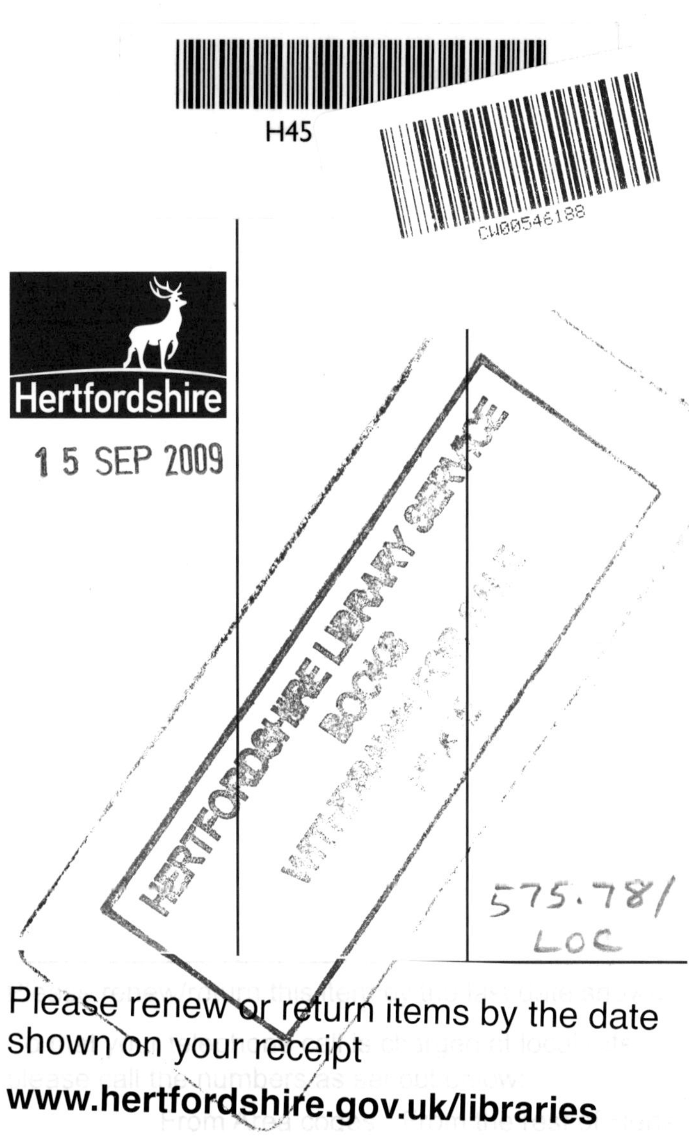
H45
CW00546188
Hertfordshire
1 5 SEP 2009
HERTFORDSHIRE LIBRARY SERVICE
575.78/
LOC

Hertfordshire

THE MOTHS OF HERTFORDSHIRE

The history, status, distribution and phenology of the micro- and macro-Lepidoptera of a south-eastern English county

compiled by
Colin W. Plant

Hertfordshire Natural History Society

2008

(see page 531)

Published in 2008 by the
Hertfordshire Natural History Society
Registered Charity number 218418
24 Mandeville Rise, Welwyn Garden City
Hertfordshire AL8 7JU

With generous assistance from

The Environment Agency;
Hertfordshire Biological Records Centre, Hertfordshire County Council;
Butterfly Conservation, Herts and Middlesex Branch and Upper Thames Branch;
London Natural History Society;
Ecological Planning & Research Ltd, Micheldever, Winchester;
Bioscan Environmental Consultancy, Little Baldon, Oxford;
Ecology Consultancy, London;
Lee Valley Regional Park Authority;
Liz Lake Associates, Bishops Stortford
Herts & Middlesex Wildlife Trust
and individual moth enthusiasts
Andy and Melissa Banthorpe, Alan Cockburn, Rob Souter, Stephen Waters and Shirley Watson
and others who wish to remain anonymous.

Printed in Great Britain by
Cravitz Printing Company Ltd
1 Tower Hill, Brentwood, Essex CM14 4TA

British Library Cataloguing-in-publication Date

A catalogue record for this book is available from the British Library

ISBN: 978-0-9521685-7-7

To
Rosie and Ed

A small fly or moth had fluttered across our path, and in an instant Stapleton was rushing with extraordinary energy and speed in pursuit of it. To my dismay the creature flew straight for the great Mire, but my acquaintance never paused for an instant, bounding from tuft to tuft behind it, his green net waving in the air.

From *The Hound of the Baskervilles* by Arthur Conan Doyle

Summary

The moth fauna (Lepidoptera other than Rhopalocera) of the English county of Hertfordshire (Watsonian Vice-county 20), is examined. A total of 1548 species is recorded for all time to the end of December 2006 representing 62% of British Isles moths at that date. Recorded species fall within 58 families (42 families of micro-Lepidoptera, and 16 of macro-Lepidoptera); only the Limacodidae, Douglasiidae, Heliodinidae and Endromidae amongst British families are not represented in Hertfordshire by at least one reliable record. A small number of species of 'micro' moths may be overlooked. Information is presented on the status and distribution of each of the 1548 recorded species within the county, and distribution maps are presented for 1428 of these. These maps employ hierarchical symbols to distinguish distribution in three date bands and to permit changes in patterns to be shown over time. Larval foodplants as recorded in Hertfordshire are listed where data are available. Adult flight periods are listed for the period 1995 to 2006 and for 595 species where there are sufficient numerical data histograms are plotted showing the flight period by standard weeks. The year of the first and last record is given for all species along with the number of records upon which a free-text discussion is based; the earliest record was made in the year 1710. Maps depicting solid and drift geology, soil types, and various climatic parameters are presented as an aid to interpretation of the data. Rarity and Threat Status Categories are introduced and defined for Hertfordshire's moths; all 1548 recorded species are allocated to one of these categories. Using these data, a *Red List* of Hertfordshire moths is presented and from this formal recommendations are made for species to be included in the county's biodiversity action planning process. Twenty-seven of the 81 moths that are currently regarded as Priority Species within the UK Biodiversity Action Plan are recorded, but of these only eight are still present or may be present. These, and a further 68 species not listed as UK Priority Species are regarded as Endangered (in danger of extinction) within Hertfordshire. A further 47 species are Vulnerable and are expected to become Endangered if the causes of their declines are not remedied urgently. These 123 Endangered and Vulnerable species are recommended for designation as *Priority Species* within Hertfordshire's *Biodiversity Action Plan*. A further 22 species are regarded as Threatened in the county and another 115 are Rare, but under no immediate or apparent threat. The role of these as indicators of the ecological significance of discrete sites is discussed. A total of 157 species has apparently become extinct in the county. Forty-nine species that have been reported in the literature, but for which there is no reliable supporting evidence, are formally deleted from the Hertfordshire fauna; a summary list of these is presented.

Contents

Acknowledgements

A great many people have contributed in a great many ways to the production of this book. I shall attempt to mention them all, but if I have accidentally left someone out, please accept my profound apologies.

The Hertfordshire Natural History Society is the organisation responsible for appointing me as the formal Hertfordshire Moth Recorder and for re-appointing me on an annual basis. I shall leave the reader to decide if that is a good or a bad thing! Active field work on the part of a great many interested people, mostly amateurs, has been crucial in the generation of this review. I am extremely grateful to these people, not only for undertaking species recording in the county, but also for passing their data to me and for giving me permission to use it. In addition, several other people have contributed by identifying moths for others, by commenting on identifications, or by looking for voucher specimens in museums. I have combined all these people in the following single list of people without whom this book simply would not have been possible:

Agar, Nigel.; Agassiz, D. J. L.; Albertini, M.; Aldridge, B.; Alexander, K. N. A.; Allen, D.; Allen, P.; Alston, P.; Alton, P.; Anderson, N.; Anderson, S.; Andrews, D.; Arnold, V.; Ashby, M.; Ashdown, Mrs; Atkinson, L.; Austin, T.; Bailey, M.; Baker, C.; Baker, P.; Banthorpe, A.; Banthorpe, Martin; Banthorpe, Melissa; Bantock, H.; Bantock, T.; Barnacle, J.; Bartlett, J.; Barton, B.; Beaumont, H. E.; Beechey, A.; Bennett, P.; Bensted, A.; Bernard, A.; Best, M.; Bevan, D.; Bigg, R.; Birdsall, J.; Blake, A.; Bland, K. P. ; Bolitho, A.; Bowden, S. R. (deceased); Bowman N.; Boyd, G.; Bradford, Andy; Bradford, E. S. (deceased); Bradley, J. D. (deceased); Bremner, M.; Briggs, B.; Bristow, A.; Bristow, T.; Brown, L.; Brown, T.; Browne, L.; Buller, G.; Bunn, W.; Burrows, A.; Burrows, C.; Burrus, I.; Burton, P.; Byerley, B.L.; Bygate, P.; Byrne, C.; Callewaert, A.; Campbell, F. M.; Campbell, M.; Carpenter, C.; Carter, J.; Casey, T.; Chainey, J.; Chapman, D.; Chapman, J.; Chapman, T.; Cheeseman, A.; Cheeseman R.; Cherry, K.; Childs, J.; Churchman, K.; Clack, P.; Clancy, T.; Clark, D.; Clark, P.; Clarke, J.; Clifton, J.; Cockburn, A.; Coletta, A.; Colston, J.; Conroy, C.; Cook, R. (deceased); Cooper, H.; Cooper, M.; Cope, R.; Court, C.; Cripps, R.; Culshaw, A.; d'Arcy, J.; Davies, J.; Davies, S.; Davis, T.; Dawson, J.; de Maria, E.; Dee, C.; Dickerson, B.; Dickinson, A.; Donahaye, J.; Doncaster, C.; Downie, A.; Downie, S.; d'Souza, J.; Durose, K., Dunk, H. C. ; Dyke, R.; Dymond, N.; Edwards, F. W.; Edwards, S. J.; Elliot, B.; Ellis, H.; Ellis, R.; Emmet, A. Maitland (deceased); Evans, D.; Everett, C. M.; Fairclough, R.; Farrell, S.; Field, P.; Fish, J..; Fisher, A.; Fitzpatrick, M. J.; Fletcher, N.; Ford, T.; Foy, A.; Francis, V.; Fraser, D.; Freed, T.; Freeman, M., Fullforth, V.; Gamble, I.; Gamble, P.; Gardener, T.; Gaskell, J.; Gatward, H.; George, A. M. 'Ched'; Gibbs, D.; Gibson, Seth; Gladwin, J.; Gladwin, T..; Glenister, C.; Goater, Barry; Gonzales, G.; Goodall, G.; Goodey, B.; Goodyear, E.; Gould, P.; Grant, C.; Grant, M.; Green, M.; Green, T.; Greenham, W. D. W.; Grey, C.; Groom, L.; Gurney, M.; Hackett, D.; Hall, K.; Halstead, A.; Harcourt, E.; Hardacre, A.; Harding, G.; Harrington, R.; Harris, A.; Harris, S.; Harris S. R.; Harrison, Miss; Harvey, P. R.; Hatton, W.; Hawkwy, K.; Hayes, J.; Healy, M.; Heath, Dug; Heath, G. H.; Heaton, N.; Henderson, C.; Herbert, C.; Hicks, M.; Hill, L.; Hill, Tim; Hindson, F.; Hindson, F.; Hobbs, R.; Hollingdale, J.; Holt, C.; Homan, R.; Horrocks, J.; Horton, C.; Howdon, D.; Hudson, D.; Hughes, A.; Hughes, S.; Inward, D.; Jackson, E.; James, T.; Jefferies, P.; Jeffery, P.; Jenner P.; Jessop, B.; Johnson, E. E.; Johnson, S.; Joiner, C.; Judd, B.; Judd, V.; Kallmer, D.; Katz, P.; Katz, R.; Kindley, A.; King, J.; King, T.; Kingsey, J.; Kirk, D.; Kirke, C. M. StG.; Knaggs, D.; Lambert, C.; Lambert, L.; Lane, B.; Lane, S.; Langford, Mrs; Langmaid, J. R. ; Lansdown H.; Latchmore, F.; Law, G.; Lawrence, M.; Leeming, D. J.; Lewis, A.; Lewis, P.; Lewis, T.; Loftus, Arti; Lowe, S.; Lowry, A.; Loxdale, H.; Lumley, P.; Lyal ,C. H. C.; Lyle, T.; Manning, D.; Marett, A.; Marks, S. R.; Marriott, D.; Martin, George; Martin, Geoff.; May, E.; McCormick, Roy; McLelland, P.; Middleton, A.; Middleton, R.; Millbank, S.; Millis, D.; Milner, E.; Minnion, W. E. (deceased); Mitchell, K.; Mitchell-Finch, J.; Mole, A.; Mole, G.; Moore, A.; Moss, J.; Moverley, T.; Murray, C. Murray, D.; Murray, J.; Murray, S.; Murray, T.; Neal, P.; Newland, M.; Newton, J.; Noakes, J.; Noakes, M.; Northfield, R.; Oakenfull, P.; O.Malley, M.; Orchard, M.; Orwind, D.; Osborn, S.; Otter, D.; Outen, A.; Page, B.; Page, P; Palme, A.; Palmer, A.; Palmer, S. M.; Parsons, M.; Paynter, S.; Pearson, R.; Peart, S.; Peck, B.; Penn, S.; Penney, C.; Penrose, R.; Perkins, J.; Perkins, J.; Perry, G.; Piffard, A.; Piffard, B.; Pilbrow, C. F.; Piper, A.; Piper, R.; Pittman, S.; Plant, E.; Plant, R.; Pledger, M.; Ponting, E.; Postelthwaite, S.; Prior, G.; Powell, A.; Prue, R.; Quantrill, T.; Reed, R.; Reeves, J.; Reid, J.; Reynolds, A.; Riley, A.; Robinson, K.; Robinson, M.; Rodbard, T.; Rogers, J.; Roper, P.; Russell, M.; Rye Meads Ringing Group; Sainsbury, A.; Salisbury, G.; Sampford, N.; Sandifer, R.; Saunders, Andrew; Sawford, B.; Scrivens, H.; Sears, E. J.; Selby, Miss; Self, A.; Sell, G.; Senior, G.; Shepherd, A.; Shepperson, C.; Silvester, F.W.; Skinner, Bernard; Skinner, P.; Small, I.; Smart, L.A.; Smith, C. R.; Smith, C.; Smith, G.; Smith, J.; Smith, K.; Smith, M.; Smith, N. A.; Smith, R.; Softly, R.A.; Sokoloff, P.; Souter, R.; Spence, J.; Standbridge, K.; Staniforth, S.; Starkey, J.; Stead, A.; Stead, P.; Stephenson, P. M.; Stephenson, P.; Sterling, M.; Stevens, J.; Stevens, P.; Stirling, P.; Stroud, R. W.; Stroyan, H. L .G.; Syme, L.; Taggart, B.; Tanner, D.; Taylor, A.; Taylor, G.; Terry, R.; Thomas, S.; Thompson, J.; Thompson, K.; Thompson, V.; Thomson, R.; Thorne, G. W.; Tindall-Lucas, C. H.; Tomkins, J.; Townsend, M.; Tuck, F.; Tyler-Smith, C.; Uffen, R. W. J.; Ustin, T.; van Stone, P.; Vicary, G.; Wakeley, S.; Walker, T.; Wall, M.; Ward, L.; Waring, P.; Warrington, S.; Waters, R.; Waters, S.; Waterton, P.; Watson, C.; Watson, S.; Watts, M.; Webb, J.; Webster, D.; Whalley, G.; Wheeler, P.; White, G.; Whitebread, S.; Whiteman, J.; Williams, B.; Williams, S. A.; Williamson, M.; Wilson, D.; Wilson, T.; Wingrove, D. A.; Wistow, R.; Woiwod, I.; Wood, A.; Wood, J.; Woodward, I. D. and Yeates, M.

For specialist help with the identification of various difficult 'micro' specimens I am grateful to several friends, in particular David Agassiz and the late Maitland Emmet. Many people who profess not to be interested in 'micros' nevertheless provided me with many hundreds of these moths from their traps over the past few years, mostly quite unrecognisable without dissection. Steve Palmer, David Manning, Brian Goodey and Rachel Terry between them carried out large numbers of such dissections for me; without this assistance the 'micro' section of this book could not yet have been produced.

Shirley Watson has identified a great many plant species for me, adding considerably to our knowledge of caterpillar foodplants in Hertfordshire. Trevor James answered numerous queries concerning the distribution of various larval foodplants in Hertfordshire; his encyclopaedic knowledge of both the county and its flora never ceases to amaze and I look forward to his Hertfordshire *Flora* with eager anticipation.

John Langmaid kindly provided the data behind some of the map dots shown in the distribution maps for 'micros' in the series *Moths and butterflies of Great Britain and Ireland* (Harley Books) and Martin Honey, David Agassiz, Raymond Uffen, Keith Bland and Klaus Sattler have all assisted with the tracking down and checking of museum specimens for me. Henry Arnold of the Biological Records Centre at Monks Wood provided background data on several historical records of 'macros'. The Curator and staff at Mill Green Museum provided me with facilities to examine the moth collections in their care. Tony Davis has checked most records of pyralid moths along the way, pointing out a few that 'didn't quite fit' and so enabling voucher specimens of these to be traced and dissected.

Modern-day moth recording has centred upon the activities of the Herts Moth Group. This was formed by me with considerable assistance from Rob Souter and I am also grateful to Tom Gladwin for arranging the free use of Digswell Village Hall for the group's inaugural meeting in April 2000. The success of the Herts Moth Group has been greatly aided by the generosity of

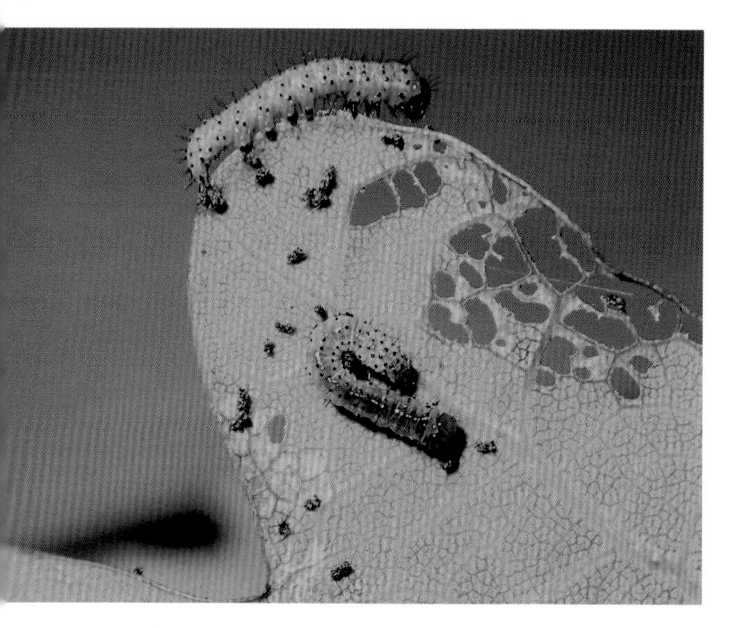

various landowners and agents who have happily granted the group permission to record moths on their properties. These owners and agents include:

Andrew Easby (Broad Colney Lakes); Andy Fleckney (Beds, Cambs & Northants Wildlife Trust); Andy Hardstaff (Countryside Management Service); Andy May (Essex Wildlife Trust); Barry Trevis (Lemsford Springs); Brian Hudgell (Redbourne Meadows); Brian Planton (Hare's Garden Wood); Buckinghamshire County Council; Carol Horton (Ravensdell Wood); Christine James (Ashwell Chalk Quarry); Clive Thomas (Balls Park); Conservators of Chorleywood Common; Conservators of Therfield Heath; D. Beales (Mrs) & staff (Hilmead School); Dave Kirk (Boxmoor Trust); David Ford (Friends of Brook Farm); Don Otter and colleagues (National Trust); Edward Carter (Home Wood, Gilston); Geoff Foreman (Home Wood, Gilston); Geoffrey Sell (Birchanger Wood); Graeme Cannon (Aldbury Common); Graham Black (St Edmunds College); Hannah Fearnley (Strutton Parker); Heidi Hutton (Countryside Management Service); Herts and Middlesex Wildlife Trust; Hon. C. A. Savile (Youngsbury Estate); Ian Mather (Watford Borough Council); James Carter (Eastwick Lodge Farm); James Gemmil (Golden Grove/Sayes Coppice); Jim Ashley-Cooper (Hexton Chalk Pit); John Jenkins (farmer at Therfield Heath); John Langham (Gascoyne Cecil Estates); John & Margaret Noakes (Millhoppers Pasture); John Wells (Brockett Hall); Jon Green (St Albans City and District Council); Julie Hughes (Three Rivers District Council); Kay Fitzgerald (Three Rivers District Council); Les Young (Pryors Wood, Stevenage); Lord and Lady Salisbury; Lord and Lady Verulam; Mark Carter (Herts County Council); Matt Soley (Golden Grove); Michelle Dixon (University of Hertfordshire); Mike Clarke (Tewin Orchard); Neil Ireland (London Wildlife Trust); Nigel Hawkins (Gascoyne Cecil Estates); P. Sinfield (Zouches Farm, Dunstable); Patrick Ashley-Cooper (Hexton Chalk Pit); Paul Jarczewski (Hertfordshire County Council); Paul Palmer (Conservators of Therfield Heath); Paul Sargent (Kensworth Quarry); Peter Clegg (Gascoyne Cecil Estates); Peter Heath (Astonbury Wood); Peter Neal (Bricketwood Common); Phil Lumley (Oughtonhead); Phil Pennington (Boxmoor Trust); Ray Hobbs (Astonbury Wood); Richard Pierce (Bramfield Wood); Richard Playdell-Bouverie (Lawrence End Estate); Richard Sweetland (Nomansland Common); Rob Hopkins (Herts & Middlesex Wildlife Trust); Sean Clarke (Therfield Heath Golf Club); Simon Smith (Astonbury Wood); Steve Carling (Gascoyne Cecil Estates); Steve Waller (Gilston Park); Stuart Tinney (Golden Grove); Ted Darling (Conservators of Therfield Heath); Teresa Wurr (Buntingford); Tom Casey (Bayfordbury and Pinetum);

Three Counties Radio interviewed me about this project and subsequently broadcast a number of appeals for records. Keyboard wizard Rick Wakeman, in his current incarnation as a DJ on the digital radio station *Planet Rock*, twice aired my appeal for people to tell me of any references to moths in the lyrics of rock music.

The first electronic version of the Herts Moth Database was created by me using Lotus Approach software; this involved considerable assistance from Brian Goodey, the then Essex Lepidoptera Recorder. Terri Tarpey, a noted Essex botanist, wrote me a computer 'macro' that allowed me to transfer selected data from that Lotus database to maps created using the DMap software written by Alan Morton. When it became clear that MapMate was becoming the standard software for moth recording in Britain, Peter Harvey of the Essex Field Club spent a huge amount of time and effort converting the Lotus database into a format suitable for me to import into MapMate and subsequently Andrew Wood has been responsible for converting records received electronically at the end of each year into a format that could be 'absorbed' by Map Mate without the loss of the editing facility that is inherent in the 'sync' process associated with the latter programme.

In terms of preparing the data for publication I must mention the efforts of several people. Les Hill and Peter Harvey provided the SQL computer code for several 'user queries' by which means the MapMate database could be interrogated in various unconventional ways dreamed up by me. Les was also almost entirely responsible for 'tweaking' the software to create the distribution maps (including the provision of boundary files). He also rescued me on numerous occasions when my computer became 'un-cooperative' – as computers seem liable to do from time to time. Chris Dee electronically altered the flight charts so that they adopted the form in which they now appear and has been responsible for various statistical analyses.

My original text of the species accounts was very kindly peer-reviewed by experts in various areas. John Langmaid read the text for all the micro families up to the start of the Tortricidae; Raymond Uffen offered helpful criticism on the draft of the early micros. Colin Hart examined the text for the Pterophoridae and Bernard Skinner did the same for all the macros and the Crambidae and Pyralidae. When the peer-reviewers had finished and their comments had been accommodated, Graham Wenman (France) and Keith Hyatt (Wales) proof-read the entire text, pointing out numerous spelling, punctuation and grammatical errors requiring my attention. Text other than that concerned with the moth species and their distribution has been read and corrected by Linda Smith of the Herts Natural History Society. Gillian Church and Roger Pamaby at British Geological Survey and Timothy Farewell at National Soil Resources Institute prepared the geology and soil maps respectively. For help with biographical data searches I record my gratitude to Martin Honey (Natural History Museum), Carol Osman (Archivist, Haileybury School), Maggie Garret (The Library, Bishops Stortford College) and Eleanor Cowland (St Albans Museum) as well as to Raymond Uffen and David Wilson.

The overall design of the book also required the efforts of more than one person. Marcel Ashby, Jack Fearnside, Linda Smith and Rachel Terry all commented on various aspects of presentation and page layout at various stages. At Cravitz Printing, Andrew Smith has been driven to distraction by my constant telephone calls and e-mails calling for yet more changes to the design and Matthew Cravitz has kindly permitted all these to be incorporated without raising his fees!

Linda Smith has been single-handedly responsible for approaching our sponsors and for general fund-raising. My son, Edward Plant, designed the cover of the finished book.

What and where is Hertfordshire

Lying to the north of London and bounded, additionally, by the counties of Middlesex, Buckinghamshire, Bedfordshire, Cambridgeshire and Essex, the modern administrative county of Hertfordshire covers some 634 squares miles (1643 square kilometres) making it the 36th largest British county. At the end of 2007 it supports a human population of 1,058,600, a density of 644 people per square kilometre. The county town, Hertford, derives its name from the place where Harts (Fallow Deer) crossed the River Lea (Ford = a crossing point on a river) and originates in the Anglo-Saxon period of British history, attesting to the wooded nature of the area at that time; the Roman Road that is Ermine Street crosses the River Lea further east in the town of Ware and was not constructed until much later.

However, political boundaries are liable to change, so that the Hertfordshire we know today was not the same as the Hertfordshire of the 1930s, when the last county list of moths was produced by Arthur Foster. Foster's Hertfordshire was different again to that understood by Gibbs when he wrote the moth list for the *Victoria County History of Hertfordshire* in 1902. In order to standardise, biologists and naturalists use something called a vice county. The vice county system for Great Britain was devised by an English botanist called Hewett Cottrell Watson (1804 – 1881). Watson began to look at the distribution of the British Flora on a nation-wide scale when he wrote *Outlines of the Geographical Distribution of British Plants* published in Edinburgh in 1832. He followed this with *Remarks on Geographical Distribution of British Plants* published in London in 1835, *Geographical Distribution of British Plants*, London 1843, *Cybele Britannica* published in London in 1847 and finally his magnum opus *Topographical Botany*, the First edition of which was published in 1873 and a revised Second Edition, two years after his death, in 1883. Watson started his work by dividing Great Britain into recording areas – six in the *Outlines* – but by the *Topographical Botany* of 1873 he divided the country into 112 Vice-Counties which are still used today with the addition of the 40 Irish Vice-Counties, defined in 1901 by Robert Lloyd Praeger (1865 – 1953).

Watson's Vice County map showed little detail being at a scale of 1:4,000,000 and even an updated version which appeared in the journal *Topographical Botany* in 1883 was only at 1:3,000,000. The current definitive boundaries were hand drawn on a set of one inch to one mile maps by A. J. Wilmott and J. E. Dandy under the auspices of the Systematics Association in the mid 20th Century. These maps together with written descriptions were used to prepare a two-map set at a scale of 10 miles to the inch, published by the Ray Society in 1969, which is still widely used by naturalists today. More recently, staff at the National Biodiversity Network have digitised the Vice County Boundaries at a scale of 1:10,000, much more detailed than ever before.

Throughout this book, therefore, when I say 'Hertfordshire' I imply the Hertfordshire that is Watsonian vice county number 20 and **not** the present or any past administrative area. This extends to include Kensworth and the southern part of Dunstable in administrative Bedfordshire, but excludes Potters Bar and surrounding countryside which is in Middlesex (vice county 21). This will undoubtedly annoy some people, but unless the same boundary is used throughout history there would be little point in using the county at all.

Solid lines denote the Watsonian county boundaries, the dashed line shows the current administrative county boundary where it differs.

Soils and Stones: Essential Hertfordshire Geology

The underlying geology of an area has a profound effect upon the distribution of plants and animals. Apart from affecting soil type and drainage it is also responsible for hills and valleys. A very quick tour of Hertfordshire's main geological features is essential towards a full understanding of the patterns of moth distribution.

The main underlying geological features of Hertfordshire (the 'solid geology') are relatively simple. The entire of south-east England rests on a band of chalk and associated Upper Greensand that is continuous with adjacent parts of France. This was laid down under the warm seas of the Cretaceous period (in three sessions, resulting in Lower, Middle and Upper Chalk, which have different geological properties but similar ecological effects). When those seas retreated about 65 million years ago they left a more or less level chalk landscape that was, over the next few million years, uplifted to form the Chiltern Hills, which just reach Hertfordshire in the west. Approximately fifty million years ago during the early stages of the Eocene period, the seas returned across much of south-east England. This smoothed the chalk and at the same time deposited layers of pebble-rich sands and clays (the Reading Beds) on top of it. In some places, this deposit combined with silica and iron oxides to form the famous 'Hertfordshire Pudding Stone'. The seas again retreated and the earth was again uplifted before they returned once more. Throughout the course of this next inundation, a fine sediment of clay was deposited on top of the Reading Beds in a broad band from Newbury in Berkshire to Felixstowe in Suffolk to form the London Clay Basin.

All this has resulted in a series of geological bands running from north-east to south-west, with the whole county tilted so that the high ground lies in the north-west. These bands are shown in the solid geology map on this page.

From the end of the Eocene period various other geological materials have been deposited on top of the solid geology; remnants of these remain today and form the surface or 'drift' or 'surface' geology of the county. First, around 40 million years ago, fine clay deposits were laid down to form the Claygate Beds. Over the next few million years, earth movements and the weathering of the rocks caused a number of changes. Chalk started to dissolve, leaving behind various lumps of Flint. As the adjacent Reading Beds also weathered, their clay component was washed over the chalk and filled the gaps around the flints to create the Clay-with-Flints substrate that dominates much of western Hertfordshire today. Many other similar events took place and then, around one and a half million years ago, during the various Pleistocene 'Ice Ages' Hertfordshire was invaded from the north-east by an ice sheet. This, when it eventually melted, left behind the layer of 'glacial till' (in the form of clay) containing 'erratics' of various sizes (in this case, mostly chalk boulders) – our modern day Chalky Boulder Clay. This now dominates the north-east of the county. In more recent times, rivers cut through the surface geology at intervals, depositing sands and gravels along their margins as they flowed, to create the River Terrace Gravels, whilst on their flood plains a deposit of fine-particled and organically rich alluvium was left behind. The surface geology is summarised in map form on page 8.

All these events had a profound effect on modern day soil type and hence on the flora and fauna, including the moths. In the north-west, from Tring to Royston, are there significant areas of chalk at the surface, although much of the original chalk grassland has been degraded by human activity. Chalk also remains at the surface is a number of unexpected places as can be seen from the drift (surface) geology map below. The relatively uniform cover of Chalky Boulder Clay in the north-east of the county has created a rather monotonous, undulating landscape and it is reasonable to expect this region to support a lower diversity of habitats and hence fewer moth species; the farming community is only partly to blame for this observed fact. In more southerly areas where the ice sheet failed to reach, the landscape has a more varied surface geology and a more diverse topography that together give the area its 'character'. Gravel-based plateaux permit the development of acid grasslands, whilst rich alluvial sediments in the river valleys allow for the formation of marshland (most of which man has drained). The poorly-draining London Clay became colonized by damp woodlands and small areas of glacial gravels deposited on top of the clay supported heathland.

Solid Geology of Hertfordshire

Derived from 1:625000 BGS geological digital data. British Geological Survey © NERC 2008

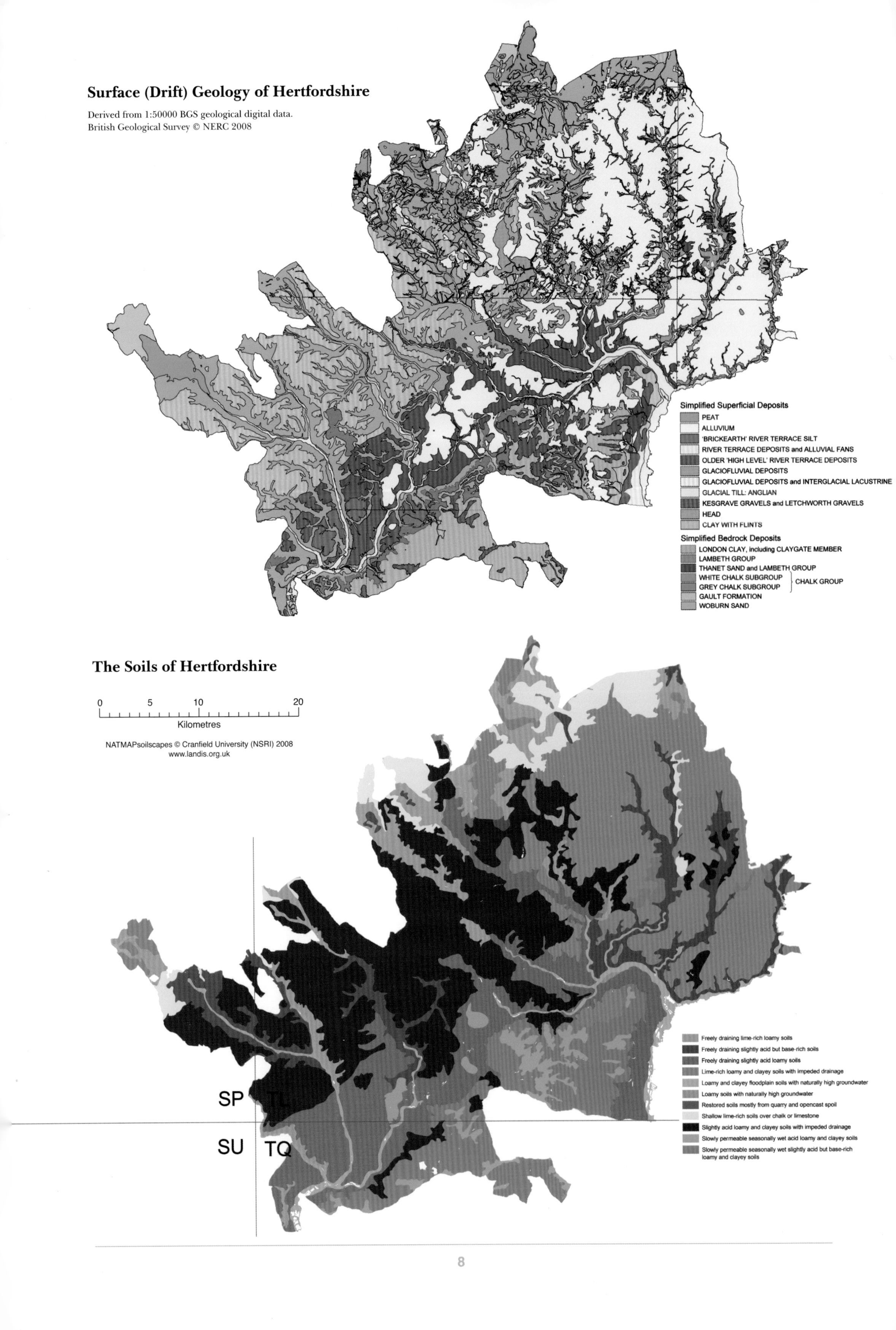

Surface (Drift) Geology of Hertfordshire
Derived from 1:50000 BGS geological digital data.
British Geological Survey © NERC 2008
Simplified Superficial Deposits
PEAT
ALLUVIUM
'BRICKEARTH' RIVER TERRACE SILT
RIVER TERRACE DEPOSITS and ALLUVIAL FANS
OLDER 'HIGH LEVEL' RIVER TERRACE DEPOSITS
GLACIOFLUVIAL DEPOSITS
GLACIOFLUVIAL DEPOSITS and INTERGLACIAL LACUSTRINE
GLACIAL TILL: ANGLIAN
KESGRAVE GRAVELS and LETCHWORTH GRAVELS
HEAD
CLAY WITH FLINTS
Simplified Bedrock Deposits
LONDON CLAY, including CLAYGATE MEMBER
LAMBETH GROUP
THANET SAND and LAMBETH GROUP
WHITE CHALK SUBGROUP
GREY CHALK SUBGROUP
CHALK GROUP
GAULT FORMATION
WOBURN SAND
The Soils of Hertfordshire
0
5
10
20
Kilometres
NATMAPsoilscapes © Cranfield University (NSRI) 2008
www.landis.org.uk
SP
TL
SU
TQ
Freely draining lime-rich loamy soils
Freely draining slightly acid but base-rich soils
Freely draining slightly acid loamy soils
Lime-rich loamy and clayey soils with impeded drainage
Loamy and clayey floodplain soils with naturally high groundwater
Loamy soils with naturally high groundwater
Restored soils mostly from quarry and opencast spoil
Shallow lime-rich soils over chalk or limestone
Slightly acid loamy and clayey soils with impeded drainage
Slowly permeable seasonally wet acid loamy and clayey soils
Slowly permeable seasonally wet slightly acid but base-rich loamy and clayey soils

The Effects of Man on the Hertfordshire Environment

Hertfordshire has a history of land use dating back to the Mesolithic period (Middle Stone Age) and was first farmed during the Neolithic period, about 7,000 years ago, when most of the 'wildwood' was probably cleared. Permanent habitation appeared at the beginning of the Bronze Age around 3500 years ago and after the Roman conquest of Britain a little less than 2000 years ago Hertfordshire adapted quickly to the Roman way of life, and one of several new towns, Verulamium – modern-day St Albans – became the third largest town in Roman Britain. The town was built alongside the River Ver and Verulamium means 'settlement above the marsh', providing a clue to the nature of the habitats available in those distant times. After the Romans left Britain, the Anglo-Saxons occupied the area, creating their own towns, including the future county town of Hertford. After the Norman conquest of 1066, castles were built in places such as Bishop's Stortford and Berkhamsted and these areas became the centres of what must have passed as 'culture' in those far off times. At this stage the human population was, of course, still at a very low density and man's effect on the natural landscape and its incumbent flora and fauna was minuscule. There are no available figures for what we now recognise as Hertfordshire, but by way of example when William, Bishop of London, bought the Stortford Manor and Estate in the year 1060 (for the princely sum of £8), the new 'Bishop's Stortford' had a recorded population of 120 people.

As nearby London grew bigger, however, much of the county was bought or otherwise acquired by the nobility, whose patronage helped to boost the local economy. However, even by the time of the first National Census, in 1891, the population of the administrative county was still less than a quarter of a million people. Indeed, almost all of the increase in Hertfordshire's human population took place in the twentieth century as a consequence of repeated influxes of people from other areas. Two initiatives, in particular, were responsible for this. In 1903, Letchworth became the world's first Garden City, a novel approach to urban planning, pioneered by Sir Ebenezer Howard in 1898. Other garden cities followed, including at Welwyn. Then, during 1945, the Government set up a New Towns Committee to consider how best to repair and rebuild urban communities after World War II. This led to the New Towns Act of 1946 and the new 'satellite' towns around London started to appear, with Stevenage the first for Hertfordshire. These completely new towns, built on open countryside, largely accommodated the 'overspill' from London and represented the first 'major' land-take actions in the county.

Thus, in summary, for the first two thousand years of its existence Hertfordshire supported less than a quarter of a million people and man had minimal, if any, lasting effect on the natural environment in general and moth populations in particular. In the first fifty years of the twentieth century, however, this doubled to half a million and in the last fifty years it doubled again to a little over one million.

So, since from the Neolithic clearance of the wildwood, the effects of humans on the now 'semi-natural' landscape seem to have been delayed and then dramatic, in parallel with human population changes. The ownership of large parts of the county by a few rich noblemen probably helped to prevent industrialisation of the county, and most of the changes that have taken place at the landscape level did so during the twentieth century.

New housing, roads and other developments are taking an increasing share of land in the county. Note the very small size of the gardens associated with new homes. Photo: J. C. K. Webb at webbaviation.co.uk

Moth Habitats in Hertfordshire

An excellent summary of Hertfordshire's semi-natural habitats is readily available in Brian Sawford's book *Butterflies of Hertfordshire* (1987) and doubtless elsewhere too – there is little point in repeating that information here. However, a brief overview of the habitats present during our 'current' period of 1995 to 2006 is necessary to set the moth distributions in some sort of context.

Arable farmland

The rise in human population throughout Britain resulted, inevitably, on an increased demand for food production. A much improved infrastructure, making possible the movement of goods from one end of the country to the other stimulated the effective division of England into different 'food production regions' and whilst some wetter regions were better suited to livestock rearing, the drier south-east saw a huge in increase in the use of land for arable crop production. In Hertfordshire, the gently undulating Chalky Boulder Clay soils in the north-east of the county proved to be ideal for this activity. The wholesale removal of hedges became necessary from the 1950s onwards as new, bigger machines took over from the horse whilst both the removal of hedges and the ploughing up of every spare scrap of land had been actively encouraged during the 1940s as a part of the 'Dig for Victory' campaign of the Second World War. During the fifties and sixties, agrochemicals made their debut. Fertilisers of various types were added to the relatively nutrient-poor soils and with the aid of wind drift and (in those less enlightened times) deliberate spraying of verges, many native plants were unable to survive – as were the moth caterpillars that fed upon them. Dieldrin, DDT and other pesticides had direct effect on moth populations. As a result of this broad onslaught, much of modern north-east Hertfordshire presents an extremely poor habitat for moths and this is reflected in the distribution maps.

Extensive, monocultural fields dominate the landscape in much of north-east Hertfordshire and hedges are mostly absent (Photograph copyright © Colin W. Plant)

Field margins in the arable areas of the north-east are generally confined to the sides of roads like these here at Bygrave and mown 'to enable motorists to have clear visibility at all times'. This 'arable desert' supports extremely few moths. (Photograph copyright © Brian Sawford)

Woodland

Woodland, however, remains a prominent feature in the county, especially in the south and the west. The original cover of 'wildwood' would have developed between 13,000 and 12,000 years ago and the pollen record suggests that the dominant trees were Small-leaved Lime, English Elm, Oak and Hazel in the more calcareous areas with Birch, Hornbeam, Holly, Yew and Rowan on the more acidic gravel plateaux. On the chalk slopes adjoining Buckinghamshire, the mix included Ash, Wych Elm, Field Maple and Cherry; the Beech woodlands that dominate in the west of the county today were all artificially planted during the nineteenth century to provide timber for the furniture trade (Sawford, 1987). Around 7,000 years ago, Neolithic farmers began to clear it all to make way for small fields and over the next couple of thousand years the wildwood was all but lost. It is interesting to speculate on the changes in the moth fauna that may have taken place in this period. Of course, we have no means of knowing how many completely unknown species may have been present in those days, but there will certainly have been drastic reductions in the numbers of canopy-feeding species and, presumably, a slow but gradual rise in populations of species associated with the herb layer. Generally held opinion is that woodland had been completely cleared from the chalk in Hertfordshire by Roman times, but that it persisted in the south of the county as a part of the mosaic of fields, woods, hedged lanes and small hamlets that made up the English countryside; between Roman times and the start of the twentieth century there would have been little or no significant change to the Hertfordshire landscape and a correspondingly minimal effect on its moth populations. In today's Hertfordshire, the mosaic persists but the components parts have become considerably fragmented and isolated by urban expansion during the twentieth century.

Thus, although a glance at the map or any of the various sources of satellite images on the Internet shows that the county is not short of woodlands – the problem, from a moth point of view, is that their quality is rather variable and generally poor. In the north, many smaller woodlands are used for rearing pheasants, so that there is both a raised predation rate of birds on invertebrates and a general lack of herbaceous plants. These conditions are exacerbated by the usual isolation of the woodlands within an arable landscape, which prevents the birds from wandering to new areas when local food supplies are depleted. Though detailed surveys are still ongoing (few gamekeepers in charge of woodlands used for intensive pheasant rearing are keen to allow overnight moth surveys in July and August), the moth fauna in these areas appears, unsurprisingly, to be dominated by canopy-feeders.

The better woodlands for moths are mostly in the south, where in many cases they can be related to the various gravels shown in the geology map on page 8. Here, perhaps because of the raised disturbance levels provided by people and dogs, pheasant rearing is less prevalent and woodlands tend to sport better-developed under-storeys whilst herbaceous plants often dominate in the edge zones along tracks and at the woodland margins. Examination of the moth fauna here usually reveals raised species diversity in comparison with the northern pheasant woods and in most cases this increase is a result of the presence of species whose caterpillars are associated with the herb layer. Nevertheless, most southern Hertfordshire woodland is just as fragmented and isolated as that elsewhere. Our most extensive, continuous tract is that which forms the Broxbourne Woods complex, parts of which are now a National Nature Reserve, extending from Hertford Heath and Balls Wood in the north-east to Wormley Wood in the south-west. This area is amongst the best in the county for woodland moths, both in terms of the number of species and the number of 'rarities'.

However, it also owes some of its significance to the variation in micro-habitat made possible by the underlying surface geology – the woods are partly on the London Clay, providing damp areas and partly on the Pleistocene Pebble Gravel, which creates well drained areas that support acid grassland and heathland in the clearings. The damper areas have a more humid microclimate and appear to support different moths of which the most striking, in terms of its county distribution, might be 2037: Rosy Footman (*Miltochrista miniata*). Many smaller woodland units

Beechwood at High Scrubs, near Tring. Note the lack of an under-storey and the absence of a herb layer. Typical moths here include Lobster Moth (*Stauropus fagi*) and 1647: Barred Hook-tip (*Watsonalla cultraria*) (Photograph copyright: © Brian Sawford)

Small isolated woods used for pheasant rearing, such as this one near High Wych, are typically dominated by young trees growing close together to provide cover. Dead wood has been gathered up and used to create 'bivouacs' as shelter for the birds. The feeding habits of the pheasants reduce the ground flora and the invertebrate numbers so that moths within these woods tend to be those associated with the canopy layer. (Photograph copyright © Colin W. Plant).

to the west at Bayfordbury, at Northaw Great Wood and at the Hatfield Estate share this geological combination of London Clay and Pebble Gravel and their moth lists contain some overlap of species, though the Broxbourne complex has a longer list simply because it is a larger tract of woodland. Much further to the west, beyond Watford, Whippendell Wood stands out as an important site in the county for moths and this too rests on a gravel geology. Mid-way between Broxbourne and Whippendell, Bricket Wood Common supports recently developed woodland on our most southerly deposit of Chalky Boulder Clay. The moths here are poorly studied in recent years, but there are subtle differences in the assemblage in comparison with the gravel/London Clay woodlands and Bricket Wood Common provides the only Hertfordshire site for 2040: Four-dotted Footman (*Cybosia mesomella*).

Balls Wood, a part of the Broxbourne Woods National Nature Reserve. (Photograph copyright © Andrew Wood).

Most Beech woodlands in the county rest on the clays which cap the chalk in the west, on our border with Buckinghamshire. Because of the way that Beech trees grow there is generally little in the way of an understorey or herb layer in the woodlands and not surprisingly there are elements of the moth fauna here that differ from that of woodlands elsewhere in the county. Species such as 1999: Lobster Moth (*Stauropus fagi*) and 1647: Barred Hook-tip (*Watsonalla cultraria*), form a significant part of the moth fauna here and these western woodlands are the only place where it is possible to find 1903: Barred Umber (*Plagodis pulveraria*).

The secondary woodland at Bricketwood Common is the only Hertfordshire site for 2040: Four-dotted Footman (*Cybosia mesomella*). (Photograph copyright © Brian Sawford).

Grassland

As wildwood was cleared, grassland became dominant in the landscape and probably remained so almost as far as the present day. However, the pressure on grasslands today is probably even greater than that on woodlands. The major decline probably started during the Second World War as grasslands were taken into arable cultivation. The epidemic of the rabbit virus myxomatosis in 1954 had an even more profound effect, since the removal of rabbits allowed for the uncontrolled encroachment of scrub. Areas such as Aldbury Nowers, which were still chalk downland in the 1930s, had become woodland by the 1950s, with the parallel loss of moths such as the Chalk Carpet (*Scotopteryx bipunctaria*). During the 1960s many more areas were subsumed into the arable desert whilst the widespread use of pesticides such as dieldrin and DDT put paid to those few moths that were able to hang on. Both the causal data submitted to county moth recorders over the years and the statistically reliable data gathered in the Rothamsted Insect Survey light traps at Harpenden show very clearly that most of the losses to the county's moth fauna occurred during the two decades of the 1950s and 1960s. In addition to scrub invasion, the withdrawal of grazing also caused other, more subtle changes to take place. Coarse, competitive grasses start to dominate the sward and eventually choke out the finer species. Broad-leaved plants that would normally have been grazed start to take hold and in no time at all the character of the grassland had changed beyond recognition. From a moth point of view, the loss of specialist food plants spells extinction for many species.

Although chalk reaches the surface and affects the macro-habitat type in a narrow band along the entire north-west edge of the county from Buckinghamshire to Cambridgeshire, modern land use has rendered good quality calcareous grassland a rare habitat in Hertfordshire today. Most chalk grasslands had been ploughed or allowed to develop into woodland and by the 1930s the only significant areas remaining were in isolated sites at Tring Park, Aldbury Nowers, between Hexton and Hitchin, at Weston Hills and Therfield Heath. Further losses occurred during the 1940s including our only Chalk Heath site, at Lilley Hoo. In 1940, there were 500 acres of chalk downland remaining in the county; by 1984 this had reduced to a mere 70 acres. Today, in early 2008, it has all but completely vanished. The best surviving example is probably on Church Hill, where management aimed at preserving the Pasque Flower (*Pulsatilla vulgaris*) has inadvertently allowed less common chalkland moths to flourish. Here, 914: *Scythris crassiuscula* (which feeds on rock rose and is also present in the Pirton area) and 482: *Epermenia insecurella*, an Endangered species in Hertfordshire known only from Church Hill and whose caterpillars feed on Bastard Toadflax are to be found.

According to research undertaken by the North Herts Museum Service, over 90 percent of the unimproved neutral grasslands of North Hertfordshire present in 1940, including nearly all our ancient flower-rich meadows, had been lost by 1984. There has been a corresponding decline in specialist moths associated with that habitat. Acid grassland is now all but absent and confined to isolated small patches at places such as Croxley Common Moor, Patmore Heath, Nomansland Common and Hertford Heath. Here, moth assemblages that are characteristic of the habitat hang on and contain some quite rare species. However, whilst all of these sites are formally designated, in some form or other, as sites of ecological interest, there is a pressing need to revisit their management plans. Secondary woodland dominates over a large area of Nomansland Common, and is beginning to do so at Patmore Heath, whilst falling ground water levels may be responsible for subtle habitat changes at Croxley Common Moor, which supports some of the counties rarest moths.

Acid heath is an even rarer feature of the county today and is all but absent. Small, but extremely important patches can be found at Nomansland Common and Hertford Heath.

Church Hill supports one of the few remaining chalk downland habitats of significance in Hertfordshire. Note the purple blooms of Pasque Flowers (*Pulsatilla vulgaris*) for which this site is famous. This is the only Hertfordshire site for 487: *Epermenia insecurella*. (Photograph copyright © Brian Sawford)

The acid grassland at Croxley Common Moor supports an assemblage of invertebrates that include some of the county's rarest moths. (Photograph copyright © Brian Sawford).

Aldbury Nowers. Most of the downland habitat has become scrub-invaded and although several characteristic moths remain, some of the more sensitive species such as 164: Cistus Forester (*Adscita geryon*) and 1731: Chalk Carpet (*Scotopteryx bipunctaria*) may have already become extinct here. (Photograph copyright © Brian Sawford).

Trees now dominate the acid grassland habitat at Patmore Heath; these ought to be completely removed before the remaining grassland is degraded beyond recovery. (Photograph copyright © Brian Sawford)

Though largely dominated by semi-mature secondary woodland, Nomansland Common is one of the few areas of the county that supports heather heathland. (Photograph copyright © Brian Sawford)

In recent years the heather heath areas of Hertford Heath have been saved from extinction by extensive tree removal. This process ought to continue across a far greater area in the next few years before the seed bank is exhausted. (Photograph copyright © Brian Sawford)

Wetland

In the days when the wildwood covered much of the county there were probably freshwater marshes in most Hertfordshire river valleys, but today all of the county's marshland habitat is justifiably regarded as endangered. The threats are many. Because of their position in low-lying and level river valleys, many have been lost through the construction of first railways and then roads, closely followed by the encroachment of the urban environment. A simple train ride from Bishops Stortford to London Liverpool Street, travelling first along the Stort and then the Lea will amply demonstrate this latter point. Happily, recent flooding in Britain has alerted planners and developers to the risks associated with building on flood plains, though the cynic in me now fears for the areas of high ground formerly regarded as too expensive to develop. Another, rather more sinister threat to wetland habitats, however, is the general lowering of the water table – the level to which ground water rises. The causes of this are perhaps farther reaching.

Hertfordshire wetlands are now rather few. Sawbridgeworth Marsh Nature Reserve probably supports the single-most important wetland moth assemblage in the county and this includes a strong population of the pyralid moth 1387: *Nascia cilialis* as well as 2370: Twin-spotted Wainscot (*Archanara geminipuncta*), 2371: Brown-veined Wainscot (*Archanara dissoluta*) and 2377: Fen Wainscot (*Arenostola phragmitidis*). Other, non-designated marshland areas exist in the Stort Valley between Bishops Stortford and Rye Meads – those investigated certainly warrant nature reserve status and there is probably a good case for incorporating all of the remaining wetland habitat in the valley within a single National Nature Reserve. At the confluence of the Rivers Lea and Stort are larger areas of wetland, centred on Rye Meads and Amwell, where important assemblages of wetland moths combine with important bird communities. Upstream along the River Lea most of the habitat is severely degraded, but the watercress beds at Lemsford Springs have generated a list of moths with a raised wetland component and include a population of 2362: Butterbur moth (*Hydraecia petasitis*). In the north of the county, the River Oughton at Ickleford also creates a wetland of major importance in the county whilst in the west the reed beds at the Wilstone Reservoirs and Tring Sewage Farm support another major wetland species assemblage and provide the only known Hertfordshire populations of 2204: Obscure Wainscot (*Mythimna obsoleta*). A few other wetland habitats persist, such as at Broad Colney Lakes, but most are very small and somewhat isolated. There is enormous scope for wetland habitat creation in Hertfordshire and all existing areas ought to be designated as sites of ecological importance.

Rye Meads, at the confluence of the rivers Lea and Stort support a diverse assemblage of wetland moths.
(Photograph copyright © Joan Childs)

Marshland around Sawbridgeworth Station is not formally designated and is becoming invaded by young woodland. There is a pressing need to incorporate all of the Stort Valley wetland sites within a single nature reserve framework. (Photograph copyright © Colin W. Plant)

Sawbridgeworth Marsh has a regionally important assemblage of wetland moths, including a strong population of the pyralid *Nascia cilialis*. (Photograph copyright © Colin W. Plant)

Reed beds at the Tring Reservoirs support 2204: Obscure Wainscot (*Mythimna obsoleta*). (Photograph copyright © Brian Sawford)

Oughtonhead Common, in the north of the county is a structurally diverse wetland site. (Photograph copyright © Brian Sawford)

The disused watercress beds at Lemsford Springs create a different kind of wetland habitat. This site is especially productive for aquatic species such as the China-mark moths (Crambidae). The slightly raised ground in the distance is dominated by plants of Butterbur and supports a regionally important population of the Butterbur Moth (*Hydraecia petsitis*). (Photo © Brian Sawford)

Edge habitats

Where vertical and horizontal features, such as a hedgerow and grassland, coincide edge habitats are formed. This much-neglected micro-habitat feature is of profound importance to invertebrates in general and to moths in particular. On the one hand they form physical corridors across the landscape along which invertebrates can move ('green corridors') and in some areas of southern Hertfordshire may be the only means by which small and isolated woodland units are rendered continuous. This continuity of green habitat is invariably present in farmland sites that produce the richest invertebrate species lists and absent in those that produce poor lists. At the same time, they often provide a habitat in its own right and in intensely farmed areas may be the only places where herbaceous plants can grow. Thus, in spite of the indisputably poor ecological value of arable fields, the hedges in between them, as well as field margins and any header strips, should be treated with greater respect than they have in the past. interestingly, recent (2007) research by Dr Thomas Merckx and Dr Martin Townsend of the Wildlife Conservation Research Unit (WildCRU) at Oxford University has shown that where trees are present in hedges the numbers of moths (as opposed to the number of species) is significantly raised and it is clear that hedges with standard trees are far better for moths than hedges without.

The best hedges for moths are those that merge gradually with the adjacent grassland habitat. This one, at Sawbridgeworth Marsh, is one of the few remaining hedges in the county that supports 1642: Lappet (*Gastropacha quercifolia*) – even though the other side, against a road, is regularly trimmed. (Photograph copyright © Colin W. Plant)

The all too familiar winter flailing of hedges is an act of sheer vandalism. It removes over-wintering eggs and is very largely responsible for the loss of many species that overwinter in this stage. The resultant opening up of the hedge at the coldest time of year lets the frost in to kill hibernating adults, larvae and pupae. (Photograph copyright © Colin W. Plant)

The urban and suburban environments

Much modern moth data for Britain originate from light traps operated in domestic gardens, ranking this habitat amongst the most thoroughly recorded in the country. Inevitably, garden lists will include both primary immigrants and moths that have 'wandered' from nearby specialist habitats, but the resident moth fauna of the 'average' garden is characterised by species whose larvae feed on herbaceous plants or bushes or on plants associated with disturbed (ruderal) habitats. By and large, the canopy-feeders are poorly represented

The Robinson trap in the author's garden at Bishops Stortford. Even the smallest of gardens can generate a lengthy list of moths. (Photograph copyright © Colin W. Plant)

(though seldom absent) and it is interesting that, to a degree, the moth inventory will vary with the socio-economic class of the garden owner (for example, 1788: Scarce Tissue *Rheumaptera cervinalis* is typically found in large, well-maintained gardens, but is generally absent from areas of local authority owned housing, whilst the reverse is true for many species that feed on annual weeds).

Away from gardens, the ruderal flora that typically develops on the disturbed ground of post-industrial ('brownfield') sites can support a varied moth fauna. Species such as 382: Six-belted Clearwing (*Bembecia ichneumoniformis*), 1867: Treble-bar (*Aplocera plagiata*), 1868: Lesser Treble-bar (*A. efformata*) and 2221: Mullein (*Shargacucullia verbasci*) are typical.

Bovingdon Brick Pits. The ruderal flora of post-industrial sites supports a varied and rich moth fauna. (Photograph copyright © Colin W. Plant).

Over-wintering sites

Moth recording is certainly more pleasant in the warm, summer months, but the insects themselves are, of course, available for examination all year round. Many of the losses from the moth fauna may result from the excessive desire for 'tidying up' the countryside, which destroys hibernation sites. Neatly mown verges alongside roads, dead branches removed from trees, hedges cut square, dilapidated wooden fences replaced with metal and the uncontrollable desire to burn anything that falls or can be felled from a tree – the list is endless. These, and many others, are important micro-habitats for a wide range of invertebrates. Caterpillars of 2475: Waved Black (*Parascotia fuliginaria*) feed on fungi under the bark of fallen logs and those of 371: Lunar Hornet Moth (*Sesia bembeciformis*) tunnel within the bases of sallow trunks; both probably owe much of their rarity to burning following conservation management work on nature reserves. As well as eliminating over-wintering eggs on twigs, winter flailing of hedges exposes old nests of birds to the frost and so kills a range of hibernating moths, especially micros. A great many wetland moths pass the winter, in one stage or another, in or on stems of reeds or other amphibious vegetation; in Hertfordshire, we simply do not have enough of this habitat to allow burning to feature in the rotational management of reed beds, sedge beds and similar places. In general, tidying is a bad thing; burning has no place at all in conservation management.

Synanthropic habitats

Synanthropy is the association by a species with humans and their dwellings. In many cases it results from a species normally associated with a natural micro-habitat, for example a bird's nest, adapting to an easier life in association with humans. It is interesting to speculate whether the ubiquitous 647: Brown House Moth (*Hofmannophila pseudospretella*) or 648: White-shouldered House Moth (*Endrosis sarcitrella*) may have been rare before the advent of human habitation. Certainly, many of the clothes moths (Tineidae) that were such a nuisance in my grandfather's day (who can forget he smell of 'moth balls' in every cupboard and drawer) have been reduced to comparative rarity by the replacement of wool and cotton with artificial materials such as nylon and rayon, though occasional outbreaks can occur.

Accumulations of leaves and other debris in the epicormic growth around tree bases such as this at Gilston provide hibernation sites for many species of moths. (Photograph copyright © Colin W. Plant).

Road verge at Sawbridgeworth. Good verge management involves leaving dead stems of annual plants *in situ*. The ivy-clad tree in the background also provides an important over-wintering area. (Photograph copyright © Colin W. Plant).

Hertfordshire's Weather

The climate of Britain is notoriously variable and changeable from day to day; it is also apparently changing in the longer term. Nevertheless, some of the more 'freak' weather events of recent years are not new. Events such as the exceptionally cold winter of 1962/1963, the drought summers of 1976 and 2003 and the famous hurricane of October 1987 are not unique to modern times. Examination of the weather reports in past issues of the *Transactions of the Hertfordshire Natural History Society* reveals some interesting facts, including that the year 1881 had them all. On 18th January 1881, there was an easterly gale which brought blizzards which 'for two or three days impeded, and in many cases stopped, all traffic by road and rail'. Temperatures fell to 5° Fahrenheit (approximately minus 15° Celsius). On 15th July 1881, there was a sudden heat wave, with the temperature rising to 91°F (approximately 33°C) at Watford and on 14th October 1881 the entire of Britain was affected by a hurricane which resulted in many blank pages appearing in *The Times* newspaper ('Owing to the hurricane which raged over the country yesterday from very early morning, and which, though less fierce, had by no means abated when we went to press this morning, we have been almost entirely deprived of telegraphic news, communications being interrupted in all directions').

Longer term changes to the underlying weather pattern, however, are of greater relevance to interpretation of moth distributions and especially of any shifts observed in seasonality of appearance. These climatic changes are likely to have a far reaching effect on the natural environment, perhaps in particular on the hydrological aspects of the county. Summer droughts and winter flooding may become the norm.

The following comments are based on data supplied by The Met Office for the years 1971 to 2000. These years only partly overlap with our 'current' moth recording period of 1995 to 2006, but are the most recent for which data is available.

British weather is generally cool to mild with frequent cloud and rain, but occasional settled spells of weather occur in all seasons. The eastern side of Britain tends to be a little colder in winter and warmer in summer and is drier the year round than the rest of the country, with a tendency for summer rain to be heavier than that of winter. The south-east in particular has more temperature variations with warmer summers and cooler winters. The climate of Hertfordshire is most easily presented pictorially and the maps below require little interpretation. Based on average July temperatures, Hertfordshire falls entirely in the warmest part of Britain and receives a good deal of sunshine (though southern counties receive more); as a consequence, it falls in the area of the country most prone to thunder storms, even though the average precipitation (rainfall) is the lowest in Britain. During the winter, however, the temperature varies across the county with the south-east being, on average, three of four degrees warmer than the higher ground in the north-west, and this means that when snow falls, something of a rarity these days, it is more likely in the north-west and it usually melts fairly quickly.

I have not the space to explore in detail here the implications of the climate on the moth fauna of Hertfordshire, nor to speculate on any changes that might take place as the global climate alters. However, as with the geology map, the reader is encouraged to interpret distribution patterns of moths in the light of information presented here and to reach his or her own conclusions.

January temperature

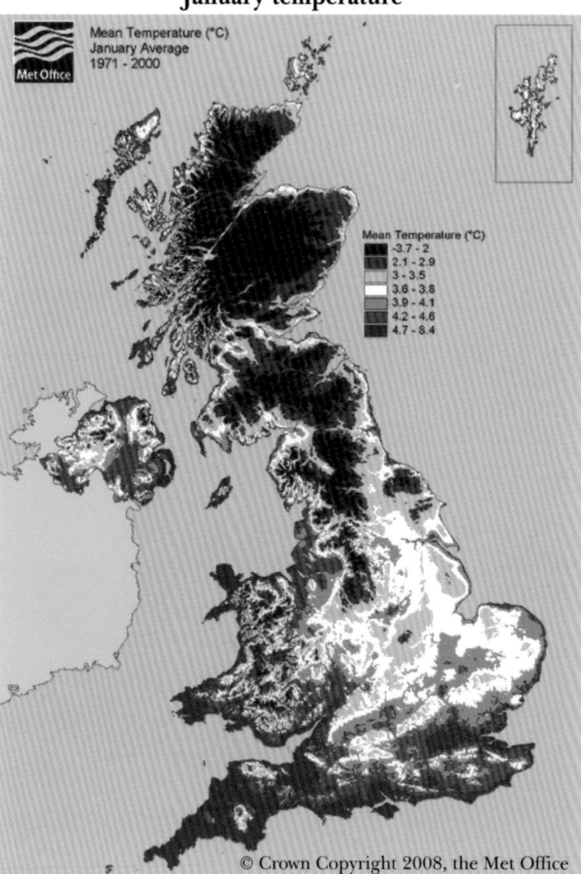

July temperature

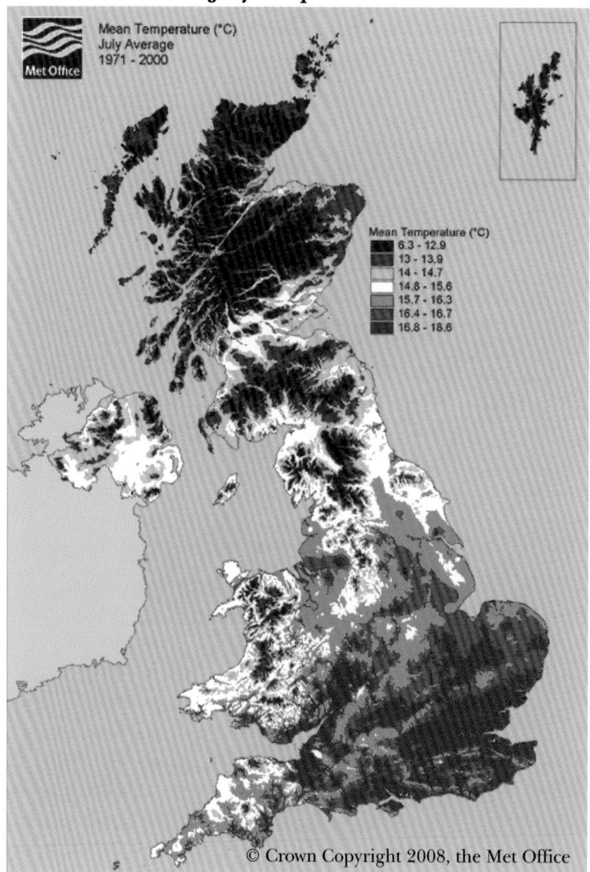

Rainfall

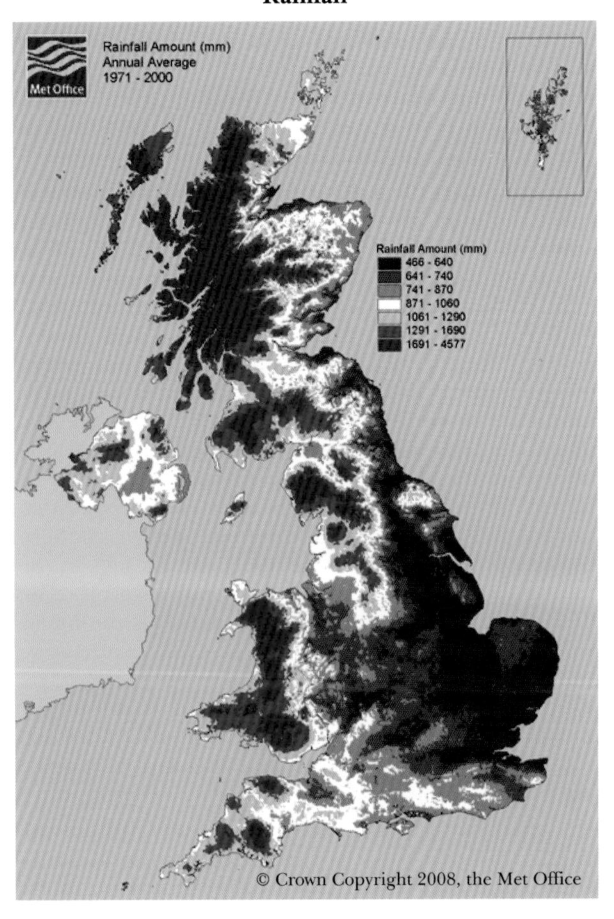

Sunshine

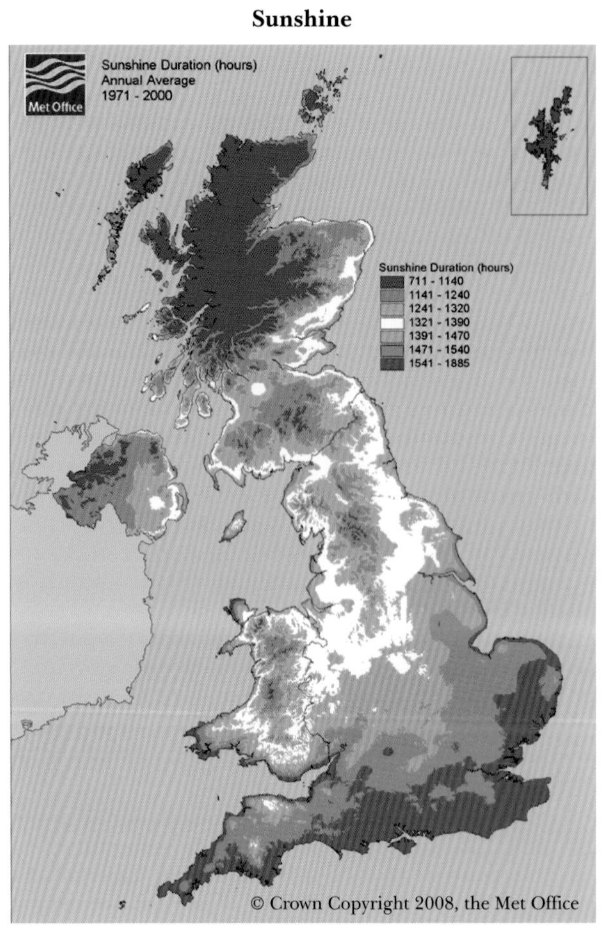

Snow

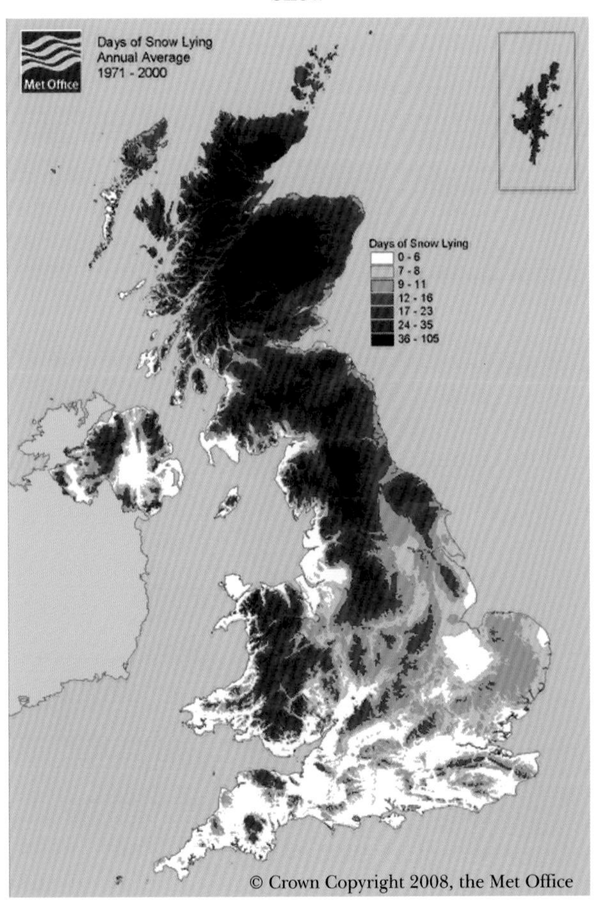

Thunder

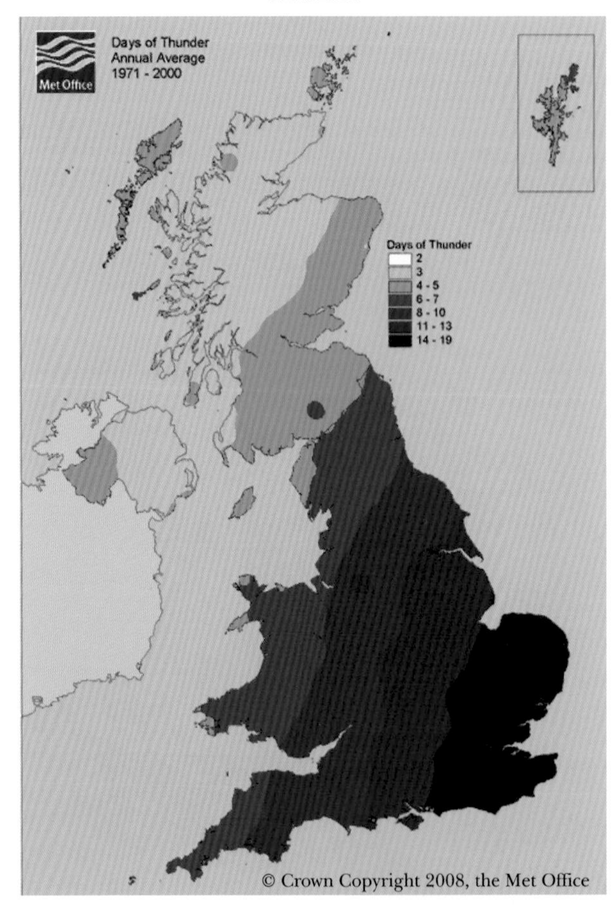

Introducing Moths

Scientific classification for beginners

Oh-oh! It's a moth! I blew it!
Ode to a grasshopper
Jim Morrison (The Doors)
Hollywood Bowl, 5th July 1968

Moths, along with butterflies, belong to a group of insects known as the Lepidoptera. That word is derived from the two ancient Greek words *Lepidos* = scales and *Ptera* = wings. The wings of all butterflies and moths consist of a flat, transparent membrane which is covered, usually completely, with minute scales. The scales also cover the rest of the body including the antennae and legs and in most species only the eyes are bare. It is these scales which carry the colours that can be seen on the wings of butterflies and moths. Some Lepidoptera can be confused with caddis flies, which are known scientifically as the Trichoptera from the Greek *trichos* = a hair with *ptera* = wings, to give hairy wings. It is the fact that there are hairs arising from the wing *membrane* that distinguishes them from the Lepidoptera. Small caddis flies often enter moth traps and are mistaken for 'micro' moths.

The Lepidoptera share their ancestry with caddis flies; we think they 'diverged' during the Jurassic Period (206 – 144 million years ago). Today there are around 165,000 species worldwide (McGavin, 2001). There is great diversity within the Lepidoptera. Wingspans range from 3 mm in some of the leaf-mining nepticulids to 300 mm in tropical species and whilst most have a long tongue (properly called the *haustellum*), which they use to feed on nectar from flowers and which is usually coiled when not in use, others have sideways operating jaws and feed on pollen grains. Yet others, including some British species, do not feed in the adult stage and so have no functional mouthparts at all. There are other variations too, most notably the means by which the fore and hind wings are connected, or not, during flight. A great many species have a stiff spine, or a group of spines, the *frenulum* that projects forward from the leading edge of the hind wing at its base and hook into a part of the adjacent forewing called the *retinaculum* thus connecting the wings to function as a single unit in flight. However, this is absent from others, notably the swifts (Hepialidae) in Britain, so that all four wings operate independently.

These, and other fundamental differences that have arisen during the evolutionary history of the group, rather than more ephemeral things such as wing colour, are used to subdivide the Lepidoptera into five 'Suborders' (of which three are represented in both Britain and Hertfordshire). These are further split into 42 Superfamilies (names always ending in *–oidea*) containing 127 Families (names always ending in *–idae*) as shown in the following table (adapted from McGavin, 2001, which is a recommended source of further information).

Order Lepidoptera

Suborder Zeugloptera
Superfamily Micropterigoidea
Functional jaws present: 1 British family – Micropterigidae, species 1 to 5 in the British list

Suborder Aglossata
Non-British

Suborder Heterobathmiina
Non-British

Suborder Glossata
Species with a proboscis (which may be reduced or vestigial) instead of jaws

Monotrysia
Species with a single genital opening used for mating and egg-laying

Superfamily Eriocranoidea (1 British family – Eriocraniidae, species 6 to 13 in the British list)

Superfamily Hepialoidea (1 British family – Hepialidae, species 14 to 18 in the British list)

Superfamily Incurvarioidea (4 British families – Incurvariidae, Prodoxidae, Adelidae and Heliozelidae, species 128 to 159 in the British list)

Superfamily Nepticuloidea (1 British family – Nepticulidae, species 19 to 122 in the British list)

Superfamily Tischerioidea (1 British family – Tischeriidae, species 123 to 127 in the British list)

Ditrysia
Species with two genital openings – one for mating and one for egg-laying

Superfamily Papilionoidea (true butterflies)
Superfamily Hesperioidea (skipper butterflies)
} together, the 'Rhopalocera' or butterflies

Plus 18 Superfamilies containing all remaining British moths

What's the difference between a moth and a butterfly?

According to contemporary poet Rob Walker,

Moths
go about their work
stoically in grey suits
or grimy blue overalls
pollinating flowers
feed birds and frogs
need fur coats for warmth
working the graveyard shift

Butterflies are showy socialites
sipping nectar at
A-list cocktail parties
all show, no substance.
superficial in their beauty
mwah-mwahing incincere air kisses
to the Beautiful Pupae.

Moths are the working class
waiting for the revolution

Our slightly more scientific scheme, however, is based on evolutionary trends, placing the most primitive groups first and the most highly evolved last. This process is usually repeated in the ordering of both families and the species within the families. True butterflies fall into a single superfamily called Papilionoidea whilst the skippers form a completely separate grouping, the Hesperioidea. Collectively, they are just two Superfamilies of the Ditrysian Glossata and significantly, because the scheme puts things into evolutionary sequence, butterflies fall in the middle of the Lepidoptera series, with moths before and moths after, rather than being at one end. So, the separation of butterflies from moths begs the question 'what do you mean by butterflies?' The answer for the papilionids will be different to that given for the hesperiids and trying to find common links between the two is difficult. In Britain, true papilionid butterflies have clubbed antennae, fly by day rather than at night and have brightly-coloured wings (as clearly observed in Rob Walker's poem, above), which are held closed above the body at rest, but these are all features that can also be found amongst the moths (though admittedly, not all in combination). The skippers have close affinities with the true butterflies, but they also have greater affinities with several moths; more than any other group, skippers are best regarded as 'honorary moths' rather than 'honorary butterflies'. However, in keeping with the non-scientific convention I have not included the skippers in this present review of Hertfordshire's moths.

Why do we need 'Latin' names and who invents them anyway?

What's in a name? that which we call a rose,
By any other name would smell as sweet;
William Shakespeare
Romeo and Juliet (1594)

The fundamental need for a 'scientific' name (they are actually a combination of a Greek first name and a Latin second name in most cases) is a simple matter of the need to be understood in different countries. If I write about *L'Écaille hérissonne* most British readers would have no idea what I was talking about. Similarly, if whilst on holiday in France I made a record of a Garden Tiger the French recorder for the region where I found it would probably be equally in the dark. Both could, of course, look up the name I used, but actually knowing where to look presents a problem and then there's the effort of actually doing the research – and probably repeating if for the hundred or so other names on my list. However, in both countries, the name *Arctia caja* would either be immediately recognised or could be immediately looked up in a checklist – all three names refer to the same species.

Latin names are in fact just a further subdivision of the hierarchy of classification discussed above. Back in the mists of time, scholars described new species of insects by a brief sentence in Latin. For example, if I may be forgiven for using a butterfly as an example rather than a moth, James Petiver writing in 1699 in his work *Musei Petiverana centuria prima – decima* describes a species which after translation reads '*the brown-eyed butterfly with yellow circles*' – a species which today we know as the Ringlet. In the days before global communication when the bulk of the population didn't care and couldn't read in any case, this scarcely mattered a great deal, but it should be obvious to all that both Petiver's Latin description and the subsequently contrived English name could probably be applied to many species elsewhere in the world. Some sort of standard naming system was called for!

Enter a clever young Swedish chap called Carl von Linné (1697 – 1778). Linnaeus, by which latinised form of his name he is better known, came up with the brilliantly simple system of giving everything a name comprising just two words – the now universally used *binomial* system. This system was launched upon the unsuspecting scientific community in 1758 in his book *Systema Naturae*. The model was, presumably, the human system (remembering that outside Britain, many countries put family name first and given name second). The first part of the Linnaean binomial affects a group of species that have characters in common, just like close family members such as brothers, sisters and parents. The word that covers 'having things in common' is *generic* and so this first name is the generic name – which we call the *genus* (plural *genera*). Linnaeus had only a limited number of genera, though he freely admitted '*ea quae scimus sunt pars minima eorum, quae ignoramus*' which translates as ' the ones we know form only a fraction of the many of which we have no knowledge'. The second part is the name given to the individual species within each genus and is often referred to as the 'specific epithet'.

By analogy with names of people, Smith John, Smith George and Smith Mary are all different individuals (species), but all have something in common – they are all Smiths (in this model, that would be their genus). Similarly, Jones Tom, Jones Dick and Jones Harry are also all different whilst sharing something (surname – genus) in common), but they are also all three different from the three Smiths; their relationship is higher up the chain – they are all from Hertfordshire. If you can understand this, then you can understand scientific names!

Why do scientific names change?

When I was at school there were two 'Plants' in my Form, Michael A. Plant and myself, Colin W. Plant. In order to distinguish us, I was referred to as 'Plant Major' and the other chap was 'Plant Minor' (though after a remarkably short while the teachers, in a move led rather surprisingly by my Latin Master, slipped into a less formal 'CW' and 'MA'). Essentially, we were renamed – twice! Yet we remain the same people.

So it was that as soon as Linnaeus told everyone about his binomial system they all set about applying it and, inevitably, started to encounter all those '*many of which we have no knowledge*' species. The intention always was to encourage others to apply names to these new discoveries, so it was not long before scientists in Austria, France and England started to apply their own scientific names to the same species that occurred in all three countries. The result – confusion: same species, but two or three different names! This problem required resolution. Enter the *International Commission for Zoological Nomenclature* (ICZN). The origins of this body are not relevant to the present discussion; suffice to say that they are the final arbiter in matters of repeated names. In order to achieve a satisfactory resolution in such situations, a set of rigid rules is applied. Essentially, it's a case of 'first come first served' – whichever name was applied to the species first is the name that applies (this is called the Rule of Priority).

To take a real example from amongst Hertfordshire's moths, during 1766 the German entomologist Hufnagel discovered a new species of moth which we call the Dotted Rustic. He recognised that it had characters of the genus *Phalaena* which had been created by Linnaeus, but it was a completely new species. Perhaps because its habit of aestivation (summer hibernation) caused early observers to think that it was feigning death, Hufnagel gave it the specific epithet *simulans* (= pretending). The full name of the moth was, therefore, *Phalaena simulans*. A few years later, in 1775, the Viennese entomologists Denis and Schiffermüller also discovered a new species of moth. They considered that it was a member of the Linnaean genus *Phalaena*, but that it was a species not previously described. They called it *Phalaena pyrophila*.

This was all well and good until the Germans started talking to the Austrians. In those days there was no radio, television, telephone and certainly no Internet, whilst sending a letter took even longer than it does today. Books were rare items, owned only by a few and written by even fewer and there would be little reason to expect that Denis and Schiffermüller would have had access to the publications of Hufnagel. It comes as no surprise, therefore, to learn that both sets of authors had independently discovered and described the same species. Rigid application of the '*Law of Priorities*' says that the first name is the correct one, and so the moth is correctly called *simulans* and the name *pyrophila* is referred to as a synonym.

It's the same with genus names

As we learn more and more about moths, through field work, breeding experiments and more recently from examination of DNA structure, we often have to revise our opinions concerning the relationships between species. In our example above, closer investigation of the moths after the initial impetus provided by Linnaeus showed that there were rather more than the mere five or six genera that he had created. His *Phalaena* was 'split' into a great many new genera, one of which is called *Rhyacia* and it is into this genus that *simulans* was placed and still remains.

Brackets or no brackets

For absolute clarity, it is conventional to place the names of the authors who described a moth after the name that they created. Thus, in our example using the Dotted Rustic, the full original name is *Phalaena simulans* Hufnagel, 1766 and the full name for the Austrian species is *Phalaena pyrophila* Denis & Schiffermüller, 1775. By placing the dates after the authors it is clear when the name was applied. However, when in 1821 another German, Hübner, created the genus *Rhyacia* he realised that the species *simulans* of Hufnagel belonged there. In making the move there is a risk that the origin of the name could be lost and so following convention we place Hufnagel's name, and the date, within brackets to indicate that Hufnagel himself, whilst being the author of the same *simulans* did not place his species in *Rhyacia*. Thus, in our example, the correct and full citation of the name for the Dotted Rustic should be *Rhyacia simulans* (Hufnagel, 1766).

Thus, it is now instantly possible to know that *Sphinx ligustri* Linnaeus, 1758 (the Privet Hawk) was not only named as '*ligustri*' by Linnaeus in 1758, but also that when he created that name he also placed the moth with others in the genus *Sphinx* whilst *Deilephila porcellus* (Linnaeus, 1758) was named *porcellus* by Linnaeus in 1758, but was not placed in *Deilephila* at that stage (in fact, Linnaeus called it *Sphinx porcellus*). So, the presence or absence of brackets surrounding authors' names follows set rules and is not a random act on the part of an editor! All this becomes of particular importance when trying to work out which species are implied in

some of the older British literature or, indeed, in foreign works.

This same system may require us to 'move' a moth species to a different part of the checklist for similar reasons. This has been done, for example, with 2268: *Parastichtis suspecta* (The Suspected), which for a long time was placed, for want of adequate knowledge, within the subfamily Acronictinae before it was realised that it actually belonged to the Amphipyrinae. What's more, research also showed that it belongs to the same genus as a species that was already there – 2314: *Parastichtis ypsillon* (Dingy Shears). At the time, the latter species was known as *Enargia ypsillon*, but when it was realised that the two species were members of one and the same genus the oldest name, *Parastichtis*, was adopted for it using the Rule of Priority.

Validity of names

It is not permitted to change a name without good reason and all the valid 'good reasons' are listed in a regularly updated *Code* produced by the ICZN. Different names used by the various authors of identification guides and other popular works (including this one) have no scientific validity significance unless they are backed by argument and/or data. Such names, not supported by argument, are sometimes included in name lists with the words *nomen nudum* ('naked name') afterwards. However, peer-reviewed publications that are in effect a formal 'taxonomic review' need to be taken into account. Of relevance to British moths are the ten currently published volumes of *Noctuidae Europaea*. These have introduced some radical changes, including the revelation that the British species known as Barrett's Marbled Coronet (not known from Hertfordshire) is in fact *Conisana* (was *Hadena*) *andalusica* (Staudinger) and not *Conisania luteago* ([Denis & Schiffermüller]) or the lumping of our *Aporophyla lutulenta* (Deep-brown Dart) with *Aporophyla lueneburgensis* (Northern Deep-brown Dart) under the latter name on the basis that the true *lutulenta* is an Eastern European species that does not occur in Britain.

Anybody can describe a new species of moth if they are lucky enough to find one, provided that a few simple rules are followed. These inevitably include doing some research to make sure that you are not re-describing a species that someone else has already named. There are two principal ways in which this lack of duplication is achieved. First, new species should be described only in established, easily accessible (at a world-wide level), peer-reviewed journals, so that subsequent research by others is made easy. 'Peer-reviewed' means that submitted papers are scrutinised, usually severely so and almost always anonymously, by 'experts' in the area of your research. Suitable British journals for describing new species of moths are, at the end of 2007, the *Entomologist's Record and Journal of Variation* and *Entomologist's Gazette*. Suitable European journals include *Nota Lepidopterologica* and *SHILAP Revista Lepidopterologia*. Publication of a new species in a magazine or a popular work such as an identification guide is severely frowned upon and because of the lack of peer-review might subsequently be shown to be invalid.

What are type specimens?

If you decide that you have a new species, a 'type' specimen must be elected and deposited in a suitable safe place. This is the single specimen upon which the original diagnostic description of the moth must be based. This specimen is referred to as the Holotype and must always be labelled as such. If you also describe an example of the opposite sex then the selected specimen becomes the Allotype. The holotype is in fact **the** species, which is why it is so important. If you catch another example in your garden light trap, this is, technically, not the same species – it is merely *referable to* your species. Thus, when describing a new species you need to borrow (or travel to see) and examine the type specimens of similar species before rushing into publication; this can take time, which is why it sometimes takes ages for new species to be published. It is also why it is essential (and according to the rules compulsory) to state where the type specimen is finally deposited. This will usually be a museum, though as one who worked in a museum that was subsequently closed and its collections dispersed or discarded this is not a rule to which I adhere as strictly as do my peers.

On rare occasions, where a moth may vary in appearance, a selection of specimens can be described alongside the Holotype, and these specimens are described as being the Type Series. Of course, you need to be absolutely sure that all the examples in a type series really are the same species. The classic failure in this regard is, of course, with the Common Rustic, described from a series of variable specimens as *Mesapamea secalis* until it was later discovered that some dark examples were a different species, *Mesapamea didyma* – the Lesser Common Rustic.

Why is the collecting of specimens important?

> *The caterpillar on the leaf*
> *Repeats to thee thy mother's grief*
> *Kill not the moth nor butterfly*
> *For the Last Judgment draweth nigh!*

So said William Blake in *Auguries of Innocence* (1803), perhaps reflecting the misunderstanding of the uneducated majority more than any genuine ethical objection to collecting. Certainly, in Blake's day collecting was, with a few notable exceptions, undertaken for pure leisure purposes which would today be widely regarded as unacceptable. However, whilst the days of collectors travelling the country to amass long 'series' of rare butterflies and moths are largely a thing of the past and arguably have no place in today's conservation-conscious world, discouraging children and students from making a collection is potentially depriving us of the scientists of the future.

The study of invertebrates and the formation of reference collections, complete with their inherent recorded data, are important sources of information which make a vital contribution to the conservation of the invertebrate fauna and to conservation in general. To this end, accurate identification of species is essential; this often requires the examination of dead specimens. Good environmental conservation is based upon the sound ecological knowledge that results from diligent research; in Britain, the pitiful lack of state funding means that such research is almost entirely carried out by amateurs. A good teacher will not discourage a hobbyist, but will steer the student in a direction that results, ultimately, in the creation of a potential scientist.

It goes without saying that all material collected should have a purpose; that purpose will usually be pre-defined, but may be as simple as the provision of a 'voucher specimen' to support a record submitted to a recording scheme. Specimens should be individually labelled with the place and date of capture as well as the name of the collector and they should be preserved in a suitable safe place. Further provision ought to be made for them following the death of the collector – many an important specimen has been discarded by unsympathetic relatives following his or her death.

Moth trapping, as undertaken by a growing army of amateur enthusiasts, does not harm moths: they remain alive and can be released in the morning. But even if all the moth traps in Britain killed all the moths attracted to them there would be no effect on the populations of moths – those who profess to disagree are likely to be unfamiliar with the population dynamics of insects. The numbers of insects are huge; whilst a bird might be rare if it is down to the last few hundred breeding pairs, for a moth to be rare its numbers may well remain in the millions (and there is, of course, a difference between 'animal rights' and conservation). The problem with rare moths is that their habitat is also likely to be threatened. Removal of a few dozen individuals of a rare moth from a particular habitat is very unlikely to adversely effect the survival of the species in question since, if populations are so low that they can be wiped out by killing the catch in a moth trap then the species is destined for extinction in any event. Damage to the habitat could easily eliminate the entire population in a single go; collecting an individual might well lead to the site being recognised and protected. Since we do not know now what we will know in fifty years from today, all we can do is adopt the precautionary approach and to my mind *scientific* collecting of insects, including moths, is not only justifiable but an essential part of the fight to maintain the survival of the human race. Standardised sampling of moths in the network of RIS traps (discussed in the contributed chapter commencing on page 31), has provided a means of assessing long term trends in moth population (and continues to do so) and is *the* reason why the organisation *Butterfly Conservation* has been able to state, unequivocally, that a number of our species are in serious decline.

Restraint is already exercised by most people who study moths in the field. The *Code of Conduct* on page 26 has been adapted for moths from the code issued by Invertebrate Link (Joint Committee for the Conservation of British Invertebrates) covering all invertebrates. The full version of that code is available at many invertebrate conservation websites, in volume 15 of *Journal of British Entomology and Natural History* (2002), and on sale from AES Publications, www.amentsoc.org. By subscribing to this code entomologists can show themselves to be a concerned and responsible body of committed naturalists who wish to maximise the value of their data for conservation.

The lepidopterist with happy cries,
devotes his days to catching butterflies.
The leopard, through some feline mental twist,
would rather hunt the lepidopterist.
That's why I never adopted lepidoptery:
I do not wish to live in jeopardoptery.

The Lepidopterist by Ogden Nash

Introducing Moth Recording

The reasons for recording moths are surely founded in plain, old-fashioned human curiosity? Starting with Thomas Moffet (1553 – 1634), whose book *Insectorum sive minimorum Animalium Theatrum* was the first known book about insects to be published in Britain, then through John Ray (1627 – 1705) whose name is perpetuated in 'The Ray Society' – publishers of the two important volumes *British Tortricoid Moths* and James Petiver (1663 – 1718), whose pamphlets and broadsheets published from 1695 onwards contain the first mention of a great many British insects, to more recent entomologists such as J. W. Tutt (1858 – 1911) founder (in 1890) of the journal *Entomologist's Record and Journal of Variation* and Edward Meyrick (1854 – 1938), an entirely amateur lepidopterist whose '*Handbook of British Lepidoptera*', first published in 1895, provided the primary basis for the development of the science throughout the twentieth century, the emphasis has been on the discovery of new things.

In a much more recent period of history, the realisation by an enlightened few that profound change was being imposed upon the Earth as a result of acts of pure folly by the human race, led to the desire to discover being gradually replaced by a desire to understand. The natural sciences, formerly the preserve of an educated few whose emphasis was, essentially, on collecting specimens, began to enjoy an expanded popularity. The passing of the *National Parks and Access to the Countryside Act*, in 1949 allowed, for the first time, access to areas of the countryside that had previously been 'out of bounds' to ordinary people. Environmental awareness, albeit still largely species-based, had been heightened by the enactment of the *Protection of Birds Act* in 1933, prior to which birds were pretty much fair game for collectors, pet traders, egg collectors and gamekeepers alike, though there was no legal protection for any moth species until the Wildlife and Countryside Act, was enacted in 1981.

With this expanded popularity was born the concept of distribution mapping, first undertaken for plants in 1960, but very quickly picked up by entomologists. Of course, 'county lists' were not new. The 'Victoria County History of ...' series, generated at the start of the twentieth century included lists of the Lepidoptera for most of the counties covered, that for Hertfordshire was published in 1902. The historical aspects of moth recording in Hertfordshire are now discussed in greater detail.

A Code of Conduct for Collecting Moths

1 Collecting – general

- Never take more specimens from the wild than you need for your specific purpose.
- Avoid killing or removing moths from the wild without good reason (e.g. if essential for scientific study or identification, but not for trade).
- Do as little damage to the habitat as possible.
- Take care of collected specimens and ensure their availability for study in perpetuity.

2 Collecting – rare, local and endangered species

- Obey all laws and bylaws that prohibit or control collecting on protected sites or the collection of protected species.
- Exercise the utmost restraint if collecting taxa listed as being of 'Conservation Concern'
- If, for reasons of *bona fide* scientific study, you need to sample populations of listed taxa, do so only if the proposed sampling is known not to be damaging.
- Always report new findings of rare species to the appropriate conservation agencies, records centres and organisers of recording schemes.

3 Collecting - traps and lights

- Use live trapping (without anaesthetics) where possible and release the catch in cool, shady conditions near the trap site after examining, recording and retaining voucher specimens if essential.
- If a trap used for repeated sampling is found to be catching rare or local species unnecessarily it should be re-sited.
- Traps and lights should be sited with care so as not to annoy or confuse other people.

4 Collecting - permissions and conditions

- Always seek permission from the landowner or occupier before collecting on private land, or obtain appropriate permit(s) for access and/or collecting on any site controlled by a statutory or conservation body. Collecting on a Site of Special Scientific Interest (SSSI) requires permission from both the owner and the national conservation agency (Natural England, Scottish Natural Heritage or Countryside Council for Wales)
- Always comply with any conditions laid down with the granting of access and the permission to collect.
- Always report your findings to the person who gave you permission, at least by commenting orally on the ecological requirements of a few species of interest. If the site is protected or managed for wildlife, send the organisation(s) concerned a full list of the species recorded, annotated with habitat data.

5 Collecting - protecting the environment

- Protect the environment and do as little damage as possible; remember the interests of other naturalists and avoid harm to nesting birds and vegetation, particularly rare or fragile plants.
- If you collect or dismantle any habitat items (e.g. seed heads, loose bark or dead wood), always leave a good proportion intact.
- Do not apply 'sugar' to tree trunks or other surfaces that support lichens or that would appear unsightly (e.g. in sight of roads, rides etc.). Consider using 'wine ropes' instead.
- Do not uproot plants or dig up turf without permission from the landowner, as this is generally illegal in the UK. Also, observe the law regarding protected plant species.
- If collecting litter from vertebrate nests or roosts, do so only in compliance with the laws applying to the species concerned.
- Follow the Country Code and comply with all bylaws that apply to the site concerned.

6 Recording - general

- Keep full and relevant data together with all specimens, even if you also duplicate the data in databases, notebooks and other media.
- Species lists, together with habitat and other data, should be sent to the relevant county and national recording schemes.

7 Rearing and breeding

- If obtaining breeding stock of scarce species, try to do so from established captive colonies, rather than from wild-caught sources.
- If taking larvae or other livestock from the wild, never take more than you can adequately feed and maintain in captivity.
- If you have surplus invertebrates from rearing or breeding, observe genetic and ecological precautions, i.e. do not release them except into their parental population and do not release large numbers back into the population if it is small and localised.
- Do not attempt to establish new populations or to reinforce existing ones except within an ecologically sound programme. This would have to be well prepared in consultation with the appropriate conservation agencies, agreed with the owner or occupier of the site concerned and notified to other appropriate organisations, including wildlife trusts and recording schemes.
- Obey any laws relating to the release of invertebrates into the wild; the release in the UK of any non-native kinds is illegal, except under special licence.

A Brief History of Moth Recording in Hertfordshire

One of the earliest of Hertfordshire Lepidopterists was **James Francis Stephens**, who was employed in the Admiralty office, Somerset House, 1807 – 1845, but also assisted in arranging the insect collection at the British Museum (Natural History). He was educated at The Bluecoat School, Hertford and collected insects extensively in southern Hertfordshire and North London, especially the Hertford area. He was author the of the four volume work *Illustrations of British Entomology (Haustellata),* published from 1828 to 1834, in which there are references to 129 Hertfordshire Lepidoptera – most of which are the earliest Hertfordshire references to the species concerned.

In 1862, the **Haileybury and Imperial Service College** was established and on 6th November 1872 the Haileybury Natural Science Society was founded, with the object of studying natural history in the college grounds and nearby areas. Under the guidance of the Masters, the boys established a museum and set about recording work, producing several annual reports. In 1888 the first list of the moths at the school and its surrounds was produced by Robert William Bowyer (? – 1905), a master at the school from 1869 to 1901, under the title '*Some methods of moth collecting*', and published in *Transactions of the Hertfordshire Natural History Society* **5**: 23 – 32. Revisions were published in 1902 and 1926, but these were apparently authored by the schoolboys with minimal validation of the records and, as a consequence, they are to a large extent unreliable. Sawford (1987. *The Butterflies of Hertfordshire*) says that 'specimens still survive in the Haileybury Museum, but, most unfortunately, data labels were not attached to the majority and it is not possible to be absolutely certain of their provenances'. The school museum was closed in 1993. In spite of the less than convincing nature of many records the list is an important source of data for many moth species from what is the northern part of the Broxbourne Woods complex, including Hertford Heath, Hailey Wood, High Wood, Goldings Wood and probably also Balls Wood.

On 23rd January 1875 the **Watford Natural History Society and Hertfordshire Field Club** was founded with, as its objective, '*the investigation of the natural history of the neighbourhood of Watford and the County of Hertford and the dissemination of information amongst its members*'. They too set up a museum, though it is interesting to note that the Society's objects also included the statement that they '... shall discourage the practice of removing are plants ... and of exterminating rare birds, fish and other animals'. Their first *Transactions* were published in 1875 and contained a paper entitled '*Notes on the observation of insects in connexion with investigations of seasonal phenomena*' by Arthur Cottam (pages 50 – 51). The Convolvulus Hawk-moth (*Agrius convolvuli*) is the only moth mentioned. This is in the following paragraph, from which the ignorance which prevailed at that date of immigration by Lepidoptera is apparent:

> *Occasional appearances in unusual numbers. It is well known that certain insects appear occasionally in enormous numbers, and then are comparatively rare, or disappear altogether, for a series of years.* Vanessa Cardui *(the painted lady butterfly),* Colias Edusa *and* Hyale *(the clouded-yellow butterflies),* Sphinx Convolvuli *(the convolvulus hawk-moth), are familiar examples. Such exceptional occurrences should be carefully noticed. Meteorologists may thus possibly throw light upon phenomena that have never been satisfactorily accounted for by naturalists.*

On 1st July 1879, the Watford society was renamed as the **Hertfordshire Natural History Society and Field Club (HNHS)**. Their *Transactions of the Hertfordshire Natural History Society* (*Trans. HNHS*), replaced the *Transactions of the Watford Natural History Society*, which had seen only two volumes, although the emphasis of the Society was, inevitably, still concentrated in the west.

John Hopkinson, FLS, FZS, FRMetSoc, (1844-1919) co-founder of the Hertfordshire Natural History Society and eminent local phenologist.

The Hertfordshire society's first entomological Recorder seems to have been **Miss Eleanor Anne Ormerod**, who was consulting entomologist (unpaid) to the Royal Agricultural Society. Apparently a somewhat fearsome, lady, she devised many cheap-and-easy methods for destroying some of the world's worst agricultural pests but, whilst nobody objected to her schemes to control codling moth or wipe out warble fly, when she determined to completely eradicate the house sparrow, she found herself hanged in effigy. For more details, read the article by Stephanie Pain in the *New Scientist*, volume 172, issue 2316 for 10th November 2001. Although she does not seem to have recorded any moths in the county, she encouraged observers to submit records (*Trans. Watford NHS* **2**: 77) and references in the *Transactions* indicate that Miss Ormerod attended several of the meetings and frequently gave advice and opinion on such matters as how to eradicate common pests such as Goat Moth (*Cossus cossus*) larvae from apple trees in one's garden!

From 1883, the HNHS has appointed specific Lepidoptera Recorders for the county, commencing with **Arthur Forster Griffith**, who stayed in post until 1888. Griffith contributed two important papers to the Hertfordshire entomological literature in the form of *Notes on Lepidoptera observed in the neighbourhood of Sandridge, Herts* in 1884 (*Trans. HNHS* **3**: 58-66), which recorded moths found by himself and his brother F. Ll. Griffith "in a district about 6 miles long and 2 miles wide , having the village of Sandridge at about its middle point" and *Notes on Tineina and other Lepidoptera observed in the neighbourhood of Sandridge,*

Herts in 1890 (*Tran. HNHS* **6**: 97-102). Looking at the modern map, their recording area (10 kilometres by three and a bit kilometres in modern equivalent) must (if we assume that "wide" means east to west) have included all of St Albans as far south as the A.414 road and north to include all of Wheathampstead, then from the A.1 road in the east to the River Ver in the west. In those days, the continuity of semi-natural habitat must have been such that many of the recorded species could be found in many places, but these days that is not at all the case and we need to exercise far greater precision in recording findings. Clearly, it is not practical to map the records in these works.

In 1888, Griffith was succeeded as Hertfordshire Lepidoptera Recorder by **John Hartley Durrant**, who remained in post until 1893. Durrant was Entomological Secretary to Lord Walsingham and an accomplished expert on the microlepidoptera. A Native of Hitchin, Durrant wrote, in 1885, a *List of Lepidoptera observed in the neighbourhood of Hitchin and Knebworth, Herts* (*Trans. HNHS* **3**: 261-266). In the *Transactions* for 1888, he wrote *Contributions to the knowledge of the entomological fauna of Hertfordshire. No. 1 – Lepidoptera.* An especially interesting aspect of the latter work was Durrant's analysis of numbers Hertfordshire Lepidoptera records cited in the entomological literature up to that date. These are summarised in the following table and although most also include butterflies, they are interesting nevertheless. The significant contribution made by J. F. Stephens is apparent in the list.

SOURCE QUOTED BY DURRANT	NUMBER OF HERTFORDSHIRE LEPIDOPTERA REFERENCES CITED
Haworth, A. H. *Lepidoptera Britannica.* 1803-29.	0
Stephens, J. F. *Illustrations of British Entomology (Haustellata)*, vols. i-iv, 1828-34.	192
Crewe, Rev. H. Harpur. The Prominent Moths of Buckinghamshire, 1869. *Quarterly Magazine of the High Wycombe Natural History Society*, vol. ii, pp. 97-104.	1
Newman, E. *An Illustrated Natural History of British Moths.* 1874.	0
The Entomological Magazine, 1833-38.	0
The Entomologist, 20 vols., vol. i, 1840, vol. ii, 1864, to vol. xx, 1887.	21
The Entomologists' Annual, 20 vols., 1855-74.	7
The Entomologists' Weekly Intelligencer, 10 vols., 1856-61.	7
The Journal of Entomology, 2 vols., 1862-66.	0
The Entomologists' Monthly Magazine, 24 vols., 1864-87.	24
Transactions of the Watford Natural History Society and Hertfordshire Field Club, 2 vols., 1875-80.	31
Transactions of the Hertfordshire Natural History Society and Field Club, 4 vols., 1880-88.	1,065

In 1893, the role of Lepidoptera Recorder for Hertfordshire was taken over by **Arthur Ernest Gibbs**, who remained in post until his death. Gibbs was born and bred in St Albans and lived there for much of his life. From 1889 to 1899 he was Curator of the society's collections and he was a lead figure in the establishment of the present day museum in St Albans. From 1912 to his death he was also the President of the HNHS. In his annual report to the Society for 1900, he writes 'During the past twelve months I have been collecting information for the articles on the Insecta of the county which will appear in the forthcoming Victoria History of Hertfordshire'. That work was eventually published in 1902. In his report for 1900, Gibbs also noted that the county moth fauna then stood at 1139 – 'rather more than half' the species listed as British by Meyrick's *Handbook of British Lepidoptera*. Foster (1937) revised the total downwards to 1136; his justification is lost deep in his text but is, essentially, that three of Gibbs' species were incorrectly identified. Meyrick recognised 2061 species, so the Hertfordshire total actually represented 55% of the British fauna. As County Recorder, Gibbs produced occasional annual reports of moths recorded in Hertfordshire in the *Transactions* from 1889 (covering up to 1888) to 1896 (covering 1895). The 1896 report seems to have been replaced by Spencer's paper on Lepidoptera in the Watford area (Spencer, 1897) and that for the period from 1897 to 1899 by Cottam's paper covering western Hertfordshire (Cottam, 1901). The reasons for these gaps are unclear. Gibbs presented a report on Lepidoptera in the county during 1900 in the 1901 *Transactions*, but there is no report for 1901 and the 1902 report was presented by Philip J. Barraud, who explained that '*In the absence of Mr A. E. Gibbs, your Recorder of Insecta, who, I regret to say, has been seriously ill, I have been asked to lay before the members of the Society the annual report on the Lepidoptera observed in the county in the past year*' (*Trans. HNHS* **12**: 21 – 25). Gibbs evidently recovered and in 1904 presented a report covering 1903 and continued these until 1907 when they ceased. Gibbs final contribution was in 1909, when his list of '*Lepidoptera from St Albans and its neighbourhood*' appeared in *Trans. HNHS* **14**: 236 – 238. At Gibbs's death in 1917, the number of recorded Hertfordshire moths had risen to 1155 species. Regrettably, moth specimens collected by Gibbs, originally deposited in the society's museum, can no longer be traced.

On Gibbs death in 1917, John Hartley Durrant acquired his manuscript lists and other papers and through these evidently provided A. H. Foster (see below) with much valuable information and clarification on the lists published in the *Victoria County History*.

Recording seems to have received a boost in the early 1890s, as it is during this period that the first references to moths taken 'at the electric lamp in Watford' start to appear. Word evidently got around fast and references to moths taken at electric lights become progressively more numerous – as much a statement of the social class of members of the HNHS as of the efficacy of moth recording! In 1893, we see the first county records of Purple Thorn (*Selenia tetralunaria*), Light Brocade (*Lacanobia w-latinum*) and Dog's-tooth (*Lacanobia suasa*), for example – all taken at electric light in Gladstone Road, Watford by S. H. Spencer. This begs the question as to what was common and what was rare. In his report for 1893, Gibbs (*Trans. HNHS* **8**: 74 – 84) talks about larvae of Small Eggar (*Eriogaster lanestris*) almost in passing, but then refers to Barred Red (*Hylaea fasciaria*), Small Elephant Hawk-moth (*Deilephila porcellus*) and Ruby Tiger (*Phragmatobia fuliginosa*) *'and other rare insects'* whilst in 1896 he reports the discovery of the Shuttle-shaped Dart (*Agrotis puta*) for the first time in the county, also at light in Gladstone Road, and comments on its great rarity. How times have changed.

During 1901, the Hertfordshire moth list received another major boost in the form of a publication by **William Christopher Boyd** entitled '*List of the Lepidoptera of Cheshunt and its neighbourhood*'. His list contained 745 species, but covered the previous half century and gave no years for the records. The area covered included '*on the east ... the long extent of marshland which runs from Hackney northwards to Hertford and Bishops Stortford, and on the north and west there are many good woods, while at the pollards near Wormley West End, on the north, there is a most excellent little patch of heather, mixed with* Genista anglica, *bracken, and bushes of oak and poplar*'. Also incorporated were three gardens where '*I have sugared pretty regularly ... namely at my father's house in Cheshunt Street for 18 years, then three quarters of a mile farther south at College Road for 14 years; and lastly, another half mile farther south, in Crossbrook Street, for 9 years*'. The latter locality is probably the same as the address given at the head of the paper (The Grange, Waltham Cross). Boyd's list nicely complements the Haileybury list, which covered an adjacent area slightly further north and the two together form a comprehensive list for the Lea Valley/Broxbourne Woods area of south-east Hertfordshire. Interestingly, Boyd's paper was presented to the HNHS on 23rd April 1901, not by himself but by A. E. Gibbs.

During about 1918, Lepidoptera recording in Hertfordshire was taken on board by **Arthur Herbert Foster**, who had joined the HNHS in 1904. In 1916, he prepared *A list of macrolepidoptera occurring in north Hertfordshire, with notes on each species* in the *Trans. HNHS*:**16**: 237 – 258) and then in 1934 he contributed the chapter *Butterflies and Moths* in the book *The Natural History of the Hitchin Region*, edited by R. L. Hine for the Hitchin and District Regional Survey Association. However, Foster's major contribution to our knowledge of Hertfordshire's moths came in 1937 with the publication of his *magnum opus* entitled *A list of the Lepidoptera of Hertfordshire* in *Trans. HNHS* **20**: 157 – 259. Unfortunately, this list is a little less than representative of the true situation in the late 1930s since it is largely a collation of previously published records presented with the collector's name in brackets, but in almost all cases without any date or even a year appended. Some early twentieth century records are included, but these cannot be discerned amongst the rest and the list is, essentially, a simple summary of all species ever recorded in the county, amounting to a total of 1259 species out of 2143 in Meyrick's revised *Handbook* (1928) – some 59% of the British total.

Additions, deletions and corrections to the 1937 list were published in the same journal in 1940, 1941, 1942, 1944 and 1945. At the request of the Council of the HNHS, he revived the annual reports on Lepidoptera that Gibbs had started in 1892, but his death in 1946 meant that only one was produced – covering 1945 and published posthumously in 1946. Foster's collections were donated to the North Herts Museum Service.

On the death of Foster, his Recorder role was filled by **Sir John Claud Forteuseue Fryer**. Fryer lived at Harpenden and was Entomologist to the Ministry of Agriculture from 1914, soon after becoming Director of the Ministry's Plant Pathology Laboratory which, in 1920, was established at Harpenden. He produced annual reports on Hertfordshire Lepidoptera for 1946 and 1947, but promptly died, leaving the Recorder post vacant.

Captain Peter J. Bell was appointed the next Recorder, holding office until 1976, in the first year sharing the task with his father **J. H. Bell**. Bell lived variously in Berkhamsted and Tring and continued the annual Lepidoptera reports in the *Transactions* until he stood down in 1976. It is, at least to some degree, more probably a reflection of declining general interest in entomology than it is of the abilities of Bell that the annual reports become progressively shorter and shorter over the years, often comprising less than two pages of print. However, his last report, published in 1977 and covering the years 1973 to 1976, was especially notable for its incompleteness, listing several interesting records without localities!

We now see the first split of moth recording in the county into the two wholly artificial groups of 'micros' and 'macros'. **Dr. D. A. B MacNicol,** a resident of Welwyn, undertook the role of micro-moth Recorder from 1953 to 1971, though he almost immediately moved to live in Edinburgh and it seems that he did not produce any published reports on Hertfordshire 'micros'. By 1972, **Peter Bell** is again listed (*Trans. HNHS* **27**: 229) as the Recorder for all Lepidoptera, though his report for that year dealt only with rather few macros and butterflies.

Peter Waterton replaced Bell in 1977 and continued as Recorder to 1981, in which year he moved from his home in Welwyn to Middlesborough for reasons associated with his employment. Waterton's first Lepidoptera report for Hertfordshire was for the year 1977 (published in the *Transactions* for 1979) and his last was for 1981, published in 1983.

From 1981 to 1987 there was no formally appointed moth Recorder for Hertfordshire, although butterflies were monitored separately from this period. During this interim period, the national organisation Butterfly Conservation was establishing its own network of county moth officers and in Hertfordshire this task was undertaken by **Rob Souter**. Souter had been undertaking moth surveys at the Bayfordbury Campus of the

University of Hertfordshire and became involved with the Herts and Middlesex Branch of Butterfly Conservation from 1994 to 2000, sitting on the main and conservation committees as Branch Moth Officer. He wrote regular articles about moths for the branch newsletter and an article for the national magazine on day-flying moths.

In 1987, the present writer was appointed to fill the formal position of Hertfordshire Moth Recorder, having moved to live in the county at Bishops Stortford during October 1986. This position is still held in 2008 but is, of course, elected annually by the HNHS.

Hertfordshire Moth Recorders and the years that they held office

From	To	Name
1883	1888	Arthur F. Griffiths
1888	1893	John H. Durrant
1893	1917	Arthur E. Gibbs
1918	1946	Arthur H. Foster
1946	1948	J. C. F. Fryer
1949	1976	Captain Peter J. Bell*
1953	1971	D. A. B MacNicol**
1977	1981	Peter Waterton
1981	1987	No Recorder for moths
1987	present	Colin W. Plant

* macrolepidoptera : 1949 – 1971; all moths: 1972 – 1976.
** microlepidoptera only

The London Natural History Society was formed in 1914 by the amalgamation of the North London Natural History Society (established in 1892) with the City of London Entomological and Natural History Society (established in 1858). From as early as 1899, those associated with recording in London had defined an area of operations of '*a circle of ten mile radius centred upon Charing Cross Station*' but with the formation of the new society this was extended and the present LNHS recording area is based upon a circle of radius 20 miles (32 kilometres) from St Paul's Cathedral. Thus, about one third of Hertfordshire, in the south, is common both the LNHS and the HNHS, though the circumference of the circle now follows the Ordnance Survey's grid lines along the map tetrads (see page 45) through which the circle passes. The post of London Area Moth Recorder is also occupied, currently, by the writer, who was appointed in 1978. A full list of earlier recorders and their publications is given in *Larger Moths of the London Area* (Plant, 1993). Several of the records presented in this latter work also affect Hertfordshire and have also been incorporated into the present study.

The Herts Moth Group was formed during April 2000, by the present writer and Rob Souter, with the

intention of revitalising interest in studying the county's moths. The inaugural meeting took place on Saturday 8th April 2000 at Digswell Church Hall. A total of 50 people were invited, 34 attended and a further seven wished to come, but were unable to do so and sent apologies. This was judged encouraging. At December 2007, the Herts Moth Group has 229 members. The aim of the group was to organise recording effort and work towards the production of the book that you are now reading – which means that if you are in fact reading it we were successful! The group continues to hold informal recording trips to a range of sites across Watsonian Hertfordshire and has a single indoor meeting in each year.

At the end of March 2000 the database, then kept using Lotus Approach software, contained 21,565 records of Hertfordshire moths. The total comprised 1431 species of which 589 are traditionally regarded as larger moths (macrolepidoptera) and 842 were microlepidoptera. The success or otherwise of the Herts Moth Group is for others to judge, but by the end of 2006 the database, now transferred into MapMate software, contained 209,392 records of 1550 species, comprising 618 macros (66% of British macros) and 932 micros (59 % of British micros). It is these species, representing 62% of the overall British lepidopteran fauna, which are discussed in this present book.

Progress in recording Hertfordshire's moths, measured at each of the three publications covering the whole county, can be summarised as follows:

Author	To year	All species all time	British species (all Lepidoptera)	Percentage of British Lepidoptera in Hertfordshire
Gibbs	**1902**	1136	2061	55%
Foster	**1937**	1259	2143	59%
This work	**2006**	1548	2542	62%

Of course, all the figures in the chart above are merely a measure of recording effort on the part of humans. Many of the recorded species are no longer present in the county. The moth fauna is analysed on page 499, after the species accounts.

Long-term Moth Studies at Rothamsted

Ian P. Woiwod and Philip J. L. Gould

The Rothamsted Insect Survey, Plant and Invertebrate Ecology Department, Rothamsted Research, Harpenden, Hertfordshire AL5 2JQ

Hertfordshire is fortunate in having quantitative moth data which goes back to the 1930s. These are from the Rothamsted Estate on the edge of the suburban town of Harpenden and are amongst the longest runs of moth population data anywhere in the world. In this chapter we describe the historical background to these unique datasets and present some of the scientific insights that they continue to provide.

Rothamsted Research (known as Rothamsted Experimental Station until 2002) is one of the largest agricultural research institutes in the UK, with a strong international scientific reputation. It is also famous worldwide as the oldest agricultural research station in the world and known particularly for its long-term 'Classical' fertilizer field experiments. These include the Broadbalk continuous wheat experiment started in 1843 and the Park Grass pasture experiment started in 1856. Both of these experiments continue to the present day and are still providing original research insights, with Park Grass in particular being regarded as the first and longest-running ecological experiment in the world (Silvertown *et al.* 2006). It is undoubtedly this background of long-term experiments that inspired the moth studies on the Rothamsted Estate that eventually resulted in the UK-wide national moth recording scheme known as the Rothamsted Insect Survey (RIS).

The light-trap studies of Carrington Bonsor (C.B.) Williams

Entomological studies at Rothamsted began in 1915 and an Entomology Department was established under the leadership of Dr. A.D. Imms in 1918 (Lewis 1993). However, the story of moth related research really begins with the arrival of Dr. C.B. Williams as head of the department in 1932, a post he held until his retirement in 1955. C.B. (as he was universally known, even by his wife) was a top research scientist, perhaps best known by naturalists for his work on butterfly migration (Williams 1958). More importantly, he was one of the world's first truly quantitative ecologists. That is, someone who appreciated the need for this particular branch of science to get past the purely descriptive stage where it originated and start to make full use of mathematical and statistical insights that can only come after quantitative measurements have been taken. Such views are fully accepted by today's ecologists without further consideration and so it is easy to forget how alien this idea was in the 1920s and 30s. For example, C.B. Williams had a paper rejected from one of the top ecological publications of the time on the grounds that he had used logarithms and the editor was not having any of that mathematical nonsense in his journal.

Before he came to Rothamsted C.B. had worked in Egypt where he had designed a light trap to monitor moth pests in cotton (Williams 1923; Williams 1924) (see page 519). On arriving at Rothamsted he refined the design, where it eventually became known as the Rothamsted light trap (Williams 1948). For continuity, this design of trap with the same light source, a 200 watt clear tungsten filament bulb, is still in use today, with the immediate advantage that nearly all the data collected on the Rothamsted Estate from the 1930s onward is directly comparable.

In 1933 C.B. placed his standard light trap beside Barnfield, one of the 'Classical' fields on the estate, and started to collect daily insect population data with particular emphasis on the macrolepidoptera, or larger macro-moths. This trap ran almost continuously for a four-year period. During the 1939-45 war it was not possible to run a bright light in a field overnight so it had to wait until 1946 until the trap could be restarted at the same site for a further four-year period. Initially this data was collected to look at the relationship between insect activity and meteorological variables; however this study was soon extended to a whole range of basic questions relating to sex proportions, phenology, height of flight, time of flight, and the effect of moonlight on trap catches. Williams published the results of these studies in a series of important papers which are classics of their type and still well worth reading (e.g. Williams & Killington 1935; Williams 1935; Williams 1936; Williams 1939; Williams 1940a; Williams 1940b; Williams 1951a). As part of these studies additional traps were run during this period to provide complementary data, for example one on the roof of the laboratories at Rothamsted and another on a tripod 10.6 metres (35 feet) above the low level trap at Barnfield to study the height of flight of different moth species (Figure 1; Williams 1939).

One innovative way that C.B. Williams made use of the long runs of moth data was to look at the pattern when data were presented as species frequency distributions. He found that it always had a rather typical shape with an excess of species with only a single individual and a long tail of a few very abundant or dominant species. In collaboration with the famous statistician R.A. Fisher and biologist A.S. Corbet, who had some similar tropical butterfly data, he published a paper showing that such species frequency data was well fitted by a particular statistical distribution, the logarithmic series, and that this provided a parameter, α, which was independent of sample size and could be considered as an index of diversity (Fisher *et al.* 1943; Williams 1944; Williams 1947; Williams 1951c; Williams 1953; Williams 1964). The need for such an index follows from the fact that the more obvious measure, number of species in the samples, is almost entirely dependent on the number of individuals examined and is therefore usually very uninformative. This was again very original work at the time as it was one of the first attempts to quantify what is now known as biodiversity. Many other diversity measures have been proposed over the years but log-series α has stood the test of time, particularly when it was re-examined with the more extensive replicated moth datasets obtained later by the Insect Survey (Kempton 1979; Kempton & Taylor 1974; Kempton & Taylor 1979; Taylor 1978; Taylor *et al.* 1976; Magurran 2004).

Figure 1. In May and June 1936 a second light trap was suspended above the long-running Barnfield trap to study the height at which moths fly. It is believed that the figure in the photograph is C.B. Williams.

In addition to these major pieces of research, C.B. found time to conduct light-trap experiments comparing standard Rothamsted traps with the widely used Robinson MV design (Williams 1951b; Williams *et al.* 1955). Again these experiments were innovative, for they showed for the first time how such experiments needed to be spatially and temporally replicated to provide statistically valid results. Building on these early experiments further light-trap comparison experiments were done both at Rothamsted (Taylor & French 1974) and in the tropics (Taylor & Brown 1972; Intachat & Woiwod 1999). These various experiments provide valuable background information of importance in long-term sampling studies. For example, they showed a lack of effect of one night's catch on the following night, even for the more powerful MV Robinson trap design (Williams *et al.* 1955). They also suggest that the Rothamsted trap has been a good choice for long-term quantitative studies as its sample, although usually smaller than that from the Robinson trap, is more consistent from night to night and therefore provides a small standardised sample which is ideal for long-term monitoring (Taylor & French 1974).

One other publication by C.B. Williams is worthy of note as it concerns the often contentious subject of the ethics of killing insect samples in the interest of scientific research. Generally, the samples collected by Rothamsted traps are killed for a number of good reasons including: quality assurance; transport; long-term storage; and to prevent double recording. Indeed, it is certain that the results presented later would not have been possible to obtain without this necessity. Typically, C.B. tackled this question head on in a publication that makes many points that remain valid (Williams 1952). In that paper he makes full use of the results on moth numbers from the eight years of Barnfield trap data available at that time to show the complete lack of effect of such sampling on moth populations. These days the conservation of insects has a much higher profile but these results and more extensive sampling since provide convincing evidence that the long-term sampling of moths on the Rothamsted Estate and nationally will have no deleterious effects on our insect fauna and indeed are a vital weapon in our attempts to conserve them (Woiwod *et al.* 2005).

Roy Taylor and the birth of the Rothamsted Insect Survey

The next milestone in moth recording at Rothamsted came with the appointment in 1948, by C.B. Williams, of L.R. (Roy) Taylor to work on aphid ecology in the Entomology Department. His early work involved the development of suction traps for sampling aerial insect populations but by the late 1950s he was turning his attention to the way insect, and more specifically aphid, populations worked. Insect population models at that time did not consider the role of movement, although for many very mobile species such as moths and aphids the role of movement was crucial to an understanding of population dynamics. He soon realised that this study could not progress until spatially replicated population data became available. Collecting such data on aphids was not financially viable at that time so he turned his attention to the army of expert amateur moth experts in the UK as a cost-effective way around the problem. Many such amateurs were already running light traps but it soon became apparent that these were not being run consistently enough for his purpose and so it was decided to set up a network of volunteers to run cheap and robust light traps based on the well established standard light-trap design of C.B. Williams (Williams 1948).

In 1960 the first trap was placed at the side of Barnfield, in the same place that Williams had sampled in the 1930s and 1940s, and it has run daily ever since. Immediately, it became apparent that large changes had taken place in the moth fauna in the intervening years and these will be discussed in detail later. In 1965 and 1966 two further traps were installed on the Rothamsted Estate and have operated daily ever since. Gradually, a network of volunteer trap operators and identifiers were recruited throughout the UK so that by 1968 there were over 60 sites in operation with a good spatial coverage. Since then traps have been operated at over 450 sites, with 54 sites operating for more than 15 years. Currently, in 2007, there are over 80 traps in operation throughout Great Britain and Northern Ireland, with additional single sites in Southern Ireland, Finland, France and Gibraltar.

Following the publication of *Silent Spring* (Carson 1963) and resulting public concern about possible pesticide hazards, money became available for research aimed at the reduction of unnecessary application of insecticides. Roy Taylor took the opportunity offered to set up a complementary network of 12m high suction traps to sample aphid populations and issue timely warning of pest aphid abundance, as well as providing the data he required for his population studies. The first suction trap was installed at Rothamsted in 1965 and is still in daily operation. Currently there are 16 suction traps in England and Scotland, and a further 50 are run by collaborators in 16 other European countries. Such traps are expensive to make and maintain, and aphid identification is done by a skilled team of dedicated taxonomists. As a result, they have to be run on a professional basis at various permanent sites, such as experimental farms and research establishments. Together, the UK light-trap and suction-trap networks have become known as the Rothamsted Insect Survey (Taylor 1986; Woiwod & Harrington 1994; Harrington & Woiwod 2007). These two networks have recently been augmented by two vertical-looking insect radars (VLR), one based at Chilbolton in Hampshire since 2003 and the other at Rothamsted, which has been in operation continuously since 2000. These VLRs are operated by the Rothamsted Radar Entomology Unit and are being used to study high level migration behaviour in various insects including moths (Chapman *et al.* 2002a; Chapman *et al.* 2002b).

The resulting RIS databases are unique in the world in terms of the number of species included, the geographical spread of sites and the long-term nature of the daily sampling regime. The moth data have been used for a wide range of studies on biodiversity, population dynamics and climate change (e.g. Taylor *et al.* 1976; Taylor *et al.* 1978; Taylor *et al.* 1979; Taylor & Woiwod 1980; Taylor *et al.* 1980; Taylor & Woiwod 1982; Hanski & Woiwod 1991; Woiwod & Hanski 1992; Hanski & Woiwod 1993a; Hanski & Woiwod 1993b; Woiwod & Harrington 1994; Woiwod 1997a). More recently, they have also been used in a conservation context to study long-term trends in moth populations. Initially these analyses were concerned with a single species, the Garden Tiger Moth *Arctia caja*, which was known to have declined and changed its spatial distribution over the 35 period, 1968 to 2002. The decline of this species was found to be particularly severe in the south-east of Britain and seemed to be related to poor overwintering success following a series of wet winters and warm springs (Conrad *et al.* 2001; Conrad *et al.* 2002; Conrad *et al.* 2003; Conrad *et al.* 2006a).

When the trend analysis used in the Garden Tiger Moth study was extended to other common and widespread moth species for which there is adequate RIS data, the results were surprising and rather alarming. Of the 337 species analysed, two thirds (226 species) showed a downward trend whereas only one third (111 species) were increasing. In addition, the rate at which some species were declining was so rapid that if IUCN (the World Conservation Union) criteria were applied then 71 species could be considered 'threatened', with 15 species qualifying as 'endangered' and 56 species as 'vulnerable' (Woiwod 2003; Conrad *et al.* 2004; Woiwod *et al.* 2005; Parsons *et al.* 2005; Conrad *et al.* 2006b; Fox *et al.* 2006). Whether it is appropriate to apply these IUCN criteria to such common and widespread species is arguable, but the results do highlight the serious nature of the decline of many of our common moths and these 'endangered' and 'vulnerable' species have now been given Biodiversity Action Plan (BAP) status in the UK, indicating that further research is required at the national level. These declines of individual species are mirrored in an analysis of total numbers of macro-moths from the RIS National Light-trap Network, which show an overall decline of 31% in 35 years. However, this decline is not distributed evenly throughout Britain, for if the country is split in half (along the 4500 grid line, approximately level with the Humber Estuary) then the southern half exhibits a larger decline of 44%, whereas the northern half has a slight increase of 5% (Conrad *et al.* 2006b). The reason for these recent large scale southern declines of our larger moths is still under investigation but possible factors include climate change, agricultural intensification, urbanisation and air and light pollution. Fortunately not all species are faring badly and some are actually increasing in abundance and range. Of particular note in this respect are winter-flying species and those whose larvae feed on conifers or lichens. The long-running sites on the Rothamsted Estate formed an important core set of data in these analyses; therefore the national trends provide a useful perspective on the local Rothamsted moth trends which are discussed later in this chapter.

The Rothamsted Farm Traps

Since moth recording began at Rothamsted in 1933 numerous light and suction traps have operated on the Rothamsted Estate to sample moths and other insects. Many of these have just operated over short periods for experimental purposes (e.g. Williams *et al.* 1955; Taylor & French 1974). In this account we will be concentrating mainly on results from three long-running sites: Barnfield, Geescroft I and Allotments, that have operated continuously since the mid 1960s, and two additional traps: Geescroft II and Park Grass, which have also run over extended periods. In addition we will be considering some spatially extensive data that was collected between 1990 and 1993 when the four existing traps were supplemented by an additional 22 sites so that the pattern of moth populations could be studied right across the Rothamsted Farm landscape. Details of trapping periods and grid references for these sites are given in Table 1. A more complete list and map of all moth trapping sites at Rothamsted is given in Riley (1999).

To understand some of the later results it will be worthwhile describing the longer-running Rothamsted trap sites in more detail:

Figure 2a. Barnfield 1975

Figure 2b. Barnfield 1980

Figure 2c. Barnfield 2006

Figure 2d. Geescroft I 2006

Figure 2e. Allotments 1966

Figure 2f. Allotments 1968

Figure 2g. Allotments 1968

Figure 2h. Allotments 2007

Site 1 Barnfield

This is the original 1933 site of C.B. Williams as already described (Fig 1). The trap was placed by the western edge of the first long-term 'Classical' Rothamsted fertilizer experiment in which root crops were grown for 126 years from 1843 until 1969. Since then a range of arable crops have been grown on the field and from 1984 it has been grass or a grass-clover ley. By the time the trap was re-placed there in 1960 the field was being managed intensively as typical of arable agriculture at that time (Fig 2a). Gradually the field margin has become less intensively managed (Fig 2b) until currently the trap is surrounded by a woody mixed hedge that has developed by natural regeneration (Fig 2c).

Site 22 Geescroft I

This trap is in a small (1.3 ha) experimental woodland known as Geescroft Wilderness. The area was originally a piece of agricultural land which was sown to clover in 1888 and then allowed to revert to woodland by natural succession. This now has a flora approaching climax woodland. A trap was placed there in 1965 and has operated daily ever since (Fig 2d).

Site 34 Allotments

In 1966 a trap was put in an area consisting of 2.8 ha. of mature allotments, founded around 1852 (Lawes, 1877) but about to cease operation (Fig. 2e). The allotments were cultivated until 1967 and were cleared and ploughed in 1968 (Fig. 2f and g) and the area sown to wheat and beans. In 1969 and 1970 the immediate surroundings of the trap were fallow with high weeds. Since then the area has been used for dumping soil and debris from a building site, partly paved for car parking and used for building. The immediate vicinity of the trap is now parkland, i.e. closely cut grassland with small trees and bushes, but an experimental area near the trap has recently been planted with fast growing willows with a surrounding uncultivated area (Fig. 2h). In other words this is a site that has changed markedly over the years and become more urbanised.

Site no.	Trap name	Grid reference	Data available	Dominant land use
1	Barnfield	132135	1933-1936 1946-1949 1960-2007	arable
22	Geescroft I	132128	1965-2007	woodland
34	Allotments	134134	1966-2007	parkland
99	Geescroft II	131127	1973-1998	woodland
601	Parklands	127133	1990-1994	grassland
602	Stackyard	125134	1990-1994	arable
603	Little Knott	121135	1990-1993	arable
604	Broadbalk	122137	1990-1993	grassland
605	Sawyers	121142	1990-1993	arable
606	Long Hoos	121139	1990-1993, 1996	arable
607	Farm	120137	1990-1993	grassland
608	Knott Wood I	117134	1990-1993	woodland
609	Knott Wood II	115132	1990-1993	woodland
610	White Horse	114131	1990-1993	arable
611	White Horse Spinney	114129	1990-1993	woodland
612	Apiary	121129	1990-1993	parkland
613	Park Grass	122129	1990-2007	grassland
614	Manor Wood I	121132	1990-1993	woodland
615	Pastures	121133	1990-1993	woodland
616	Manor Wood II	123133	1990-1993	woodland
617	Geescroft Field	131129	1990-1993, 1998	arable
618	Road Piece	130127	1990-1993	arable
619	Lodge	133131	1990-1993	arable
620	Great Field	132132	1990-1993	arable
621	Garden Plots	130134	1990-1993	grassland
622	Ninnings	132136	1990-1993	parkland

Table 1. List of sites and names of long-running Rothamsted core traps and the additional traps of the Farmland Light-trap Network.

Site 99 Geescroft II

In 1973 a second trap was placed in Geescroft Wilderness and run for a period of 26 years. This was out of sight of the original trap and was in effect a replicate sample of Geescroft I.

Site 613 Park Grass

This is the only survivor of the additional 22 sites that were started on the estate in 1990. It is by the side of the 'Classical' Park Grass Experiment (Silvertown *et al.* 2006) (Fig 2i) and became the official Rothamsted light trap for the national Environmental Change Network (ECN).

Long-term moth population and diversity trends

One of the main interests of the unique Rothamsted data is what it can tell us about long-term changes in moth abundance and diversity over the last 70 years. In this section we discuss some of these changes and their possible causes.

Declines in the 1950s

Immediately after the Barnfield trapping was resumed in 1960 it became apparent that there had been a big decline, both in moth numbers and the range of species present. This is most clearly seen when mean annual macro-moth abundance is plotted for each decade that the Barnfield trap has operated (Fig. 3). These are geometric means (de-transformed means of logged annual abundances to remove over-emphasis of any particular year) and show a distinct reduction during the 1950s when unfortunately no sampling was being done. Indeed there is a 71% reduction in average numbers when the pre-1950 data is compared to average catches between 1960 and 1979. There has been a slight recovery in populations as the Barnfield field margin became less intensively managed since the 1980s (Fig 2c) but there are still 59% fewer moths on average being caught now compared to the 1930s and 40s.

A very similar pattern would be apparent if we plotted the average number of species recorded over the same period. However, this would be misleading as the number of species recorded is very closely related to the number of individuals examined, even if there is no real change in diversity. This sampling artefact can be overcome to some extent by using a diversity index which is independent of sample size and, as previously mentioned, log-series α has proved to be the most powerful index to use in such studies (Taylor *et al.* 1976).

In effect, ∝ is a measure of the rate at which new species are added as sample size increases, with a higher value probably denoting a larger pool of species but also indicating that species are distributed more evenly amongst individuals. The change in diversity does indeed follow the pattern of abundance as there was also a significant decline during the 1950s (Fig. 4), although the pattern since 1960 has been rather different and will be discussed in more detail in the next section.

The large decline in moth abundance and diversity during the 1950s is alarming, but does corroborate many anecdotal accounts by lepidopterists which indicate that moth populations used to be much larger before the 1950s and particularly pre-war (Paul Waring *pers. comm.*). The explanation for the decline at Rothamsted seems to be a combination of land-use change and agricultural intensification. We have been able to reconstruct the land-use in the immediate vicinity of the Barnfield trap for 1933 and 1972 (Fig. 5). As can be seen, there were considerable changes between these dates with a large move from grassland to arable, removal of many hedges and uncultivated areas to increase field sizes for mechanised farming and the replacement of allotments with buildings. Some of these changes are typical of what happened more widely in agricultural areas in the east of England after the war in response to real food shortages at that time. In addition to land-use change it was at this time that pesticides, particularly herbicides, started to be more widely used and mechanisation of farming became widespread. Rothamsted, as an agricultural research institute, very much followed the latest developments in farming practice as they were more widely adopted throughout the UK.

Unfortunately we were not sampling the moths in the 1950s when many of these changes in farming practices took place. If we had we might have been able to see what happened in what order and which of these many changes had the largest and most immediate effects on moth populations. Unfortunately this is impossible to do in retrospect and underlines the importance of keeping long-term monitoring going once it has been established.

Figure 2i. Park Grass May 2006. Notice the heavily mown area round the trap Geescroft Wilderness is the block of woodland on the horizon.

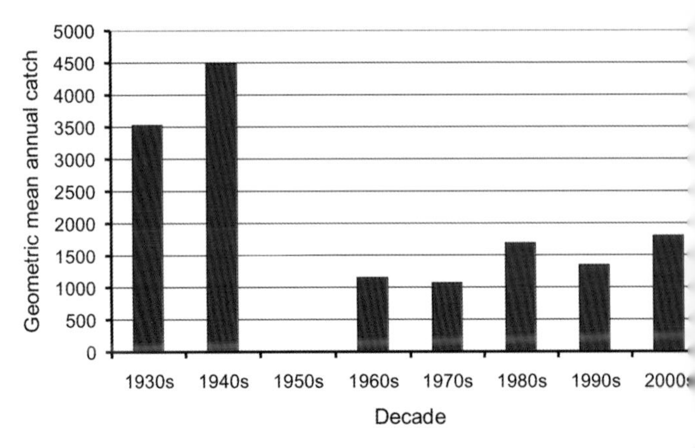

Figure 3. Geometric mean annual catch of macrolepidoptera in Barnfield light t

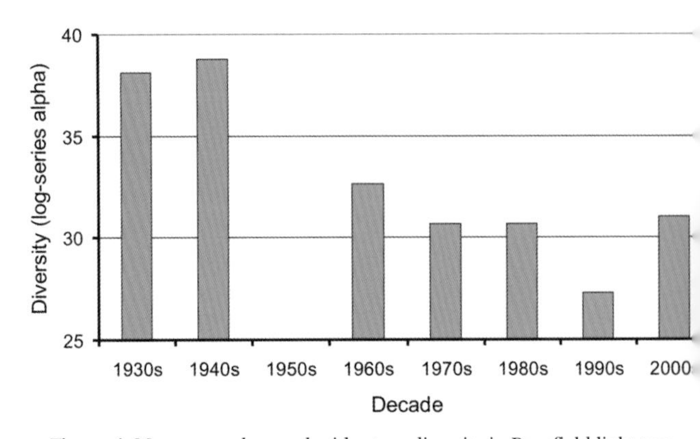

Figure 4. Mean annual macrolepidoptera diversity in Barnfield light trap.

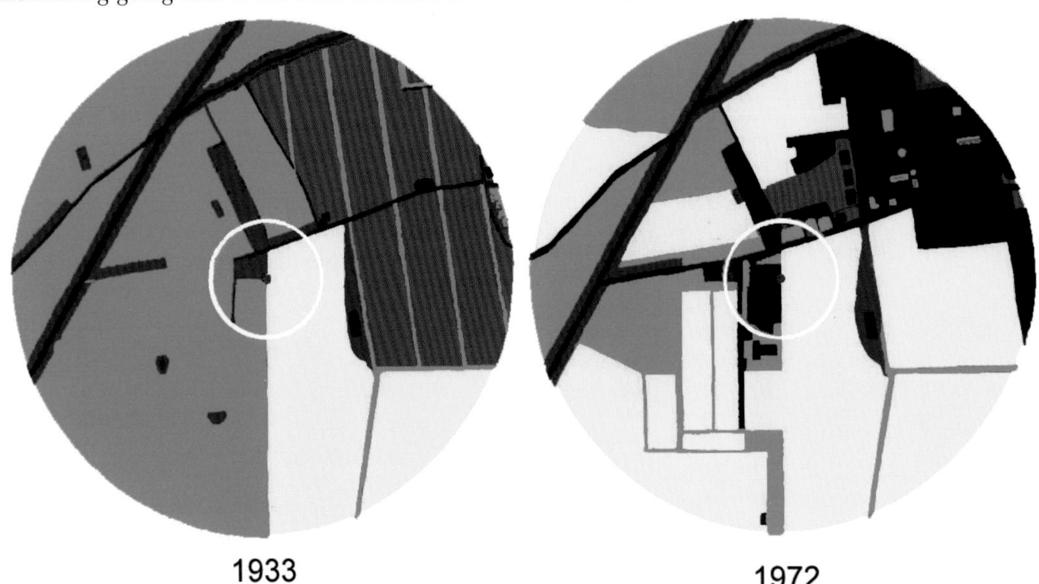

Figure 5. Land use around Barnfield trap in 1933 and 1972.
Light green =grassland, dark green=hedges, yellow=arable, brown=allotments and gardens, black=buildings and paved roads. The inner circle represents a radius of approximately 50 metres around the trap.

Because Barnfield is a single site in Britain with no replication it is not possible to separate the local effects at Rothamsted from wider changes in the countryside. However, we have run RIS traps beside a wide range of arable fields throughout the UK since the 1960s and have compared these with Barnfield. In all cases arable populations are very similar to post-1960 Barnfield levels rather than those found pre-1950. Populations next to improved agricultural grassland were only slightly higher suggesting that similar declines in moth numbers may have occurred very widely across farmed landscapes throughout Britain (Woiwod 1991). This evidence also suggests that moth populations may have declined very widely at about the same time. This is contrary to many peoples' perception that the decline of farmland wildlife due to agricultural intensification is a relatively recent phenomenon, i.e. over the last 20 years or so. It looks like there was a much bigger decline in the 1950s and 60s that went largely unnoticed because wildlife monitoring schemes were not in place at that time and conservation concerns were largely centred around rarer species living in non-agricultural habitats.

It is interesting to compare the moth declines at Barnfield with the only other insect group for which there is equivalent data. These are the Heteroptera (true bugs) which have been identified and counted from many of the same Barnfield samples (Southwood *et al.* 2003). Changes in the annual abundances of bugs closely followed those of the moths. However, diversity changes showed a very different pattern, with the bugs currently having very similar diversity values to those found in the 1930s and 40s (Southwood *et al.* 2003). This ties in with the fact that bugs seem to be responding positively to recent increases in temperature, with many species extending their distribution and several new species becoming established (Kirby & Stewart 2001).

If individual moth species totals are examined then they tend to follow overall abundance with most species showing dramatic declines after the 1940s. In fact there are 35 species caught in the Barnfield trap before 1950 which have not been caught there since and to these there are an additional 38 species that have large step-like declines in the 1950s. Of particular note amongst the locally extinct species are: the Heart Moth, *Dicycla oo*, a singleton of which was caught in 1933 and hasn't been seen since; the Lappet, *Gastropacha quercifolia*, 10 of which were caught before 1950 and none since; the Mottled Grey, *Colostygia multistrigaria*, 16 recorded up to 1935 and none since; the Bordered Gothic, *Heliophobus reticulata*, caught 10 times up to 1946 and none since, the Four-spotted, *Tyta luctuosa*, 26 of which were caught before 1950 and none since. Several of these species have declined widely across the UK and now have their own Biodiversity Action Plans. However, to balance out these extinctions there are 67 species that were not caught before 1960 but have turned up in the Barnfield trap since then. Some of these additional species are known to be spreading, such as the Least Carpet, *Idaea rusticata*, and Blair's Shoulder-knot, *Lithophane leautieri*. However, most of the additional species are purely down to the fact that we are comparing eight years sampling before 1960 to 46 years after and underlines how species richness can be a very unreliable measure of diversity when sample sizes differ.

Changes post 1960

Since 1960 we have the advantage of continuous trapping and some replication in different parts of the estate. The trends in both abundance and diversity are rather idiosyncratic but informative. As expected the general pattern of abundance at the two Geescroft sites are similar, although Geescroft II consistently caught fewer individuals (Fig. 6), probably because the trap was nearer the edge of the woodland. However, there is generally a statistically significant log-linear 49% decline in moth populations in Geescroft over the last 42 years. This is almost identical to the general 43% decline in moth populations throughout the south of Britain measured over a slightly shorter period (Conrad *et al.* 2006b). It therefore seems that Geescroft I, by being in a stable environment little effected by local factors, is providing a very useful barometer of the wider moth community, unfortunately the message from this barometer is not good (Fox *et al.* 2006).

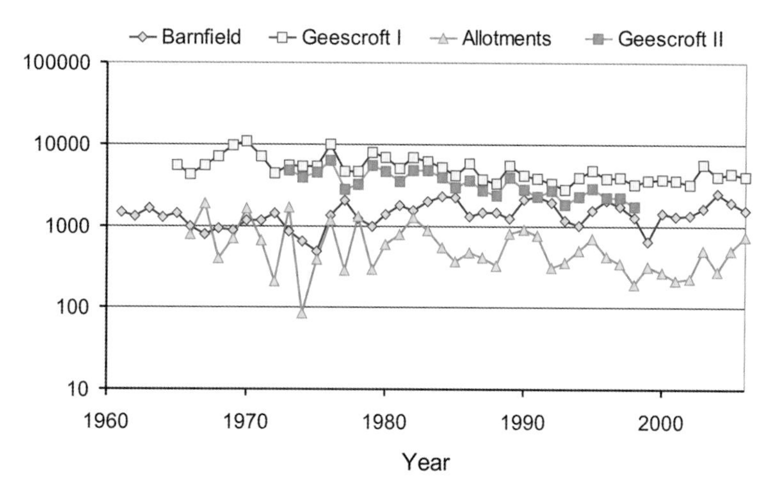

Figure 6. Annual total of macro-moths (logarithmic scale) at four long-running Rothamsted trap sites.

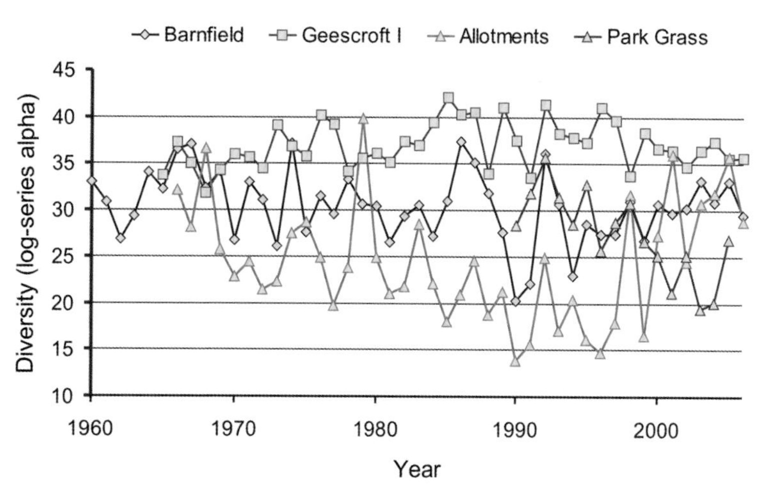

Figure 7. Annual macro-moth diversity for the three longest-running Rothamsted trap sites.

At Barnfield it seems that moth numbers continued to decline, probably to a nadir during the mid 1970s when the field was being managed very intensively (Fig 2a; Fig 6). Since then numbers seem to have recovered as the field became grassland rather than arable, as adjacent farmland became set-aside, and perhaps more importantly, as the field margin was allowed to revert to hedgerow by natural regeneration (Fig. 2c). As a result, between 1965 and 2006 there has been a significant positive log-linear trend indicating an overall increase in moth abundance of 23% over the period.

Numbers in the Allotment trap have fluctuated widely, particularly in the earlier years when there were very rapid changes in land-use and management in the immediate vicinity of the trap (Taylor *et al.* 1978). However, the overall pattern is of a significant decline that again is best fitted by linear regression on logged abundances. This analysis indicates an overall decline of 54% since 1966, which is probably a good indication of the negative response of moths to rapid environmental change and the poor environment provided by the intensively managed formal parkland and gardens that now surround the trap (Fig. 2h). There has been a slight recovery in numbers over the last few years, possibly in response to the adjacent willow plantation and increases in set-aside farmland nearby.

The moth diversity trends of the three long-running traps are slightly more complicated than abundance (Fig. 7). There is no overall statistically significant diversity trend in the Geescroft I trap even when the data is split into different time intervals. So it seems to have kept its species abundance structure despite overall declines in moth populations. The diversity at Barnfield also shows no overall trend from 1960 to 2006 although when a split line is fitted to the data there is an indication that there was a 13% decline up to 1996 with a 12% recovery since then (Figs. 4 & 7). Perhaps there was a delayed effect on diversity following the moth declines up to the mid 1970s and we are now seeing a welcome return to former levels. The Allotments diversity tells a particularly interesting story. Again there is no overall linear trend from 1966 to 2006 but by fitting a split-line regression it is clear, and statistically significant, that there was a decline of 48% during the 30 years until 1996 and a linear increase of 51% in the 10 years since then. It is interesting that both Allotments and Barnfield diversity seemed to take a turn for the better in 1996. These traps are only a couple of hundred metres apart so this suggests a general improvement in the environment for moth diversity in the area and that this was particularly pronounced at the Allotments trap site. Up to 2003 this could have been due to a nearby set-aside field and the maturation of the formal planting around the trap, since 2003 the establishment of a willow plantation surrounded by semi-natural grassland (Fig. 2h) will also have helped diversify the moth fauna, although it clearly has not yet increased total moth numbers.

The latest long-running trap, Park Grass, which was started in 1990, shows a different pattern from the other sites. As this was placed next to a 'Classical' field whose management has remained basically consistent for 150 years we would expect a relatively stable moth community. In terms of moth abundance there is an almost significant decline of 37% over 16 years,

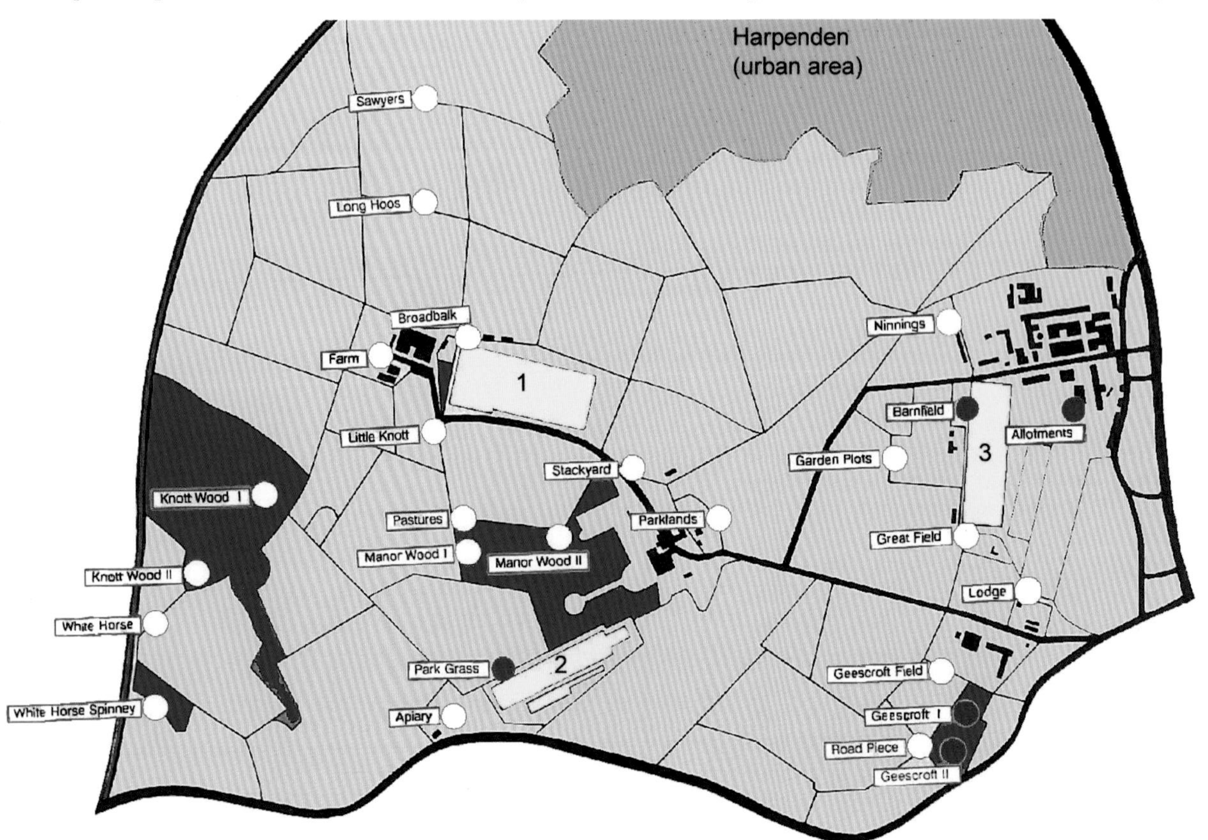

Figure 8. The Rothamsted Farm Light-trap Network 1990-1993. Three 'Classical' experiments are shown: 1) Broadbalk, continuous wheat since 1843, 2) Park Grass, continuous hay since 1856, 3) Barnfield. Note also the distribution of three areas of woodland: Knott Wood, Manor Wood and Geescroft Wilderness.

probably reflecting the widespread national moth declines already mentioned. However, in contrast to the other three long-running sites, there has also been a highly significant 33% reduction in diversity over the same period (Fig. 7). As the management of the Park Grass experiment has not changed then we must look elsewhere for the cause of this decline. The most likely explanation lies in the management of the non-experimental grassland in the immediate vicinity of the trap site. Originally this was rough grass, cut at most once a year, and was outside the Park Grass perimeter fence. This fence line was recently moved to ease management of the experiment with a result that the trap site now lies within the experimental field and as a result has been subject to a much more frequent mowing regime, which although tidier does nothing for the moths. Following the discovery of this decline in moth biodiversity it has been agreed that the grassland around the trap will revert to its previous frequency of management so it will be interesting to see how quickly the moth diversity recovers. In the next section the importance of such local land use and management on both moth abundance and diversity will become apparent.

Patterns of moth abundance and diversity across the farm

The temporary establishment in 1990 of a network of 26 traps across Rothamsted Farm has a given us a unique opportunity to study how moth populations are structured at a local scale. Although the traps were not placed evenly across the farm because of practical issues relating to electricity supply, we managed to get a fairly representative selection of the various habitats around the estate, including woodland, arable, grassland and urban areas (Table 1; Fig. 8). At the species level moth distributions are normally structured very much by their foodplant requirements. As an example, density maps of two relatively common species are given here. The Setaceous Hebrew Character, *Xestia c-nigrum,* is a generalist feeder on low growing plants and common in all the open areas, however there are noticeably fewer individuals in the woodland areas such as Geescroft, which has a relatively sparse understorey (Fig. 2d; Fig 9). In contrast, the November Moth, *Epirrita dilutata,* which is a tree-feeder, is very much confined to the more wooded areas of the farm (Fig. 10). Many other species showed this dichotomy of either favouring the woodland areas or the more open areas of the farm. One species

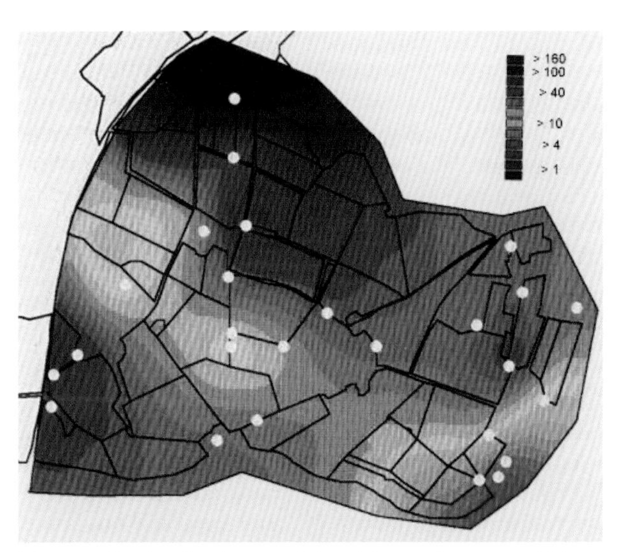

Figure 9. Density distribution of the widespread Setaceous Hebrew Character, *Xestia c-nigrum*, across Rothamsted Farm in 1990.

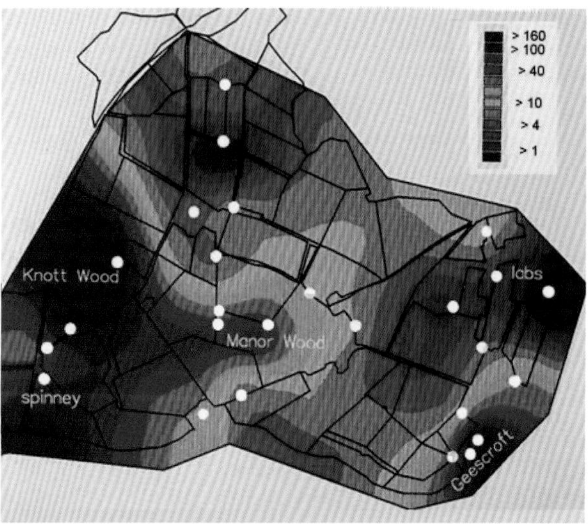

Figure 10. Density distribution of the November Moth, *Epirrita dilutata*, in 1990.

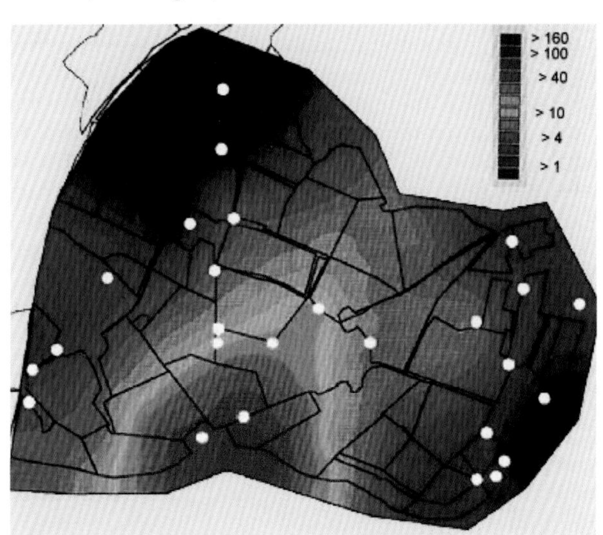

Figure 11. Density distribution of the Ear Moth, *Amphipoea oculea*, in 1990.

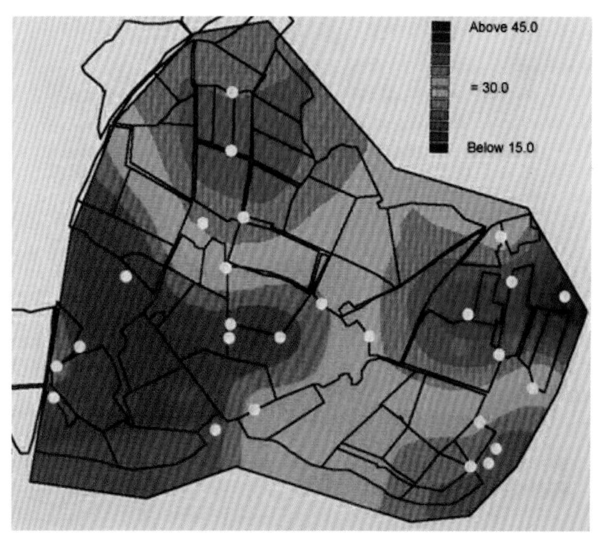

Figure 12. Distribution of moth diversity (log-series α) across Rothamsted Farm in 1990.

that showed a very different pattern was the Ear Moth, *Amphipoea oculea*, which has a very restricted distribution centred around Park Grass but is found very rarely elsewhere on the farm (Fig 11). The traditionally managed hay meadow of Park Grass seems to suit this species well but exactly why is unclear.

When the farm network was set up, genetic studies were made of *E. dilutata* and the results were interesting. Not only was this species largely confined to woodland areas but the populations could be genetically differentiated in the three woodland patches, Knott Wood, Manor Wood and Geescroft Wilderness (Woiwod & Wynne 1994; Wynne *et al.* 2003). This suggest surprisingly little movement between woodland patches at the farm scale even though Knott Wood and Manor Wood were continuous woodland up to the 1930s and none of these woods are more than a few fields distant from each other.

The pattern of diversity across the farm is shown in Figure 12 and the pattern for moth abundance is almost identical. There is a very definite structure to this pattern with low diversity and abundance in the north and east parts of the estate and high diversity and abundance in a large patch in the south-west corner of the farm with a smaller high diversity patch in the south-east. This general pattern is explicable in terms of the general environment across the farm. For example, the large high diversity and abundance area in the south-west contains Knott Wood, Manor Wood and also has more fields that have retained their hedgerows. In contrast, the low diversity area to the north is mainly intensively managed arable fields and experimental plots with few semi-natural areas and the low diversity area to the east contains the Rothamsted laboratories, tennis courts and a playing field, none of which are likely to be very productive for moths.

We can look at the importance of local environment in more detail by constructing land-use maps (similar to those in Figure 5) around each trap and then formally analysing the influence on both diversity and abundance of local land-use. This was done using the 1990 and 1991 data from the Rothamsted Farm Network and the results are striking. Table 2 gives the rankings in importance of different land uses in the immediate vicinity of the traps in promoting moth diversity and abundance. Although the ordering differs slightly between diversity and abundance, it can be seen that woodland and hedgerows dominate the provision of both diversity and abundance. In contrast mown grass, tarmac and building are, not surprisingly, uniformly bad for moth populations. These relationships were optimised for distance round the trap and it was found that the land-use within a 100 metre radius had the most influence. This in itself is interesting as it suggests that light traps are not attracting insects from long distances, as is often thought, and that the majority of the sample is of locally bred individuals. The percentage variance accounted for, given at the foot of Table 12, indicates that 58% of the pattern visible in the diversity map (Fig. 12) is accounted for by this local land use, and a similar value of 50% for moth abundance. These are surprisingly high values considering the relatively general nature of the categories used and a host of other factors that must be involved in determining such patterns.

Land Use (area within 100m radius from trap)	Importance Ranking Diversity (log-series α)	Annual abundance (log N)
Bushes and Hedges	1	3
Mixed Woodland	2	1
Deciduous Woodland	3	2
Gardens	4	5
Arable	5	6
Permanent Grass (grazed/cut)	6	4
Unproductive (roads, buildings, etc)	7	8
Permanent Grass (regularly mown)	8	7
Variability accounted for	58%	50%

Table 2. Influence of local land use on moth diversity and abundance based on the Rothamsted Farm Network.

Phenology and climate change

It is now widely accepted that climate change is with us and is mainly the result of human activity (IPCC 2007). The predictable effects of climate change on moth populations are changes in distribution, abundance and phenology (Woiwod 1997a; Woiwod 1997b). Climate related changes in distribution are already being observed in some species and such changes will be well monitored by the intensive amateur moth recording that is the basis for much of this book. In future, moth distribution data is likely to be co-ordinated by county recorders and collated throughout the UK by the National Moth Recording Scheme (NMRS). Widespread changes in moth abundance have been recorded by the RIS National Light-trap Network and are certainly mirrored in the long-term Rothamsted Farm datasets. There are indications that these changes in abundance may be, at least partly, climate related and that was certainly so for the only species so far studied in detail, the Garden Tiger Moth, *Arctia caja*, which is badly affected by wet winters and warm springs (Conrad et al. 2002).

Phenology, the timing of regularly occurring natural biological events, is often temperature related and there has been increasing public and scientific interest in the subject as climate change becomes apparent (Sparks *et al.* 2001). Not only are any changes in phenology of interest in their own right but they may have important conservation implications, particularly if interdependent species in different trophic levels get out of synchronisation as a result, e.g. a moth with its food supply (Harrington *et al.* 1999). A classic example of this is found in those moths that lay eggs in the autumn or winter so that their eggs can hatch to coincide with budburst on the trees and bushes on which they feed. If egg hatch and budburst coincide then food quality is ideal and caterpillar populations of some species can explode leading to defoliation. However, if they get out of synchrony then high quality food quality becomes scarce and moth populations decline and it is notable that many species that overwinter as eggs have indeed been declining recently (Conrad *et al.* 2004).

Regular long-term moth trapping at Rothamsted enables us to study one particular aspect of moth phenology, flight time, in some detail. Table 3 contains the result of such an analysis on the 27 single-generation species for which we have good numbers of individuals in the Rothamsted traps from 1965 to 2005. The analysis was in two parts, firstly a linear regression (single straight line) was fitted to median flight time

Species	Mean flight time (Julian day and date)	Days earlier (-) or later (+) per decade pre-breakpoint	Breakpoint (significant change in trend)	Days earlier (-) or later (+) per decade post-breakpoint	% variance accounted for
Alsophila aescularia	75 (16th March)	NS	1980	-10.7	32.7
Agriopis marginaria	80 (21st March)	+8.2	1980	-12.5	42.8
Orthosia cruda	87 (28th March)	NS	1980	-7.2	23.3
Orthosia gothica	104 (14th April)	NS	1979	-14.4	77.7
Odontopera bidentata	145 (25th May)	-	none	-3.7	25.4
Hepialus lupulinus	162 (11th June)	-	none	-1.4	6.6
Xanthorhoe montanata	163 (12th June)	NS	1979	-4.4	28.4
Spilosoma lubricipeda	165 (14th June)	NS	1985	-6.9	47.2
Diarsia mendica	175 (24th June)	-	none	-2.4	17.4
Spilosoma luteum	178 (27th June)	+9.1	1973	-4.6	23.3
Rusina ferruginea	178 (27th June)	NS	1985	-4.2	11.9
Herminia grisealis	181 (30th June)	NS	1979	-5.8	28.5
Alcis repandata	186 (5th July)	NS	1983	-4.3	29.2
Idaea dimidiata	199 (18th July)	+11.4	1977	0	18.1
Eilema lurideola	201 (20th July)	NS	1980	-4.8	22.3
Hydriomena furcata	202 (21st July)	NS	1979	-4	18.5
Perizoma alchemillata	212 (31st July)	-	none	NS	-
Abraxas grossulariata	217 (5th August)	-	none	-4.2	34.4
Mesoligia furuncula	219 (7th August)	-	none	-2	12.7
Crocallis elinguaria	219 (7th August)	NS	1984	-8.2	49.8
Cosmia trapezina	220 (8th August)	-	none	-4.1	32.4
Luperina testacea	238 (26th August)	-	none	-0.9	12.7
Noctua pronuba	239 (27th August)	-	none	+2.7	16.4
Xestia xanthographa	245 (2nd Sept.)	+4.4	1979	0	30.7
Agrochola macilenta	292 (19th Oct.)	-	none	NS	-
Epirrita dilutata	293 (20th Oct.)	-	none	+1.7	31.4
Colotois pennaria	301 (28th Oct.)	-	none	+2.4	21.3

Table 3. Trends in median flight time from long-running Rothamsted traps based on data from 1965 to 2005.

against year and then a split-line regression was fitted (two separate straight lines with different slopes), as many species seemed to be showing a sharply different response at different periods across the 40 years of study. The best fit of these two models is presented in the table and the species have been ordered according to their mean flight time to help bring out the patterns (Table 3).

It is noticeable that most of the split-line regressions occur in species that fly before the end of July and that the mean breakpoint, where the regressions change slope, is about 1980 (Table 3, column 4). Only two species show no significant trend in flight time over the last 40 years and 20 of the 27 species have flight phenologies that are getting earlier, at least after the breakpoint. Eleven out of the fifteen species that have a significant breakpoint have no trend before the breakpoint and the remaining four actually have flight times getting later, rather than earlier, until the breakpoint. The other noticeable feature is that species that have a mean flight time from the end of August tend to have no trend or are tending to fly later in the year.

Two species with advancing flight times, both fitted with a split-line, are shown in Fig. 13. These are species that fly early in spring and it appears that it is such species that currently have the most rapidly advancing flight phenologies. Indeed, as can be seen, the Hebrew Character, *Orthosia gothica* is now flying on average over 37 days earlier on the Rothamsted estate than it was in 1979 and the March Moth, *Alsophila aescularia* over 24 days earlier than 1980. In contrast Figure 14 has examples of three species, the Square-spot Rustic, *Xestia xanthographa,* the November Moth, *E. dilutata* and the Feathered Thorn, *Colotois pennaria*, which are now flying later than they did 40 years ago. These are all late summer or autumn flying species in which it may be an advantage to be able to fly later as autumn climate gets warmer.

There is likely to be a direct relationship between flight time trends and temperature, but as can be seen from these results not all species are responding in exactly the same way, and indeed two species do not seem to be responding at all. At Rothamsted we have one of the longest continuous temperature records in the UK with readings going back to 1878. There is certainly an upward trend in mean temperature in this record, with an estimated overall increase of 0.65°C between 1878 and 1995 (Woiwod 1997a). If we look at the Rothamsted temperature data between 1965 and 2006 (Fig. 15) then we can see a possible explanation for the split-line relationship as there is a similar discontinuity, although a bit later as it occurs between 1985 and 1986 rather than 1980 for the moths. The lack of any trend in temperature up to 1985 makes the increase in the twenty years since then even more astounding. For mean annual temperature there is an average increase of 1.54°C, for mean maximum annual temperature the increase is 1.44°C but for mean minimum annual temperature there has been a 1.64 °C increase since 1986. These are all very large temperature rises and go some way to explain some of the big changes that are becoming apparent in moth population, distribution and phenology. The idiosyncratic nature of some of the changes in moth phenology between species are almost certainly caused by the different rates of change in temperature at different times of the year combined with differences in the life-histories of the various moth species and clearly justify further study.

Conclusion

From a moth perspective there is nothing particularly special about Rothamsted Farm or its surroundings and its fauna is likely to be fairly representative of farms in the area. However, the intensity and long-term nature of the moth recording has inevitably turned up a few interesting species. A full list of macro-species recorded on the estate has been published and altogether over 450 species have been recorded (Riley 1999). Some species are very rare migrants that have only turned up as singletons and are unlikely to have bred. Examples of these include the Brother, *Raphia frater*, which was found in a trap run on a laboratory roof in 1949 and was the first British record; the Goosefoot Pug, *Eupithecia sinuosaria*, in one of the farm network traps in 1992, which was the second British record; and the Dusky Peacock, *Macaria signaria*, which was also caught in a farm network trap in 1992. Some other species are noteworthy because they used to occur regularly but are now very rare if not extinct. Some of these have already been mentioned in the Barnfield trap account, for example the Lappet Moth, *G. quercifolia*, which had disappeared from Barnfield by 1960 and has only been seen once since, in 1990 from a trap in a more diverse part of the farm. The Heart Moth, *D. oo*, which is now regarded as a very rare species nationally but was caught 11 times at Rothamsted between 1933 and 1952 but not since. Similarly, the Four-spotted, *T. luctuosa*, which, other than the 26 in Barnfield, was recorded 6 times in other traps up to 1952 and has not been seen since. Other examples are to be found in Riley (1999), where there is some discussion of the likely local factors responsible.

These extinctions and trends from the Barnfield trap and elsewhere on the Rothamsted estate underline the fact that moths are just not as abundant and diverse as they were before 1960 and unfortunately the

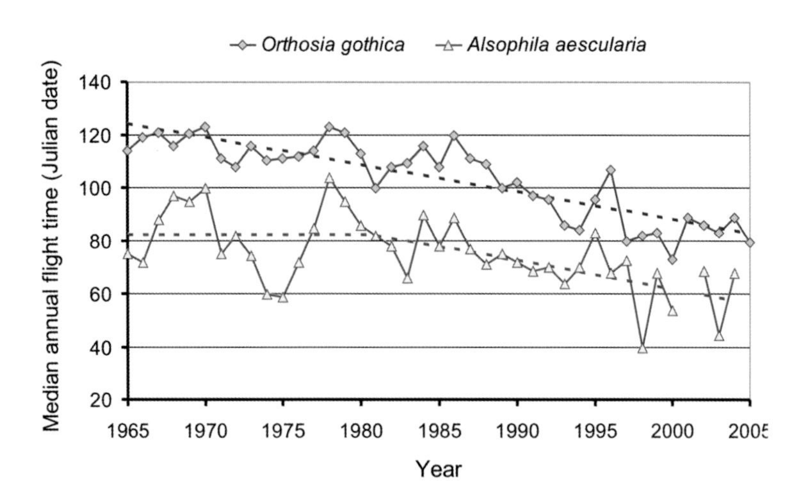

Figure 13. Example of flight time trends in two species which are flying earlier, *O. gothica* and *A. aescularia*. Both are best fit with two lines with breakpoints at 1979 and 1980 respectively (see Table 3).

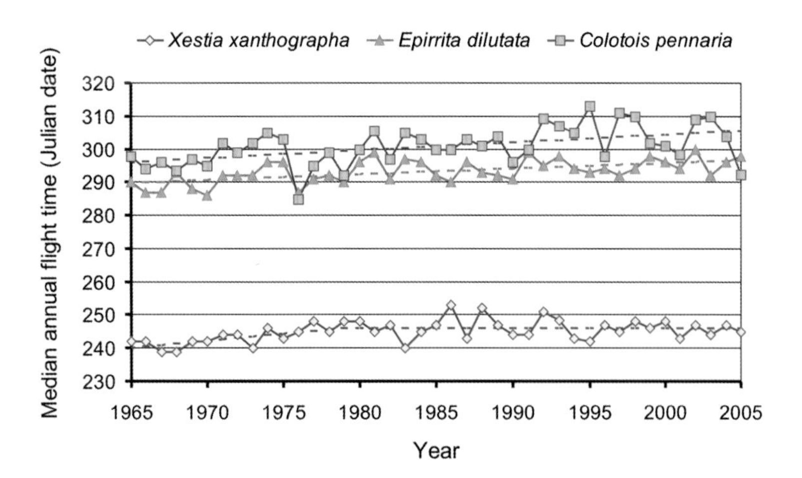

Figure 14. Example of flight time trends in three species which are flying later. The trends in *E. dilutata* and *C. pennaria* are best summarised by a single line whereas *X. xanthographa* is best summarised by two lines with a breakpoint at 1979.

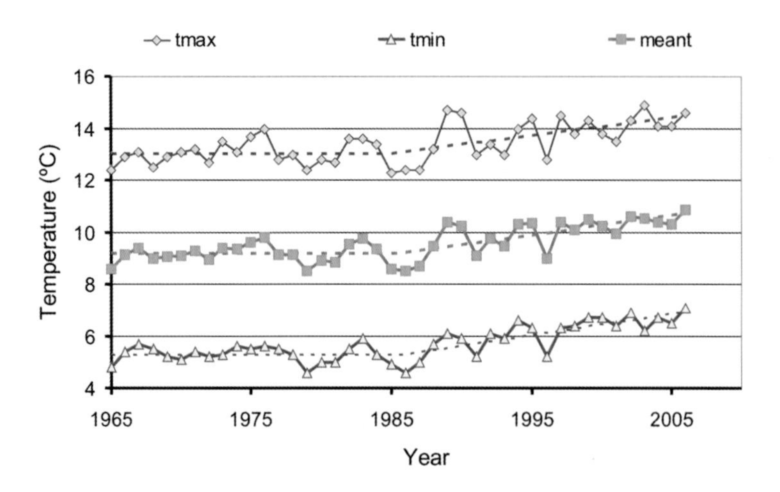

Figure 15. Rothamsted annual minimum, maximum and mean temperatures 1965-2006 with fitted split-line regressions.

decline in abundance seems to be continuing both locally and nationally (Fox *et al.* 2006). Data reported elsewhere in this book also suggest that major local extinctions of species occurred throughout Hertfordshire from about 1960, as would be expected following the extensive changes in land use and farming practice which took place immediately after the last war. We are fortunate that the long runs of abundance data from Rothamsted and distribution data collected more widely in the county give us a quantitative glimpse of what biodiversity has been lost over the last 60 years, both in Hertfordshire and almost certainly more widely. In future we have the prospect of more and better information being available, not only from national schemes such as the RIS and the NMRS but also because there are so many more active moth recorders regularly running light traps at fixed locations as well as doing other important surveys. Changes in climate, pollution and land-use are certain to continue and we need to fully understand the implications of these if future moth conservation policies are to be realistic and fruitful. The results from the Rothamsted Estate underline the importance of long-term quantitative records for this purpose.

The Rothamsted Insect Survey continues to require trap operators in Hertfordshire and throughout the UK (equipment provided). If you are interested please contact phil.gould@bbsrc.ac.uk.

Acknowledgements

The late C.B. Williams, R.A. French and L.R. Taylor provided the original inspiration behind the data presented here. We would like to thank, Joan Nicklen, Peter Hugo, Adrian Riley, Lynda Alderson, John Bater, Suzanne Clark, Sue Parker, Martin Townsend and all present and past Rothamsted staff that have contributed to the collection, identification and processing of the massive Rothamsted dataset over the years.

References

Carson, R. 1963 *Silent Spring*. London: Hamish Hamilton.

Chapman, J. A., Smith, A. D., Woiwod, I. P., Reynolds, D. R. & Riley, J. R. 2002a Development of vertical-looking radar technology for monitoring insect migration. *Computers and Electronics in Agriculture* **35**, 95-110.

Chapman, J. W., Reynolds, D. R., Smith, A. D., Riley, J. R., Pedgley, D. E. & Woiwod, I. P. 2002b The high-altitude migration of the diamondback moth, *Plutella xylostella*, in the UK: a study using radar, aerial netting and ground trapping. *Ecological Entomology* **27**, 641-650.

Conrad, K. F., Perry, J. N. & Woiwod, I. P. 2001 An abundance-occupancy time-lag during the decline of an arctiid tiger moth. *Ecology Letters* **4**, 300-304.

Conrad, K. F., Perry, J. N., Woiwod, I. P. & Alexander, C. J. 2006a Large-scale temporal changes in spatial pattern during declines of abundance and occupancy in a common moth. *Journal of Insect Conservation* **10**, 53-64.

Conrad, K. F., Warren, M. S., Fox, R., Parsons, M. & Woiwod, I. P. 2006b Rapid declines in common moths underscore a biodiversity crisis. *Biological Conservation* **132**, 279-291.

Conrad, K. F., Woiwod, I. P., Parsons, M., Fox, R. & Warren, M. S. 2004 Long-term population trends in widespread British moths. *Journal of Insect Conservation* **8**, 119-136.

Conrad, K. F., Woiwod, I. P. & Perry, J. N. 2002 Long-term decline in abundance and distribution of the garden tiger moth (*Arctia caja*) in Great Britain. *Biological Conservation* **106**, 329-337.

Conrad, K. F., Woiwod, I. P. & Perry, J. N. 2003 East Atlantic teleconnection pattern and the decline of a common arctiid moth. *Global Change Biology* **9**, 125-130.

Fisher, R. A., Corbet, A. S. & Williams, C. B. 1943 The relation between the number of species and the number of individuals in a random sample of an animal population, Part 2 - Results obtained by means of a light-trap at Rothamsted. *Journal of Animal Ecology* **12**, 42-58.

Fox, R., Conrad, K. F., Parsons, M., Warren, M. S. & Woiwod, I. P. 2006 *The state of Britain's larger moths.*: Butterfly Conservation and Rothamsted Research, Wareham, Dorset.

Hanski, I. & Woiwod, I. P. 1991 Delayed density-dependence. *Nature, London* **350**, 28.

Hanski, I. & Woiwod, I. P. 1993a Mean-related stochasticity and population variability. *Oikos* **67**, 29-39.

Hanski, I. & Woiwod, I. P. 1993b Spatial synchrony in the dynamics of moth and aphid populations. *Journal of Animal Ecology* **62**, 656-668.

Harrington, R. & Woiwod, I. 2007 Foresight from hindsight: The Rothamsted Insect Survey. *Outlooks on Pest Management* **18**, 9-14.

Harrington, R., Woiwod, I. P. & Sparks, T. H. 1999 Climate change and trophic interactions. *Trends in Ecology and Evolution* **14**, 146-150.

Intachat, J. & Woiwod, I. P. 1999 Trap design for monitoring moth biodiversity in tropical rainforests. *Bulletin of Entomological Research* **89**, 153-163.

IPCC 2007 *Climate Change 2007:* the *Intergovernmental Panel on Climate Change Fourth assessment report*. See www.ipcc.ch

Kempton, R. A. 1979 The structure and species abundance and measurement of diversity. *Biometrics* **35**, 307-321.

Kempton, R. A. & Taylor, L. R. 1974 Log-series and log-normal parameters as diversity discriminants for the Lepidoptera. *Journal of Animal Ecology* **473**, 381-399.

Kempton, R. A. & Taylor, L. R. 1979 Some observations of the yearly variability of species abundance at a site and the consistency of measures of diversity. In *Contemporary Quantitative Ecology and Related Econometrics*, vol. 12 (ed. G. P. Patil & M. L. Rozenzweig). Maryland, U.S.A.: International Co-operative Publishing House.

Kirby, P. & Stewart, A. J. A. 2001 True bugs, leaf- and planthoppers, and their allies. In *The Changing Wildlife of Great Britain and Ireland* (ed. D. L. Hawksworth), pp. 262-299. London: Taylor & France.

Lawes J. B. 1877 The Rothamsted Allotment Club. *Journal of the Royal Agricultural Society* **13**, 387-393.

Lewis, T. 1993 The contribution of Rothamsted to British entomology. *Bulletin of Entomological Research* **83**, 309-312.

Magurran, A. E. 2004 *Measuring Biological Diversity*. Oxford: Blackwell Publishing.

Parsons, M. S., Fox, R., Conrad, K. F., Woiwod, I. P. & Warren, M. S. 2005 British moths: throwing light on a new conservation challenge. *British Wildlife* **16**, 386 - 394.

Riley, A. M. 1999 The macrolepidoptera of the Rothamsted Estate, Harpenden, Hertfordshire. *Entomologist's Record* **111**, 71-94.

Silvertown, J., Poulton, P., Johnston, E., Edwards, G., Heard, M. & Biss, P. M. 2006 The Park Grass Experiment 1856-2006: its contribution to ecology. *Journal of Ecology* **94**, 801-814.

Southwood, T. R. E., Henderson, P. A. & Woiwod, I. P. 2003 Stability and change over 67 years - the community of Heteroptera as caught in a light-trap at Rothamsted, UK. *European Journal of Entomology* **100**, 557-561.

Sparks, T., Crick, H., Woiwod, I. & Beebee, T. 2001 Climate change and phenology in the United Kingdom. In *Impacts of climate change on wildlife* (ed. R. E. Green, M. Harley, M. Spalding & C. Zockler), pp. 53-55: RSPB.

Taylor, L. R. 1978 Bates, Williams and Hutchinson - A variety of diversities. In *The Diversity of Insect Faunas* (ed. L. A. Mound & N. Waloff), pp. 1-18. Oxford: Blackwell Scientific Publications.

Taylor, L. R. 1986 Synoptic dynamics, migration and the Rothamsted Insect Survey. *Journal of Animal Ecology* **55**, 1-38.

Taylor, L. R. & Brown, E. S. 1972 Effects of light-trap design and illumination on samples of moths in the Kenya highlands. *Bulletin of Entomological Research* **62**, 91-112.

Taylor, L. R. & French, R. A. 1974 Effect of light trap design and illumination on samples of moths in an English woodland. *Bulletin of Entomological Research* **63**, 583-594.

Taylor, L. R., French, R. A. & Woiwod, I. P. 1978 The Rothamsted Insect Survey and the urbanization of land in Great Britain. In *Perspectives in Urban Entomology* (ed. G. W. Frankie & C. S. Koehler), pp. 31-65. New York: Academic Press.

Taylor, L. R., Kempton, R. A. & Woiwod, I. P. 1976 Diversity statistics and the log-series model. *Journal of Animal Ecology* **45**, 255-272.

Taylor, L. R. & Woiwod, I. P. 1980 Temporal stability as a density dependent species characteristic. *Journal of Animal Ecology* **49**, 209 - 224.

Taylor, L. R. & Woiwod, I. P. 1982 Comparative synoptic dynamics. I. Relationship between inter and intra specific spatial and temporal variance/mean population parameters. *Journal of Animal Ecology* **51**, 879 -906.

Taylor, L. R., Woiwod, I. P. & Perry, J. N. 1979 The negative binomial as a dynamic ecological model for aggregation, and the density dependence of k. *Journal of Animal Ecology* **48**, 289-304.

Taylor, L. R., Woiwod, I. P. & Perry, J. N. 1980 Variance and the large scale spatial stability of aphids, moths and birds. *Journal of Animal Ecology* **49**, 831-854.

Williams, C. B. 1923 A new type of light trap for insects. *Ministry of Agriculture, Egypt, Technical and Science Service Bulletin* **No. 28**.

Williams, C. B. 1924 An improved light trap for insects. *Bulletin of Entomological Research* **15**, 57-60.

Williams, C. B. 1935 The times of activity of certain nocturnal insects, chiefly Lepidoptera, as indicated by a light trap. *Transactions of the Royal Entomological Society of London* **83**, 523-555.

Williams, C. B. 1936 The influence of moonlight on the activity of certain nocturnal insects, particularly of the family noctuiidae, as indicated by a light trap. *Philosophical Transactions of the Royal Society of London (B)* **226**, 357-389.

Williams, C. B. 1939 An analysis of four years captures of insects in a light trap, Part 1: General survey; sex proportions; phenology; and time of flight. *Transactions of the Royal Entomological Society of London* **89**, 79-132.

Williams, C. B. 1940a An analysis of four years captures of insects in a light trap, Part II: The effect of weather conditions on insect activity; and the estimation and forecasting of changes in the insect population. *Transactions of the Royal Entomological Society of London* **90**, 227-306.

Williams, C. B. 1940b The number of insects caught in a light trap at Rothamsted during four years 1933-1937. *Proceedings of the Royal Entomological Society of London (A)* **15**, 78-80.

Williams, C. B. 1944 Some applications of the logarithmic series and the index of diversity to ecological problems. *Journal of Ecology* **32**, 1-44.

Williams, C. B. 1947 The logarithmic series and its application to biological problems. *Journal of Ecology* **34**, 253-272.

Williams, C. B. 1948 The Rothamsted light trap. *Proceedings of the Royal Entomological Society of London (A)* **23**, 80-85.

Williams, C. B. 1951a Changes in insect populations in the field in relation to preceding weather conditions. *Proceedings of the Royal Society of London (B)* **138**, 130-156.

Williams, C. B. 1951b Comparing the efficiency of insect traps. *Bulletin of Entomological Research* **42**, 513-517.

Williams, C. B. 1951c Diversity as a measurable character of an animal or plant population. *Année Biologique* **27**, 129-141.

Williams, C. B. 1952 Some notes on killing insects for collections and for scientific research. *The Entomologist* **85**, 271-279.

Williams, C. B. 1953 The relative abundance of different species in wild animal populations. *Journal of Animal Ecology* **22**, 14-31.

Williams, C. B. 1958 *Insect Migration*. The New Naturalist. London: Collins.

Williams, C. B. 1964 *Patterns in the balance of nature*. London and New York: Academic Press.

Williams, C. B., French, R. A. & Hosni, M. M. 1955 A second experiment in testing the relative efficiency of insect traps. *Bulletin of Entomological Research* **46**, 193-204.

Williams C. B. & Killington F. J. 1935 Hemerobiidae and Chrysopidae (Neur.) in a light trap at Rothamsted Experimental Station. *Transactions of the Society for British Entomology* **2**, 145-150.

Woiwod, I. P. 1991 The ecological importance of long-term synoptic monitoring. In *The Ecology of Temperate Cereal Fields* (ed. L. G. Firbank, N. Carter, J. F. Darbyshire & G. R. Potts), pp. 275-304. Oxford: Blackwell.

Woiwod, I. P. 1997a Detecting the effects of climate change on Lepidoptera. *Journal of Insect Conservation* **1**, 149-158.

Woiwod, I. P. 1997b Monitoring population change and diversity. In *The Butterflies and Moths of Bedfordshire* (ed. V. W. Arnold, C. R. B. Baker, D. V. Manning & I. P. Woiwod), pp. 61 - 78: Bedfordshire Natural History Society.

Woiwod, I. P. 2003 Are common moths in trouble? In *Butterfly Conservation News*, vol. 82, pp. 9-11.

Woiwod, I., Gould, P. & Conrad, K. 2005 The Rothamsted Light-trap Network - shedding light on a common moth problem. *Atropos* **26**, 5-18.

Woiwod, I. P. & Hanski, I. 1992 Patterns of density dependence in moths and aphids. *Journal of Animal Ecology* **61**, 619-629.

Woiwod, I. P. & Harrington, R. 1994 Flying in the face of change: The Rothamsted Insect Survey. In *Long-term Experiments in Agricultural and Ecological Sciences* (ed. R. A. Leigh & A. E. Johnston), pp. 321-342. Wallingford: CAB International.

Woiwod, I. P. & Wynne, I. R. 1994 The distribution and genetic structure of farmland moth communities. In *Fragmentation in Agricultural Landscapes* (ed. J. Dover), pp. 137-144. Preston: IALE (UK).

Wynne, I. R., Loxdale, H. D., Brookes, C. P. & Woiwod, I. P. 2003 Population genetic structure of fragmented November moth (Lepidoptera: Geometridae) populations in the farmland agroecosystem. *Biological Journal of the Linnean Society* **78**, 467-477.

Present-day Moth Recording in Hertfordshire

A century ago, all that really seemed to matter within a county list of moths was the approximate locality and the name of the gentleman who had recorded it. This enabled other gentlemen collectors to make contact and either visit the locality or have the original recorder obtain specimens for him. Additional information must have seemed un-necessary; the notion that such extra data might be of some unforeseen future use was beyond the comprehension of all but the most enlightened of collectors.

Today, whilst knowing where less common moths are to be found remains of importance, the reasons are more conservation-based and the overall emphasis is on assessing the pattern of distribution presented by each species and interpreting this in terms of geology, habitat, weather patterns and, of course, recorder bias. We also religiously record dates of observations: if only we had such detailed phenological data from a century ago the changes of flight period currently attributed to climate change could perhaps have been detected earlier. Foodplant data are equally important. Slavishly copying what others have already written masks new discoveries. Are the larval foodplants in Hertfordshire the same as those used elsewhere?

So 'good' recording involves obtaining as much data as possible whether or not it is of immediate use. Data labels on specimens are an absolute requirement and where these are cross-referenced to diaries or record books even better. A year ago I would not have expected that I would be involved in a project to produce DNA profiles for European moths, yet because I have not only recorded the date of capture but have a record of how the specimen was killed and whether it was subsequently relaxed before being 'set' I have been able to select recently collected material, despatched by freezing or other non-chemical means and not subjected to the relaxing box to send to scientists in Canada for just such a project. It is not at all possible to predict what other future use my collection may be – but I hope that my data recording process will serve as adequate when new uses do arise.

Distribution maps explained

Each map in this book show the physical distribution of the moth concerned within vice county 20 (Hertfordshire). I have used three different symbols in the maps:

- ● A red dot represents records made in that map square from 1st January 1995 to 31st December 2005
- + A plus sign represents records made in that map square from 1st January 1950 to 31st December 1994
- O An open circle represents records made in that map square prior to 1950

The presence of a dot, plus sign or a circle means that there is at least one record of the moth under discussion from that map square in the date period indicated by the symbol. This does not give any indication at all of numbers of individuals, which may, in some cases, vary from one side of the county to the other. These are *distribution* maps – not *status* maps. They present an overall impression of the *pattern* of distribution and are only very rarely 'complete'. Distribution maps such as these should never be interpreted in isolation; always read the accompanying text. The three symbols have been selected so that older records are not masked by those made more recently; this allows changes in distribution to be detected. In particular, it should be noted that a red spot with a black circle around it represents two date bands – a pre-1950 'open circle' and a post-1994 red spot – where a species is recorded only in the period 1995 to 2006 the red dot will not have a black outline.

The symbols are placed on imaginary map squares, each measuring 2 kilometres by 2 kilometres and called tetrads. These are not random. They defined by the lines of the Ordnance Survey's National grid and are the same lines used to derive grid references from maps. The large squares of the grid overlaid upon the map are each 10 kilometres by 10 kilometres (centads). Each 10 Km square, as it is usually referred to, clearly holds 5 x 5 = 25 tetrads.

Tetrads may be defined in two ways – by an alphabetic 'user friendly' system or by a more logical numeric notation. In the alphabetic system, the 25 tetrads in each ten-kilometre square are indicated by the letters A to Z, omitting the letter O, from bottom-left to top-right, working vertically as in the flowing diagram:

E	J	P	U	Z
D	I	N	T	Y
C	H	M	S	X
B	G	L	R	W
A	F	K	Q	V

In this system, the tetrads are referred to by the alpha-numeric ten-kilometre square reference followed by the alphabetic symbol of the particular tetrad – e.g., TL42Q or SP91Y. Hertford town centre lies in tetrad TL31G.

In the numerical notation, the tetrads are numbered according to the grid reference of their south-west corner as follows:

08	28	48	68	88
06	26	46	66	86
04	24	44	64	84
02	22	42	62	82
00	20	40	60	80

The tetrads may now be referred to in the same way as above. Thus, Hertford town centre is in tetrad TL31T22. By inserting an upper case 'T' between the ten-kilometre reference and the tetrad reference the reference is distinguished from TL3122, which is a one kilometre grid square.

Allocating records with insufficient data to tetrads

The maps show all records from the Hertfordshire vice-county that can be accurately allocated to a tetrad using the data available. However, just as the place you are looking for often seems to be on the fold of the map, in some cases records cannot be accurately positioned. In these situations it may be best not to map the record at all, but in species with very few mapped records it may be visually more misleading to omit it than to place it incorrectly – after all, distribution maps are intended to convey only a *pattern* of distribution. Therefore, in a few cases we have assigned a record to a tetrad either by careful reasoning or, in the cases where the record could be in one of two or three tetrads, by placing it *downwards and to the left*. Thus, a record that cannot be placed accurately to the east or west of a north-south dividing line is always placed westwards and one that cannot be distinguished between north and south is always placed south. In cases were the record affects one of four tetrads, both rules apply and the record is mapped in the south-west tetrad. This means that if it is later proved incorrect then we at least know which direction to move it back again. Records that are even more vague have not been not mapped.

Boundary sites

All records from the Hertfordshire Vice-county are included. Inevitably, however, some sites straddle our border with neighbouring counties and, when recording moths there it is either impractical or rather ridiculous to decide which site of the arbitrary line the insect was seen; the moth almost certainly flies across the line on a regular basis. I have used another rigid rule in deciding whether or not to include the moth on our maps for Hertfordshire and it is simply this: the record **is** included **if** it is made in an area of habitat that is continuous across the county boundary **and** there is no discernible difference in habitat on either side of the boundary. If, however, the moth is a rare species or a new county record, we allocate it accurately to the correct vice-county and do not include it in the Hertfordshire maps if it was found next door! The places where this rule has applied are as follows, clockwise from Bishops Stortford in the far east of the map:

Birchanger Wood, Bishops Stortford	Continuous hornbeam-dominated woodland across the Herts/North Essex border. Many records were made at light traps on an adjacent school playing field in North Essex and the moths were watched flying out of the Hertfordshire portion of the wood and over the county boundary to travel the three metres to the traps!
Sawbridgeworth Marsh	Freshwater marsh affecting both Hertfordshire and North Essex. In reality, we have probably recorded all the species on both sides of the boundary in any case.
urban area of Barnet	Some garden records are mapped because the trap site, although a few yards into Middlesex, is a part of the urban habitat continuum here. Had the owner chosen to buy a house a few yards up the same road the garden list would be the same.
Chorleywood	Some garden records are mapped because the trap site, although a few yards into Buckinghamshire, is a part of the suburban habitat continuum here. Had the owner chosen to buy a house a few yards up the same road the garden list would be the same.
Pavis & Grove Woods, Tring	Continuous woodland across the county boundary with Buckinghamshire – the footpath forms the county boundary.

Although the Ashridge Estate straddles the border between Hertfordshire and Buckinghamshire in the west all included records have been made firmly on the Hertfordshire side of the somewhat convoluted vice-county boundary.

Flight periods of adults

There are, of course, four stages to the development of a moth – egg (ovum, plural ova), caterpillar (larva, plural larvae), chrysalis (pupa, plural pupae) and adult (imago, plural imagines). All show remarkable consistency, under normal circumstances, in the timing of their appearance throughout the year, though most moth enthusiasts concentrate their efforts only on the adults. Of course, there are always 'freak' appearances of adults at the wrong time of year, but these are rare exceptions and are usually brought about by artificial circumstances. For example, a few years ago I had a whole load of 'summer' flies (Diptera) in my greenhouse during March – because a week earlier I had dug some of my compost heap in preparation for growing tomatoes. When I opened the door, most flew out and if found by a Dipterist would doubtless have caused excitement.

However, if the bulk of adults of a species suddenly start to appear earlier or later than the expected norm, there is probably an underlying reason; if there is a shift of the flight period over a number of years then it is likely that one or more wider environmental issues may be responsible. Turning the situation around, if there is a supposed environmental change taking place, such as global climate change, for example, then moth flight period may act as both as an early warning system and as monitors of change over time. This is the reason why I really do want dates and numbers for all your Large Yellow Underwings and other very common species.

In order to make the flight period data useable, the charts in this book include only data gathered from 1995 to 2006 inclusive. It is most unfortunate that other than from the Rothamsted light trap from Harpenden we do not have an adequate data set of numbers against dates for earlier years and so we cannot truly tell if most species are now flying earlier or later than in, say, the 1930s. However, by placing the 1995 – 2006 data on record here, future researchers will indeed be able to detect such alterations. I have excluded the Harpenden trap data from the charts and have also avoided using them as a direct comparison with our current data set for one very simple reason: the Harpenden trap retains all the moths that go in and so the nightly counts are a measure of the number of new examples entering the trap (recruitment) whilst all other trapping in the county involves the release of most or all individuals, so that catches inevitably include a high proportion of retrapped moths. Data are plotted by standard weeks as indicated in the following chart:

Table of Standard Weeks (from Plant, 1994)

Week No	Dates	Week No.	Dates	Week No	Dates	Week No	Dates
1	1 Jan – 7 Jan	**14**	2 Apr – 8 Apr	**27**	2 Jul – 8 Jul	**40**	1 Oct – 7 Oct
2	8 Jan – 1 4 Jan	**15**	9 Apr – 15 Apr	**28**	9 Jul – 15 Jul	**41**	8 Oct – 14 Oct
3	15 Jan – 21 Jan	**16**	16 Apr – 22 Apr	**29**	16 Jul – 22 Jul	**42**	15 Oct – 21 Oct
4	22 Jan – 28 Jan	**17**	23 Apr – 29 Apr	**30**	23 Jul – 29 Jul	**43**	22 Oct – 28 Oct
5	29 Jan – 4 Feb	**18**	30 Apr – 6 May	**31**	30 Jul – 5 Aug	**44**	29 Oct – 4 Nov
6	5 Feb – 1 1 Feb	**19**	7 May – 13 May	**32**	6 Aug – 12 Aug	**45**	5 Nov – 11 Nov
7	12 Feb – 18 Feb	**20**	14 May – 20 May	**33**	13 Aug – 19 Aug	**46**	12 Nov – 18 Nov
8	19 Feb – 25 Feb	**21**	21 May – 27 May	**34**	20 Aug – 26 Aug	**47**	19 Nov – 25 Nov
9	26 Feb – 4 Mar	**22**	28 May – 3 Jun	**35**	27 Aug – 2 Sep	**48**	26 Nov – 2 Dec
10	5 Mar – 11 Mar	**23**	4 Jun – 10 Jun	**36**	3 Sep – 9 Sep	**49**	3 Dec – 9 Dec
11	12 Mar – 18 Mar	**24**	11 Jun – 17 Jun	**37**	10 Sep – 16 Sep	**50**	10 Dec – 16 Dec
12	19 Mar – 25 Mar	**25**	18 Jim – 24 Jun	**38**	17 Sep – 23 Sep	**51**	17 Dec – 23 Dec
13	26 Mar – 1 Apr	**26**	25 Jun – 1 Jul	**39**	24 Sep – 30 Sep	**52**	24 Dec – 31 Dec

It is worth discussing the likely statistical significance of the flight period data used. If I run my trap every night of the year and count each species, that would provide a complete data set. If several people do likewise at different places across the whole county, we would have a data set as near perfect as possible. However, this does not happen. Few people actually trap every single night and most people take holidays so that there is a period when the nightly counts *appear* in the data set to be zero. If all the moth catchers of Hertfordshire took their holiday in the same two weeks of August, the charts would show a significant dip that was not a true reflection of reality. Happily, this latter problem does not actually exist in the Hertfordshire data set and although there are gaps in almost everybody's nightly counts these are all at different periods and any anomalies are considered to have been 'smoothed' out from the charts. People who trap moths at a fixed site on a regular basis but who do not yet count the numbers of individuals of each species are warmly invited to start counting at least the macro moths and make sure that the data is sent to me at the end of the year.

2166: *Hadena rivularis* Campion (© Colin W. Plant)

Verification of records

Like most branches of natural history in Britain, the study of moths is largely an amateur enterprise, undertaken as a leisure activity. However, whilst entirely agreeing with the idea that people should enjoy looking at moths, it is nevertheless absolutely essential that records sent in to recording schemes relate to moths that have been correctly identified. For Hertfordshire, I have always erred on the side of caution and the 'default' position has been to reject records that I do not feel 100 percent happy about after a thorough examination of the evidence. Although modern-day recording does not compel the recorder to collect a specimen, he or she should be aware that situations exist where such proof of identity may be required. In many cases a photograph may help, but although several species can be named at rest from the appearance of the upper surface of their forewings some may need to be viewed from beneath or have their hind wings examined; non-collectors should at least be aware of which species require a specimen, even if they are unwilling to engage in that activity themselves.

A small number of species require what is termed 'critical' examination to be correctly named. Fortunately for us, the process of evolution has ensured that different species are not able to interbreed and produce offspring and in the case of insects this is usually expressed by the fact that the various bit simply don't fit another species. We can, therefore, use these physical differences in genital structure to name individual insects. A macro-moth species included in the Hertfordshire fauna for which I have insisted on examination of the genitalia follows, on page 48.

Beyond these is a further set of species groups which, though they do not require their reproductive apparatus to be scrutinised, are nevertheless regarded as problematic. To these, I have added a number of further groups which have been drawn to my attention as difficult by the less experienced contributors to this book. It has not been my intention to put anyone off enjoying looking at moths, but records of these species sent in by less experienced observers were queried by me unless a specimen or a photograph showing the relevant features was also supplied.

Hertfordshire moth species whose identification depends upon genitalia examination.

Species	Notes
Dark-barred Twin-spot/Red Twin-spot Carpet	*Xanthorhoe ferrugata/spadicearia*. Fresh examples can usually be named, but worn examples require dissection
Lead/July Belle	*Scotopteryx mucronata/luridata*
November/Pale November/Autumnal Moth	*Epirrita* species
Brindled/Oak-tree Pug	*Eupithecia abbreviate/dodoneata*.
Eupithecine pugs (some examples)	Unicolorous or melanic *Eupithecia* specimens and worn examples with the exception of distinctive species such as *linariata, pulchellata, venosata, centaureata, icterata, succentureata* etc
Sloe/Green Pugs (worn examples)	*Pasiphila chloerata/rectangulata*
Grey/Dark Dagger	*Acronicta psi/tridens*
Marbled/Tawny Marbled/Rufous Minor	*Oligia strigilis/ latruncula/ versicolor*
Common/Lesser Common Rustic	*Mesapamea secalis/didyma*
Ear/Large Ear	*Amphipoea oculea/ fucosa*

Hertfordshire moth species that are difficult to separate and may require expert examination.

Species	Scientific name	Notes
Orange/Light Orange Underwing	*Archiearis parthenias/notha*	Impossible to name correctly unless handled
Plain Wave	*Idaea straminata*	Rare species confused with Riband Wave *Idaea aversata*
Balsam Carpet	*Xanthorhoe biriviata*	Rare species confused with Dark-barred Twin-spot/Red Twin-spot Carpet *Xanthorhoe ferrugata/spadicearia*
Wood Carpet	*Epirrhoe rivata*	Rare species confused with Common Carpet *Epirrhoe alternata*
Dark Marbled Carpet	*Chloroclysta citrata*	Requires examination of underside of hind wing to separate from Common Marbled Carpet *Chloroclysta truncata*
Foxglove/Toadflax Pugs	*Eupithecia pulchellata/linariata*	Easily confused
Dentated Pug	*Anticollix sparsata*	Absent from Herts: closely resembles male Brown Scallop *Philereme vetulata*
Treble-bar/Lesser Treble-bar	*Aplocera plagiata/efformata*	Easily confused
Peacock/Sharp-angled Peacock	*Semiothisa notata/alternata*	Easily confused
Great Oak/Pale Oak Beauty	*Hypomecis roboraria/punctinalis*	Easily confused
Small Engrailed/Engrailed	*Ectropis crepuscularia/bistortata*	Refer to text
Common Wave/Common White Wave	*Cabera exanthemata/pusaria*	Easily confused
Sloe Carpet/Early Moth	*Aleucis distinctata/Theria primaria*	Easily confused
Alder/Poplar/Sallow Kitten	*Furcula bicuspis/bifida/furcula*	Easily confused
Swallow/Lesser Swallow Prominent	*Pheosia tremula/gnoma*	Easily confused
Scarce/Common Footman	*Eilema complana/lurideota*	Easily confused
Lunar Yellow Underwing	*Noctua orbona*	Extremely rare species easily confused with Lesser Yellow Underwing *Noctua comes*
Triple-spotted Clay (except in western Herts)	*Xestia ditrapezium*	Apparently confined to the west of the county and easily confused with Double Square-spot *Xestia triangulum*
Gothic/Feathered Gothic	*Naenia typica/Tholera decimalis*	Easily confused
Lychnis/Campion	*Hadena rivularis/bicruris*	Easily confused
Marbled/Varied Coronet	*Hadena confusa/compta*	Easily confused
Lead-coloured/Clouded Drab	*Orthosta populeti/incerta*	Easily confused
Shark/Chamomile Shark	*Cucullia umbratica/chamomillae*	Easily confused
Tawny/Pale Pinion	*Lithophane semibrunnea/hepatica*	Easily confused
Chestnut/Dark Chestnut	*Conistra vaccinii/ligula*	Easily confused
Copper/Dusky Copper Underwing	*Aniphipyra pyramidea/berbera*	Easily confused
Reddish Light Arches/ Light Arches/Clouded Brindle	*Apamea sublustris/ lithoxylaea/crenata*	Easily confused Easily confused
Uncertain/Rustic	*Hoplodrina alsines/blanda*	Easily confused
Beautiful/Plain Golden Y	*Autographa pulchrina/jota*	Easily confused
Dark Spectacle	*Abrostola triplasia*	Rare species, easily confused with Spectacle *Abrostola tripartita*

How well-recorded are Hertfordshire's moths?

	Number or recorded species of			Number of species new to Herts during this year			Number of		New species expressed as a percentage of all records	Average number of records per recorder
	micros	macros	all moths	micros	macros	all moths	records in database	recorders contributing		
pre-1995	821	612	1433	0	0	0	19,519	-	0	-
1995	166	369	535	6	1	7	1,947	36	0.34	5,408
1996	108	373	481	2	1	3	1,776	33	0.17	5,382
1997	283	404	687	12	0	12	3,222	34	0.37	9,476
1998	203	380	583	8	1	9	3,124	28	0.29	11,157
1999	269	436	705	6	0	6	5,812	43	0.10	13,516
2000	405	432	837	18	1	19	15,723	66	0.12	23,823
2001	401	435	836	12	1	13	18,379	57	0.07	32,244
2002	468	440	908	13	0	13	25,609	74	0.05	34,607
2003	508	436	944	9	0	9	29,166	75*	0.03	38,888
2004	511	437	948	9	0	9	22,793	77	0.04	29,602
2005	465	437	902	10	0	10	27,382	72	0.03	38,031
2006	402	446	848	6	1	7	34,194	64	0.02	53,428

*value corrected by the removal of 30 recorders who only submitted single records of Humming-bird Hawk Moth (*Macroglossum stellatarum*).

Progress in modern moth recording in Hertfordshire, during the years 1995 to 2006, can be more effectively analysed than that undertaken in earlier years. The table above allows a number of comparisons.

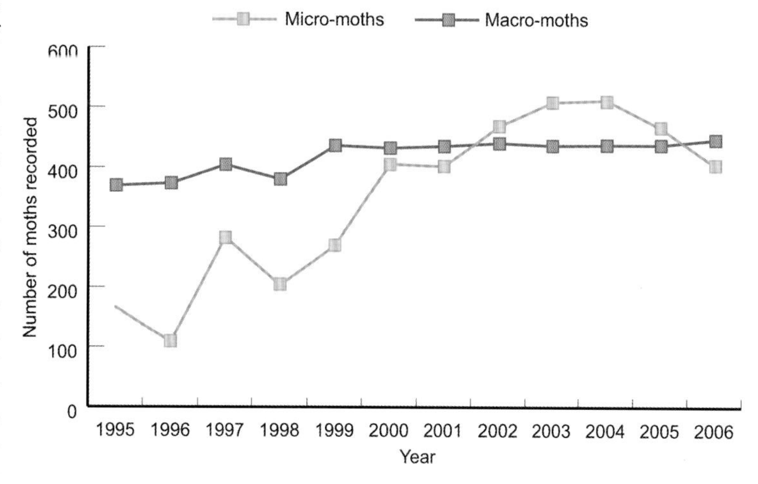

Using these data, graphs can be drawn to aid interpretation. It is clear that the number of larger moth (macro) species recorded each year is more or less constant, perhaps suggesting that, ignoring random influxes of immigrants, the fauna is more or less completely known.

However, the graph line for micro moths rises steeply at first, indicating a group that has been seriously under-recorded in the past (easy to find new species) and then starts to level off a bit before actually declining in the last two years – an indication that perhaps the easy-to-find micros have now been ticked off whilst those that require specialist searching are the ones that remain under-recorded.

The graph of all moth records received shows a slow start from 1995 and a dramatic peak in 2000 – correspondingly precisely with the formation of the Herts Moth Group. Records continue to rise as more people get interested in moths, though the decline in 2004 is both surprising and unexplained.

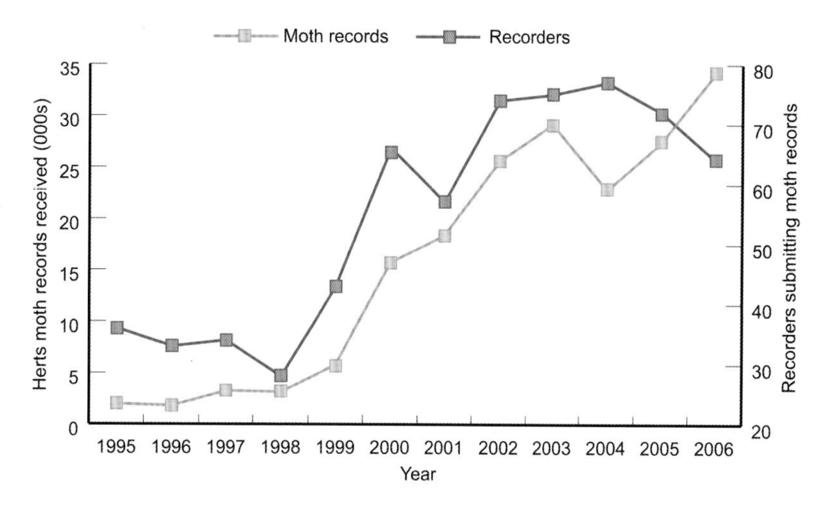

Examination of the number of recorders sending in Hertfordshire moth records does not show a corresponding dip during 2004, although the average number of records does; together these data suggest that 2004 was a poor year for moths rather than a poor year for recording them. They also suggest that 2005 and 2006 were markedly better (an increase in records from a declining number of observers raises the average number of moths reported by each person by a significant amount).

Introduction to the Species Accounts

The entry for each individual moth species follows a set five-point format, as follows:

1. Code number and name of the moth

The sequence in which the moths are presented follows, more or less, the latest British checklist (Bradley, 2000) even though I may personally take issue with some points. We are lucky in Britain to have the checklist numbers that were originally introduced by Bradley & Fletcher (1979); we are equally fortunate to have survived the well-intentioned, but premature attempts by some to re-number the species from scratch. The checklist numbers, repeated in Bradley (2000) are given for each species so that the reader can be in no doubt, either now or in the future, over which species is intended. In general, the scientific names of the moths are also those of the Bradley checklist; where they differ the fact is pointed out and discussed. Where an established English name exists, this is also given.

2. Summarised data

In order to make it easier for the reader to compare different moth species with each other, I have tried to standardise the text as far as practical. Each species account opens with summarised statements under the following six headings:

Recorded

The years in which the species under discussion was first and last recorded are given. This usually implies that the moth is thought to have been continuously present throughout that period, but it does not imply that I have a record on the database for each intervening year. In some cases the year is the earliest/latest *possible*, not necessarily the actual year of the record. For example, the many un-dated records given by Foster (1937 list) may relate to earlier years, but we have no means of knowing when; these are given as '1937'.

Distribution and status

A statement, for the period 1995 to 2006, based on both the distribution map and on an assessment of how well-recorded the species might be. A good measure of 'gut feeling' has also been inserted in places; some species with rather few map dots might be defined as widespread, because I think they will be so if looked for. The following categories have been used to define distribution:

Absent/apparently absent – Self-explanatory

Local – Unlike Widespread species these are not to be found in every site. If we could achieve 100 percent coverage there would be more gaps than dots on the maps.

Widespread – These species are almost everywhere, but not *actually* everywhere. If we could achieve 100 percent coverage there would be more dots than gaps on the maps, but there would indeed be gaps.

Ubiquitous – Present, or expected to be present, in just about every map tetrad.

These are used in combination with the following definitions of status.

Immigrant – Recorded only as a visitor from overseas. Immigrant species may produce one or more generation of larvae, but the species is not thought to survive the winter in any stage and so depends upon immigration for its continued presence in the county

Vagrant – Recorded only as a wanderer from elsewhere in Britain.

Temporary resident – A species that may breed occasionally, but which does not become established. Typically, these may be immigrants whose progeny do not survive the subsequent winter. As the climate warms, some of these species may become established and so recording their temporary residency or otherwise now provides valuable baseline data for the future.

Extinct – The rules vary, though as a guiding principle extinction should not be declared until 50 years have elapsed without the species being found in spite of adequate and appropriate searching. Even then, some species have a habit of staging surprise returns – for example 2165: Small Ranunculus (*Hecatera dysodea*) that became extinct in Britain in 1912 and reappeared in Kent during the 1990s. My personal opinion has been used freely in designations of extinction in Hertfordshire; knowledge of the year of the last record will help the reader to form an independent opinion.

Resident – A species that has either bred continuously in the county from 1995 to 2006 inclusive or which has colonised the county since the end of 1994 and appears to have become permanently established here. This is refined as follows:

- Rare resident – a species that appears to be numerically infrequent wherever it is found
- Uncommon resident – a species arbitrarily assigned to the void between Rare and Common
- Common resident – a species that appears to be represented in good number whenever it is found
- Abundant resident – a species that is regularly recorded in colossal numbers

Alien – Non-British species that have arrived here with human assistance, not by immigration, for example, imported with foreign produce. These have no significance in terms of biodiversity conservation in Hertfordshire unless they establish feral colonies that appear likely to persist.

Doubtfully recorded – The jury is out. They may be incorrectly identified, but contrary evidence exists to suggest that the record may be correct.

Erroneously recorded – Square brackets are traditionally placed around the *entire* entry for a species that is erroneously recorded. Such species are only included if they have appeared in the published literature or in newsletters and similar. Unpublished erroneous records (e.g., on web sites) are not mentioned unless there is some reason why they ought to be placed on permanent record. Erroneously recorded species are summarised after the species accounts, on page 500.

In some cases the status has been modified with an indication of numerical abundance. This is both subjective and independent of distribution; it is possible for a rare moth (status) to be widespread (distribution) or for a common moth to be extremely local or restricted.

Conservation status

The conservation status of each species is given in accordance with the guidelines on page 504.

Caterpillar foodplants

I list *only those recorded in Hertfordshire*, but in most cases I have added those used, allegedly, elsewhere in Britain so that the reader may be guided in his or her searches. A Hertfordshire foodplant is mentioned only if it was actually being eaten in the wild – not a plant upon which a caterpillar was resting nor plants force-fed to captive larvae. I have used English names for foodplants since many moth enthusiasts (like me!) are hopeless botanists. However, the scientific names of all are presented in Appendix 4 on page 526. Proper names start with an initial capital; generic names are entirely in lower case. Thus, 'Common Hawthorn' means *Crataegus monogyna* and whilst 'hawthorn' means *Crataegus* species.

Flight period

The approximate flight periods of adults in Hertfordshire are given using data from the period 1995 to 2006 only. Extremes and anomalies are mentioned in the text.

Records in database

The total number of records in the database is given. A record is a report of a species on a date by a person and is independent of the number of individuals or the degree of detail attached to the date.

3. A distribution map

For a fuller discussion, see page 45.

● A red dot represents records made in that map square from 1st January 1995 to 31st December 2006

+ A plus sign represents records made in that map square from 1st January 1950 to 31st December 1994

O An open circle represents records made in that map square prior to 1950

The three symbols have been selected so that older records are not masked by those made more recently, so allowing any changes to be seen. thus, a red dot without a black ring around it is not the same as a red dot *with* a black circle around its circumference.

4. An adult flight-period chart

For species where there is sufficient data, the flight period is also expressed as a bar chart to illustrate when the adult moth flies in Hertfordshire. The data plotted are the numbers of *individuals*, which is not the same as the number of *records* in the database. Records are plotted for 'standard Weeks' (see page 47) and reflect the years 1995 – 2006 only.

5. Free text discussing the species

Each species account ends with free-text, the length of which varies depending on how much additional information remains to be imparted.

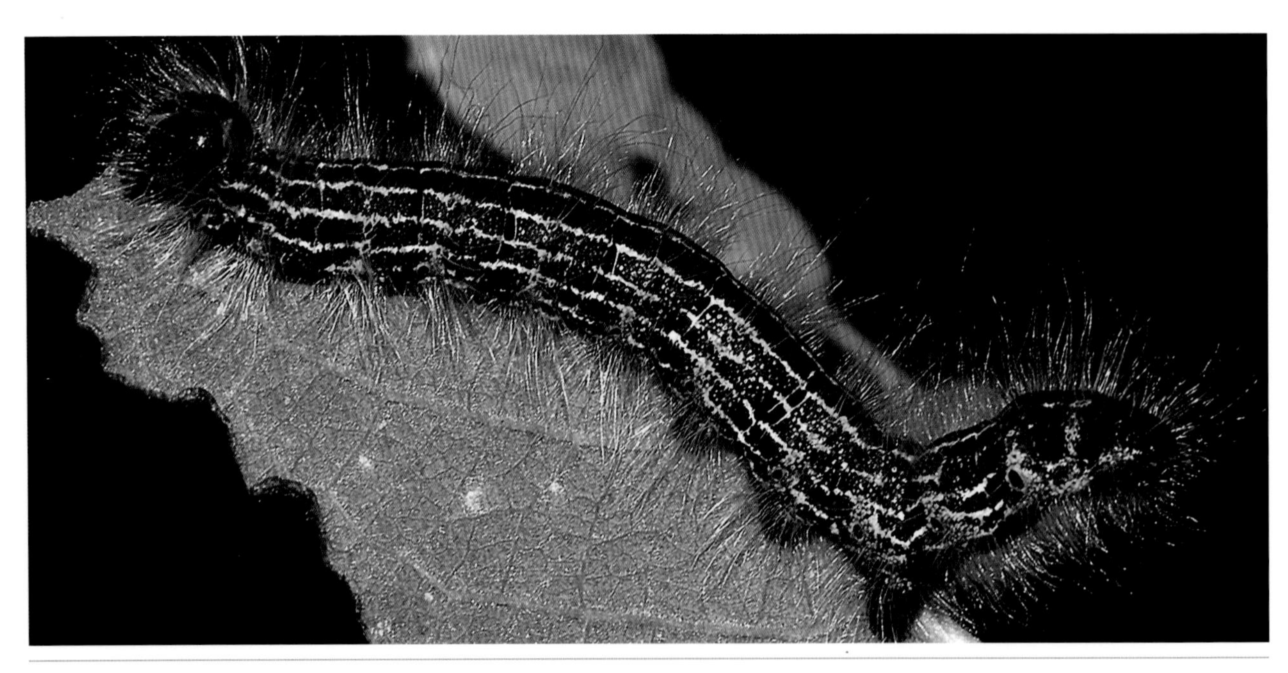

ZEUGLOPTERA
MICROPTERIGOIDEA
MICROPTERIGIDAE

The Micropterigidae are our only representatives of the lepidopteran suborder Zeugloptera. This group of small, metallic-coloured day-flying moths is unique in that the species have jaws that are used for feeding on pollen. There are five British species, all of which are known from Hertfordshire. All are very much under-recorded, though two may be extinct as their preferred habitat is extremely rare in the county.

0001 *Micropterix tunbergella* (Fabr.)

Recorded:	1890 – 1997
Distribution / Status:	Extremely local / Resident
Conservation status:	Herts Rare
Caterpillar food plants:	Completely unknown
Flight period:	Unrecorded. Elsewhere in May and June
Records in database:	4

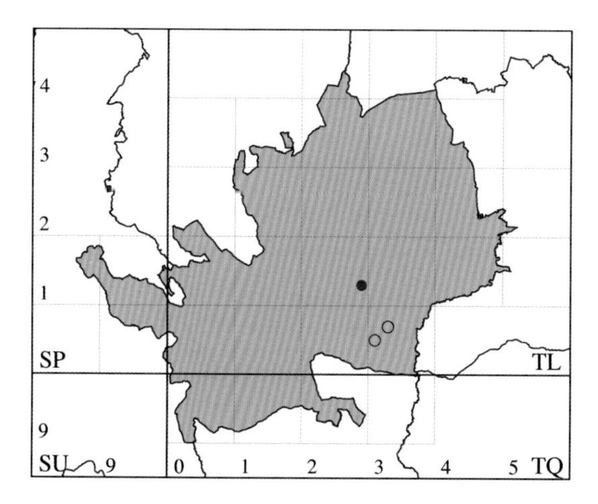

The two open-circle records on the map relate to Wormley Wood/Broxbourne Wood complex (Boyd, 1901); a record from the Sandridge area, prior to 1890, cannot be mapped accurately. The only current record is from Panshanger Park where it was noted by Tom Gladwin in 1997. The adult moths feed on the pollen of oak, Sycamore and perhaps other plants.

0002 *Micropterix mansuetella* Zell.

Recorded:	1890 – 1900
Distribution / Status:	Absent? / Extinct, or under-recorded?
Conservation status:	Herts Extinct
Caterpillar food plants:	Unknown
Flight period:	Not recorded. Elsewhere in May and June
Records in database:	3

Our older records are from the Sandridge area prior to 1890 (A. F. Griffith) and from Cheshunt prior to 1901 (W. C. Boyd). The apparent scarcity of this species today is surprising. It seems to prefer wet woodland, a habitat that is scarce in Hertfordshire, in which there are plenty of sedges upon which the females sit, feeding on the pollen and are easily captured for identification.

0003 *Micropterix aureatella* (Scop.)

Recorded:	1834
Distribution / Status:	Absent? / Extinct or under-recorded
Conservation status:	Herts Extinct
Caterpillar food plants:	Unknown
Flight period:	Not recorded. Elsewhere in May and June
Records in database:	1

Our only record is that given by J. F. Stephens, who illustrated this species from a Hertford specimen in his *Illustrations of British Entomology* **4**: 362, published in 1834. The exact locality is not known and so no map can be presented. Like *M. mansuetella,* this moth seems to prefer wet woodland in which there are plenty of sedges upon which the adults sit, feeding on the pollen, but unlike all the other *Micropterix* species *M. aureatella* is possibly absent from much of East Anglia so may in fact be extinct in Hertfordshire.

0004 *Micropterix aruncella* (Scop.)

Recorded:	1890 – 2005
Distribution / Status:	Local / Resident
Conservation status:	No perceived threats
Caterpillar food plants:	Not recorded. Elsewhere on plant debris in tussocks of the grass *Dactylis*
Flight period:	Late May to mid-June. Elsewhere, from May to August
Records in database:	11

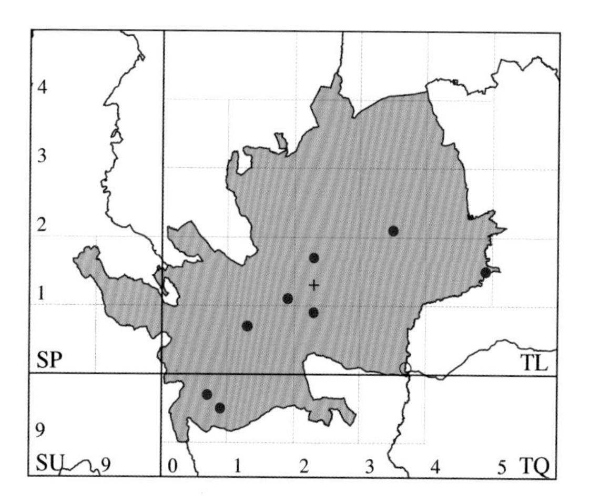

Recent records are from Lemsford Springs in 1979 (Tom Gladwin), Croxley Common Moor on 13th June 1999 (Raymond Uffen), Sawbridgeworth Marsh on 29th May 2004 (Colin Plant) and Oxlease, 9th June 2005 (Wendy Hatton). The Sawbridgeworth Marsh examples were sitting inside flowers of buttercups and may have been feeding on the pollen. The moth is likely to be widespread and relatively common in Hertfordshire, but is currently under-recorded everywhere.

0005 *Micropterix calthella* (L.)

Recorded:	1890 – 2004
Distribution / Status:	Probably widespread / Resident
Conservation status:	No perceived threats
Caterpillar food plants:	Elsewhere in Britain on 'young shoots of herbaceous plants'
Flight period:	May.
Records in database:	16

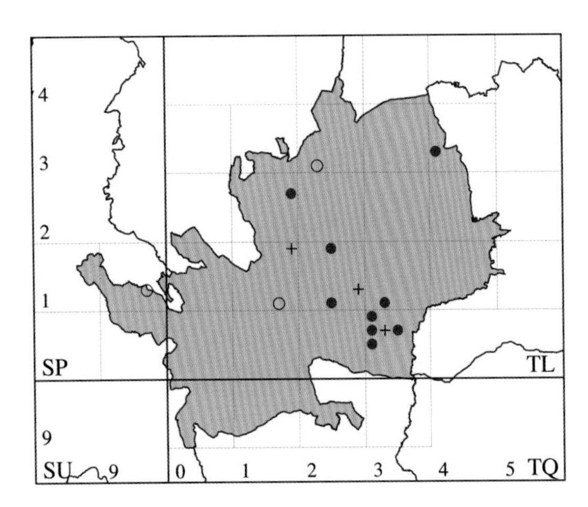

Adults have been found feeding on the pollen of Pendulous Sedge in damp woodland by Raymond Uffen, who also noted mating pairs on this plant at Bayfordbury, in 1996. Adults have also been found on nettles growing beneath poplar trees, on buttercups (also beneath poplars and also under sallow), on Bugle, Dandelion and Marjoram.

DACNONYPHA
ERIOCRANIOIDEA
ERIOCRANIIDAE

The Eriocraniidae are a primitive group of moths, representing the lepidopteran suborder Dacnonypha in Britain. Some members of this suborder have jaws in the adult stage, but in the Eriocraniidae these are reduced to rounded lobes and are presumably non-functional. We have records of all eight British species from Hertfordshire. All are leaf-miners in the caterpillar stage; the blotch-mines made by *Eriocrania subpurpurella* on oak leaves will be familiar to all, but recognised by few. The realisation that the form of the mine can, in combination with certain features of the larva, be used to correctly identify the species has led to a rise in the number of recent reports and it is likely that all are under-recorded.

0006 *Eriocrania subpurpurella* (Haw.)

Recorded:	1888 – 2006
Distribution / Status:	Widespread / Common resident
Conservation status:	No perceived threats
Caterpillar food plants:	oak – mining the leaves
Flight period:	Mid-April to end May
Records in database:	88

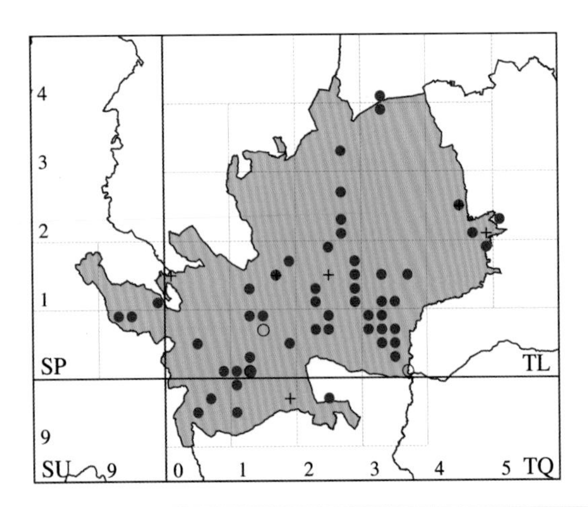

Our earliest records come from St Albans, within two or three miles of the Town Hall, and from Bricket Wood, both in the period before 1889 (Gibbs, 1889). Today it is found wherever there is an oak tree. Adults come readily to light traps and, unusually for a leaf-mining species, most of our records are made in this manner. This is, however, more likely to be a reflection of the inability of many modern entomologists to recognise the mines than anything to do with light trap efficiency. The other species in the genus are almost never reported from light traps in Hertfordshire.

0007 *Eriocrania chrysolepidella* Zell.

Recorded:	1985 – 2005
Distribution / Status:	Local / Resident
Conservation status:	No perceived threats
Caterpillar food plants:	Hazel and Hornbeam, mining the leaves
Flight period:	Mid-April to mid-May
Records in database:	16

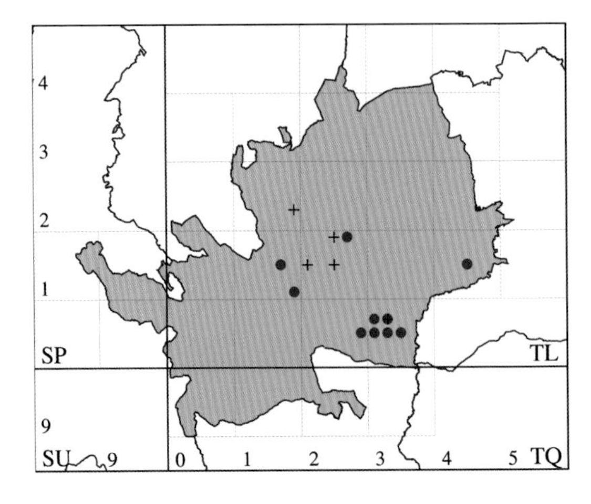

The absence of historical records for this species is surprising, though apparently correct; writing in volume 1 of *Moths and Butterflies of Great Britain and Ireland* John Heath noted, in 1976, that the moth was only recorded from the vice-counties of North Wiltshire, Sussex, North Essex, Cambridgeshire and Herefordshire. Our first reported Hertfordshire record was made at Dowdells Wood on 2nd June 1985, where Raymond Uffen found two vacated mines on Hazel. Adults moths, and mines on Hornbeam, were found at Lockleys Wood, Digswell on 18th April 1987, also by Raymond Uffen. Since then we have recorded a small number of additional occurrences, almost all as larval mines in the years 2004 and 2005. Searching for the mines is likely to reveal that this is now a widespread species.

0008 *Eriocrania unimaculella* (Zett.)

Recorded:	1925 – 2000
Distribution / Status:	Local / Resident
Conservation status:	Herts Rare
Caterpillar food plants:	Not recorded. Elsewhere, mining birch leaves
Flight period:	April
Records in database:	5

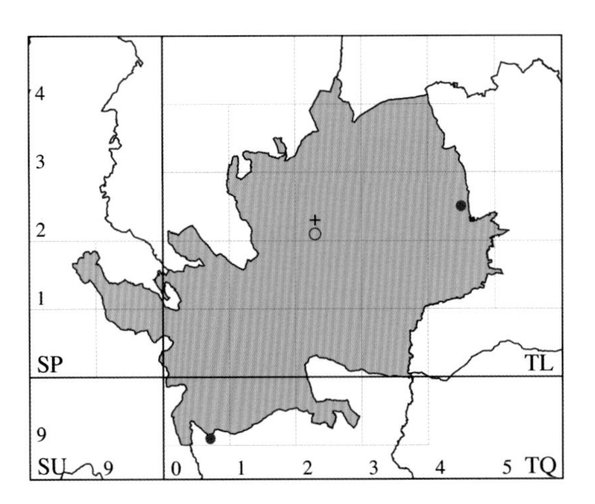

Our earliest county record is from Great Wood at Knebworth in 1925, where it was found by A. H. Foster. Our only other records are of adults in association with birch trees at Watery Grove, Stevenage on 16th April 1993, Patmore Heath on 23rd April 1995 and Bishop's Wood near Rickmansworth on 6th April 2000 – all recorded by Raymond Uffen. Oddly, we have not yet found the mines of this species in the county.

0009 *Eriocrania sparrmanella* (Bosc)

Recorded:	1884 – 2006
Distribution / Status:	Local / Rare resident
Conservation status:	No perceived threats
Caterpillar food plants:	birch
Flight period:	Not recorded – elsewhere April and May
Records in database:	3

Griffith (1890) lists this species for the Sandridge area – almost certainly for the year 1884, but there are no further records until mines were found in birch leaves on Mardley Heath by Raymond Uffen on 8th June 1995. Mines were still present several years later, on 27th June 2006, some containing larvae from second to final instar and some recently vacated. There are no other Hertfordshire records of this species. Although the moth appears scarce in the south-east of Britain it may be under-recorded in Hertfordshire. The larval mines, which are discussed under the next species, are the latest of all the *Eriocrania* mines to appear and may be seen in June and July.

0010 *Eriocrania salopiella* (Stt.)

Recorded:	1995 – 2005
Distribution / Status:	Local / Resident
Conservation status:	No perceived threats
Caterpillar food plants:	Silver Birch. Elsewhere, also on Downy Birch
Flight period:	Not recorded. Elsewhere, April/May
Records in database:	4

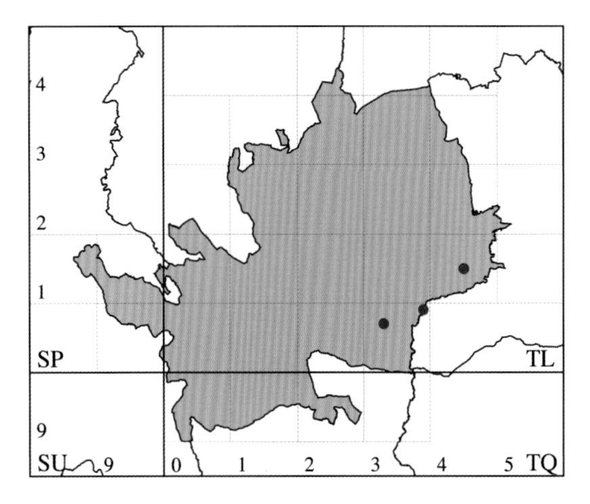

Recent advances in the identification of leaf-mines are responsible for the addition of *Eriocrania salopiella* to the Hertfordshire fauna – from Broxbourne Wood, Rye House Power Station and Golden Grove at Gilston. Mines of *E. salopiella* appear two or three weeks later than those of *unimaculella*, *sangii*, *cicatricella* and *semipurpurella*, but slightly before those of *sparrmannella*.

0011 *Eriocrania cicatricella* (Zett.) = *haworthi* Bradley

Recorded:	1890 – 2004
Distribution / Status:	Probably widespread / Resident
Conservation status:	No perceived threats
Caterpillar food plants:	Silver Birch; Downy Birch
Flight period:	April
Records in database:	10

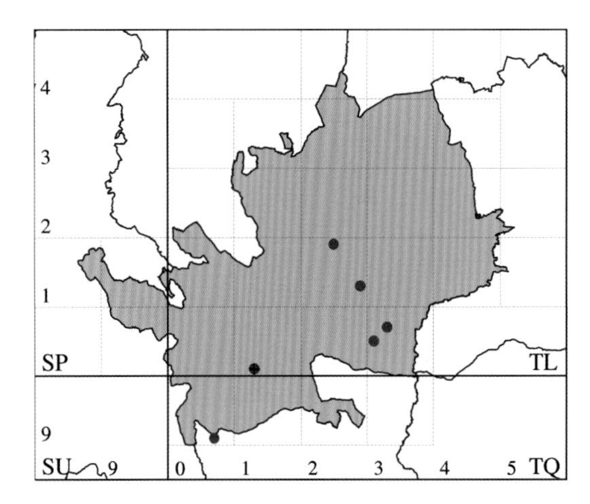

The mines of this species, which affect the edge of birch leaves from the end of April and throughout May, are easily recognised in the field because they frequently contain more than one caterpillar, though caution should be exercised in case two mines, each with a single larva of a different species, have accidentally joined up. The caterpillars of confusion species differ in colouration, those of *cicatricella* being entirely translucent white and lacking a dark head capsule. This species is almost certainly under-recorded in Hertfordshire and will be found in many new places if looked for.

0012 *Eriocrania sangii* (Wood)

Recorded: 1928 – 2004
Distribution / Status: Probably widespread / Resident
Conservation status: No perceived threats
Caterpillar food plants: Silver Birch. Elsewhere, also on Downy Birch
Flight period: Not recorded. Elsewhere April
Records in database: 10

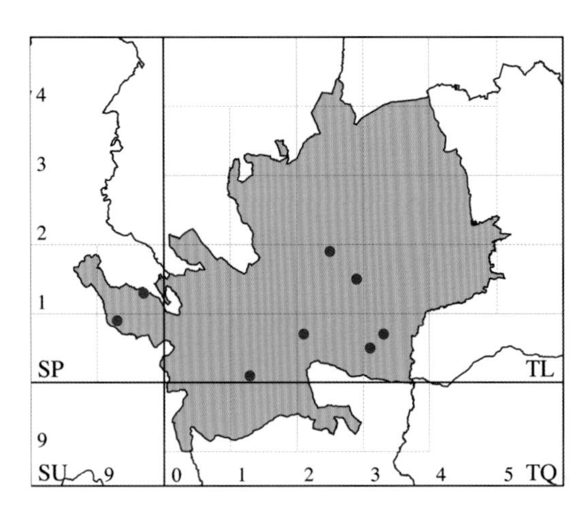

The poorly recorded state of *Eriocrania* in general is reflected well in this species – it was first recorded for the county in Meyrick's *Handbook* in 1928, but the next records were not for another 71 years, when Raymond Uffen caught a female at Broxbourne Wood on 3rd April 1999 and a male at Mardley Heath on 7th April 2000. Remaining records since that date are exclusively of leaf mines and it seems probable that this will prove to be a widespread and common species with us.

0013 *Eriocrania semipurpurella* (Steph.)

Recorded: 1890 – 2004
Distribution / Status: Loca / Resident
Conservation status: No perceived threats
Caterpillar food plants: Silver Birch. Elsewhere, also on Downy Birch
Flight period: April
Records in database: 8

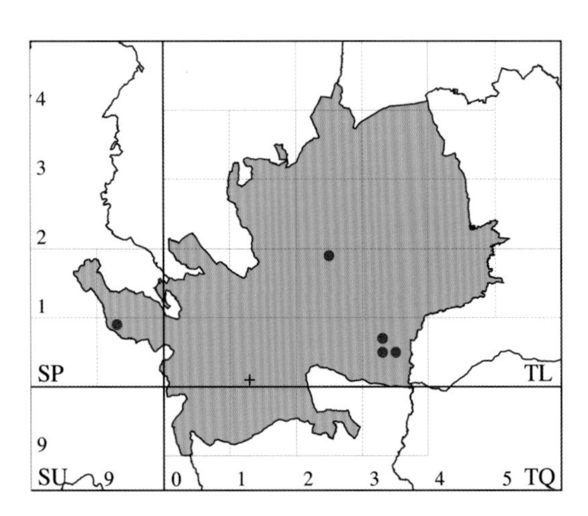

Allegedly, this is the most common of the birch-feeding species of *Eriocrania*, though there is no evidence from Hertfordshire to support that supposition. Mines are rather similar to those made by *E. unimaculella* from which they can only be reliably separated by examining the larva, which has lateral projections on the first abdominal segment (these are on the second segment in *unimaculella*). As with the other members of this group, both mines and adults are very much under-recorded.

MONOTRYSIA
HEPIALOIDEA
HEPIALIDAE

The Swifts are recognised immediately by their incredibly short antennae and long, narrow wings that lack any sort of coupling mechanism so that the wings appear to the human eye to flap about independently. Indeed, they derive their family name from their manner of flight, the females dashing about and depositing their eggs at random as they do so. The Greek *Hepialos* means "fever" and is also supposed to relate to their "fitful and alternating" flight (Emmet, 1991). All hepialid larvae are subterranean, feeding on the roots of plants. All five British species are recorded in Hertfordshire.

0014 *Hepialus humuli* (L.) Ghost Moth

Recorded: 1883 – 2005
Distribution: Widespread
Status: Common resident
Conservation status: UK BAP Watch List
Caterpillar food plants: Not recorded. Elsewhere on and in the roots of grasses and other plants including dock, Mugwort, Yarrow and Garden Mint.
Flight period: June/July
Records in database: 181

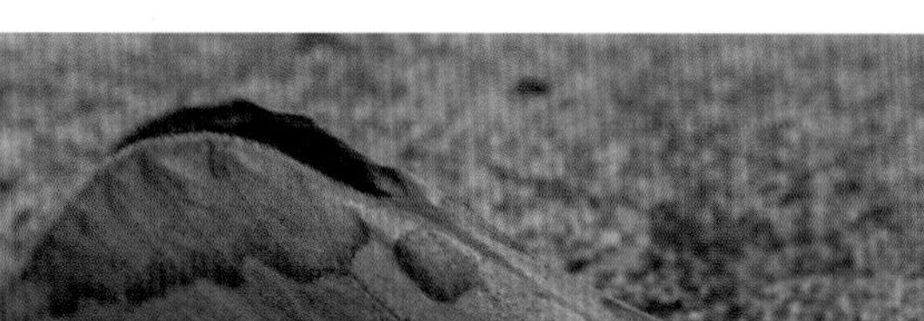

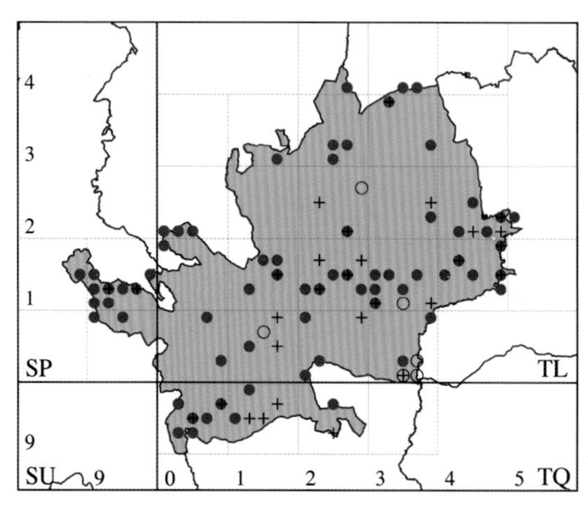

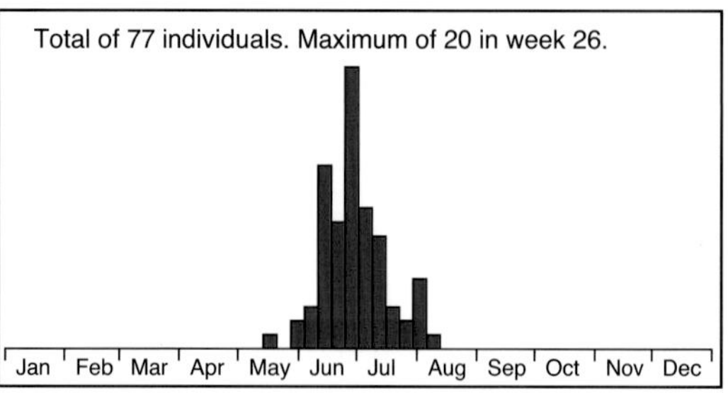

This is an easily recorded species because the all-white males perform a highly visible hovering flight in the early evening – presumably to attract the yellow/brown females – 'dancing' over grasslands in a ghostly manner and so giving rise to the English name. In the 1937 list, Foster stated, simply, that this moth was "Common in all districts" and gave no further details. This situation has probably changed somewhat since then, for although the moth remains a common sight for those out and about at dusk in June and July there are certainly several grassland areas where the moth is not recorded. The distribution map may suggest that there has been a small decline in predominantly urban areas and in the arable north-east – both parts of the county where there has been a significant reduction in available habitat. Whilst records suggest that acid, neutral and calcareous swards are all capable of supporting populations, longevity of habitat appears to be a crucial factor, with newer, planted or regenerated grasslands apparently not usually able to support populations of the moth. The larvae overwinter twice.

0015 *Hepialus sylvina* (L.) Orange Swift

Recorded: 1828 – 2005
Distribution / Status: Widespread / Common resident
Conservation status: No perceived threats
Caterpillar food plants: Not recorded. Elsewhere in and on the roots of herbaceous plants
Flight period: August to early September
Records in database: 591

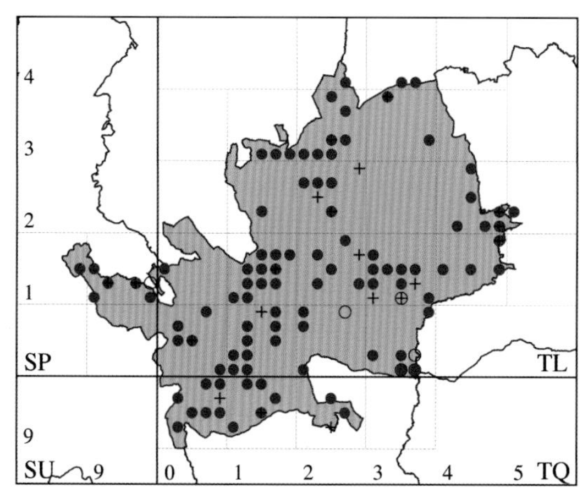

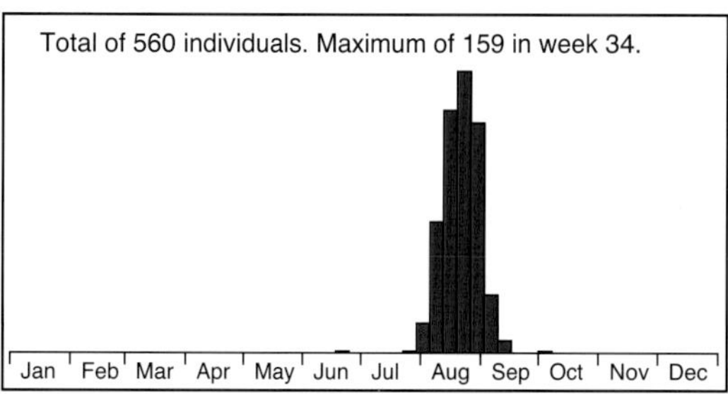

First listed for the county by J. F. Stephens from Hertford in his *Illustrations of British Entomology* **1:** 8, published in 1828, it appears to have been widespread when Foster wrote his 1937 Hertfordshire inventory, although many of the 15 localities that he noted relate to lists made tens of years earlier. Interestingly, this moth is also poorly represented in the county's strictly calcareous grasslands, evidently preferring those of a more mesotrophic nature; this may partly explain the blank area in the north-east of the map where the Chalky Boulder Clay provides a basis for an intensely arable area. Large, pale forms of the female can look confusingly like similar forms of female Common Swifts. Separation is easily effected by looking at the diagonal white line on the forewing, which runs to the apex in Common Swift and to the leading edge of the wing, just before the apex, in Orange Swift.

0016 *Hepialus hecta* (L.) Gold Swift

Recorded: 1834 – 2005
Distribution / Status: Local / Common resident
Conservation status: No perceived threats
Caterpillar food plants: Not recorded. Elsewhere in the roots of Bracken and 'other plants' and mosses.
Flight period: Late May to early June
Records in database: 53

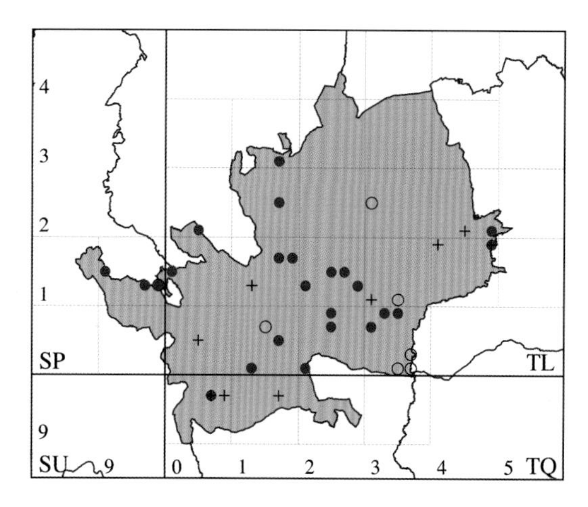

This member of the Swift family is evidently more restricted in its distribution than either of the preceding two species or the next, perhaps because of its more specific caterpillar foodplant requirements. Old records listed by Foster (1937) cover fifteen areas, though it is not practical to allocate all of them to a map tetrad. The present day distribution pattern shows a clear absence of the moth from the north-east sector and suggests that it may have disappeared from some more southerly sites. All apart from two records, both the solid dots and open circles on the distribution map relate to map tetrads that are either entirely on clay or contain an area of clay soil. However, unlike the Map-winged Swift, which appears to be restricted to a Clay-with-Flints substrate, the Gold Swift is also reported from the Chalky Boulder Clay around Bishops Stortford and to the south of Hertford and from the London Clay in the south. The Map-winged Swift may prefer relatively large areas of longer-established Bracken, whilst the Gold Swift appears more able to thrive in smaller areas.

0017 *Hepialus lupulinus* (L.) Common Swift

Recorded: 1868 – 2005
Distribution / Status: Ubiquitous / Common resident
Conservation status: No perceived threats
Caterpillar food plants: Roots of grasses. Elsewhere also on roots of herbaceous plants
Flight period: Mid-May/June
Records in database: 798

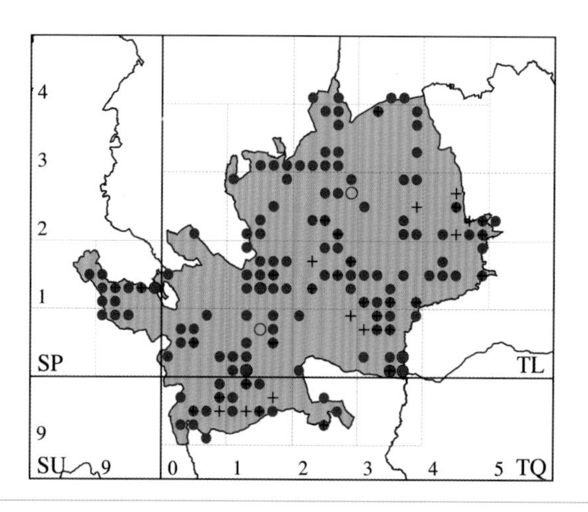

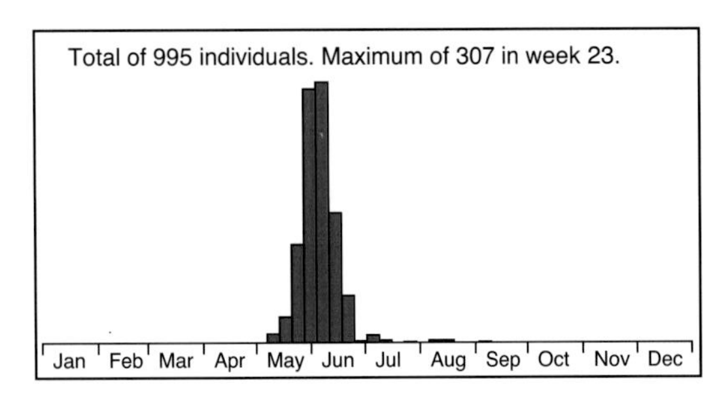

Large, pale forms of the female can look confusingly like similar forms of female Orange Swifts and the possibility exists that the seven records from August, all unsupported by specimens, may relate to this other species, though these do not affect the distribution map in any way. The species will be found wherever there is grassland and larvae have even been recorded in lawns in the North London area (although it is possible that this may have related to imported turf). The success of this species in comparison with the other four Swift species is doubtless due in no small part to its annual life cycle – all of the other four having a requirement to over-winter twice in the larval stage and thus being unable to colonise regularly disturbed areas.

0018 *Hepialus fusconebulosa* (DeGeer) Map-winged Swift

Recorded:	1888 – 2005
Distribution / Status:	Local / Uncommon resident
Conservation status:	Herts Scarce
Caterpillar food plants:	Not recorded. Elsewhere in the roots and stems of Bracken
Flight period:	Late May/June
Records in database:	30

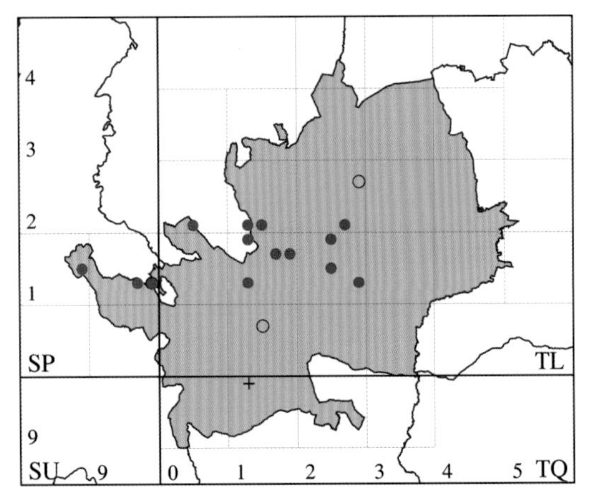

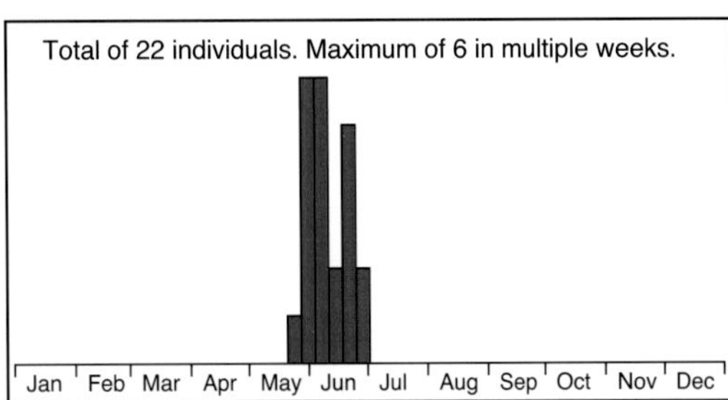

Old records in Foster's 1937 list number just five – St Albans, Watford, Hitchin, Tring and Berkhamsted, though all relate to the period prior to 1920. The rather peculiar present-day distribution shown in the map appears to be real. Of the 14 current maps dots, one lies on the Gault Clay and 13 lie on Clay-with-Flints. The old records also emanate from areas with a Clay-with-Flints geology and the species appears to be quite absent from the London Clay-dominated South Herts Plateau and from the Chalky Boulder Clay areas of the north and east, as indeed it is from the Chalk proper. It seems that a Clay-with-Flints geology is necessary for the moth to persist and within this it may require extensive areas of long-established Bracken in older woodlands. In adjacent Essex, Jermyn (1974) shows a complete absence of Clay-with-Flints substrate and according to Goodey (2004) the Map-winged Swift is represented on the county list by just two examples (in the years 1842 and 1860) and is apparently now absent. Similar comparisons can be made with the Drift Geology map of the London Area (Plant, 1994) and the map of the moth's extremely sparing distribution in that area given in Plant (1993). In Bedfordshire, to our north, at least the five most southerly of their eight records appear to be related to a Clay-with-Flints soil.

NEPTICULOIDEA

NEPTICULIDAE

This is a large family with just under one hundred species listed for Britain, the exact number varying with opinion on the taxonomy of some taxa, including the *Stigmella aurella*-complex in particular. All are small, the adults having a wingspan of between 3 and 10 millimetres, mostly at the smaller end of that range. The top of the head is roughly haired and the first antennal segment, called the scape, is enlarged to form a characteristic eye-cap. Confusion is possible, by the inexperienced, with species of *Bucculatrix*, which also have eye-caps and a long-coiled haustellum (tongue). The Opostegidae, which follow the Nepticulidae in the list, have much larger eye-caps, but are recognised by the presence of a smooth, flat-scaled area on the head behind the vertex (the vertex itself bears erect hair-like scales as in the Nepticulidae). Identification of some species is difficult. The larvae of all our nepticulids are miners of leaves, stems or bark and identification of many species is far easier from the mine than from the adult. However, the reverse is true for some species, especially those that feed on hawthorn or other rosaceous plants and those that feed on deciduous species of oak, many of which require rearing of the adult and sometimes and examination of genitalia for positive naming. Existing British literature on this family is woefully inadequate and the supposed standard text is hopelessly out of date and does not include drawings of the genitalia. Reference to the Continental literature is essential – especially as there remains scope for additional species to be found in Britain. At 2006, the favoured text is the two volume work by Johansson *et al*. (1990).

To date, we have reliable records for 69 species of Nepticulidae in Hertfordshire, but we know more or less nothing of them in the county beyond the information that is imparted by the distribution maps; for this reason, most of the species accounts that follow are accompanied by the bare minimum of text. In particular, we have no significant data on adult flight period for most species and this line is, accordingly, omitted from the summary at the start of each species text; where available, such information is placed in the text.

0019 *Bohemannia quadrimaculella* (Boh.)

Recorded: 1992 – 2003
Distribution / Status: Local / Rare resident
Conservation status: Herts Rare
Caterpillar food plants: No data. Elsewhere, on Alder
Mines evident: Unknown in Britain
Records in database: 2

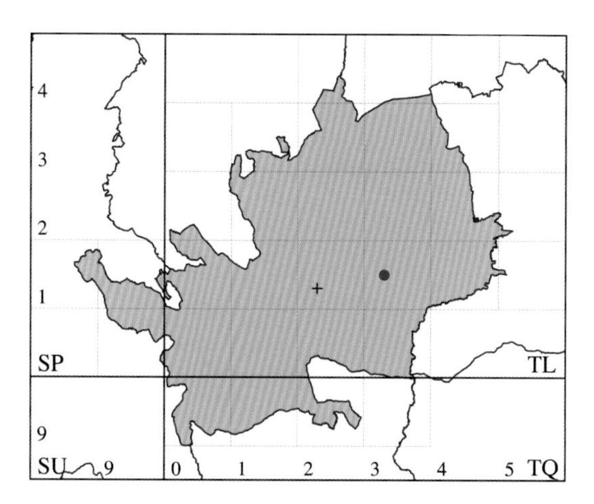

Adults at Lemsford Springs on 12th July 1992 (Raymond Uffen) and Hertford on 8th July 2003 (Andrew Wood) are our only records.

0040 *Bohemannia pulverosella* (Stt.)

Recorded: 1890 – 2004
Distribution / Status: Local / Rare resident
Conservation status: Herts Rare
Caterpillar food plants: apple
Mines evident: June/July
Records in database: 3

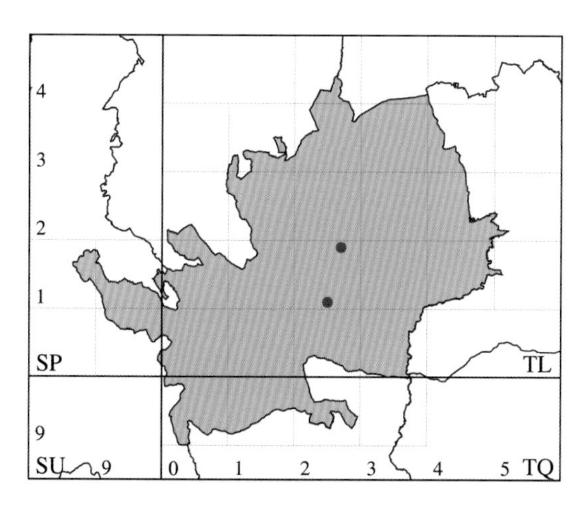

There is an old record from the area around Sandridge, prior to 1890 then two modern records, from Ascots Lane, Welwyn Garden City on 5th September 1995 (Raymond Uffen) and Raffin Park, Datchworth on 20th June 2004 (Steve Palmer). The moth has scattered stations in Bedfordshire and north-west Essex so may be present at more Hertfordshire sites than the present data suggest.

0020 *Ectoedemia decentella* (H.-S.)

Recorded: 2002 – 2005
Distribution / Status: Local / Uncommon resident
Conservation status: No perceived threats
Caterpillar food plants: Sycamore
Mines evident: July – In buds
September/October – in keys
Records in database: 15

Ectoedemia decentella (H.-S.)

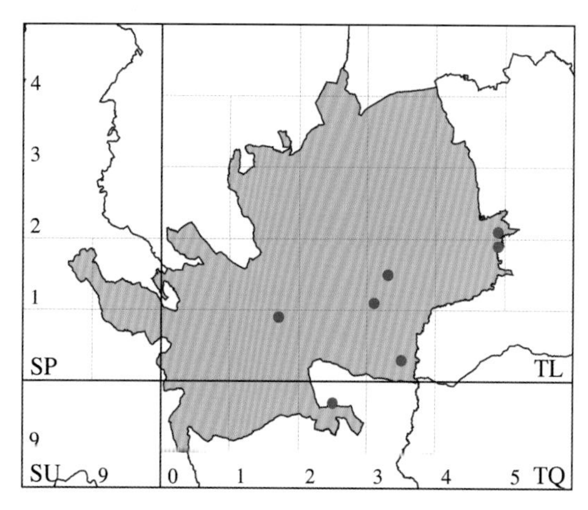

There are two generations per year. The first is reared from larvae that feed in the buds of the tree to give adults in August. Second generation larvae feed in the blade, but apparently not in the seed, of sycamore keys, leaving these and overwintering on the ground before climbing trunks to pupate the following May. This moth is surely under-recorded in Hertfordshire, where sycamore trees are to be found almost everywhere.

0022 *Ectoedemia louisella* (Sircom) = *sphendamni* (Hering)

Recorded: 2003 – 2004
Distribution / Status: Local / Uncommon resident
Conservation status: No perceived threats
Caterpillar food plants: Field Maple
Mines evident: September
Records in database: 2

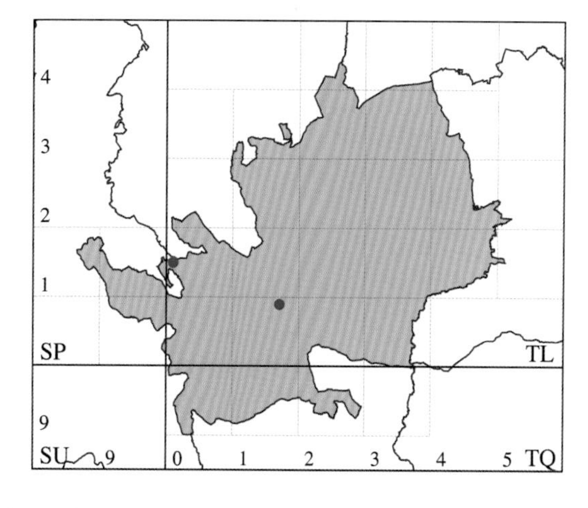

The rather attractive adult was taken at light in Ravensdell Wood on 31st May 2003 by myself and Mark Cooper whilst mines were found in the samara (keys) of Maple by Wendy Hatton on 26th September 2004 in Jersey Farm Woodland, St Albans. There are no other Hertfordshire records, but the species is surely under-recorded.

0023 *Ectoedemia argyropeza* (Zell.)

Recorded: 1860 – 2006
Distribution / Status: Probably local / Uncommon resident
Conservation status: No perceived threats
Caterpillar food plants: Aspen
Mines evident: September – in petioles
October/November – in leaf blade
Records in database: 8

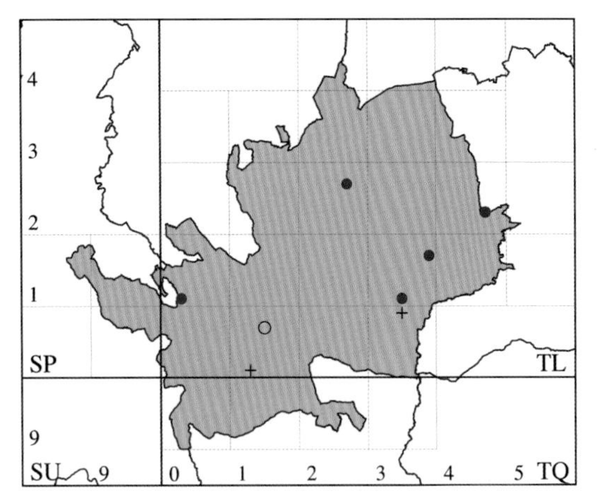

Old records are from Sandridge, probably in the 1860s (Griffith, 1890) and St. Albans 'within two or three miles of the Town Hall' in the period before 1889 (Gibbs, *Trans. Herts.* **5:** 181 – 186). The spread of recent records suggests the moth is under-recorded.

0024 *Ectoedemia turbidella* (Zell.)

Recorded: 2004 only
Distribution / Status: Local / Uncommon resident
Conservation status: Herts Rare
Caterpillar food plants: Grey Poplar
Mines evident: September – in petiole
October – in leaf blade
Records in database: 1

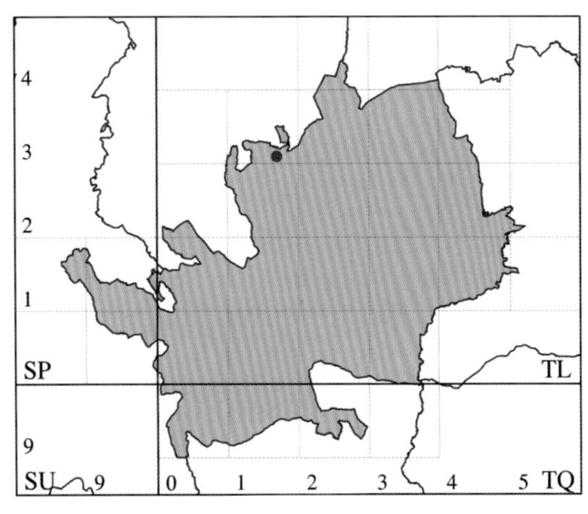

Our single record is from Oughton Head, near the Bedfordshire border during 2004 (Mark Sterling). The caterpillar feeds first in the petiole and later moves into in the leaf blade forming a triangular blotch. It is recorded as widespread and common in *The Butterflies and Moths of Bedfordshire* (published in 1997) and rare in *The Moths of Essex* (published in 2004). This puts us in the overlap zone; there are probably more sites for this moth in Hertfordshire.

0025 *Ectoedemia intimella* (Zell.)

Recorded: 1890 – 2005
Distribution: Local / Uncommon resident
Conservation status: No perceived threats
Caterpillar food plants: Sallow and probably other *Salix* spp.
Mines evident: October/November
Records in database: 7

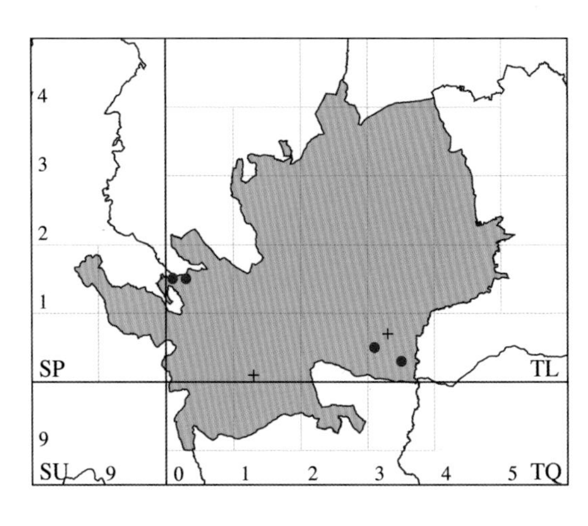

Records are from woodland and roadside verge situations and the moth is probably far more widespread than our few records indicate. Like the preceding species, *E. intimella* is reported as common in Bedfordshire to our north-west and rare in Essex, to our east.

0028 *Ectoedemia angulifasciella* (Stt.)

Recorded: 1901 – 2006
Distribution / Status: Widespread / Common resident
Conservation status: No perceived threats
Caterpillar food plants: rose
Mines evident: September to November
Records in database: 57

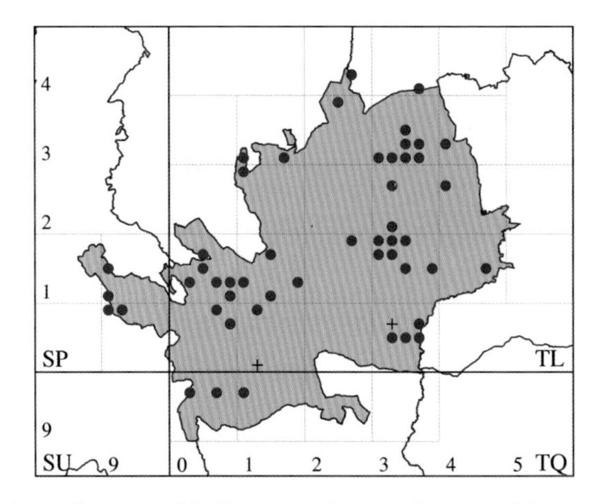

The earliest record is from Wormley Wood, reported by W. C. Boyd in 1901. Our records suggest that only wild rose species are mined by the larvae, as we have no records from any variety of cultivated rose.

0029 *Ectoedemia atricollis* (Stt.)

Recorded: 1901 – 2005
Distribution/ Status: Ubiquitous / Common resident
Conservation status: No perceived threats
Caterpillar food plants: Common Hawthorn; pear. Elsewhere on apple and other rosaceous shrubs and trees
Mines evident: August to October
Records in database: 126

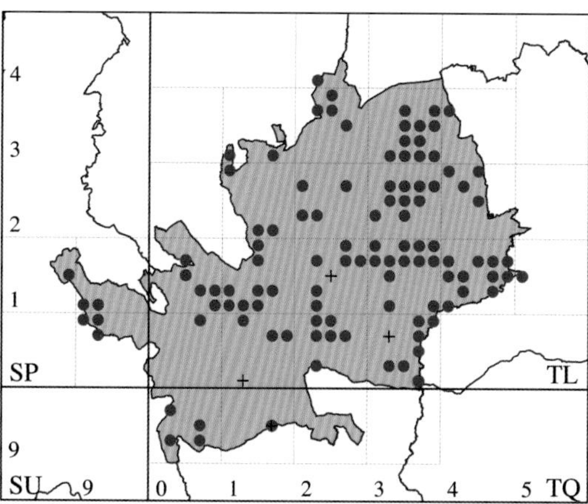

All of our mine records are from leaves of Common Hawthorn; there are none so far from Midland Hawthorn. This moth is probably present in most, if not all, map tetrads in Hertfordshire.

0030 *Ectoedemia arcuatella* (H.- S.)

Recorded: Pre-1976
Distribution / Status: Absent / Former resident
Conservation status: Herts Extinct
Caterpillar food plants: No data. Elsewhere on Strawberry and Barren Strawberry
Mines evident: August to October
Records in database: 1

The map in volume 1 of *The Moths and Butterflies of Great Britain and Ireland* (Harley Books, 1976) shows this species as present in Hertfordshire. Discussion with the late Maitland Emmet, who was responsible for the map, revealed that the occurrence was not supported by a specific record. However, Maitland was meticulously careful over the validation of data, as well as being a leading European authority on the Nepticulidae and would not have entered the record had he not believed it; it is far more likely that he may have lost the supporting documentation during his later years. It is possible that the record from the Pegsdon Hills given in the 1997 book *The Butterflies and Moths of Bedfordshire* relates to the same individual; this area ought to be searched on the Hertfordshire side of the border.

0031 *Ectoedemia rubivora* (Wocke)

Recorded: 1976 – 2003
Distribution / Status: Extremely local / Rare resident
Conservation status: Herts Rare
Caterpillar food plants: Bramble – elsewhere preferring Dewberry
Mines evident: September to November
Records in database: 3

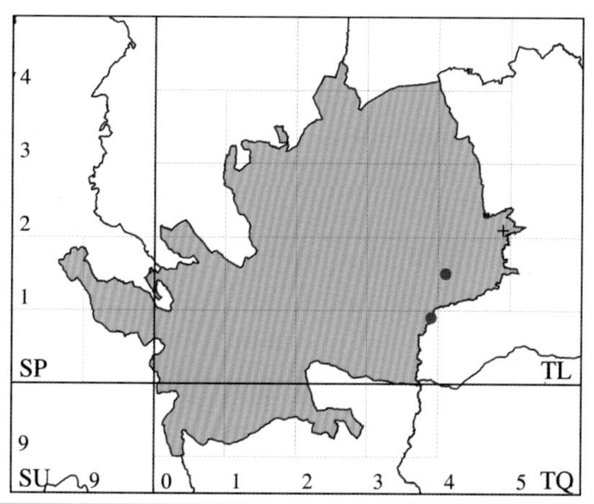

This species is noted for Hertfordshire in volume 1 of *The Moths and Butterflies of Great Britain and Ireland* (1976), but there are no supporting data with the record. More recently it was located at Dobbs Weir (mines collected 7th November 2002) and at Widford Station (mines collected 12th October 2003) – both by Elizabeth Goodyear.

0034 *Ectoedemia occultella* (L.) = *argentipedella* (Zell.)

Recorded: 1976 – 2006
Distribution / Status: Widespread / Common resident
Conservation status: No perceived threats
Caterpillar food plants: Silver Birch; Downy Birch
Mines evident: August to November
Records in database: 56

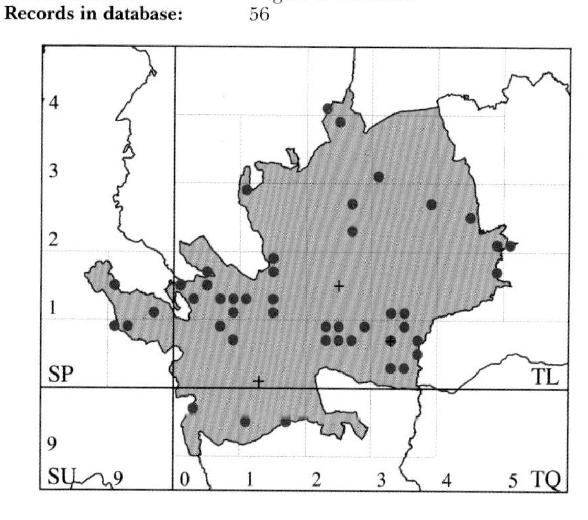

Where we have been able to identify the species of birch tree affected it has always been Silver Birch, but there is no reason to suppose that the caterpillar may not also make its distinctive mines on Downy Birch or even the hybrid. However, every time we have looked on alien species of *Betula* the mine has been absent.

0035 *Ectoedemia minimella* (Zett.) = *mediofasciella* (auctt.).

Recorded: 1980 – 2005
Distribution / Status: Local / Uncommon resident
Conservation status: Herts Scarce
Caterpillar food plants: birch
Mines evident: July to October
Records in database: 15

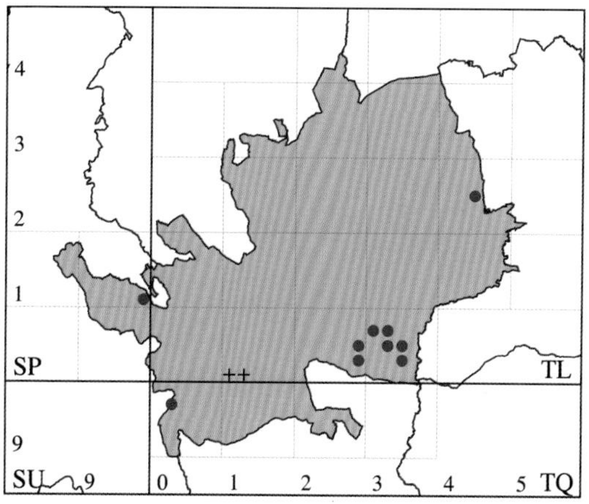

In *Moths and Butterflies of Great Britain and Ireland* this species is incorrectly called *mediofasciella* (Haworth). There are no old Hertfordshire records, our first not being made until as recently as 1980 when Maitland Emmet found mines at Bricket Wood on 2nd November, subsequently rearing the adults. Since then, there have been only a handful of discoveries of the mines of this species.

0036 *Ectoedemia quinquella* (Bedell)

Recorded: 2001 only
Distribution / Status: Local / Uncommon resident
Conservation status: Herts Rare
Caterpillar food plants: English Oak
Mines evident: October
Records in database: 1

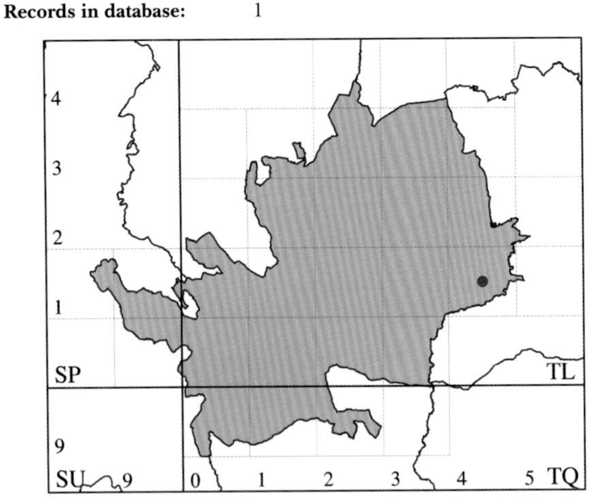

Our only record is from Gilston on 18th October 2001, when I found the distinctive, highly contorted mines on a veteran oak tree on the verge of a country lane near to Golden Grove. Adults were reared. The moth appears more widespread in Bedfordshire and so may be under-recorded in our north-west sector, yet perversely our only record is nearer to the border with Essex where it is evidently less frequent.

0036a *Ectoedemia heringella* Mariani

Recorded: 2006 only
Distribution / Status: Local, but spreading / Rare resident
Conservation status: No perceived threats
Caterpillar food plants: Holm Oak
Mines evident: January
Records in database: 2

Recently discovered new to Britain at a site in central London, this species started to expand its range in the winter of 2006/2007. Mines were found at Ware Cemetery on 26th January 2007 (Elizabeth Goodyear) and at Bricketwood Common on 7th April 2007 (Mark Cooper & Colin Plant). Both clearly indicate a female laying eggs in 2006 (the last year of the 'current' period) and so justifiably included here!

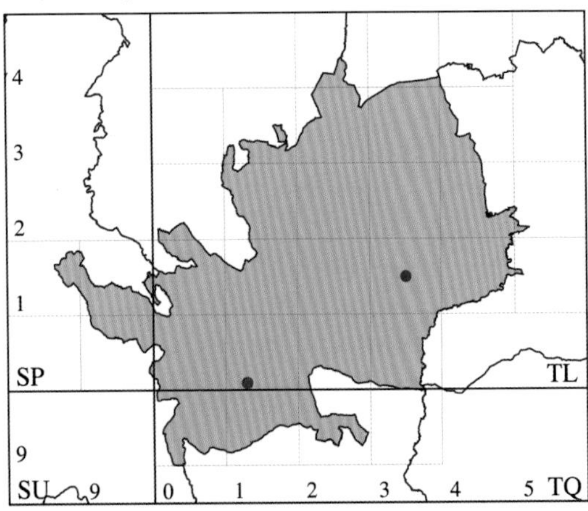

0037 *Ectoedemia albifasciella* (Hein.)

Recorded: 1981 – 2006
Distribution / Status: Widespread / Common resident
Conservation status: No perceived threats
Caterpillar food plants: English Oak; Sessile Oak
Mines evident: August/September/October
Records in database: 38

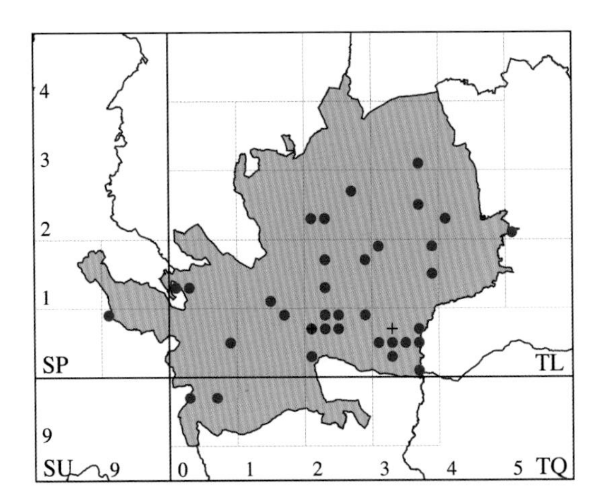

This species is likely to be found wherever there is an oak tree and the paucity of dots in the map indicates the high level of caution adopted in accepting records. The mines are easily confused during October with those of 38: *Ectoedemia subbimaculella*. It is important to note whether or not the mine is tenanted or empty – *E. albifasciella* feeds earlier than *subbimaculella*, mostly during September, so the mature but vacated mines will be present on the same tree when *subbimaculella* starts feeding in October. Just occasionally, a late larva of *albifasciella* can be found in early October. In all cases of doubt, the adults must be reared.

0038 *Ectoedemia subbimaculella* (Haw.)

Recorded: 1868 – 2006
Distribution / Status: Widespread / Common resident
Conservation status: No perceived threats
Caterpillar food plants: English Oak
Mines evident: October/November
Records in database: 112

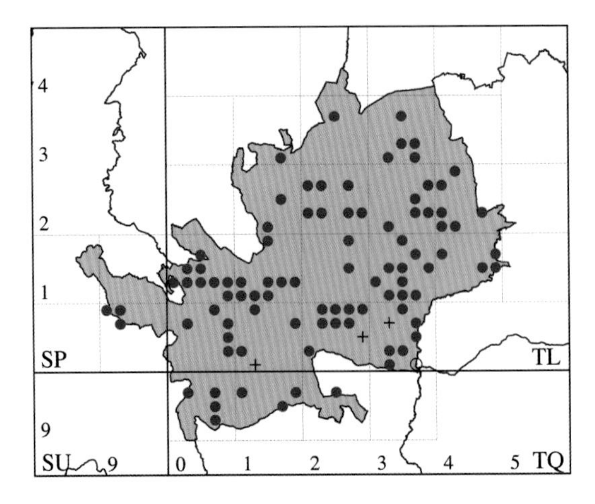

A widespread and common species, mining the under surface of oak leaves. Confusion with 37: *Ectoedemia albifasciella* has been discussed under that species.

0039 *Ectoedemia heringi* (Toll) = *quercifoliae* (Toll)

Recorded: 1987 – 2006
Distribution / Status: Widespread / Common resident
Conservation status: No perceived threats
Caterpillar food plants: English Oak
Mines evident: October/November
Records in database: 30

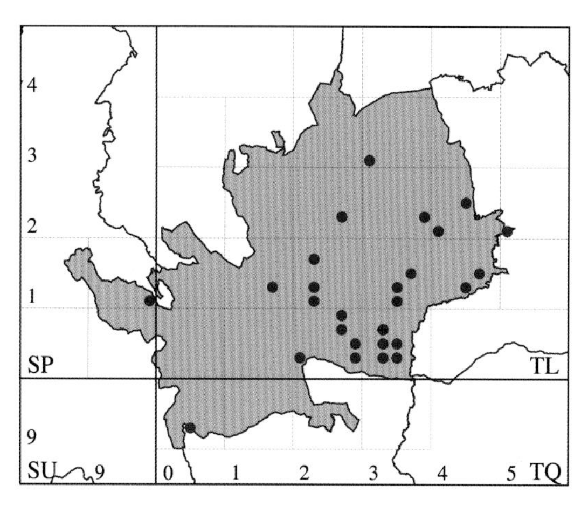

Another common species, likely to be found on every oak tree in the county, though so far only recorded here on English Oak; it is important to name the host tree if at all possible when submitting records. The larval mine, on the lower surface of an oak leaf, is distinguished from that of 38: *E. subbimaculella* because the caterpillar does not slit the leaf surface to allow the frass to fall out.

0042 *Ectoedemia septembrella* (Stt.)

Recorded:	1890 – 2006
Distribution / Status:	Local / Uncommon resident
Conservation status:	No perceived threats
Caterpillar food plants:	Perforate St. John's-wort and an ornamental St. John's-wort in a garden
Mines evident:	July/August and October/November
Records in database:	21

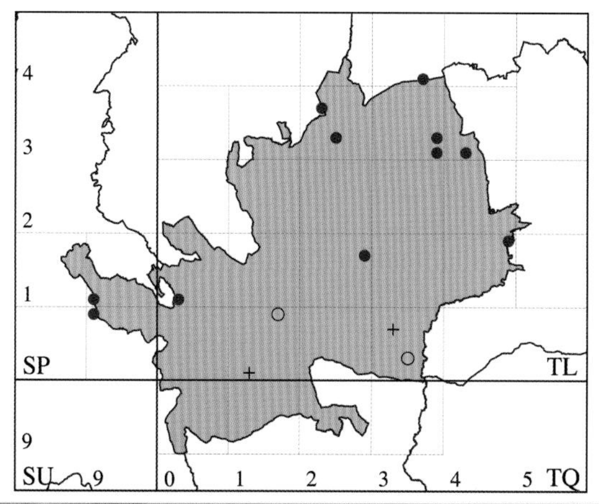

Examination of the data shows that almost all the mapped records relate to mines on wild St. John's-wort plants and, with this in mind, the apparent absence of the moth from the south of the county is interesting. Of course, it may just mean that people are not looking for this species on their garden *Hypericum* plants – when I looked in my garden I found it straight away!

0046 *Ectoedemia immundella* (Zell.)

Recorded:	1890 – 1987
Distribution / Status:	Extremely local / Rare resident
Conservation status:	Herts Rare
Caterpillar food plants:	Broom
Mines evident:	Elsewhere, September and throughout the winter
Records in database:	3

The paucity of records for this species in our county is surprising, though it is very local in Bedfordshire and there are no recent records from the western half of Essex; perhaps it has declined? The caterpillar mines the shoots of Broom plants, creating a long, brown gallery that initially runs downwards, away from the egg, which is laid about six inches (15 centimetres) from the tip. The egg is distinctive, and its presence, together with the downwards direction of the early mine, distinguish it from the otherwise similar mine of 256: *Leucoptera spartifoliella*. The mines are evident, and remain occupied, throughout the winter months.

0047 *Trifurcula beirnei* Puplesis = *pallidella* (Zell)

Recorded:	1885 only
Distribution / Status:	Absent / Extinct
Conservation status:	Herts Extinct
Caterpillar food plants:	Unknown – elsewhere probably Dyer's Greenweed
Mines evident:	Unknown
Records in database:	1

Two specimens were taken in 1885 'Near Symonds Hyde Great Wood' (A. F. Griffith, *Entomologist's Monthly Magazine* **22**: 65). The record is also mentioned by H. T. Stainton in *Entomologist's Monthly Magazine* **22**: 263 and by Griffith again in *Transactions of the Hertfordshire Natural History Society and Field Club* **6**: 98. Prior to this there had been only one British example of the species, at Preston (Lancashire). Today, it is extremely rare in Britain having been rediscovered in Hampshire during 2003 after a period of presumed extinction. The foodplant is now regarded as absent from the Symondshyde area.

The *Stigmella aurella* complex

The Bramble Leaf-miner (50: *Stigmella aurella*), is popularly regarded as one of our commonest and most easily recorded moths. One has only to look at any bramble patch to find the distinctive white gallery mines. However, it is not at all clear if the recognition of mines of *aurella* is as clear cut as it seems. Related species, in particular 53: *S. splendidissimella* traditionally feed on other foodplants, but in recent years a number of people have become concerned that some mines of *aurella* on brambles look more like those of *splendidissimella* whilst occasional mines on raspberry leaves, always presumed to belong to *splendidissimella*, look more like those of *aurella*. The two species are clearly separate, with different adult appearance and differing genital structures, but it is unclear if *aurella* has a monopoly on bramble as a foodplant. Certainly *aurella* can also feed on other related plants and it is worth mentioning that both *Stigmella gei* and *S. fragariella* (as listed in volume 1 in the series *Moths and Butterflies of Great Britain and Ireland*), are now known to be forms of *S. aurella*. Typical mines of *aurella* on bramble take the form of a long, sinuous gallery, with the frass at first linear or broken linear and later expanding to almost or completely fill the gallery width. Typical mines of *splendidissimella* on raspberry are longer and narrower and have the frass in a near continuous, narrow central line leaving clear margins. The leaf surface alongside *aurella* mines frequently turns purple, but this never seems to happen in *splendidissimella* mines on raspberry nor on the long, narrow, clear-margined mines on bramble.

When recording *Stigmella* species in general, and especially if recording species in the *aurella* complex, it is enormously important also to record the foodplant (get a botanist to check it!) and to record whether the mine was occupied or empty on the date it was collected. The larvae of true *aurella* can be found in the mine over winter, but if no such larvae are found it may not be possible to determine the species. Wherever possible, adults should be reared for examination. There are old records for 55: *S. aeneofasciella* (H.- S.) from both Essex and Bedfordshire, but we have not yet found it in Hertfordshire.

0050 *Stigmella aurella* (Fabr.) = *gei* Wocke; = *fragariella* Heyden

Recorded:	1890 – 2006
Distribution / Status:	Ubiquitous / Abundant resident
Conservation status:	No perceived threats
Caterpillar food plants:	Bramble; possibly other *Rubus* species. Elsewhere, also on Herb Bennet, strawberries and agrimonies
Mines evident:	All year – larvae may be present all year
Records in database:	372

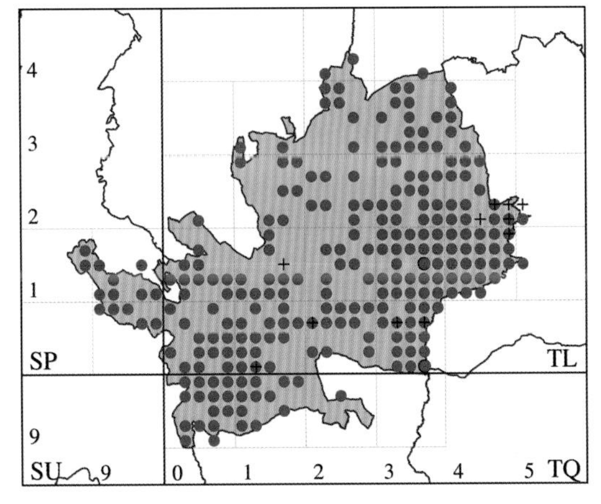

The species formerly known as *Stigmella gei*, now regarded as a form of *S. aurella*, is shown as occurring in Hertfordshire in volume 1 of *Moths and Butterflies of Great Britain and Ireland* (1976). The same work indicates that the taxon *fragariella* was absent at that time. Foster's 1937 list gives Sandridge, Cheshunt and Ashridge, but he records as synonyms not only *fragariella* and *gei*, but also *dulcella*, which is actually *splendidissimella*. Consequently, these old records are treated as unverified and are ignored. Typical *aurella* mines on bramble, containing overwintering larvae are common across the entire county and these are the records that are mapped here.

0053 *Stigmella splendidissimella* (H.- S.)

Recorded:	1976 – 2006
Distribution / Status:	Widespread / Uncommon resident
Conservation status:	No perceived threats
Caterpillar food plants:	Raspberry; Bramble. Elsewhere, also on Herb Bennet and strawberries
Mines evident:	All year, larvae present only from June to October
Records in database:	36

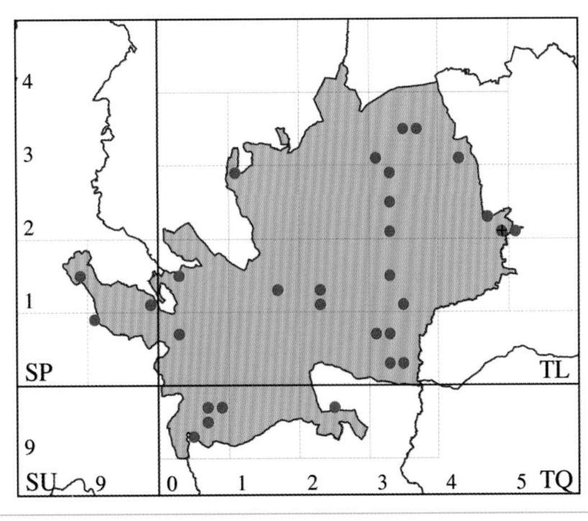

The mapped records include long, narrow mines with linear central frass and unequivocally clear margins on bramble, as well as those on Raspberry leaves, to which the bulk of the mapped records relate. The foodplant name should always accompany submitted reports of mines so that, if we eventually discover that more than one species is involved, we will be able to separate out the records for each.

0057 *Stigmella filipendulae* (Wocke)

Recorded:	pre-1976 only
Distribution / Status:	Absent / Extinct
Conservation status:	Herts Endangered
Caterpillar food plants:	Dropwort
Mines evident:	June to September
Records in database:	1

The map in volume 1 of *Moths and Butterflies of Great Britain and Ireland*, published in 1976, shows a past record for Hertfordshire. The source of this record cannot be traced. The moth is rather uncommon in Britain and is found on chalk downland; it may be worth looking for it in areas where the foodplant may grow along our border with Bedfordshire and Cambridgeshire.

0058 *Stigmella ulmariae* (Wocke)

Recorded:	2002 only
Distribution / Status:	Extremely local or absent / Rare resident, perhaps now extinct
Conservation status:	Herts Endangered
Caterpillar food plants:	Meadowsweet
Mines evident:	June to October – in two generations
Records in database:	1

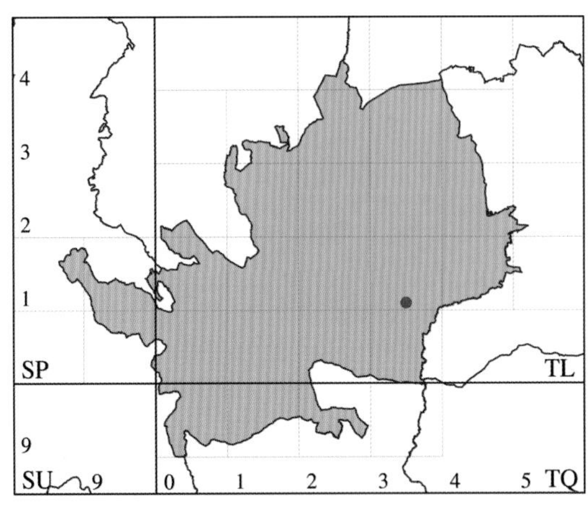

I found mines of this Nationally Scarce moth in a single clump of Meadowsweet along the track leading from the western part of Hertford Heath down to Balls Wood on 26th October 2002. Regrettably, in spite of identifying this specific group of plants to the land managers it was cut and burned by conservation volunteers; this may have caused the extinction of this moth in Hertfordshire. The foodplant is widespread in the county and the reasons for the apparent rarity of the moth are unclear.

0059 *Stigmella poterii* (Stt.)

Recorded:	1900 only
Distribution / Status:	Absent / Extinct
Conservation status:	Herts Extinct
Caterpillar food plants:	Not recorded. Elsewhere, on burnets (both *Sanguisorba* and *Poterium*) and Cloudberry
Mines evident:	Unknown
Records in database:	1

The map in volume 1 of *Moths and Butterflies of Great Britain and Ireland*, published in 1976, shows a past record for Hertfordshire; the text implies that the record was made prior to 1900, but the original data cannot be traced. The 1997 book *Butterflies and Moths of Bedfordshire* lists Pegsdon Hills and Dunstable Downs for this species; parts of both of these places fall within vice-county 20, and may be the source of the record.

0063 *Stigmella lemniscella* (Zell.) = *marginicolella* Stt.

Recorded: 1890 – 2006
Distribution / Status: Ubiquitous / Uncommon resident
Conservation status: No perceived threats
Caterpillar food plants: English Elm; Wych Elm
Mines evident: June to October – in two generations
Records in database: 159

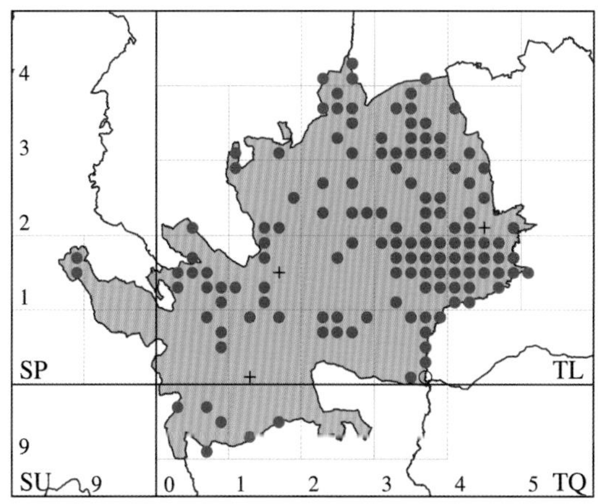

Mines of this very common species are polymorphic so that they may often resemble those of 80: *Stigmella ulmivora*, and *vice versa*. However, the exit hole is always on the upper surface of the leaf with *lemniscella* and always on the lower surface in *ulmivora*. In almost all cases where the species of elm on which the mine was found is recorded this is English Elm. In just one case Wych Elm is reported. The moth does not appear to have suffered any decline in the aftermath of the Dutch Elm Disease epidemic of the 1970s and is a common site on elm leaves in hedgerows. It is of interest, though perhaps not surprising, that leaves which are heavily galled by eriophyid mites tend not to be mined by the moth and where a moth mine is found it is very rare for any mite galls also to be present.

0064 *Stigmella continuella* (Stt.)

Recorded: 1981 – 2006
Distribution / Status: Local / Uncommon resident
Conservation status: No perceived threats
Caterpillar food plants: Silver Birch; Downy Birch
Mines evident: June/July and September/October – in two generations
Records in database: 10

The paucity of records, in spite of much searching, suggests that this moth may be absent from a wide area of the county.

0065 *Stigmella speciosa* (Frey)

Recorded: 1976 – 2005
Distribution / Status: Widespread / Common resident
Conservation status: No perceived threats
Caterpillar food plants: Sycamore
Mines evident: July to October, in two generations
Records in database: 44

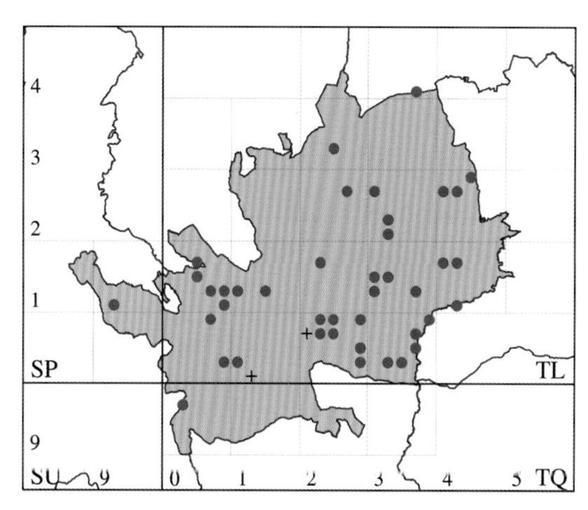

Likely to be found across the county wherever the Sycamore tree grows, the moth is most easily recorded by standing below the tree and looking upwards, when the larval mines will be silhouetted against the sky.

0067 *Stigmella plagicolella* (Stt.)

Recorded: 1890 – 2006
Distribution / Status: Ubiquitous / Abundant resident
Conservation status: No perceived threats
Caterpillar food plants: Blackthorn; Wild Damson; Plum
Mines evident: July to October in two generations
Records in database: 189

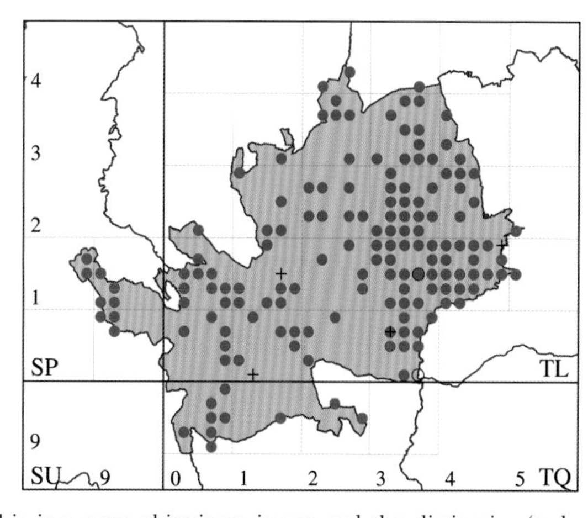

This is a near ubiquitous insect and the distinctive 'tadpole' mines are likely to be found on every *Prunus* bush or tree in the county at the appropriate time of year.

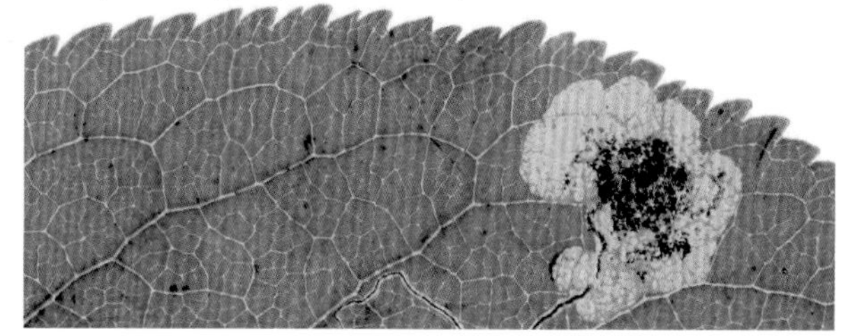

0068 *Stigmella salicis* (Stt.)

Recorded: 1976 – 2006
Distribution / Status: Widespread / Common resident
Conservation status: No perceived threats
Caterpillar food plants: Goat Willow; Common Sallow
Mines evident: June to October in two generations
Records in database: 67

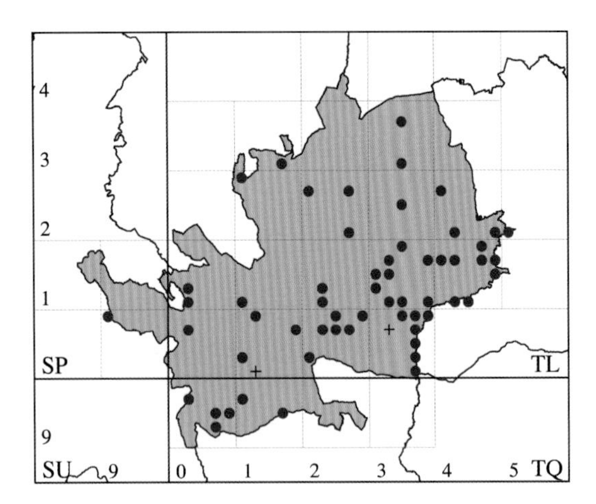

Older records of this species, including those given in Foster's 1937 county moth list, cannot be distinguished from those of 70: *Stigmella obliquella*. The moth is abundant on sallow leaves wherever these are found, but population densities may vary enormously from year to year.

0070 *Stigmella obliquella* (Hein.)

Recorded: 1976 – 2006
Distribution / Status: Local Uncommon resident
Conservation status: No perceived threats
Caterpillar food plants: Weeping Willows (*Salix babylonica*, and *S. alba* var. *pendula*); Crack Willow
Mines evident: June to October in two generations
Records in database: 27

Apparently more local in occurrence than *Stigmella salicis*, larval leaf mines of this species are nevertheless a common feature of willow trees in a variety of habitats, including on trees in parks and gardens.

0073 *Stigmella trimaculella* (Haw.)

Recorded: 1890 – 2006
Distribution / Status: Local / Uncommon resident
Conservation status: No perceived threats
Caterpillar food plants: poplars, including native Black and Lombardy
Mines evident: June to October in two generations
Records in database: 43

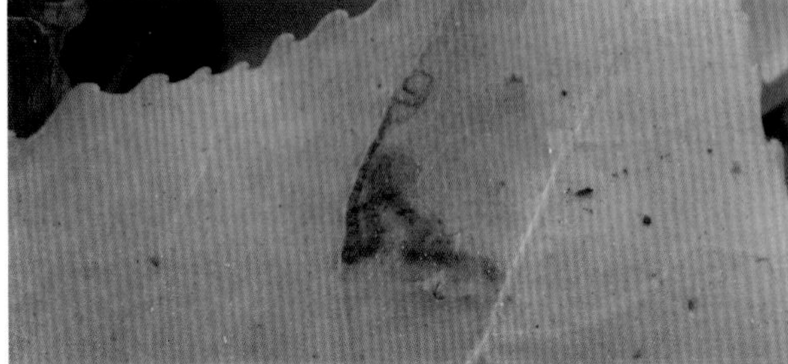

The apparent absence of this moth in the south of the county is surprising and just may reflect poor recording effort. Whilst native Black Poplar is largely confined to the extreme west of Hertfordshire, the hybrid tree is widely planted.

0074 *Stigmella assimilella (Zell.)*

Recorded: 2007 only
Distribution / Status: Local / Resident
Conservation status: Herts Rare
Caterpillar food plants: Aspen. Elsewhere also on Grey Poplar
Mines evident: October
Records in database: 1

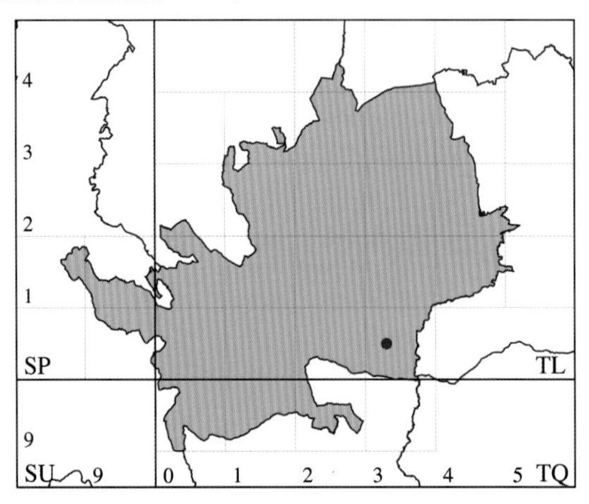

This species was added to the Hertfordshire list by Mark Cooper, who found mines on Aspen leaves at Thunderfield Grove on 23rd October 2007. Technically, this is after the 31st December 2006 cut-off date, but it seems silly to ignore it.

0075 *Stigmella floslactella* (Haw.)

Recorded: 1890 – 2006
Distribution / Status: Widespread / Common resident
Conservation status: No perceived threats
Caterpillar food plants: Hazel and Hornbeam
Mines evident: June to October, in two generations
Records in database: 85

A familiar sight in woodlands and in hedgerows, the mines are usually easy to separate from those of 111: *Stigmella*

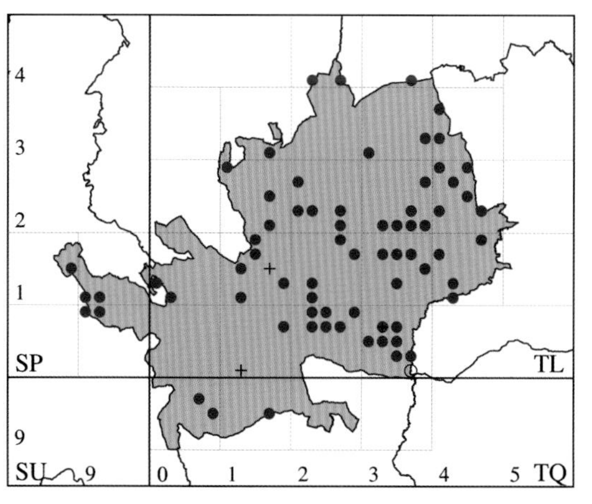

microtheriella, a parthenogenetic species that feeds on the same two foodplants. Records of mines should always be accompanied by the name of the foodplant.

0077 *Stigmella tityrella* (Stt.)

Recorded:	1890 – 2006
Distribution / Status:	Widespread / Common resident
Conservation status:	No perceived threats
Caterpillar food plants:	Beech
Mines evident:	July to November, in two generations
Records in database:	119

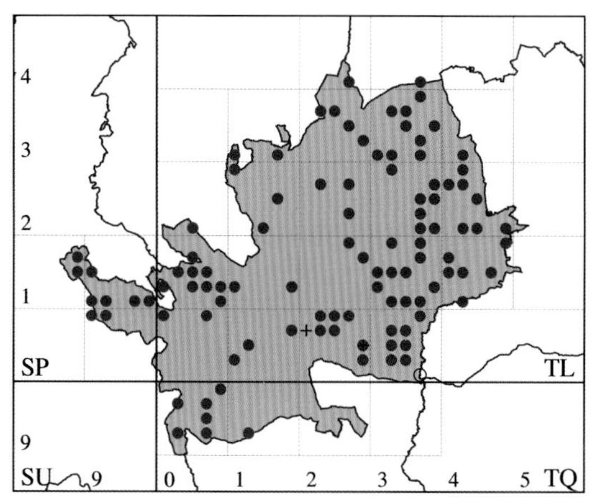

Although variable in form, the mine of this species is usually adequate to record the moth without rearing the adults.

0078 *Stigmella incognitella* (H.- S.) = *pomella* (Vaughn)

Recorded:	1890 – 2004
Distribution / Status:	Very local / Rare resident
Conservation status:	Herts Rare
Caterpillar food plants:	Domestic Apple
Mines evident:	June to November, in two generations
Records in database:	5

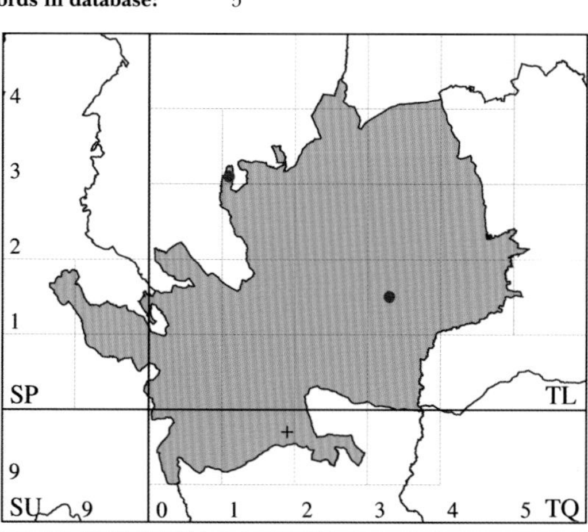

First recorded for the county within six miles of Sandridge, probably in the 1880s, but the year was not specified when it was reported in Griffith (1890); this record cannot be accurately mapped. The insect appears genuinely rare and our only other records are from the ATV Studios at Borehamwood, on 11th Nov 1981 (Eric Bradford), in the garden at Hexton Manor, where I collected mines on 20th October 2001 and from north Hertford, where Andrew Wood found mines on 24th October 2001 and 11th August 2004.

0079 *Stigmella perpygmaeella* (Doubl.)

Recorded:	1890 – 2006
Distribution / Status:	Widespread / Abundant resident
Conservation status:	No perceived threats
Caterpillar food plants:	Common Hawthorn
Mines evident:	June to October, in two generations
Records in database:	74

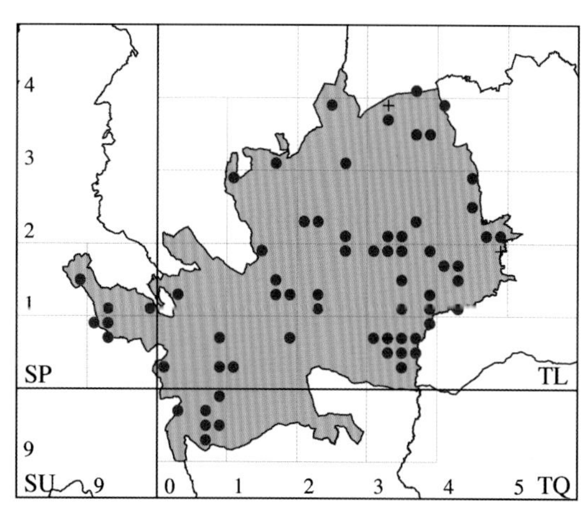

Although some mines are distinctive, most mines on hawthorns will require rearing of the adults for successful identification of the species.

0080 *Stigmella ulmivora* (Fol.)

Recorded:	1976 – 2005
Distribution / Status:	Local / Uncommon resident
Conservation status:	No perceived threats
Caterpillar food plants:	Wych Elm. Elsewhere on other elms
Mines evident:	June to September, usually in a single generation
Records in database:	20

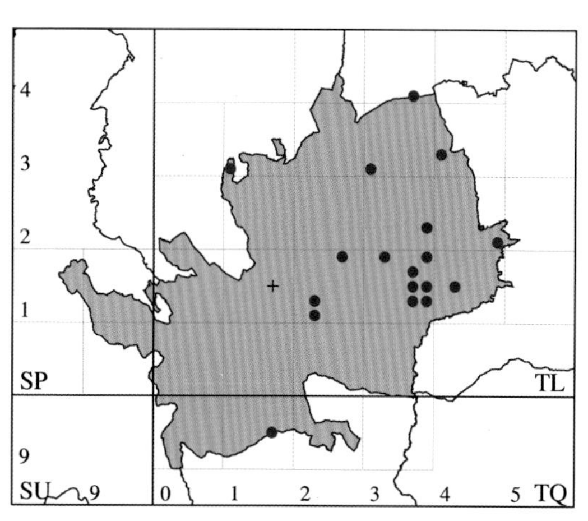

Mines of this apparently uncommon species are polymorphic so that they may often resemble those of 63: *Stigmella lemniscella* and vice versa. However, the exit hole is always on the upper surface of the leaf with *lemniscella* and always on the lower surface in *ulmivora*. Mines of *ulmivora* are usually quite hard to find and to date have only been found on Wych Elm in Hertfordshire.

0081 *Stigmella hemargyrella* (Kol.)

Recorded: 1989 – 2006
Distribution / Status: Widespread / Common resident
Conservation status: No perceived threats
Caterpillar food plants: Beech
Mines evident: June to September in two generations
Records in database: 50

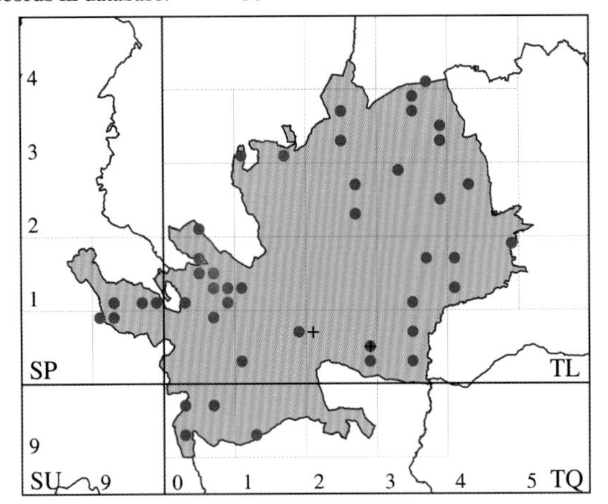

A widespread and common species, limited only by the availability of Beech trees. Beech hedges sometimes support mines of this species, but summer pruning is not compatible with their longer term survival.

0082 *Stigmella paradoxa* (Frey)

Recorded: 1976 – 2000
Distribution / Status: Extremely Local / Rare resident
Conservation status: Herts Rare
Caterpillar food plants: Hawthorn
Mines evident: June and July, but remaining on the bushes until the autumn
Records in database: 2

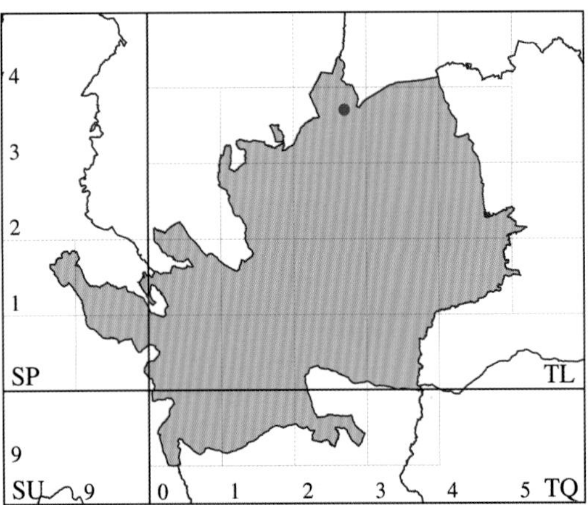

This moth is locally common in southern Cambridgeshire and so the fact that our only definable Hertfordshire record is up against the border with that county, at Bygrave, where I found a small number of mines during 2000, is no real surprise. A 1976 dot in *Moths and Butterflies of Great Britain and Ireland* is thought to have been made by Maitland Emmet in the north of the county during the early 1970s. The moth is not expected any further south, but may yet be found elsewhere in our northern border area. There are also records from Bedfordshire in map squares that border our county.

0083 *Stigmella atricapitella* (Haw.)

Recorded: 1980 – 2006
Distribution / Status: Widespread / Common resident
Conservation status: No perceived threats
Caterpillar food plants: English Oak; Sessile Oak
Mines evident: June to November in two generations
Records in database: 59

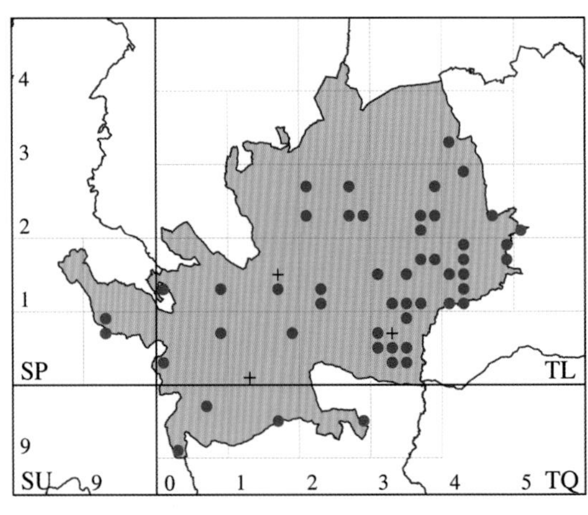

The mines of this species cannot always be separated from those of 84: *S. ruficapitella* or 86: *S. roborella*, because these latter species sometimes lay their eggs on the under-surface of the leaf. Rearing of adults is often crucial for correct identification.

0084 *Stigmella ruficapitella* (Haw.)

Recorded: 1980 – 2006
Distribution / Status: Widespread / Common resident
Conservation status: No perceived threats
Caterpillar food plants: English Oak; Sessile Oak; Sweet Chestnut
Mines evident: June to November in two generations
Records in database: 104

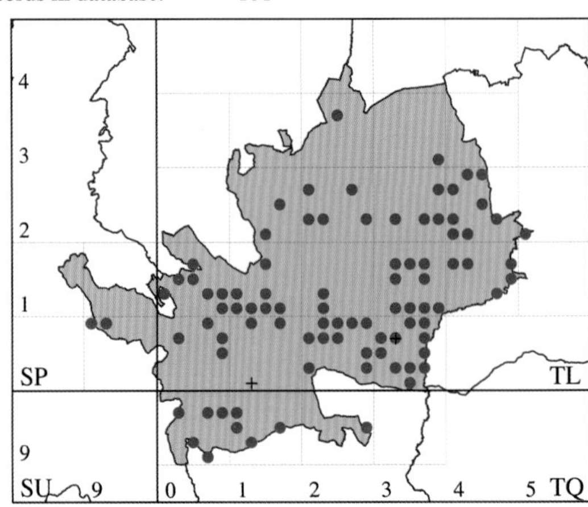

There is considerable difficulty in separating the mines of *Stigmella* species on oak. *Stigmella ruficapitella* is popularly supposed to be confined to deciduous species of oak, but I have reared one example from a mine originally thought to have been made by *S. samiatella* on Sweet Chestnut, collected at Chorleywood Common. It is important in all cases to rear adults for examination. The dots on the map include all rearing records and wild caught adults, but a few, where insufficient detail has been supplied, probably represent mines on oaks where the form of the mine was typical of *ruficapitella* and the egg is specifically recorded as being on the upper surface. The situation is complicated by the fact that *Stigmella samiatella* is also known to mine deciduous oaks elsewhere (see Emmet, 1976) and typically lays its egg on the upper surface of the leaf. Eggs laid on the underside may have come from *ruficapitella*, but are more likely to relate to 83: *S. atricapitella*; these are treated as unconfirmed and so are not mapped.

0085 *Stigmella suberivora* (Stt.)

Recorded: 1970 – 2006
Distribution / Status: Local / Uncommon resident
Conservation status: No perceived threats
Caterpillar food plants: Holm Oak
Mines evident: June and July then October/November, but as the leaves do not fall old mines may be evident at other times too
Records in database: 11

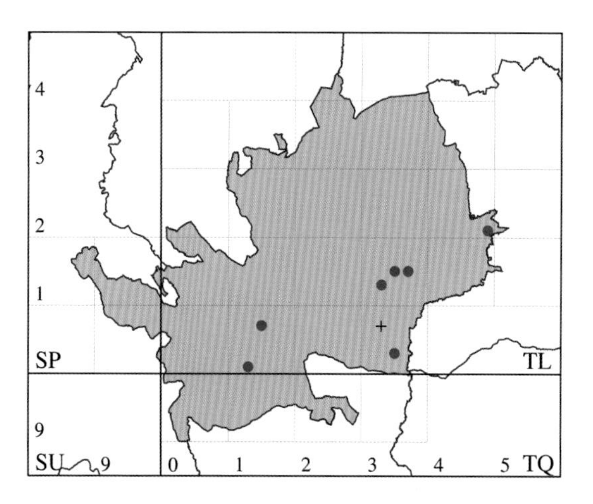

The lack of Holm Oak trees is likely to be the only factor restricting the spread of this species, which is usually found wherever the tree grows.

0086 *Stigmella roborella* (Johan.)

Recorded:	2000 – 2006
Distribution / Status:	Widespread / Common resident
Conservation status:	No perceived threats
Caterpillar food plants:	English Oak; Sessile Oak
Mines evident:	June to November in two generations
Records in database:	41

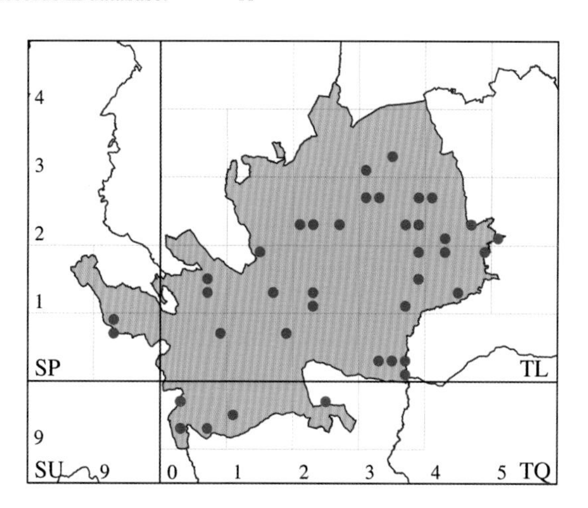

The revelation that there are no Hertfordshire records for this species prior to year 2000 is very surprising and reflects the neglect that the micro-moths have suffered at the hands of local lepidopterists over the years. In many cases, satisfactory naming of this moth requires adults to be reared from collected mines.

0087 *Stigmella svenssoni* (Johan.)

Recorded:	1987 – 2005
Distribution / Status:	Very local / Rare resident
Conservation status:	Herts Scarce
Caterpillar food plants:	English Oak
Mines evident:	July to October (but see text)
Records in database:	5

The text under this species in *Moths and Butterflies of Great Britain and Ireland*, authored by the late Maitland Emmet and published in 1976, suggests that larvae feed as late as November and it is unclear if there are two generations, or just one protracted emergence. This is at odds with the information Maitland provided in his *Life History Chart of the British Lepidoptera* in volume 7(2) of the same work, published in 1991, in which larvae are indicated for July and August only. One of our records, mapped here, was of a tenanted mine found by

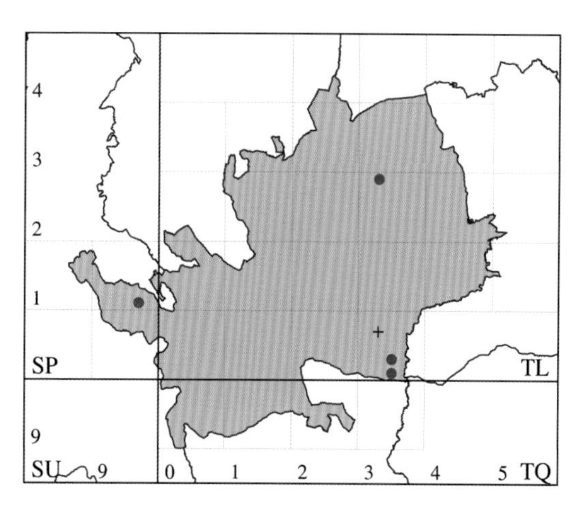

Maitland himself on 25th October 1987 (at Broxbourne Wood West Car Park). Of the remaining four, two are mine, on 8th September 2001 at Ashridge Estate and on 16th October 2001 at Cottered. One agrees with the July date in the Life History Chart – on 25th July 2004 at Theobalds Park, courtesy of Elizabeth Goodyear and one is undated from Cheshunt in 2005 (Mark Cooper).

0088 *Stigmella samiatella* (Zell.)

Recorded:	2000 – 2005
Distribution / Status:	Local, but spreading / Uncommon resident
Conservation status:	No perceived threats
Caterpillar food plants:	Sweet Chestnut. Elsewhere on deciduous oak
Mines evident:	June to October in two generations
Records in database:	13

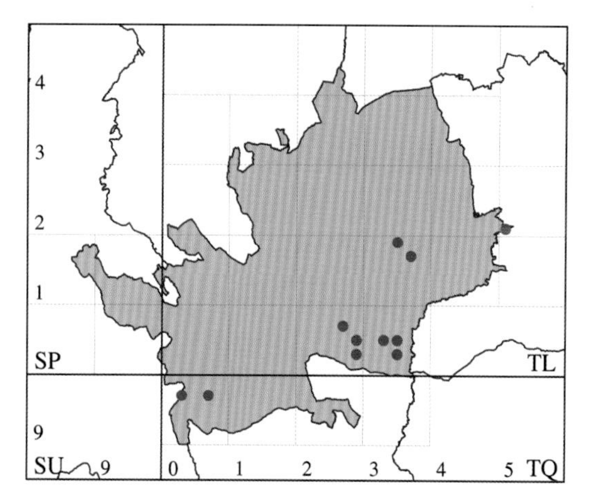

Mines resembling those of *Stigmella ruficapitella* on leaves of Sweet Chestnut are very likely to be this species, although *ruficapitella* has also been bred from this host on a single occasion. The eggs are variously laid on the upper or lower surface so the position is not of any help. It is likely that the single occurrence of *ruficapitella* was of a freak nature; more research, including breeding out of adults from mines is highly desirable. *Stigmella samiatella* is also known to mine deciduous oaks elsewhere (see Emmet, 1976).

0089 *Stigmella basiguttella* (Hein.)

Recorded:	1900 – 2006
Distribution / Status:	Widespread, Common resident
Conservation status:	No perceived threats
Caterpillar food plants:	English Oak
Mines evident:	June to November in two generations
Records in database:	65

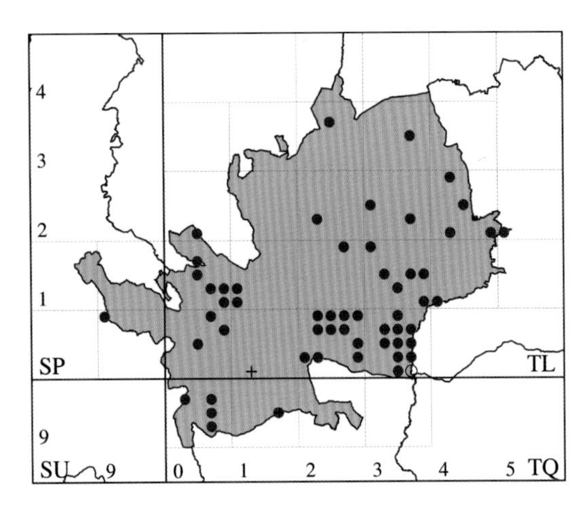

The very character that renders this mine instantly identifiable is, perversely, also responsible for its under-recorded status – it is completely filled with green frass that renders it very hard to spot when fresh!

0090 *Stigmella tiliae* (Frey)

Recorded: 2002 – 2006
Distribution / Status: Local – probably spreading / Rare resident (recent colonist)
Conservation status: No perceived threats
Caterpillar food plants: Lime (street trees)
Mines evident: July to October in two generations
Records in database: 11

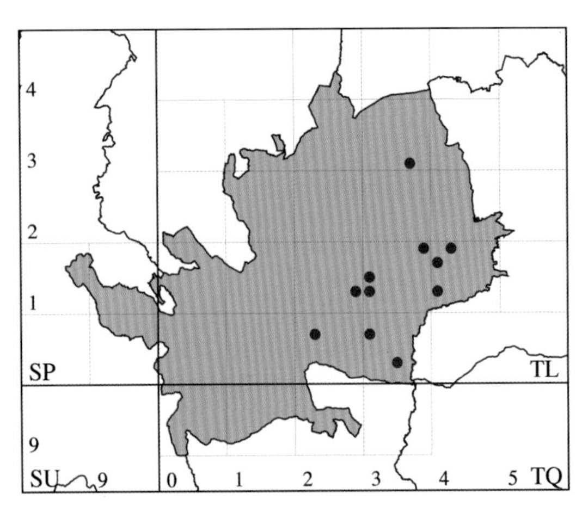

This moth seems to be a very recent arrival in Hertfordshire. It was almost certainly absent for the duration of the twentieth century; the late Charles Watson and I looked for it over several years and failed to find it in sites where it is now present. It may prefer to mine the epicormic leaves that grow from the trunks of lime trees.

0091 *Stigmella minusculella* (H.- S.)

Recorded: 1868 only
Distribution / Status: Absent / Extinct resident
Conservation status: Herts Extinct
Caterpillar food plants: Pear
Mines evident: June to September in two generations
Records in database: 1

This moth was recorded as new to Britain from Cheshunt during August 1868 (Boyd, 1868. *Entomologist's Monthly Magazine* **5**: 280); it was also reported by H. T. Stainton in *Entomologists' Annual* **1870**: 159. There are no other known records for the county. The larvae are said to prefer wild varieties of pear over cultivated forms in gardens; a thorough examination of wild pear trees might prove profitable and has undoubtedly not yet been undertaken.

0092 *Stigmella anomalella* (Goeze)

Recorded: 1868 – 2006
Distribution / Status: Ubiquitous / Common resident
Conservation status: No perceived threats
Caterpillar food plants: Dog Rose; Rugose Rose; 'wild rose'. Elsewhere, also on garden roses
Mines evident: July to October in two generations
Records in database: 137

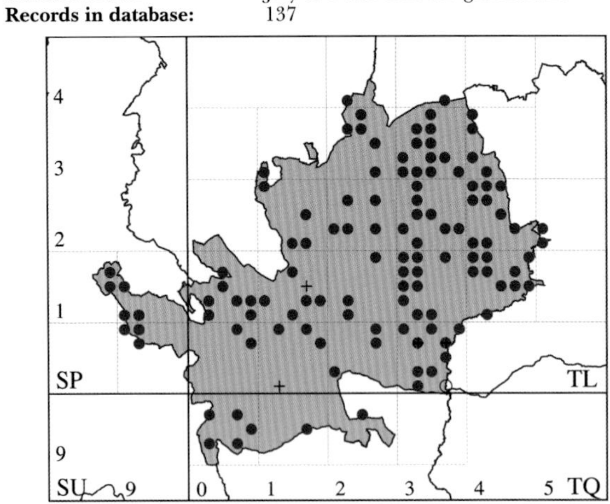

This is by far the more frequently encountered of the two common *Stigmella* species on rose (the other being 93: *S. centifoliella*). Most records are on Dog Rose or other wild rose species, but Charles Watson and I have occasionally found it on the introduced Rugose Rose, which is often planted in roadside situations in towns. We have never found it in ordinary garden roses, though it has to be said our searching of rose gardens in the county has not been thorough.

0093 *Stigmella centifoliella* (Zell.)

Recorded: 1900 – 2006
Distribution / Status: Local / Uncommon resident
Conservation status: Herts Scarce
Caterpillar food plants: Dog Rose; 'wild rose'
Mines evident: June to October in two generations
Records in database: 14

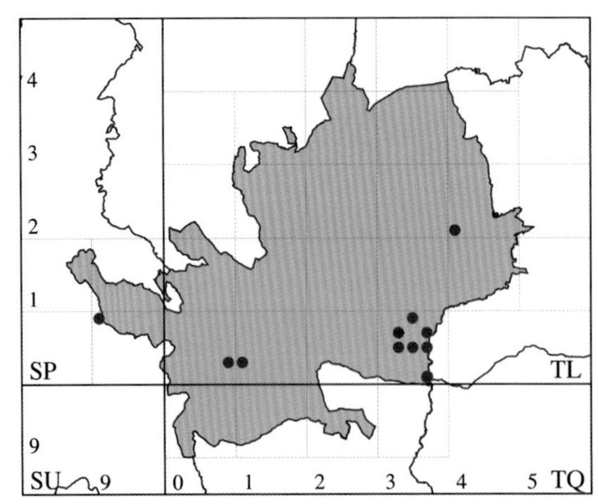

Recorded as new to Britain at Cheshunt, April 1866 by W. C. Boyd (1866. *Entomologist's Monthly Magazine* **3**: 115; 1868. *Entomologist's Monthly Magazine* **5**: 147 and 1870. *Entomologist* **3**: 187) and by Stainton (*Entomologists' Annual* **1867**: 163 and **1870**: 18). The moth is still found at Cheshunt, but is apparently local and very scarce in the county as a whole. Given the number of roses searched, successfully, for 92: *S. anomalella*, the lack of records is unlikely to reflect under-recording.

0095 *Stigmella viscerella* (Stt.)

Recorded: 1976 – 2006
Distribution / Status: Widespread / Common resident
Conservation status: No perceived threats
Caterpillar food plants: English Elm; elms
Mines evident: August to October
Records in database: 48

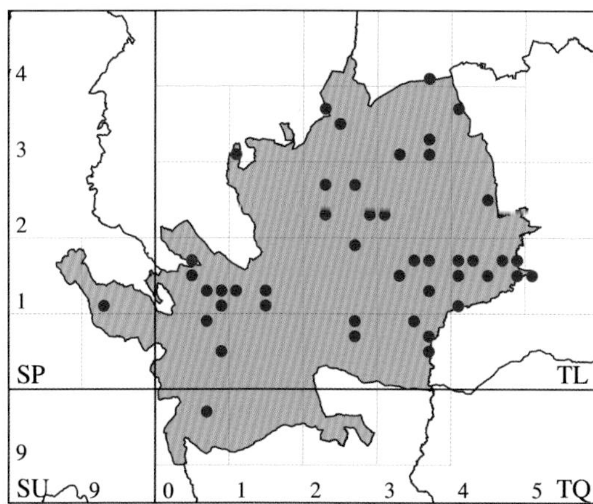

If the map for 63: *Stigmella lemniscella* reflects recording effort in searching for mines on elm, then *S. viscerella* appears to be a far less common and more localised species.

0097 *Stigmella malella* (Stt.)

Recorded: 1976 – 2006
Distribution / Status: Local / Uncommon resident
Conservation status: No perceived threats
Caterpillar food plants: Domestic Apple
Mines evident: June to October in two generations
Records in database: 20

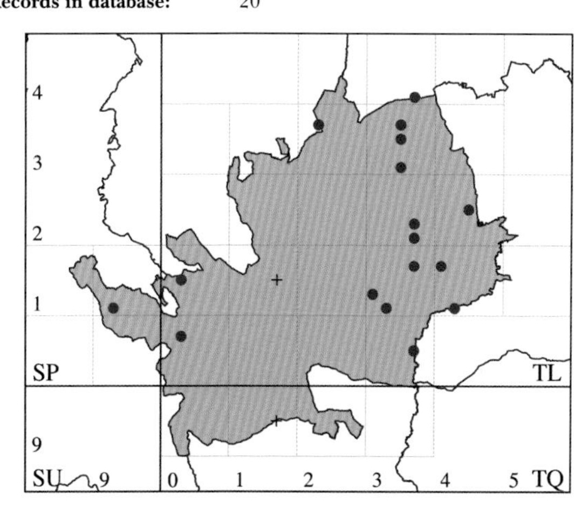

Nepticulid mines on apple, like those on hawthorn, are very hard to identify and in almost all cases the adults need to be reared for detailed examination. This may account for the eastern bias indicated in the map: most records are near to where I live!

0098 *Stigmella catharticella* (Stt.)

Recorded: 1890 – 2006
Distribution / Status: Local / Uncommon resident
Conservation status: Herts Scarce
Caterpillar food plants: Buckthorn
Mines evident: June to October in two generations
Records in database: 12

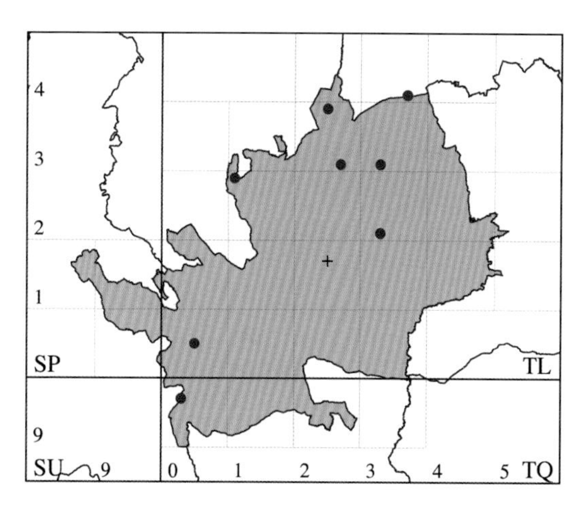

This is probably an under-recorded moth that will be present wherever the foodplant grows wild. The 1995 central Hertfordshire record was made at Dane End, where the foodplant grows on the Chalky Boulder Clay; all other records are on chalk.

0099 *Stigmella hybnerella* (Hb.)

Recorded: 1900 – 2006
Distribution / Status: Widespread / Common resident
Conservation status: No perceived threats
Caterpillar food plants: Common Hawthorn
Mines evident: May to September in two generations
Records in database: 42

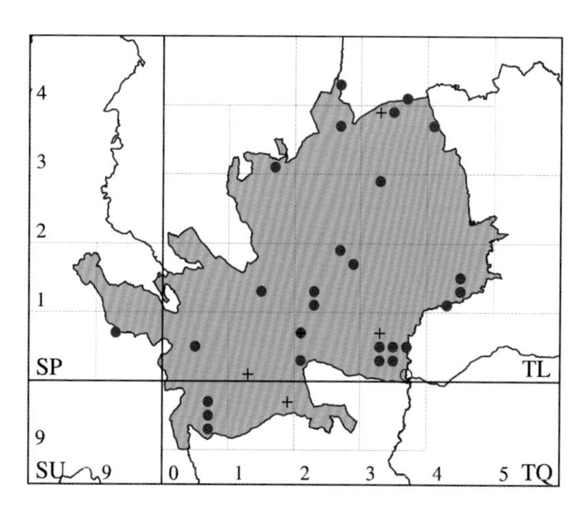

The populations of this species seem to fluctuate; in some years it is easy to find mines, but in others they appear only at very low density.

0100 *Stigmella oxyacanthella* (Stt.)

Recorded: 1890 – 2006
Distribution / Status: Ubiquitous / Abundant resident
Conservation status: No perceived threats
Caterpillar food plants: Common Hawthorn; Midland Hawthorn; Domestic Apple; Crab Apple; Whitebeam
Mines evident: September/October
Records in database: 182

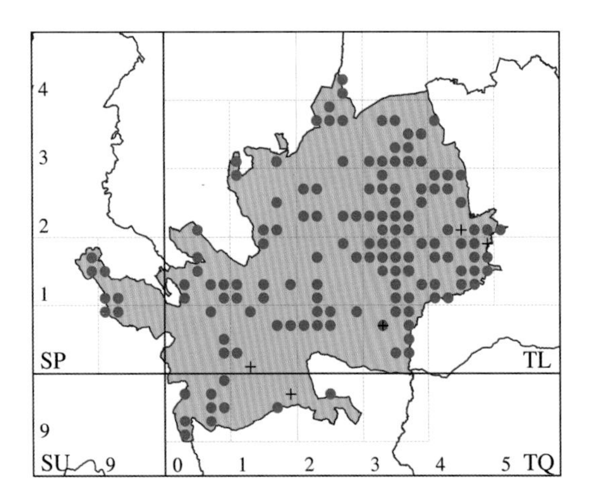

One of our commonest nepticulids, it feeds in a wide range of rosaceous shrubs and the list of host plants recorded for Hertfordshire is probably far from complete.

0102 *Stigmella aceris* (Frey)

Recorded:	2003 only
Distribution / Status:	Extremely local, probably spreading / Uncommon resident
Conservation status:	No perceived threats
Caterpillar food plants:	Field Maple. Elsewhere, on Norway Maple. In Europe, apparently on Sycamore
Mines evident:	June to September, in two generations
Records in database:	1

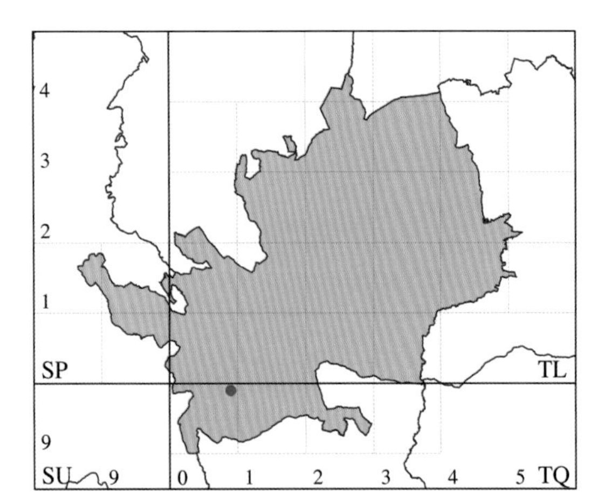

Our only record to the end of 2006 is from Leavesden Green where I recorded tenanted mines on 18th October 2003. This species is a recent arrival in the county and is likely to spread.

0103 *Stigmella nylandriella* (Tengst.) = *aucuparia* (Frey) sensu *MBGBI*

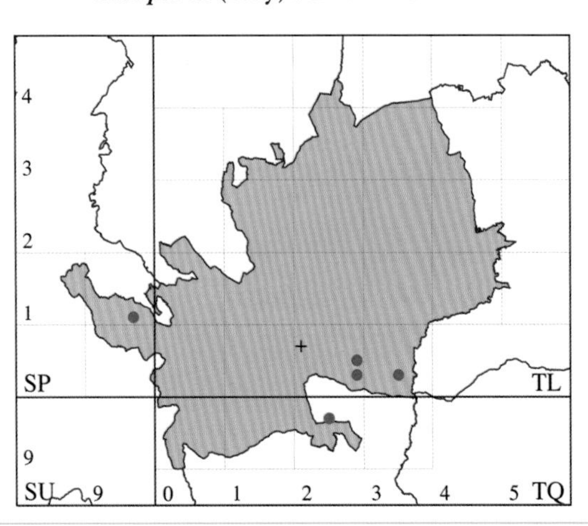

Recorded:	1990 – 2005
Distribution / Status:	Local / Uncommon resident
Conservation status:	No perceived threats
Caterpillar food plants:	Rowan
Mines evident:	July/August
Records in database:	8

The absence of records in the north of the county may reflect under-recording. This is the species referred to as *S. aucupariae* on page 255 of volume 1 in the series *Moths and Butterflies of Great Britain and Ireland*; the text relating to *S. nylandriella* in that work is in fact concerned with *S. magdalenae* (Klim.), a species not recorded in Hertfordshire.

0107 *Stigmella regiella* (H.- S.)

Recorded:	1978 – 2002
Distribution / Status:	Very local / Rare resident
Conservation status:	Herts Rare
Caterpillar food plants:	Common Hawthorn
Mines evident:	July to September
Records in database:	3

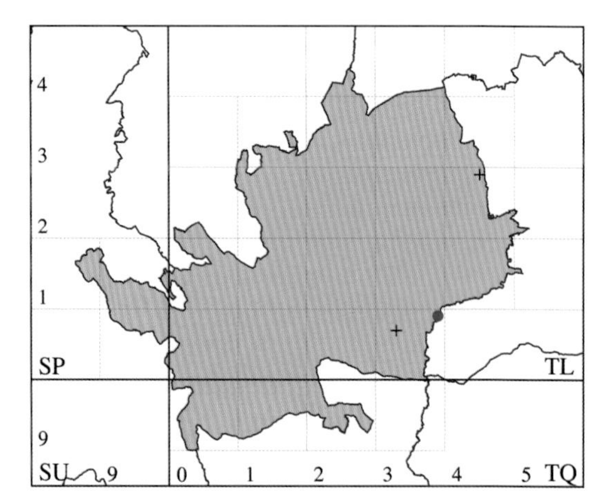

We have only three records: Stocking Pelham, 31st October 1978, Broxbourne Wood, 25th October 1987 (Maitland Emmet) and Dobbs Weir, 7th November 2002 (Elizabeth Goodyear) – all recorded as mines on Common Hawthorn. The species is widespread and common in neighbouring Bedfordshire, but scarce to the east in Essex with no recent records from the west of the county.

0108 *Stigmella crataegella* (Klim.)

Recorded:	1976 – 2005
Distribution / Status:	Widespread / Common resident
Conservation status:	No perceived threats
Caterpillar food plants:	Common Hawthorn
Mines evident:	June to August
Records in database:	46

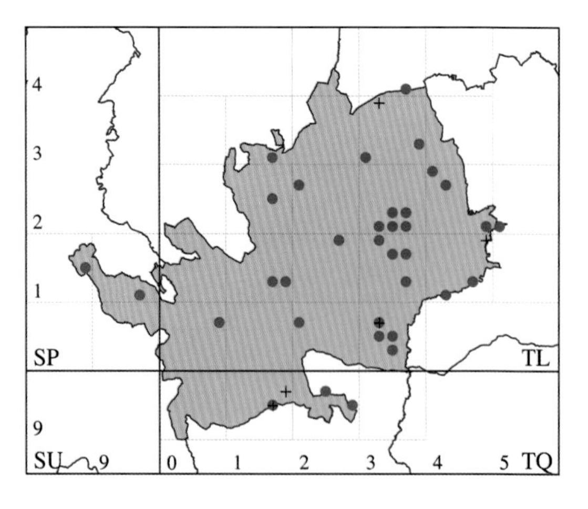

Most people start looking for leaf mines in the autumn, when the catches fall off in their moth traps, and this earlier mining species is probably under-recorded for this reason. It is likely to be on most if not all hawthorn bushes.

0110 *Stigmella betulicola* (Stt.)

Recorded: 1890 – 2004
Distribution / Status: Extremely local / Rare resident
Conservation status: Herts Scarce
Caterpillar food plants: Seedling birches
Mines evident: July to October in two generations
Records in database: 8

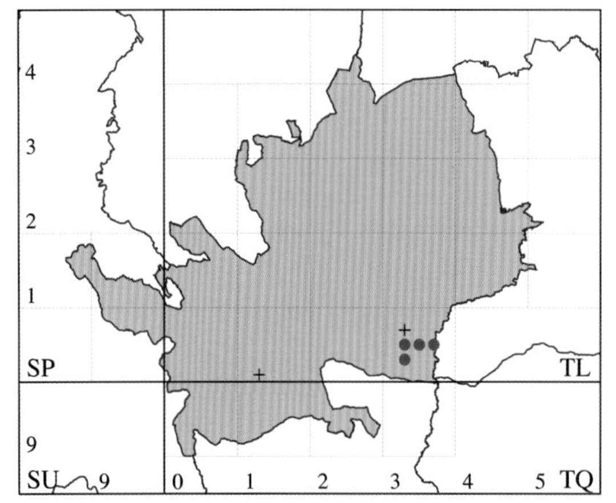

Modern records of this moth seems to be restricted in Hertfordshire to the Broxbourne Woods complex, from where it has been recorded in several locations by the late Maitland Emmet and more recently by Mark Cooper. There is an older record from Bricketwood common, where Maitland Emmet found mines in November 1980, and it is also listed for the Sandridge area by Griffith (1890).

0111 *Stigmella microtheriella* (Stt.)

Recorded: 1890 – 2006
Distribution / Status: Ubiquitous / Abundant resident
Conservation status: No perceived threats
Caterpillar food plants: Hazel and Hornbeam
Mines evident: June to November, in two generations
Records in database: 229

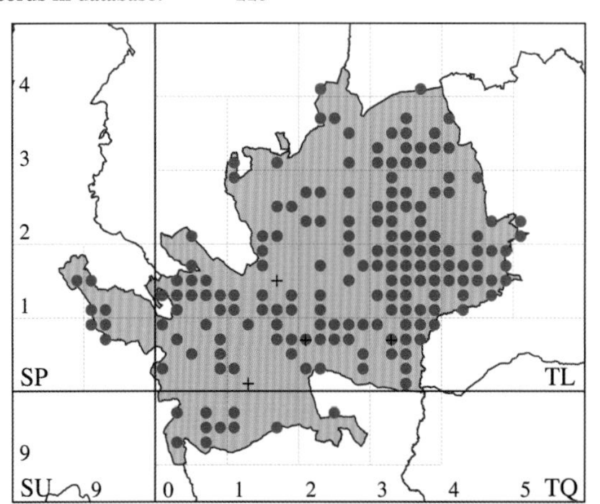

The mines of this species are a familiar site in woodlands and hedgerows throughout the county. Records of mines should always be accompanied with the name of the host tree.

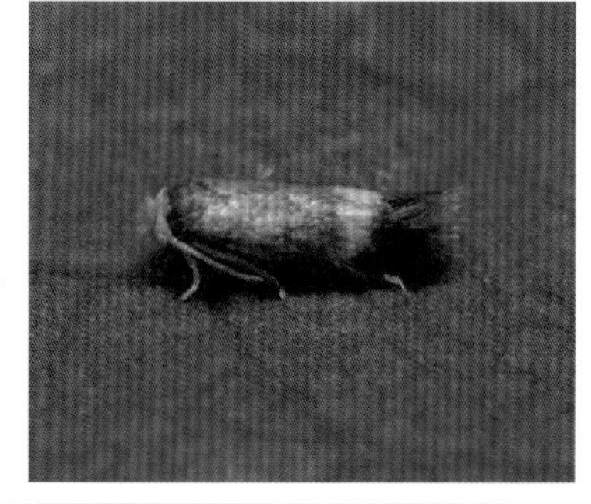

0112 *Stigmella luteella* (Stt.)

Recorded: 1890 – 2006
Distribution / Status: Local / Rare resident
Conservation status: Herts Scarce
Caterpillar food plants: Silver Birch
Mines evident: August to October
Records in database: 15

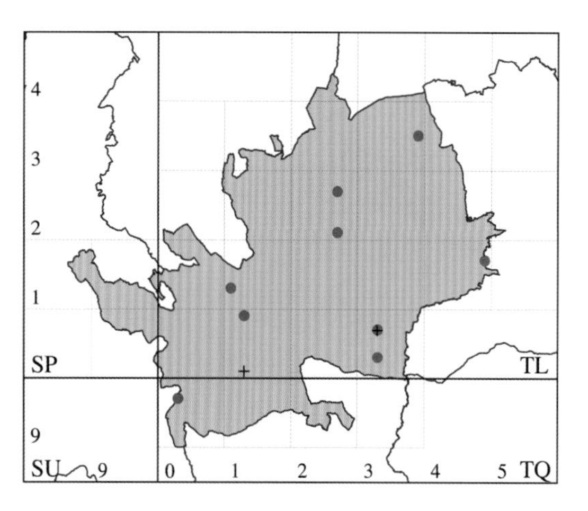

An 1890 record for the Sandridge area is not mapped. Leaf mines seem to be numerically uncommon at sites where we have found them at all.

0113 *Stigmella sakhalinella* (Pupl.) = *distinguenda* (Hein.) sensu *MBGBI*

Recorded: 1976 – 2005
Distribution / Status: Local / Uncommon resident
Conservation status: Herts Scarce
Caterpillar food plants: Silver Birch. Elsewhere, also on Downy Birch
Mines evident: June to September
Records in database: 14

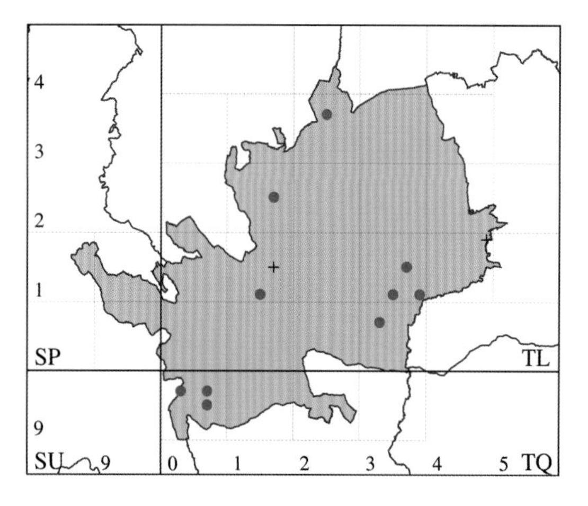

This is the birch-feeding *Stigmella distinguenda* (Heinemann) on page 262 of volume 1 of *Moths and Butterflies of Great Britain and Ireland* – in spite of apparently misleading entries in the chart on page 72 of volume 7(2) in which *distinguenda* of Heinemann is said to be the *glutinosae* of Stainton. In common with all the birch-mining nepticulids, which are hard to identify, it is very much under-recorded.

0114 *Stigmella glutinosae* (Stt.)

Recorded: 1984 – 2006
Distribution / Status: Local / Uncommon resident
Conservation status: Herts Scarce
Caterpillar food plants: Alder
Mines evident: July to October, in two generations
Records in database: 13

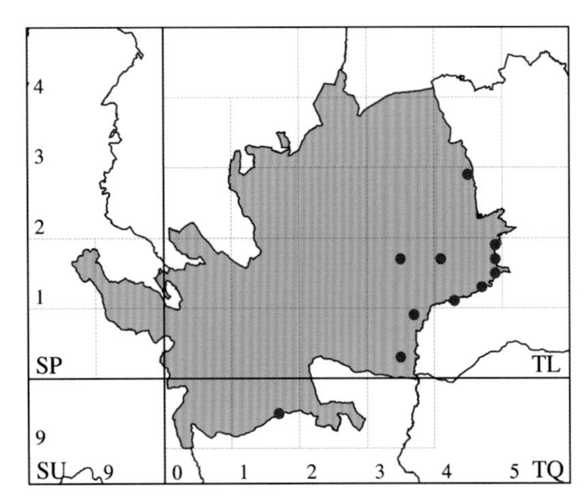

Our records suggest that only native Alder growing by streams and other watercourses is utilised by the larva and searching on the leaves of Grey Alder and other imported species has to date failed to reveal the moth. The mines of this species and the next are usually impossible to separate and adults need to be reared.

0115 *Stigmella alnetella* (Stt.)

Recorded: 2001 – 2006
Distribution / Status: Local / Uncommon resident
Conservation status: Herts Scarce
Caterpillar food plants: Alder
Mines evident: July to October, in two generations
Records in database: 9

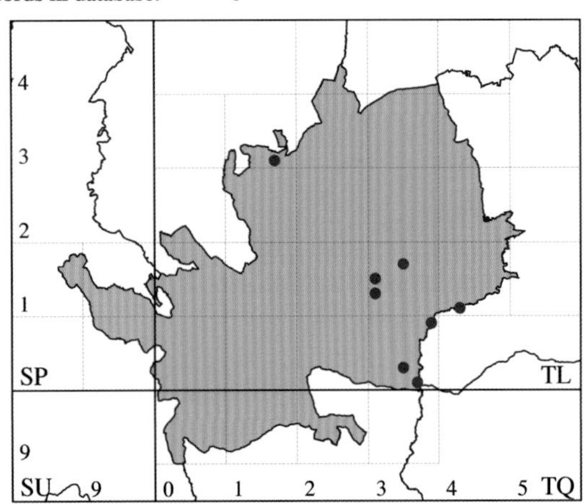

Adults need to be reared in order to be certain of the identity of this species, whose mines are very similar to those of 114: *S. glutinosae*. This requires effort on the part of the entomologist and may be partly responsible for the low number of acceptable records.

0116 *Stigmella lapponica* (Wocke)

Recorded: 1979 – 2005
Distribution / Status: Local / Uncommon resident
Conservation status: No perceived threats
Caterpillar food plants: Silver Birch
Mines evident: June and July
Records in database: 11

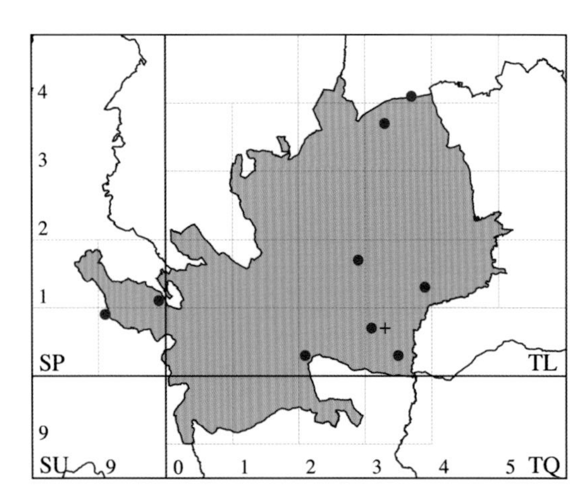

This is a species that mines the leaves of birch in midsummer and may be under-recorded, since most people don't consider looking for leaf-miners until the autumn period.

0117 *Stigmella confusella* (Wood)

Recorded: 1976 – 2005
Distribution / Status: Local / Uncommon resident
Conservation status: No perceived threats
Caterpillar food plants: Silver Birch. Elsewhere, also on Downy Birch
Mines evident: July and August
Records in database: 9

This is another birch-feeding species that is under-recorded because of the early date when it mines leaves and because of the difficulty of naming most of the birch-feeding nepticulids.

OPOSTEGIDAE

Our four British members of the Opostegidae are very similar to the Nepticulidae. They are slightly larger than most "neps", with a wingspan around 9 or 10 millimetres, they have a large eye-cap, much larger than that of nepticulids and the back of the head, behind the vertex, there is an area of flat-scales so that this part of the head is smooth. The larvae of the four British species are unknown; we have records for two species in Hertfordshire.

0119 *Opostega salaciella* (Tr.)

Recorded: 1885 – 2006
Distribution / Status: Extremely local / Resident
Conservation status: Herts Vulnerable
Caterpillar food plants: Sheep's Sorrel
Flight period: June/July
Records in database: 9

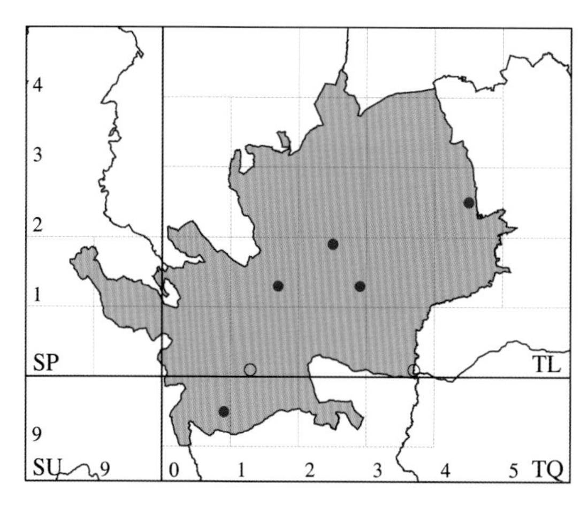

A record from "Hitchin" made in 1885 by J. H. Durrant is not mapped because it is not clear where in the Hitchin area the species was found. Other historical records are from Bricket Wood before 1890 (A. F. Griffith) and at Cheshunt prior to 1901 (W. C. Boyd). Modern records are all a result of hard work and dedication on the part of Raymond Uffen, who has found it at Croxley Common Moor, Nomansland Common and Panshanger – all acid-grassland sites. At Panshanger Park on 19th June 2005 and at Nomansland Common on 10th July 2005, Raymond noted that the adults climb up the stems of the foodplant from 6 pm (at Panshanger) or from 7 pm (Nomansland – a month later), and then take to the wing at dusk. Eggs were laid singly on the stems and on the lower surface of leaves.

0121 *Pseudopostega crepusculella* (Zell.)

Recorded:	1890 – 1971
Distribution / Status:	Absent / Extinct resident
Conservation status:	Herts Extinct
Caterpillar food plants:	Unknown. Elsewhere probably on mint
Flight period:	July
Records in database:	4

A record from the Sandridge area by A. F. Griffith, published in 1890, lacks sufficient detail to allow mapping here. There is one other historical record, from Cheshunt before 1901 (W. C. Boyd). The only records since that date were made by the late Eric Bradford at the Associated Television Studios in Borehamwood on 12th July 1969 and 23rd July 1971.

TISCHERIOIDEA
TISCHERIIDAE

The taxonomy of the species in this family is undergoing revision. At one stage, all the British species were regarded as belonging to the genus *Tischeria*, but this was 'split' recently by the French entomologist Patrice Leraut and the genus *Emmetia* was created for four of our six British species. Though this name met with the thorough approval of those of us who were privileged to know Lt. Col. Maitland Emmet, in whose honour it was created, even more recent research has put some species back into *Tischeria* and others into a new genus *Coptotriche*. For now, however, I prefer to retain the genus *Emmetia*. Of the six known British species one has not been seen for over a hundred years and has only been found once – at Colchester in Essex. Four species are recorded for Hertfordshire. All are leaf miners in the larval stage.

0123 *Tischeria ekebladella* (Bjerk.)

Recorded:	1890 to 2006
Distribution / Status:	Widespread / Common resident
Conservation status:	No perceived threats
Caterpillar food plants:	English Oak; Sessile Oak; Sweet Chestnut
Flight period:	June
Mines evident:	September/October
Records in database:	98

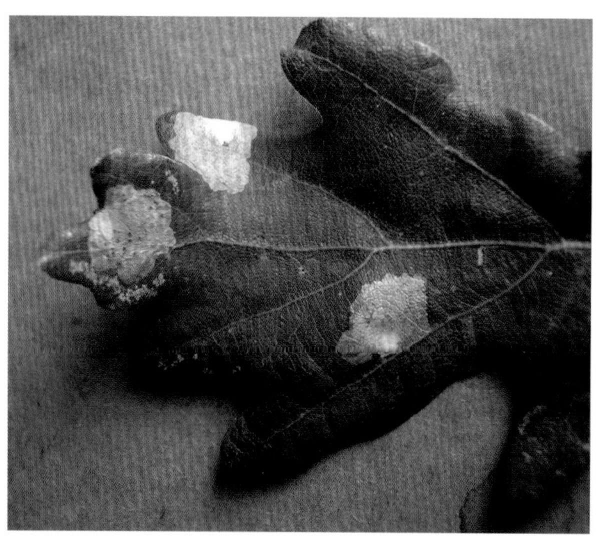

The adults are rarely seen and we have just two records: from my garden trap at Bishops Stortford on 19th June 2000 and from Datchworth on 21st June 2005, where it was found by Steve Palmer. The mines, however, are not only common on oak leaves, but are easy to recognise without confusion. The moth will surely be found wherever there is an oak tree.

0124 *Tischeria dodonaea* Stt.

Recorded:	1890 to 2006
Distribution / Status:	Extremely local / Rare resident
Conservation status:	Herts Scarce
Caterpillar food plants:	English Oak
Flight period:	Not recorded
Mines evident:	September/October
Records in database:	5

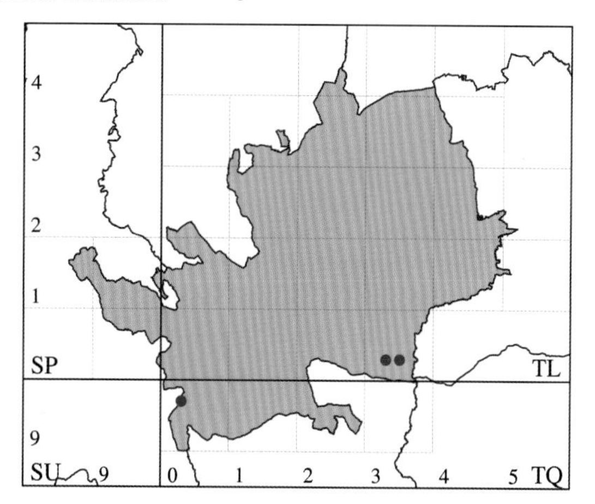

This is evidently a rare moth with us. Apart from a record made in the Sandridge area prior to 1890 by A. F. Griffith (not mapped) our only records are of mines in the Cheshunt area in

2003, 2004 and 2005 (Mark Cooper) and a mine at Chorleywood Common on 21st October 2006 – the latter during a Herts Moth Group recording trip. The mine is distinctive, but we have no records of adult moths.

0125 *Emmetia marginea* (Haw.)

Recorded:	1890 to 2006
Distribution / Status:	Widespread / Abundant resident
Conservation status:	No perceived threats
Caterpillar food plants:	Bramble
Flight period:	Not recorded
Mines evident:	July to October, in two generations, but old mines all year
Records in database:	187

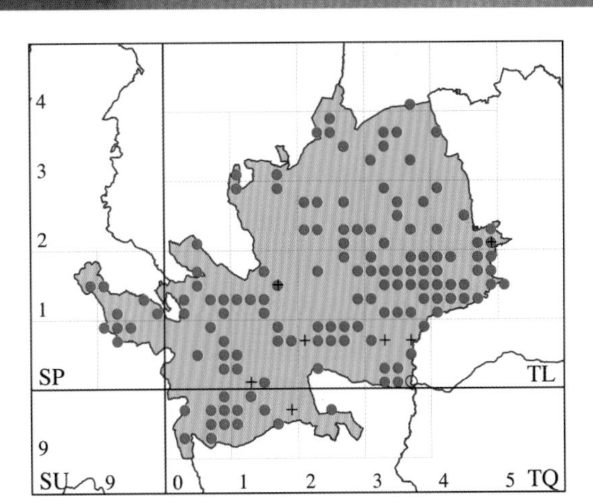

The autumn generation mines of this species are familiar to most of us, though to the casual observer they may resemble a spread-out bird dropping. During 2005, Rob Edmunds and John Langmaid found, in Hampshire and Surrey, examples of summer-brood mines that were not typical. These large, flat mines were transparent when held up to the light and there was only limited evidence of silk in the centre of the mine. Some larvae were pale in colour and had a pale colouration to the head capsule, in contrast to the autumn generation, which is a darker green colour and has more pronounced capsule pigmentation. Rearing of the adults proved that they were *E. marginea*; it is worth noting that the summer generation mines may look different from the more familiar autumn workings.

0127 *Emmetia angusticollella* (Dup.)

Recorded:	1987 only
Distribution / Status:	Extremely local / Rare resident
Conservation status:	Herts Rare
Caterpillar food plants:	Dog Rose
Flight period:	Not recorded
Mines evident:	September/October
Records in database:	2

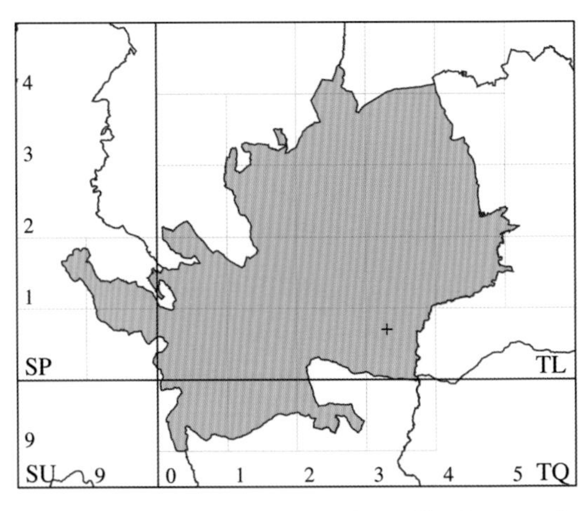

We have only two reports of this moth. Maitland Emmet found mines at Broxbourne Wood West Car Park on 25th October 1987 and kindly informed me so that I was able to see these myself a few days later on 31st October, when I also found them deeper into the wood. It seems inconceivable that this moth is no longer with us and diligent searching is likely to turn it up at least in the south of the county.

INCURVARIOIDEA

Originally, the Incurvariidae were divided into three sub-families, the Incurvariinae, Prodoxinae and Adelinae but all are now treated as full families: the leaf-mining *Phyllophora* and *Incurvaria* species are placed in the Incurvariidae, family Prodoxidae accommodates the members of genus *Lampronia* whilst *Adela*, *Nemophora* and *Nematopogon*, all of which have larvae that construct portable cases, are separated to the Adelidae.

INCURVARIIDAE

There are five British representatives of the Incurvariidae, all of which are noted in Hertfordshire, though one is probably extinct here.

0128 *Phylloporia bistrigella* (Haw.)

Recorded:	1890 – 2004
Distribution / Status:	Extremely local / Resident
Conservation status:	Herts Rare
Caterpillar food plants:	birch (mining leaves)
Flight period:	May
Records in database:	3

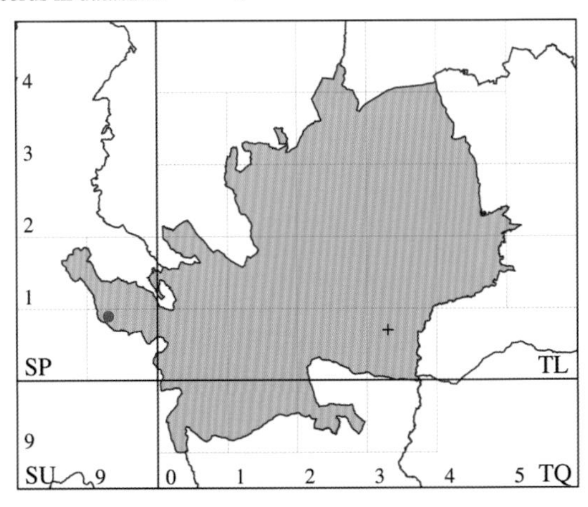

An old record from the Sandridge area (Griffith, 1890), cannot be mapped accurately. Since then we have only two reports: of mines at Broxbourne Wood on 12th September 1981 (Maitland Emmet) and an adult at Hares Garden Wood on 10th May 2004 – in a light trap run by myself, Marcel Ashby and the wood's owner, Brian Planton.

0129 *Incurvaria pectinea* Haw.

Recorded:	2004 – 2005
Distribution / Status:	Local / Uncommon resident
Conservation status:	Herts Scarce
Caterpillar food plants:	Silver Birch (mining leaves). Elsewhere also on other deciduous trees
Flight period:	April. Elsewhere, April/May
Records in database:	2

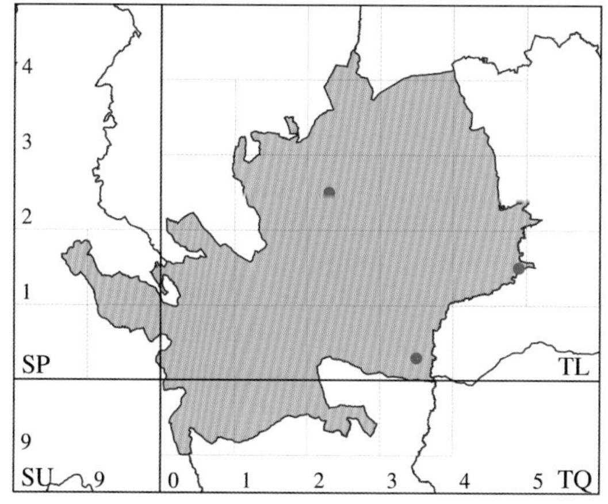

We have records for mature mines and 'cut-outs' on birch leaves at Sawbridgeworth Marsh, which I found on 29th May 2004 and of an adult from Cheshunt on 1st April 2005 by Mark Cooper. A few weeks later, on 30th April 2005, Raymond Uffen encountered adult males flying about young foliage of a clipped Hornbeam hedge at King George Fields, Stevenage. The absence of old records is interesting.

0130 *Incurvaria masculella* ([D.& S.])

Recorded:	1890 – 2006
Distribution / Status:	Widespread / Common resident
Conservation status:	No perceived threats
Caterpillar food plants:	Not recorded. Elsewhere, mining leaves of hawthorn and rose
Flight period:	April/May
Records in database:	47

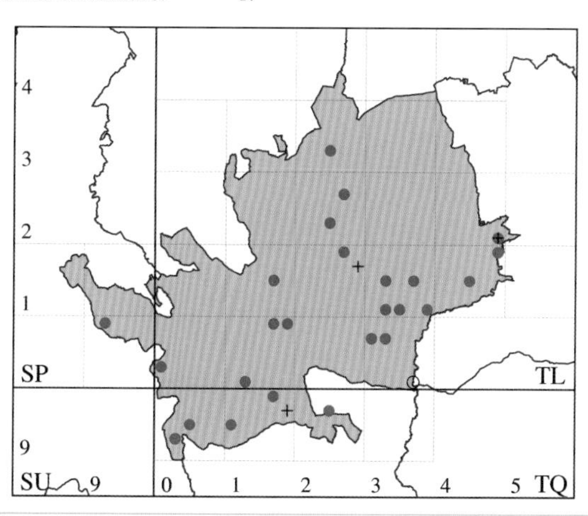

The larvae first mine leaves, then cut out a protective case from the leaf and fall to the ground to continue feeding on dead vegetation. All of our records are of adults and so we have no knowledge of tree species used here.

0131 *Incurvaria oehlmanniella* (Hb.)

Recorded:	1900 – 2005
Distribution / Status:	Local / Common resident
Conservation status:	Herts Scarce
Caterpillar food plants:	Not recorded. Elsewhere, mining leaves of deciduous trees and brambles
Flight period:	Late May. Elsewhere June/July
Records in database:	11

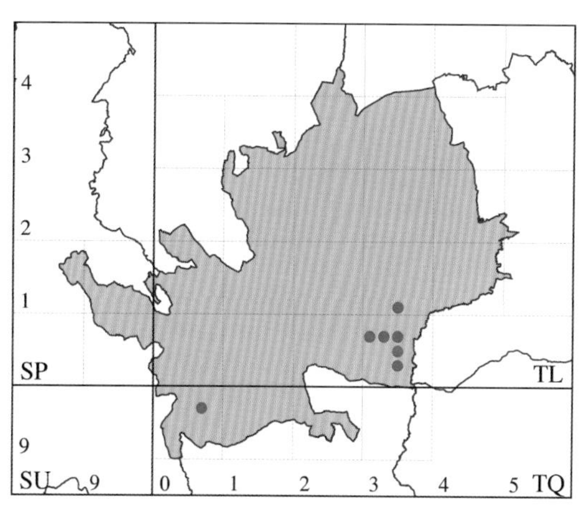

Woodlands in the Broxbourne area support a strong population of this species, but given that it is also recorded from Whippendell Wood near Watford it must surely be elsewhere in the various woodlands in southern Hertfordshire.

0132 *Incurvaria praelatella* ([D.& S.])

Recorded:	pre-1890 only
Distribution / Status:	Absent / Extinct
Conservation status:	Herts Extinct
Caterpillar food plants:	Elsewhere mining leaves of various Rosaceae, especially strawberry
Flight period:	Elsewhere, June/July
Records in database:	1

Our only Hertfordshire record is from the Sandridge area (Griffith, 1890). Griffith defined his area as 'a vertically aligned rectangle of 6 x 3 miles centred upon Sandridge'. The moth has never been recorded in our neighbouring county of Bedfordshire and has not been seen in Essex since 1916 and so is probably extinct in Hertfordshire.

PRODOXIDAE

Three of the seven British species are represented in the Hertfordshire list, though at least two are probably extinct and the third might be so. *Lampronia luzella* (Hb.) is noted in Bedfordshire for 1900 only and in Essex at Rowney Wood in the north-west, last recorded in 1980. The remaining three species are not expected in our county.

0133 *Lampronia capitella* (Cl.)

Recorded:	1901 – 1970
Distribution / Status:	Absent / Possibly extinct
Conservation status:	UK BAP Priority Species. Herts Extinct
Caterpillar food plants:	Not recorded. Elsewhere on Redcurrant and Gooseberry
Flight period:	May/June
Records in database:	2

We have only two records: from Cheshunt prior to 1901 (W. C. Boyd) and from Borehamwood on 2nd June 1970 (Eric Bradford). It was last seen in Essex in 1979 and has apparently never been recorded in Bedfordshire or Middlesex. It seems likely that this species may have been lost from the Hertfordshire fauna.

0136 *Lampronia corticella* (L.) = *rubiella* (Bjerk.)

Recorded:	1901 – 1969
Distribution / Status:	Extremely local or absent / Rare resident or Extinct
Conservation status:	Herts Extinct
Caterpillar food plants:	Not recorded. Elsewhere on Raspberry
Flight period:	Not recorded. Elsewhere, June
Records in database:	2

Our two reports are from the Cheshunt area (Boyd, 1901) and from Borehamwood on 28th May 1969 (Eric Bradford). However, it seems unlikely that the moth is extinct with us, since during 2005 Rachel Terry recorded it in her garden at Barnet, on the Middlesex side of the border just a few yards outside Hertfordshire. This species should be searched for in areas where raspberries are grown free of chemical applications.

0137 *Lampronia morosa* (Zell.)

Recorded:	1890 – 1900
Distribution / Status:	Absent / Extinct
Conservation status:	Herts Extinct
Caterpillar food plants:	Rose
Flight period:	June
Records in database:	2

Our only records are from the Sandridge area prior to 1890 and from the Cheshunt area prior to 1901. In neighbouring Essex it was last seen in 1980 in the south-east of the county and in Bedfordshire there is a single nineteenth century from the Luton area and one 1989 record from the north of the county. It has never been recorded in Middlesex. There can be no real reason to doubt that it is now extinct in Hertfordshire.

ADELIDAE

Members of subfamily Adelidae are characterised by their densely hairy hind legs and by the enormous eyes of the males and contain members of genera *Adela* and *Nemophora*. Of the fifteen British species (five in each of the three genera), Hertfordshire boasts eleven.

0140 *Nematopogon swammerdamella* (L.)

Recorded:	1890 – 2006
Distribution / Status:	Local / Common resident
Conservation status:	No perceived threats
Caterpillar food plants:	Not recorded. Elsewhere on dead leaves
Flight period:	May to early June
Records in database:	57

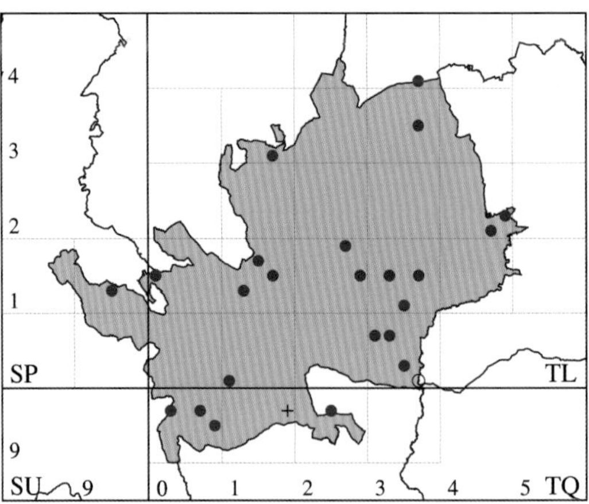

A widespread and common species, though it can be confused with 141: *N. schwarziellus*, which appears to be less frequently encountered.

0141 *Nematopogon schwarziellus* (Zell.)

Recorded:	1834 – 2006
Distribution / Status:	Local / Uncommon resident
Conservation status:	Herts Scarce
Caterpillar food plants:	Not recorded. Elsewhere on dead leaves
Flight period:	Mid-May to June
Records in database:	16

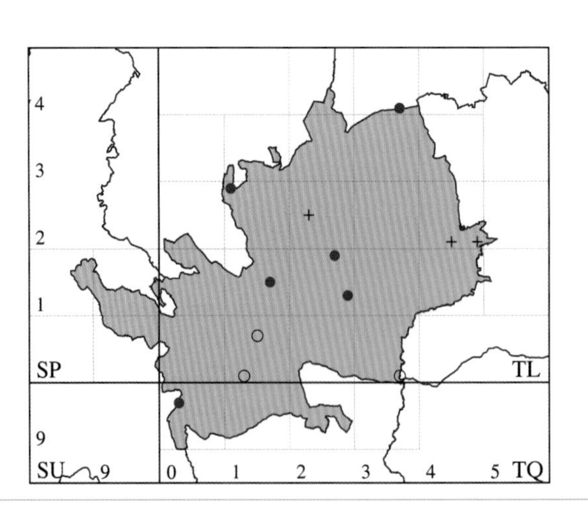

First noted in Hertfordshire by J. F. Stephens, who used a specimen he had collected near Hertford for his *Illustrations of British Entomology* **4:** 232, published in 1834, there are also old records from St Albans, within two or three miles of the Town Hall, and Bricket Wood, both in the period before 1889 (Gibbs). Modern records show a spread across the county and suggest that the species is under-recorded here.

0143 *Nematopogon metaxella* (Hb.)

Recorded: 1834 – 2005
Distribution / Status: Very local / Rare resident
Conservation status: Herts Scarce
Caterpillar food plants: Not recorded. Elsewhere on 'dead and living leaves'
Flight period: Mid-June to early July
Records in database: 4

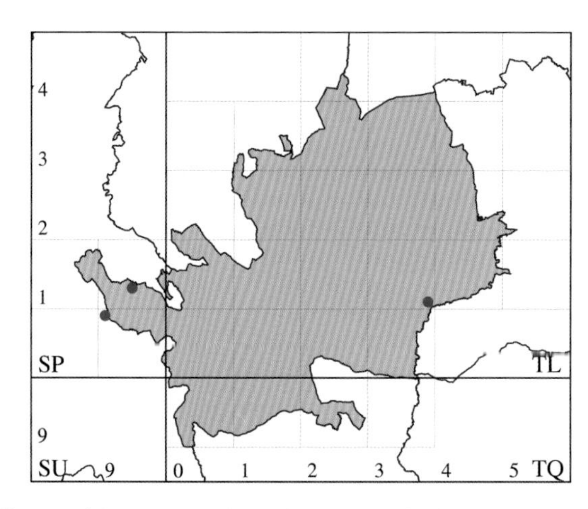

Illustrated by J. F. Stephens from a Hertford specimen in his *Illustrations of British Entomology* **4**: 232 (published in 1834) and noted from the Sandridge area by Griffith (1890), there are no more records until 17th June 2000 when I found it at Rye Meads, then 2nd July 2005 when I light trapped an adult at Grove Wood. The considerable gap between the two groups of records clearly illustrates difficulty in declaring species extinct, even after a hundred years of absence, if there has not been a specifically targetted survey.

0144 *Nemophora fasciella* (Fabr.)

Recorded: 2002 – 2006
Distribution / Status: Extremely local / Rare resident
Conservation status: UK BAP species. Herts Rare
Caterpillar food plants: Not known. Elsewhere, Black Horehound
Flight period: June/July
Records in database: 2

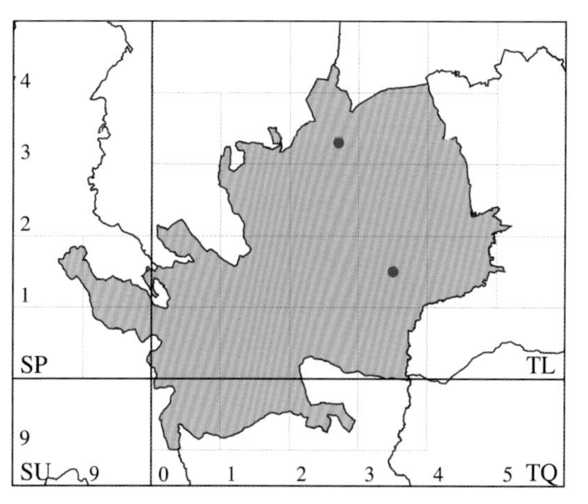

A single adult was caught in a light trap at Quickswood by Dug Heath in July 2002 and the identification was confirmed by myself. This rather surprising event was followed by Andrew Wood catching another on the meads along the River Lea, east of Hertford, on 14th June 2006. The caterpillar feeds on the seeds of Black Horehound then later eats the lower leaves; personal observations on post-industrial sites in eastern London suggest that it rarely moves far from its foodplant. This might suggest that there may be more populations of this evidently sedentary species in the county and stands of the foodplant would repay searching. The adult cannot be confused with any other species.

0145 *Nemophora minimella* ([D.& S.])

Recorded: 1887 – 2006
Distribution / Status: Extremely local / Rare resident
Conservation status: Herts Threatened
Caterpillar food plants: Not recorded. Elsewhere on Devil's-bit Scabious; Small Scabious
Flight period: Mid-August. Elsewhere July
Records in database: 4

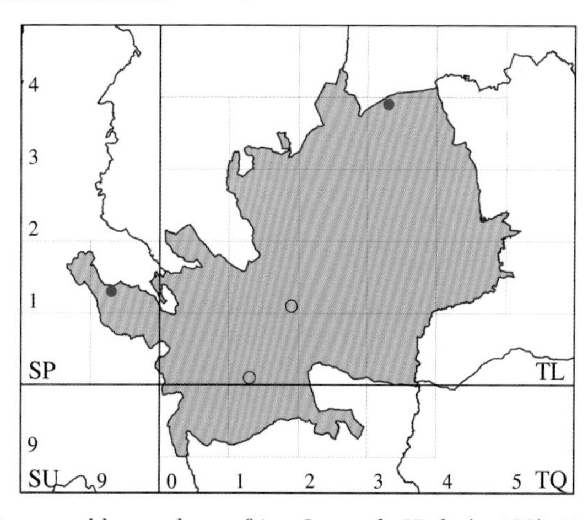

The two old records are from Symonds Hyde in 1887 (A. F. Griffith) and Bricket Wood in 1888 (A. E. Gibbs); the recent ones are from Church Hill at Therfield Heath on 17th August 1996 (Raymond Uffen) and Wilstone Sewage Works on 21st June 2006 (Colin Lambert). The larval foodplants are not common in Hertfordshire, but the moth may be present undetected at a small number of sites along the north-west boundary area on the chalk.

0146 *Nemophora cupriacella* (Hb.)

Recorded: 1998 – 2004
Distribution / Status: Extremely local / Rare resident
Conservation status: Herts Rare
Caterpillar food plants: Not recorded. Elsewhere on Scabious species and Teasel
Flight period: Late June to mid-July. Elsewhere July
Records in database: 2

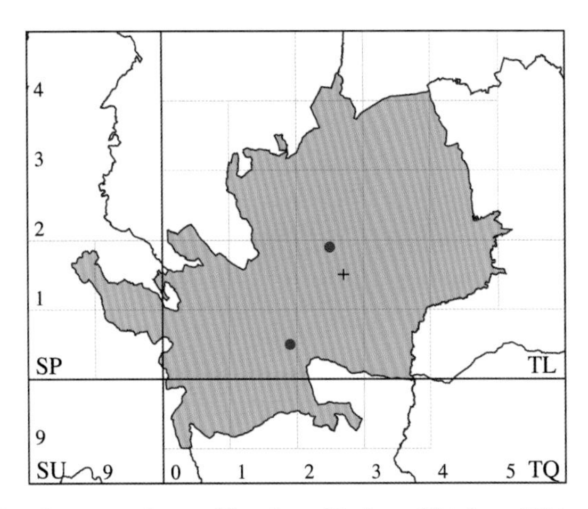

Our three records are of females at Tewin on 25th June 1994 and adults at Mardley Heath on 16th July 1998 (Raymond Uffen) then at Tyttenhanger on 27th June 2004 (Trevor Chapman). Foodplant distribution will limit the range of this species, but it is likely to be present at a small number of other sites in the county.

0147 *Nemophora metallica* (Poda) = *scabiosella* (Scop.)

Recorded:	1933 – 2004
Distribution / Status:	Extremely local / Rare resident
Conservation status:	Herts Rare
Caterpillar food plants:	Not recorded. Elsewhere on Scabious species
Flight period:	Mid-July to early August. Elsewhere July
Records in database:	5

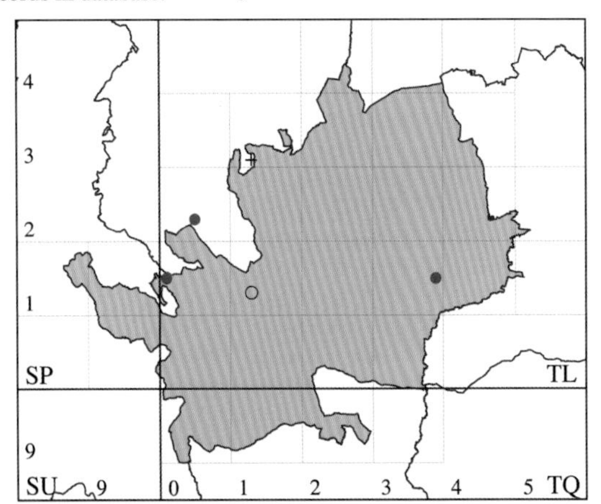

The earliest record, in 1933, is from Harpenden (J. C. F. Fryer); the more recent discoveries are from Tingley Wood at Pirton on 16th July 1994 (Raymond Uffen), Ravensdell Wood on 23rd July 1997 (David Manning), Blows Down near Dunstable on 13th July 2004 (myself) and over in the east at Mardocks, Wareside on 2nd August 1998 (Raymond Uffen).

0148 *Nemophora degeerella* (L.)

Recorded:	1890 – 2006
Distribution / Status:	Widespread / Common resident
Conservation status:	No perceived threats
Caterpillar food plants:	Not recorded. Elsewhere on dead leaves in late instars, but food of early instars is unknown
Flight period:	late May/June
Records in database:	60

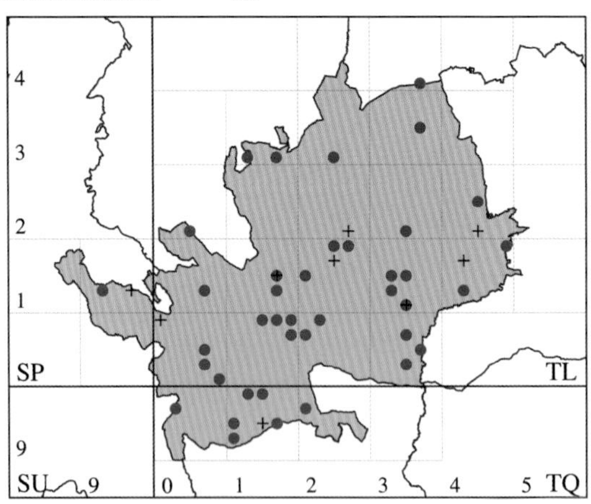

A widespread and common species across the county, most frequent in woodland edge and similar habitats.

0150 *Adela reaumurella* (L.)

Recorded:	1890 – 2006
Distribution / Status:	Widespread / Common resident
Conservation status:	No perceived threats
Caterpillar food plants:	Not recorded. Elsewhere on dead leaves in late instars, but food of early instars is unknown
Flight period:	End April to start June. Elsewhere May/June
Records in database:	72

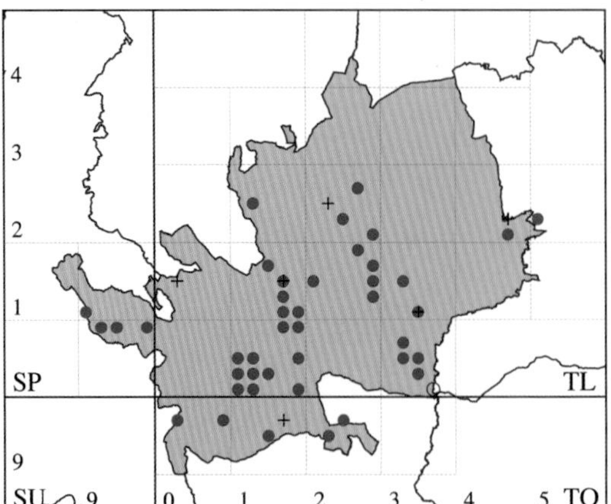

A widespread and very common moth in woodland edge, hedgerow and similar habitat. There is a very strong association with deciduous oaks and all the male swarms for which any detail is available appear to be associated with these trees. Most Hertfordshire records have been made in the first three weeks of May.

0152 *Adela rufimitrella* (Scop.)

Recorded: 1900 – 2006
Distribution / Status: Local / Uncommon resident
Conservation status: No perceived threats
Caterpillar food plants: Not recorded. Elsewhere on Cruciferae
Flight period: May to mid-June
Records in database: 33

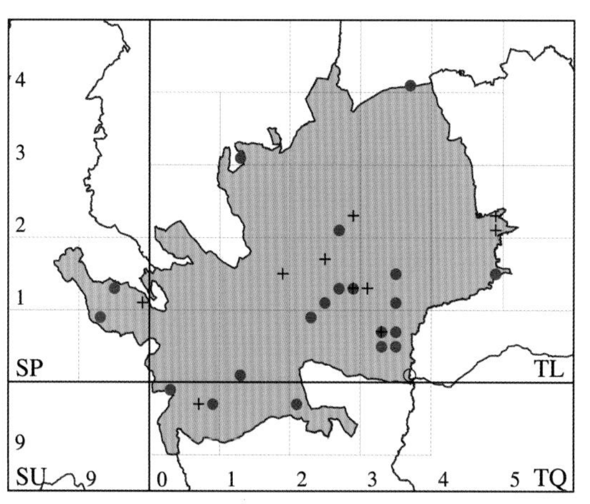

Although far less frequently encountered than 150: *Adela reaumurella*, this species is nevertheless likely to prove a widespread moth in Hertfordshire. There is a preponderance of records from areas that are either damp or else near to damp habitats. Though we have no confirmed foodplant records, adults have been found in association with Shepherd's-purse, Hedge Garlic, Lady's Smock and Winter Cress plants.

0153 *Adela fibulella* ([D.& S.])

Recorded: 1890 – 1999
Distribution / Status: Local / Rare resident
Conservation status: Herts Scarce
Caterpillar food plants: Not recorded. Elsewhere on Germander Speedwell and other *Veronica* spp.
Flight period: Late May. Elsewhere, June
Records in database: 18

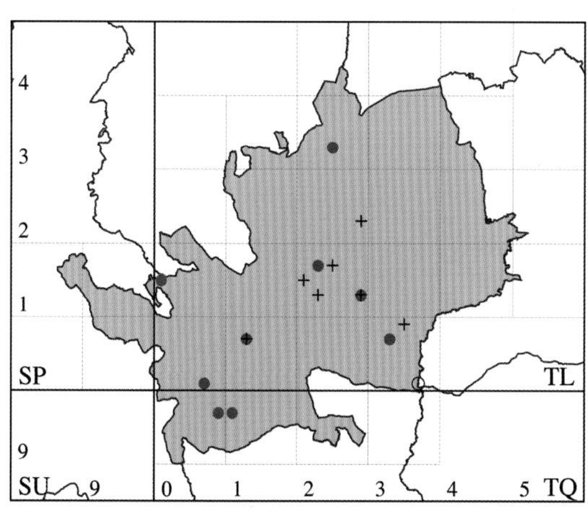

Gently sweeping flowers of Germander Speedwell with a net in late May or June may well reveal that this moth is more widespread than the small number of existing records suggest; we also have records of adults associated with Common Speedwell at Broxbourne Wood on 27th May 1999 (Raymond Uffen).

HELIOZELIDAE

The Heliozelidae are miners in the larval stage. Species of *Heliozela* mine stems or leaf petioles and are almost impossible to find; when almost mature they migrate into the leaf, but even here mines are rarely found because within about 24 hours the caterpillar cuts a portion of the leaf and uses it to make a case, heavily spun inside with silk, in which to pupate on the ground. In contrast, species of *Antispila* lay their eggs in a slit cut in the leaf edge and the larvae mine throughout until ready to cut out a case, so that they are always conspicuous. The shape and size of the cut-out are very precise and help identification. The adults are day-flying. All five of the British species are recorded in Hertfordshire and all are recorded in recent years.

0154 *Heliozela sericiella* (Haw.)

Recorded: 1890-2004
Distribution / Status: Very local / Uncommon resident
Conservation status: Herts Rare
Caterpillar food plants: English Oak
Flight period: April/May
Records in database: 7

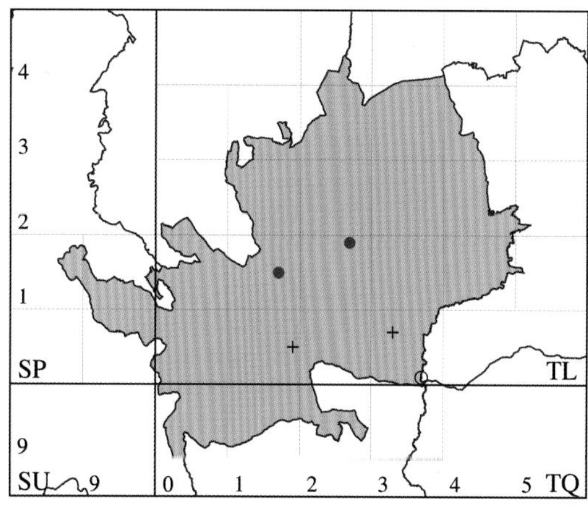

The larva first mines a twig, then a leaf petiole before moving to the midrib, which swells to form a gall. It then moves into the leaf base, hollows out a blotch and immediately cuts a case measuring from 4 to 5 millimetres long by two to three millimetres wide, seals itself inside and drops to the ground to pupate. It is almost certainly under-recorded in Hertfordshire. Cut-outs are usually made around the end of July; adults fly in May and may 'swarm' under oak branches.

0156 *Heliozela resplendella* (Stt.)

Recorded: 1900 – 1998
Distribution / Status: Very local / Uncommon resident
Conservation status: Herts Rare
Caterpillar food plants: Alder
Flight period: Not recorded. Elsewhere May to July
Records in database: 2

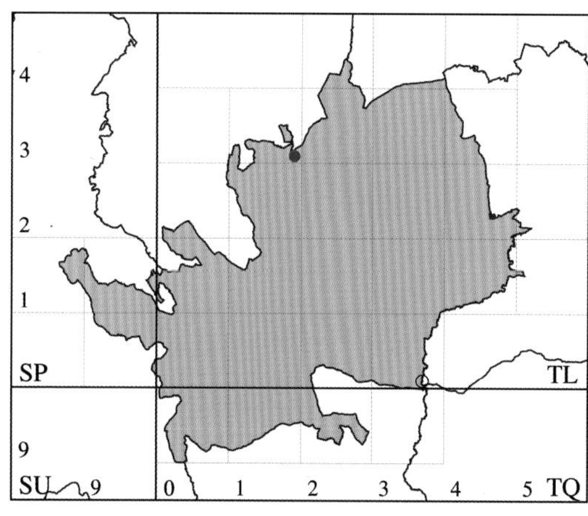

After mining the midrib and leaf, the larva cuts an oval case measuring five by three millimetres in which to pupate. Larvae are evident from June to September and the species is apparently double-brooded. Though there are only two records, from Cheshunt (Boyd, 1900) and Purwell Nine-springs, Hitchin, 17th September 1998, (Raymond Uffen), the gap between them indicates strongly that the species has not been looked for adequately.

0157 *Heliozela hammoniella* (Sorhagen)

Recorded: 1937 – 1998
Distribution / Status: Very local / Uncommon resident
Conservation status: Herts Rare
Caterpillar food plants: birch. Elsewhere, Downy Birch is usually favoured over Silver Birch
Flight period: Not recorded. Elsewhere, May/June
Records in database: 6

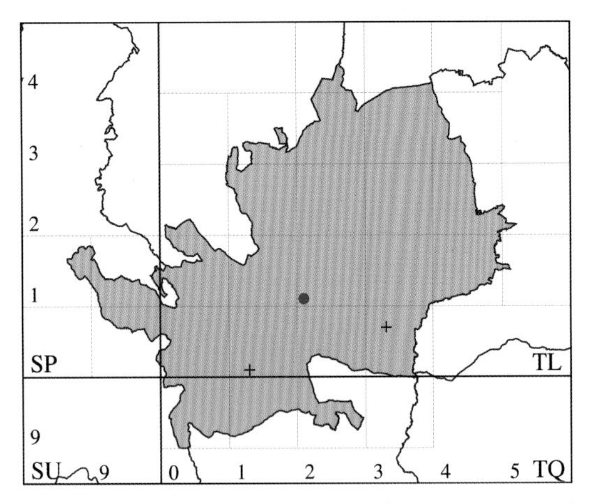

First recorded at Berkhamsted in 1937 by J. Hervey, mines were seen regularly throughout the 1980s in Broxbourne Wood, but have not been noticed there since 1987. Mines were also noted in Bricket Wood in 1980. The only recent record is from Furzefield Wood, Symondshyde on 18th September 1998, made by Raymond Uffen.

0158 *Antispila metallella* ([D.& S.]) = *pfeifferella* (Hb.)

Recorded: 1890 – 2003
Distribution / Status: Very local / Uncommon resident
Conservation status: Herts Rare
Caterpillar food plants: Dogwood
Flight period: Not recorded. Elsewhere, May
Records in database: 5

This species flies earlier than 159: *A. treitschkiella*, which also feeds on dogwood. It cuts a larger oval of leaf for its case – the hole measuring 5.5 – 7.0 millimetres lengthways. Recent records are from Wheathampstead in 1995 (Raymond Uffen) and my garden in Bishops Stortford in 2003. It is judged likely to be under-recorded.

0159 *Antispila treitschkiella* (Fisch. von Roesl.)

Recorded: 1997 – 2006
Distribution / Status: Very local / Resident
Conservation status: Herts Scarce
Caterpillar food plants: Dogwood
Flight period: Not recorded. Elsewhere, June/July
Records in database: 5

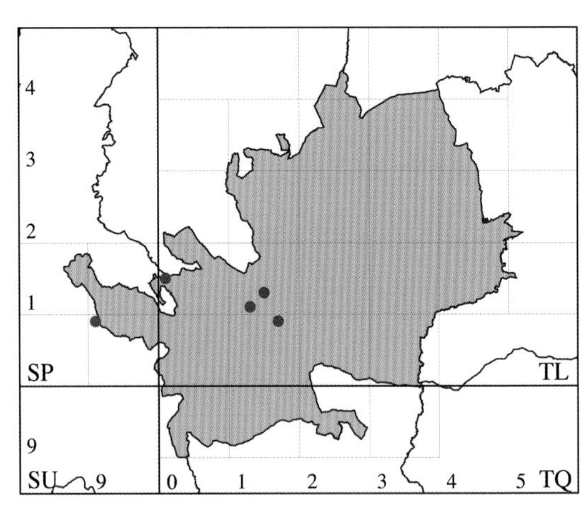

The larva cuts a smaller oval than that of 158: *Antispila metallella*, measuring 4.0 – 5.0 millimetres lengthways, so enabling reliable separation. The adult flies later than *metallella*. Our records seem to be concentrated in the west, though there is no reason why the moth should not be found elsewhere and as with the previous species, it is almost certainly under-recorded.

DITRYSIA
COSSOIDEA
COSSIDAE

Like the Hepialidae (swifts) the Cossidae are regarded as primitive moths. The larvae of all species feed internally in plant tissue, either in wood or in the pith, and have a large sclerotised prothoracic plate that presumably affords them a degree of protection from the hard surface of the tunnel in which they live. Of 85 Palaearctic species, we have just three in Britain, in three different genera, all of which are recorded for Hertfordshire.

0160 *Phragmataecia castanea* (Hb.) Reed Leopard

Recorded: Pre-1900 only
Distribution / Status: Absent / Extinct
Conservation status: Herts Extinct
Caterpillar food plants: Not recorded. Elsewhere, in reed stems
Flight period: Not recorded. Elsewhere, June/July
Records in database: 1

One adult found in a spider's web near the River Lea at Hoddesdon by G. V. Bull, undated but certainly prior to 1900, possibly represents the end of a population of this species in what must have been perfect habitat in the Lea Valley during the nineteenth century. Not withstanding this possibility, there are no other records from either the Hertfordshire or the Essex side of the valley.

0161 *Zeuzera pyrina* (L.) Leopard Moth

Recorded: 1883 – 2005
Distribution / Status: Widespread / Common resident
Conservation status: No perceived threats
Caterpillar food plants: Not recorded. Elsewhere, internally in small trunks and branches of trees
Flight period: Mid-June to mid-August
Records in database: 221

Most older lists for the county include this species, suggesting that it has always been widespread and common in spite of concerted efforts to eradicate it from orchards and larger gardens. It comes readily to light, but almost all records from traps relate to males and the flight period noted above is based on this sex almost exclusively. The larva feeds internally in the woody tissue of trees. Emmet (1991) states that stems and branches up to 10 centimetres diameter are used. The larval phase can extend over three calendar years, from August in the first to May in the third, but this may not always be the case.

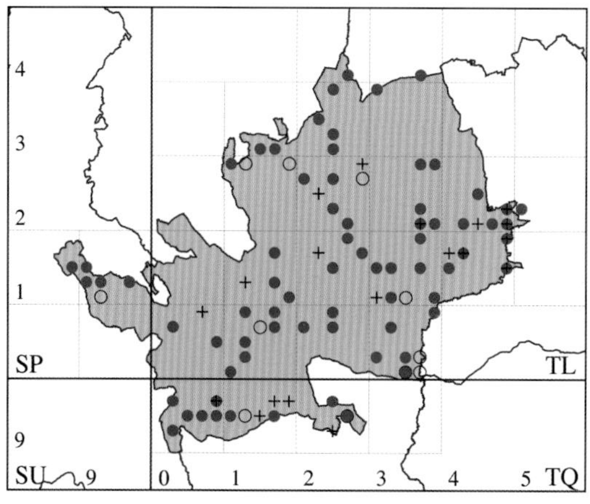

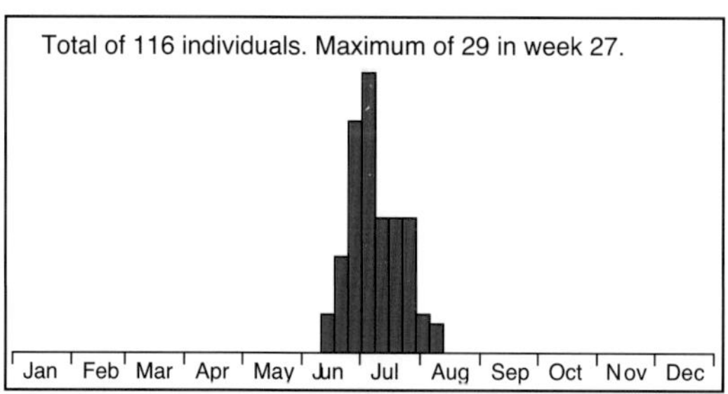

0162 *Cossus cossus* (L.) Goat moth

Recorded: 1873 – 1999
Distribution / Status: Extremely Local or absent / Extremely rare resident, perhaps extinct
Conservation status: UK BAP Priority Species; Herts Endangered
Caterpillar food plants: oak; Ash; Aspen; Balsam poplar; poplar – under the bark of large girth live timber
Flight period: Not recorded. Elsewhere, June/July
Records in database: 16

In the London Area, which adjoins the southern boundary area of Hertfordshire, I recorded Goat Moth as *'an extremely local and very rare resident. Declining and considered to be in danger of extinction in the London Area'* (Plant, 1993). Almost identical

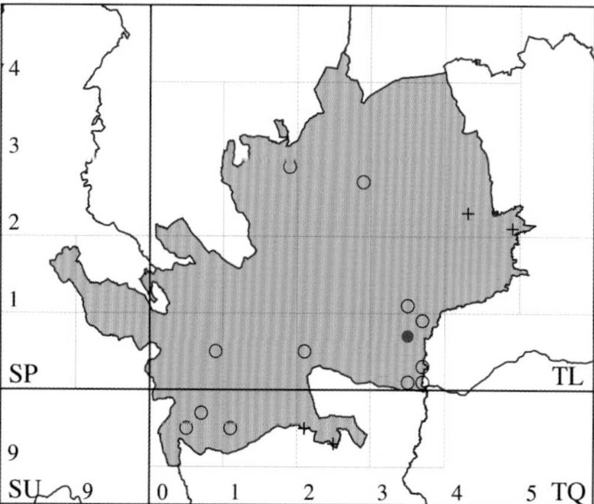

comments are now applied to Hertfordshire, from where it may or may not already have vanished. J. H. James (1875. *Transactions of the Watford Natural History Society* **1**: 64) records an oak tree on his farm at Kingswood, Watford, affected by goat moth larvae 'for the last three years' Upon felling the tree in April 1875, he recorded larvae of various ages in profusion in the east side of the trunk, but none on the western aspect. This gives us our earliest county record. Our latest is at the Danemead Nature Reserve, where an affected oak tree was discovered by myself in 1999. However, none of the larval workings appeared to be populated and the characteristic smell of goat was absent. The tree appeared to have been excessively 'worked' for larvae and, judging from the large pile of chiselled timber and the extent of the damage, a degree of restraint might better have been exercised. Prior to this, the last Hertfordshire record was made by Ian Lorimer at Totteridge in 1979. Foster (1916), had the moth as 'Common everywhere [in north Hertfordshire] in larval stage', but this statement is not supported by the list of localities that Foster has presented in various publications over the years. Indeed, the map above shows only two north Hertfordshire localities. Later (Foster, 1937) he extends the range of this large moth to 'Common in the county, frequently destructive', but did not support this statement by listing any localities. In reality, the moth has evidently always been local in its Hertfordshire distribution, but typically was abundant when found. For example, during 1892 over 200 larvae were discovered "wandering about a small walled garden in Station Road, Hitchin in search of a place to spin up. Two or three young aspen trees in the garden were literally riddled with 'goat-holes' (Gibbs, 1893). Although there were clearly lots of larvae, this relates to a single garden. There are no other records for the Hitchin area and the only other report from north Hertfordshire comes from Walkern, in 1940 (J. Birdsall). The statement that it was 'very common' in the Cheshunt area' (Boyd, 1901) holds slightly greater credence as our map indicates, and it seems possible that the Lea Valley may have been one region where the moth might have affected a wider area. With this in mind, it is interesting that all the records mapped are coincident with water courses.

All our reports of this species relate to larvae and we do not appear have a record of a wild caught adult in the county.

ZYGAENOIDEA

ZYGAENIDAE

A familiar group of moths that contains two major groups – the Foresters and the Burnets. All are aposematic – they are brightly coloured and contain toxins in all stages that render them at least inedible, if not directly poisonous to predators. In Hertfordshire, we boast records of two of the three British species of Forester Moth, though one is extinct here and the other possibly so. Of the Burnets, we have three out of the seven British species, two of which are common and one of which is no longer present and is represented by a single reliable record.

0163 *Adscita statices* (L.) Forester

Recorded:	1828 – 1947
Distribution / Status:	Absent / Extinct resident
Conservation status:	UK BAP Priority Species. Herts Extinct
Caterpillar food plants:	Not recorded. Elsewhere on Sorrel
Flight period:	Not recorded. Elsewhere, late May to late July
Records in database:	13

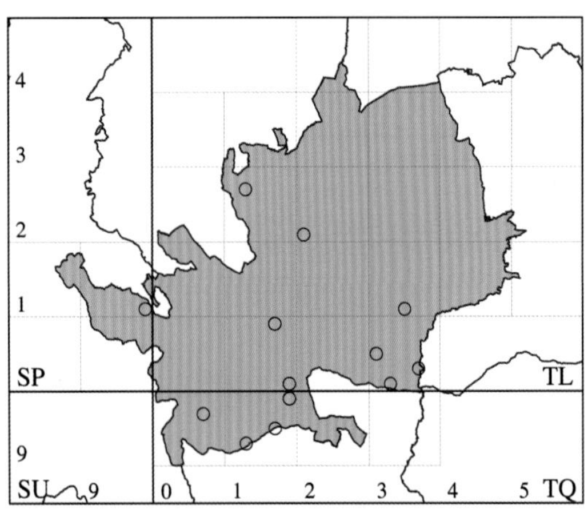

The Forester has never been a common moth in Hertfordshire, but plotting all the records on the map shows clearly that it was once resident in the south and west of the county on clay-dominated soils. A record from Lilley Hoo, made in 1893 by F. Latchmore and represented by the most northerly open circle on our map, in TL 1226, is in a chalk-dominated landscape, but reference to the soils map of the county on page 8 shows that the site in fact rests on a small band of decalcified boulder clay that runs between two chalk outcrops then extends south-eastwards and also supports a Knebworth record at TL 2120. Our first record is the painting of an example taken at 'Hertford' (Stephens, 1828); the last reliable record of the Forester in Hertfordshire was made in 1947, at Cheshunt. In between, dated records are from the Sandridge area (Griffith, 1884), Wormley, 1894 by Edelsten, Haileybury, 1888 by Bowyer, Goffs Oak (Boyd, 1901), Green Street and Shenley prior to 1902 by A. E. Gibbs and Knebworth in 1916 by Durrant (Foster, 1916). Foster (1937) also lists undated records from Berkhamsted School, Rowse [*sic*] Barn Lane, Watford (Spencer, Heaton) and a railway bank at Oxhey (Rowland-Brown), Aldbury (Rothschild). It is clear that most of these last few pre-date the 1937 publication by several years; although the last record was as late as 1947, this moth appears to have vanished from the Hertfordshire fauna in the early years of the twentieth century.

0164 *Adscita geryon* (Hb.) Cistus Forester

Recorded:	1899 – 1992
Distribution / Status:	Extremely local or absent / Extremely rare resident or extinct
Conservation status:	Herts Endangered or Extinct
Caterpillar food plants:	Not recorded. Elsewhere on rock rose
Flight period:	June
Records in database:	9

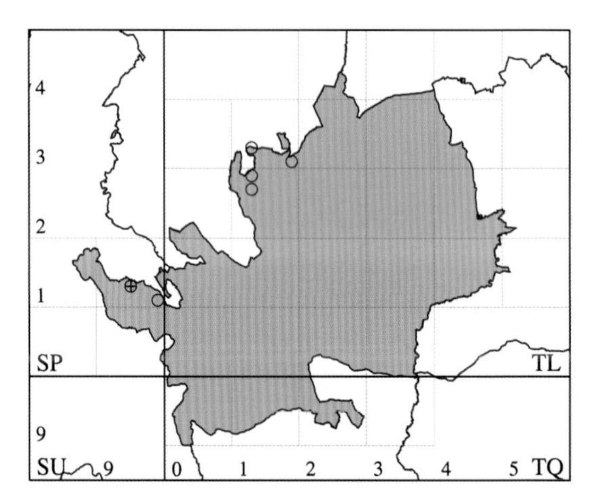

Our only recent records are from Aldbury Nowers in the extreme west of the county on the border with Buckinghamshire. Alan Bernard last saw it there on 13th June 1981 and again during June 1982 whilst two were seen by Trevor James on 6th June 1992. Thorough site searches in this area during 2004 failed to reveal any at all, which was not especially surprising given the exceedingly degraded state of the chalk grassland. Records from 'Tring' by Goodson in 1904, given in Gibbs (1905) and in Foster (1937) all relate to Aldbury Nowers. It was abundant at Pegsdon Hills on both the Hertfordshire and Bedfordshire side in the period around the First World War (Foster, 1916), but the last record held by the current Bedfordshire macro-moth recorder for Pegsdon Hills was made on 23rd June 1947 by the late Sydney Bowden. Foster's 1937 county list gives records from Hitchin, Lilley Hoo and hills near Hexton, Berkhamsted, Apsley End and Tring. Two years later, Hodgson (1939) lists this moth as locally common on the downs at Ashridge and Aldbury Nowers. There are records between 1977 and 1982 for Dunstable Downs in Bedfordshire, but the moth does not appear to have flown across the Whipsnade to Dunstable road on a day when an entomologist was present and so we cannot count any Dunstable records for the Hertfordshire vice-county! The last Bedfordshire record in any case was in 1987 – also just outside our boundary (at Bison Hill, SP 9918).

It seems then, that the Cistus Forester was once a feature of the narrow band of chalk grasslands that affect the extreme north-west edge of Hertfordshire on the border with Bedfordshire and Buckinghamshire. This is no longer the case and although it is possible, perhaps even likely, that a few overlooked populations persist in this area today, there can be no doubt that the moth has been lost from most of its former sites. The cause of this decline is likely to relate to habitat loss through scrub-invasion. This may have been a direct consequence of the loss of rabbits through myxomatosis during the 1950s, but there is an unfortunate gap in the records from the early part of the twentieth century to the 1980s. If nothing else, this provides a real-life example of why repeat records from the same site year after year *are* important.

0169 *Zygaena filipendulae* (L.) ssp. *stephensi* Dupont Six-spot Burnet

Recorded: 1887 – 2006
Distribution / Status: Widespread / Common resident
Conservation status: No perceived threats
Caterpillar food plants: Bird's-foot trefoil. Elsewhere also on Slender Bird's-foot Trefoil
Flight period: Mid-June to mid-August
Records in database: 124

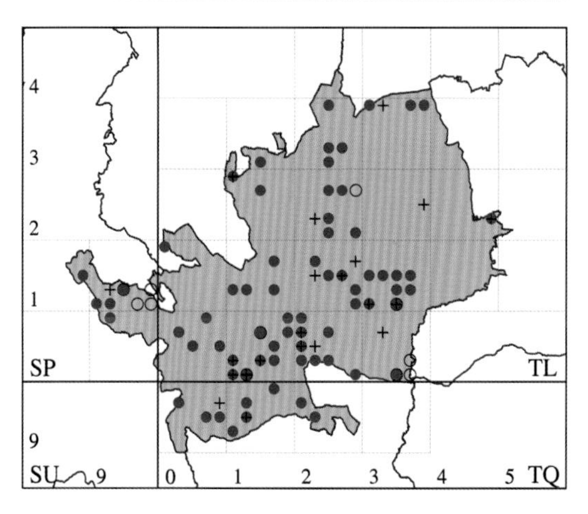

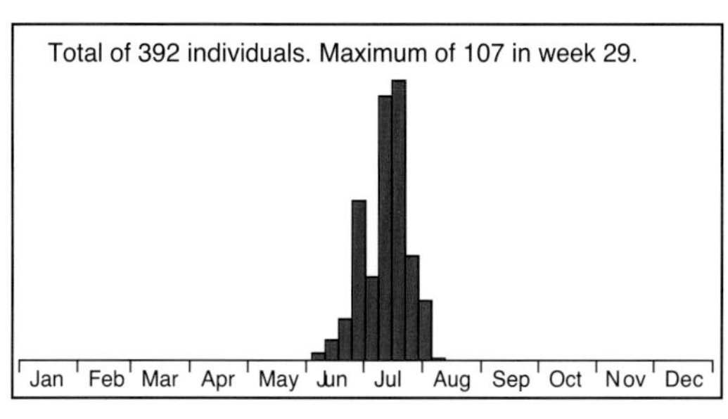

The nominate subspecies *filipendulae* Linnaeus is not found in Britain, where it is replaced by *stephensi* Dupont. Almost all published lists of moths from any part of Hertfordshire include this species which was given by Foster, in his 1937 county list as 'Noted from all districts'. This remains more or less the case today, with both the caterpillars and the day-flying adults being found just about everywhere that the foodplant grows. The exception may prove to be in parts of the arable and largely featureless north-east sector which, although certainly under-recorded in comparison with the remainder of the county, supports few areas where the foodplant is able to thrive. An example with the normal left hind wing replaced with the forewing pattern – a case of extreme homoeosis – emerged on 2nd July 1949 from a wild pupa taken at Therfield Heath (Hyde, 1951. *Proceedings of the South London Entomological & Natural History Society 1949 – 50*: 34 & Plate 3, Fig. F). Examination of the Plate that accompanies the report also shows clearly that the shape of the left hind wing is that of a typical forewing.

0170 *Zygaena trifolii* (Esp.) Five-spot Burnet

Recorded: 1894 – 1894
Distribution / Status: Absent / Extinct
Conservation status: Herts Extinct
Caterpillar food plants: Not recorded
Flight period: Not recorded
Records in database: 1

Separating this species from the very similar 171: Narrow-bordered Five-spot Burnet is likely to prove extremely difficult for the inexperienced. It takes the form of two subspecies: ssp. *decreta* Verity is associated with Large Bird's-foot Trefoil in wet habitats whilst ssp. *palustrella* Verity is associated with ordinary Bird's-foot Trefoil on chalkland sites. In terms of the wider national picture, the Five-spot Burnet is to be found on the western edge of England and Wales and along the southern edge of England as far east as about Sussex, whilst the Narrow-bordered Five-spot Burnet is found throughout the rest of England (including Hertfordshire) and very sparingly in both Scotland and Ireland. There is a limited amount of overlap in the range of the two species, but Hertfordshire is well outside this 'danger zone'. Thus, all records of the pair in our county *ought* to relate to the Narrow-bordered Five-spot Burnet. However, there are a number of claimed occurrences of *Z. trifolii* for Hertfordshire; these require careful examination. Records from Oughton Head and St Ipollyts 'on marshy ground' in 1892 given in Gibbs (1893), are also mentioned by Foster (1916) who says that these relate to 'the marsh form var. *palustris*' [now called *decreta*] and credits the records to Tutt (recording the sites as Ippolyts Common and Oughton Head Common). He goes on to say that at the Ippolyts Common site there have been no records for the past five years [to 1916], but that at the Oughton Head site both 'the type and var. *palustris* are still very abundant'. He concludes by saying that 'Other localities for the type are Pegsdon Hills, Royston, North Road [the A1 Great North Road], near Gravely, Willbury Hill and Offley Park'. He also lists Narrow-bordered Five-spot Burnet on the same page, but says that it is very scarce with only one site near Hitchin. Hitchin, Hemel Hempstead, Cheshunt, Bayford, Watford, Berkhamsted and Broxbourne are all listed for this species by Foster (1937). In 1934 – 35 there was said to be a small colony on the south side of Berkhamsted Common, but it had disappeared when this information was published by Hodgson (1939). More recently, at least in terms of publication date, there is one open-circle record shown for ten-kilometre square TL 30, indicating a 1960 record, volume 2 of *The Moths and Butterflies of Great Britain and Ireland* (Harley Books). The square TL 30 is entirely within vice county 20 and is the one that includes the Broxbourne Woods complex. This chapter was prepared by W. G. Tremewan, one of the world's foremost authorities on the Zygaenidae, to whom I am grateful for helpful correspondence in this matter. Gerry Tremewan wrote, in March 2005: 'I can no longer remember where in Hertfordshire the record for the open circle came from, but it must have been genuine, otherwise I would not have accepted it. However, I do remember that there was a record for Broxbourne in 1894, (cited by Tutt, 1899, *Nat. Hist. Br. Lepidoptera* **1:** 498) and I think this must refer to one published in the literature. Tutt cites the recorder as Battley. I do remember reading a note that said that the species was so common that the "air was red with them" or something to that effect. Moreover, comments on the variation showed that it was *trifolii*, not *lonicerae*. Regarding the other references you cite, I obviously did not accept them for one reason or another. The problem in those days was that almost always people cited *'trifolii'* when it should have been *lonicerae*. Apart from a genuine record from Norfolk during the past decade or so, the wetland subspecies of *trifolii* [= ssp. *decreta* Verity] seems to be extinct in south-east England. Moreover, *lonicerae* does occur in wetlands where the larvae feeds on *Lotus uliginosus*, to make matters complicated! See Tremewan, 1980, *Entomologist's Gazette* **31**: 143-143; 1982, *Entomologist's Gazette* **33**: 9-11'. On the basis of this expert opinion I am inclined to dismiss all but the 1894 Broxbourne record.

0171 *Zygaena lonicerae* (Schev.) Narrow-bordered Five-Spot Burnet

Recorded:	1887 – 2006
Distribution / Status:	Widespread / Common resident
Conservation status:	No perceived threats
Caterpillar food plants:	Not recorded. Elsewhere mainly on Red Clover and Meadow Vetchling
Flight period:	Mid-June to early August
Records in database:	100

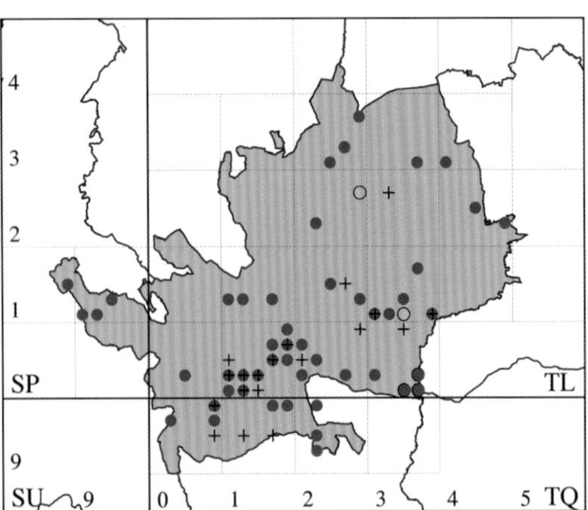

Confusion between this species and 170: Five-spot Burnet has been discussed above and all recent reports of Five-spot Burnet have been treated as referring to Narrow-bordered Five-spots. The present day distribution indicates a widespread and common species with a pattern that is remarkably similar to that of the Six-spot Burnet. It seems surprising that all of our records relate to adults and that the highly distinctive caterpillars appear never to have been found.

LIMACODIDAE

A small family of only around 15 species in the Palaearctic Region, of which two occur in Britain. One species has been reported in a published work as occurring in Hertfordshire, but this record is unreliable. The family is not represented in the Hertfordshire fauna.

[0173 *Apoda limacodes* (Hufn.) Festoon

The Festoon is an extremely local species of ancient beech and oak woodlands in the southern part of England and Hertfordshire is outside both its known and its expected ranges. A single record of this species from a garden in central Hertfordshire on 17th July 1999 is not supported by either a voucher specimen or a photograph and cannot be substantiated.]

TINEOIDEA

PSYCHIDAE

The psychids are amongst our least well-recorded moths. Sometimes referred to as 'bag worms' the larvae feed on lichens, algae and similar material on tree trunks, walls and elsewhere from within a silk case that is decorated externally with bits of vegetation, dead insects and other debris. A key to cases may be found in volume 2 of *Moths and Butterflies of Great Britain and Ireland*. Fully-winged females are found in only two of the British species – 175: *Narycia duplicella* and 180: *Diplodoma laichartingella* – both of which are recorded in Hertfordshire. In the remainder the females lack wings, legs and antennae and never leave the larval case. Three species, *Dahlica triquetrella*, *D. lichenella* and *Luffia ferchaultella*, are parthenogenetic (reproduce without sex). Males of both the *Dahlica* species are known from elsewhere in Europe, but apparently not from Britain; neither species is yet recorded from Hertfordshire, but may be overlooked here. The offspring of parthenogenesis possess only half the number of chromosomes (because any male contribution via spermatozoa is absent) and are referred to as 'haploid' (individuals with a full set of chromosomes are 'diploid'). Some may be surprised to discover that this condition is quite prevalent in nature. For example, it is found in many of the insects that create galls on plants, especially on oak. Periodically, mating between males and females does take place to produce diploid individuals; these then continue to reproduce parthenogenetically. This cycle is often referred to as the 'alternation of generations'. It seems improbable that a species could survive in the very long term in a purely haploid form and it is surmised here that males of the *Dahlica* species are therefore probably overlooked in Britain. There is some debate over the status of *Luffia ferchaultella* and many consider that it is not a distinct species, but is instead a form of *L. lapidella* (Goeze) – which does have a male form. This view is shared by the present author, who regards the female of *ferchaultella* as a haploid form of *lapidella*. Seven of the eighteen 'species' reliably recorded in Britain are so far known from Hertfordshire. All are very much under-recorded and the possibility exists that other species have been overlooked.

0175 *Narycia duplicella* Goeze = *monilifera* (Geoff.) sensu Bradley, 2000

Recorded:	1900 – 2004
Distribution / Status:	Local / Resident
Conservation status:	Herts Scarce
Caterpillar food plants:	Not recorded. Presumed on lichens on tree trunks
Flight period:	Not recorded. Elsewhere June and July
Records in database:	3

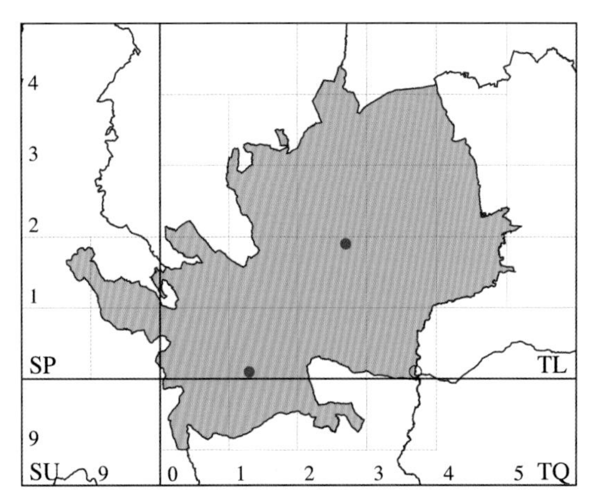

Our earliest record is from Cheshunt in about 1900, perhaps earlier (Boyd, 1901) and since then there have been just two encounters with this moth – near Datchworth on 29th July 1997 (Steve Palmer) and larval cases at Bricket Wood on 28th March 2004 (Mark Sterling).

0180 *Diplodoma laichartingella* Goeze = *herminata* (Geoff.) sensu Bradley, 2000

Recorded:	1900 – 2004
Distribution / Status:	Local / Resident
Conservation status:	Herts Scarce
Caterpillar food plants:	Not recorded. Cases found on Hornbeam
Flight period:	June. Elsewhere, May/June
Records in database:	5

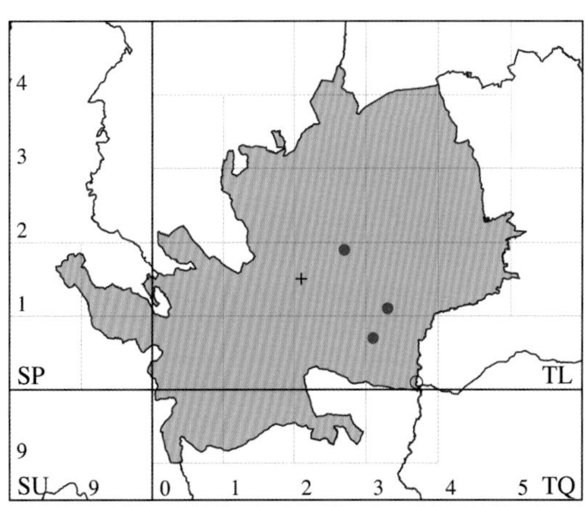

Our only old record is from Cheshunt, made at the end of the nineteenth century by Boyd (1901). It has been recorded in recent years from Dowdells Wood, April 1993 (Raymond Uffen), Datchworth in 1996 (Steve Palmer), Balls Park, Hertford in 2001 (Colin Plant) and Wormley Wood in 2004 (Mark Cooper).

0181 *Taleporia tubulosa* (Retzius)

Recorded:	1834 – 2005
Distribution / Status:	Local / Resident
Conservation status:	Herts Scarce
Caterpillar food plants:	Not recorded. Cases found on beech
Flight period:	Not recorded. Elsewhere May and June
Records in database:	7

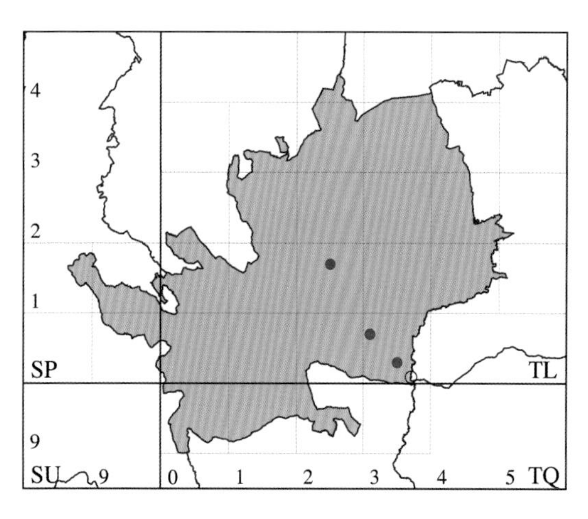

Our first record is that given by J. F. Stephens for 'Hertford' in *Illustrations of British Entomology* **4**: 233 (published in 1834). This record is not mapped as Stephens applied the label of 'Hertford' to a very wide area of Hertfordshire. There are nineteenth century records from the Sandridge area (Griffith, 1890) and Cheshunt (Boyd, 1901). Since then, we have three reports, from Harmer Green Wood, where Raymond Uffen found larval cases in January 2001, from Hobbs Close, Cheshunt in 2004 and from Old Grove in December 2005 – the last two by Mark Cooper.

0185 *Luffia ferchaultella* (Stephens)

Recorded:	1987 – 2006
Distribution / Status:	Widespread / Resident
Conservation status:	No perceived threats
Caterpillar food plants:	Green algae on a wooden garage door; cases also found on trunks of beech, oak and lime, on fence posts
Adult period:	Not recorded
Records in database:	9

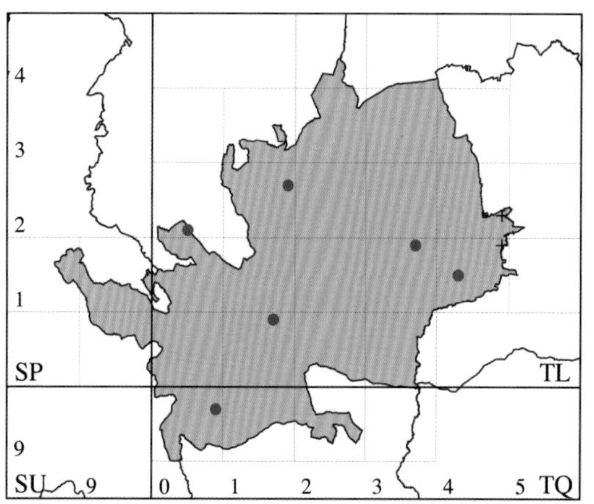

A thriving population of this wingless species existed for many years on the green algae growing on the late Charles Watson's untreated, wooden, garage doors in Bishops Stortford, first noted there in 1987. Most of the scattered other records are from tree trunks and a few are from old, well-rotten fence posts covered in algae and lichens. This moth is surely under-recorded and is likely to be present in most of Hertfordshire.

0186 *Psyche casta* (Pallas)

Recorded: 1890 – 2006
Distribution / Status: Widespread / Common resident
Conservation status: No perceived threats
Caterpillar food plants: Not recorded. Larval cases found in many situations
Flight period: May and June
Records in database: 42

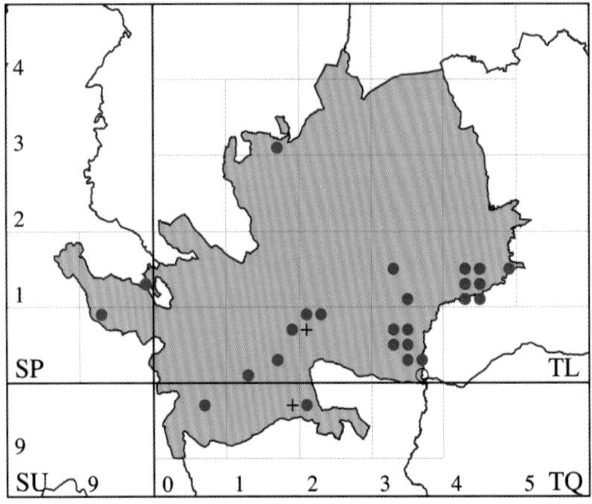

Our earliest record is from the Sandridge area (Griffith, 1890). The distinctive larval cases are currently frequent low down on the trunks of trees of a great many species, on fence posts, grave stones, walls and various plants in the south of the county and the insect is likely to be pretty much everywhere here. However, cases appear to be much harder to find in the north-east of the county and in places here are perhaps genuinely absent. Adults are occasionally caught in light traps.

0188 *Proutia betulina* (Zeller)

Recorded: 1980 – 2000
Distribution / Status: Local / Resident
Conservation status: Herts Rare
Caterpillar food plants: Not recorded
Flight period: Late May to July
Records in database: 3

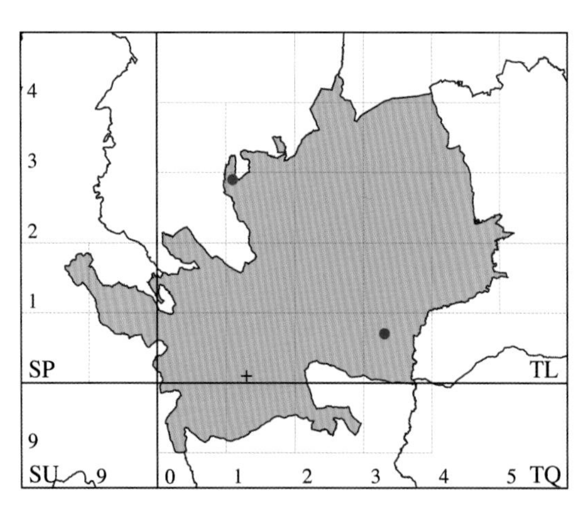

This is apparently a scarce species in Hertfordshire, with just three records – from Bricket Wood in 1980 (Maitland Emmet) and Broxbourne Wood and Hexton Chalk Pit in 2000 (Raymond Uffen). At the national level, it appears to be largely confined to the south-east and it is probably genuinely rare in Hertfordshire.

0189 *Epichnopterix plumella* ([D. & S.])

Recorded: 1834 – 1995
Distribution / Status: Local / Resident
Conservation status: No perceived threats
Caterpillar food plants: Not recorded. Elsewhere on grasses
Flight period: Not recorded. Elsewhere, May/June
Records in database: 4

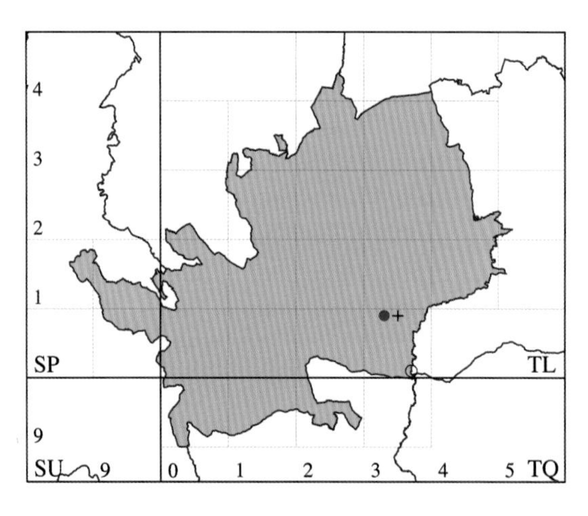

Listed by J. F. Stephens for 'Hertford' in *Illustrations of British Entomology* **2**: 82 (published in 1829) and from Cheshunt in the late nineteenth century (Boyd, 1901), there are no further records until 1977 when it was found at Hoddesdon Park Wood by David Agassiz and 1995 when cases were found by Raymond Uffen at Highfield Wood, Brickendon.

TINEIDAE

This group of 'micro' moths includes the once familiar 'clothes moths', many of which have declined drastically in the last fifty or so years as natural fibres such as wool and cotton have been gradually replaced by synthetics such a rayon and nylon. Out-of-doors, they are threatened as a group by the modern trend of 'tidying' woodland and other habitats. The need for specialist searching for larvae and the requirement to rear and dissect adults of many species for successful identification has resulted in many people neglecting the group, with the result that it is very poorly-studied in Hertfordshire. A total of 61 species of tineid is listed in John Bradley's checklist, published in 2000, though some of these are importations with produce from overseas and the number of resident species, including some now regarded as extinct, is just under 50. In our county, we have records for 26 species, though the records for three of these (211: *Haplotinea ditella*, 239: *Tinea columbariella* and 243: *Tinea dubiella*) are not supported by data.

0196 *Morophaga choragella* ([D.& S.])

Recorded: 1901 - 2006
Distribution / Status: Widespread / Common
Conservation status: No perceived threats
Caterpillar food: Not recorded. Elsewhere in bracket fungi and rotting wood
Flight period: June to August.
Records in database: 39

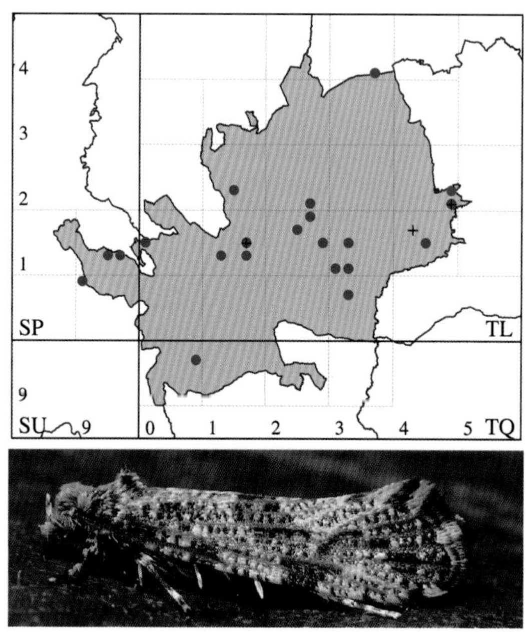

Meyrick lists Hertfordshire for this moth in his 1928 *Handbook* whilst Foster (1937) lists this species (as *Scardia boleti* Fabr.) as reared in considerable numbers from 'Broxbourne' by Fryer. Sir John C. F. Fryer lived from 1886 – 1947. The large size and markedly bipectinate (feathery) antennae render this species immediately recognisable. It is an expected species in Hertfordshire woodlands and so may be absent from large areas of the north-east of the county, which is largely an arable desert.

0199 *Psychoides verhuella* Bruand

Recorded: 2006 only
Distribution / Status: Local / Rare resident
Conservation status: Herts Rare
Caterpillar food: Fronds and sporangia of Hart's-tongue Fern
Flight period: No data. Elsewhere, June and July
Records in database: 1

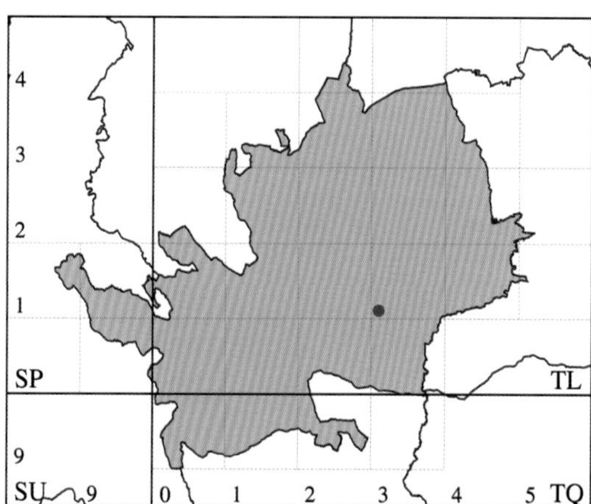

At Bayfordbury Pinetum Grotto, on 4th May 2006, Raymond Uffen managed to find one larva and one pupa of this species under the spores of a leaf of Hart's-tongue Fern along with a vacated mine alongside the midrib of the leaf. This is the only Hertfordshire record for this moth, which is expected in the south-west of England, but is rather unusual here. Raymond and others have been searching Hart's-tongue Fern for this moth for some while and failed to find it elsewhere; given the nature of the locality the possibility exists that the foodplant could have been brought in from elsewhere in Britain.

0203 *Infurcitinea argentimaculella* (Stt.)

Recorded: 2006 only
Distribution / Status: Local / Common
Conservation status: Herts Scarce
Caterpillar food: *Lepraria* (a lichen) on tree trunks
Flight period: Not recorded. Elsewhere, July/August
Records in database: 4

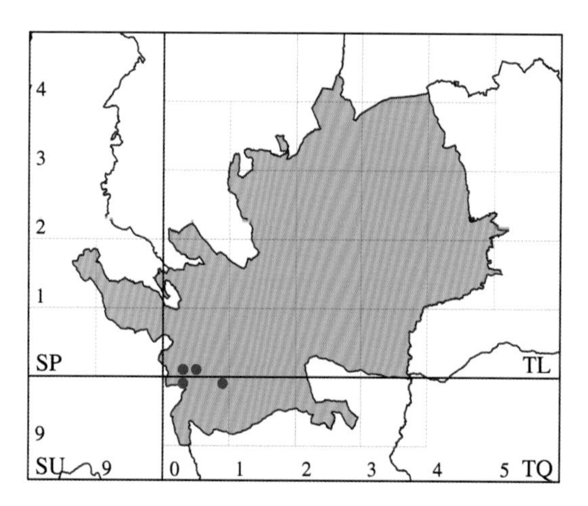

This species is mapped for Hertfordshire in volume 2 of *Moths and butterflies of Great Britain and Ireland*, but the late Maitland Emmet, who produced the maps, was not in possession of the supporting data for the record. The larvae feed from a distinctive silk tunnel constructed on lichens growing on walls and tree trunks, but since few people can recognise these the species is certainly overlooked. The recent discovery that it is quite common in another county led to the realisation that several distinguished colleagues had overlooked it for want of experience. During September 2007, Seth Gibson made a trip to Hertfordshire specifically to find this species and succeeded in doing so at Whippendell Woods (a larval tube on Scots Pine and another on oak), Dawes Common (five on oak), Woodman's Wood (one on hawthorn) and Chipperfield Common (six on Scots Pine). Though these are technically beyond the December 2006 cut-off date for records there can be no doubt that the adult moths were present at all four sites prior to 2007.

0211 *Haplotinea ditella* (Pierce & Metcalfe)

This species is mapped for Hertfordshire in volume 2 (1985) of *Moths and butterflies of Great Britain and Ireland* but the late Maitland Emmet, who produced the maps, was not in possession of the supporting data for the record. The adult moth requires dissection for separation from *H. insectella*; the latter is not yet recorded in Hertfordshire, but both species are present in surrounding counties and are probably overlooked.

0215 *Nemapogon granella* (L.) Corn Moth

Recorded: 1889 – 1997
Distribution / Status: Local / Uncommon
Conservation status: Insufficiently known
Caterpillar food: Not recorded. Elsewhere on stored vegetable products indoors and outdoors in bracket fungi
Flight period: May (one record). Continuously brooded elsewhere
Records in database: 4

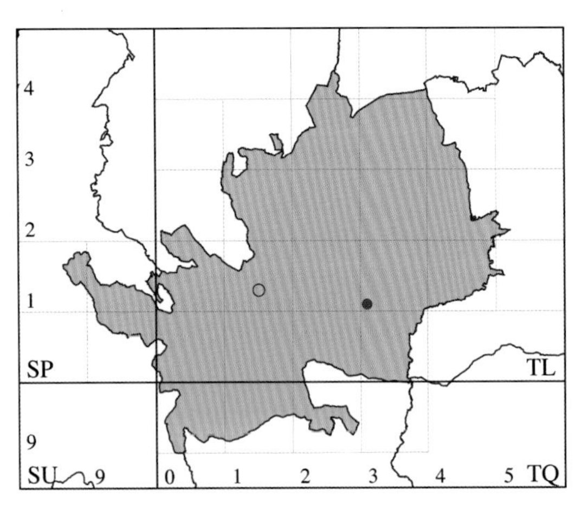

Recorded in the area east of Bamville Wood Farm, near Harpenden Common (Gibbs, 1889). In March 1905, Gibbs (*Trans. Herts.* **12**: 159 – 164) lists the 'first county record' from St Albans, caught by himself, in 1904. The specimen was identified by both Revd. E. N. Bloomfield and C. G. Barrett. It is unclear how Gibbs overlooked his own earlier record from Bamville Wood Farm, but reality suggests he was probably just having a bad day when he prepared his report as he also overlooked earlier records of 1736**:** *Catarhoe cuculata* which he claimed as new to the county on the same page. One year earlier, his annual report had been prepared and presented by P. J. Barraud (*Trans. Herts.* **12**: 21 – 25) because Gibbs 'has been seriously ill'. Foster (1937) also lists Letchworth. More recently, there is a single record from Bayfordbury in 1997 (Raymond Uffen).

0216 *Nemapogon cloacella* (Haw.) Cork Moth

Recorded: 1967 – 2005
Distribution / Status: Local / Resident
Conservation status: No perceived threats
Caterpillar food: *Ganoderma* sp. and other unidentified bracket fungi on trees. Elsewhere on bracket fungi outdoors; occasionally indoors on stored vegetable products
Flight period: May to August
Records in database: 30

This species is first recorded in the county from St Albans, within two or three miles of the Town Hall, in the period before 1889 (Gibbs, 1889). Whilst there is no reason to suppose that the record is incorrect, this species was confused with *N. ruricolella* and for many years *ruricolella* Stt. was treated as a synonym of *cloacella*, For this reason, older, unconfirmed records are excluded from the map, which presents only those records that have been verified by examination of a specimen.

0217 *Nemapogon wolffiella* Karsh. & Niels.

This moth was added to the county fauna by A. E. Gibbs (as *Tinea albipunctella*) from the St Albans area in June 1902 (Barraud, 1903). The record cannot be accurately mapped and there are no other known occurrences in the county.

0218 *Nemapogon variatella* (Clemens)

Recorded: 2006 only
Distribution / Status: Local / Uncommon
Conservation status: Insufficiently known
Caterpillar food: Unidentified fungus
Flight period: Elsewhere, March to August
Records in database: 1

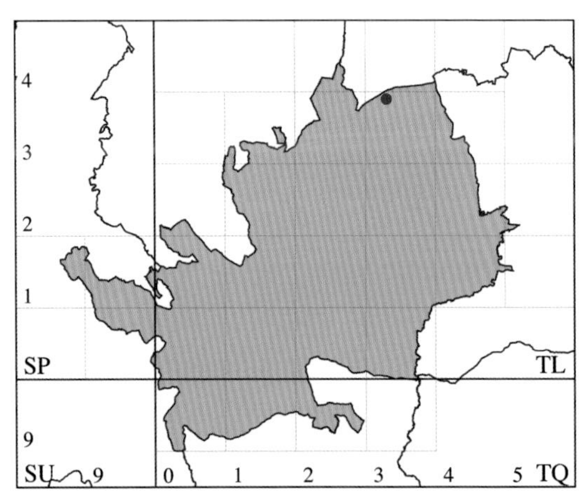

Brian Elliot reared adults during May 2007 from an unidentified fungus collected from a rot hole in a Beech tree in Fox Covert Nature Reserve, on 21st April 2007. On the basis that the female must have laid eggs during 2006, this species qualifies for inclusion in this review, which considers records up to 31st December 2006. Large numbers of adults were reared. It is likely that this species will be present in other areas of the county.

0219 *Nemapogon ruricolella* (Stt.)

Recorded: 2002 – 2005
Distribution / Status: Local / Uncommon
Conservation status: Insufficiently known
Caterpillar food: Not recorded. Elsewhere in bracket fungi and rotten wood
Flight period: June to August
Records in database: 6

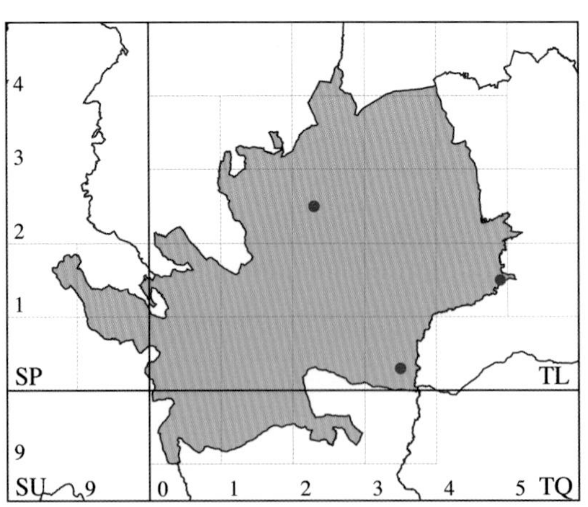

The most southerly dot on the map, at Barnet, was actually made about 100 metres into Middlesex, but the garden where it was recorded is part of a continuous habitat that straddles the border and it would be incredible to suppose that the moth's range ended at this invisible line. Other records are from Marshall's Heath, Hertford and Bishops Stortford. All four sites coincide neatly with garden light traps whose operators actively seek out and name the 'micros' and there can be no doubt that equal or greater effort applied elsewhere would also turn up this species.

0220 *Nemapogon clematella* (Fabr.)

Recorded:	1889 – 2004
Distribution / Status:	Local / Resident
Conservation status:	Herts Scarce
Caterpillar food:	Not recorded. Elsewhere, on fungus *Hypoxylon fuscum* growing on dead Hazel
Flight period:	June to August
Records in database:	9

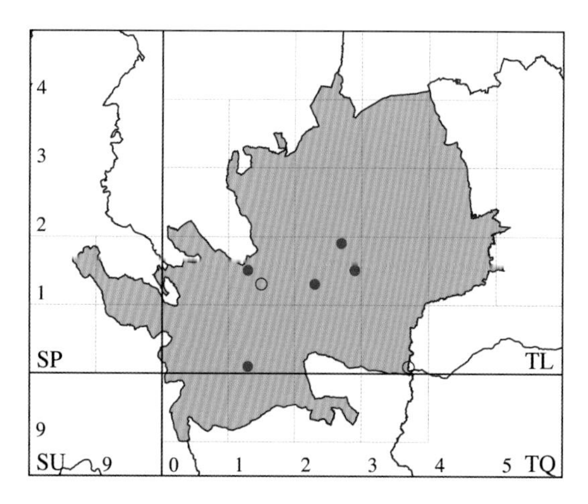

Recorded in the area east of Bamville Wood Farm, near Harpenden Common (Gibbs, 1889) and also noted from Sandridge (Griffith, 1890) and Cheshunt (Boyd, 1901) in the nineteenth century and at Harpenden (Fryer) at the start of the twentieth. More recently, this distinctive and rather pretty moth, which is unlikely to be confused with other species, is surprisingly under-represented in the records.

0223 *Nemaxera betulinella* (Paykull)

Recorded:	1937 – 2000
Distribution / Status:	Local / Uncommon
Conservation status:	Herts Rare
Caterpillar food:	Not recorded. Elsewhere in bracket fungi and rotten wood
Flight period:	Late July (one record). Elsewhere, May to August
Records in database:	2

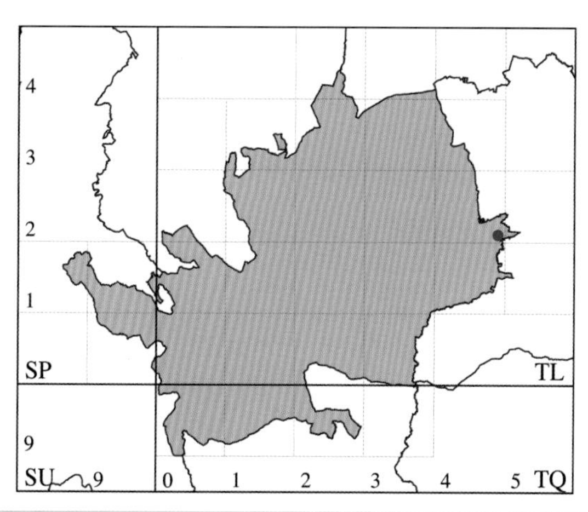

Foster (1937) lists '*Tinea costicella* Curt.' from Ashridge by Fryer; this is presumably a typographical error for *corticella* Curtis, 1834 – a synonym of the present species. The record is not mapped as the precise location is unclear. Our only other record is from the light trap in my own garden at Bishops Stortford on 28th July 2000.

0224 *Triaxomera parasitella* (Hb.)

Recorded:	1890 – 2006
Distribution / Status:	Local / Uncommon
Conservation status:	Insufficiently known
Caterpillar food:	Not recorded. Elsewhere in bracket fungi and rotten wood
Flight period:	May to June. Elsewhere, May to August
Records in database:	11

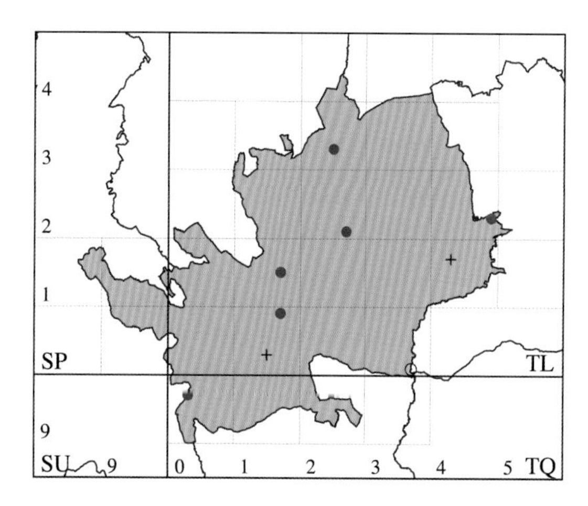

Foster (1937) tells us of records from Sandridge (Griffith), Cheshunt (Boyd), Knebworth (Edwards), Ashridge and Broxbourne (Fryer); the first two are from the last twenty years or so of the 1800s and the last two are more likely to have been made between 1900 and 1937. The six records made post-1994 indicate a species that is probably under-recorded in many parts of the county.

0225 *Triaxomera fulvimitrella* Sodof.

Recorded:	Pre-1937
Distribution / Status:	Absent / Extinct
Conservation status:	Herts Extinct
Caterpillar food:	Not recorded. Elsewhere in bracket fungi and rotten wood
Flight period:	Not recorded. Elsewhere, May to July
Records in database:	1

The only Hertfordshire record of this species, whose larvae feed in bracket fungi and on fungal hyphae inside rotten wood, is from Ashridge (Fryer), given in Foster (1937) and relating to the early part of the twentieth century. The Ashridge Estate spans the Hertfordshire Buckinghamshire border yet, in keeping with almost all of Foster's other summarised reports, no more precise detail is given. Since it was reported as a Hertfordshire moth, and there is no evidence to the contrary, I assume it was found on our side of the border!

0227 *Monopis laevigella* ([D.& S.]) Skin Moth = *rusticella* (Hb.)

Recorded:	1885 – 2006
Distribution / Status:	Probably Widespread / Common resident
Conservation status:	No perceived threats
Caterpillar food:	Reared from Blackbird and Song Thrush nests. Elsewhere on dry dead mammals and birds, dry owl pellets and similar
Flight period:	May to September
Records in database:	23

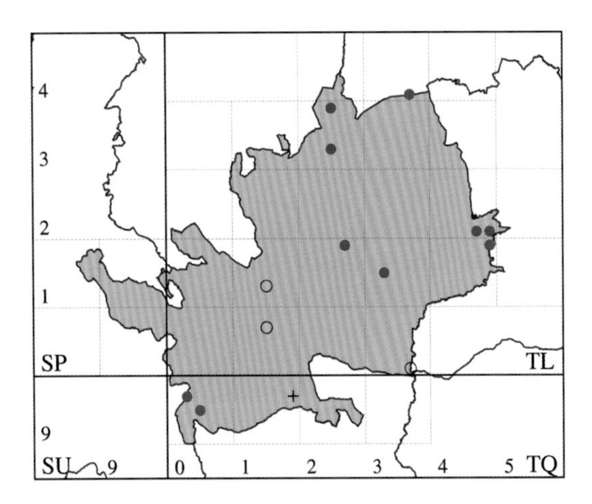

Although 228: *M. weaverella* was described in 1858, there seems to have been some reluctance to treat this species as separate from *laevigella* until Banks (1910) provided clarification. Thus, the earliest published records of *laevigella*, from Hitchin (Durrant, 1885), the St Albans area (Gibbs, 1889) and near Harpenden Common (Gibbs, 1889) are taken on trust that they are this species. Regrettably, none of these are dated and so it is unclear which is the earliest. Boyd (1901) also lists Cheshunt and Foster (1937) adds Letchworth in 1918 (Edwards) and Bushey Heath, undated (Hervey). Modern-day records indicate it is likely to be a fairly widespread and not uncommon moth in most parts of the county.

0228 *Monopis weaverella* (Scott)

Recorded:	1972 – 2006
Distribution / Status:	Local / Resident
Conservation status:	No perceived threats
Caterpillar food:	Not recorded. Elsewhere, reared from dry fox faeces and dry dead mammals
Flight period:	May to August
Records in database:	26

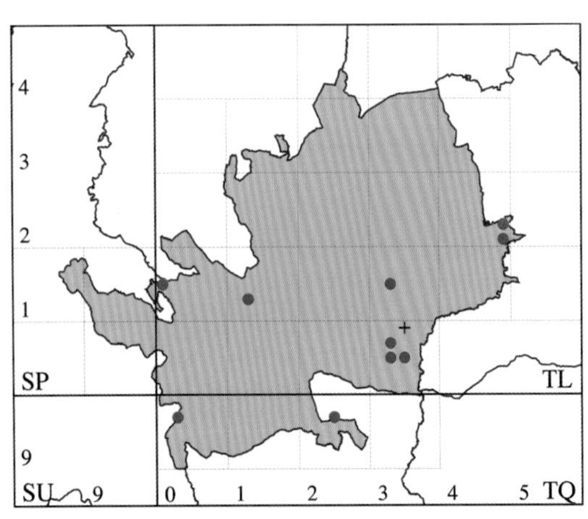

There are no Hertfordshire records of this species prior to those made by David Agassiz at Hoddesdonpark Wood on 17th May 1972. As stated under the previous species, Banks (1910) provided clarification of the separation of *weaverella* from *laevigella* nearly a hundred years ago. Modern records suggest that the species is now fairly widespread and not uncommon, so it remains a mystery whether it was absent or just not recorded for most of the twentieth century.

0229 *Monopis obviella* ([D.& S.]) = *ferruginella* (Hb.)

Recorded:	1901 – 2006
Distribution / Status:	Local / Resident
Conservation status:	No perceived threats
Caterpillar food:	Not recorded. Elsewhere, on dry dead animal matter or occasionally in vegetable matter
Flight period:	Elsewhere, May to August, then October
Records in database:	41

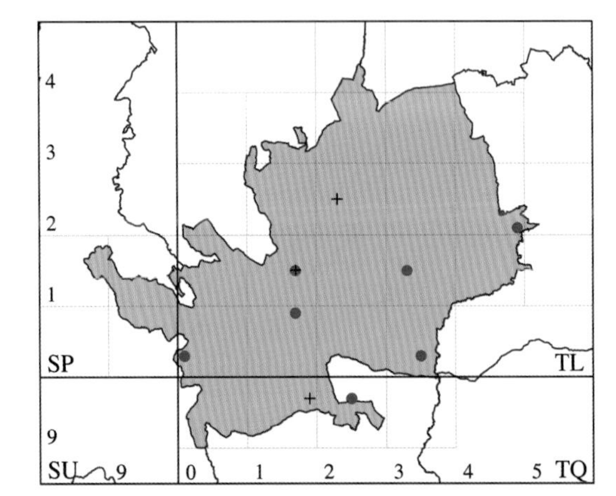

Boyd (1901) provides the first Hertfordshire mention of this species, from Waltham Cross; this record pre-dates the resolution of the confusion between this species and the next (230: *Monopis crocicapitella*) and so the record should be treated with caution as should the next which was not made until 1923, when it was found at Knebworth. These, old records as well as one from Bushey Heath in 1933 (J. K. A. Hervey) are not mapped here. More recent records have been confirmed as correct. Today, it appears to be likely to turn up in most places and is not numerically uncommon in light traps.

0230 *Monopis crocicapitella* (Clem.)

Recorded: 1990 – 2006
Distribution / Status: Local / Uncommon resident
Conservation status: No perceived threats
Caterpillar food: Not recorded. Elsewhere, on dry dead animal matter or occasionally in vegetable matter
Flight period: Elsewhere, June to October
Records in database: 11

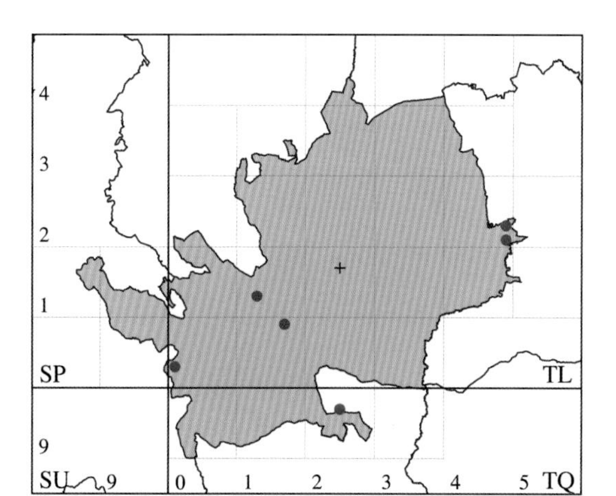

This species was not recognised as distinct from 229: *Monopis obviella* until the early part of the twentieth century (Bankes, 1912), but that does little to explain the apparent total absence of any records prior to 1990 and as with 228: *Monopis weaverella* it remains a mystery whether it was absent or just not recorded for most of the twentieth century.

0234 *Trichophaga tapetzella* (L.) Tapestry Moth

Recorded: 1885 – 1901
Distribution / Status: Absent / Extinct
Conservation status: Herts Extinct
Caterpillar food: Not recorded. Elsewhere, on dry dead animal matter or stored produce
Flight period: Elsewhere, May to August
Records in database: 4

There are only four Hertfordshire records of this formerly abundant pest species, which declined nationally soon after the Second World War and which is now very scarce everywhere in Britain. These are from Hitchin (Durrant, 1885), Sandridge (Griffith, 1890), Cheshunt (Boyd, 1901) and Tring (Gibbs, undated in Foster's 1937 list). The moth is now presumed to be extinct in Hertfordshire.

0236 *Tineola bisselliella* (Hummel) Common Clothes Moth

Recorded: 1885 – 1923
Distribution / Status: Absent / Extinct
Conservation status: Herts Extinct
Caterpillar food: On dried animal and vegetable matter
Flight period: Elsewhere, all year
Records in database: 4

A synanthropic pest species that is probably unable to thrive out of doors and which appears to have been recorded only four times in the county – at Hitchin (Durrant, 1885), in the Sandridge area (Griffith, 1890), at Cheshunt (Boyd, 1901) and at Letchworth (Edwards, 1923). Thus, it has not been reliably reported in the county for 83 years at the time of writing and is considered likely to be Extinct. A record from Watford in 1958 is not supported by a voucher specimen and is regarded as incorrect.

0237 *Niditinea fuscella* (L.) Brown-dotted Clothes Moth

Recorded: 1902 – 2000
Distribution / Status: Local / Uncommon resident
Conservation status: Herts Rare
Caterpillar food: Not recorded. Elsewhere, mainly in birds' nests
Flight period: August. Elsewhere, May to September
Records in database: 5

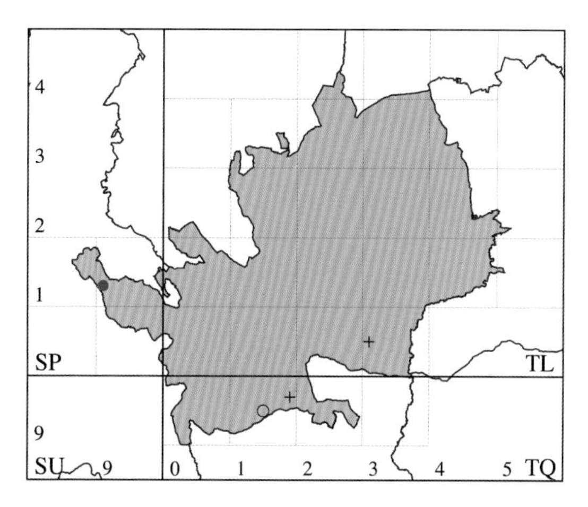

Added to the county fauna by A. E. Gibbs (as *Tinea fuscipunctella*) from St Albans in June and October 1902 (Barraud, 1903) this seems to be a rather locally distributed moth in our county. Foster (1937) also lists Bushey Heath (Hervey), which subsequent research has shown to relate to the year 1933. Since then there are rather few records: Borehamwood in both May (Raymond Uffen) and June (Eric Bradford) 1968; Newgate Street, 7th July 1993 (Raymond Uffen) and near Wilstone Reservoir, in flight underneath an oak tree on 19th August 2000 by myself. The chance nature of the last record suggests that under-recording might feature prominent in the interpretation of this moth's status. It was casually netted over the cars parked under an oak tree on the verge of the lane as we awaited the arrival of other Herts Moth Group members for a night's light trapping in the adjacent reed beds.

0239 *Tinea columbariella* Wocke

This species is mapped for Hertfordshire in volume 2 (1985) of *Moths and butterflies of Great Britain and Ireland* (Harley Books), but the late Maitland Emmet, who produced the maps, was not in possession of the supporting data for the record when I quizzed him on this several years ago. Emmet was meticulously careful over records and there is no suspicion that the record is incorrect – only that the supporting documentation is not available. Recent records, from Rachel Terry's garden at Barnet are a few tens of metres into Middlesex (VC 21), but are in any event certainly not the source.

0240 *Tinea pellionella* L. Case-bearing Clothes Moth

Recorded: 1890 – 2006
Distribution / Status: Local / Uncommon resident
Conservation status: Herts Scarce
Caterpillar food: Not recorded. Elsewhere on wool, hair and feathers indoors; birds' nests outdoors
Flight period: Not recorded. Elsewhere, June to October
Records in database: 11

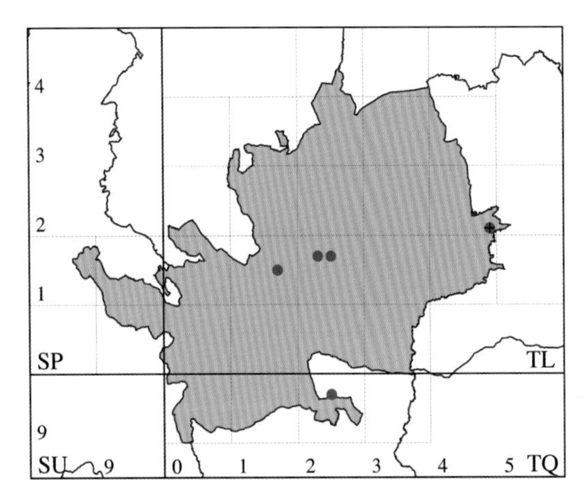

Foster (1937) noted that this moth was 'Only too abundant everywhere'. Whilst this may well have been the case, the statement is tempered somewhat by the work of Robinson (1979), who showed that about half of the '*Tinea pellionella*' in British collections were in fact *T. dubiella*, so emphasising the need for dissection of adult specimens for correct identification. The map shows only reliable records. Elsewhere in Britain, owl pellets and the nests of Swallows seem to be particularly good places to find larvae out of doors, but as a synanthropic species inside buildings it has become extremely rare.

0243 *Tinea dubiella* Stt.

This species is mapped for Hertfordshire in volume 2 (1985) of *Moths and butterflies of Great Britain and Ireland* (Harley Books) but the late Maitland Emmet, who produced the maps, was not in possession of the supporting data for the record. The discovery of Robinson (1979) mentioned under the heading of 240: *Tinea pellionella* is also relevant to this species.

0245 *Tinea pallescentella* Stt. Large Pale Clothes Moth

Recorded:	1890 – 1901
Distribution / Status:	Absent / Extinct
Conservation status:	Insufficient data
Caterpillar food:	Not recorded. Elsewhere, on stored products
Flight period:	Not recorded. Elsewhere, continuously brooded
Records in database:	2

There are only two Hertfordshire records of this species, from the Sandridge area (Griffith, 1890) and from Cheshunt (Boyd, 1901). However, unlike some of the other potential pest species mentioned above, *pallescentella* does not appear to have suffered a particularly significant national decline and so its apparent absence from our county may reflect under-recording. Whatever the reason, we have no records for at least 105 years.

0246 *Tinea semifulvella* Haw.

Recorded:	1901 – 2006
Distribution / Status:	Widespread / Common resident
Conservation status:	No perceived threats
Caterpillar food:	Reared from a Blackbird's nest. Elsewhere in birds' nests, animal debris and similar
Flight period:	May to late August. Elsewhere, May to September
Records in database:	64

Early records are from Broxbourne Woods (Boyd, 1901) and Berkhamsted (Griffith, 1890). There are no further reports until 1969, when it is recorded from Borehamwood by Eric Bradford. In the years since the inception of the Herts Moth Group, however, it has proved to be widespread and common

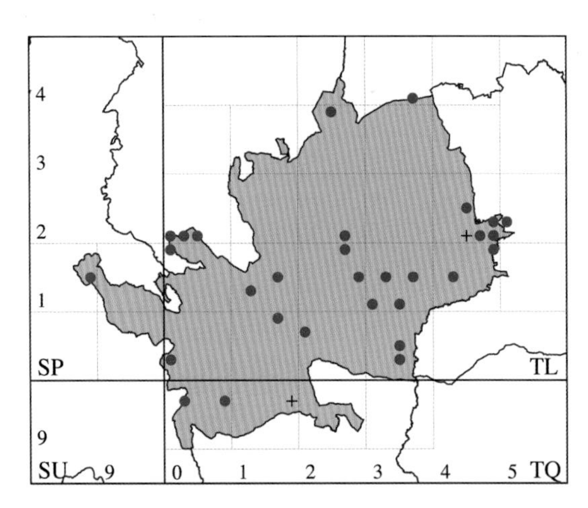

across the county, though with a probable blank in the north-east arable desert area. There is a clear peak of adult records in June.

0247 *Tinea trinotella* Thunb.

Recorded:	1890 – 2006
Distribution / Status:	Widespread / Common resident
Conservation status:	No perceived threats
Caterpillar food plants:	Not recorded. Elsewhere in birds' nests and on animal matter such as feathers and fur, owl pellets and similar
Flight period:	Extreme end of April to early September in two generations.
Records in database:	140

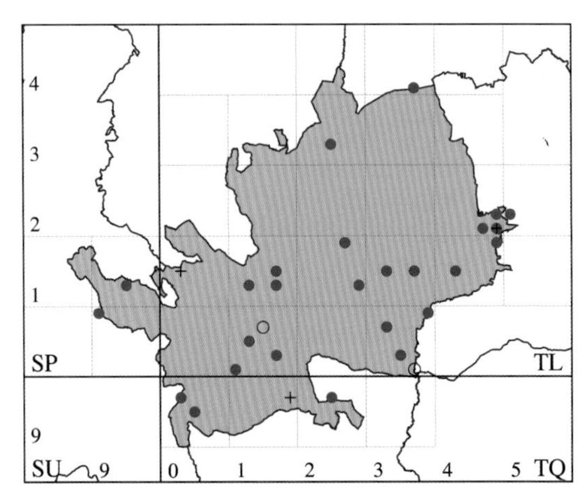

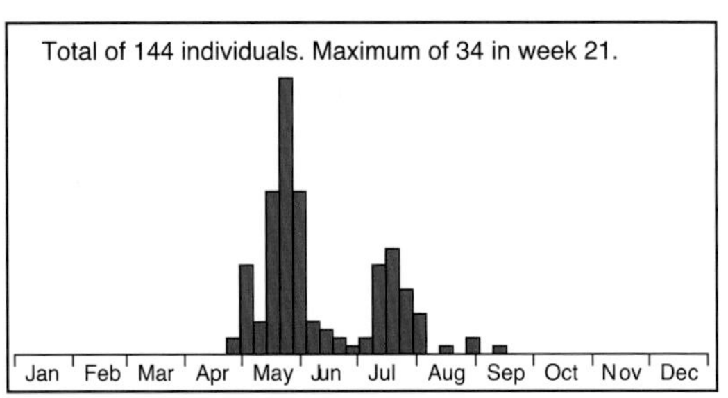

Our earliest report is from St Albans, within two or three miles of the Town Hall (Gibbs, 1889); other late nineteenth century records are from Sandridge, Cheshunt, Letchworth Hitchin, Harpenden and Bushey Heath and are given in Foster (1937). Modern records indicate a species that is widespread and very common in almost all areas. Modern Hertfordshire data confirms the supposed existence of two generations in the south of England; the phenology chart above is presented in evidence of this.

OCHSENHEIMERIIDAE

Now included within YPONOMEUTIDAE (see after species 463).

LYONETIIDAE

Now follow Yponomeutidae, before the Coleophoridae (see after species 476).

GRACILLARIOIDEA
BUCCULATRICIDAE

A large family of moths that in Britain is represented by 12 species, of which nine are recorded in Hertfordshire, although one of these has not been seen here since the late nineteenth century. All are leaf-miners in the early larval stage, making galleries rather than blotches; in later stages they feed externally, ecdysis taking place within a silk cocoon. Mines are sometimes confused with those of *Stigmella* species (in which the vacated egg-shell is smooth and shiny) and with early, leaf-mining stages of some other families. All are hopelessly under-recorded in the county.

0265 *Bucculatrix cristatella* Zell.

Recorded: 1890 – 2006
Distribution / Status: Local / Rare resident
Conservation status: Herts Rare
Caterpillar food plants: Yarrow
Mines evident: April, May and July
Records in database: 4

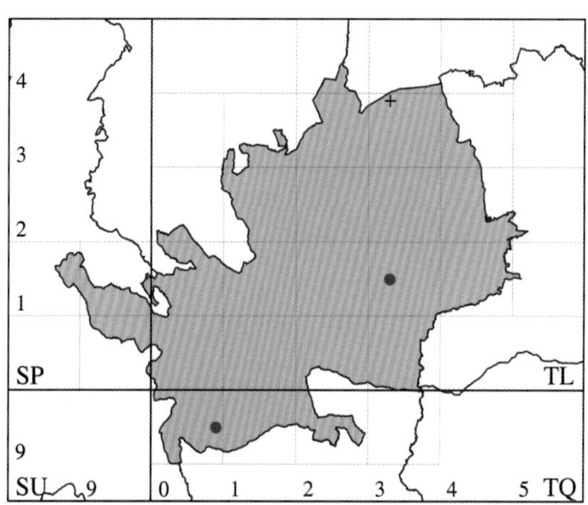

Although undoubtedly overlooked in places where the foodplant is able to grow undisturbed long enough for the moth to complete its life-cycle, such places are, in reality, rather few and so the moth is regarded as rare in Hertfordshire. An 1890 record from the Sandridge area is not mapped as the locality is unclear. The northerly record is my own from Therfield Heath in 1987, but I have not looked for it there since and it may still be present. The southerly dot is from Croxley Common Moor, a site that has a very rich moth fauna, recorded by Raymond Uffen in 1999 and the remaining record is from Hertford in 2006 (Andrew Wood).

0266 *Bucculatrix nigricomella* Zell.

Recorded: 1890 – 2006
Distribution / Status: Local / Uncommon resident
Conservation status: Herts Scarce
Caterpillar food plants: Ox-eye Daisy
Mines evident: July and September to April/May
Records in database: 16

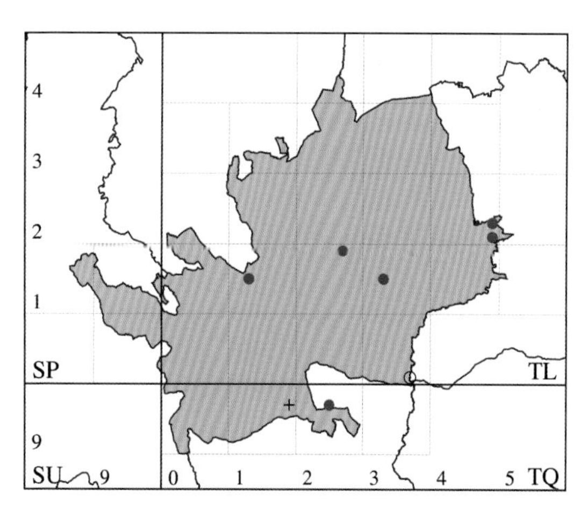

The foodplant is abundant in much of the county, especially in the west, and it is likely that adequate searching will shown this moth to be quite prevalent. Mined leaves of Ox-eye Daisy are often ignored by lepidopterists on the assumption that the mines belong to one of the two flies that also mine the plant, but the larvae of flies lack legs – a feature easily seen with a normal hand lens.

0270 *Bucculatrix frangutella* (Goeze)

Recorded: 1890 only
Distribution / Status: Extremely local or absent / Rare or extinct
Conservation status: Herts Extinct
Caterpillar food plants: Not recorded. Elsewhere, Buckthorn and Alder Buckthorn
Mines evident: Not recorded. Elsewhere, August/September
Records in database: 1

Our only record is from the Sandridge area, prior to 1890. However, the moth is recorded over the border in Middlesex at Barnet, and is surely overlooked in Hertfordshire? Given the foodplants it seems sensible that searches ought to commence on the chalky areas of the county, though gardens should not be ignored.

0271 *Bucculatrix albedinella* Zell.

Recorded: 1900 – 2003
Distribution / Status: Local / Rare resident
Conservation status: Herts Rare
Caterpillar food plants: Elm
Mines evident: July to September
Records in database: 3

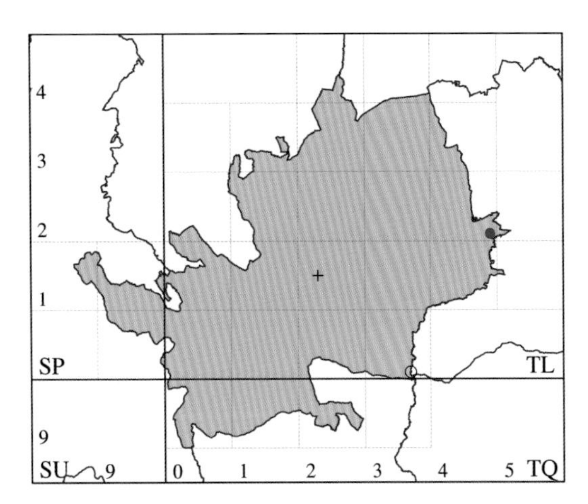

It is unfortunate that moth recording in the county in the years prior to the devastating outbreak of Dutch Elm Disease in the 1970s largely failed to recognise the existence of 'micros'. We can, as a consequence, only guess that the loss of elms from the Hertfordshire landscape had an equally devastating effect on elm-feeding micros. Whatever the reasons, this is now a rare moth with us, with only three records: Cheshunt area (Boyd, 1901), Welwyn, 23rd May 1993 (Raymond Uffen) and mines on unidentified elm leaves at Bishops Stortford, 4th August 2003 by myself.

0272 *Bucculatrix cidarella* Zell.

Recorded:	2000 only
Distribution / Status:	Local / Rare resident
Conservation status:	Herts Rare
Caterpillar food plants:	Alder. Elsewhere, also on Bog Myrtle
Mines evident:	August – September
Records in database:	1

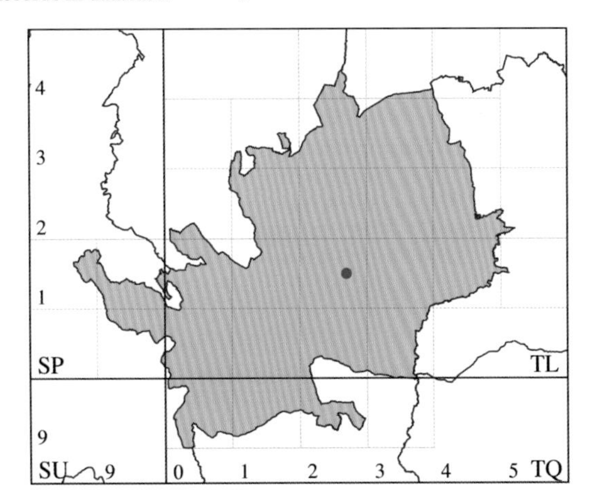

We have a single record of this moth in Hertfordshire, with mines reported at Tewinbury, 12th September 2000 by Raymond Uffen.

0273 *Bucculatrix thoracella* (Thunb.)

Recorded:	1995 – 2006
Distribution / Status:	Probably Widespread / Abundant resident
Conservation status:	No perceived threats
Caterpillar food plants:	Street Lime
Mines evident:	July/August
Records in database:	9

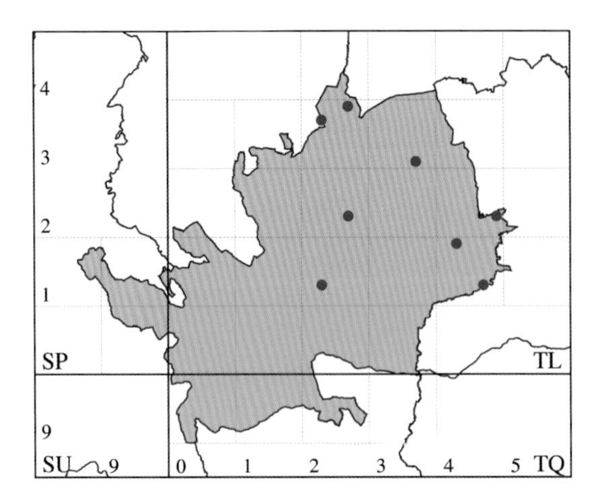

This moth is most easily spotted when the minute caterpillars leave their mines and hang from the foliage on long silk threads; there are no other species that do this on lime trees. The characteristic, longitudinally ribbed cocoons, housing the pupae, are also very easy to find in crevices on the bark of lime trees once you 'get your eye in'; adults may be found resting on trunks during the day in May. Two aspects of this moth in Hertfordshire are rather surprising, however: First, the apparent lack of any records prior to 1995, and second the concentration of records in the north-eastern half of the county. The moth is to be found on almost every 'street' lime in northern and eastern London, so presumably we have simply not looked for it in southern Hertfordshire?

0274 *Bucculatrix ulmella* Zell.

Recorded:	1890 – 2006
Distribution / Status:	Widespread / Common resident
Conservation status:	No perceived threats
Caterpillar food plants:	English Oak
Mines evident:	September – October
Records in database:	39

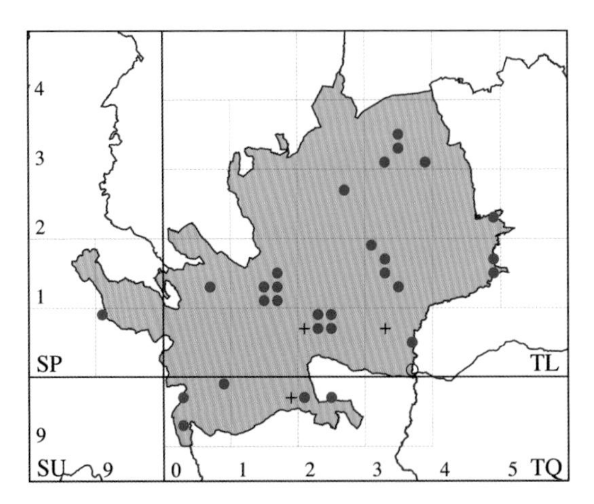

This is a widespread and numerically common moth across the whole county wherever deciduous oaks are present, being equally easy to find in the southern woodlands and on isolated trees on the Chalky Boulder Clay in the arable north-east. Mines tend to be on larger, older leaves rather than on fresh leaves, though this is not exclusively the case.

0275 *Bucculatrix bechsteinella* (D.& S.) = *crataegi* (Zell.)

Recorded: 1890 – 2006
Distribution / Status: Probably Widespread / Uncommon resident
Conservation status: No perceived threats
Caterpillar food plants: Common Hawthorn. Elsewhere also on pear, apple and Rowan
Mines evident: July to August, but vacated mines persisting to October
Records in database: 8

The spread of records affects the northern and southern extremes of the county as well as the better-recorded central area and suggests that specific searching might turn up this moth in other areas too. There is no reason to suppose that Midland Hawthorn is not equally attractive as a foodplant, though we have only recorded it here on Common Hawthorn. The southerly record, from Barnet, was made just within the county boundary and the moth is also present in Middlesex.

0276 *Bucculatrix demaryella* (Dup.)

Recorded: 1890 – 2006
Distribution / Status: Local / Rare resident
Conservation status: Herts Rare
Caterpillar food plants: Sweet Chestnut. Elsewhere also on Birch
Mines evident: July and August
Records in database: 2

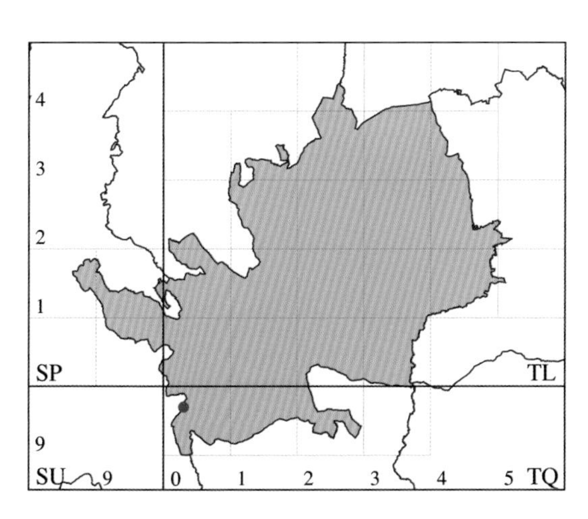

There are only two Hertfordshire records: the first was from the Sandridge area (Griffith, 1890) and is not mapped as the precise locality is unclear. The next was not until 21st October 2006, when I found a vacated mine on Sweet Chestnut and, after searching, an associated pupal cocoon, at Chorleywood Common.

ROESLERSTAMMIIDAE

Formerly regarded as belonging to the Yponomeutidae, Roeslerstammiidae is now regarded as a family in its own right. Scientific opinion varies on its position within the grand scheme of things, but following a brief stay in the Tineoidea current thinking places it here within the Gracillarioidea. For ease of reference, the original Bradley and Fletcher (1979) code numbers are retained. There are two British species, one of which is recorded in Hertfordshire. The second species may be separable only on male genitalia and it seems sensible that Hertfordshire examples *Roeslerstammia erxlebella* should be confirmed in this way in case the second species is here undetected.

0447 *Roeslerstammia erxlebella* (Fabr.)

Recorded: 1834 – 2003
Distribution / Status: Local / Common resident
Conservation status: Herts Scarce
Caterpillar food plants: Not recorded. Elsewhere on Lime and birch
Mines evident: No data. Elsewhere, July then September/October
Flight period: Late July and all August. Elsewhere, May/June and August/September
Records in database: 11

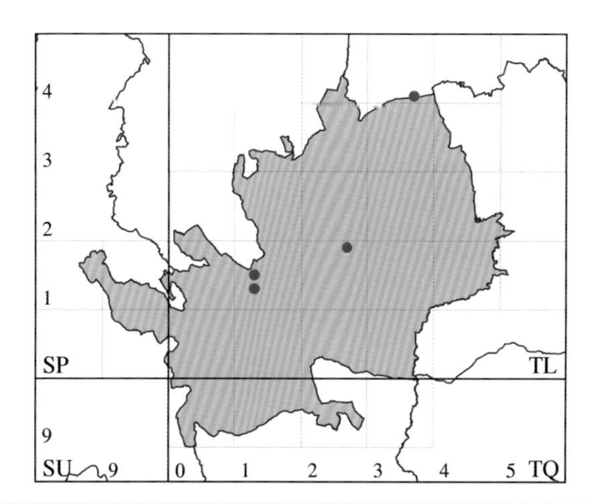

Our earliest reference for this species is for Hertford in J. F. Stephens' *Illustrations of British Entomology* **4:** 278, published in 1834. The record is not mapped, as Stephens' definition of 'Hertford' incorporated a large area around the town. Since then, there are records from only three localities, although the moth is seemingly common in at least two of these, with repeat records in particular at the Rothamsted Light Trap in Harpenden.

GRACILLARIIDAE

The Gracillariidae are all leaf-mining moths, creating the familiar 'pucker' or 'tentiform' mines rather than linear galleries. There are two major subfamilies – members of the Lithocolletinae, including all of the species of *Phyllonorycter* and the infamous Horse-chestnut Leaf Miner (366a: *Cameraria ohridella*), mine inside leaves (or soft bark) throughout their entire larval stage, whilst members of the Gracillariinae, including *Parornix* and *Caloptilia* species, feed externally in the final larval stages – a process that necessitates them exiting the mine and then folding a leaf-edge over to create a protective feeding chamber. A third subfamily, the Phyllocnistinae, is regarded by many as a family in its own right, the Phyllocnistidae, on the basis of changes to the larval head capsule at various stages of its development. This is of no concern to the present work and I have, for convenience, followed the Bradley (2000) checklist in retaining Phyllocnistinae as a subfamily of Gracillariidae. In Britain we have, at the latest count, 35 Gracillariinae, 55 Lithocolletinae and 3 Phyllocnistinae, giving a total of 93 British Gracillariidae. In Hertfordshire, we can boast 27 Gracillariinae, 45 Lithocolletinae and 2 Phyllocnistinae, making 74 in all – 80 per cent of the British fauna.

GRACILLARIINAE

0280 *Caloptilia cuculipennella* (Hb.)

Recorded: 1890 – 2006
Distribution / Status: Local / Rare resident
Conservation status: Herts Scarce
Caterpillar food plants: Ash. Elsewhere also on privet
Flight period: Not recorded. Elsewhere October to May
Records in database: 5

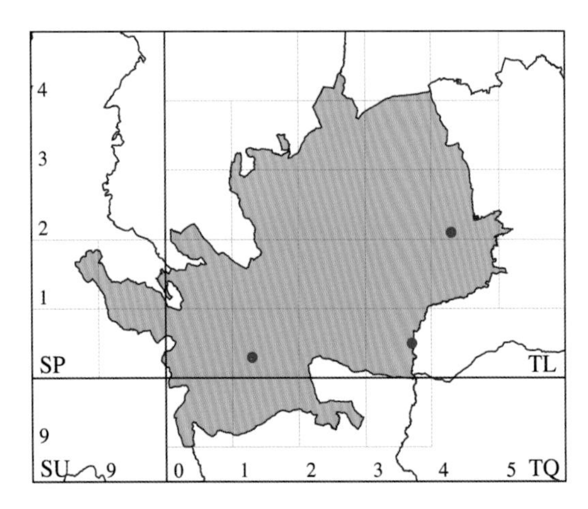

There is a single nineteenth-century record from the Sandridge area and then no more until two separate and widely-spaced discoveries of larval stages at Danebridge on 30th September and Turnford Marsh on 2nd October, both during 2003 and an adult in a garden trap at Bricketwood on 6th July 2006 (Henry Ellis). There have been no further examples since these.

0281 *Caloptilia populetorum* (Zell.)

Recorded: 2002 – 2005
Distribution / Status: Local / Uncommon resident
Conservation status: Herts Scarce
Caterpillar food plants: Not recorded. Elsewhere on birch
Flight period: Late July to mid-October. Elsewhere September to May
Records in database: 3

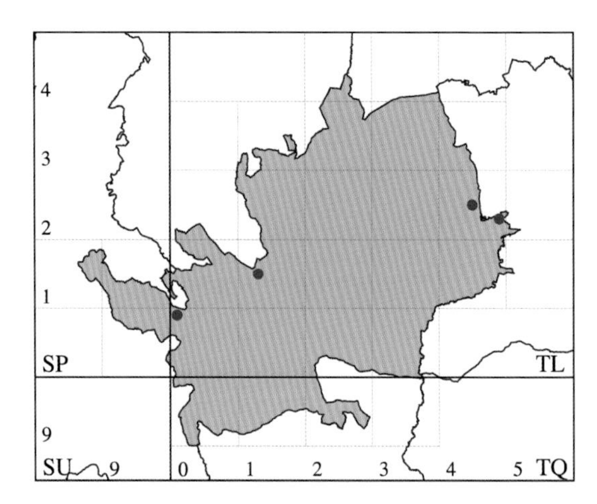

Three records are available, all from the present century and all relating to adults at light. A male was caught on the Herts Moth Group recording trip to Frithsden Beeches, in the west, on 31st August 2002 and another was caught by me amongst young birches on Patmore Heath, in the east, on 14th October 2002. The third was caught in the garden light trap operated by James Fish and Julian Reeves in Bishops Stortford, on 31st July 2005 (identified by Rachel Terry). All three were named by genitalia dissection.

0282 *Caloptilia elongella* (L.)

Recorded: 1890 – 2006
Distribution / Status: Local / Uncommon resident
Conservation status: No perceived threats
Caterpillar food plants: Alder
Flight period: August to May
Records in database: 24

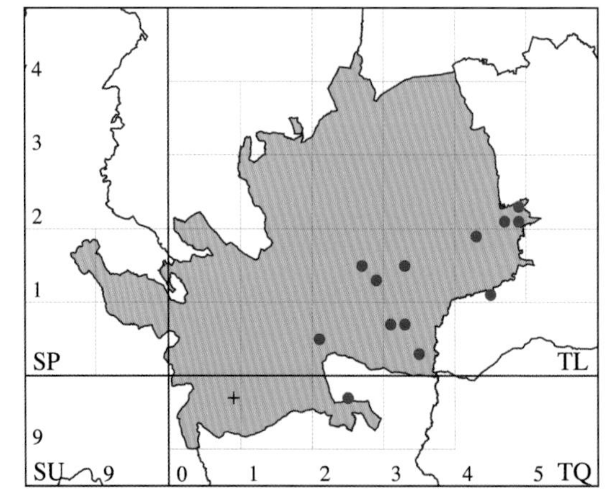

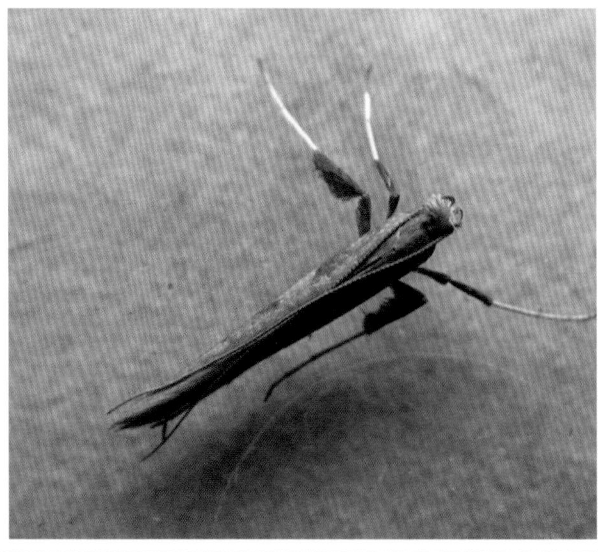

The apparent restriction of this species to the south-east of the county seems likely to be real as it has been searched for assiduously in other areas to no avail. Availability of native Alder is a contributing factor and in keeping with several other alder-associates it is genuinely absent from the north-east and most of the chalk-dominated north-west border with Bedfordshire. However, by no means all the alder bushes affected by mines are associated with wetland habitat or water courses and isolated alders in gardens are likely to support larvae (though they appear to be unable to thrive on ornamental varieties).

0283 *Caloptilia betulicola* (Her.)

Recorded:	1973 – 2005
Distribution / Status:	Local / Uncommon resident
Conservation status:	Herts Scarce
Caterpillar food plants:	Silver Birch; Downy Birch
Flight period:	July to April
Records in database:	25

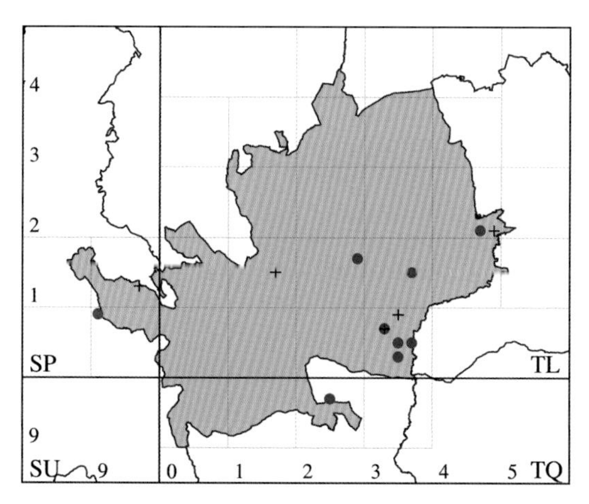

Not recorded in the county until 1973, when an adult was taken at light on the Ashridge Estate by Jack Newton on 7th March. Intensive collection of leaf mines in the years since 1999 appear to indicate that at the present time the moth is widespread, though rather local, wherever birch trees grow. The absence from the north-east section and the north-west border is likely to be largely genuine.

0284 *Caloptilia rufipennella* (Hb.)

Recorded:	1991 – 2006
Distribution / Status:	Ubiquitous / Abundant resident
Conservation status:	No perceived threats
Caterpillar food plants:	Sycamore. Elsewhere perhaps also on Field Maple?
Flight period:	Insufficient data. Elsewhere October to April
Records in database:	73

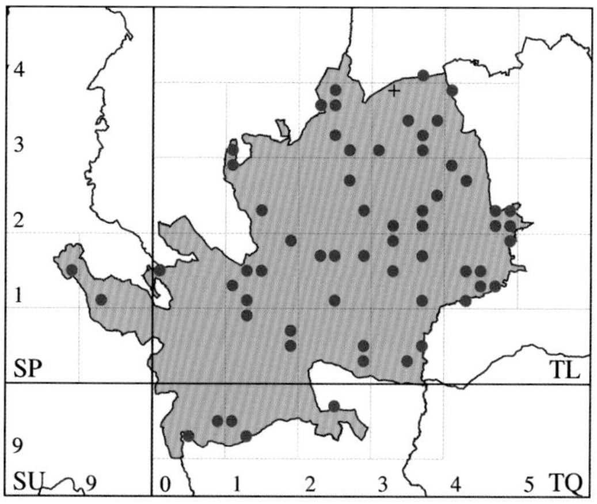

The first report in the county was from Therfield Heath, where Maitland Emmet recorded it on 14th October 1991; prior to that period it may well have been genuinely rare with us. Today, however, it is an expected species on almost every Sycamore tree, although the population will inevitably fluctuate in inverse proportion to that of their parasites.

0285 *Caloptilia azaleella* (Brants)

Recorded:	2001 – 2006
Distribution / Status:	Local – spreading / Common
Conservation status:	No perceived threats
Caterpillar food plants:	Not recorded. Elsewhere on several species of Azalea
Flight period:	Late May, mid July and early August for outdoor examples.
Records in database:	15

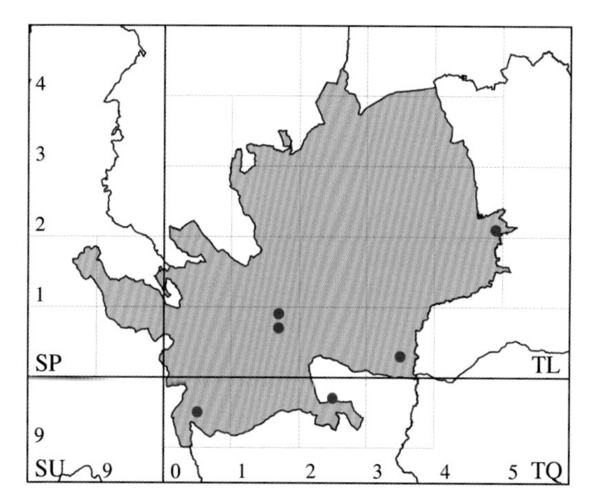

This small moth was recently introduced to Britain with imported azalea plants, particularly *Rhododendron simssi* and *R. indicum*. In the north of the country it survives only in glasshouses, but in the south-east it appears to have become established on feral *Rhododendron* plants out of doors. In Hertfordshire, our first record was associated with azalea plants in an indoor setting in Rickmansworth (Paul Clack) and this was the only report for that year. It was still thriving there in 2003. Most of the other records, however, are of free-flying adults taken at light from 2003 to 2006. This suggests that the species has colonised the county from somewhere other than Rickmansworth.

0286 *Caloptilia alchimiella* (Scop.)

Recorded:	2000 – 2006
Distribution / Status:	Widespread / Common resident
Conservation status:	No perceived threats
Caterpillar food plants:	English Oak; Sessile Oak
Flight period:	May to August, perhaps in two broods
Records in database:	39

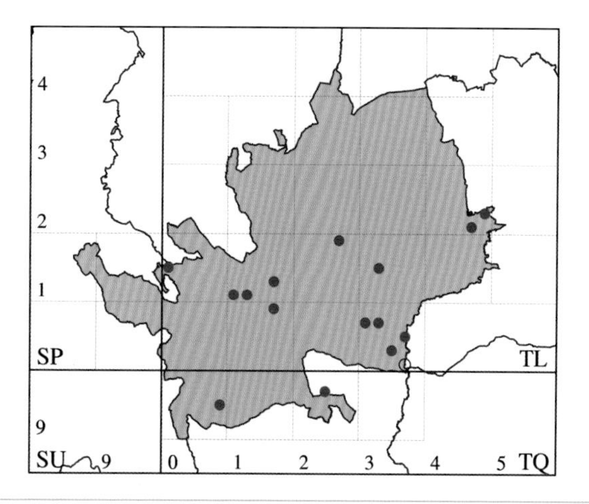

From the first alleged record in the vicinity of Hertford in 1834 (J. F. Stephens) to the present day, this appears to have been a widespread and common species in Hertfordshire. However, separation of the mines from those of 287: *Caloptilia robustella* is impossible without rearing the adults and the separation of adults is generally unsafe without examination of the genitalia and random re-examination of specimens named in the past by 'experts' indicates that many were incorrectly determined. Consequently, I have accepted here only those records based on genitalia examination. The distribution maps for both species thus reflect only positively identified examples and for this reason may give a false impression of distribution; both species are abundant wherever deciduous oak trees are to be found.

0287 *Caloptilia robustella* Jackh

Recorded: 1975 – 2006
Distribution / Status: Widespread / Common resident
Conservation status: No perceived threats
Caterpillar food plants: English Oak; Sessile Oak
Flight period: May/June and July/August, apparently in two generations
Records in database: 35

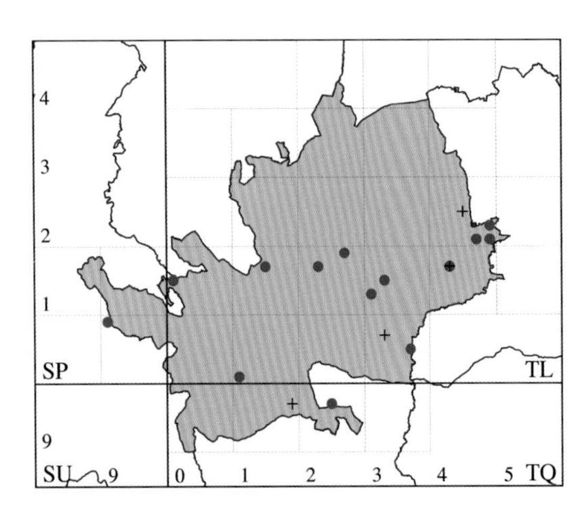

The first record for the county was from Borehamwood, on 4th June 1975 (Eric Bradford); we have not examined this specimen, but Eric was likely to have performed the appropriate dissection. The moth is widespread and common wherever oak grows and the comments under 286: *Caloptilia alchimiella* apply here too.

0288 *Caloptilia stigmatella* (Fabr.)

Recorded: 1885 – 2005
Distribution / Status: Widespread / Common resident
Conservation status: No perceived threats
Caterpillar food plants: poplar, Aspen and Sallow
Flight period: June to August
Records in database: 39

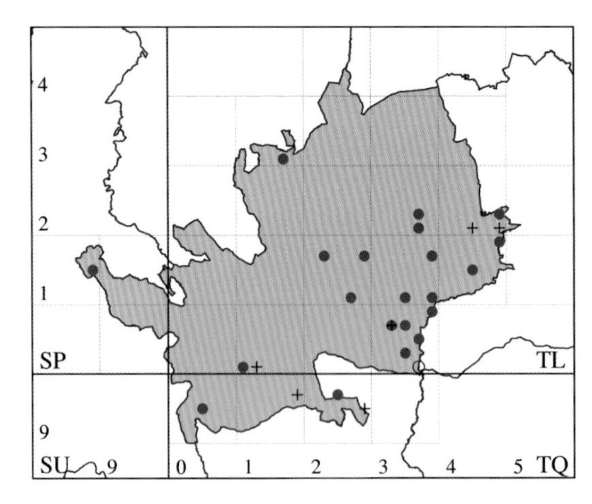

The adult of this species is immediately recognisable and it is no surprise then that most records are of adults from light traps. Foodplant records confirmed by rearing the adult include a single record from aspen, one from an unknown species of poplar and several from Sallow. The species is likely to be found in most places where one or other of these foodplants grows.

0289 *Caloptilia falconipennella* (Hb.)

Recorded: 2000 – 2006
Distribution / Status: Local – spreading / Uncommon
Conservation status: Herts Scarce
Caterpillar food plants: Alder. Elsewhere, also on Italian and Grey Alders
Flight period: September to May
Records in database: 9

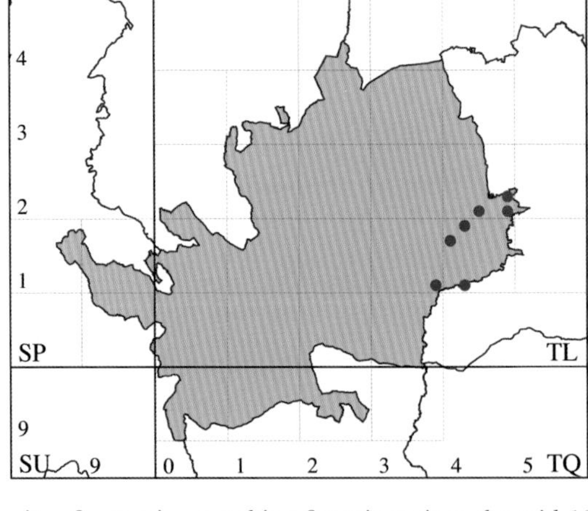

In spite of extensive searching for mines since the mid 1980s by a keen few, and at least a few trips out to run lights in places where alder grows, there are no records for *falconipennella* in Hertfordshire prior to 2000; the moth appears to have colonised us in the last six years. It is possible, of course, that a very small population has persisted undetected for a longer period in the east of the county, but as this area has had a high concentration of lepidopterists for many years this seems unlikely. The records give the impression that this species is actively extending its range and it is expected to spread to cover a greater proportion of the county in the next few years. The moth is usually double-brooded in southern England.

0290 *Caloptilia semifascia* (Haw.)

Recorded: 1885 – 2004
Distribution / Status: Local / Rare resident
Conservation status: Herts Rare
Caterpillar food plants: Not recorded. Elsewhere on Field Maple
Flight period: No data. Elsewhere September to May (double-brooded in the south)
Records in database: 2

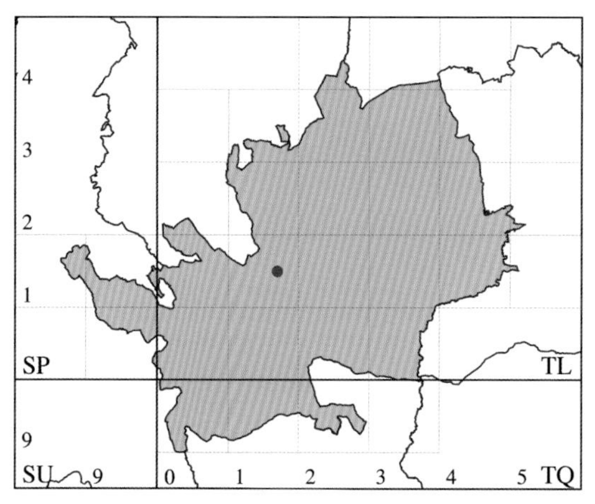

There are only two Hertfordshire records: from the Sandridge area prior to 1885 (A. F. Griffith) and Marshall's Heath in 2004 (Mark Sterling). Mines have been searched for intensively since 2004 and have not been found and it seems that the moth is genuinely rare with us.

0293 *Caloptilia syringella* (Fabr.)

Recorded: 1890 – 2006
Distribution / Status: Ubiquitous / Abundant resident
Conservation status: No perceived threats
Caterpillar food plants: Ash, Garden Privet, Lilac
Flight period: April to June; July to September; October/November
Records in database: 216

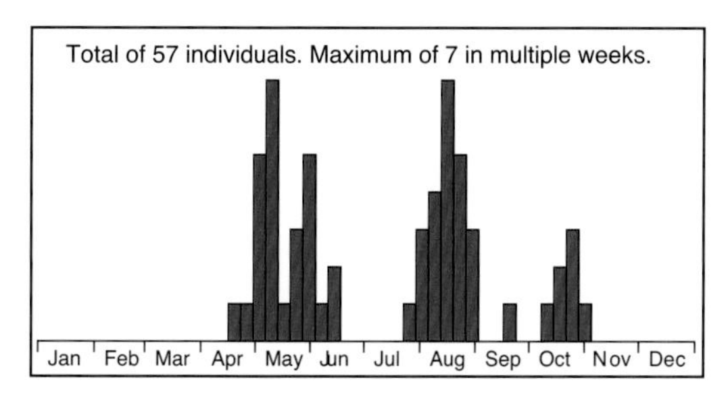

The appearance of adults in Hertfordshire is at odds with published data for the rest of Britain, which has the moth flying around May (as here) and then in July. Our moths fly

through August and (from records made 2000 to 2006) into September with occasional verified captures in late October and early November. The larval mines and cones of this distinctive moth are a familiar sight on almost every ash tree and most un-pruned privet and lilac bushes. It is predicted that adequate searching would find this moth in every map tetrad where one or other of the foodplants grow.

0294 *Aspilapteryx tringipennella* (Zell.)

Recorded: 1900 – 2005
Distribution / Status: Local / Common resident
Conservation status: No perceived threats
Caterpillar food plants: Ribwort Plantain
Flight period: August. Elsewhere May and August
Records in database: 12

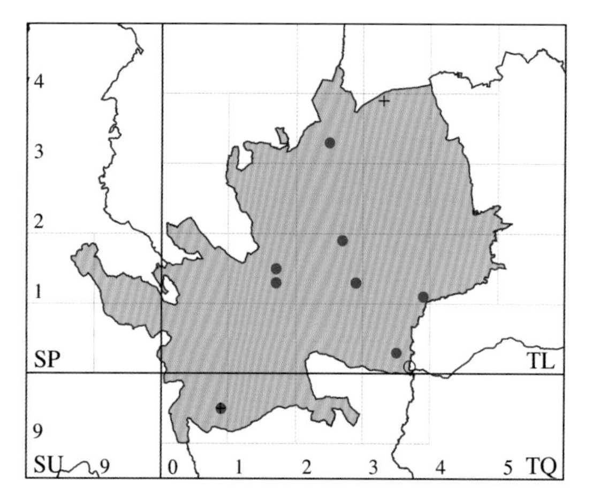

The paucity of dots on the distribution map most likely reflects the failure by lepidopterists to get down on their hands and knees and examine the upper surface of plantain leaves for the larval mines (which at first glance resemble those of a *Phyllonorycter* species), during June and July or over the winter. The adult moth flies in afternoon and early evening sunshine and can be netted over the foodplant without effort.

0296 *Calybites phasianipennella* (Hb.)

Recorded: 1992 – 2004
Distribution / Status: Local / Rare resident
Conservation status: Herts Rare
Caterpillar food plants: Not recorded. Elsewhere on *Rumex*, *Polygonum* and *Lysimachia*
Flight period: No data. Elsewhere October to May.
Records in database: 2

We have only two records of this species, from Croxley Common Moor SSSI where Raymond Uffen disturbed two adults from Petty Whin plants on 19th July 1992 and from the

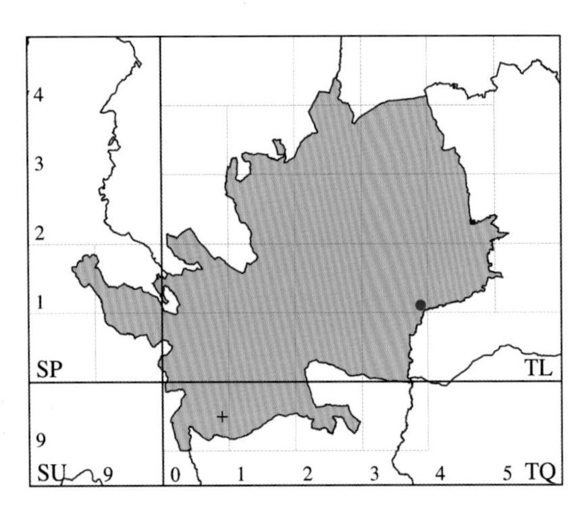

North Area of the RSPB owned portion of Rye Meads Nature Reserve in 2004 (Paul Roper). The larvae are sensitive to inappropriate grazing regimes.

0297 *Eucalybites aurogutella* (Steph.)

Recorded:	1890 – 2006
Distribution / Status:	Local / Uncommon resident
Conservation status:	No perceived threats
Caterpillar food plants:	Perforate St. John's-wort. Elsewhere, also on other St. John's-worts
Flight period:	May
Records in database:	19

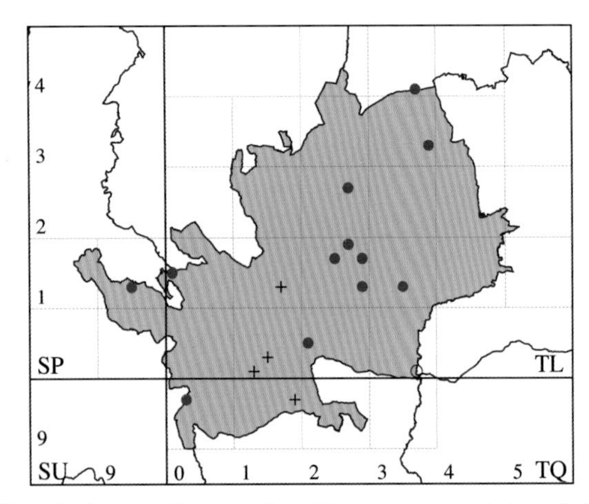

Though there are few map dots this attractive moth is probably under-recorded since finding mines or folded leaves involves getting down to ground level and searching – mines on trees and shrubs are far better recorded! It is likely to be found in most woodland edge situations where the foodplant grows.

0299 *Parectopa ononidis* (Zell.)

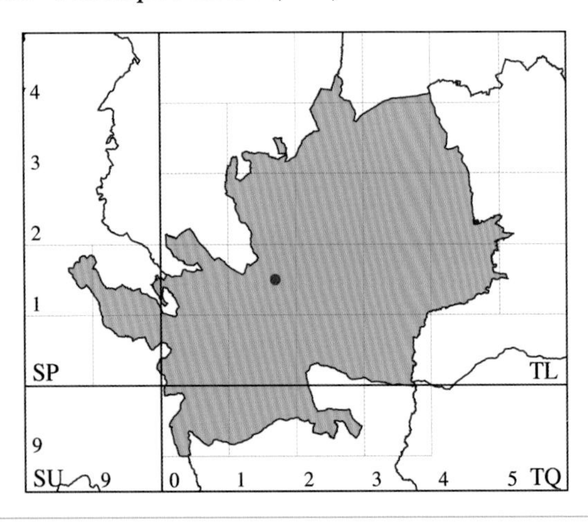

Recorded:	2002 only
Distribution / Status:	Extremely local / Rare resident
Conservation status:	Herts Rare
Caterpillar food plants:	Not recorded. Elsewhere on clover, especially Red Clover
Flight period:	Not recorded. Elsewhere in May/June and August
Records in database:	2

There are just two records of this elusive moth, both from the same site – at Marshall's Heath on 29th July and 13th August 2002 (John Murray). Young caterpillars mine the underside of young leaves of clovers and can be difficult to spot, though as the larva gets more mature the mines become full-depth. Nevertheless, this species is perhaps overlooked.

0301 *Parornix betulae* (Stt.)

Recorded:	1890 – 2005
Distribution / Status:	Local / Uncommon resident
Conservation status:	No perceived threats
Caterpillar food plants:	Silver Birch; Downy Birch
Flight period:	May. Elsewhere also in August
Records in database:	20

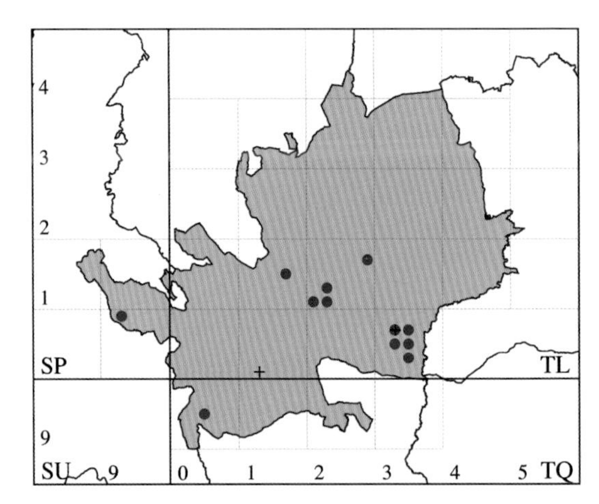

The wide spread of records from different habitats suggest that this moth is likely to be found over a much wider area than the map indicates. The mines of this species are unfailingly found on seedling birches rather than on semi-mature and mature trees so that populations probably succumb as younger areas of woodland become progressively more mature. This suggests that the overall population is likely to be mobile.

0302 *Parornix fagivora* (Frey.)

Recorded:	2001 – 2005
Distribution / Status:	Local / Uncommon resident
Conservation status:	No perceived threats
Caterpillar food plants:	Beech
Flight period:	No data
Records in database:	11

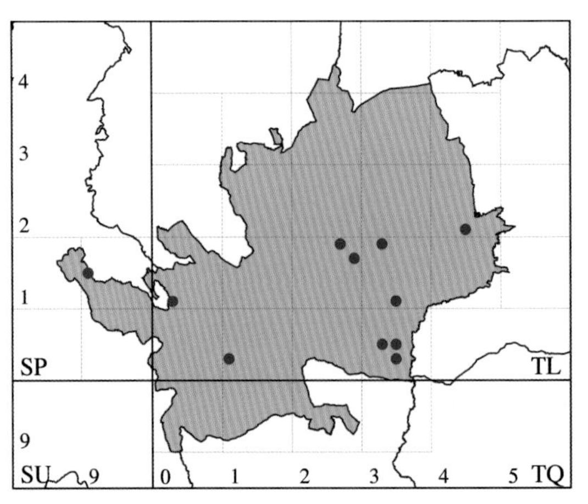

There has been confusion in the past between this species and 302a: *Parornix carpinella*, but it is now clear that the *Parornix* on Hornbeam is *carpinella* whilst that on Beech leaves is *fagivora*. For further discussion see Emmet (1986). There is an unfortunate tendency on the part of some field workers not to record the foodplant of larvae that are not widely polyphagous and so some older records of mines and leaf folds of this species might have been on hornbeam. Therefore, the distribution map has been compiled from records relating only to mines and/or folds on beech trees. Separation of adult *fagivora* from adult *carpinella* requires dissection of the genitalia; there are no adult records in the map. *Parornix fagivora* is widespread, but very locally distributed in the southern two thirds of Hertfordshire and probably very much under-recorded across our entire area.

0302a *Parornix carpinella* (Frey)

Recorded: 1990 – 2006
Distribution / Status: Local / Rare resident
Conservation status: Herts Scarce
Caterpillar food plants: Hornbeam
Flight period: No data
Records in database: 4

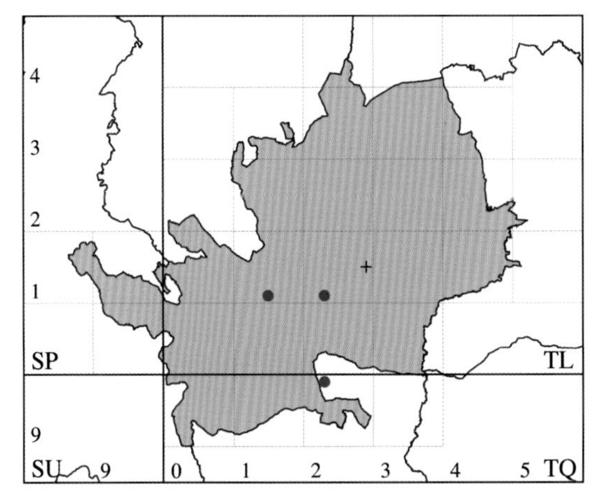

Past confusion with 302: *Parornix fagivora* has been mentioned under that species. Emmet (1986) commented that *carpinella* appeared to be uncommon, being reported from Kent and Essex only. However, he also noted that it was hard to find because larvae occur at very low density. In spite of some twenty years elapsing since that statement we have just four records in Hertfordshire: Mines and folds were found at Bramfield during 1990 by Mark Sterling; mines and folds were found by Wendy Hatton in October 2006 at Lemsford Recreation Ground, on Harpenden Common Golf Course and along Galley Lane at Dyrham Park, just inside the Hertfordshire vice-county boundary in the south of our area.

0303 *Parornix anglicella* (Stt.)

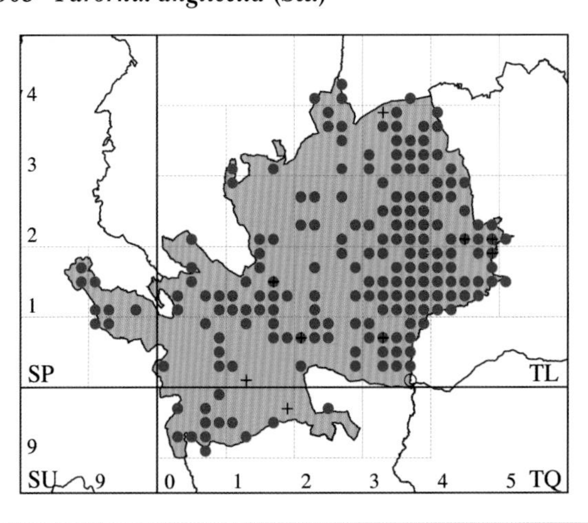

Recorded: 1890 – 2006
Distribution / Status: Ubiquitous / Abundant resident
Conservation status: No perceived threats
Caterpillar food plants: Common Hawthorn; Midland Hawthorn
Flight period: May and August
Records in database: 270

The conical folds of this numerically abundant species are likely to be found on every hawthorn bush in the county. Adults sometimes come to light traps, but there are few records.

0304 *Parornix devoniella* (Stt.)

Recorded: 1885 – 2006
Distribution / Status: Ubiquitous / Abundant resident
Conservation status: No perceived threats
Caterpillar food plants: Hazel
Flight period: May and August
Records in database: 177

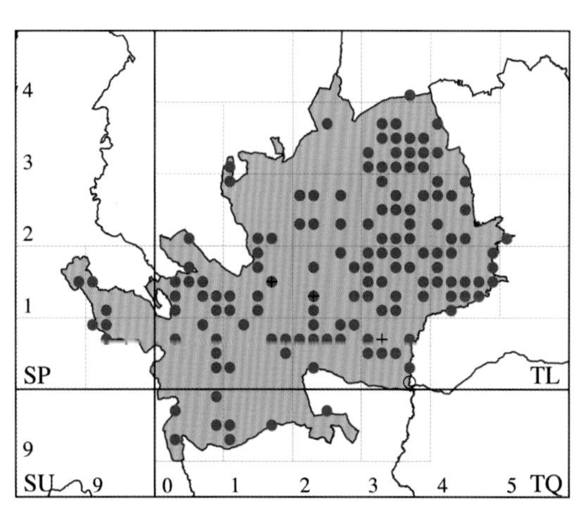

The caterpillar makes easily recognised sub-rectangular mines on the underside of hazel leaves before later feeding in a folded leaf edge – usually the same leaf. Hazel grows more or less everywhere in Hertfordshire and finding a bush without mines would be unusual.

0305 *Parornix scoticella* (Stt.)

Recorded: 1900 – 2006
Distribution / Status: Local / Uncommon resident
Conservation status: No perceived threats
Caterpillar food plants: Not recorded. Elsewhere, on Whitebeam, Rowan and occasionally apple and *Cotoneaster* species
Flight period: May and August
Records in database: 22

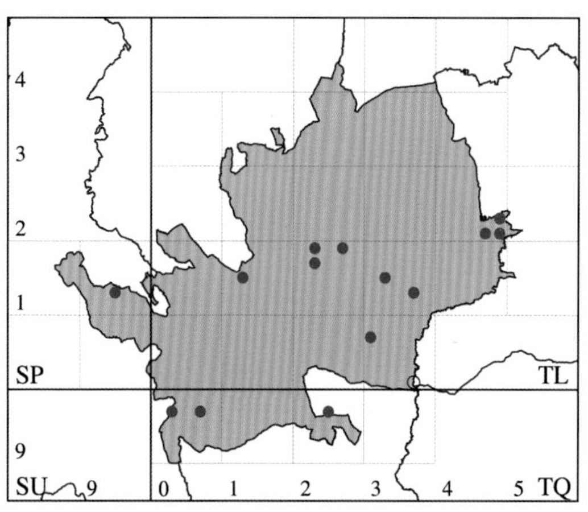

Although reports are widely spread across the county, the moth appears to be genuinely local and numerically scarce compared with other members of the genus.

0308 *Parornix finitimella* (Zell.)

Recorded: 1981 – 2006
Distribution / Status: Widespread / Common resident
Conservation status: No perceived threats
Caterpillar food plants: Blackthorn
Flight period: Insufficient data. Elsewhere in May
Records in database: 51

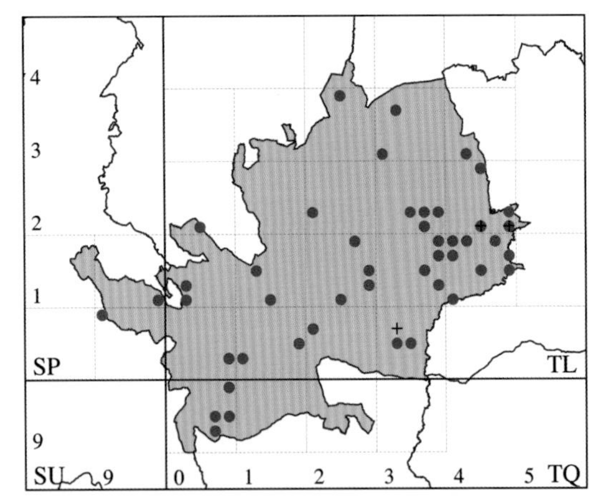

Separation of the blackthorn-feeding *Parornix* is often difficult, but rearing adults from collected mines seems to suggest that *finitimella* is far more frequent than 309: *Deltaornix torquillella*. It was not recognised as British until 1917 when it was discovered in Essex (Pierce, 1917); this explains the absence of nineteenth century records, but it is surprising that there are no Hertfordshire records prior to 1981, when Maitland Emmet found mines in Broxbourne Wood on 12th September and later reared adults.

0309 *Deltaornix torquillella* (Zell.)

Recorded: 1890 – 2004
Distribution / Status: Local / Uncommon resident
Conservation status: Herts Scarce
Caterpillar food plants: Not recorded.
Flight period: No data. Elsewhere May to July
Records in database: 12

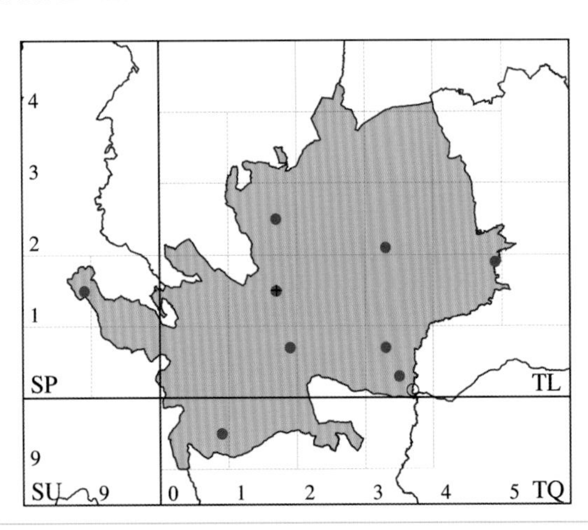

As with the other blackthorn feeding species, records are best confirmed by rearing adults from collected mines; only confirmed records are included in the distribution map.

0310 *Callisto denticulella* (Thunb.)

Recorded: 1885 – 2006
Distribution / Status: Widespread / Common resident
Conservation status: No perceived threats
Caterpillar food plants: Domestic Apple; Crab Apple
Flight period: Not recorded. Elsewhere, May/June
Records in database: 46

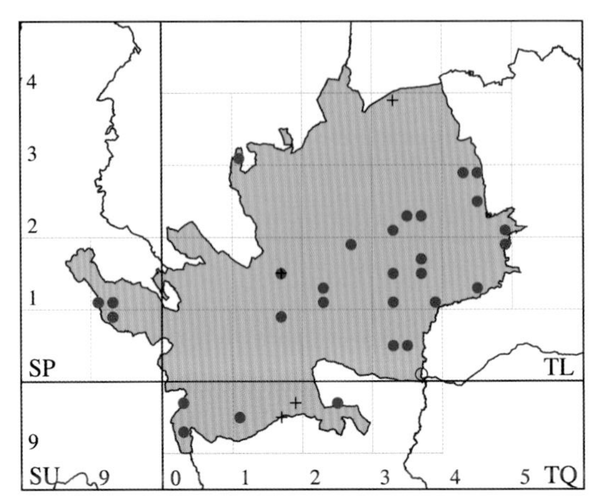

Although recorded as mines on both domestic and crab apple, most records are from domestic cultivars. It is likely that if we could get access to peoples' gardens at the right time of year the number of dots on the distribution map would rise considerably.

0313 *Acrocercops brongniardella* (Fabr.)

Recorded: 1985 – 2005
Distribution / Status: Local / Uncommon resident
Conservation status: No perceived threats
Caterpillar food plants: English Oak; Sessile Oak. Elsewhere, also on Holm Oak
Flight period: Not recorded. Elsewhere July, overwintering to May
Records in database: 18

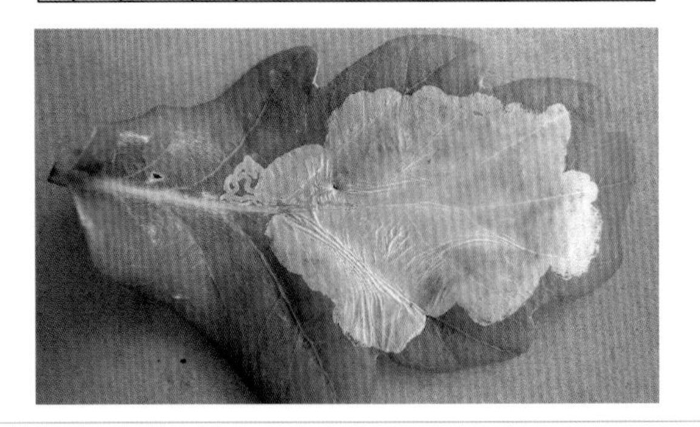

The mines of this species are fairly distinctive, though they may be confused by the inexperienced with those of the sawfly *Profenusa pygmaea*, which is widespread and common in Hertfordshire. The moth is also said to mine evergreen oaks, which the sawfly does not do, but we have no records on this host plant for the county.

0314 *Leucospilapteryx omissella* (Stt.)

Recorded:	1965 – 2004
Distribution / Status:	Local / Uncommon resident
Conservation status:	Herts Scarce
Caterpillar food plants:	Mugwort
Flight period:	May
Records in database:	14

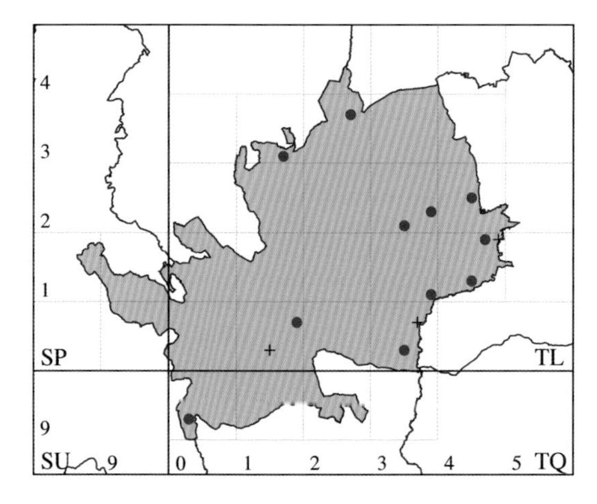

The larvae mine the lower leaves of Mugwort plants and in the final stages these inflate and become purple, making recognition easy. However, Mugwort affects ruderal sites which are, by definition, temporary, and so the plant and the moth are relatively mobile. Unfortunately, many of the sites where mugwort is left alone to thrive for an entire year are secured behind fences and the plants cannot be inspected without considerable organisation. The moth is likely to be more frequent than the map indicates.

LITHOCOLLETINAE

0315 *Phyllonorycter harrisella* (L.)

Recorded:	1890 – 2006
Distribution / Status:	Ubiquitous / Abundant resident
Conservation status:	No perceived threats
Caterpillar food plants:	English Oak; Sessile Oak
Flight period:	Not recorded. Elsewhere, April/May and August/September
Mines evident:	June; September to leaf-fall
Records in database:	133

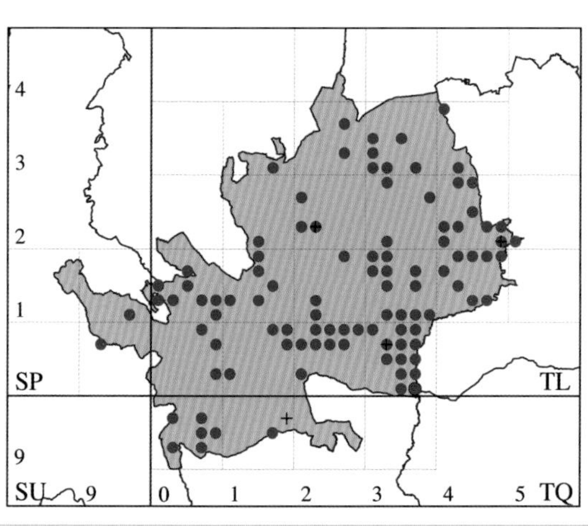

This whitish moth is the cause of one of the most frequently encountered mines on oak leaves. Mines of the summer generation are mostly easy to name once the pupa has formed, as the cocoon is fixed firmly to both upper and lower surface inside the mine. However, most autumn mines are impossible to separate from those of *P. quercifoliella* and *P. messaniella*: the discussion under 320: *P. quercifoliella* applies.

0316 *Phyllonorycter roboris* (Zell.)

This species is listed by Griffith (1890) for the Sandridge area – a large area extending several miles around the village; this is the source of the Hertfordshire 'dot' in volume 2 of *Moths and Butterflies of Great Britain an Ireland*. Although generally scarce in the south-east of England, it is possible that it is overlooked because it mines oak leaves in July and August whilst the main thrust of leaf-miner recording appears to take place in the autumn period. There do not appear to be any records for the adjacent counties of Essex or Bedfordshire and there are certainly none for Middlesex. It should be added that I have not been able to validate the Griffith record by examining a voucher specimen.

0317 *Phyllonorycter heegeriella* (Zell.)

Recorded:	1980 – 2003
Distribution / Status:	Local / Common resident
Conservation status:	No perceived threats
Caterpillar food plants:	English Oak
Flight period:	Insufficient data. Elsewhere, May and August
Mines evident:	July; September to leaf-fall.
Records in database:	42

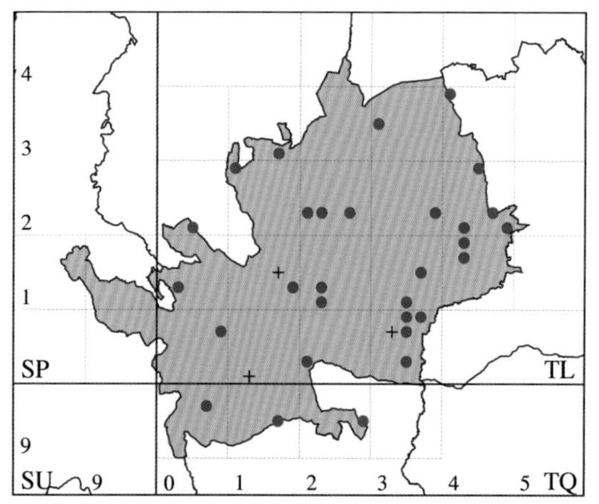

It is odd that we have no records prior to 1980 and none since the end of 2003. It has certainly been searched for in the years 2004 to 2006 and appears to be absent. The database lists ten records for year 2000, ten for 2001 and ten for 2002, but then only two for 2003 and none thereafter. Of course, populations of *Phyllonorycter* species undergo drastic rises and falls in tune with their parasites, so it may just be a good time for the latter at the moment. We have not found mines on Sessile Oak in spite of searching.

0318 *Phyllonorycter tenerella* (Joannis)

Recorded: 1900 – 2006
Distribution / Status: Widespread / Common resident
Conservation status: No perceived threats
Caterpillar food plants: Hornbeam
Flight period: No data. Elsewhere, May and August
Mines evident: June/July; September to leaf-fall
Records in database: 80

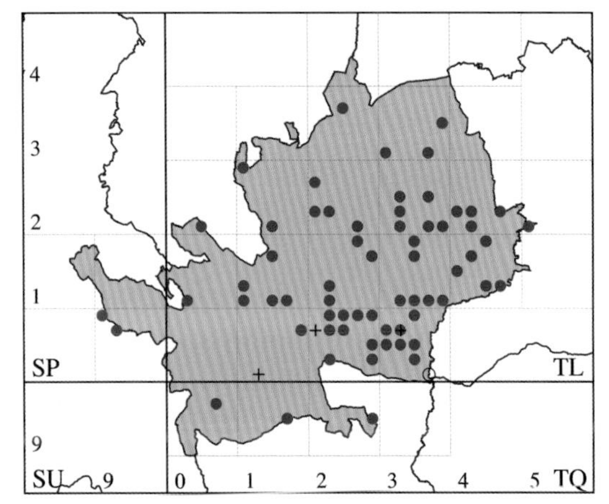

The distinctive mines on the under-surface of Hornbeam leaves are a common feature of Hertfordshire's woodlands, but the moth also utilises trees growing in isolation, in hedges and elsewhere and is likely to be found wherever hornbeam grows.

0319 *Phyllonorycter kuhlweiniella* (Zell.) = *saportella* (Dup.)

We have a single record, from the Sandridge area prior to 1890 (Griffith). As with 316: *P. roboris* this is the source of the Hertfordshire 'dot' in volume 2 of *Moths and Butterflies of Great Britain an Ireland*. Although generally scarce in the south-east of England, it has increased its range in recent years and may be overlooked with us. Emmet (1983) notes that it prefers to mine leaves high up in oak trees; this may be a factor in our failure to record it.

0320 *Phyllonorycter quercifoliella* (Zell.)

Recorded: 1890 – 2006
Distribution / Status: Ubiquitous / Abundant resident
Conservation status: No perceived threats
Caterpillar food plants: English Oak
Flight period: Insufficient data. Elsewhere, April/May and August/September
Mines evident: July; September to leaf-fall
Records in database: 213

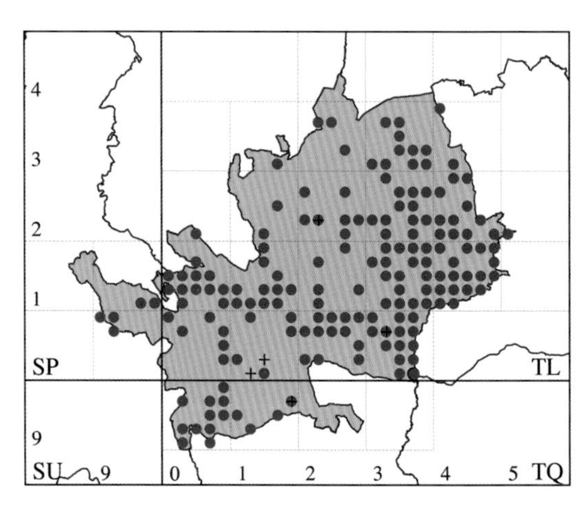

Experience has demonstrated emphatically that the mines of this species cannot be separated from those of 321: *P. messaniella* nor from the bulk of those of 315: *P. harrisella* and in order to generate the maps it has been necessary to embark upon and extensive programme of rearing adults. This has involved collecting batches of mines, putting all those from each site together inside the cut-off foot of a pair of nylon tights and staking the latter out on the ground under bushes in the garden until the following year. These were brought indoors during March and ignored until May, when they were opened and the dead, dried adults scooped up and dissected. This time-consuming exercise has ensured that the maps presented for all three species are valid.

0321 *Phyllonorycter messaniella* (Zell.)

Recorded: 1890 – 2006
Distribution / Status: Ubiquitous / Abundant resident
Conservation status: No perceived threats
Caterpillar food plants: English Oak; Sessile Oak; Beech; Sweet Chestnut. Elsewhere, also on Holm Oak and Hornbeam
Flight period: Insufficient data. Elsewhere, May and August
Mines evident: July; September to leaf-fall
Records in database: 177

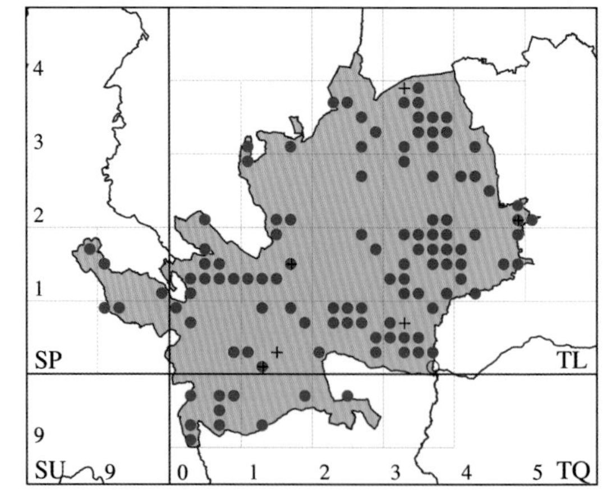

The comments under 320: *P. quercifoliella* in relation to naming the mines of this species also apply here.

0321a *Phyllonorycter platani* (Stdgr.)

Recorded: 1997 – 2006
Distribution / Status: Local / Abundant resident
Conservation status: No perceived threats
Caterpillar food plants: London Plane
Flight period: No data.
Mines evident: October/November
Records in database: 22

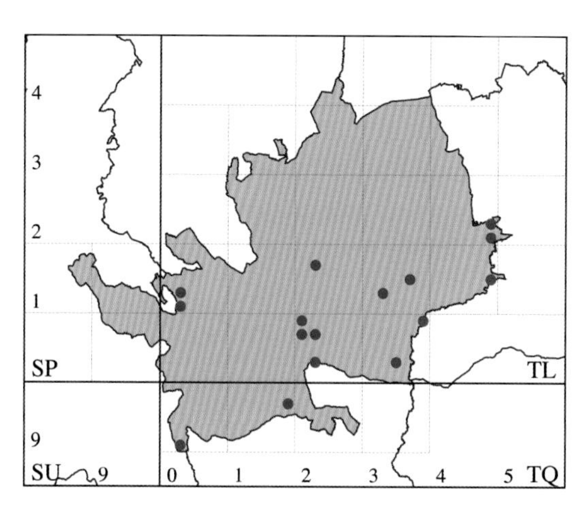

This is a relatively new species to the British Isles. It was first found here in October 1990 by the late Maitland Emmet during the course of the Annual Exhibition of the British Entomological and Natural History Society in South Kensington, London (Middlesex). It has spread rapidly since then. It was first found in Hertfordshire at Bishops Stortford in 1997 (Charles Watson), but this is quite a leap from London and surely it must have been overlooked in the south of the county between 1990 and 1997? During 2006 it can be expected wherever there are London Plane trees and there are often many mines on a single leaf.

0323 *Phyllonorycter oxyacanthae* (Frey)

Recorded: 1885 – 2006
Distribution / Status: Ubiquitous / Abundant resident
Conservation status: No perceived threats
Caterpillar food plants: Common Hawthorn; Midland Hawthorn; a non-native *Crataegus* species. Elsewhere, also on pear, quince and Wild Service
Flight period: Insufficient data. Elsewhere, May and August
Mines evident: July; September to leaf-fall
Records in database: 251

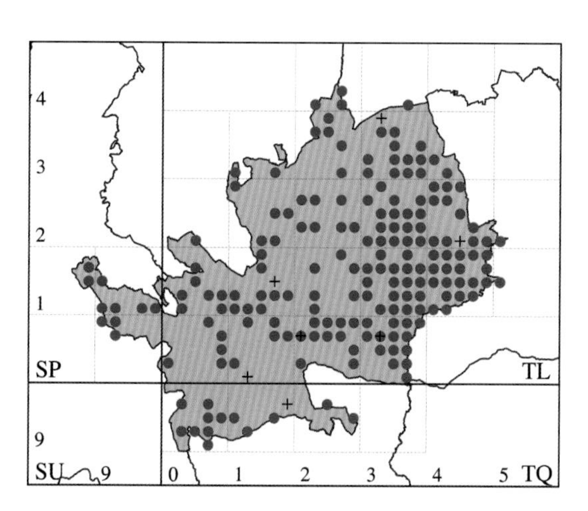

The caterpillar creates an unmistakable pucker mine on the underside of a hawthorn leaf and just about every hawthorn in the county is affected. Mines are frequently abundant on the bushes, though only very rarely more than one on a single leaf.

0324 *Phyllonorycter sorbi* (Frey)

Recorded: 1990 – 2006
Distribution / Status: Local / Common resident
Conservation status: No perceived threats
Caterpillar food plants: Rowan
Flight period: Insufficient data. Elsewhere, April/May and August
Mines evident: July; September to leaf-fall
Records in database: 23

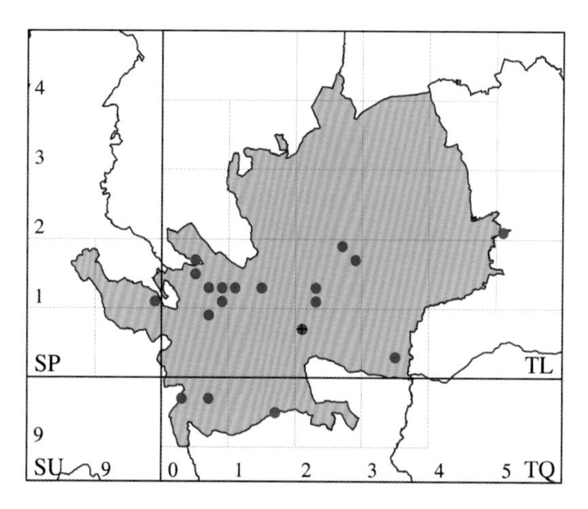

Elsewhere, the caterpillar sometimes mines Whitebeam and Bird-cherry, but in Hertfordshire we have only found it on Rowan. It is often present in great numbers, with almost every leaflet on a tree being mined, but mined trees themselves seem particularly local and in spite of searching I have been unable to find this species in the north of the county. Readers will hopefully take this as a challenge! Though most mines on Rowan will be this species, at least in Hertfordshire, this tree is also mined by 325: *P. mespilella* and 331: *P. lantanella*, so adults must be reared to confirm identifications.

0325 *Phyllonorycter mespilella* (Hb.)

Recorded: 1885 – 2005
Distribution / Status: Local / Common resident
Conservation status: Herts Scarce
Caterpillar food plants: Rowan; Wild Service
Flight period: No data. Elsewhere, May and August
Mines evident: October. Elsewhere July and September to November
Records in database: 5

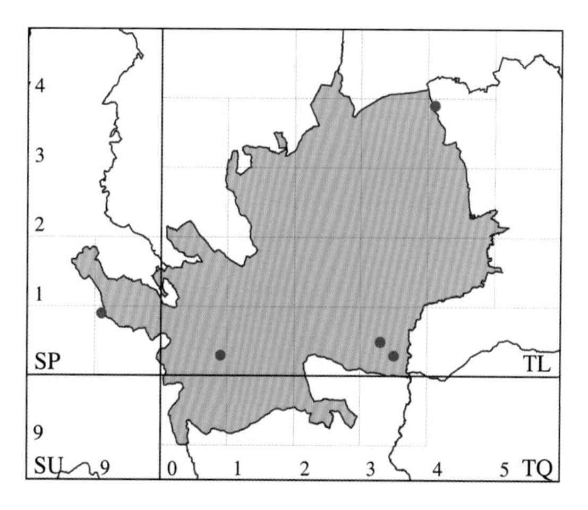

This is said to be the most frequent mine on leaves of Wild Service trees, but elsewhere in Britain the leaves of this rather rare tree are sometimes mined by 323: *P. oxyacanthae* and 324: *P. sorbi* so it is important to rear adults to confirm the identity. *Phyllonorycter mespilella* also mines Rowan and, elsewhere in Britain, pear. It is rarely found in Hertfordshire.

0326 *Phyllonorycter blancardella* Fabr.

Recorded: 1923 – 2006
Distribution / Status: Widespread / Common resident
Conservation status: No perceived threats
Caterpillar food plants: Domestic Apple; Crab Apple
Flight period: No data. Elsewhere, May and August
Mines evident: July; September to leaf-fall
Records in database: 45

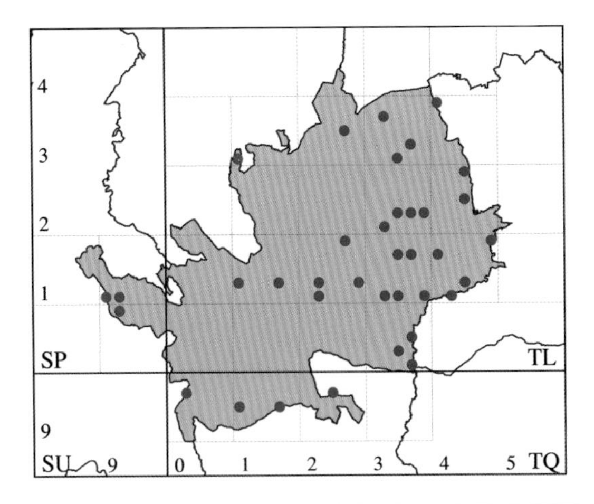

Considerable care must be exercised in interpreting old records of *blancardella*, *cydoniella* and *mespilella*. The name *blancardella* has been used for both the current understanding of *blancardella* and for *cydoniella*, whilst *pomifoliella* has been used for both *cydoniella* and *mespilella*. It is my opinion that the current *blancardella* was intended by Foster (1937) in recording *Lithocolletis concomitella* Bankes, for 'Letchworth, Knebworth '1923' (Edwards); Hitchin (Durrant)'. A few years later, Foster (1942) adds *blancardella* Fabr. (= *pomifoliella* Zell.) to the county list from Hitchin, in 1941, and I take this to be present-day *cydoniella*. Other old records are less easy to interpret and have been disregarded for the present exercise. The map shows only confirmed modern records of what we currently call *blancardella*.

0327 *Phyllonorycter cydoniella* ([D.& S.])

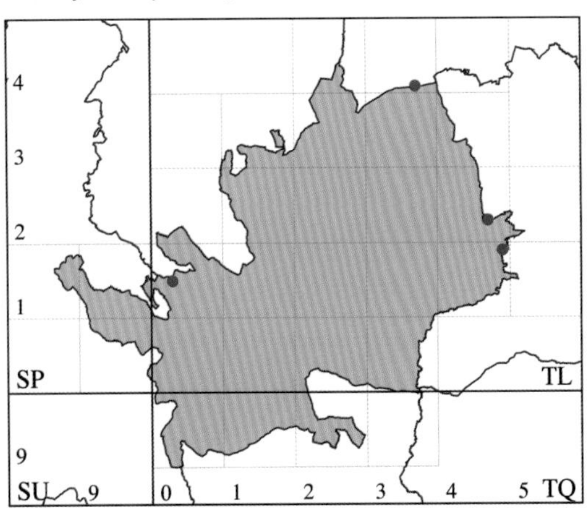

Recorded: 2000 – 2006
Distribution / Status: Local / Uncommon resident
Conservation status: Herts Scarce
Caterpillar food plants: Quince; Crab Apple
Flight period: No data. Elsewhere, May and August
Mines evident: October/November. Elsewhere, also June and July
Records in database: 4

Comments on synonymy are given under the last species. In Hertfordshire, it appears that *P. cydoniella* is not common and most candidate mines have produced *blancardella* adults – demonstrating, if nothing else, the absolute need to rear adults for positive identification.

0329 *Phyllonorycter spinicolella* (Zell.) = *pomonella* auct.

Recorded: 1890 – 2006
Distribution / Status: Ubiquitous / Common resident
Conservation status: No perceived threats
Caterpillar food plants: Blackthorn; Domestic Plum (=Bullace)
Flight period: No data. Elsewhere, May and August
Mines evident: July; September to leaf-fall
Records in database: 135

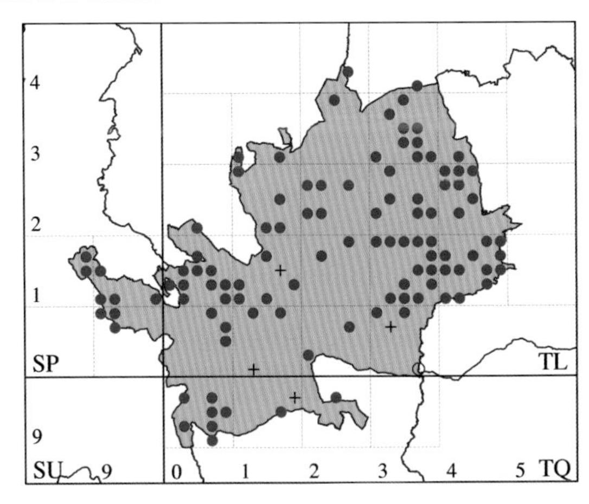

This is the only *Phyllonorycter* on Blackthorn in Britain and it is usually easy to distinguish from the mines of both 308: *Parornix finitimella* and 309: *Deltaornix torquillella*, which also mine the underside of the leaves, because the lower epidermis of the leaf remains green. *Phyllonorycter* species also pupate within the mine, whilst the larvae of the other two species leave the mine and feed in a folded leaf in later instars.

0330 *Phyllonorycter cerasicolella* (H.- S.)

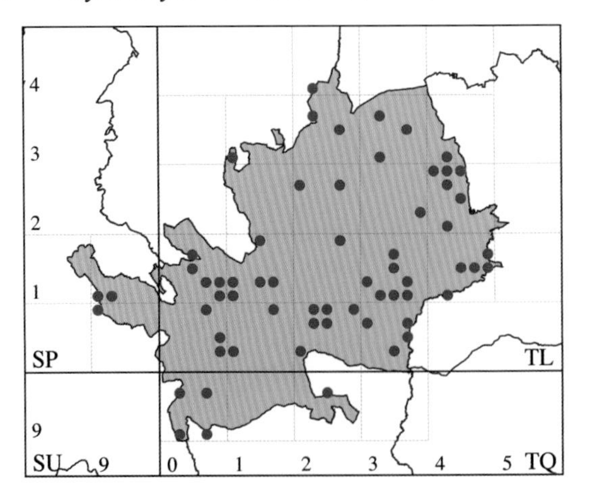

Recorded: 2000 – 2006
Distribution / Status: Ubiquitous / Common resident
Conservation status: No perceived threats
Caterpillar food plants: Wild Cherry (native); Sour Cherry; ornamental cherry

Flight period: No data. Elsewhere, May and August
Mines evident: July; September to leaf-fall
Records in database: 76

A common species that is likely to be found on most if not all cherry trees in the county.

0331 *Phyllonorycter lantanella* (Schrank)

Recorded: 1890 – 2006
Distribution / Status: Local / Common resident
Conservation status: No perceived threats
Caterpillar food plants: Wayfaring Tree (most records); Guelder Rose (few)
Flight period: No data. Elsewhere, May and August
Mines evident: July; September to leaf-fall
Records in database: 14

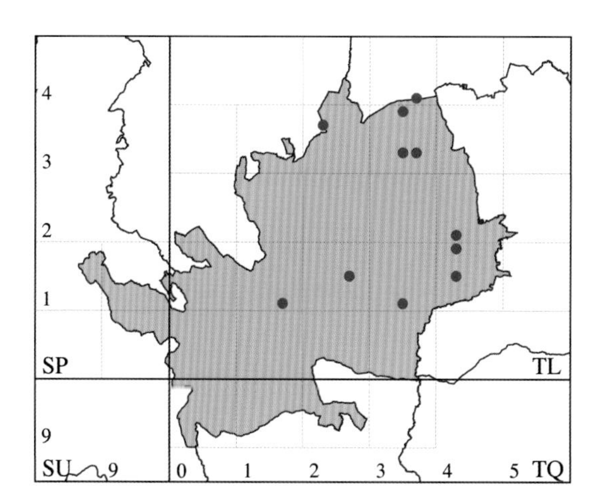

Most records are from established semi-natural *Viburnum* in woodlands and hedgerows, but since about 2002 we have started to find occasional mines in the ornamental *Viburnum* that are sometimes densely planted on new road verges. It would be nice to think that this may reflect a move towards native strains of shrubs, and away from ornamental varieties, as a result of greater ecological awareness on the part of the environmental consultancies who manage the planting. There is scope for original research in this area.

0332 *Phyllonorycter corylifoliella* (Hb.)

Recorded: 1890 – 2006
Distribution / Status: Ubiquitous / Abundant resident
Conservation status: No perceived threats
Caterpillar food plants: Common Hawthorn; Midland Hawthorn; Crab Apple; Domestic apple; ornamental cherry; *Cotoneaster* sp., Rowan, Whitebeam.
Flight period: No data. Elsewhere, May/June and August
Mines evident: July; September to leaf-fall
Records in database: 252

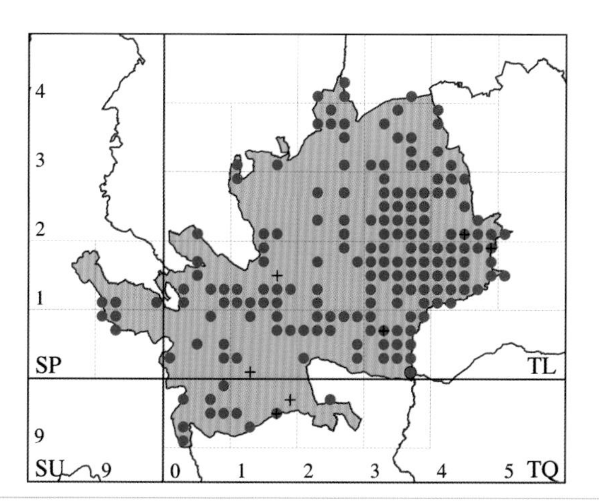

Hawthorn is the most frequent foodplant, but the larva probably feeds in the leaves of almost all rosaceous trees and shrubs. The mine is made on the upper surface of the leaf and is speckled with brownish frass pellets making it easily separated from 332a: *P. leucographella* which appears to be starting to make the leap away from its original *Pyracantha* to hawthorn and perhaps other rosaceous trees and bushes. This moth is surely to be found in every map tetrad in Hertfordshire?

0332a *Phyllonorycter leucographella* (Zell.)

Recorded: 1989 – 2006
Distribution / Status: Ubiquitous / Abundant resident
Conservation status: No perceived threats
Caterpillar food plants: Firethorn. Elsewhere, also on hawthorn, pear, apple and species of *Sorbus*
Flight period: May and October
Mines evident: November to April
Records in database: 106

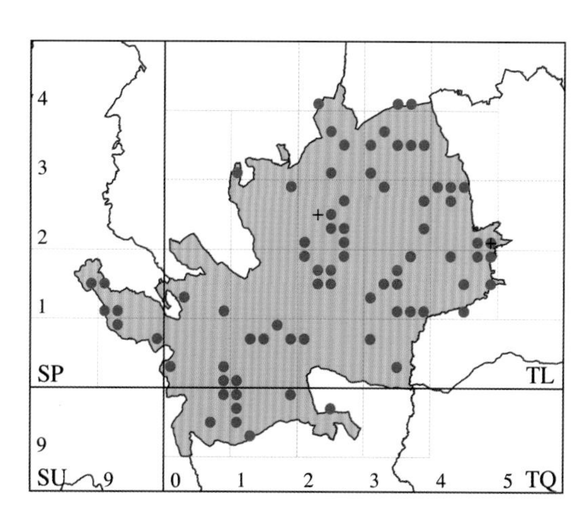

The first British record of this species was made in 1989 when mines were discovered in Essex (Emmet, 1989); I found the first Hertfordshire mines a few weeks later on the Firethorn bush in front of my study window in Bishops Stortford. As far as I am aware they were not there previously and although the spread of the moth was, and perhaps still is, assisted by the garden trade it seems that mine arrived unaided from some nearby site. The spread in Britain has been documented by Nash *et al* (1995). The next day, Charles Watson found mines on plants at his nursery in Bishops Stortford. Most of Hertfordshire had been 'colonised' by the end of 1991 and today the bright white mines may be seen easily during the winter months on the upper surface of Firethorn leaves in front gardens and elsewhere across the county. Away from Hertfordshire, mines have now been found on hawthorn, and so it is important to note that *leucographella* mines have a shining white 'skin' that is not speckled with frass like the translucent 'skin' of 332: *P. corylifoliella* mines.

0333 *Phyllonorycter salictella* (Zell.) ssp. *viminiella* (Sirc.)

Recorded: 1890 – 2006
Distribution / Status: Local / Common resident
Conservation status: No perceived threats
Caterpillar food plants: White Willow, Weeping Willow, Crack Willow, Osier and unidentified willows
Flight period: No data. Elsewhere, May and August
Mines evident: July; September to leaf-fall
Records in database: 50

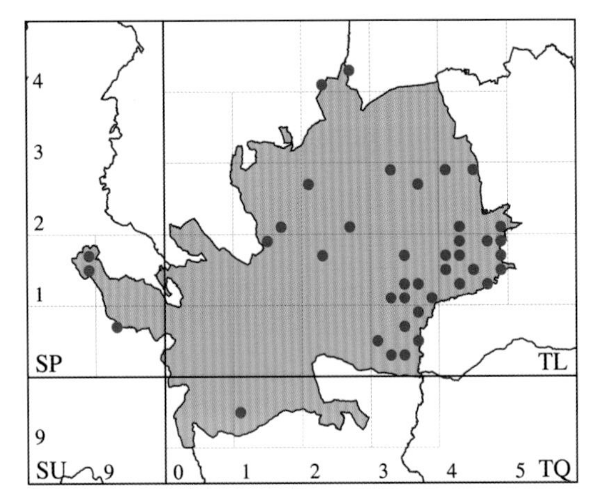

The unusual distribution pattern, showing a concentration of records in the south-east of the county and a lack of reports from much of the south-west probably reflects a concerted effort to rear adults from willow leaves by entomologists living in this area. The moth is quite able to thrive on weeping willow varieties in gardens and so ought to be widespread.

0334 *Phyllonorycter viminetorum* (Stt.)

Recorded: 1900 – 2006
Distribution / Status: Local / Uncommon resident
Conservation status: Herts Scarce
Caterpillar food plants: Common Osier
Flight period: No data. Elsewhere, May and August
Mines evident: October and November. Elsewhere June/July and September to November
Records in database: 6

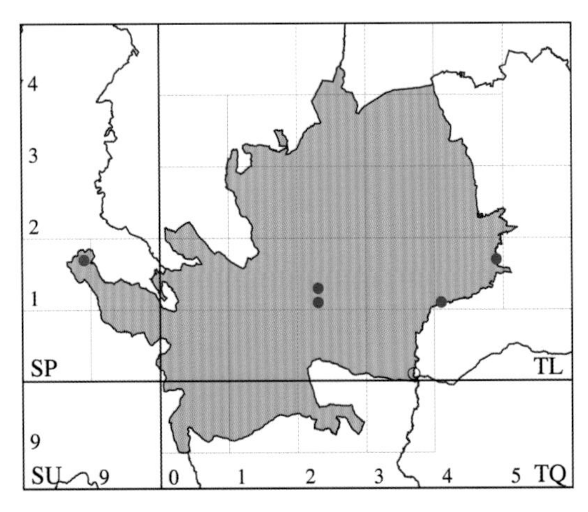

The apparent inability of this species to feed in any leaves other than those of Common Osier is likely to be the reason behind its scarcity. We have no records of mines on any of the hybrid willows involving *Salix viminalis* as a parent.

0335 *Phyllonorycter salicicolella* (Sirc.)

Recorded: 1890 – 2006
Distribution / Status: Widespread / Common resident
Conservation status: No perceived threats
Caterpillar food plants: Common Sallow, Goat Willow; unidentified sallows, including hybrids
Flight period: No data. Elsewhere, May and August
Mines evident: July; September to leaf-fall
Records in database: 53

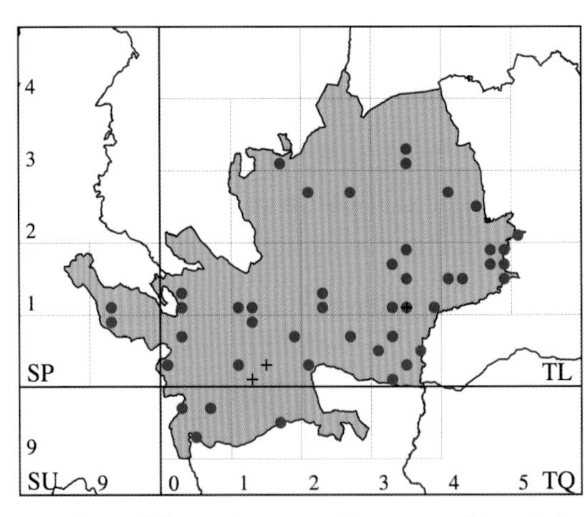

Almost all candidate mines on sallows (round/rough-leaved *Salix* species) in Hertfordshire will be this species, but it is necessary to rear adults to separate out any 336**:** *P. dubitella* and 337**:** *P. hilarella* which also mine these plants.

0336 *Phyllonorycter dubitella* (H.- S.)

Recorded: 1980 only
Distribution / Status: Extremely local or absent / Rare resident or extinct
Conservation status: Insufficiently known
Caterpillar food plants: Common Sallow? Elsewhere, usually on Goat Willow
Flight period: No data. Elsewhere, May/June and August
Mines evident: October/November. Elsewhere July and September/October
Records in database: 1

The only record for this species in the county is from Bricket Wood, where Maitland Emmet found mines on 2nd November 1980 and reared adults. This seems surprising and one wonders if Maitland may have misidentified *Salix caprea* as *Salix cinerea*? The sallows and willows are not easy to name. Where Hertfordshire mines on Common Sallow have been reared through, the result has always been *salicicolella*.

0337 *Phyllonorycter hilarella* (Zett.) = *spinolella* (Dup.)

Recorded: 1980 – 2001
Distribution / Status: Local / Rare resident
Conservation status: Herts Rare
Caterpillar food plants: Not recorded. Elsewhere on various *Salix* species
Flight period: No data. Elsewhere, May and August
Mines evident: October/November. Elsewhere July and September to November
Records in database: 5

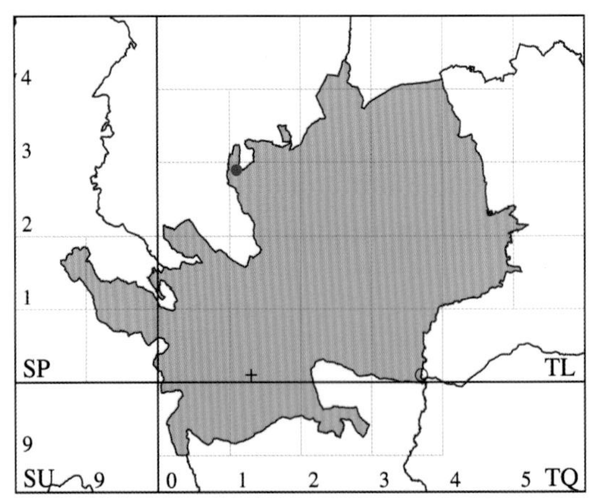

For the nineteenth century there are two record – from the Sandridge area prior to 1885 and Cheshunt prior to 1901. Foster (1937) adds a record from Ashridge. We have not mapped the Sandridge and Ashridge records as the precise locality cannot be determined adequately enough. The validity of all three records cannot be determined as there are no specimens. More recently there are only two valid records – from Bricket Wood on 2nd November 1980 (Maitland Emmet) and my own from Hexton Chalk Pit on 20th October 2001.

0339 *Phyllonorycter ulicicolella* (Stt.)

Recorded:	1966 only
Distribution / Status:	Absent or extremely local / Extinct or perhaps under-recorded
Conservation status:	Insufficiently known
Caterpillar food plants:	Not recorded. Elsewhere on Gorse
Flight period:	July.
Mines evident:	No data. Elsewhere September to May
Records in database:	1

Adults caught by Eric Bradford at Borehamwood on 30th July 1966 are our only evidence of this species in Hertfordshire. The caterpillars mine under the bark of shoots and modified leaves (spines) of Gorse from September onwards. The mines are very hard (and painful) to find and there can be no doubt that this species is likely to be found if adequate searching is undertaken.

0340 *Phyllonorycter scopariella* (Zell.)

Recorded:	1890 – 1964
Distribution / Status:	Absent or extremely local / Extinct or perhaps under-recorded
Conservation status:	Insufficiently known
Caterpillar food plants:	Not recorded. Elsewhere on Broom
Flight period:	July. Elsewhere June/July
Mines evident:	No data. Elsewhere August to October
Records in database:	3

The Sandridge area, prior to 1890 (Griffith) and Borehamwood, where adults were caught on 27th June 1962 and 27th July 1964 (Eric Bradford) are the only localities for this species in the county. Searching in recent years has failed to produce mines, though they are hard to spot and the possibility that this is an overlooked species remains. Beating broom bushes in June and early July is likely to produce adults if they are present.

0341 *Phyllonorycter maestingella* (Mull.)

Recorded:	1890 – 2006
Distribution / Status:	Ubiquitous / Abundant resident
Conservation status:	No perceived threats
Caterpillar food plants:	Beech
Flight period:	No data. Elsewhere, May/June and August
Mines evident:	July; September to leaf-fall
Records in database:	136

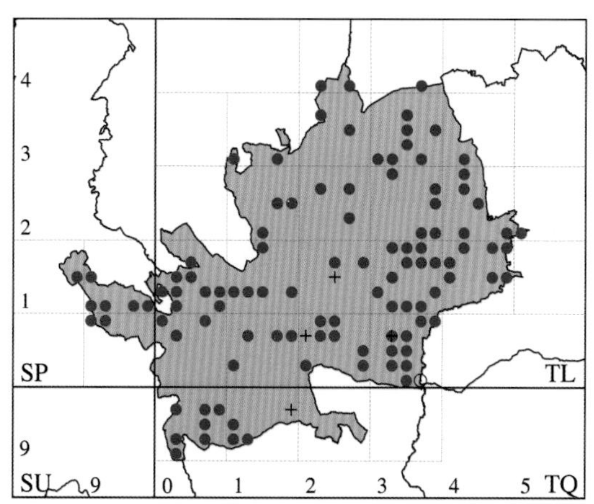

Mines of this species will be found on almost every beech tree in the county, from the mature trees that make up the woodlands over towards Buckinghamshire to the closely cropped garden hedges of the north-east. Copper Beech is also reported as a host plant from other counties.

0342 *Phyllonorycter coryli* (Nic.)

Recorded:	1890 – 2006
Distribution / Status:	Ubiquitous / Abundant resident
Conservation status:	No perceived threats
Caterpillar food plants:	Hazel
Flight period:	No data. Elsewhere, May and August
Mines evident:	July; September to leaf-fall
Records in database:	198

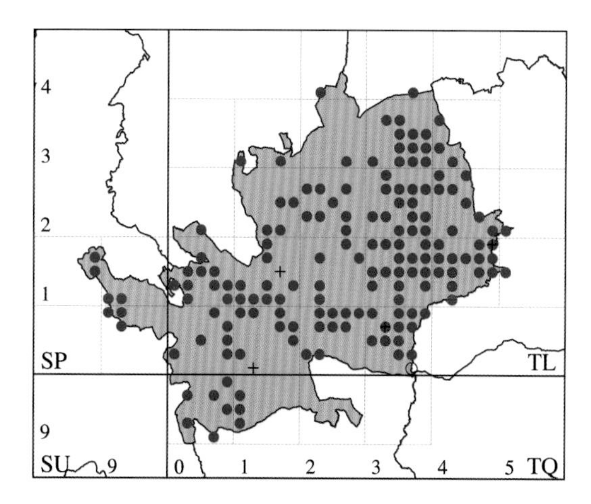

The distinctive white mines on the upper surface of Hazel leaves in hedges, woodlands and town parks makes this one of the easiest moths to record – it can be seen easily from the car window when driving along country lanes, though it is advisable to stop and check before submitting the record!

0343 *Phyllonorycter esperella* Goeze = *quinnata* (Geoff.)

Recorded:	1890 – 2006
Distribution / Status:	Widespread / Common resident
Conservation status:	No perceived threats
Caterpillar food plants:	Hornbeam
Flight period:	No data. Elsewhere, May and August
Mines evident:	July; September to leaf-fall
Records in database:	112

This is another species that makes a mine that is immediately recognisable – this one on the upper surface of Hornbeam leaves. Away from the hornbeam-dominated woodlands on the

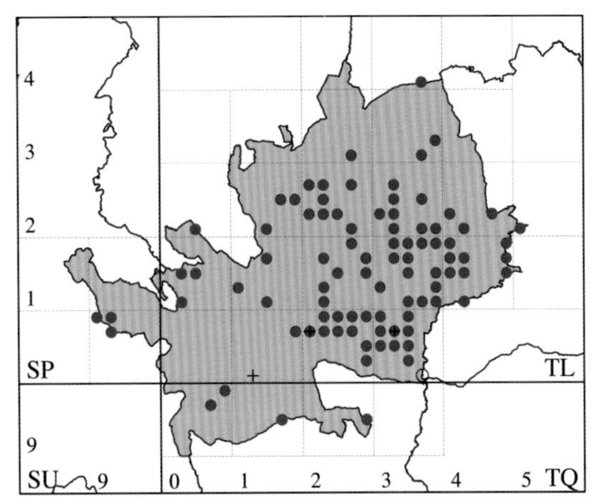

south-eastern gravels the mines are evident on trees planted in gardens.

[0344 *Phyllonorycter strigulatella* (Zell.)

The early synonymy of this species allows for confusion with modern-day *rajella* sensu Linnaeus. *Phyllonorycter strigulatella* (Zell.) was called *alnifoliella* by Duponchel whilst *rajella* has been called *alnifoliella* by Hübner. To add further confusion, *strigulatella* has been applied to Linnaeus' *rajella* by some authors. Foster's 1937 list gives only one species – *alnifoliella* Dup. (= *alniella* Zell.) – from Sandridge (Griffith) and Cheshunt (Boyd). This is thought to relate to 345: *P. rajella*. Volume 2 of *MBGBI* shows a Hertfordshire dot for *rajella*, but none for *strigulatella*, suggesting that the author of that work reached the same conclusion. *Phyllonorycter strigulatella* is, therefore, not admitted to the Hertfordshire fauna.]

0345 *Phyllonorycter rajella* (L.)

Recorded: 1890 – 2006
Distribution / Status: Local / Common resident
Conservation status: No perceived threats
Caterpillar food plants: Alder. Elsewhere also on Grey Alder and Italian Alder
Flight period: No data. Elsewhere, May and August
Mines evident: July; September to leaf-fall
Records in database: 37

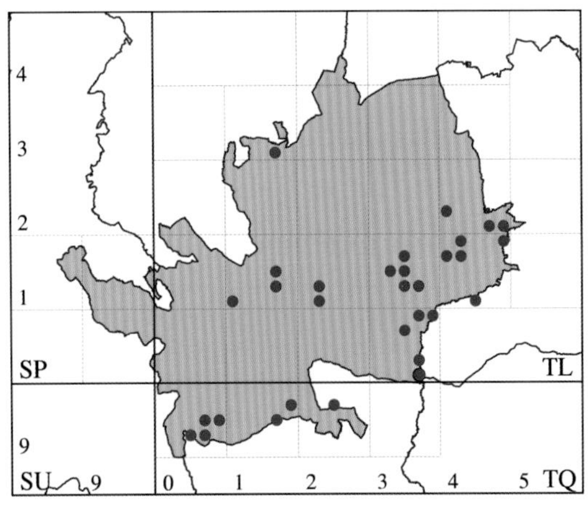

Foodplant availability may limit the range of this species in Hertfordshire, but its ability to thrive on the non-native alders elsewhere is doubtless repeated here and allows for its relatively widespread distribution in comparison with, for example, 114: *Stigmella glutinosae*.

0347 *Phyllonorycter anderidae* (Fletcher)

Volume 2 of *Moths and Butterflies of Great Britain and Ireland*, published in 1985, shows a dot for this species in the Hertfordshire vice-county, but there is no supporting evidence available. The records for were, at that date, maintained by Maitland Emmet who is perhaps the least likely person to have allowed an erroneous record of a leaf-miner to creep into the system. The caterpillars mine leaves of birch, almost always in low-growing saplings, but unlike the very common 353: *Phyllonorycter ulmifoliella* (which may also mine saplings) pupates naked in the mine without spinning a silk cocoon.

0351 *Phyllonorycter lautella* (Zell.)

Recorded: 1976 – 2003
Distribution / Status: Local / Rare resident
Conservation status: Herts Scarce
Caterpillar food plants: English Oak
Flight period: No data. Elsewhere, May and August
Mines evident: October/November. Elsewhere, July and September/October
Records in database: 10

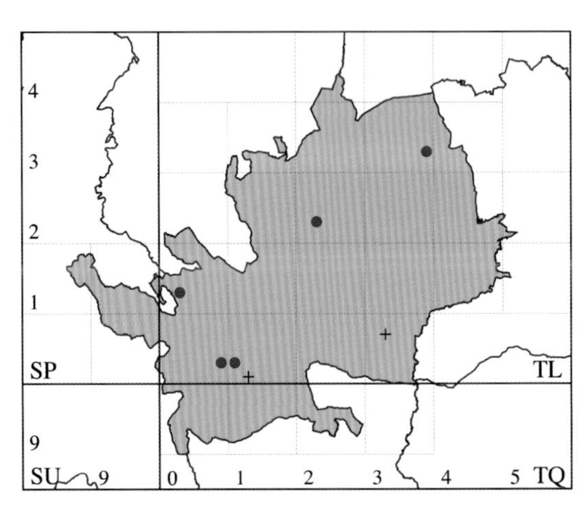

Amongst the several *Phyllonorycter* species that create larval mines on deciduous oak leaves, this one is usually fairly distinctive by reason of its colossal size in comparison with its brethren. Rearing of adults is nevertheless desirable to confirm any identification. The apparent scarcity of the species might be thought to reflect a penchant for the highest branches of oak trees, well beyond the reach and visibility of the average lepidopterist, although John Langmaid informs me that he usually finds it on sapling oaks! The map shows confirmed records only.

0352 *Phyllonorycter schreberella* Fabr.

Recorded: 1890 – 2006
Distribution / Status: Widespread / Uncommon resident
Conservation status: No perceived threats
Caterpillar food plants: Wych Elm, English Elm (suckers); unidentified elms
Flight period: No data. Elsewhere May and August
Mines evident: July; September to leaf-fall
Records in database: 32

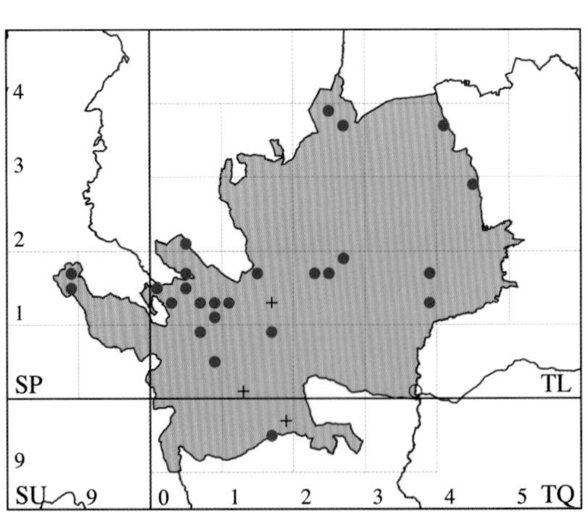

A large, sub-circular mine on elm leaves will be this species – usually easily separated from the smaller and elongated mines of 356: *P. tristrigella*. It appears to be far less prevalent than *tristrigella*, however.

0353 *Phyllonorycter ulmifoliella* (Hb.)

Recorded: 1890 – 2006
Distribution / Status: Widespread / Common resident
Conservation status: No perceived threats
Caterpillar food plants: Silver Birch; Downy Birch
Flight period: No data. Elsewhere, May and August
Mines evident: July; September to leaf-fall
Records in database: 81

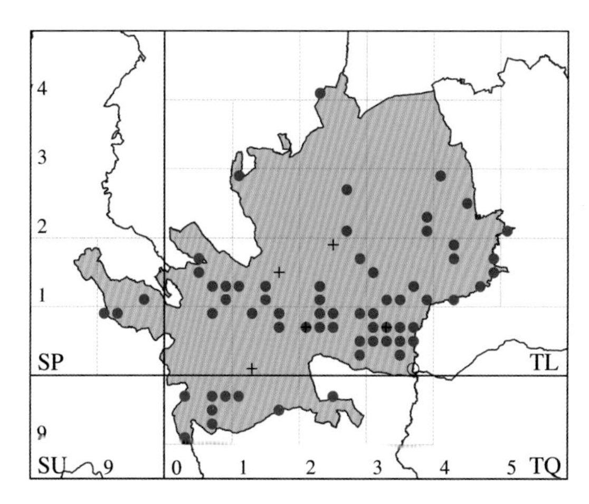

Confusion over the food plant of the specimen that was originally described by Hübner is responsible for the wholly inappropriate name of this species, which feeds on birch. It is expected wherever there are birch trees and is found on both mature trees and young saplings, though rarely on seedlings.

0354 *Phyllonorycter emberizaepenella* (Bouché)

Recorded: 1890 – 1901
Distribution / Status: Absent / Extinct
Conservation status: Herts Extinct
Caterpillar food plants: Not recorded. Elsewhere, Honeysuckle and Snowberry
Flight period: Not recorded. Elsewhere, May and August
Mines evident: July then September/October
Records in database: 2

Griffith (1890) records this species from the Sandridge area and Boyd (1901) notes it in his list for Cheshunt. The caterpillars mine the leaves of honeysuckle, which is plentiful in many of Hertfordshire's woodlands. There have been no records since 1901 and the moth is presumed extinct in Hertfordshire.

0356 *Phyllonorycter tristrigella* (Haw.)

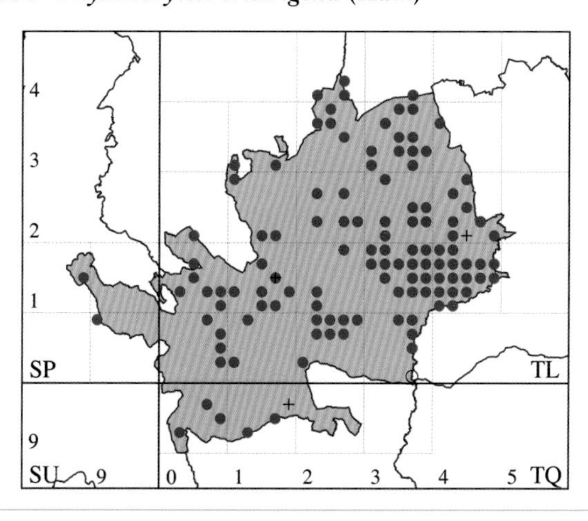

Recorded: 1885 – 2006
Distribution / Status: Widespread / Common resident
Conservation status: No perceived threats
Caterpillar food plants: English Elm; unidentified elm
Flight period: No data. Elsewhere, May and August
Mines evident: July; September to leaf-fall
Records in database: 140

This common moth appears not to favour Wych Elm as a host plant. Most mines are on leaves of English Elm 'suckers', but very rarely are they found on leaves that are also infected with mite galls.

0357 *Phyllonorycter stettinensis* (Nic.)

Recorded: 1890 – 2006
Distribution / Status: Local / Common resident
Conservation status: No perceived threats
Caterpillar food plants: Alder. Elsewhere, also on Grey and Italian Alders
Flight period: No data. Elsewhere, May and August
Mines evident: July; September to leaf-fall
Records in database: 33

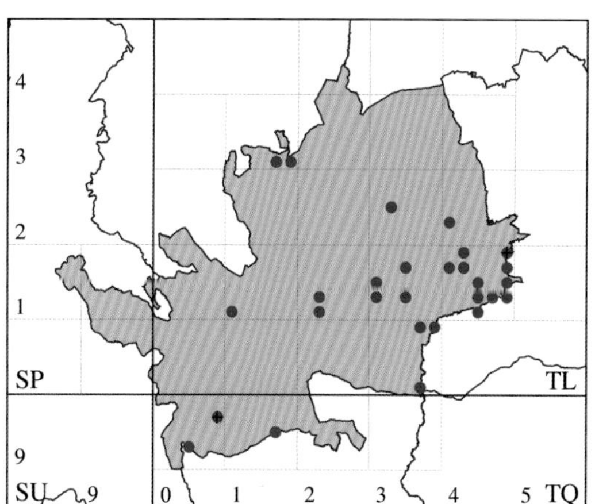

The upper surface mines of *P. stettinensis* can be confused with those of the sawflies *Heterarthrus vagans* and *Fenusa dohrnii*, both of which are common in Hertfordshire.

0358 *Phyllonorycter froelichiella* (Zell.)

Recorded: 2005 only
Distribution / Status: Local / Rare resident
Conservation status: Herts Rare
Caterpillar food plants: Alder
Flight period: Elsewhere July and August
Mines evident: August
Records in database: 1

Our only county record is of the very long mines found by me on Common Alder by the Fiddlers Bridge at Gilston in 2005. The absence of this species from elsewhere is rather surprising, although Goodey (2002) shows an equivalent absence of records on the Essex side of the Rivers Lea and Stort.

0359 *Phyllonorycter nicellii* (Stt.)

Recorded: 1890 – 2006
Distribution / Status: Ubiquitous / Common resident
Conservation status: No perceived threats
Caterpillar food plants: Hazel
Flight period: No data. Elsewhere, May and August
Mines evident: July; September to leaf-fall
Records in database: 138

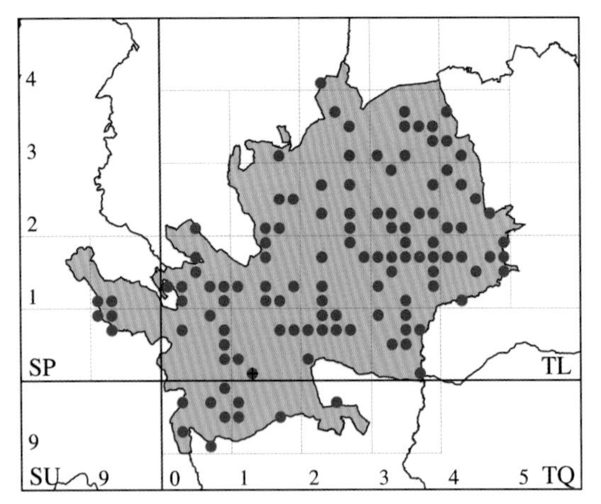

This is the only species to mine the lower surface of hazel leaves apart from 304: *Parornix devoniella*, which later vacates the mine to feed in a folded leaf-edge. It is likely to be found on every hazel bush in the county.

0360 *Phyllonorycter kleemannella* (Fabr.)

Recorded: 1890 – 2006
Distribution / Status: Local / Common resident
Conservation status: No perceived threats
Caterpillar food plants: Common Alder
Flight period: No data. Elsewhere August
Mines evident: September to leaf-fall
Records in database: 24

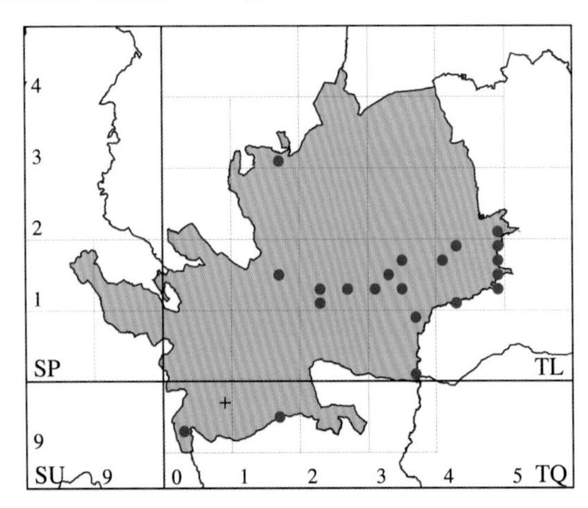

Like 345: *Phyllonorycter rajella* and 357: *P. stettinensis*, only native alder seems to be suitable and the map is similar to that for both those species.

0361 *Phyllonorycter trifasciella* (Haw.)

Recorded: 1890 – 2006
Distribution / Status: Local / Common resident
Conservation status: No perceived threats
Caterpillar food plants: Wild Honeysuckle; cultivated honeysuckle, Snowberry; Himalayan Honeysuckle
Flight period: No data. Elsewhere, May and August
Mines evident: October to leaf-fall. Elsewhere also in July
Records in database: 34

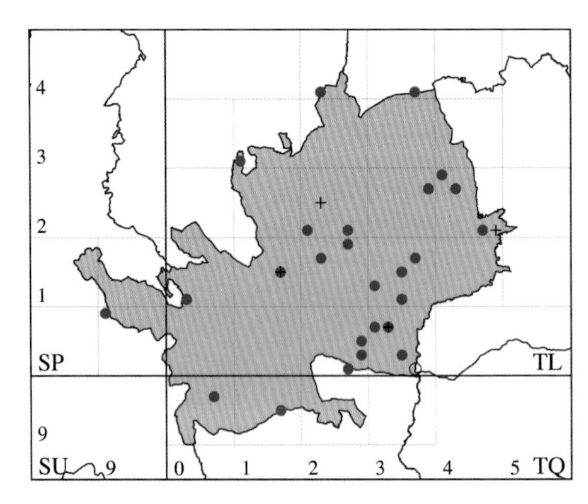

The mines of this species usually cause extreme twisting of the affected leaf so that they are at once separable from those made by 354: *Phyllonorycter emberizaepenella*, which is considered extinct in the county. The moth appears to undergo considerable swings in abundance. It was plentiful in my garden at Bishops Stortford in 1992, mining almost every leaf of my single Himalayan Honeysuckle bush. The next year it was less numerous and by 1995 it was absent and did not reappear until 2000, when it was in small number. The bush died the following winter and was removed so no further observation was possible.

0362 *Phyllonorycter acerifoliella* (Zell.) = *sylvella* (Haw.)

Recorded: 1890 – 2006
Distribution / Status: Ubiquitous / Common resident
Conservation status: No perceived threats
Caterpillar food plants: Field Maple
Flight period: No data. Elsewhere, May and August
Mines evident: July; October to leaf-fall
Records in database: 170

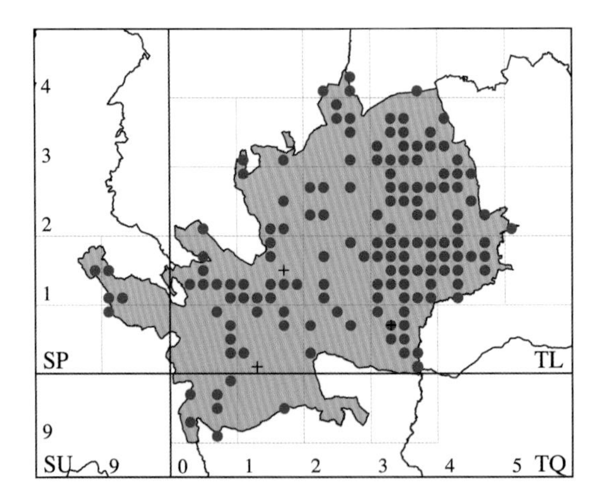

Almost every semi-mature or older Field Maple tree in Hertfordshire seems to support mines of this species, though the mines are small and often need to be searched for. Mature hedgerow maples are also affected, but saplings may not be.

0363 *Phyllonorycter platanoidella* (Joannis)

Recorded: 1981 – 2006
Distribution / Status: Widespread / Common resident
Conservation status: No perceived threats
Caterpillar food plants: Norway Maple
Flight period: No data. Elsewhere, May and August
Mines evident: October to leaf-fall
Records in database: 58

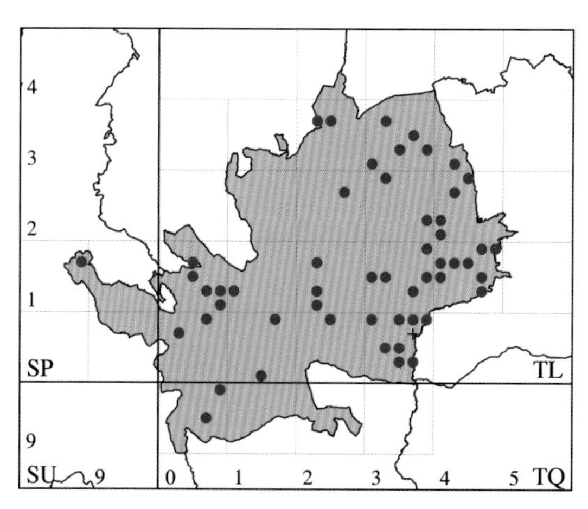

The validity of this species as one that is distinct from 362: *Phyllonorycter acerifoliella* has been questioned in the past, as they are very similar in wing pattern and genitalia. Current thinking regards the two as distinct, but whatever is eventually decided it seems sensible to segregate records. The distribution closely follows the planting of Norway Maple in parks and on road verges. Our first record was from the West Car Park at Broxbourne Wood on 12th September 1981, when Maitland Emmet found mines.

0364 *Phyllonorycter geniculella* (Ragonot)

Recorded: 1980 – 2006
Distribution / Status: Ubiquitous / Common resident
Conservation status: No perceived threats
Caterpillar food plants: Sycamore
Flight period: No data. Elsewhere, May and August
Mines evident: October to leaf-fall
Records in database: 80

Just about every Sycamore tree examined at the appropriate season will yield mines of this very common species in Hertfordshire. Surprisingly, however, our first record is as recent as 2nd November 1980, when Maitland Emmet found mines at Bricket Wood.

0365 *Phyllonorycter comparella* (Dup.)

Our only record of this moth is that made by Boyd in the Cheshunt area, and published by him in 1901. The caterpillar mines poplar leaves.

0366a *Cameraria ohridella* Deschka & Dimic Horse-chestnut Leaf Miner

Recorded: 2003 – 2006
Distribution / Status: Ubiquitous / Abundant resident
Conservation status: No perceived threats
Caterpillar food plants: Horse-chestnut.
Flight period: Insufficient data, probably continuously brooded
Mines evident: June to leaf-fall: as yet, no spring mines are recorded
Records in database: 170

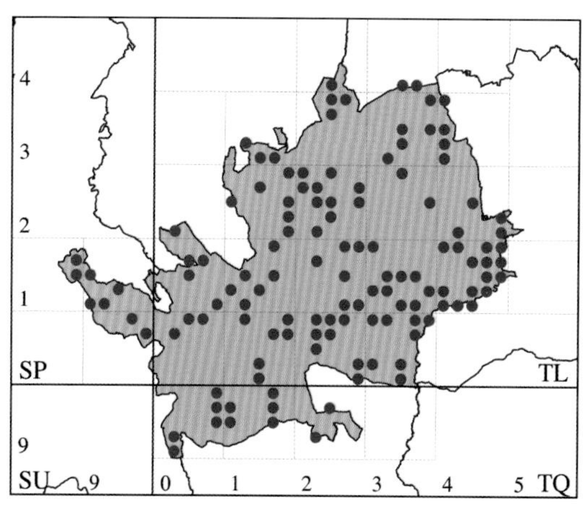

The Horse Chestnut Leaf Miner was first observed in Macedonia in northern Greece in the late 1970s, and was described as a new species in 1986. In 1989, it appeared unexpectedly in Austria and has since spread throughout central and Eastern Europe. Its current distribution includes Belgium, The Netherlands, Denmark, southern Sweden, all of Germany, Poland and the central European countries and it is currently spreading west through France and south through Italy. Since 2002 it has been reported from Spain, Albania, Turkey, Ukraine, Moldova, Belarus and western Russia. It was first found established in Britain at Wimbledon in July 2002. The moth has since spread to many parts of south-east England, and by November 2005 it had been found at separate locations as far away as Wales and the north Norfolk coast. The spread was evidently not linear, however. It arrived in Hertfordshire in the extreme south-west at West Hyde, where mines were found on 5th November 2003 by Ann Piper. In 2004 it was found in Maple Cross, Hatfield and Essendon and the following year it was located in 27 places up to about half-way up the county. During 2006 it spread to cover the entire area, but many of the sites examined did not support the moth in 2005. It is now likely to be present in large number on every Horse-chestnut tree in the county; the map does not include any record made after the end of December 2006.

PHYLOCNISTINAE

0367 *Phyllocnistis saligna* (Zell.)

Recorded: 1868 – 1997
Distribution / Status: Absent / Extinct resident
Conservation status: Herts Extinct
Caterpillar food plants: No data. Elsewhere, on Crack Willow and Purple Osier
Flight period: No data. Elsewhere July then September to April
Mines evident: No data. Elsewhere June and August
Records in database: 5

First noted in the county from Cheshunt in 1868 (Boyd, 1868) it was recorded from the Sandridge area by Griffith prior to 1890 and from Hitchin by Durrant in 1885. The only other reports are from Tom Gladwin who recorded it at Lemsford Springs in 1979 and Panshanger Park in 1997, though without voucher specimens.

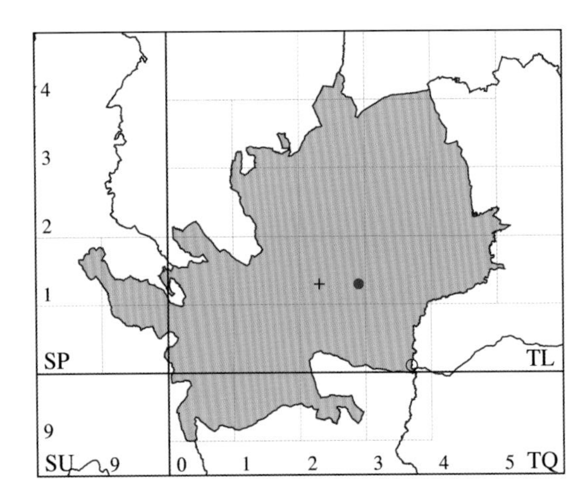

0368 *Phyllocnistis unipunctella* (Steph.)

Recorded:	1885 – 2006
Distribution / Status:	Local / Common resident
Conservation status:	No perceived threats
Caterpillar food plants:	native Black Poplar; Lombardy poplar
Flight period:	No data. Elsewhere July then September to April
Mines evident:	August to leaf-fall. Elsewhere also in June
Records in database:	38

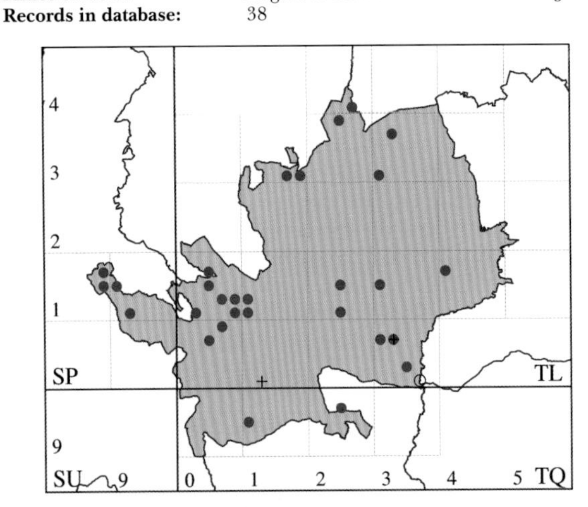

The mines of this species are quite unmistakable and resemble the slime trails of snails across the surface of poplar leaves. However, they are hard to spot unless the angle of the light is appropriate and this may well account for some under-recording.

SESIOIDEA
SESIIDAE

The 'clearwings' are amongst the most unusual of British moths by virtue of the transparent 'windows' on their wings. In newly emerged adults, these are covered with sparse scales, but on the maiden flight they are lost leaving transparent areas of wing membrane that give the group its name. Presumably there is some mimicry taking place here, although the model is not always clear. Hornet Clearwings and Lunar Hornet Clearwings may demonstrate classic Batesian mimicry in that they look like the potentially dangerous hornet (*Vespa crabro*), which may allow them to rest on tree trunks in relative safety, which is what they do for a few brief hours immediately after emergence from the pupa. I prefer to think that even this situation may not be as simple as the human eye perceives and in any case a model for some clearwings is harder to imagine. Nine of the fifteen British species are present in Hertfordshire, but all are very much under-recorded. The recent discovery and application of artificial pheromone lures has shown that most species are often to be found readily in areas where they were previously considered absent and the males at least are often numerically abundant.

0370 *Sesia apiformis* (Cl.) Hornet Moth

Recorded:	1893 – 2006
Distribution / Status:	Local / Uncommon resident
Conservation status:	No perceived threats
Caterpillar food plants:	Between the bark and the wood of hybrid black poplars and once on Grey Poplar Elsewhere on native Black Poplar
Flight period:	Mid-June/July
Records in database:	20

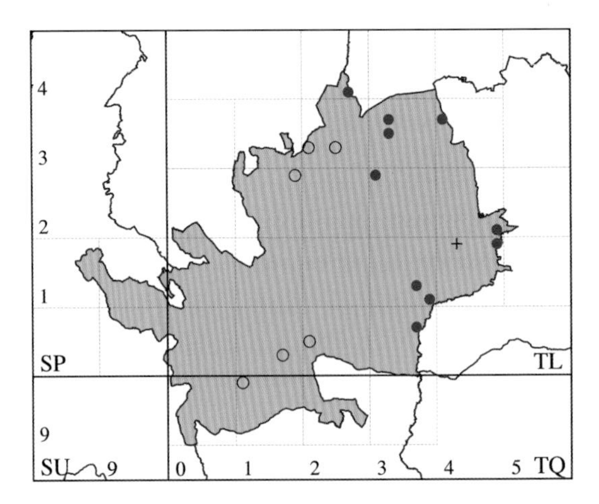

In 1916, Foster noted the Hornet Clearwing as 'not uncommon in north Herts', but gave no details and only three former localities in the north of the county have been traced. Later, in the 1937 list, Foster added Watford and Colney Heath, without any dates. Present-day records seem to be concentrated in the east of the county. Hornet Clearwing is perhaps the easiest of the group to find – one simply looks for emergence holes at the base of poplar trees to record a past presence and either protruding pupae or newly emerged adults on the trunks to determine a current population. Presumably once confined to native Black Poplar trees, the moth has evidently adapted well

to the Lombardy Poplar, a hybrid variety that was introduced to Britain in 1758. Although there are lines of apparently suitable trees from which the moth is certainly absent, mapped records coincide rather too well with the home addresses of active lepidopterists. It is worth adding that although this species is under-recorded it is nevertheless potententially threatened in Hertfordshire by the misguided felling of affected trees on grounds of safety. With this in mind it is worth pointing out that the larvae feed between the bark and the wood on the cambium of the bark and do not affect the timber of the trunk. Consequently, it does not weaken the tree nor render it unsafe.

0371 *Sesia bembeciformis* (Hb.) Lunar Hornet Moth

Recorded: 1883 – 2006
Distribution / Status: Local / Common resident
Conservation status: No perceived threats
Caterpillar food plants: Internally in the wood of Goat Willow, Common Osier and unidentified sallows
Flight period: June. Elsewhere, June/July
Records in database: 38

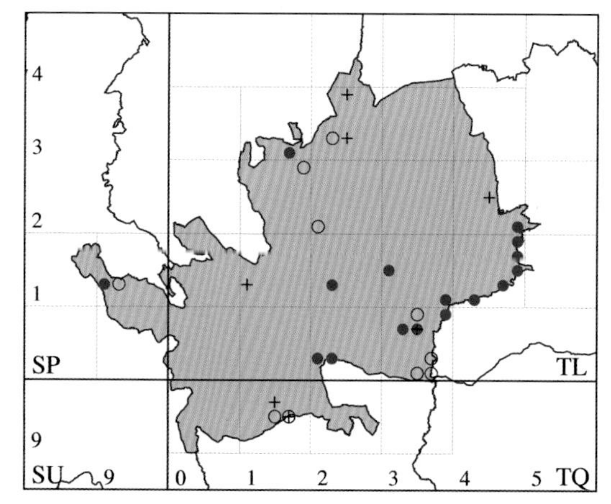

The modern distribution indicates a widespread and probably still common species, though one that is rather localised. Most records are associated with damper areas and the line of the Stort Valley in the east of the map is very clear. Larval workings are the most frequent and simple means of recording this moth, which does not respond to existing pheromone lures, and many records are made by following in the wake of scrub clearance when tunnels are frequently found in the stumps of cut sallow trunks that have achieved a diameter of at least 6 centimetres. Regrettably, the cut ends containing the larvae are usually burned – a practice that has no place in conservation management. Holes may also be spotted easily at the bases of sallow trunks when they have been widened, usually, by Lesser-spotted Woodpeckers (*Dendrocopus minor*).

0373 *Synanthedon tipuliformis* (Cl.) Currant Clearwing

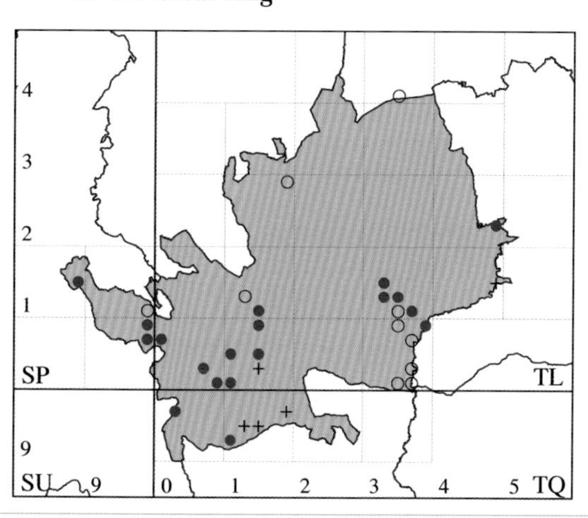

Recorded: 1883 – 2005
Distribution / Status: Local / Common resident
Conservation status: Herts Scarce
Caterpillar food plants: Blackcurrant, feeding inside the stems
Flight period: June
Records in database: 46

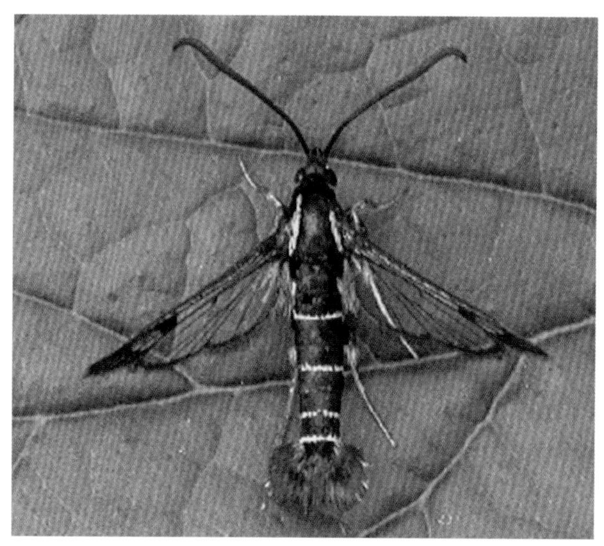

In 1916, Foster wrote of the Hitchin area that the Currant Clearwing 'Occurs all over the district but is not common'. Regrettably he omitted to list any localities and our map shows only one tetrad – relating to Foster's own garden. Later, (Foster, 1937) he again suggests this species was relatively widespread, but putting available past records as well as modern sightings on the map seems to indicate two things – first that this moth is relatively well-recorded when compared to other clearwings and second that there is a vast gap in the map in the north of the county. Currant clearwings are probably moderately well-recorded because of their association with a fruit crop that was, and to some extent still is, grown in gardens and allotments. Larval droppings (frass) spill out of the pruned ends of affected stems when the larva is feeding making spotting them quite easy; of course, most gardeners will immediately cut them out! The adults respond well to artificial pheromone lures and have turned up when these have been used. On this basis they are probably genuinely scarce in the north-east of Hertfordshire, which is largely an arable desert, and very much under-recorded in the southern part.

0374 *Synanthedon vespiformis* (L.) Yellow-legged Clearwing

Recorded: 1888 – 2002
Distribution / Status: Local / Rare resident
Conservation status: Herts Vulnerable
Caterpillar food plants: Not recorded. Elsewhere on oak, elm and other broad-leaved deciduous trees
Flight period: Mid-July/August
Records in database: 15

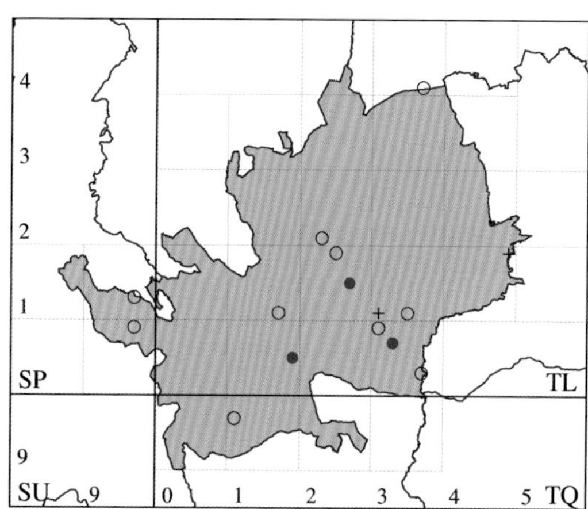

A. E. Gibbs, writing in 1893 about the year 1892 records that 'Mr J. E. Cutts, of Watford, informs me that a friend of his took the yellow-legged clearwing (*Sesia asiliformis*) near Sandridge. This is the first record of the occurrence of this moth in our county'. It is not clear if he overlooked or ignored a record on the list published in 1888 for the Haileybury School (now Haileybury College) in the Broxbourne area; that list contains some records of doubtful authenticity, though this species would have been expected there. In 1916, Foster lists Knebworth Great Wood and Hitchin whilst in the 1937 list he adds Bayford, Royston (1923), Haileybury (school list) and Ashridge. Later, in 1942, he adds Northchurch (J. Bell) and Watford (E. W. Classey). More recent records are few. Adult females lay their eggs on fresh cut stumps of oaks, occasionally other trees, and this must be a micro-habitat that is in relatively short supply over much of the county; the lack of records in the north and north-east might well be real.

0378 *Synanthedon andrenaeformis* (Lasp.) Orange-tailed Clearwing

Recorded:	1907 – 2006
Distribution / Status:	Local / Common resident
Conservation status:	No perceived threats
Caterpillar food plants:	Guelder Rose and Wayfaring Tree, perhaps Dogwood
Flight period:	Mid-June to mid-July
Records in database:	30

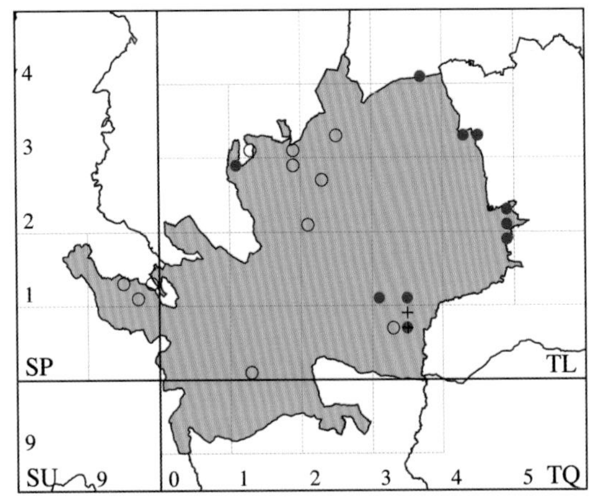

Modern-day records are concentrated in the east, but this reflects observer bias and is very largely a result of trialling artificial pheromone lures. This technique has proved very efficient in attracting male Orange-tailed Clearwings. On 21st June 2003, Andrew Palmer attracted males to the lure in his garden in Bishops Stortford and immediately telephoned me with the news. I was doubtful if the moth would be in my garden, where the foodplant is quite absent, but I attracted 2 males within 15 seconds of removing the lure from the container. The distance that the moths could have travelled in this time is minimal and this record is one of many that supports an association with Dogwood as an alternative foodplant in places where neither species of *Viburnum* are present. Further adults were attracted to pheromone lures by Jim Fish and Julian Reeves in a third area of Bishops Stortford on the same afternoon and more were attracted the next day at Meesden by Ted Ponting. It is clear that the 2003 emergence was synchronised; this is probably the normal situation.

0379 *Synanthedon myopaeformis* (Borkh.) Red-belted Clearwing

Recorded:	1828 – 2006
Distribution / Status:	Local / Common resident
Conservation status:	No perceived threats
Caterpillar food plants:	Domestic Apple and Conference Pear, beneath the bark in diseased branches and trunks.
Flight period:	Early June to late July
Records in database:	37

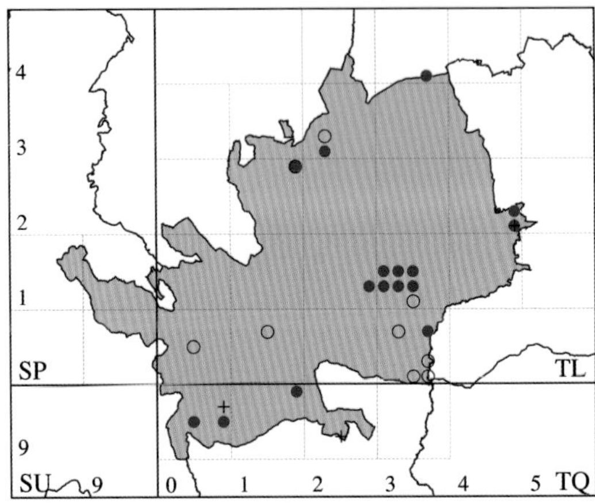

A long-term Hertfordshire resident, the Red-belted Clearwing was included by J. F. Stephens for Hertford in *Illustrations of British Entomology* **1**: 143, published in 1828). The 1937 county list records Hertford (Stephens), Haileybury (3 specimens in 1897), Cheshunt, Hitchin, St Albans (1916) Letchworth (1916) and near Broxbourne. Later, Foster (1942) adds Felden (1941) and Broxbourne [Woods, late 1930s]. This is another species that has become relatively easy to record because it responds well to artificial pheromone lures; additionally it is very easily recorded by looking for empty pupal cases protruding from trunks and major branches of old apple trees towards the end of June; the pupae usually remain evident for several days. The moth does not appear to like young or healthy trees and in Hertfordshire it has been found only on diseased or dying larger branches of apple trees (or in trunks of diseased trees). It is, as a consequence, only locally distributed in the county, yet nevertheless is probably under-recorded. Andrew Wood has commented that when he surveyed apple trees along the Lea between Ware and Hertford in 2005 he found it on every tree bar one and that was a young one. It should be added that this moth poses no threat to orchards – its presence is a consequence of diseased trees not a cause of them. However, the removal of old orchards and the "tidying" of those that are retained poses a threat to the longer-term presence of this moth in the county and the retention of older trees with dead and dying branches is urged in areas where this is acceptable. It is of interest that we have no records from our native Crab Apple.

0380 *Synanthedon formicaeformis* (Esp.) Red-tipped Clearwing

Recorded:	1884 – 2006
Distribution / Status:	Local / Uncommon resident
Conservation status:	Herts Scarce
Caterpillar food plants:	Not recorded. Elsewhere, Common Osier and other species of *Salix*, under the bark or causing a gall
Flight period:	Early June to mid-July
Records in database:	21

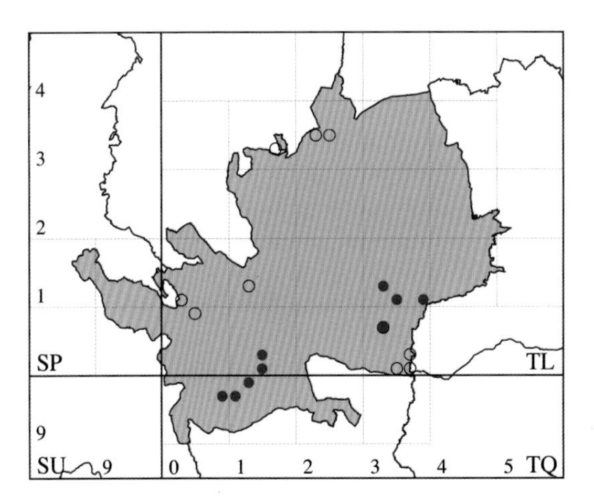

According to Foster (1916) 'Durrant mentions two specimens taken by the late Mr. Christian at Norton near Baldock previous to 1885'. Records in the 1937 list are for Norton Mill near Letchworth, Holwell near Hitchin and Harpenden. Foster (1942) adds Water End, Hemel Hempstead 'common in 1941' and Broxbourne [Woods]. Some modern records are a result of good luck and spending adequate time in the field, such as the one that Phil Jeffery was fortunate enough to see land on a thistle flower at Cowheath Wood on the morning of 13th July 2003. Most recent records, however, are from artificial pheromone lures. A lure placed on an old osier on 13th June 2004 by the River Colne at Watford by Colin Everett at 16.10 hours attracted a male after three minutes. Another placed on an old osier on 17th June 2004 on derelict ground just south of Frogmore Lakes Nature Reserve at 16.06 hours attracted a male after eight minutes. The positioning of the lure appears to be critical and the males appear reluctant to fly great distances. In adjacent Middlesex, a lure placed by me on a small oak sapling at the edge of a very wet sallow carr at Ickenham Marsh on 14th June 2002 produced no moths after 20 minutes. However, when I overcame laziness and donned my wellies to move the lure to a sallow tree less than two metres away in the wet area, a male arrived within a few seconds. The lure was placed at about 1.5 metres above the ground. The distribution map reflects under-recording, but does show a correlation with damp sallow carr – a scarce habitat in the county. Threats to this habitat, including altered hydrological regimes, are also threats to the moth. Clearance of sallows in the name of habitat management reduces the amount of trees of sufficient age to support the moth and if carried out without prior survey is likely to kill the larvae, which spend two years in the wood. Burning ensures that none are allowed to continue their development in the cut branches.

0381 *Synanthedon culiciformis* (L.)
Large Red-belted Clearwing

Recorded:	1924 – 1999
Distribution / Status:	Extremely local / Rare resident
Conservation status:	Herts Endangered
Caterpillar food plants:	Not recorded. Elsewhere on birch, rarely Alder, tunnelling into stumps that were cut the previous year
Flight period:	June (one record)
Records in database:	5

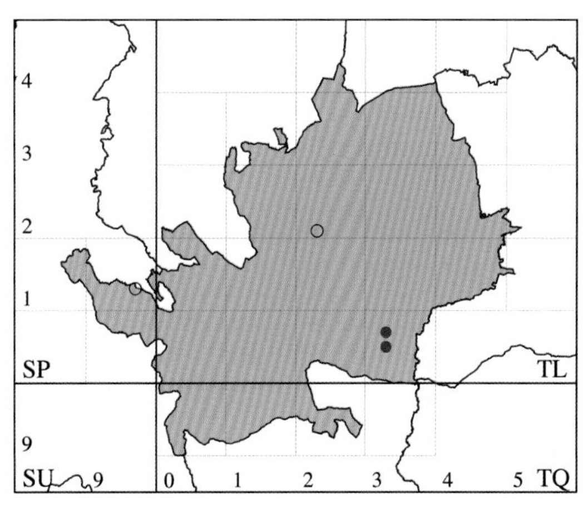

Our records of this species are very few indeed. Foster (1937) notes two pupae at Broxbourne in 1924 and [an adult] at Ashridge in 1933. One was collected by R. S. Ferry in Knebworth Great Wood during June 1947 and Maurice Pledger recorded adults during 1999 at Wormley Wood and Broxbourne Wood. Though some people have attracted this species to pheromone lures in other parts of Britain, we have not been successful in Hertfordshire. The moth seems to prefer the stumps of mature trees and the combination of mature birches and stumps cut the previous year is not frequent in the county. The current trend for the removal of mature birches from woodlands is likely to be damaging to this species.

0382 *Bembecia ichneumoniformis* ([D.& S.])
Six-belted Clearwing

Recorded:	1995 – 2004
Distribution / Status:	Local / Common resident
Conservation status:	No perceived threats
Caterpillar food plants:	Not recorded. Elsewhere on the roots of trefoil, Horse-shoe Vetch and Kidney Vetch
Flight period:	Mid-June/July
Records in database:	9

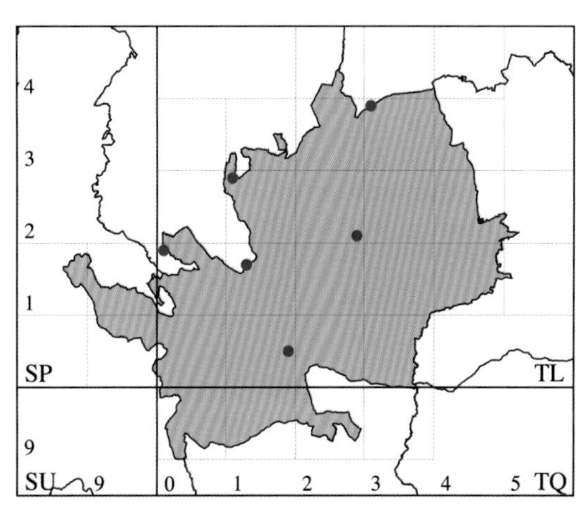

Foster (1937) lists only a single report, from 'Drayton Beauchamp, one on canal bank in 1893' but questions whether or not this site is in Hertfordshire. The village is certainly not – the vice county boundary runs some 500 metres east of it. The canal crosses the border, but as the village is named it seems likely that this record was made in Buckinghamshire not Hertfordshire; I have not included it in the map. There are no other records until 1995, though it is difficult to believe that the moth is a recent colonist. Modern pheromone lures work well to attract males and sweep-netting stands of foodplant produces both sexes. It seems probable that collectors of Foster's era would be horrified at the thought of sweep-netting, as a result of which the captured moths are rarely fit for the cabinet! Writing in *Larger Moths of the London Area* in 1993, I concluded that all records of this species were confined to areas of chalk geology. Since then, myself and others have found this insect to be abundant in association with *Lotus corniculatus* and other *Lotus* species on post-industrial sites to the east of London along the River Thames where the substrate is dominated by pulverised fuel ash (PFA). This by-product of industry is strongly alkaline and supports a calcareous flora and fauna. Three of the four tetrad dots on the Hertfordshire map are on chalk geology. The central Herts record is from Frogmore Pit where the overlying geology has a low pH value, but the derelict pit extends downwards through the sand and gravel quarry to just reach the chalk.

CHOREUTOIDEA
CHOREUTIDAE

Originally classed as belonging to the Glyphipterigidae, the choreutids have been allocated their own family since 1968, though arguments continue over where to place this family in the overall checklist; in most works they are retained within the Yponomeutoidea, but I prefer to agree with Bradley (2000) and place them in their own Superfamily – the Choreutoidea. Of the six British species, three can be found in Hertfordshire, although one has not been seen for twenty years and may have been lost. Of the three absentees, one is a rare Scottish species, one is a rare immigrant that might turn up in the future and the third (387: *Prochoreutis sehestediana*) might well be overlooked in the county. The larvae of this latter species feeds on skullcap, a trait which it shares with 388: *Prochoreutis myllerana* – the species not seen here for two decades.

0385 *Anthophila fabriciana* (L.) Nettle Tap

Recorded: 1889 – 2006
Distribution / Status: Widespread / Common resident
Conservation status: No perceived threats
Caterpillar food plants: Stinging Nettle
Flight period: May to October, perhaps in three generations
Records in database: 123

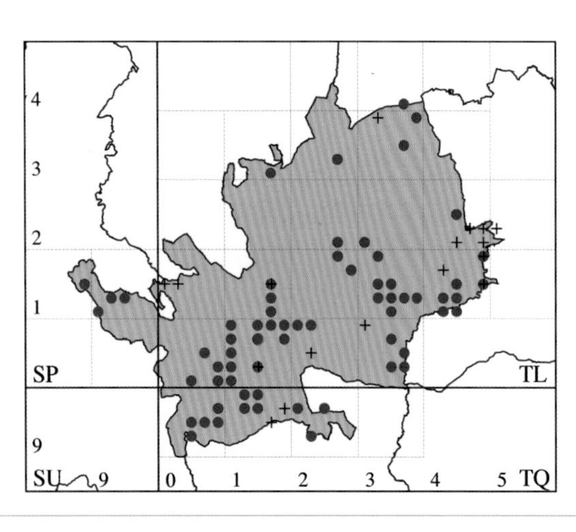

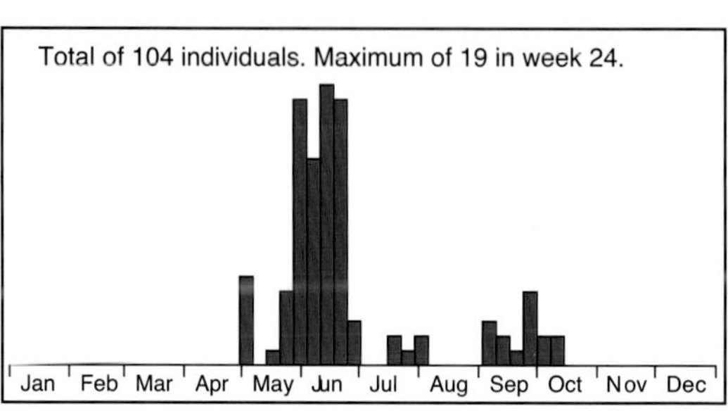

This is a near ubiquitous species of verges, wood margins and a range of other edge habitats where stinging nettles are found; the colloquial name almost certainly derives from the fact that it flies readily when nettles are tapped with a stick. The adult flies in sunshine and is also caught in light traps. Our earliest record is from near St Albans (Gibbs, 1889). Adults are recorded in Britain from May to October and the Hertfordshire flight graph suggests that there are three generations per year here, the first in May/June producing larger numbers than the others, then in July/August and September/October.

0388 *Prochoreutis myllerana* (Fabr.)

Recorded: 1987 only
Distribution / Status: Extremely Local or abscent / Rare resident or extinct
Conservation status: Herts Endangered
Caterpillar food plants: Not recorded. Elsewhere on Common Skull-cap and Lesser Skull-cap
Flight period: Not recorded. Elsewhere, May and July/August
Records in database: 1

Our only record is made by Maitland Emmet at Sawbridgeworth Marsh, on both the Essex and Hertfordshire sides of the boundary, on 25th June 1987 (Agassiz, 1989). It is unclear if he recorded adults or early stages, though both the date and Maitland's preferred method of recording suggests he probably found larvae. Common Skullcap is widespread, though rather local, across the county.

0389 *Choreutis pariana* (Cl.) Apple Leaf Skeletoniser

Recorded: 1834 – 2003
Distribution / Status: Local / Rare resident
Conservation status: Herts Rare
Caterpillar food plants: Crab apple; Domestic Apple. Elsewhere, sometimes on other rosaceous trees
Flight period: Not recorded. Elsewhere September to March
Records in database: 4

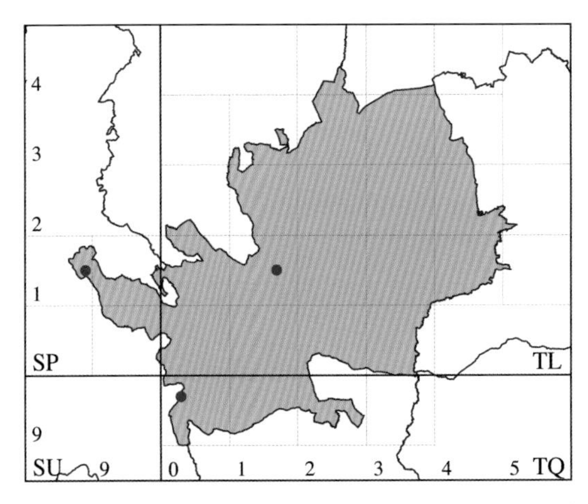

In spite of being first recorded as long ago as 1834 at Hertford, (Stephens, 1834), this appear to be a rare moth in Hertfordshire, with just two other localities – Marshall's Heath (1999 and 2002, John Murray) and Millhoppers Pasture private nature reserve, where I found it in 2003.

YPONOMEUTOIDEA

GLYPHIPTERIGIDAE

Formerly restricted to the members of the genus *Glyphipterix*, the family was expanded in 1986 by the transfer of the genus *Orthotelia* from the Yponomeutidae. The Glyphipterigidae today comprises eight species in Britain. One needs to take care over the spelling of *Glyphipterix* (with a sub-terminal 'i'), since the genus spelled *Glyphipteryx* (with a sub-terminal 'y'), is an altogether different set of moths in family Agonoxenidae; happily British *Glyphipteryx* (with a 'y') have been renamed *Chrysoclista* (see species 903), but care must be exercised in interpreting historical records. The seven British species of *Glyphipterix* are all day-flying species whilst *Orthotelia* flies at dusk and comes to light. Five *Glyphipterix* and one *Orthotelia* are recorded for Hertfordshire, a total of six for the family.

0391 *Glyphipterix simpliciella* (Stephens) Cock's-foot Moth

Recorded:	1834 – 2006
Distribution / Status:	Local / Common resident
Conservation status:	No perceived threats
Caterpillar food plants:	Not recorded. Elsewhere on *Dactylis* and *Festuca* grasses
Flight period:	May/June
Records in database:	26

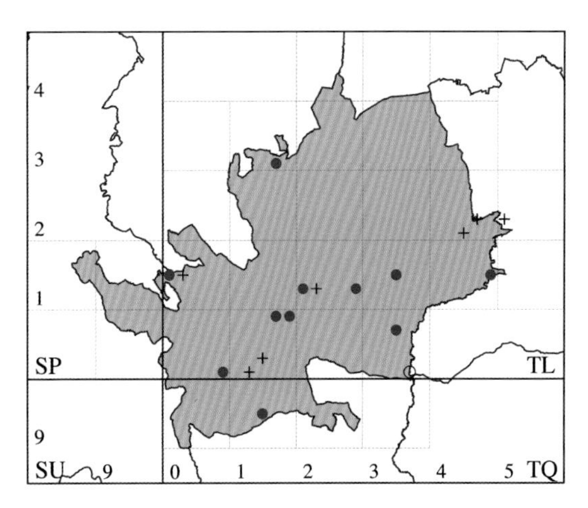

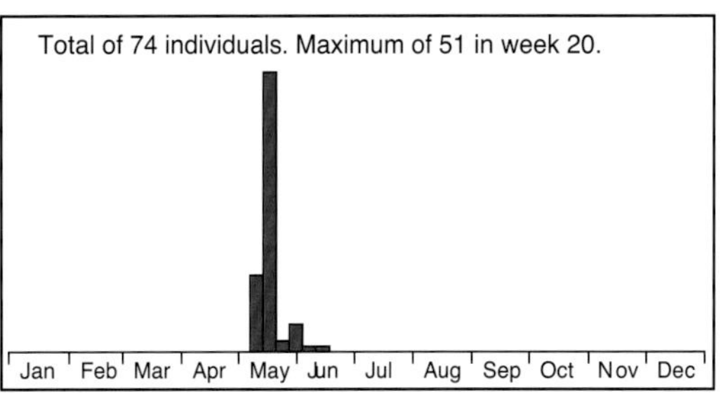

From 1834 (Hertford, in Stephens' *Illustrations of British Entomology* **4**: 263) to the present day this has evidently always been a common moth species in southern Hertfordshire, but there do not appear to be any records at all from the north, where the arable landscape is probably largely unsuitable. Note the comments concerning confusion with 393: *G. equitella* under that species. Adults are often found in sweep-net samples or at rest on flowers, especially those of buttercups.

0393 *Glyphipterix equitella* (Scopoli) = *minorella* Snellen

Recorded:	1901 only
Distribution / Status:	Absent / Extinct
Conservation status:	Insufficient data
Caterpillar food plants:	Not recorded. Elsewhere, stonecrops
Flight period:	Not recorded. Elsewhere, June
Records in database:	1

We have a single record of this species, from the Cheshunt area (Boyd, 1901). Given its wide current distribution in the south-east of England it seems improbable that it is no longer with us. The adult is very similar to the apparently common 391: *G. simpliciella* and the possibility exists that the present species is misidentified as this. Comparative differences given in volume 2 of *Moths and Butterflies of Great Britain and Ireland* are not reflected in the illustrations. The genitalia of both are drawn by Pierce & Metcalfe (1935) in which *simpliciella* is listed under the name *fischeriella*; recorders are urged to dissect their captures.

0394 *Glyphipterix forsterella* (Fabricius)

Recorded:	1834 only
Distribution / Status:	Absent / Extinct
Conservation status:	Herts Extinct
Caterpillar food plants:	Not recorded. Elsewhere, sedges
Flight period:	Not recorded. Elsewhere, May/June
Records in database:	1

J. F. Stephens records *Heribeia forsterella* Z[eller] for Hertford in his 1834 publication *Illustrations of British Entomology* **4**: 263. Durrant (1888) summarised the Lepidoptera recorded in the works by Stephens (and others) and interprets this as implying *Glyphipterix fischeriella* Zeller (a synonym of 391: *G. simpliciella*), but suffixes his opinion with a question mark, since it is *forsterella* of Fabricius, not Zeller, that we are here concerned with. However, Stephens also illustrates *Heribeia simpliciella* as a new species, on the same page, so it seems to me that Durrant was incorrect and that the *Heribeia forsterella* Z. illustrated by Stephens is *Glyphipterix forsterella* (Fabr.). There are no other records for the county.

0396 *Glyphipterix fuscoviridella* (Haworth)

Recorded:	1889 - 2006
Distribution / Status:	Local / Common resident
Conservation status:	No perceived threats
Caterpillar food plants:	Not recorded. Elsewhere on Field Wood-rush
Flight period:	June/July
Records in database:	17

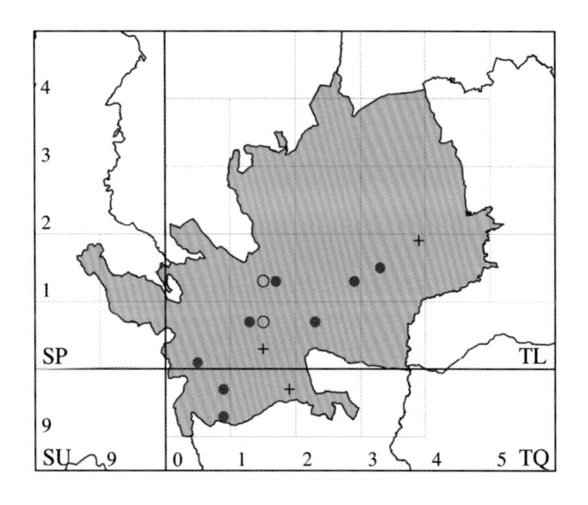

From our earliest record in the St Albans area (Gibbs, 1889) to the present day this is a common moth of grasslands in Hertfordshire.

0397 *Glyphipterix thrasonella* (Scop.)

Recorded:	1890 - 1999
Distribution / Status:	Extremely local / Rare resident
Conservation status:	Herts Rare
Caterpillar food plants:	Not recorded. Elsewhere, probably rushes
Flight period:	Not recorded. Elsewhere, May/June
Records in database:	4

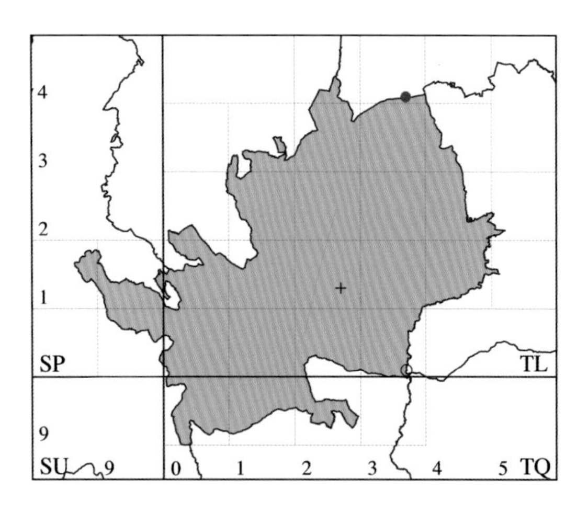

We have just four records of this moth in Hertfordshire. Griffith (1890) includes it in his list for the Sandridge area (not mapped) and Boyd (1901) lists it for Cheshunt. More recently, Raymond Uffen found adults at Tewinbury on 4th June 1992 and another turned up in John Chainey's light trap at Royston during 1999.

0470 *Orthotaelia sparganella* (Thunberg)

Recorded:	1890 - 2006
Distribution / Status:	Local / Uncommon resident
Conservation status:	Herts Vulnerable
Caterpillar food plants:	Not recorded. Elsewhere on bur-reed, Reed Sweet Grass and Iris
Flight period:	August
Records in database:	5

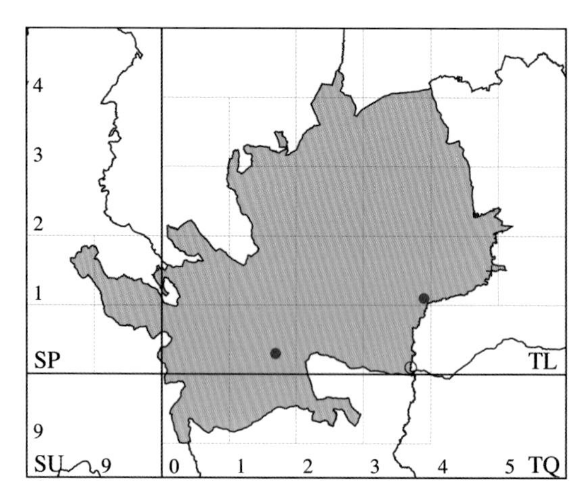

Old records are available for the Sandridge area (not mapped) and Cheshunt, both in the nineteenth century. There are only three records since then, from Sawbridgeworth Marsh, where I found it on 17th August 1988, the north area of the RSPB owned part of Rye Meads on 5th August 2004 (Paul Roper) and Broad Colney Lakes during the Herts Moth Group recording trip on 5th August 2006. The astute will realise that all three sites are wetland nature reserves. The species is probably under-recorded, but suitable sites are rather few and far between.

YPONOMEUTIDAE

This is a large family of moths and scientific opinion on which species truly belong to it is divided. For the present exercise I have followed the Bradley (2000) checklist which, although not in any way a taxonomic review, is probably the system most familiar to those who have no real interest in the taxonomic niceties. In so doing, 470: *Orthotelia sparganella* is included with the Glyphipterigidae, 447: *Roeslerstammia erxlebella* now has its own family and the British species of *Ochsenheimeria* (species 251 – 253), are transferred into the Yponomeutidae from the Tineidae. In this arrangement, there are exactly 81 species currently recognised as British, including the newly described *Prays peregrina* Agassiz known in Britain only from adjacent Middlesex. Of these, 59 are recorded within the confines of Hertfordshire.

0401 *Argyresthia laevigatella* (Heyd.)

The only claim to a place on the Hertfordshire list for this moth is the map dot for vice-county 20 in volume 3 of *Moths and Butterflies of Great Britain and Ireland*, published in 1996; I have been unable to track down the details of this record. Older reports of this Larch-feeding moth might be confused with the Spruce-feeding 403: *Argyresthia glabratella*; both species have more or less unmarked wings. In Pierce & Metcalfe (1935) this species (*laevigatella*) is called *atmoriella* and the genitalia shown under that label are correct. However, those labelled as *glabratella* are in reality also *laevigatella*. The correct drawing for *glabratella* is the one labelled as *illuminatella*. The moth flies in May and June.

0403 *Argyresthia glabratella* (Zell.)

Recorded: 1970 only
Distribution / Status: Absent or extremely Local / Extinct or a very rare resident
Conservation status: Herts Extinct
Caterpillar food plants: Not recorded. Elsewhere, on Norway Spruce
Flight period: Not recorded. Elsewhere, June
Records in database: 1

Reasons for confusion of older records with those of 401: *Argyresthia laevigatella* are discussed under that species. Unless the old, currently untraceable record of *laevigatella* turns out to relate to *glabratella* then we have only one record of this species in Hertfordshire – David Agassiz recorded it at Hertford Heath in 1970. It is likely to be present still, though Norway Spruce is not a common tree in Hertfordshire.

0405 *Argyresthia arceuthina* Zeller

Recorded: 1969 – 2004
Distribution / Status: Local / Rare resident
Conservation status: Herts Rare
Caterpillar food plants: Not recorded. Elsewhere, on Juniper
Flight period: Not recorded. Elsewhere, June/July
Records in database: 2

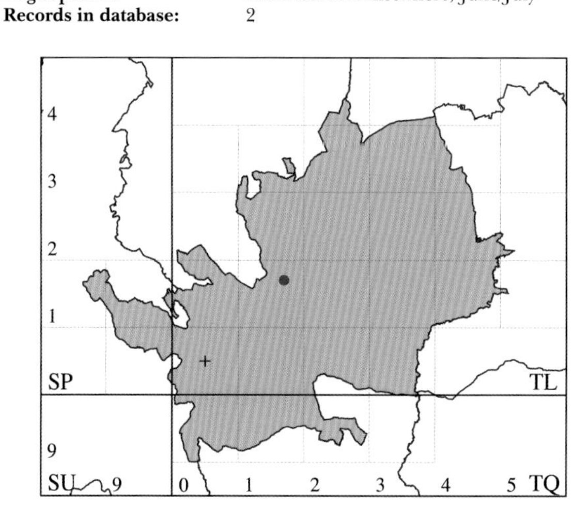

The caterpillar feeds inside shoots of Juniper bushes, overwintering there and causing die-back of the shoots in the spring. These withered shoots are easily spotted and if collected and brought indoors during May adults are likely to emerge within two or three weeks. Juniper is a rare plant in Hertfordshire and is restricted to the chalk in the west, but the moth is surely under-recorded by entomologists? Garden plantings of Juniper should not be ignored. There are just two records – from Hemel Hempstead in 1969 (Lena Ward) and from Gustard Wood Common on 17th May 2004 (Raymond Uffen).

0407 *Argyresthia dilectella* Zell.

Recorded: 1890 only
Distribution / Status: Absent or extremely Local / Extinct or rare resident
Conservation status: Herts Extinct
Caterpillar food plants: Not recorded. Elsewhere, Juniper and *Chamaecyparis* species, including Lawson's Cypress
Flight period: Not recorded. Elsewhere, July/August
Records in database: 1

Our only record is that from the Sandridge area given in Griffith (1890); given the larval foodplants it is likely to be rather more widespread. It was present continuously just over the border in the north-east at Saffron Walden, North Essex, from 1967 to 1995 (Maitland Emmet); in Bedfordshire, there is a record from Studham, on 13th July 1994.

0409 *Argyresthia ivella* (Haw.)

Recorded: 1901 only
Distribution / Status: Absent / Extinct
Conservation status: Herts Extinct
Caterpillar food plants: Not recorded. Elsewhere, apple and Hazel
Flight period: Not recorded. Elsewhere, July/August
Records in database: 1

Our only record is from Cheshunt Street, where it was described as 'Scarce' by Boyd, writing in 1901. In adjacent Bedfordshire there are no recent records and to the east in Essex it was last seen in 1980, with no old records from anywhere near the Hertfordshire border. It must be presumed Extinct in our county.

0409a *Argyresthia trifasciata* Stdgr.

Recorded: 2000 – 2006
Distribution / Status: Widespread / Abundant resident
Conservation status: No perceived threats
Caterpillar food plants: Cupressaceous trees, including *Chamaecyparis* species. Naturally, on Juniper in Europe
Flight period: May/June
Records in database: 125

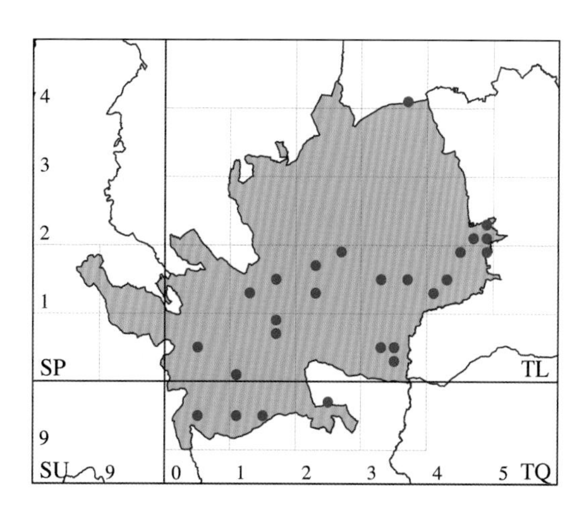

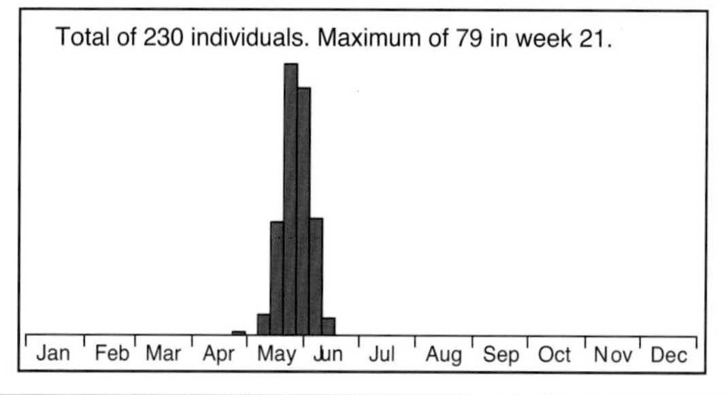

First added to the British fauna by Ray Softly from the actinic trap on the balcony of his flat in Hampstead, Middlesex (North London) this moth has spread rapidly to colonise the south-east, mining the shoots of 'cupressus' trees. These shoots turn brown in the spring and can be very easily spotted but adults need to be reared since the even more recent new arrival, 409b: *Argyresthia cupressella*, causes near identical damage. Adults are very easily found by torchlight on the foliage of the host trees on warm nights in late May, usually appearing around 22.00 hours. Inexperienced observers might initially think that they are a species of *Phyllonorycter*. Our first county record was of adults found in my own garden at Bishops Stortford in 2000. The brown tips to the shoots of my (now felled) Lawson's Cypress were evident for the first time in that year and adults appeared in the light trap a few weeks later. I am quite sure that feeding signs were absent in 1999 and earlier. During 2001 it was found at Oxhey (Joan Thompson) and Rickmansworth (Paul Clack), whilst in 2002 we added Hilfield Park Reservoir. During 2003 the spread became more rapid and there were reports from all these sites as well as Marshall's Heath (John Murray), Cheshunt (Mark and Hilary Cooper), Garston (Colin Everett), Harpenden (Phil Gould), Sandridge (Wendy Hatton), two new sites in Bishops Stortford (Andrew Hardacre; James Fish & Julian Reeves), Hertford (Andrew Wood), Danebridge and Ware (Liz Goodyear), Royston (John Chainey & Jenny Spence), Roughdown Common and St Albans (both by myself). Of course, these are only the places from which we have received records and whilst those from gardens may perhaps be treated as first dates, at those sites where we have not previously had access the moth may have become established sooner. At any rate, by 2004 it was established across the entire county and that remains the current situation.

0409b *Argyresthia cupressella* Walsingham

Recorded:	2005 only
Distribution / Status:	Extremely Local / Vagrant – likely to become resident
Conservation status:	No perceived threats
Caterpillar food plants:	Not recorded. Elsewhere, on cupressaceous trees
Flight period:	June. Elsewhere, May/June
Records in database:	1

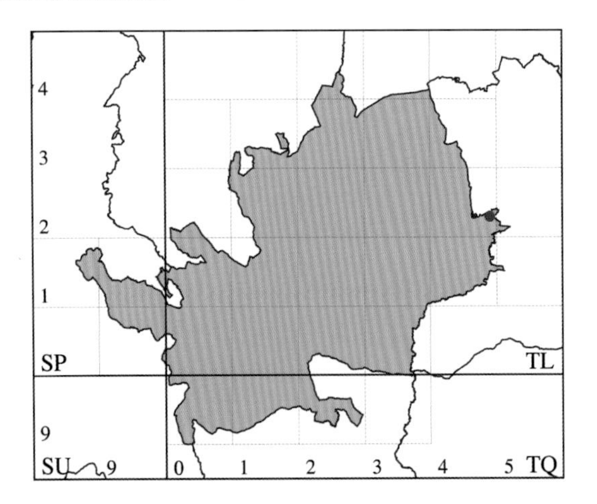

This is another recent colonist, discovered for the first time in Britain on the east coast of Suffolk during 1997 (Agassiz & Tuck, 1999). It has become established in the eastern coastal areas of Suffolk and Essex and is spreading out from that focus. Our first record in Hertfordshire was, predictably, on the eastern boundary, where one turned up on the night of 2nd June 2005 in the light trap run in the adjoining gardens of James Fish and Julian Reeves, in Bishops Stortford; it was identified by Rachel Terry in December 2006. The moth is expected to spread and observers are cautioned that the feeding damage on cupressaceous trees is identical to that caused by 409a: *Argyresthia trifasciata*, so that rearing adults is essential. This is easily achieved by cutting affected branches in May, when feeding has finished, and bringing them indoors for the adults to appear.

0410 *Argyresthia brockeella* (Hb.)

Recorded:	1834 – 2006
Distribution / Status:	Widespread / Common resident
Conservation status:	No perceived threats
Caterpillar food plants:	Birch. Elsewhere, also on Alder
Flight period:	June to August
Records in database:	59

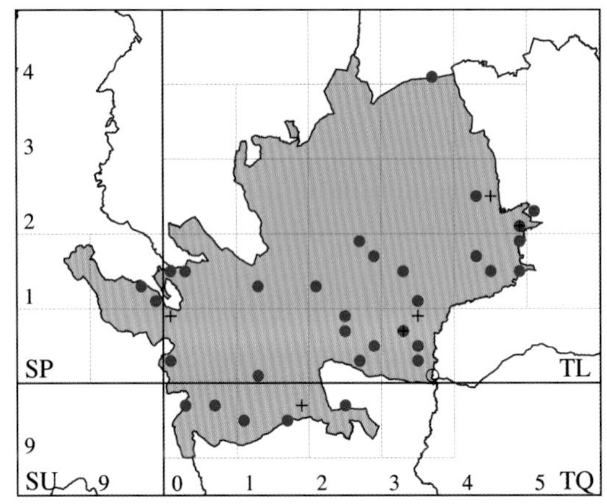

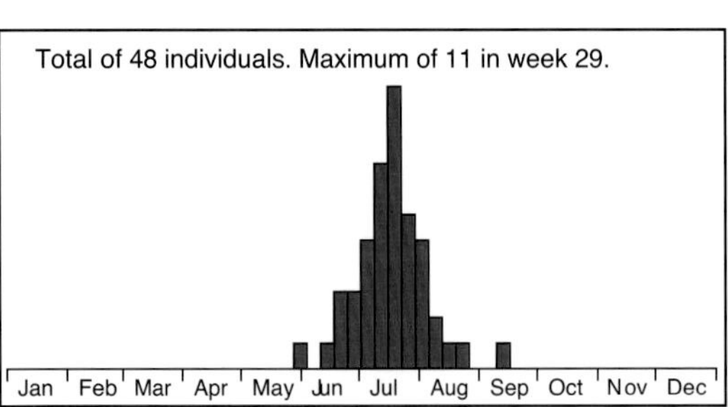

The flight period graph suggests a single extended brood, though adults that are apparently freshly emerged can be found in July and early August. The earliest was 30th May 2003 at Thunderfield Grove (Mark Cooper) and the latest was my own on 10th September at Birchanger Wood, Bishops Stortford. The absence from the north of the county may reflect, in part, the scarcity of birch trees there.

0411 *Argyresthia goedartella* (L.)

Recorded:	1834 – 2006
Distribution / Status:	Widespread / Abundant resident
Conservation status:	No perceived threats
Caterpillar food plants:	Birch. Elsewhere, also on Alder
Flight period:	June to September
Records in database:	134

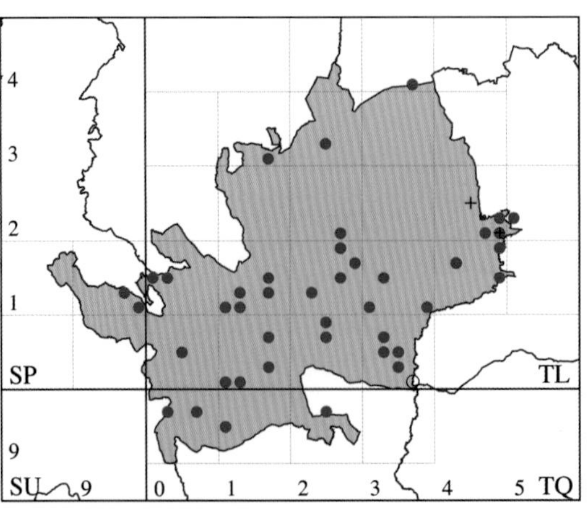

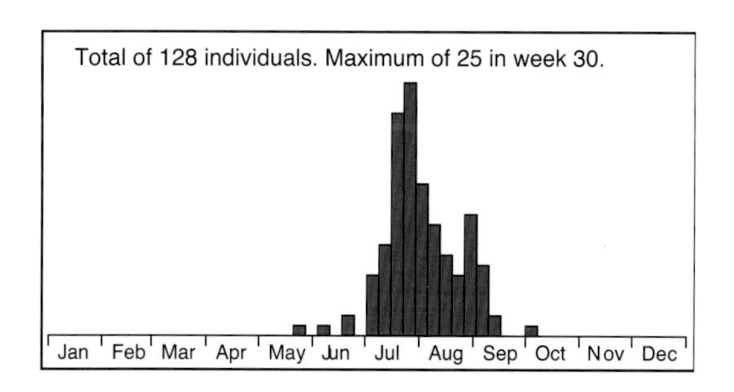

This is an abundant moth wherever birch trees grow. Extreme dates are St Albans, 23rd May 2004 (Wendy Hatton) and Whippendell Wood, 5th October 2002 (myself).

0412 *Argyresthia pygmaeella* ([D.& S.])

Recorded:	1890 – 2003
Distribution / Status:	Local / Rare resident
Conservation status:	Herts Rare
Caterpillar food plants:	Not recorded. Elsewhere, on sallows
Flight period:	June. Elsewhere, June to August
Records in database:	5

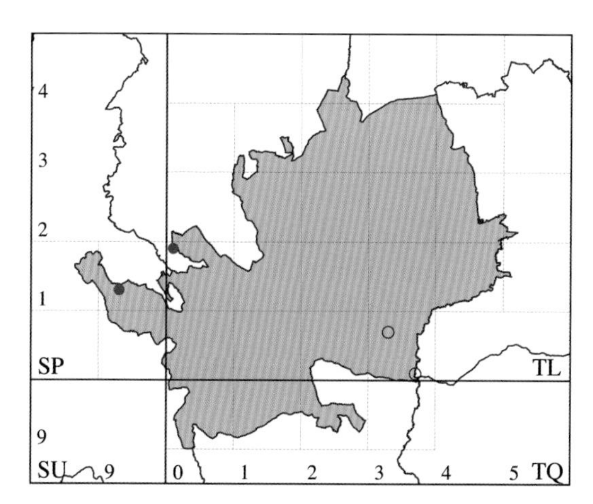

Four of the five Hertfordshire records are from the nineteenth century, at Hertford (Stephens, 1834), the Sandridge area (Griffith 1890), Cheshunt Marsh and Broxbourne Wood (Boyd, 1901). It was, therefore, something of a surprise when one came to the lights at Kensworth Chalk Quarry (in the current administrative county of Bedfordshire) on 28th June 2003. Those who were there on this Herts Moth Group recording trip will recall that we were accused at the time of 'overkill' – with no less that twelve moth traps in a circle around the rim of the quarry the site looked like the flying saucer in the film 'Close Encounters'. My comment that 'you can never have too many lights' is, however, justified! The Hertford and Sandridge records are not mapped as the exact locality is too vague.

0414 *Argyresthia curvella* (L.) = *arcella* (Fabricius)

Recorded:	1890 – 2005
Distribution / Status:	Local / Uncommon resident
Conservation status:	Herts Scarce
Caterpillar food plants:	Apple
Flight period:	June
Records in database:	15

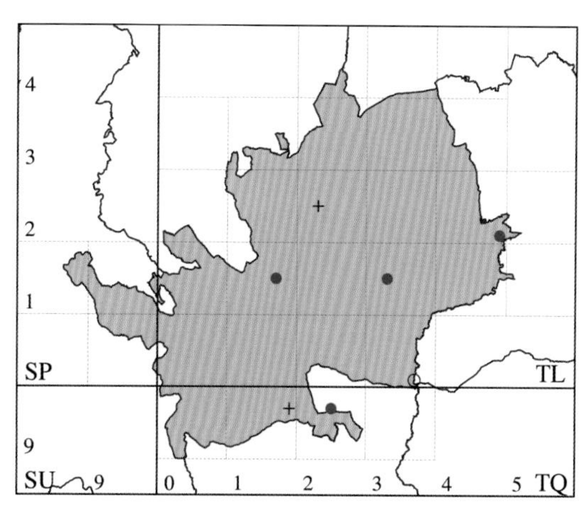

This is the *curvella* of Linnaeus, not *curvella* of Stainton and other authors (see species 421). Foster (1937) lists this species as *nitidella* Fabr. *nec* Hübn. (*purpurascentella* Stt.) from St. Albans (Gibbs), Sandridge (Griffith), Cheshunt (Boyd), Letchworth (Edwards) Harpenden (Fryer) and Hitchin (Durrant, Foster). Modern records are rather sparse as the map indicates, but this is probably a result of under-recording; worn *Argyresthia* specimens in the bottom of moth traps are often ignored by the majority who are interested only in the larger species.

0415 *Argyresthia retinella* Zell.

Recorded:	1890 – 2005
Distribution / Status:	Local / Uncommon resident
Conservation status:	No perceived threats
Caterpillar food plants:	Birch
Flight period:	June/July
Records in database:	15

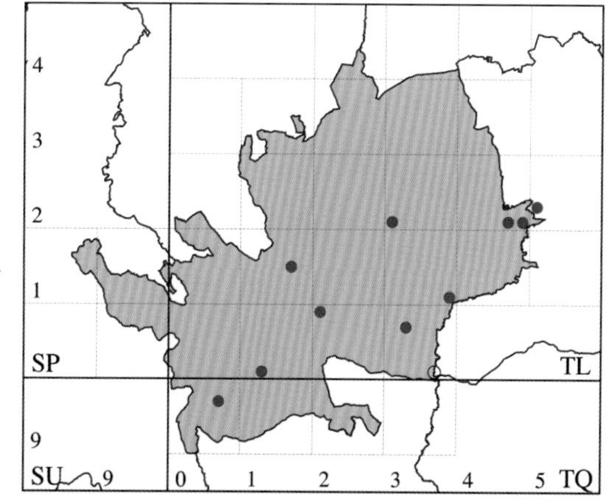

This is allegedly a common moth in the south-east of England, but interestingly the patchy distribution here, suggesting a rather localised species, is repeated for Bedfordshire (Arnold *et al.*, 1997) and Essex (Goodey, 2004). It is absent in the lists from several sites where 'micros' are positively recorded.

0416 *Argyresthia glaucinella* Zell.

Recorded: 1900 – 1995
Distribution / Status: Local / Rare resident
Conservation status: Herts Rare
Caterpillar food plants: Not recorded. Elsewhere, on oak and Horse Chestnut
Flight period: July. Elsewhere, also August
Records in database: 2

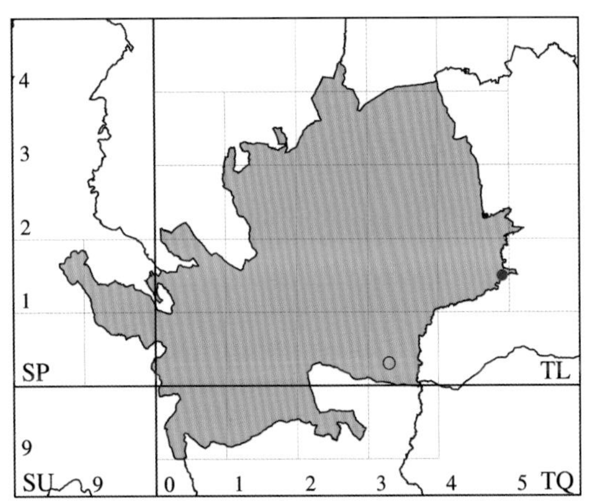

We have just two records of this species: Burton Grange, Cheshunt in 1900 (Boyd, 1901) and Sawbridgeworth Marsh nature reserve, 29th July 1995 by myself. The fact that I could find it by chance almost one hundred years after the last record suggests it is very much under-recorded. The caterpillar feeds in the bark of oak and horse chestnut trees (and in birch in Scotland) and in March/April exudes red frass from crevices in the bark. Confusion is only possible with 907: *Dystebenna stephensi*, which also exudes red frass from oak trunks (but which does not affect Horse Chestnut).

0417 *Argyresthia spinosella* Stt. = *mendica* (Haworth)

Recorded: 1834 – 2006
Distribution / Status: Widespread / Common resident
Conservation status: No perceived threats
Caterpillar food plants: Blackthorn
Flight period: June/July
Records in database: 27

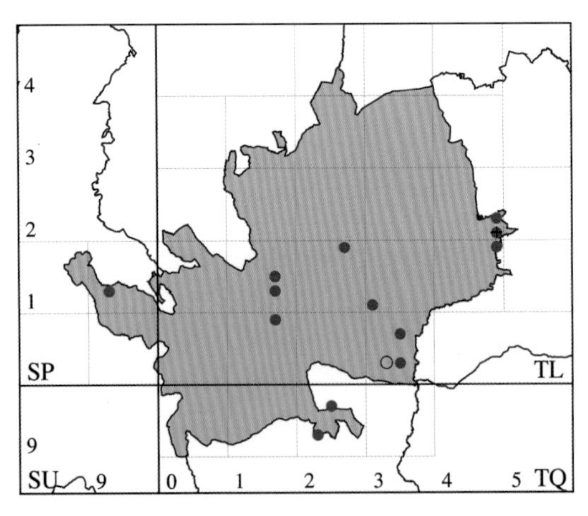

If looked for, this moth can almost always be found if lights are run near blackthorn bushes in June and July; this suggests that the species is under-recorded in the county.

0418 *Argyresthia conjugella* Zell.

Recorded: 1901 – 2005
Distribution / Status: Local / Uncommon resident
Conservation status: Herts Scarce
Caterpillar food plants: Not recorded. Elsewhere, on Rowan, Whitebeam and apple
Flight period: May/June. Elsewhere, June/July
Records in database: 5

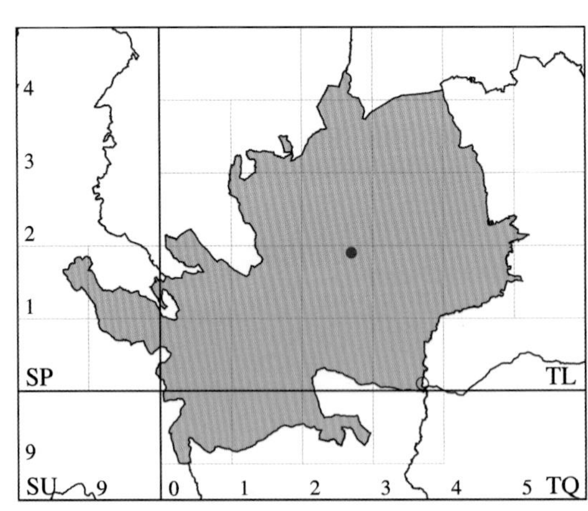

There is a single historic reference to Cheshunt (Boyd, 1901) and then no more until Steve Palmer recorded it annually from 2003 to 2005 at Datchworth (23rd June, 2003, 20th June 2004 and then 24th May and 20th June 2005). It is likely to still be there, but the site is no longer trapped.

0419 *Argyresthia semifusca* (Haw.)

Recorded: 1890 – 2004
Distribution / Status: Local / Uncommon resident
Conservation status: No perceived threats
Caterpillar food plants: Hawthorn. Elsewhere, also on Rowan and Whitebeam
Flight period: August.
Records in database: 26

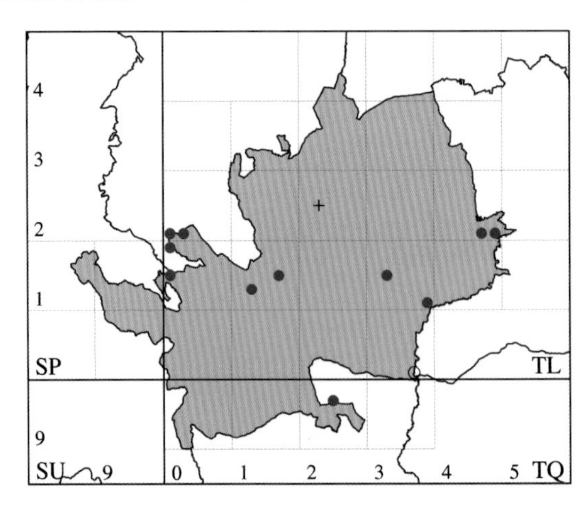

There are nineteenth century records from the Sandridge area (Griffith, 1890) and Cheshunt (Boyd, 1901) and then twentieth century sightings in 1925 at Hitchin (Foster) and on 27th August 1941 at St Albans (N. L. Birkett). There are then no more until 2002. Current data suggests a moth that is sparingly distributed.

0420 *Argyresthia pruniella* (Cl.)

Recorded: 1890 – 2005
Distribution / Status: Local / Common resident
Conservation status: No perceived threats
Caterpillar food plants: Not recorded. Elsewhere, on Sour Cherry
Flight period: June to August. Elsewhere, July
Records in database: 24

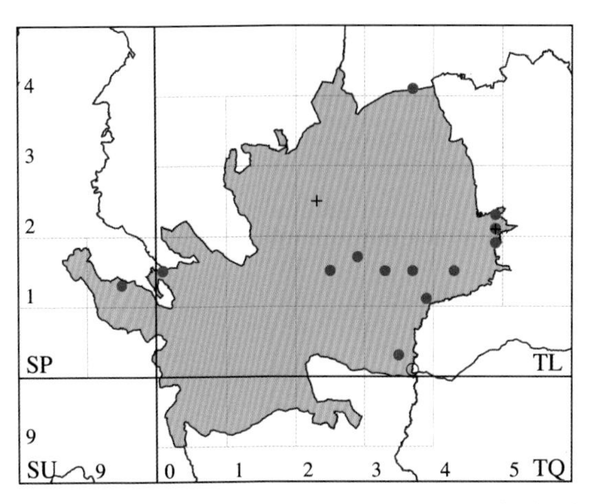

Sour Cherry is not uncommon as an ornamental planting, though not ubiquitous, and the distribution of the moth may follow that of the tree.

0421 *Argyresthia bonnetella* (L.)

Recorded: 1901 – 2005
Distribution / Status: Widespread / Common resident
Conservation status: No perceived threats
Caterpillar food plants: Common Hawthorn
Flight period: Mid-June to early September
Records in database: 34

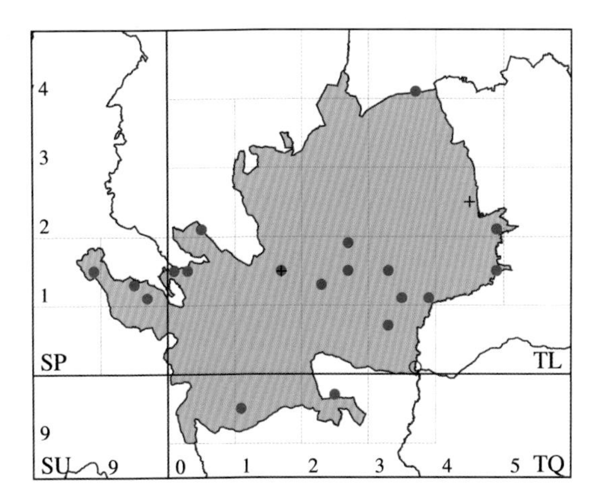

This is the *curvella* of Stainton, not the *curvella* of Linnaeus (see species 414). Foster (1937) records this species, as *cornella* Fabr. (= *curvella* Stt.) from Sandridge (Griffith) and Cheshunt (Boyd). Modern day records suggest a widespread but hopelessly under-recorded species.

0422 *Argyresthia albistria* (Haw.)

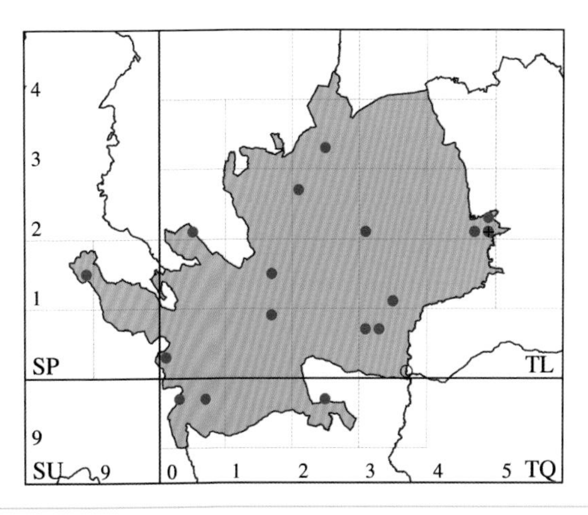

Recorded: 1890 – 2006
Distribution / Status: Widespread / Common resident
Conservation status: No perceived threats
Caterpillar food plants: Blackthorn
Flight period: July and August
Records in database: 33

The bulk of the records fall between the first week of July and the last week of August, with one late male on 14th September 2002, at Millhoppers Pasture, near Long Marston. It is likely to be present wherever blackthorn grows.

0423 *Argyresthia semitestacella* (Curtis)

Recorded: 1901 – 2002
Distribution / Status: Local / Uncommon resident
Conservation status: Herts Scarce
Caterpillar food plants: Not recorded. Elsewhere, on Beech
Flight period: August/September
Records in database: 5

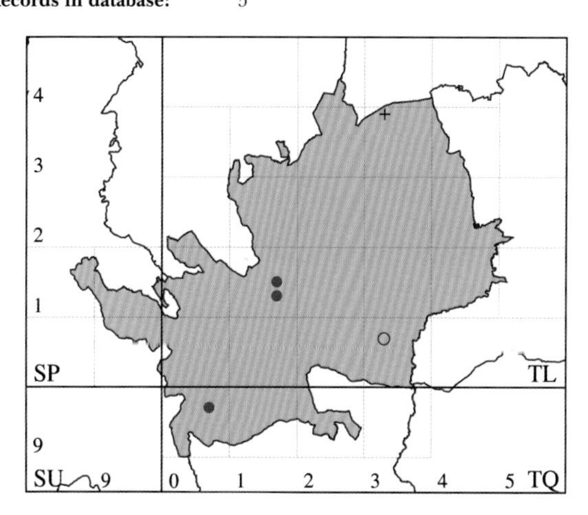

The single historic record on the map is from Broxbourne Wood in the years prior to 1901. The most northerly map symbol relates to Fox Covert at Therfield Heath, a beech woodland on the chalk, where I found it on 29th August 1987 – exactly where it would be expected to thrive. The three modern records are from Amwell Village on 1st September 1996 (Vincent & Betty Judd), Marshall's Heath in 1997 (John Murray) and Whippendell Wood on 5th October 2002 (myself) – the latter in a trap under the beech trees by the car park in Rousebarn Lane. It is likely that this moth will turn up in many other places if lights are put *under* the canopy of beech trees.

0424 *Yponomeuta evonymella* (L.)

Recorded: 1834 – 2006
Distribution / Status: Random / Immigrant and Resident
Conservation status: No perceived threats
Caterpillar food plants: Not recorded. Elsewhere, on Bird-cherry
Flight period: June to August
Records in database: 166

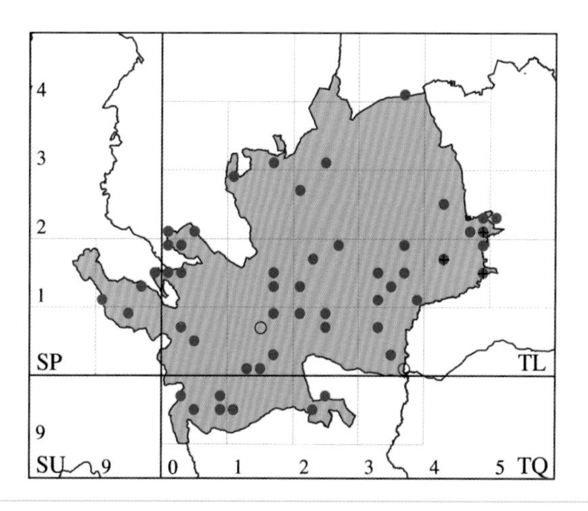

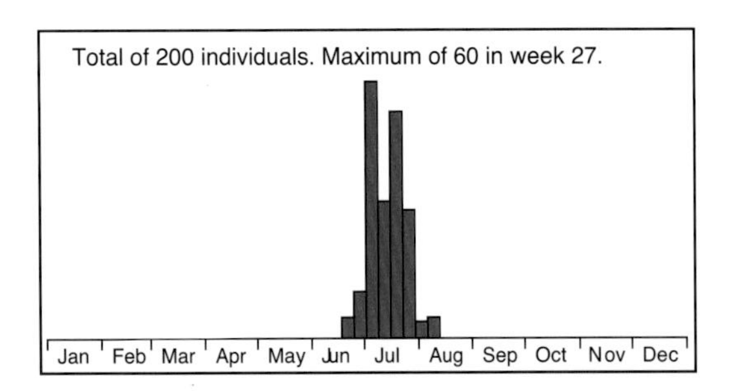

The text books inform us that there are fresh influxes of primary immigrants in most years. Based on the sudden appearance of large numbers on the same dates that other immigrant species appear, this appears to hold true in Hertfordshire – at least for some of the time. However, not all reports can be explained this conveniently. The larvae form large and very obvious silk masses on Bird-cherry trees, often defoliating the tree, yet there are no such reports from Hertfordshire and there is, to date, no evidence at all to suggest breeding here. The technique of back-tracking immigrants from further south, using meteorological criteria, is now an established tool for interpretation of immigration patterns – it would be interesting to apply this in a northerly direction for sudden occurrences of numbers of the present species.

The *padella/malinellus/cagnagella* species group

The separation of these three taxa is far from easy on general appearance and the genitalia do not provide any useful features for separation as far as I am aware. This must be borne in mind when looking at the distribution maps, which in the case of these three species may contain errors. Whilst the taxon that feeds on Spindle always seems to be *cagnagella*, separation of the other two may be less clear cut. Both *padella* and *malinellus* feed on rosaceous trees and it is a fact that many other moths that feed on one rosaceous host plant are likely to be found on another as well. For the present, *malinellus* is allegedly restricted to apple with *padella* feeding on hawthorn, blackthorn and Cherry Plum.

0425 *Yponomeuta padella* (L.)

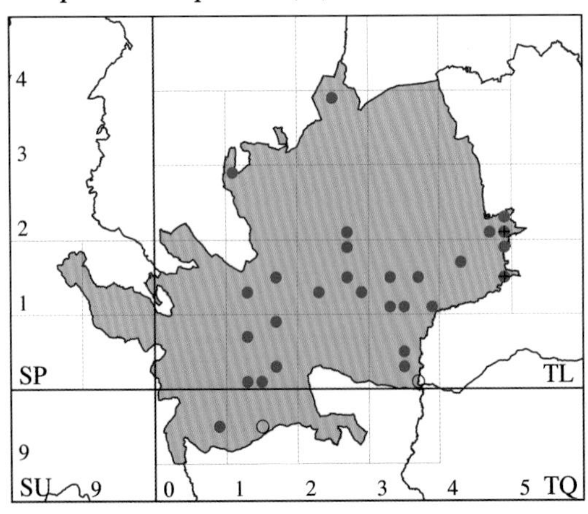

Recorded: 1890 – 2006
Distribution / Status: Widespread / Common resident
Conservation status: No perceived threats
Caterpillar food plants: Blackthorn. Elsewhere, also on Hawthorn and Cherry Plum
Flight period: June to August
Records in database: 75

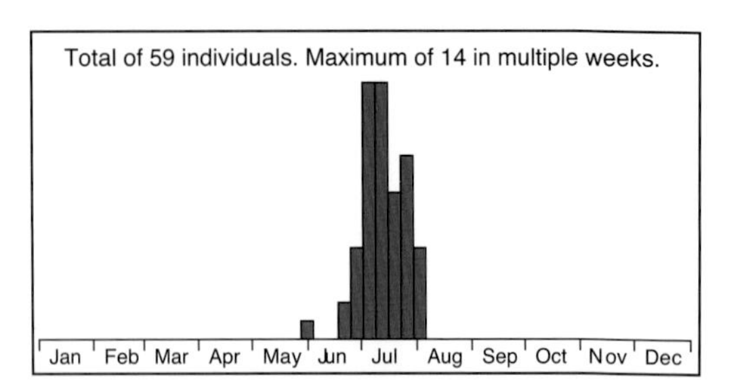

Most records are from mid-June to the first week of August; the exception in the chart is of one on 1st June 2003 at Ware (Liz Goodyear).

0426 *Yponomeuta malinellus* Zell.

Recorded: 1962 – 2006
Distribution / Status: Local / Uncommon resident
Conservation status: No perceived threats
Caterpillar food plants: Not recorded. Elsewhere, on apple
Flight period: July and August
Records in database: 18

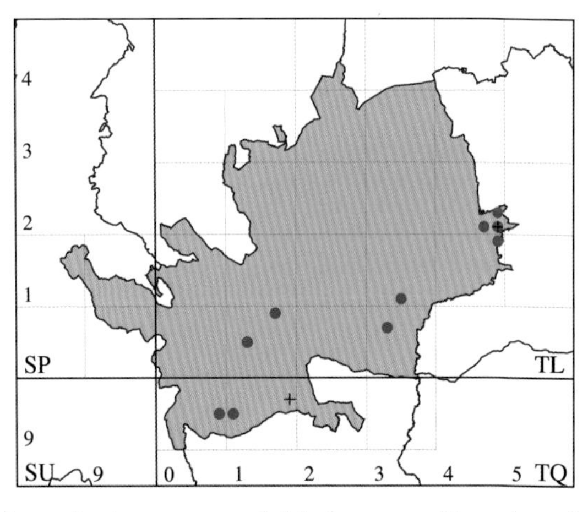

This species is never recorded in large quantity and numbers are too low on any given date for a flight chart to be plotted. The records all fall between 22nd June and 8th September

0427 *Yponomeuta cagnagella* (Hb.)

Recorded: 1902 – 2006
Distribution / Status: Local / Common resident
Conservation status: No perceived threats
Caterpillar food plants: Not recorded. Elsewhere, on Spindle and *Euonymus japonicus*
Flight period: May to September
Records in database: 49

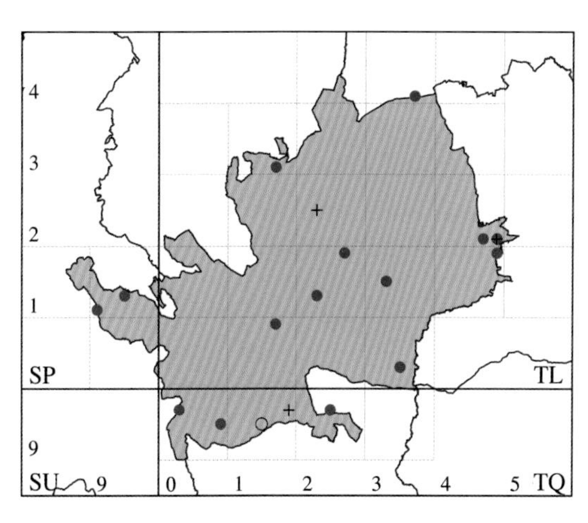

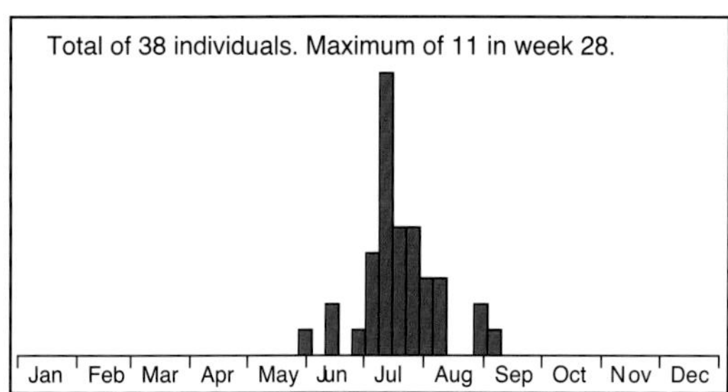

The records suggest that this may be a more widespread and numerous than 426: *Y. malinellus*.

0428 *Yponomeuta rorrella* (Hb.)

Recorded: 1995 – 2006
Distribution / Status: Local / Immigrant and temporary resident
Conservation status: Insufficiently known
Caterpillar food plants: Not recorded. Elsewhere, on White Willow, rarely Common Sallow
Flight period: July to early August
Records in database: 5

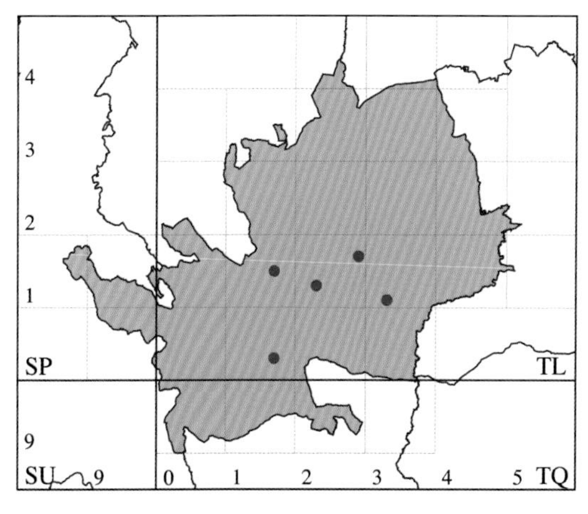

This appears to be quite a rare moth in Hertfordshire. Raymond Uffen found larvae on White Willow at Hunsdon Mead, unfortunately on the Essex side of the boundary, in 1992 following a period of immigrant activity. The colony persisted with smaller numbers in 1993, but on 22nd June 1994 there was only a single web. In 1995 there was no sign of it. This all suggests temporary residency following an initial immigration.

0430 *Yponomeuta plumbella* ([D.& S.])

Recorded: 1834 – 2004
Distribution / Status: Local / Rare resident
Conservation status: Herts Scarce
Caterpillar food plants: Not recorded. Elsewhere, on Spindle
Flight period: July/August
Records in database: 16

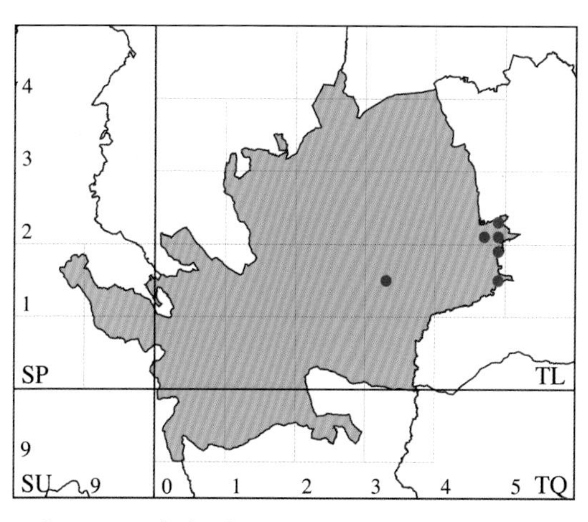

Apart from records in the Bengeo area of Hertford in both 2001 and 2002 (Andrew Wood) all our records are concentrated on the Bishops Stortford area (from several observers). This cluster-effect is unexpected and unexplained.

0431 *Yponomeuta sedella* (Tr.)

Recorded: 1868 – 2006
Distribution / Status: Local / Rare resident
Conservation status: Herts Vulnerable
Caterpillar food plants: Ice Plant; Orpine
Flight period: May and July. Elsewhere, April/May and August
Records in database: 10

Though recorded as long ago as 1868 (Cheshunt: *Entomologist's Monthly Magazine* **5:** 147) and featuring amongst some of the earliest lists from the newly established light trap at the Rothamsted Estate, in 1933 (C. B. Williams) this was and still is a rare moth in the county. In the later stages of development the caterpillars feed from a silk web spun on the flower heads of the plants making them an easy target for gardeners and horticulturists.

0435 *Zelleria hepariella* Stainton

Recorded: 2001 – 2005
Distribution / Status: Local / Resident
Conservation status: Herts Scarce
Caterpillar food plants: Not recorded. Elsewhere, on Ash
Flight period: Mid-July to April
Records in database: 6

Surprisingly, there are no records of this attractive moth for Hertfordshire until 20th October 2001, when two were attracted to my light traps at Hexton Chalk Pit in the north-west. It was next recorded in the Rothamsted Light Trap at Harpenden on 18th July 2002 (Phil Gould) and in my garden light trap in Bishops Stortford on 14th April 2003. There were two records in 2004 – from Broxbourne Wood on 31st March

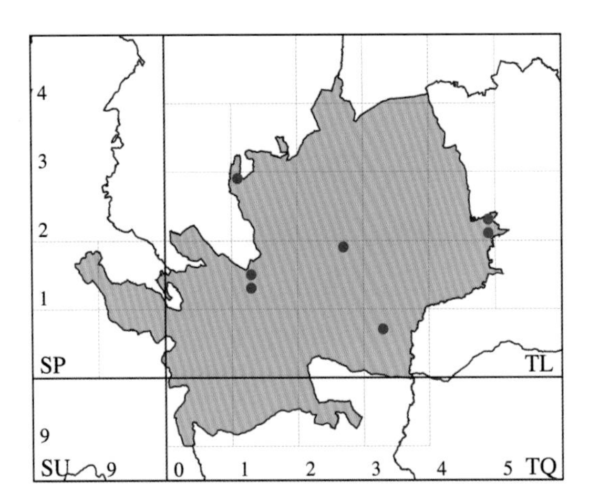

(me again) and Datchworth on 30th July (Steve Palmer) and one in 2005, on 3rd April in a different part of Bishops Stortford (James Fish and Julian Reeves). There were apparently no records in 2006. This pattern suggests a temporary population, but the spread of localities suggests that this is an unlikely explanation.

0436 *Pseudoswammerdamia combinella* (Hb.)

Recorded: 1890 – 2004
Distribution / Status: Local / Uncommon resident
Conservation status: Herts Scarce
Caterpillar food plants: Blackthorn
Flight period: May/June
Records in database: 16

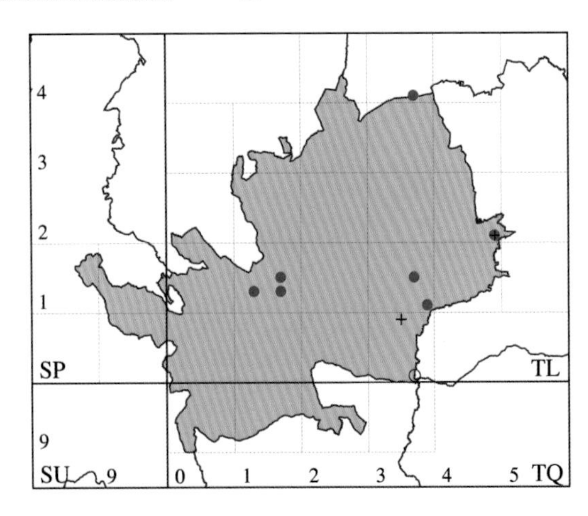

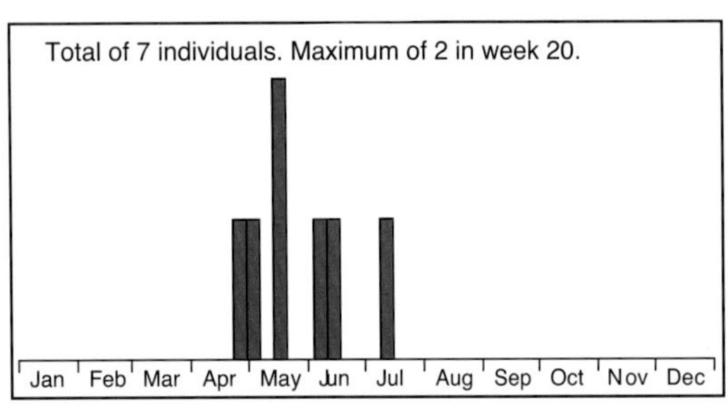

The well-defined copper-coloured patch at the wing tip of this moth makes it one of the more easily recognisable members of the *Swammerdamia* group of species. It is, therefore, surprising to discover how few records there are. That having been said, it was regular in my garden at Bishops Stortford, which is bounded on one side by an old field hedge containing mature blackthorn trees, from 1987 (my first spring there) to 2000, but has not been found since. There has been no change to the hedge, other than that the trees have become a little taller. The hedge was enclosed in the 1930s and so over-maturity seems an unlikely reason for the moth to vanish.

0437 *Swammerdamia caesiella* (Hb.)

Recorded: 1890 – 2006
Distribution / Status: Local / Uncommon resident
Conservation status: No perceived threats
Caterpillar food plants: Birch
Flight period: May/June and August
Records in database: 17

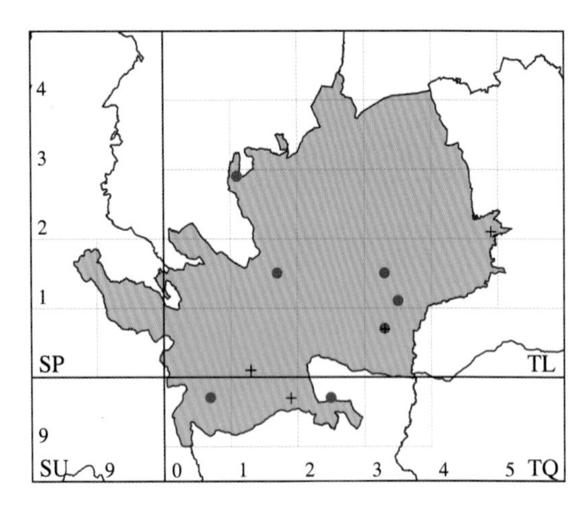

Specimens of 438: *Swammerdamia pyrella* are traditionally separated from this species by the copper-tinged cilia in the terminal area of the forewing. However, these scales are deciduous and many worn specimens are run through the identification key as if they lacked this feature and finish up being named as the present species. My insistence that this species pair be dissected before records are accepted has corrected several records and shown that *caesiella* is actually a decidedly local species in the county.

0438 *Swammerdamia pyrella* (Vill.)

Recorded: 1890 – 2005
Distribution / Status: Local / Common resident
Conservation status: No perceived threats
Caterpillar food plants: Hawthorn. Elsewhere, also on Apple and Pear
Flight period: May/June and August
Records in database: 44

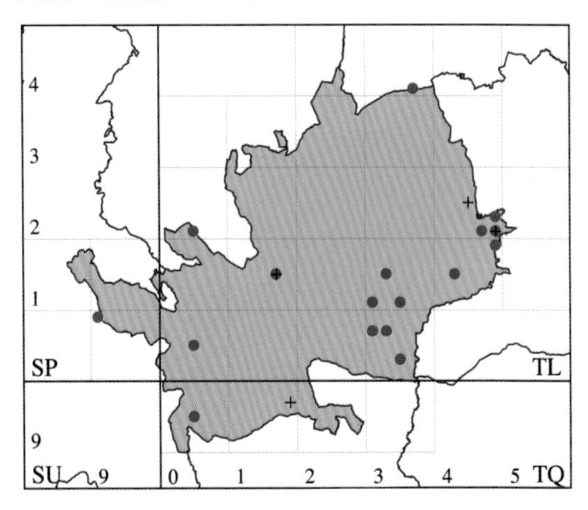

Confusion with 438: *Swammerdamia caesiella* has been mentioned under that species. The map shows distribution of confirmed records only.

0440 *Paraswammerdamia albicapitella* (Scharf.)

Recorded: 1890 – 2005
Distribution / Status: Local / Common resident
Conservation status: No perceived threats
Caterpillar food plants: Blackthorn
Flight period: June to August
Records in database: 31

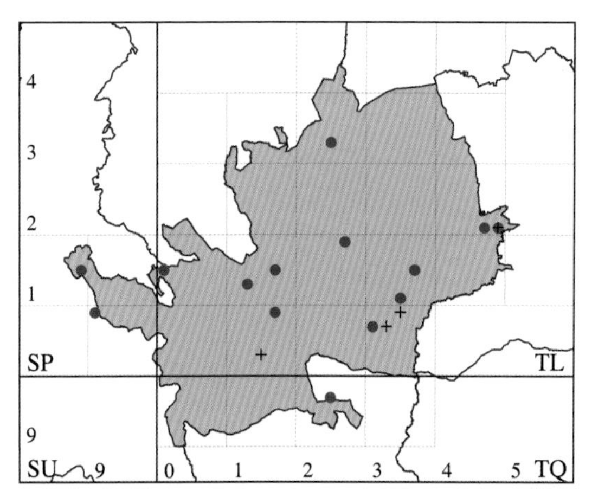

Nationally, adults of this moth seem to be quoted as flying in July and August, but confirmed records from dissections show that with us it flies continuously from the start of June to the end of August. It is probably under-recorded, like others in the group, and is likely to prove rather more widespread than the map indicates.

0441 *Paraswammerdamia nebulella* (Goeze) = *lutarea* Haw.

Recorded: 1890 – 2006
Distribution / Status: Widespread / Common resident
Conservation status: No perceived threats
Caterpillar food plants: Hawthorn. Elsewhere, also on Rowan
Flight period: June to August
Records in database: 89

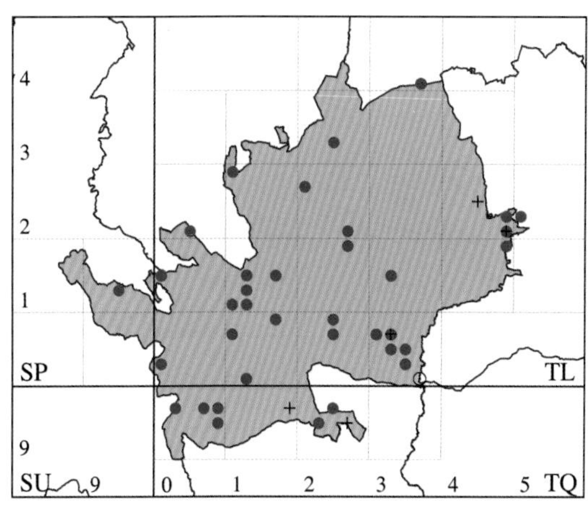

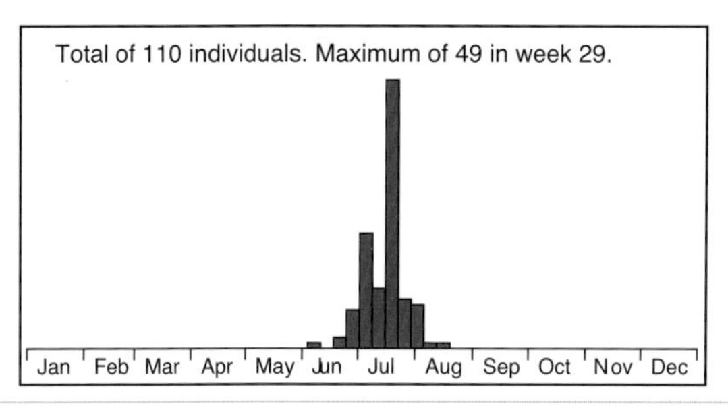

Both numerically and in terms of localities supporting it, this is the commonest member of the *Swammerdamia* group in Hertfordshire. The flight chart, which includes only records made from 2000 to 2006, shows that it can be found as an adult from June to August.

0442 *Cedestis gysseleniella* Zell.

Recorded: 1968 – 2005
Distribution / Status: Local / Rare resident
Conservation status: Insufficiently known
Caterpillar food plants: pine
Flight period: Mid-June to mid-August
Records in database: 8

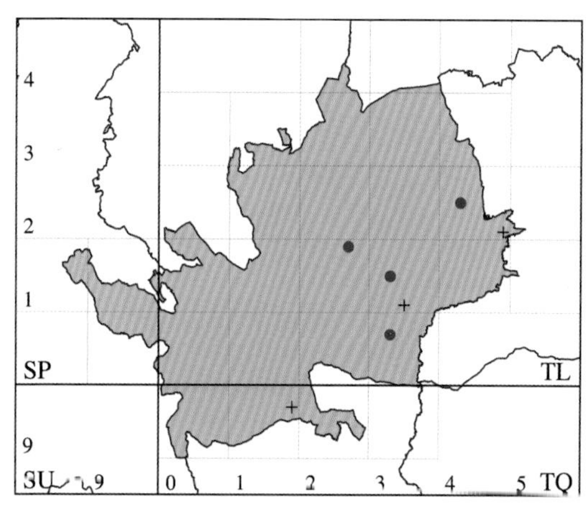

The distribution map reflects the scarcity of this pine-feeding species in Hertfordshire, which is probably a consequence of there being rather few pine trees. It is possible that small populations thrive, undetected in gardens and other inaccessible places. Our first record was from Borehamwood in 1968 (Eric Bradford).

0443 *Cedestis subfasciella* (Steph.)

Recorded: 1901 – 2002
Distribution / Status: Local / Rare resident
Conservation status: Herts Rare
Caterpillar food plants: Not recorded. Elsewhere, on pines
Flight period: May. Elsewhere, March to July
Records in database: 7

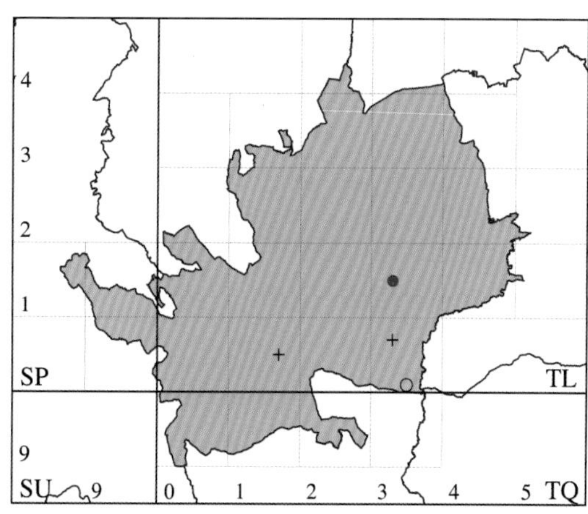

Apparently a much rarer species than 442: *Cedestis gysseleniella*, the only recent record is from Andrew Wood's garden trap in the Bengeo district of Hertford, where an example was found on 10th May 2002. Prior to this, the last records were mines from Broxbourne Wood on two dates in October 1987 (Maitland Emmet) and before then at St Albans in 1977 (David Agassiz). The open circle represents an old record from Churchgate, Cheshunt (Boyd, 1901). The caterpillars mine the pine needles from the tip downwards, so distinguishing the feeding damage from that of *gysseleniella* which mines from the base towards the tip.

0444 *Ocnerostoma piniariella* Zell.

Recorded: 2001 – 2004
Distribution / Status: Local / Rare resident
Conservation status: Herts Scarce
Caterpillar food plants: Not recorded. Elsewhere, on Scots Pine
Flight period: June. Elsewhere, July
Records in database: 5

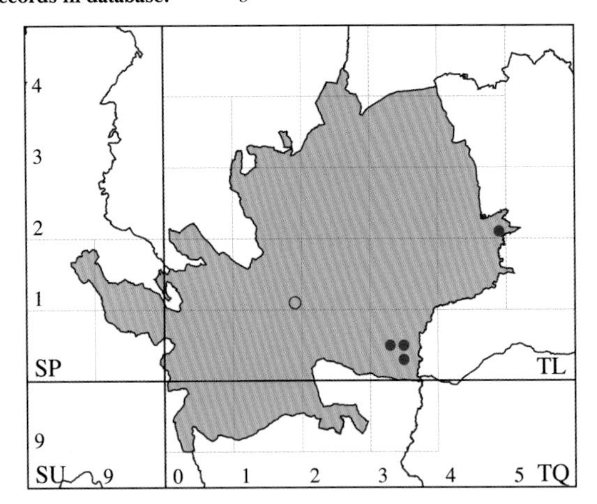

For many years this species and the next, 445: *Ocnerostoma friesei*, were confused and so the 1890 record from Symonds Hyde (Griffith) must be regarded with a degree of caution; there is no 'dot' for Hertfordshire in volume 3 of *Moths and Butterflies of Great Britain and Ireland*. Our first record thus becomes that made in my garden mv trap in Bishops Stortford on 29th June 2001 – the trap is in direct sight of mature Scots Pine trees. Other records are from the Cheshunt area in 2004, all made by Mark Cooper.

0445 *Ocnerostoma friesei* Svensson

Recorded: 1972 – 1993
Distribution / Status: Extremely local, perhaps absent / Extremely rare resident or extinct
Conservation status: Herts Extinct
Caterpillar food plants: Not recorded. Elsewhere, on Scots Pine
Flight period: July
Records in database: 3

Our two localities for this moth are Wormley Wood in 1972 and 1977 (David Agassiz) and Croxley Common Moor on 4th July 1993 (Raymond Uffen). Confusion with the previous species has been mentioned there, but the only record that is possibly affected is that currently attributed to *piniariella* from Symonds Hyde prior to 1890. All other records of both species are valid.

0447 ***Roeslerstammia erxlebella*** **(Fabr.)** – now positioned after Bucculatricidae and before Gracillariidae. See after species 276.

0449 *Prays fraxinella* (Bjerk.)

Recorded: 1834 – 2006
Distribution / Status: Widespread / Abundant resident
Conservation status: No perceived threats
Caterpillar food plants: Ash
Flight period: June /July and then end August/early September
Records in database: 77

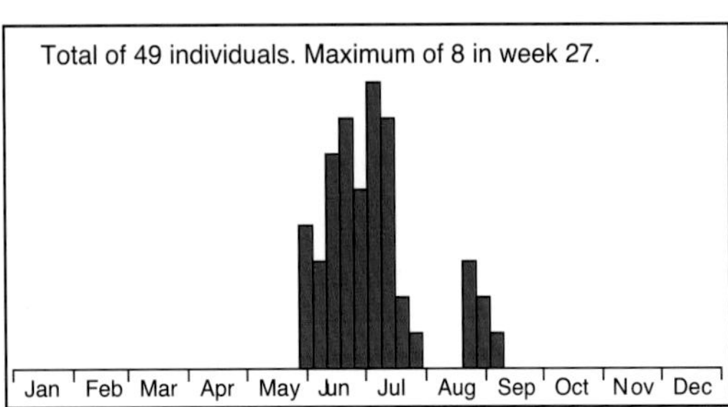

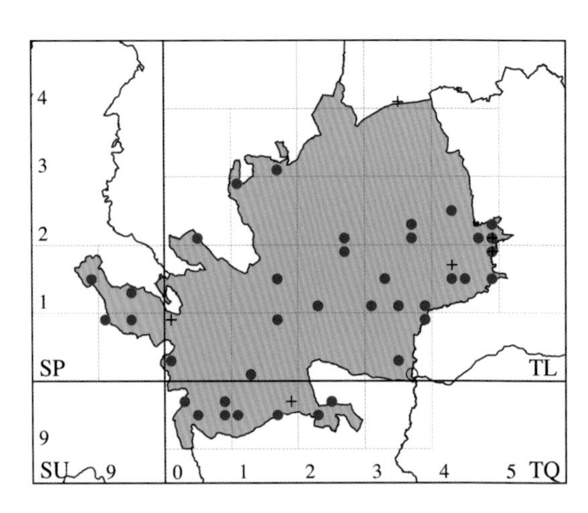

This is another species illustrated by J. F. Stephens from a Hertford specimen in his *Illustrations of British Entomology*, published in 1834. It is also mentioned in a field meeting report of the *Hertfordshire Natural History Society and Field Club* for 10th July 1886 at Hitchin. Today it is a familiar and expected species wherever there are Ash trees. David Agassiz, in *Moths and Butterflies of Great Britain and Ireland* volume 3 states that the adult flies in June and July, sometimes later, but adds that there is no clear evidence of a second generation in Britain. Our results for 2000 to 2006, shown in the graph, appear to show a clear gap between records of a large first generation and a much smaller autumn emergence, though it is noted that the numbers used in the analysis are small.

0450 *Scythropia crataegella* (L.)

Recorded: 1901 – 2006
Distribution / Status: Local / Common resident
Conservation status: No perceived threats
Caterpillar food plants: Common Hawthorn. Elsewhere, also on Blackthorn and *Cotoneaster* species
Flight period: Mid-May to September
Records in database: 107

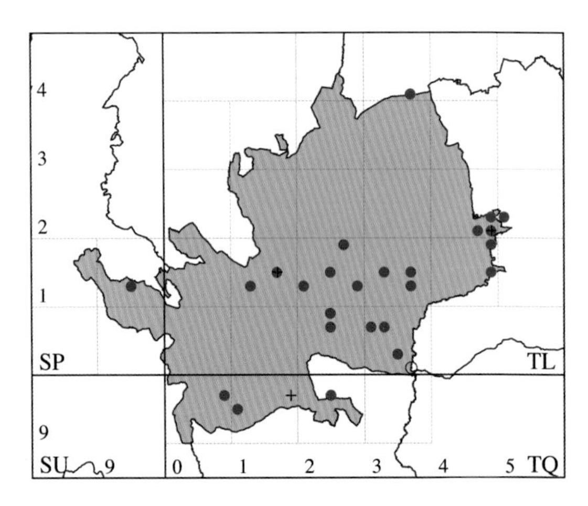

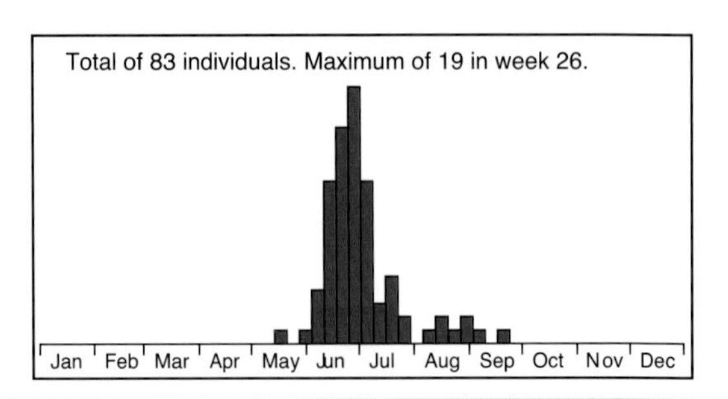

The lack of records for this usually common moth in much of the north of the county is undoubtedly a result of the winter flailing of hedges – an expression of laziness that ranks amongst the most damaging to invertebrate biodiversity of all land management techniques. Various text books give the adult flight period as July and state that there is only one generation. Our data does not disagree with the latter point, but there is evidently a prolonged emergence in Hertfordshire with adults recorded in 2000 – 2006 period from mid-May to mid-September, with a clear peak in week 26 (25th June to 1st July).

0451 *Ypsolopha mucronella* (Scop.)

Recorded:	1890 – 2006
Distribution / Status:	Local / Uncommon resident
Conservation status:	Herts Scarce
Caterpillar food plants:	Not recorded. Elsewhere, on Spindle
Flight period:	March/April. Elsewhere, September to April
Records in database:	12

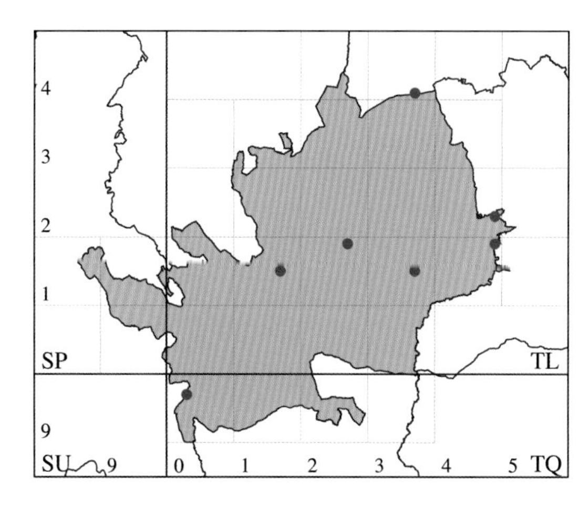

During 2004, one over-wintered adult was recorded on the very late date of 7th June at Ware (Liz Goodyear), but all our other records are done by 29th April.

0452 *Ypsolopha nemorella* (L.)

Recorded:	1998 – 2004
Distribution / Status:	Local / Uncommon resident
Conservation status:	Herts Scarce
Caterpillar food plants:	Wild Honeysuckle
Flight period:	Not recorded. Elsewhere, July/August
Records in database:	5

Three larvae collected by myself and Marcel Ashby at Balls Wood on 3rd May 2003 produced two adults and one *Microgaster* sp. parasite (Braconidae: Microgastrinae). This appears to be the first known record of a *Microgaster* species parasitising *Ypsolopha*: the identification was performed by

Mark Shaw at the National Museums of Scotland. Other localities are Welwyn in 1998 (Raymond Uffen), Hertford in 2002 and 2003 (Andrew Wood) and Hares Garden Wood, south of Tring where I caught one at light on 10th May 2004.

0453 *Ypsolopha dentella* (Fabr.)

Recorded:	1890 – 2006
Distribution / Status:	Widespread / Common resident
Conservation status:	No perceived threats
Caterpillar food plants:	Wild and garden varieties of Honeysuckle
Flight period:	July/August
Records in database:	55

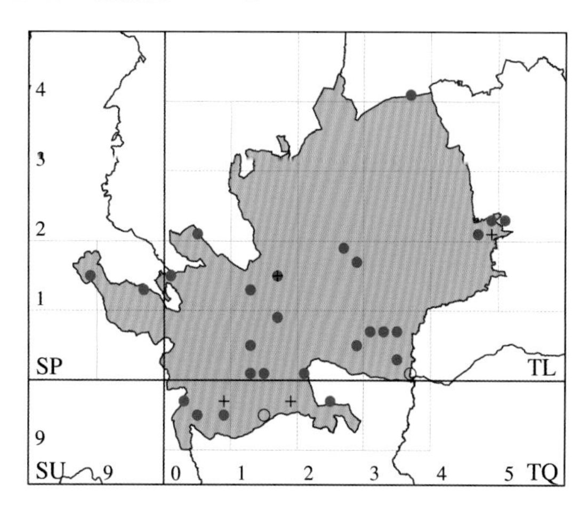

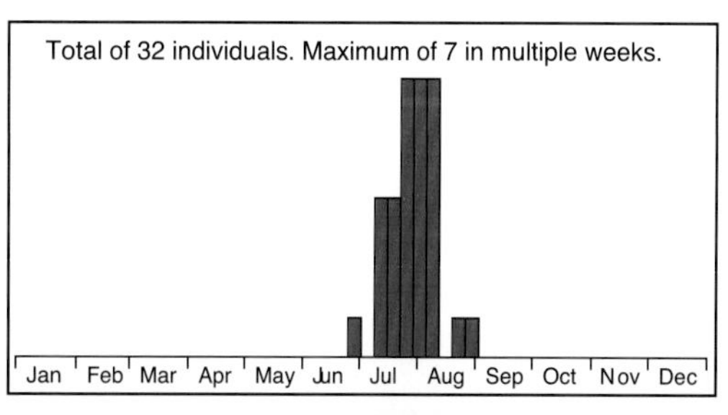

Although clearly able to thrive on garden varieties of honeysuckle, this attractive and distinctive moth is far more plentiful in association with wild honeysuckle growing in a

semi-natural woodland setting. For this reason, it appears likely to be absent from much of northern Hertfordshire and the general distribution pattern presented is probably accurate.

0455 *Ypsolopha scabrella* (L.)

Recorded: 1933 – 2006
Distribution / Status: Widespread / Common resident
Conservation status: No perceived threats
Caterpillar food plants: Not recorded. Elsewhere, on Apple, Hawthorn and *Cotoneaster* species
Flight period: July to mid-September
Records in database: 101

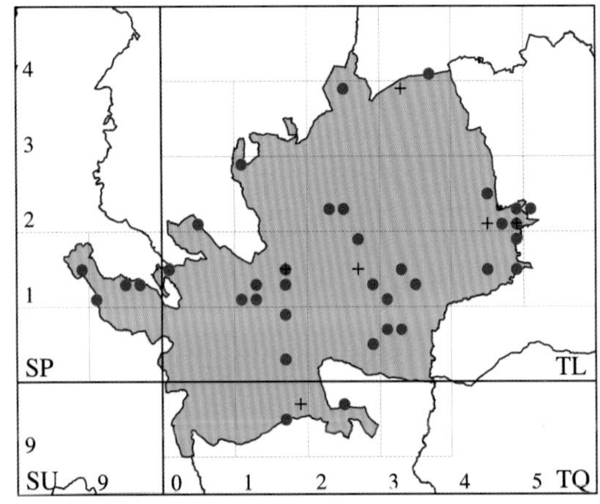

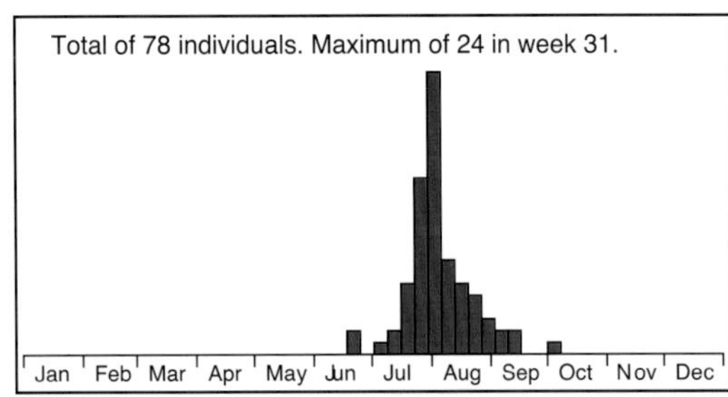

Our earliest record is from the Rothamsted light trap on the estate at Harpenden in 1933 (C. B. Williams). This same trap is the source of both our earliest and latest extreme seasonal appearances on 21st June 2003 and 6th October 2002 (Phil Gould).

0456 *Ypsolopha horridella* (Tr.)

Recorded: 1969 – 2003
Distribution / Status: Local / Rare resident
Conservation status: Herts Scarce
Caterpillar food plants: Not recorded. Elsewhere, on Blackthorn and Apple
Flight period: August to early September. Elsewhere, July/August
Records in database: 9

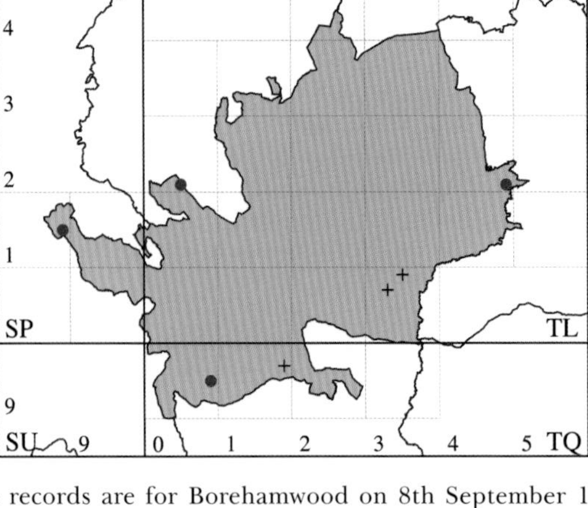

The records are for Borehamwood on 8th September 1969 (Eric Bradford), Hoddesdonpark Wood and Wormley Wood during 1977 (David Agassiz) and then nothing until a flurry of reports in 2003, from Bishops Stortford on 2nd August, Croxley Common Moor on 3rd August, Millhoppers Pasture on 23rd August and Zouches Farm near Dunstable on 6th September, all by myself. Oddly, there are no records at all since that date.

0457 *Ypsolopha lucella* (Fabr.)

Recorded: 1890 – 1929
Distribution / Status: Local or absent / Rare resident or extinct
Conservation status: Herts Extinct
Caterpillar food plants: Not recorded. Elsewhere, on oak
Flight period: August
Records in database: 2

There are just two records of this species in Hertfordshire, Griffith recorded it from the Sandridge area in his list published in 1890 and J. C. F. Fryer collected it at Bricket Wood in 1929. It was recorded just a few hundred metres over the border into Middlesex in Rachel Terry's garden at Barnet during 2003 and so may lurk undetected within our boundary. The larvae are associated with oak. Adults may be confused with those of 458: *Ypsolopha alpella* by the inexperienced.

0458 *Ypsolopha alpella* ([D.& S.])

Recorded: 1890 – 2004
Distribution / Status: Local / Rare resident
Conservation status: Herts Scarce
Caterpillar food plants: Not recorded. Elsewhere, on oak
Flight period: August
Records in database: 10

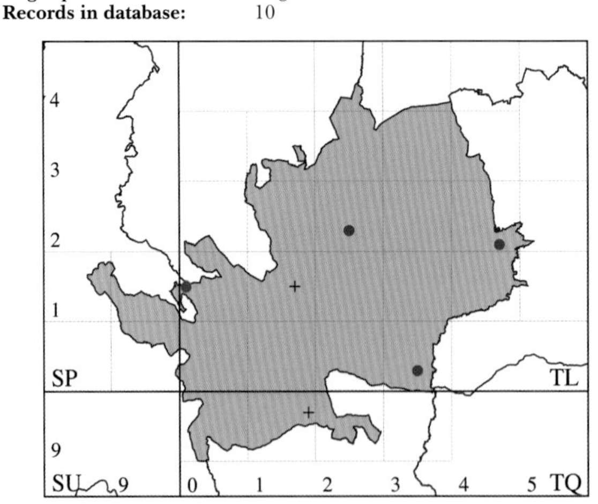

This is a moth of oak woodland, flying at night, but not always coming to light so that running light traps in a wood is not on its own sufficient to record it. As a result, it is suspected that this species is under-recorded in the southern half of the county, though probably scarce in the north.

0459 *Ypsolopha sylvella* (L.)

Recorded: 1890 – 2006
Distribution / Status: Local / Rare resident
Conservation status: Herts Scarce
Caterpillar food plants: Not recorded. Elsewhere, on oak
Flight period: August. Elsewhere, also in September
Records in database: 10

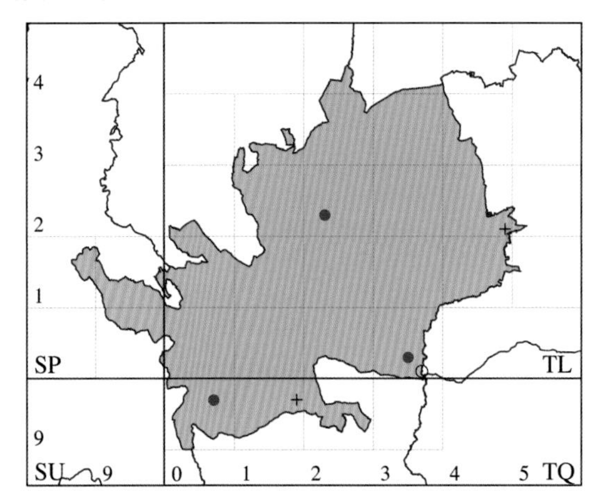

As with the last species, this is another oak woodland inhabitant that often ignores light traps and so is likely to be under-recorded. It should be looked for in the southern woodlands in the county.

0460 *Ypsolopha parenthesella* (L.)

Recorded: 1890 – 2006
Distribution / Status: Widespread / Common resident
Conservation status: No perceived threats
Caterpillar food plants: Hornbeam. Elsewhere, also on Oak, Birch, Hazel, Alder and Bog-myrtle
Flight period: July to October
Records in database: 62

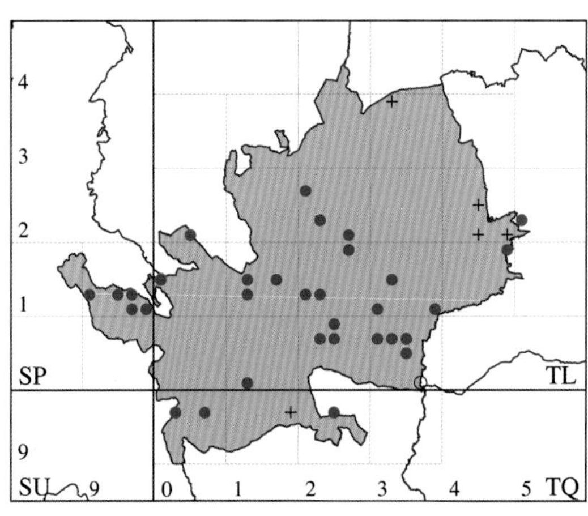

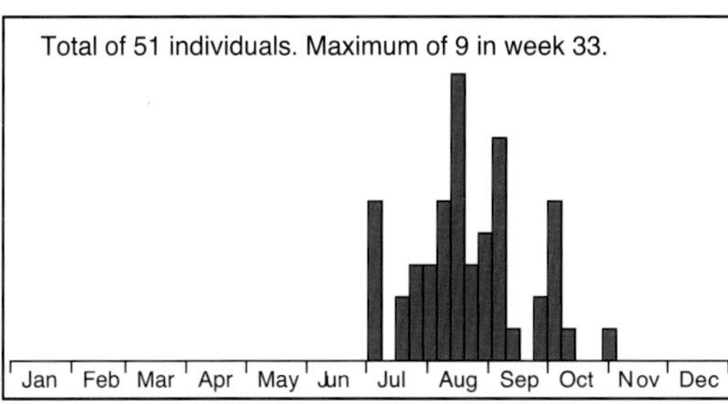

Although the larvae of this species supposedly prefer oaks, the only Hertfordshire foodplant records relate to Hornbeam. This is a common tree in the southern two thirds of Hertfordshire, but the fact that the moth is better recorded than both 458: *Ypsolopha alpella* and 459: *Ypsolopha sylvella* is probably more a reflection of its greater response to light traps. Standard text books seem to state that the adult fight period is August and September, but current Hertfordshire *parenthesella* appear from the very start of July and last until early October.

0461 *Ypsolopha ustella* (Cl.)

Recorded: 1890 – 2006
Distribution / Status: Local / Common resident
Conservation status: No perceived threats
Caterpillar food plants: Not recorded. Elsewhere, on oak
Flight period: July to March
Records in database: 35

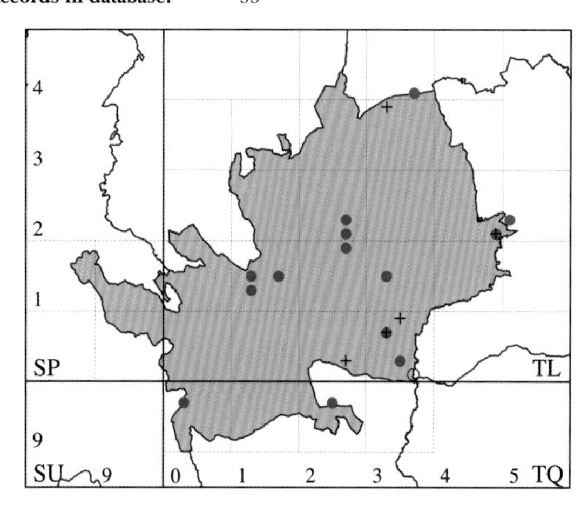

This is a very variable moth that can be confused with other species by the unwary. Recorded with us as early as 1834 (in J. F. Stephens *Illustrations of British Entomology*), it is another oak woodland species that comes readily to light traps. It is very likely to be far more widespread than the present results suggest and sometimes arrives at lights run on mild winter nights.

0462 *Ypsolopha sequella* (Cl.)

Recorded: 1890 – 2006
Distribution / Status: Widespread / Common resident
Conservation status: No perceived threats
Caterpillar food plants: Not recorded. Elsewhere, on Field Maple, rarely on Sycamore
Flight period: July to mid-September
Records in database: 68

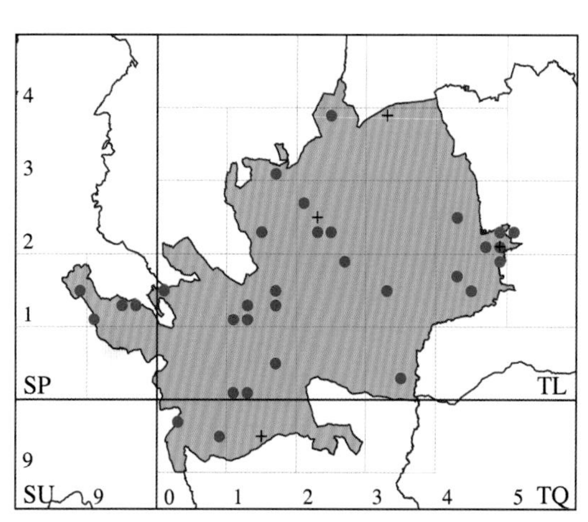

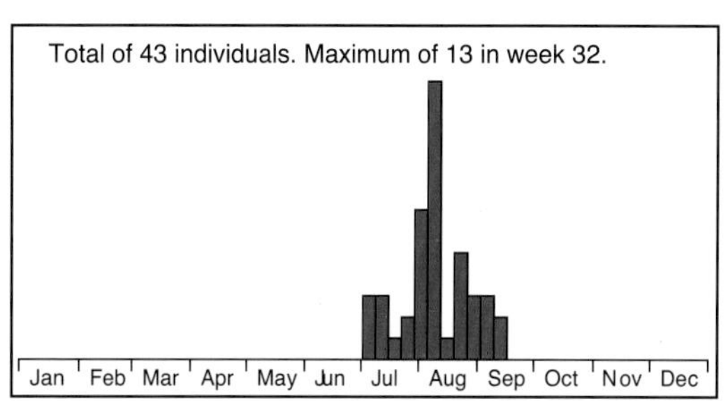

Field Maple is a widely distributed tree in most of Hertfordshire and explains the presence of this moth on many garden lists as well as those for woodlands. It is likely to be found throughout the county.

0463 *Ypsolopha vittella* (L.)

Recorded: 1890 – 2006
Distribution / Status: Extremely Local / Rare resident
Conservation status: Herts Rare
Caterpillar food plants: Not recorded. Elsewhere, on elm and Beech
Flight period: July/August
Records in database: 11

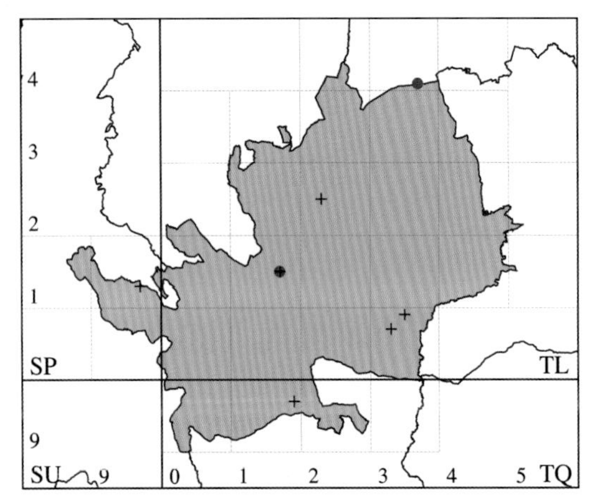

The preferred food plant is thought to be elm, and this may explain the apparent loss of this species from most of Hertfordshire. There are only two localities reported since the 1970s Dutch Elm Disease epidemic – Marshall's Heath in 1997, 1998 and 1999 (John Murray) and Royston on 27th August 2006 (John Chainey & Jenny Spence). In the latter locality, at least, the moth is more likely to be thriving on Beech.

0251 *Ochsenheimeria taurella* ([D.& S.]) = *mediopectinellus* (Haw.)

Recorded: 1834 – 2005
Distribution / Status: Local / Uncommon resident
Conservation status: Insufficiently known
Caterpillar food plants: Not recorded. Elsewhere, on various grasses
Flight period: August/September. Elsewhere, also in July
Records in database: 4

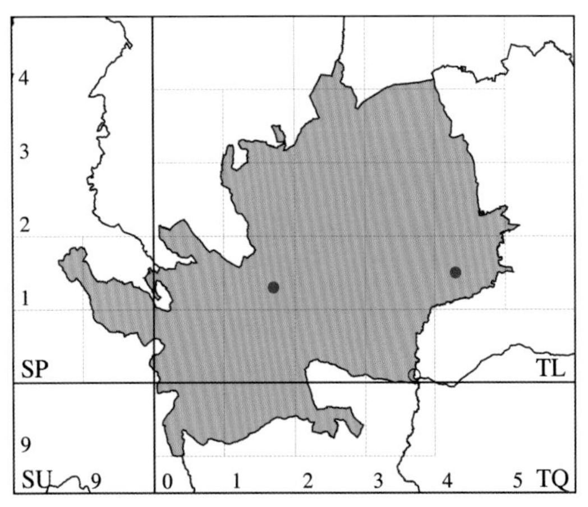

We have two old records and two modern ones: Hertford (Stephens, 1834. in *Illustrations of British Entomology* **4**: 350); Cheshunt (Boyd, 1901); Nomansland Common, 23rd August 2000 (Raymond Uffen) and Marshland Wood (north of Harlow, Essex) on 3rd September 2005 (myself). It is a grassland species that is seldom seen, but is probably common. Outside Hertfordshire I have caught it mainly by sweep-netting grassland habitat, but also in a Malaise trap amongst open scrub on a grassy motorway embankment on the M11 in Essex.

0252 *Ochsenheimeria urella* F. v. R. = *bisontella* (Lien. & Zell.)

Recorded: 1977 only
Distribution / Status: Local or Absent / Rare or Extinct
Conservation status: Herts Extinct
Caterpillar food plants: Not recorded. Elsewhere, on various grasses
Flight period: Late August. Elsewhere, July to September
Records in database: 1

Our only record is from Sawbridgeworth Marsh, on the border with Essex, where Maitland Emmet found it on 28th August 1977.

0253 *Ochsenheimeria vacculella* F. v. R.

Recorded: 1834 only
Distribution / Status: Absent / Extinct
Conservation status: Herts Extinct
Caterpillar food plants: Not recorded. Elsewhere, grasses, in haystacks and on stored grain
Flight period: Not recorded. Elsewhere, July/August
Records in database: 1

Our only record is that of J. F. Stephens whose picture in *Illustrations of British Entomology* **4**: 351, published in 1834, relates to a specimen from near Hertford.

0464 *Plutella xylostella* (L.)

Recorded: 1888 – 2006
Distribution / Status: Ubiquitous / Immigrant and temporary resident
Conservation status: No perceived threats
Caterpillar food plants: Unidentified Cruciferae
Flight period: March to November
Records in database: 479

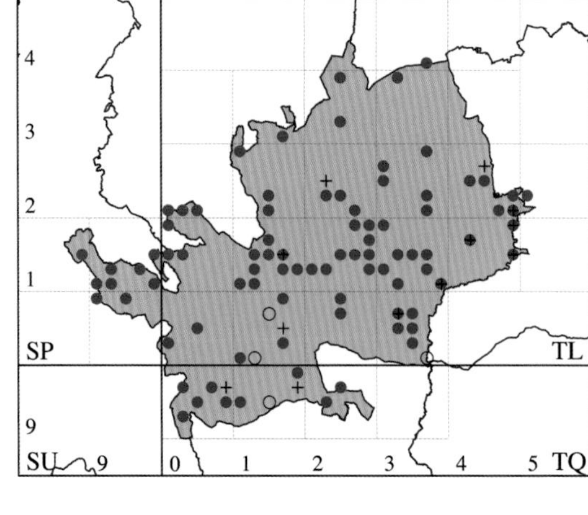

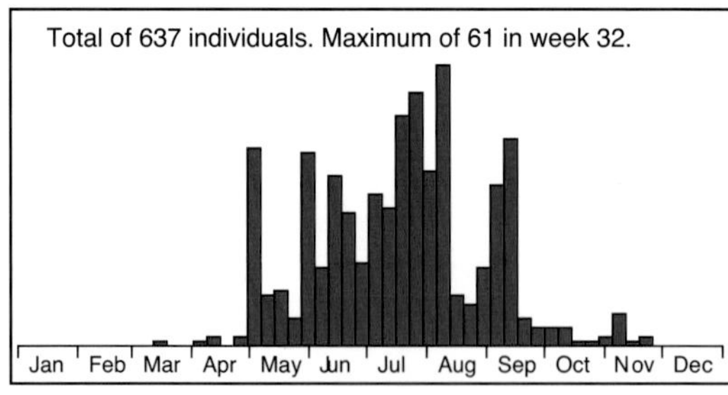

As a (probably annual) immigrant, this small moth is likely to be found in any area of the county. It is unclear if spring examples are fresh immigrants or survivors from the previous

year, but it certainly breeds here with us in the summer months. It is unfortunate that the several reports fail to identify the foodplant beyond family level.

0465 *Plutella porrectella* (L.)

Recorded:	1888 – 2006
Distribution / Status:	Local / Uncommon resident
Conservation status:	No perceived threats
Caterpillar food plants:	Dame's Violet
Flight period:	See chart. Elsewhere, May then July/August
Records in database:	41

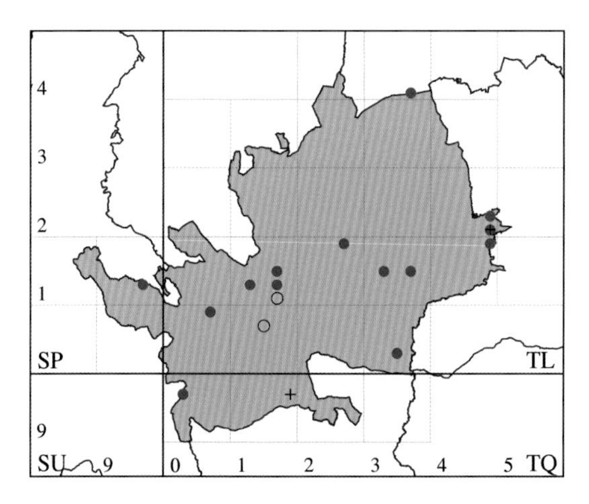

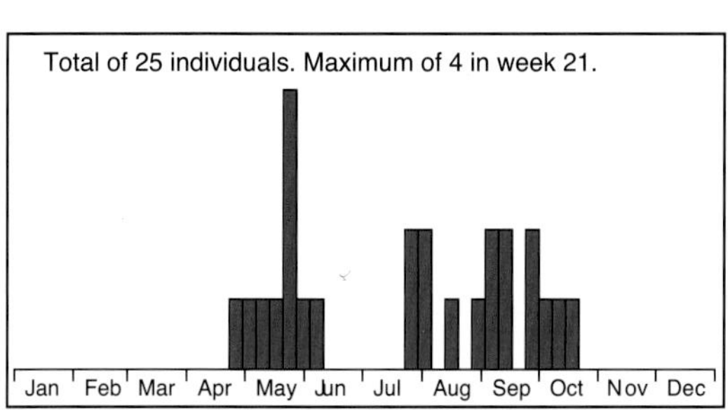

This is not a common moth in Hertfordshire, though it has been with us since at least 1889 when Gibbs recorded it within two or three miles of St Albans Town Hall. The flight data is based on very low numbers but in general agrees with there being two generations, the first flying from late April to early June but the second extending beyond the traditional July/August period to mid-October.

0469 *Eidophasia messingiella* (F. v. R.)

Recorded:	1983 – 2006
Distribution / Status:	Local / Rare resident
Conservation status:	Herts Scarce
Caterpillar food plants:	Not recorded. Elsewhere, on Hoary Pepperwort and Lady's Smock
Flight period:	June/July
Records in database:	10

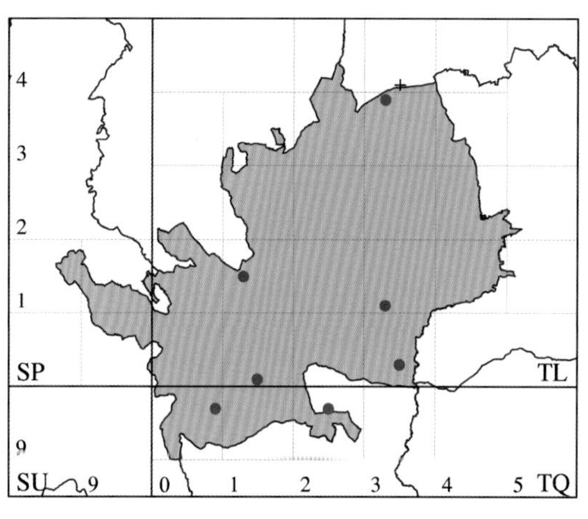

There are two unusual features of this moth in Hertfordshire. One is the apparent lack of any records prior to 1983 and the other is the absence of sightings from the well-surveyed central belt. The moth is perhaps genuinely concentrated in the south; the northern records relate to the chalk downland that is Therfield Heath.

0470 *Orthotaelia sparganella* (Thunb.) – now in Glyphipterigidae (see after species 397).

0473 *Acrolepiopsis assectella* (Zell.) Leek Moth

Recorded:	2006 only
Distribution / Status:	Local / Rare resident
Conservation status:	Herts Rare
Caterpillar food plants:	Not recorded. Elsewhere, on Leek and other *Allium* species
Flight period:	August
Records in database:	1

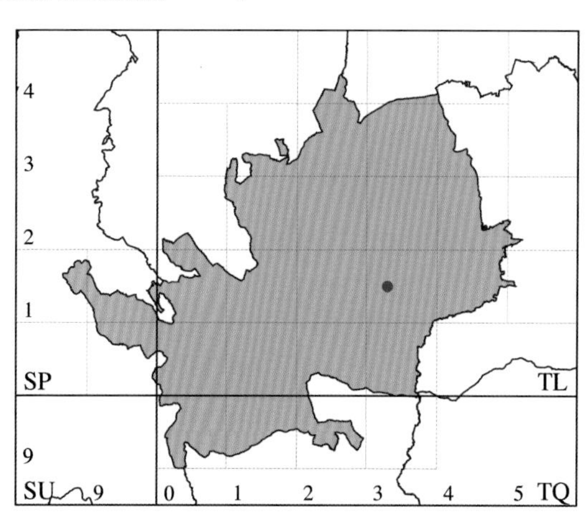

A male at light in the Bengeo area of Hertford on 17th August 2006 (Andrew Wood), confirmed by genitalia examination, is the only county record. It may be of relevance that this species was also recorded as new to adjacent Middlesex in 2005.

0476 *Acrolepia autumnitella* Curtis

Recorded: 1901 – 2005
Distribution / Status: Local / Common resident
Conservation status: No perceived threats
Caterpillar food plants: Woody Nightshade. Elsewhere, also on Deadly Nightshade
Flight period: October. Elsewhere, October to April
Records in database: 7

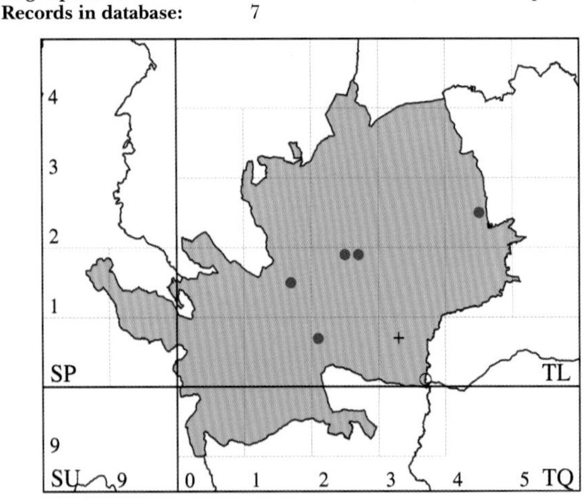

The adult moth over-winters amongst dense vegetation or other cover, but the easiest way to record the species is to look for the large and very obvious mines which are manifested as transparent patches on the leaves in both June and September. The species is probably quite common in most un-manicured woodlands where the foodplant is allowed to grow.

EPERMENIIDAE

Now in Epermenioidea after Tortricidae (see after species 1287).

SCHRECKENSTEINIIDAE

Now in Schreckensteinioidea after Epermeniidae and before Alucitidae (see before species 1288).

LYONETIIDAE

Worldwide this is a large family, but in Britain there are currently only nine members. Some recent works include the twelve British species of *Bucculatrix* in this family, but current understanding places them in a separate family, the Bucculatricidae, within the Gracillarioidea. Within this current understanding, we have five lyonetiids in Hertfordshire; all are leaf-miners in the larval stage. Originally, these species were treated as belonging to the superfamily Tineoidea, hence the Bradley and Fletcher (1979) checklist numbers are out of sequence here.

0254 *Leucoptera laburnella* (Stt.)

Recorded: 1890 – 2006
Distribution / Status: Widespread / Uncommon resident
Conservation status: No perceived threats
Caterpillar food plants: Laburnum
Flight period: Not recorded. Elsewhere, May
Records in database: 34

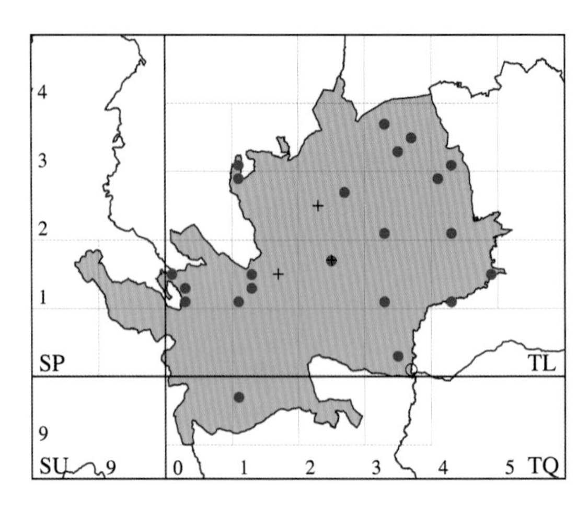

The spiral mines of this species are very distinctive and not confusable with any other species; they are likely to be found on every Laburnum tree in the county. Unfortunately for the moth, Laburnum trees are now less frequent in publicly accessible places since local authorities and others have selectively removed them in the belief that this will reduce the risk of poisoning; happily, these people seem to be unaware of the poisonous nature of a great many other plants grown in gardens and parks. Host trees are largely confined to gardens where they can be seen, but not examined by entomologists. Elsewhere, the larvae are said to occasionally mine Dyer's Greenweed, but we have no record of this host plant in Hertfordshire.

0256 *Leucoptera spartifoliella* (Hb.)

Recorded: 1890 – 2005
Distribution / Status: Local / Rare resident
Conservation status: Herts Scarce
Caterpillar food plants: Broom
Flight period: June/July
Records in database: 4

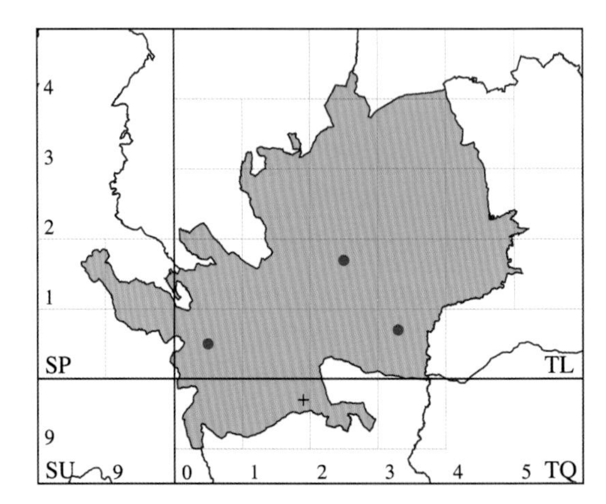

The caterpillars mine under the bark of Broom plants and the mines are not particularly easy to see, so the moth is probably under-recorded and should be searched for in new areas. We have records from the Sandridge area prior to 1890 (Griffith), Borehamwood, an adult on 20th June 1974 (Eric Bradford), Broxbourne Wood, mines on 11th

March 1999 (Raymond Uffen) and Roughdown Common, an adult on 16th July 2005 (myself).

0260 *Leucoptera malifoliella* (Costa) Pear Leaf Blister Moth

Recorded: 1901 – 2005
Distribution / Status: Local / Uncommon resident
Conservation status: Herts Scarce
Caterpillar food plants: Domestic Apple. Elsewhere, on other rosaceous trees
Flight period: June/July
Records in database: 12

Although recorded from before the turn of the nineteenth century at Cheshunt (Boyd, 1901) to the current period, this seems to have always been an uncommon moth in the county and it seems that we have no 2006 records.

0263 *Lyonetia clerkella* (L.) Apple Leaf Miner

Recorded: 1890 – 2006
Distribution / Status: Ubiquitous / Abundant resident
Conservation status: No perceived threats
Caterpillar food plants: Wild Cherry; ornamental cherry; Domestic Apple; Common Hawthorn; Midland Hawthorn; *Cotoneaster* sp.; Silver Birch; Downy Birch; Whitebeam
Flight period: May to November – see chart
Records in database: 446

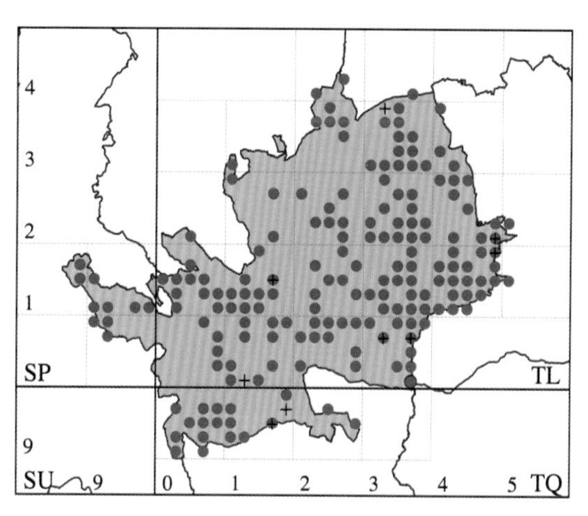

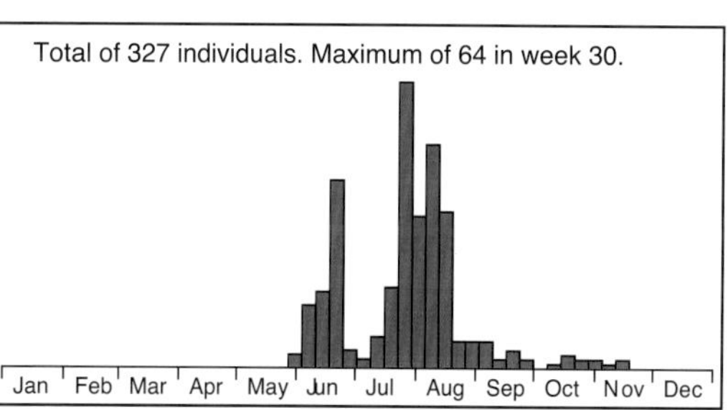

This is probably the commonest leaf-miner in the county, perhaps even the most numerically abundant micro-moth. A great many records are of the distinctive larval mines, but the adults are frequent in light traps and often recorded. The more-or-less entirely dark melanic form is recorded across the county; it is apparently scarce, perhaps not forming more than 5 per cent of catches, though county-wide counts are not available.

0264 *Bedellia somnulentella* (Zell.)

Recorded: 1901 – 2006
Distribution / Status: Local / ?Temporary resident
Conservation status: No perceived threats
Caterpillar food plants: Greater Bindweed
Flight period: Not recorded. Elsewhere, October to May
Records in database: 13

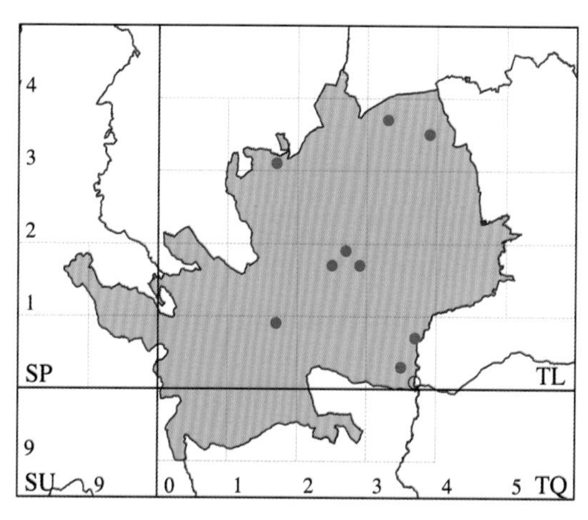

Although recorded from Cheshunt prior to 1901 (Boyd) there are no more records until Raymond Uffen found it at Welwyn in October 1996 and at Oughtonhead Common in 1998. Although doubtless under-recorded, it was probably scarce until 2003 when the larval mines, with their accompanying frass-adorned silk nets below the leaves, suddenly became common in a number of localities in south-east England. In 2006, the population appears to have declined again. This might suggest temporary residency following immigration?

GELECHIOIDEA
COLEOPHORIDAE

The Coleophoridae is a very large family with over a thousand species world-wide (Baldizzone *et al*, 2006). In Britain, some 109 species are divided into four genera – *Augasma* (one species), *Metriotes* (one species), *Goniodoma* (one species) and *Coleophora* (106). In Hertfordshire, we can muster one *Metriotes* and 58 *Coleophora*, making a total of 59. The larvae feed from specially constructed cases and these may be spun from silk or made from sections of the foodplant cut out and spun together. Some species mine leaves before creating characteristic round 'blotch' mines, which get progressively bigger as the caterpillar gets longer and can reach further whilst still keeping its rear end in the case. Such mines typically bear a small hole in the centre, marking the point where the case was attached. Other species feed in flowers heads, mostly on developing seeds and these often make the case from an empty seed capsule and so are just about impossible to see unless they move. Happily, the cases mostly allow for accurate identification, which is just as well since identification of adults caught 'blind' almost always requires dissection for correct identification. The Coleophoridae are very under-worked in Hertfordshire. Finding them and naming them are specialist activities – though very rewarding for anyone prepared to make the effort. Our records are a mixture of larval cases and adults caught in light traps – with extremely few exceptions the latter always being dissected. It should be recorded here that almost all the larval records for this family in Hertfordshire arise from the stalwart efforts of Raymond Uffen. Other specialists who wish to access the details of the records are welcome to do so.

0487 *Metriotes lutarea* (Haw.)

Recorded: 1890 – 1901
Distribution / Status: Former Resident
Conservation status: Herts Extinct
Caterpillar food plants: Greater Stitchwort
Records in database: 2

Our only two records are from the Sandridge area (Griffith, 1890) and the Cheshunt area (Boyd, 1901). Neither record can be accurately mapped. The larvae feed on the flowering heads of Greater Stitchwort and may be present in several Hertfordshire localities?

0490 *Coleophora lutipennella* (Zell.)

Recorded: 1980 – 2006
Distribution / Status: Widespread / Resident
Conservation status: No perceived threats
Caterpillar food plants: English oak (leaves)
Records in database: 36

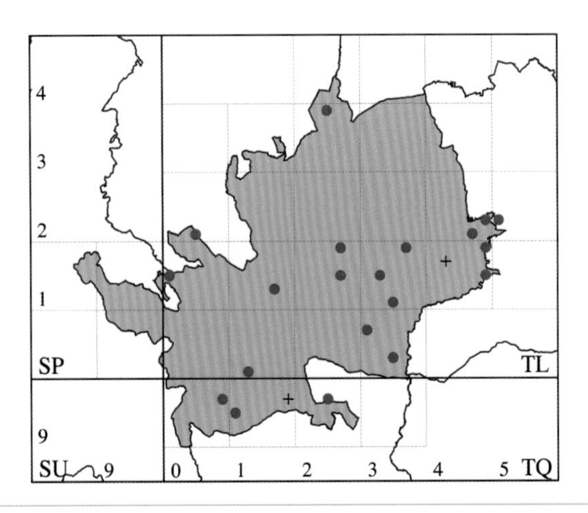

Mature spring larval cases are inseparable from those of 492: *Coleophora flavipennella* and reared adults require dissection.

0491 *Coleophora gryphipennella* (Hb.)

Recorded: 1890 – 2006
Distribution / Status: Widespread / Resident
Conservation status: No perceived threats
Caterpillar food plants: rose (leaves)
Records in database: 29

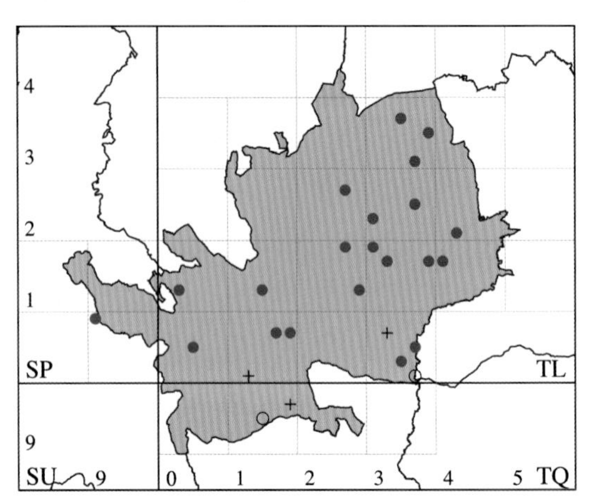

The characteristic blotch-mines on rose leaves, each with a small hole at the centre where the larval case was attached, are easily spotted and distinctive.

0492 *Coleophora flavipennella* (Dup.)

Recorded: 1991– 2006
Distribution / Status: Widespread / Resident
Conservation status: No perceived threats
Caterpillar food plants: Englsih oak (leaves)
Records in database: 41

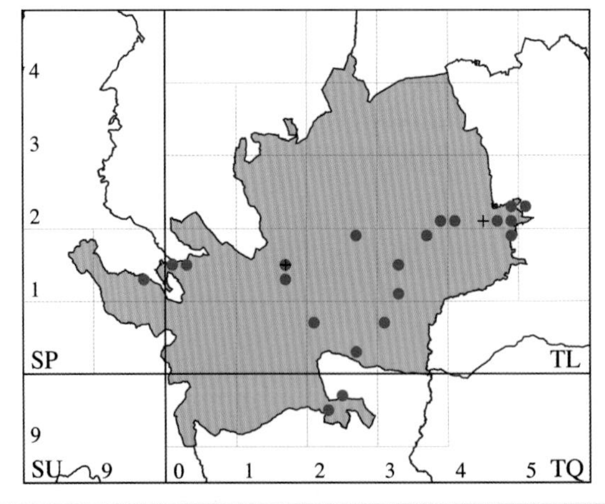

Mature spring larval cases are inseparable from those of 490: *Coleophora lutipennella* and reared adults require dissection.

0493 *Coleophora serratella* (L.)

Recorded: 1834 – 2006
Distribution / Status: Widespread / Resident
Conservation status: No perceived threats
Caterpillar food plants: Alder, Silver birch, Whitebeam, hawthorn, elm, Hazel (leaves)
Records in database: 37

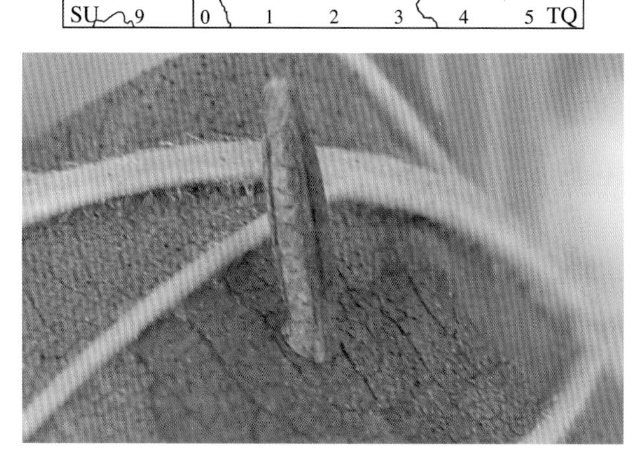

Numerically, this is probably the commonest of the *Coleophora* species in Hertfordshire. The cases appear most frequent on birch and least frequent on elm, but there is no numerical data to support this observation.

0494 *Coleophora coracipennella* (Hb.)

Recorded: 2005 – 2005
Distribution / Status: Local / Resident
Conservation status: No perceived threats
Caterpillar food plants: No data. Elsewhere, on Blackthorn, hawthorns and apples (leaves)
Records in database: 2

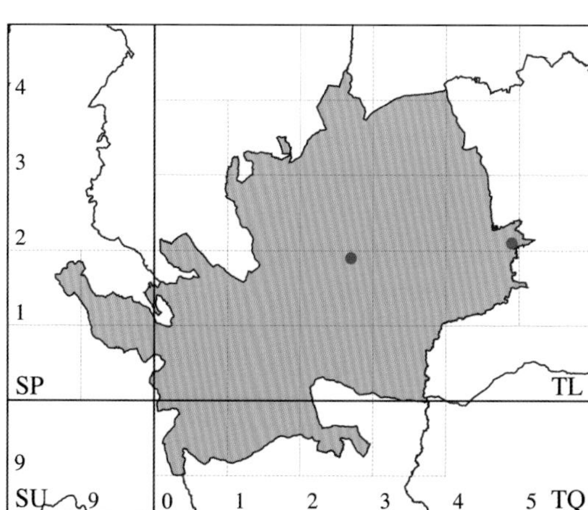

Our only records are of adults at Datchworth on 24th May (Stephen Palmer and Bishops Stortford on 13th July (myself), both in 2005.

0495 *Coleophora spinella* (Schr.) = *cerasivorella* Packard

Recorded: 1963 – 2005
Distribution / Status: Local / Resident
Conservation status: No perceived threats
Caterpillar food plants: hawthorn (leaves). Elsewhere, also on apple, pear, blackthorn and other leaves
Records in database: 16

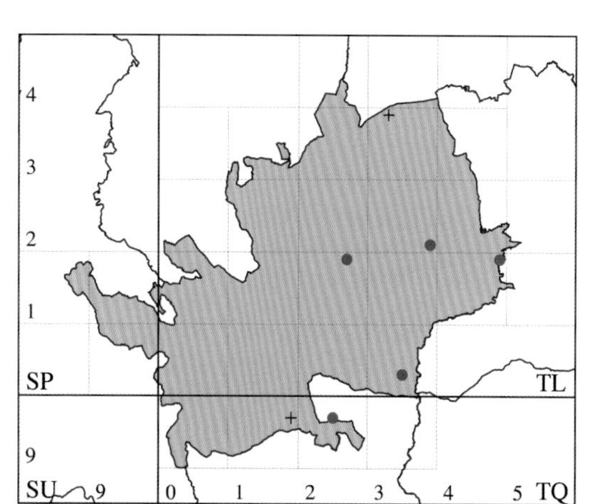

Larval cases are often indistinguishable from those of 494: *Coleophora coracipennella*. Both species ought to be widespread and common, though hedge management in the county is likely to present them with an uphill struggle for survival in some areas.

0496 *Coleophora milvipennis* Zell.

Recorded: 1937 – 2005
Distribution / Status: Local / Resident
Conservation status: No perceived threats
Caterpillar food plants: birch (leaves)
Records in database: 10

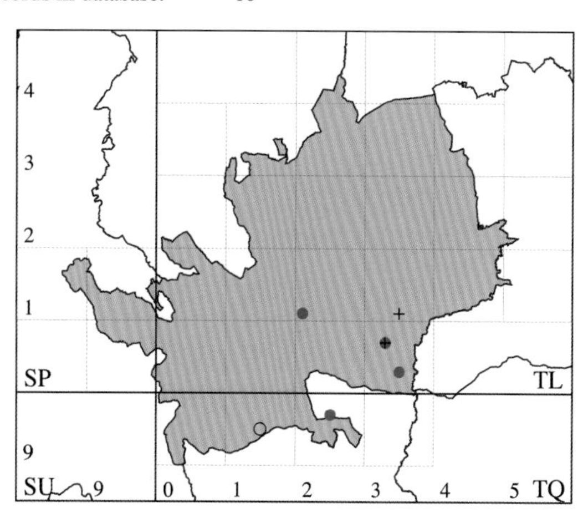

Separation from 498: *C. alnifoliae* and 499: *C. limosipennella* is often very tricky, though the former is not yet recorded from Hertfordshire. Adults should be dissected.

0497 *Coleophora badiipennella* (Dup.)

Recorded: Pre -1890 – 2000
Distribution / Status: Widespread / Resident
Conservation status: No perceived threats
Caterpillar food plants: elm (leaves)
Records in database: 14

The records suggest that this is a widespread and under-recorded moth in the county.

0499 *Coleophora limosipennella* (Dup.)

Recorded: 1998 – 2000
Distribution / Status: Local / Resident
Conservation status: No perceived threats
Caterpillar food plants: elm (leaves)
Records in database: 7

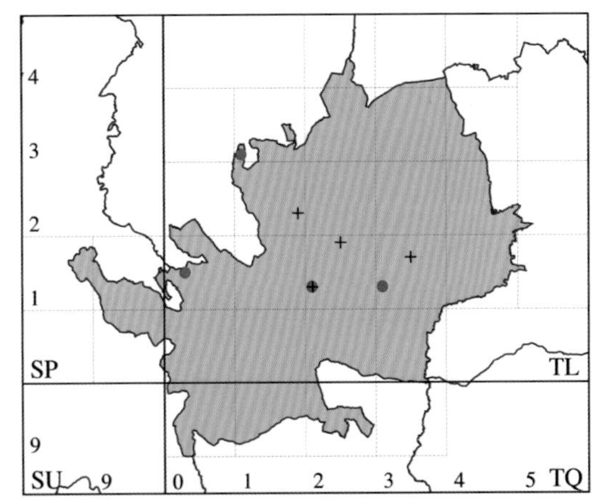

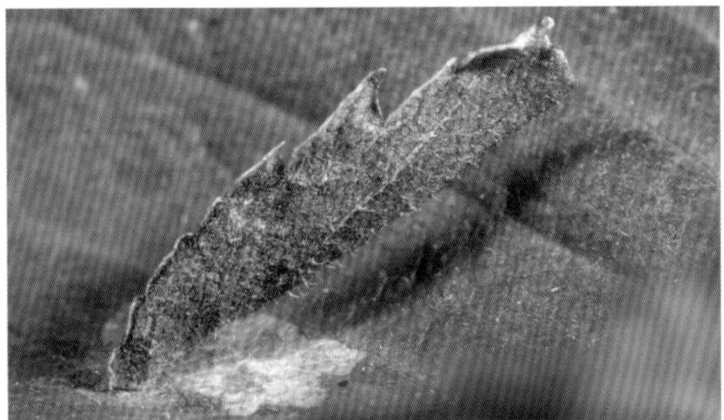

Unidentified elm suckers are favoured and Wych Elm seems to be ignored.

0501 *Coleophora siccifolia* Stt.

Recorded: 1900 – 2006
Distribution / Status: Local / Resident
Conservation status: No perceived threats
Caterpillar food plants: birches. Elsewhere, also on rosaceous trees
Records in database: 6

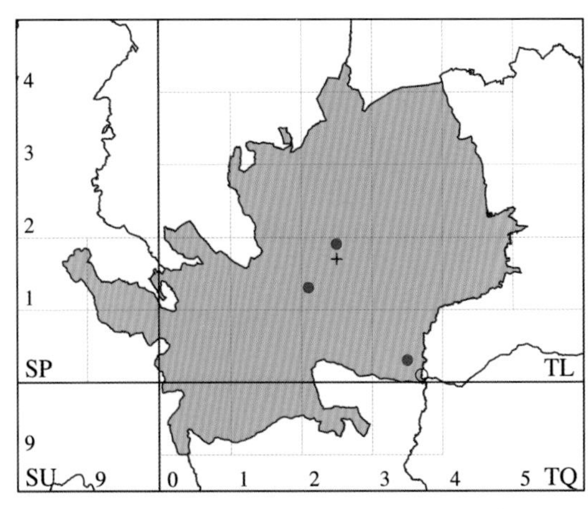

This is believed to be a biennial species, spending its first winter as a small larva and its second as a pupa, inside the larval case attached to a tree trunk.

0503 *Coleophora fuscocuprella* H.- S.

Recorded: 1971 – 1996
Distribution / Status: Local / Resident
Conservation status: No perceived threats
Caterpillar food plants: birch (leaves)
Records in database: 3

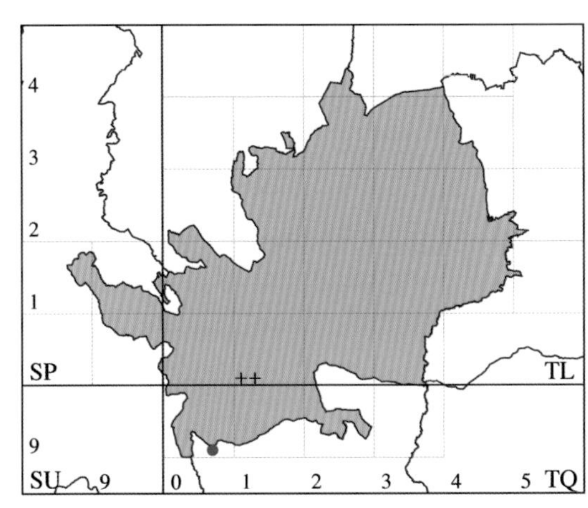

Saplings of Downy Birch are apparently preferred, but correct identification of the two birches and their hybrids can be difficult.

0504 *Coleophora lusciniaepennella* (Tr.) = *viminetella* Zell.

Recorded: 1890 – 2006
Distribution / Status: Local / Resident
Conservation status: No perceived threats
Caterpillar food plants: Eared Sallow (leaves). Elsewhere on other species of *Salix*.
Records in database: 11

Identification of sallows is a tricky business; Eared Sallow appears rare in the county but there are many hybrids and it is likely that these and others are used by the larvae.

0509 *Coleophora violacea* (Strom)

Recorded: 1890 – 2005
Distribution / Status: Local / Resident
Conservation status: No perceived threats
Caterpillar food plants: Hazel; Hawthorn; Blackthorn; elm (leaves)
Records in database: 9

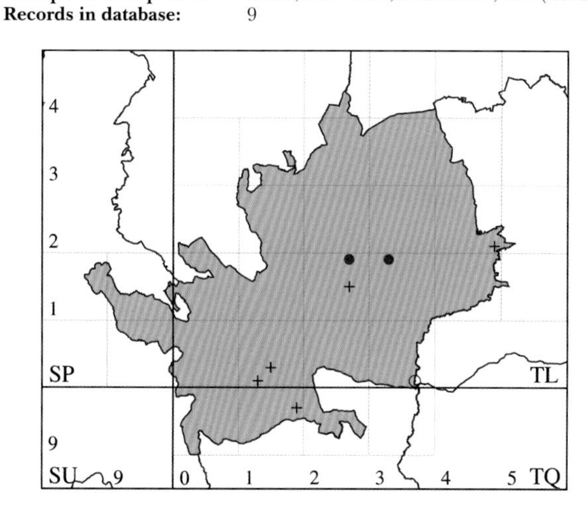

This is probably the most widely polyphagous *Coleophora* in Britain, affecting many trees and sometimes herbaceous plants as well. Its apparent rarity in Hertfordshire is surely a reflection of under-recording.

0510 *Coleophora juncicolella* Stt.

Recorded: 1901 – 2001
Distribution / Status: Extremely local / Rare resident
Conservation status: Herts Endangered
Caterpillar food plants: Heather
Records in database: 6

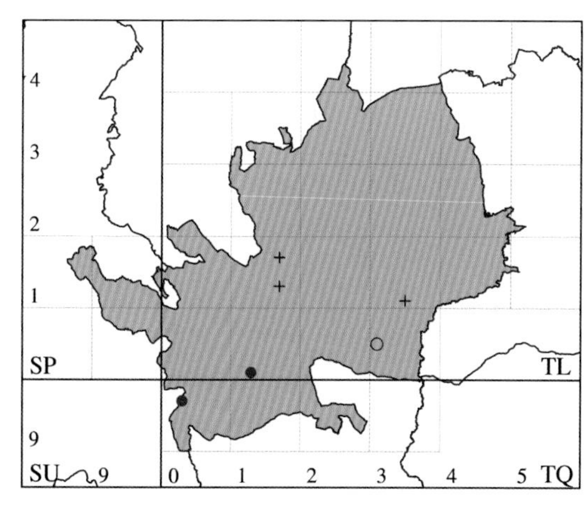

Heather is a very local plant in the county and this alone restricts the distribution of the moth, which requires long-standing patches of mature heather that has not been burned. Thus, the few relatively extensive areas of heather in the county, such as that at Bricketwood Common, do not seem to support larvae.

0511 *Coleophora orbitella* Zell.

Recorded: 1970 only
Distribution / Status: Extremely local / Resident
Conservation status: No perceived threats
Caterpillar food plants: Not recorded. Elsewhere, on birch
Records in database: 1

Eric Bradford was responsible for the only county record, of an adult at Bricket Wood in 1970. The winter is passed as a larva, in the case which is attached to a twig.

0512 *Coleophora binderella* (Kollar)

Recorded: 1890 – 2005
Distribution / Status: Local / Resident
Conservation status: No perceived threats
Caterpillar food plants: birch (leaves). Elsewhere, also on Alder and Hazel leaves
Records in database: 8

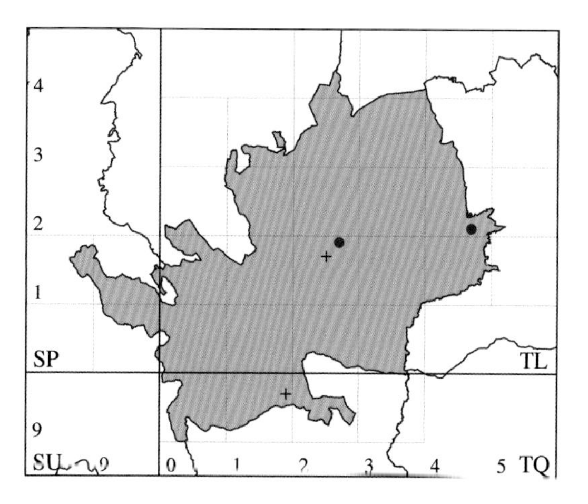

Mature birches are the favoured habitat and this might suggest that the moth is rather local in Hertfordshire.

0513 *Coleophora potentillae* Elisha

Recorded: 1980 – 1990
Distribution / Status: Rare Resident or Extinct
Conservation status: No perceived threats
Caterpillar food plants: Common Tormentil; Raspberry; Calaminth (leaves)
Records in database: 8

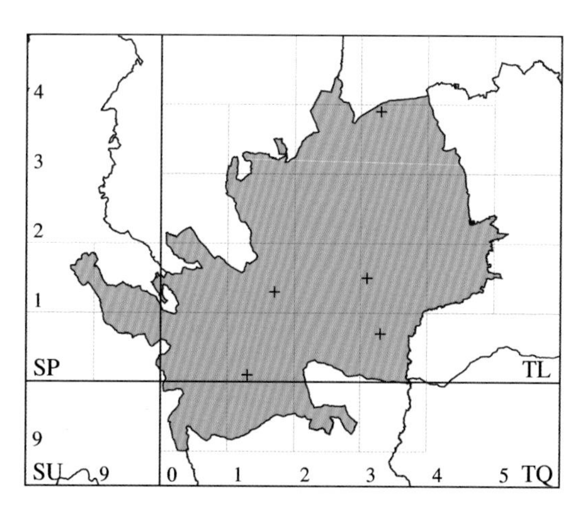

Most rosaceous herbs support the larva of this species; the case is hard to separate from that of 509: *Coleophora violacea*.

0515 *Coleophora albitarsella* Zell.

Recorded: 1890 – 2006
Distribution / Status: Local / Resident
Conservation status: No perceived threats
Caterpillar food plants: Wild Basil; Marjoram; Ground Ivy (leaves)
Records in database: 20

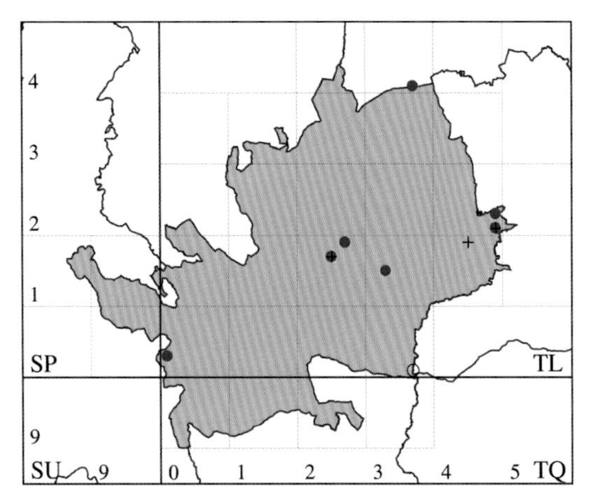

Elsewhere, a wide range of labiate plants are utilised and the Hertfordshire foodplant list is likely to expand as more people take up the study of these interesting moths.

0516 *Coleophora trifolii* (Curtis)

Recorded:	1999 – 2006
Distribution / Status:	Widespread / Abundant resident
Conservation status:	No perceived threats
Caterpillar food plants:	Common Melilot (seeds)
Records in database:	20

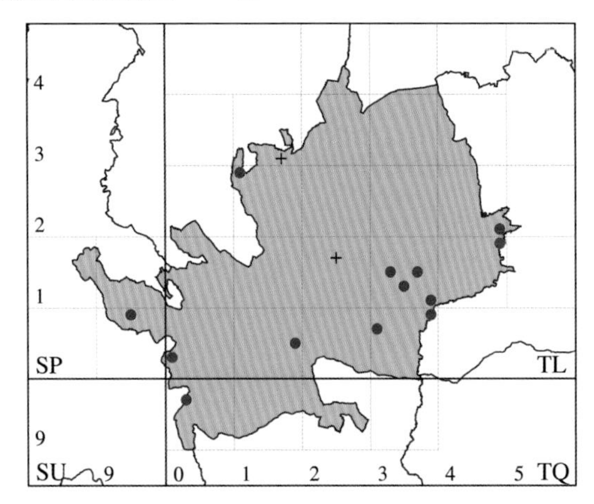

This is the easiest of the metallic green *Coleophora* to identify as it is the only one with pale yellow scales fringing its eyes – a feature seen easily in the field with the aid of a hand lens.

0517 *Coleophora alcyonipennella* (Kollar)

Recorded:	1997 – 2006
Distribution / Status:	Widespread / Abundant Resident
Conservation status:	No perceived threats
Caterpillar food plants:	White Clover (seeds)
Records in database:	33

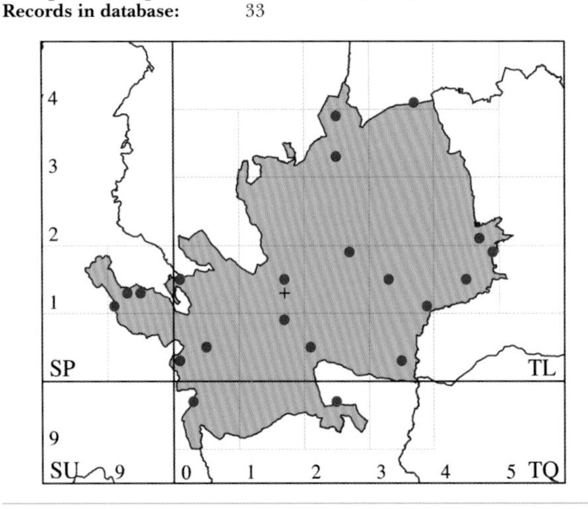

There has been past confusion with *Coleophora frischella* (L.) which is not found in Hertfordshire and probably does not occur here. All mapped records are based on dissected adults – wild caught and reared. Historical records not supported by a specimen are ignored. The text in *Moths and Butterflies of Great Britain and Ireland* volume 3 under the heading of *Coleophora frischella* in fact relates to this species (*alcyonipennella*), but the genitalia drawings do indeed relate to *frischella*. For the genitalia of *alcyonipennella* see *British Journal of Entomology & Natural History* **13**: 46 (2000).

0518 *Coleophora mayrella* (Hb.)

Recorded:	1890 – 2005
Distribution / Status:	Widespread / Resident
Conservation status:	No perceived threats
Caterpillar food plants:	White Clover (seeds)
Records in database:	24

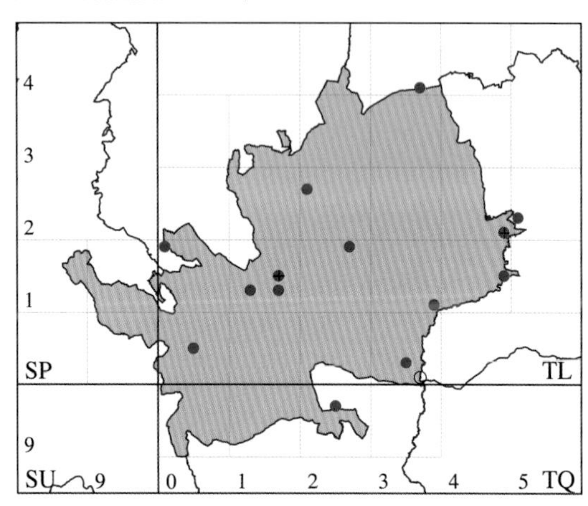

The dark (fuscous) and white ringed apical portions of the antennae immediately separate the adults from the other metallic green members of the group.

0519 *Coleophora deauratella* Lien.& Zell.

Recorded:	1834 – 2004
Distribution / Status:	Widespread / Resident
Conservation status:	No perceived threats
Caterpillar food plants:	Not recorded. Elsewhere, on Red Clover
Records in database:	14

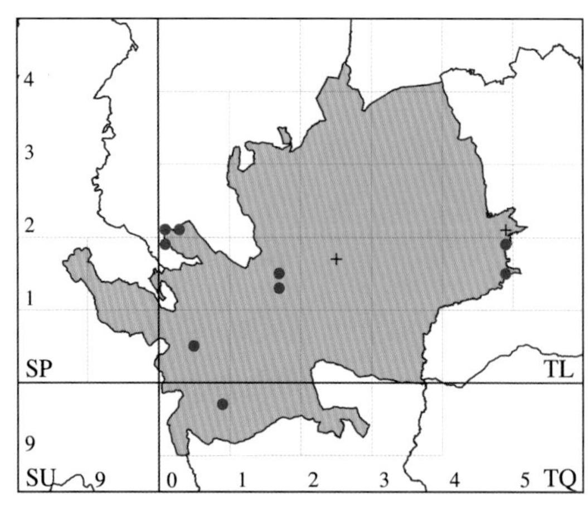

Separation of this species from 517: *C. alcyonipennella* can be problematic in many instances and dissection is often necessary.

0521 *Coleophora conyzae* Zell.

Recorded:	2002 only
Distribution / Status:	Local / Resident
Conservation status:	No perceived threats
Caterpillar food plants:	Fleabane. Elsewhere, also on Ploughman's Spikenard
Records in database:	1

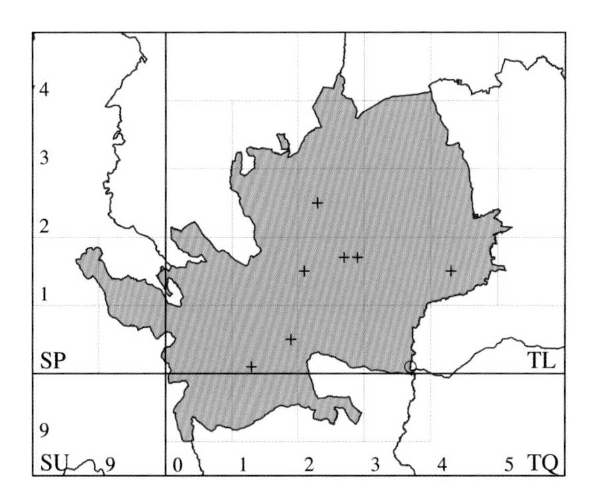

Croxley Common Moor provides the single Hertfordshire record, from where cases were found on Common Fleabane by Raymond Uffen in 2002.

0522 *Coleophora lineolea* (Haw.)

Recorded:	1997 – 2005
Distribution / Status:	Local / Resident
Conservation status:	No perceived threats
Caterpillar food plants:	White Horehound; Black Horehound; *Stachys byzantina* (leaves)
Records in database:	11

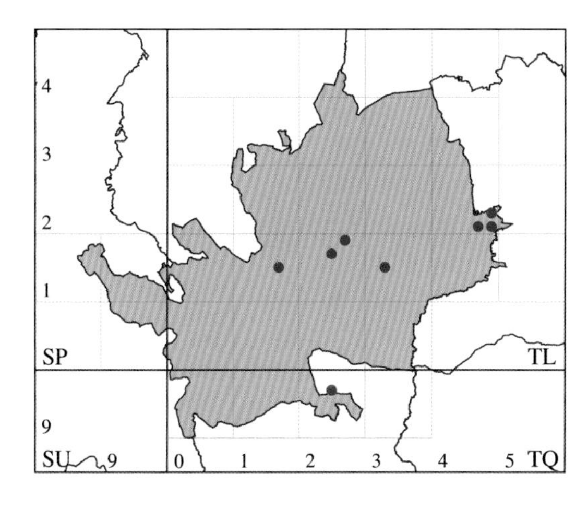

The name *lineolea* was incorrectly applied to *Coleophora striatipennella* by both Meyrick (1928) and Ford (1949) and so older literature records should always be checked by examining the voucher specimens.

0523 *Coleophora hemerobiella* (Scop.)

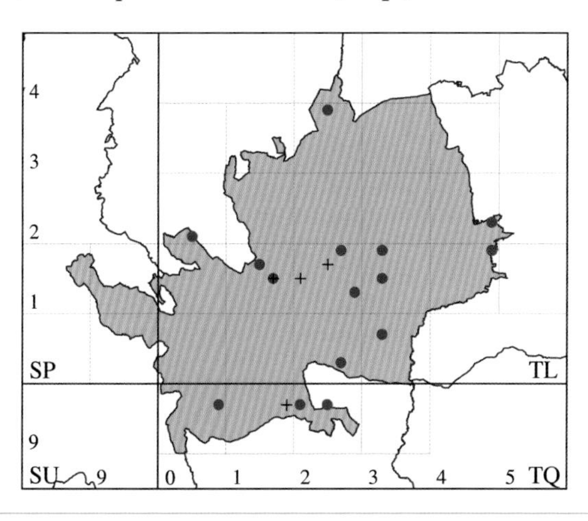

Recorded:	1968 – 2005
Distribution / Status:	Widespread / Resident
Conservation status:	No perceived threats
Caterpillar food plants:	Common Hawthorn; ornamental cherry (leaves)
Records in database:	25

Though apparently a scarce species in Britain and confined to the south-east of the country, this is nevertheless a widespread and frequently encountered species in Hertfordshire, where it is most often found feeding on the leaves of cherry trees.

0525 *Coleophora solitariella* Zell.

Now positioned after 547: *Coleophora discordella*.

0526 *Coleophora laricella* (Hb.)

Recorded:	1890 – 2005
Distribution / Status:	Local / Resident
Conservation status:	No perceived threats
Caterpillar food plants:	Larch (needles)
Records in database:	20

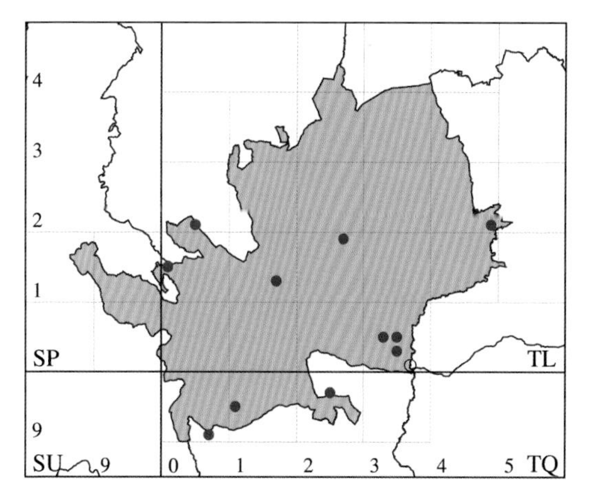

Larch trees are not common in Hertfordshire and most of our records are of adults, caught from 31st May to 19th July. Blanched needles in the crown of Larch trees are likely to indicate the presence of this moth.

0528 *Coleophora chalcogrammella* Zell.

Recorded:	1993 only
Distribution / Status:	Extremely local / Resident
Conservation status:	No perceived threats
Caterpillar food plants:	Lesser Stitchwort. Elsewhere, on Field Mouse-ear Chickweed
Records in database:	1

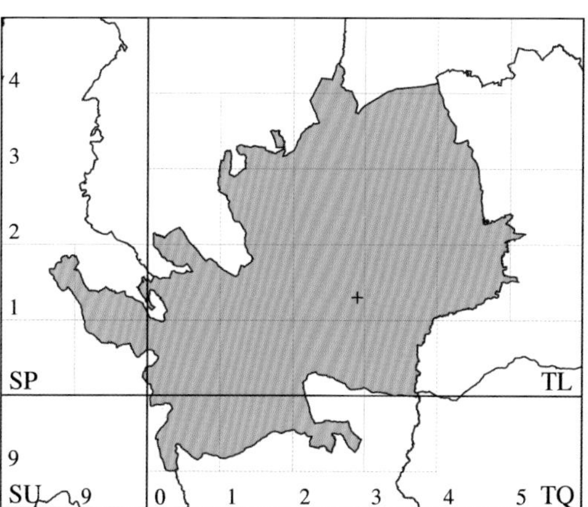

Apart from Raymond Uffen finding this species at Panshanger in 1993 there are no other Hertfordshire reports.

0530 *Coleophora lixella* Zell.

Recorded: 1890
Distribution / Status:
Conservation status: Herts Extinct
Caterpillar food plants: No data. Elsewhere, first on the seeds of Thyme, then later on grasses
Records in database: 1

Our only record is for the Sandridge area, in the years before 1890 when A. F. Griffith published his list. The location of the record is inadequately known and so it cannot be mapped here.

0532 *Coleophora albidella* ([D.& S.])

Recorded: 1933 – 2005
Distribution / Status: Local / Resident
Conservation status: No perceived threats
Caterpillar food plants: No data. Elsewhere, on first in the buds then on the leaves of *Salix* species
Records in database: 7

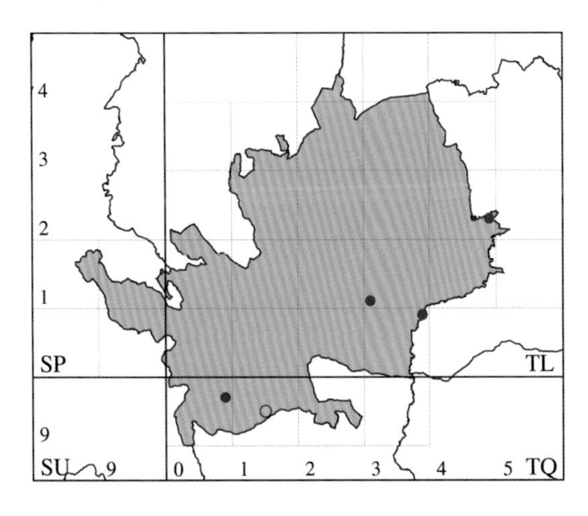

All of our records relate to adults, taken in light traps and identified by dissection.

0533 *Coleophora anatipennella* (Hb.)

Recorded: 1890 – 2005
Distribution / Status: Widespread / Resident
Conservation status: No perceived threats
Caterpillar food plants: Domestic Apple (leaves). Elsewhere, rosaceous trees, especially Blackthorn
Records in database: 13

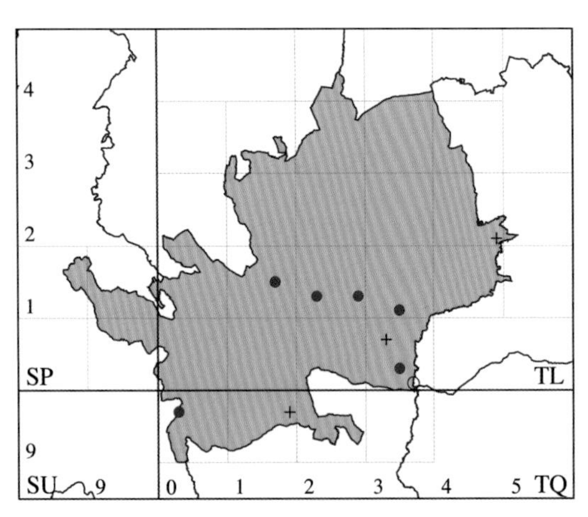

This is one of the all-white *Coleophora* species; the larvae make a characteristic pistol-shaped case on a wide range of rosaceous trees and shrubs and the scarcity of records in Hertfordshire is surprising.

0534 *Coleophora currucipennella* Zell.

Recorded: pre-1890 only
Distribution / Status: Former resident
Conservation status: Herts Extinct
Caterpillar food plants: No data. Elsewhere, oaks, Hornbeam and willows.
Records in database: 1

Our only record is for the Sandridge area, in the years before 1890 when A. F. Griffith published his list. The precise locality is not known and so cannot be mapped. It should be added that I have not been able to locate the voucher specimen for checking.

0535 *Coleophora ibipennella* Zell. = *ardeaepennella* Scott

Recorded: 1971 – 2006
Distribution / Status: Widespread / Resident
Conservation status: No perceived threats
Caterpillar food plants: English oak (leaves)
Records in database: 20

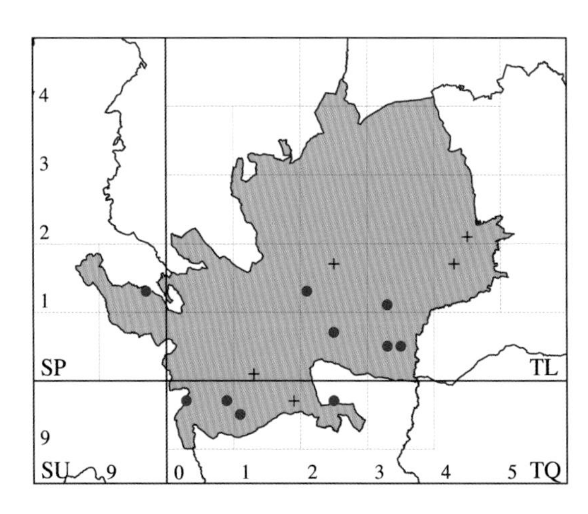

The larvae of this species graze the lower surface of oak leaves from a pistol-shaped case, so that the feeding pattern left behind is easily separated from the other oak feeding species which mine the leaves internally.

0536 *Coleophora betulella* Hein. = *ibipennella* auctt.

Recorded: 1890 – 2004
Distribution / Status: Local / Resident
Conservation status: No perceived threats
Caterpillar food plants: No data. Elsewhere, on birches
Records in database: 3

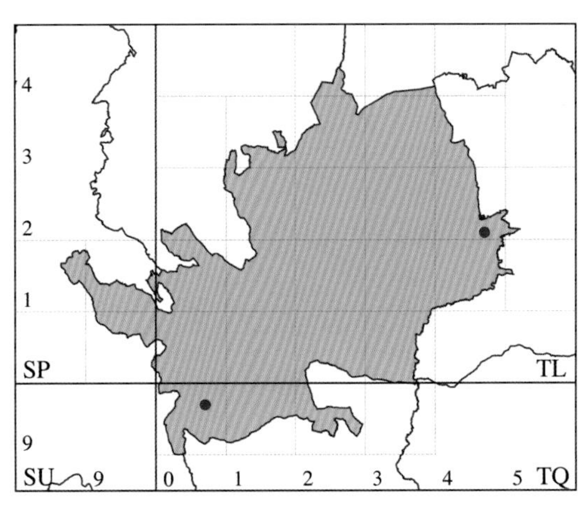

The lack of white tips to the costal cilia separate this species from the otherwise identical 535: *Coleophora ibipennella*. The larvae, of course, are on different foodplants.

0537 *Coleophora kuehnella* (Goeze) = *palliatella* (Zincken)

Recorded: 1890 – 2006
Distribution / Status: Widespread / Resident
Conservation status: No perceived threats
Caterpillar food plants: No data. Elsewhere, on oaks
Records in database: 18

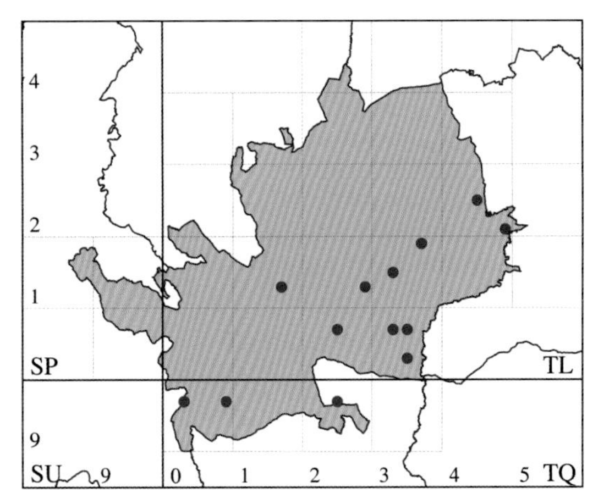

Although normally feeding on oak leaves, larvae have also been found devouring oak catkins in the spring.

0544 *Coleophora albicosta* (Haw.)

Recorded: 1890 – 2004
Distribution / Status: Widespread / Resident
Conservation status: No perceived threats
Caterpillar food plants: Not recorded. Elsewhere, on Gorse (seeds)
Records in database: 17

Although we have not recorded larval cases, all of our adults have been found in positive association with Gorse – the known foodplant elsewhere in Britain.

0545 *Coleophora saturatella* Stt.

Recorded: 1993 – 1993
Distribution / Status: Extremely local / Rare resident
Conservation status: Herts Rare
Caterpillar food plants: Not recorded. Elsewhere, on Broom
Records in database: 1

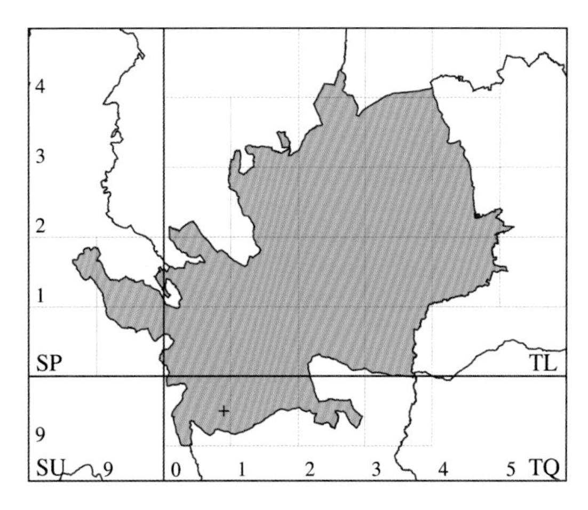

Our single record is from Croxley Common Moor, an adult in association with a Broom bush in 1993 (Raymond Uffen).

0546 *Coleophora genistae* Stt.

Recorded: 1901 – 2006
Distribution / Status: Extremely local / Very rare resident
Conservation status: Herts Endangered
Caterpillar food plants: Petty Whin (leaves and then flowers)
Records in database: 8

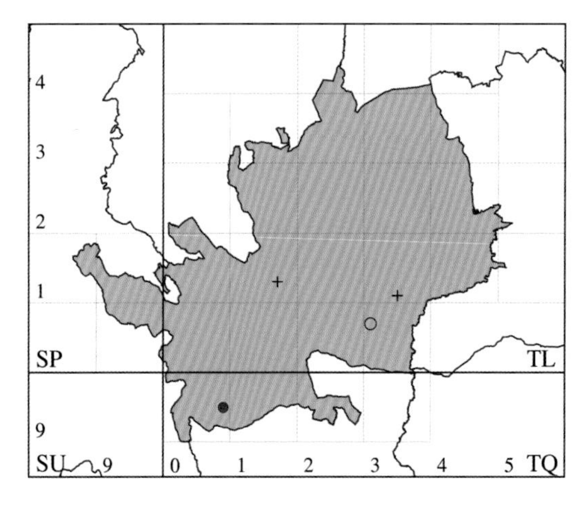

The foodplant is now apparently absent from all the sites where the moth is recorded apart from Croxley Common Moor. At this site the plant is under threat from changes in the cattle grazing regime.

0547 *Coleophora discordella* Zell.

Recorded: 1834 – 1990
Distribution / Status: Extremely local / Rare resident
Conservation status: Herts Rare
Caterpillar food plants: Greater Bird's-foot Trefoil (leaves). Elsewhere, also on Common Bird's-foot Trefoil
Records in database: 7

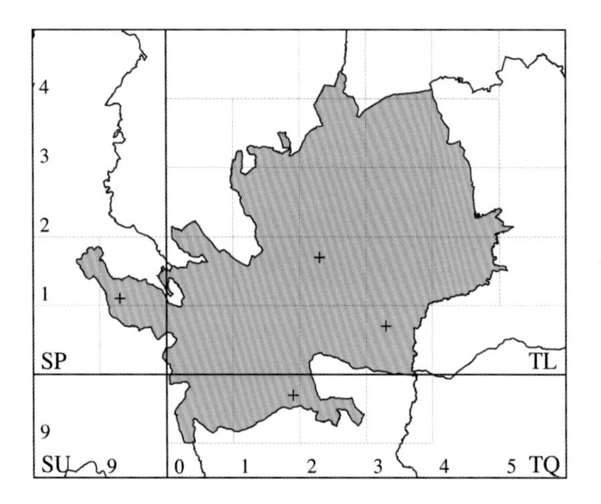

The larvae cause conspicuous blotches on the leaves of the foodplant. It is a widespread species across all of Britain and its absence from Hertfordshire is unlikely to be real. Modern entomologists seem strangely reluctant to lie on the ground and search the leaves of plants in a manner that might be described as 'close up and personal'.

0525 *Coleophora solitariella* Zell.

Recorded:	1890 – 1994
Distribution / Status:	Extremely local / Resident
Conservation status:	Herts Rare
Caterpillar food plants:	Greater Stitchwort (leaves)
Records in database:	9

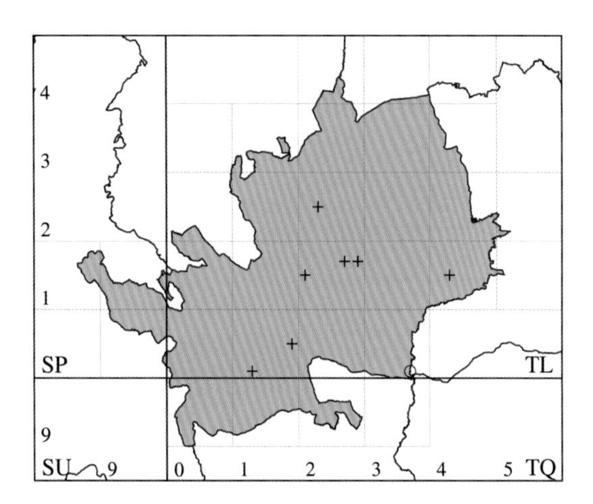

This species is hard to separate from *Coleophora lithargyrinella*, which also feeds on Greater Stitchwort and which is not yet recorded in Hertfordshire.

0550 *Coleophora silenella* H.- S.

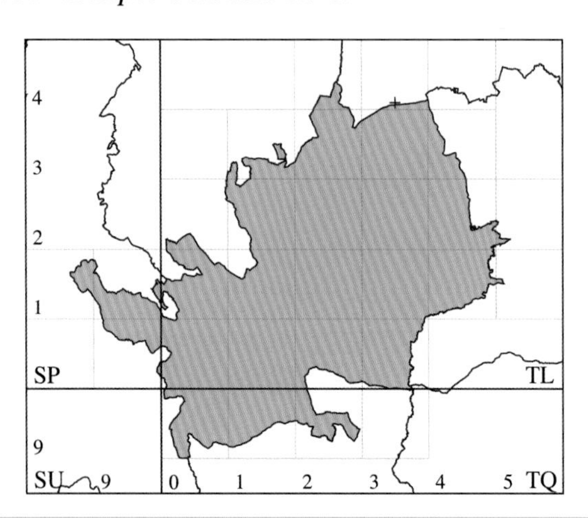

Recorded:	1985 only
Distribution / Status:	Extremely local / Rare resident
Conservation status:	Herts Rare
Caterpillar food plants:	campion (seeds). Elsewhere, Bladder Campion and Nottingham Catchfly are the listed species
Records in database:	1

Raymond Uffen's report from Therfield Heath, in 1985, is our only record. For most of its life, the larva feeds inside the seed capsule and it is only in the final stages that a case might be seen protruding; it is surely overlooked in Hertfordshire.

0553 *Coleophora striatipennella* Tengst.

Recorded:	1890 – 2004
Distribution / Status:	Widespread / Resident
Conservation status:	No perceived threats
Caterpillar food plants:	Lesser Stitchwort
Records in database:	22

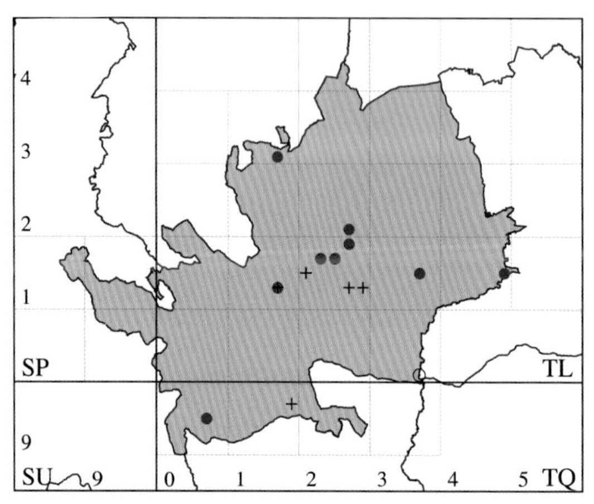

The name *lineolea* was incorrectly applied to *striatipennella* by Meyrick (1928) and Ford (1949) and so older literature records should always be checked by examining the voucher specimens.

0555 *Coleophora follicularis* (Vallot)

Recorded:	1982 – 2002
Distribution / Status:	Local / Resident
Conservation status:	No perceived threats
Caterpillar food plants:	Common Fleabane (lower leaves). Elsewhere, also on Ploughman's Spikenard and Hemp Agrimony
Records in database:	7

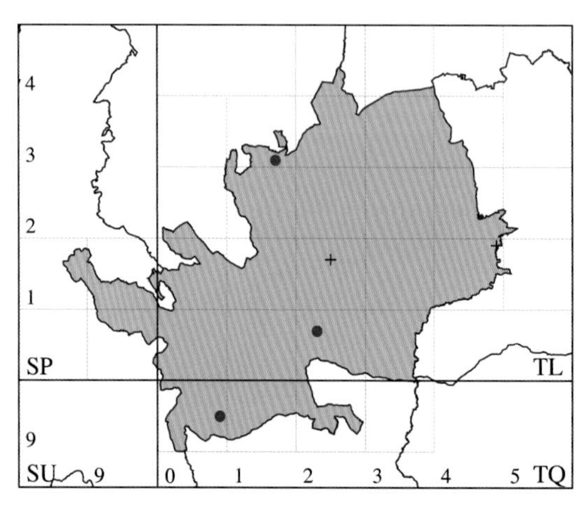

There are two biological races of this species – one feeding on Common Fleabane and flying in July and August and the other feeding on Hemp Agrimony and flying earlier, in mid-June. Until 1962, both this species and 556: *C. trochilella* (not yet recorded in Hertfordshire) were both treated as a single species under the name *Coleophora troglodytella* so that all records prior to that date must be disregarded unless a specimen can be examined.

0557 *Coleophora gardesanella* Toll

Recorded: 2001 – 2004
Distribution / Status: Local / Resident
Conservation status: No perceived threats
Caterpillar food plants: Yarrow (leaves). Elsewhere, Sea Wormwood, Mugwort, Sneezewort, Tansy and Ox-eye Daisy
Records in database: 2

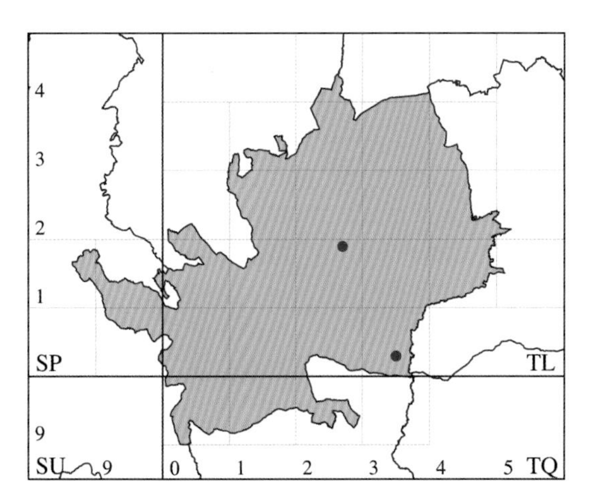

There are three races: along sea walls and in upper saltmarsh the foodplant used is Sea Wormwood, whilst those eating Sneezewort are found in damp meadows and marshes. Populations that thrive on Yarrow and Mugwort are found in dry grassland and this accounts for most inland populations including those in Hertfordshire.

0559 *Coleophora peribenanderi* Toll

Recorded: 1981 – 2006
Distribution / Status: Local / Resident
Conservation status: No perceived threats
Caterpillar food plants: Creeping thistle (leaves)
Records in database: 9

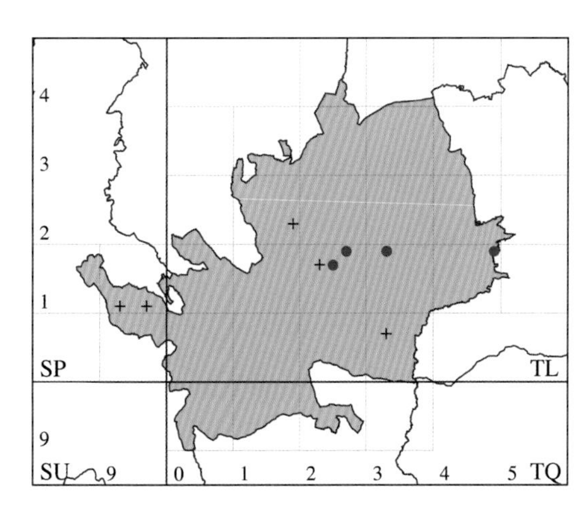

Rough grassland, roadside verges and hedge-banks are the sorts of places where this moth is usually found. It is surely under-recorded in our county.

0560 *Coleophora paripennella* Zell.

Recorded: 1890 – 2004
Distribution / Status: Local / Resident
Conservation status: No perceived threats
Caterpillar food plants: Lesser Knapweed & Greater Knapweed (leaves). Elsewhere also on thistles and burdock
Records in database: 9

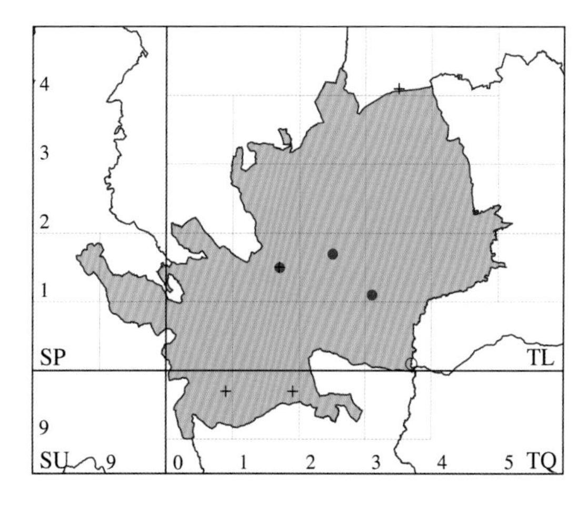

Occupying much the same habitat as the last species, the adult might be confused with the metallic green members of the *C. trifolii* group, but they fly by day whilst *C. paripennella* is nocturnal.

0561 *Coleophora therinella* (Tengström)

Recorded: 1987 – 1991
Distribution / Status: Former resident
Conservation status: Herts Extinct
Caterpillar food plants: No data. Elsewhere, on Black Bindweed
Records in database: 2

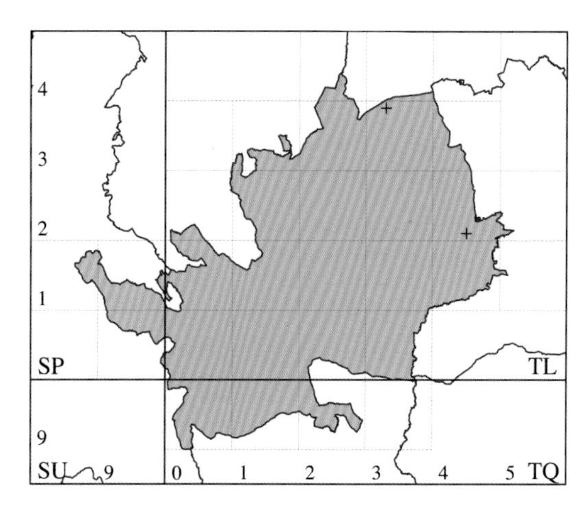

The larva feeds from its case on the seeds of the plant in August and September, overwintering in the case before pupation in May. The silk case is covered with soil particles making it very hard to find. Field edges might be the best place to find the foodplant.

0563 *Coleophora argentula* (Steph.)

Recorded: 1834 – 2005
Distribution / Status: Local / Resident
Conservation status: No perceived threats
Caterpillar food plants: Yarrow (withered flower)
Records in database: 10

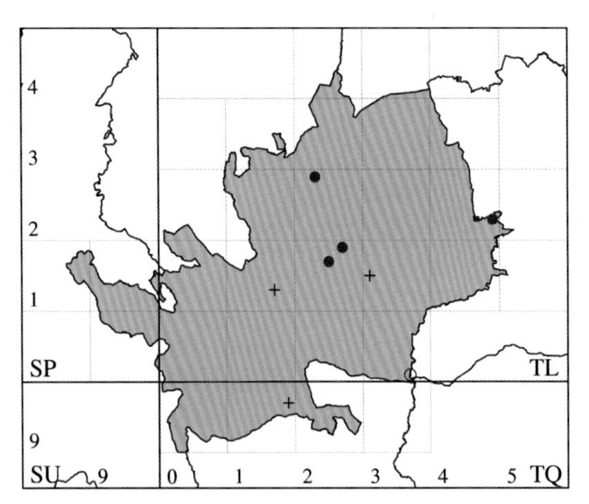

The larval case resembles a dead seed capsule but once you have 'got your eye in' it is relatively easy to spot these on the dead flower-heads of Yarrow plants.

0565 *Coleophora saxicolella* (Dup.)

Recorded: 2000 – 2005
Distribution / Status: Local / Resident
Conservation status: Herts Rare
Caterpillar food plants: No data. Elsewhere, on oraches and goosefoots (seeds)
Records in database: 4

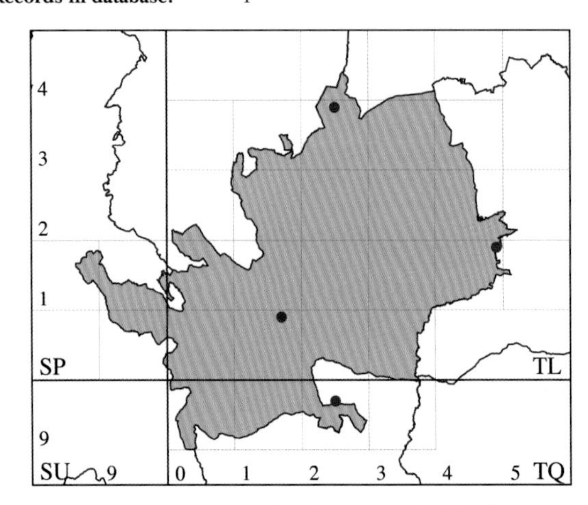

Baraud (1903) records '*Coleophora annulatella (laripennella)* taken by Mr Gibbs in August' [1902]. *Moths and Butterflies of Great Britain and Ireland*, volume 2 (1996) has both *annulatella* of Nylander and *laripennella* of Zetterstedt as synonyms of *saxicolella*, whilst also showing that *annulatella* of Nylander & Tengström and *laripennella* of Zetterstedt are both also synonyms of 572: *vestianella*. Bradley (2000) has both *annulatella* of Nylander and *laripennella* of Zetterstedt as synonyms of *vestianella*. It is not at all clear to me which species was intended and the record is, therefore, omitted from either map. Modern records are all of adults, confirmed by dissection.

0566 *Coleophora sternipennella* (Zett.)

Recorded: 1969 – 2004
Distribution / Status: Local / Resident
Conservation status: Herts Rare
Caterpillar food plants: goosefoots (seeds)
Records in database: 3

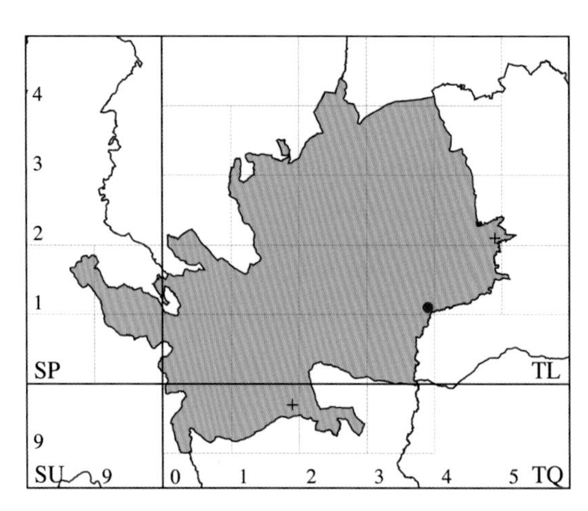

A manuscript list of species recorded in his garden at Oakwood Avenue, Borehamwood, by the late Eric Bradford, makes two entries under the heading *Coleophora moeniacella* Stt. as follows:

C. moeniacella Stt.	number bred *Chenopodium* spp. 1.6 – 27.7.69
C. moeniacella Stt.	5 ex l. *Atriplex* spp. 25.6 – 27.7.69

The entries are on the same page, but are separated by records of six other species. The epithet *moeniacella* was applied by Stainton (= Stt.) to what are now regarded as three species – *C. atriplicis* Meyrick, *C. deviella* Zeller and *C. sternipennella* (Zetterstedt). The former two are confined to saltmarshes and feed on saltmarsh Chenopodiaceae and *Sueda maritima* respectively. Neither is likely in Borehamwood. *C. sternipennella* larvae feed on *Chenopodium* and it is likely that Bradford's first entry, at least, relates to this species. However, the very similar *C. saxicolella* (Duponchel) feeds on both *Atriplex* and *Chenopodium* whilst *C. versurella* Zeller also feeds on *Atriplex* (though is less easily confused in the adult stage and it is unlikely that Eric mistook this species). Correct identification of Bradford's material necessitates examination of male genitalia of the voucher specimens. My own garden light trap in Bishops Stortford during 1988 and Rye Meads RSPB Nature Reserve in 2004 (Joan Childs) provide the two confirmed records.

0568 *Coleophora versurella* Zell.

Recorded: 1992 – 2004
Distribution / Status: Local / Resident
Conservation status: Herts Rare
Caterpillar food plants: No data. Elsewhere, on oraches and goosefoots (seeds)
Records in database: 4

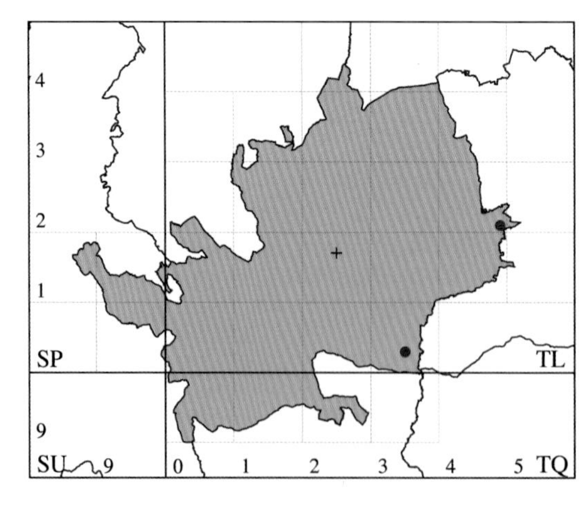

It is probably the foodplant(s) rather than the moth that is rare in our overly 'tidy' county. The few remaining ruderal habitats in the Lea Valley might be the best place to look for it.

0572 *Coleophora vestianella* (L.) = *laripennella* (Zett.)

Recorded: 1981 only
Distribution / Status: Former resident
Conservation status: Herts Extinct
Caterpillar food plants: No data. Elsewhere, on Common Orache
Records in database: 1

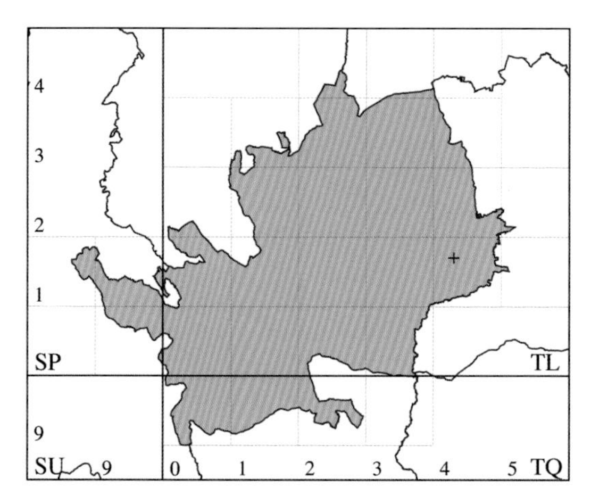

See comments at 565: *Coleophora saxicola* concerning the ignored 1902 record of '*Coleophora annulatella*', which might relate to this species. Our only confirmed record was made by Raymond Uffen at Hadham Mill Pit, in 1981. As for 568: *Coleophora versurella* the lack of foodplant must be a limiting factor.

0577 *Coleophora artemisicolella* Bruand

Recorded: 1972 – 1998
Distribution / Status: Local / Resident
Conservation status: No perceived threats
Caterpillar food plants: No data. Elsewhere, on Mugwort (seeds)
Records in database: 5

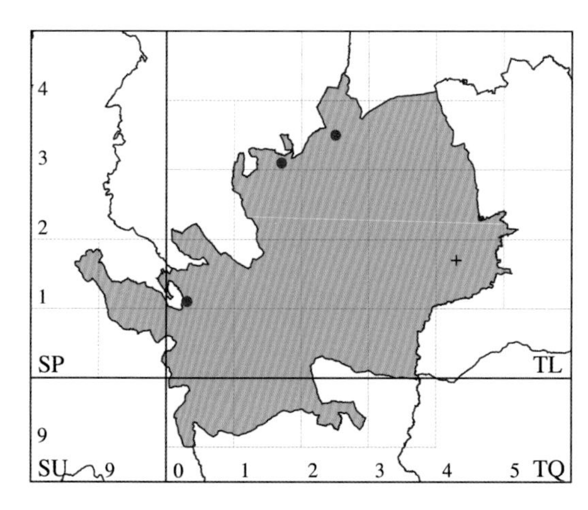

The highly camouflaged larval case is attached to the side of successive seed-heads, leaving conspicuous holes that give away its presence. Careful searching in the autumn ought to record this species elsewhere in the county.

0578 *Coleophora otidipennella* (Hb.) = *murinipennella* (Dup.)

Recorded: 1834 – 2004
Distribution / Status: Local / Resident
Conservation status: No perceived threats
Caterpillar food plants: Field Woodrush
Records in database: 13

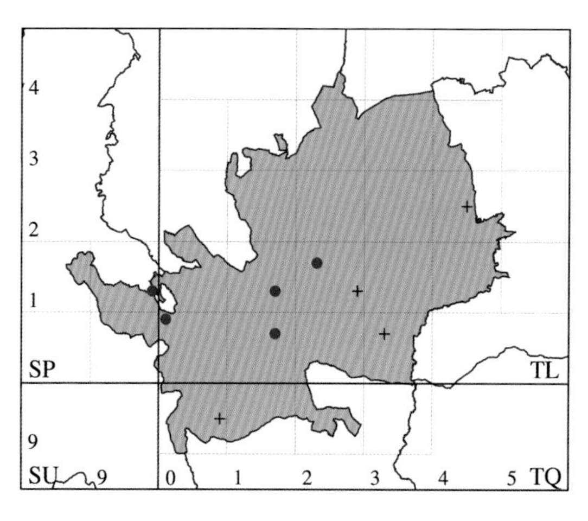

The adults fly early, in May and June; the larvae often feed on fallen seeds on the ground amongst the litter.

0581 *Coleophora taeniipennella* H.- S.

Recorded: 1990 – 2006
Distribution / Status: Local / Resident
Conservation status: No perceived threats
Caterpillar food plants: Jointed Rush; Sharp-flowered Rush (seeds)
Records in database: 6

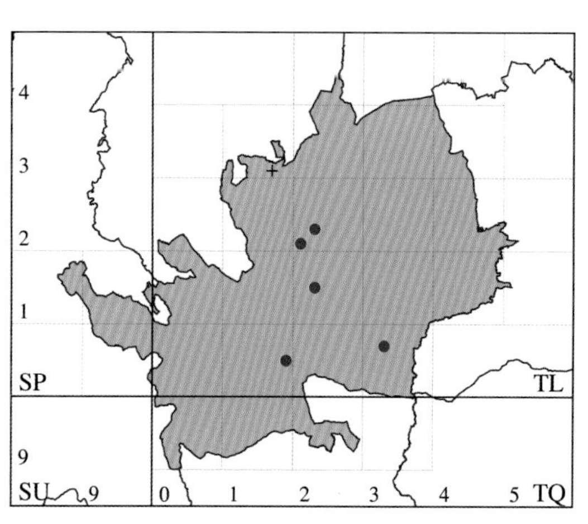

Both the recorded foodplants in Hertfordshire appear to be equally affected by the larval cases of this species.

0582 *Coleophora glaucicolella* Wood

Recorded: 1975 – 2005
Distribution / Status: Widespread / Resident
Conservation status: No perceived threats
Caterpillar food plants: Soft Rush (seeds)
Records in database: 8

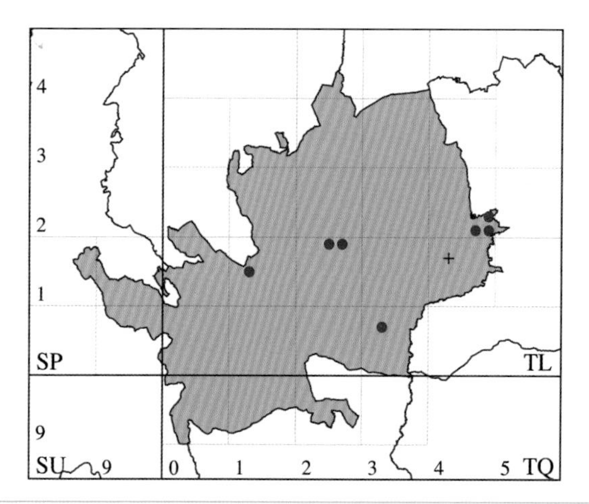

The familiar small, whitish larval cases on the seeds of rushes will be either this species, 584: *Coleophora alticolella* or 587: *C. caespititiella*. Separation requires either examination of the larva or the rearing and dissection of the adult.

0583 *Coleophora tamesis* Waters = *cratipennella* auctorum

Recorded: 1997 – 1998
Distribution / Status: Local / Resident
Conservation status: No perceived threats
Caterpillar food plants: Jointed Rush (seeds)
Records in database: 2

Marshall's Heath in 1997 (John Murray) and Tyttenhanger Farm Sandpit in 1998 (Raymond Uffen) provide the two records in the map.

0584 *Coleophora alticolella* Zell.

Recorded: 1890 – 2004
Distribution / Status: Widespread / Resident
Conservation status: No perceived threats
Caterpillar food plants: Soft Rush; Hard Rush (seeds)
Records in database: 21

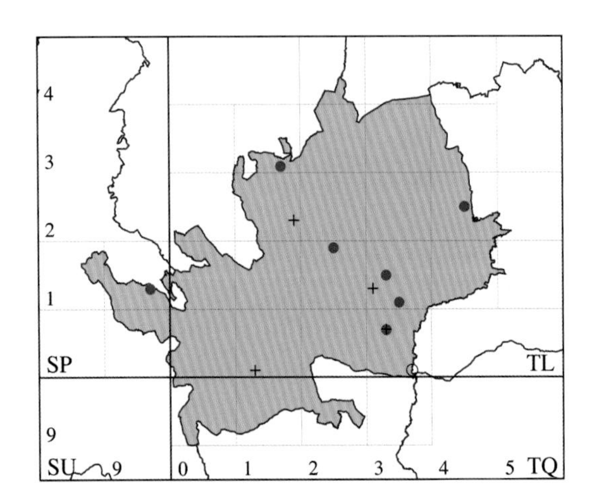

See the comments under 582: *Coleophora glaucicolella*. Both species are likely to be widespread and common in Hertfordshire.

0587 *Coleophora caespititiella* Zell.

Recorded: 1987 – 2005
Distribution / Status: Widespread / Resident
Conservation status: No perceived threats
Caterpillar food plants: Soft Rush (seeds)
Records in database: 26

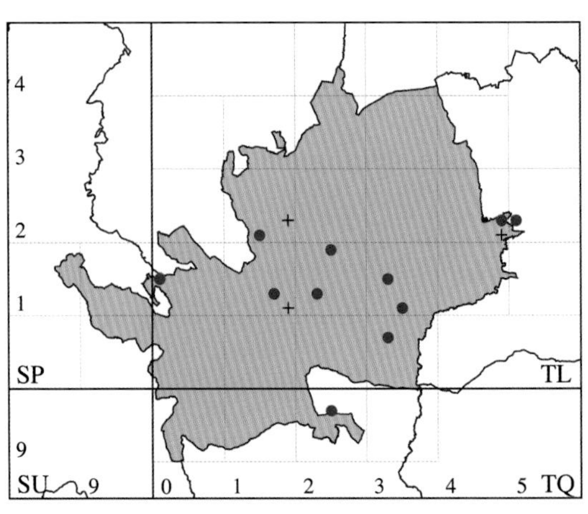

Confusion with 582: *Coleophora glaucicolella* and 584: *Coleophora alticolella* is very likely at all stages of the life cycle and dissection of adults is the favoured method of identification.

ELACHISTIDAE

The larvae of the Elachistidae are all miners, those of *Perittia* in leaves of honeysuckle, those of *Stephensia* in Wild Basil leaves, *Mendesia* on unknown Labiatae and the remainder, in *Elachista*, *Biselachista* and *Cosmiotes*, in the blades of grasses, sedges, rushes and wood rushes. The larval mines in grasses and rushes are extremely difficult to separate. A few adults are distinctive, but most, especially if worn, require dissection for correct identification. Hence, as with the Coleophoridae, this is a group of moths that are very much understudied in Hertfordshire and elsewhere and there is equally little in the way of new data that can be reported here. Discoveries are likely within this group: *Elachista nobilella* Zell. was found in Britain as recently as 2003 (Collins & Porter, 2005); it is not yet recorded in our county, but is easily confused with 594: *Elachista gleichenella* and with 602: *Elachista apicipunctella*, both of which have been reported. A few years earlier, Kaila *et al.* (2001) showed that the allegedly easily recognised 593: *Elachista regificella* comprises three species and Kaila & Langmaid (2005) have shown that all three are found in Britain. There are 49 current British species of which 25 are known from Hertfordshire.

0590 *Perittia obscurepunctella* (Stt.)

Recorded: 1890 – 2003
Distribution / Status: Local / Resident
Conservation status: No perceived threats
Caterpillar food plants: Not recorded. Elsewhere, Honeysuckle
Records in database: 4

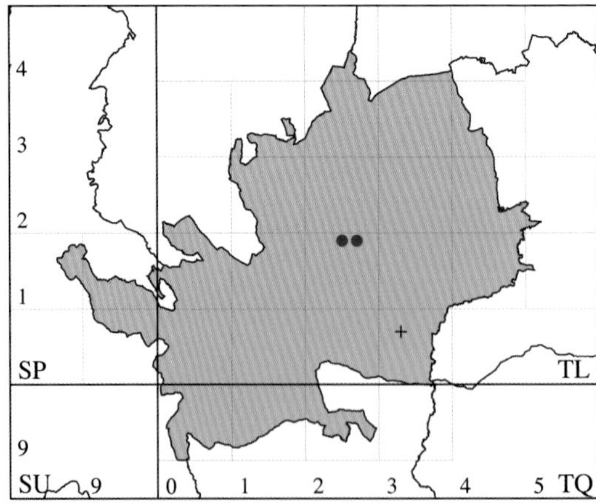

Recent records are from Broxbourne Wood, 8th July 1993 (Raymond Uffen) and Datchworth, 22nd April 2003 (Steve Palmer).

0592 *Stephensia brunnichella* (L.)

Recorded: 1890 – 2004
Distribution / Status: Local / Resident
Conservation status: No perceived threats
Caterpillar food plants: Not recorded. Elsewhere, Wild Basil
Records in database: 3

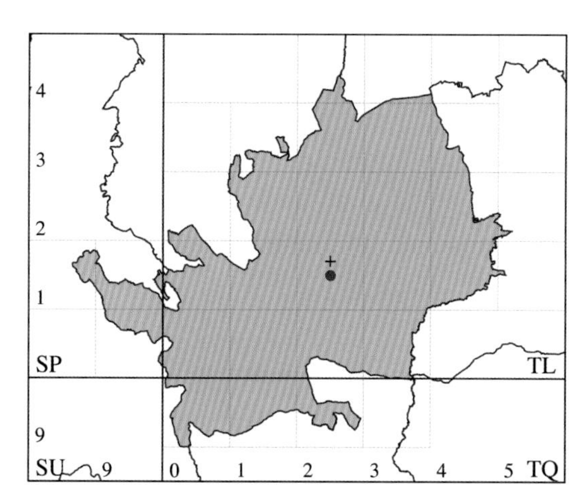

The three records are from the Sandridge area (Griffith, 1890), Harmer Green Wood, 9th November 1991 and Lockleys Wood, 5th August 2004 (both by Raymond Uffen).

0593 *Elachista regificella* Sirc. *sensu lato*

Recorded: 1901 – 1918
Distribution / Status: Unknown
Caterpillar food plants: Not recorded. Elsewhere, woodrush
Records in database: 2

There are two old reports – from Cheshunt (Boyd, 1901) and Baldock in 1918 (Foster, 1937). We have not examined any voucher specimens for these records and so we cannot determine if these are the true *regificella* or if they might be either of the recently segregated species *geminatella* and *tengstromi*.

0594 *Elachista gleichenella* (Fabr.)

Recorded: 1890 only
Distribution / Status: Extinct resident
Caterpillar food plants: Not recorded. Elsewhere, sedges
Records in database: 1

The Sandridge area (Griffith, 1890) provides the only Hertfordshire record.

0595 *Biselachista biatomella* (Stt.)

Recorded: 1890 – 1901
Distribution / Status: Extinct resident
Caterpillar food plants: Not recorded. Elsewhere, Carnation-grass
Records in database: 2

Once again, the Sandridge area (Griffith, 1890) and the Cheshunt area (Boyd, 1901) provide the only Hertfordshire reports.

0596 *Elachista poae* Stt.

Recorded: 1890 – 1964
Distribution / Status: Local / Resident
Caterpillar food plants: Not recorded. Elsewhere, Reed Sweet-grass
Records in database: 3

The most recent record is from Bricket Wood, 29th August 1964 (Eric Bradford). Old records are from the Sandridge area (Griffith, 1890) and Cheshunt (Boyd, 1901).

0597 *Elachista atricomella* Stt.

Recorded: 1890 – 2003
Distribution / Status: Local / Resident
Conservation status: No perceived threats
Caterpillar food plants: Not recorded. Elsewhere, Cock's-foot Grass
Records in database: 5

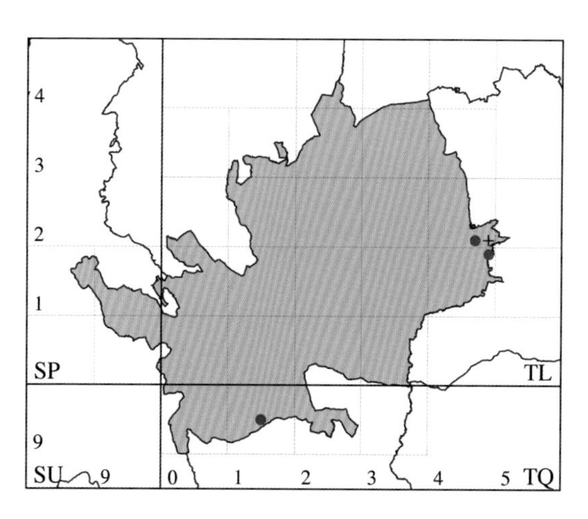

Apart from the nineteenth century record from the Sandridge area (Griffith, 1890), we have confirmed records from Bishops Stortford (town) in 1991 (my own record), the Bishops Park area of Bishops Stortford in 2002 (Andrew Palmer), Hilfield Reservoir, 23rd July 2003 (me again) and Dane O'Coys, Bishops Stortford 5th May 2003 (Andrew Hardacre).

0599 *Elachista alpinella* Stt.

Recorded: 1890 only
Distribution / Status: Extinct resident
Caterpillar food plants: Not recorded. Elsewhere, sedges
Records in database: 1

Sandridge area (Griffith, 1890) – probably now extinct in Hertfordshire.

0600 *Elachista luticomella* Zell

Recorded: 1890 – 1997
Distribution / Status: Local / Resident
Conservation status: No perceived threats
Caterpillar food plants: Not recorded. Elsewhere, Cock's-foot Grass
Records in database: 2

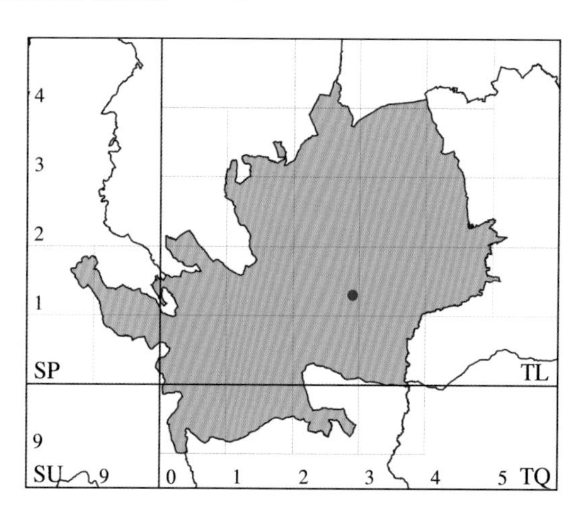

Panshanger Park in 1997 (Tom Gladwin) provides the only evidence of this species in the county since one in the Sandridge area in 1890.

0601 *Elachista albifrontella* (Hb.)

Recorded: 1890 – 2005
Distribution / Status: Local / Resident
Conservation status: No perceived threats
Caterpillar food plants: Not recorded. Elsewhere, various grasses
Records in database: 6

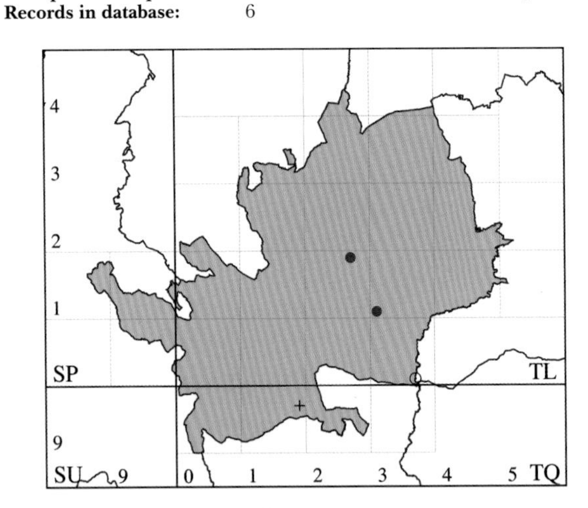

Relatively recent captures are from Borehamwood, 18th June 1966 (Eric Bradford), Datchworth, 22nd April 2003 and 21st June 2005 (Steve Palmer) and Bayfordbury, 18th June 2005 (Colin Plant).

0602 *Elachista apicipunctella* Stt.

Recorded: 2001 – 2004
Distribution / Status: Local / Resident
Conservation status: No perceived threats
Caterpillar food plants: Not recorded. Elsewhere, various grasses
Records in database: 7

All the records are listed: Marshall's Heath 2002, 2003 and 2004 (John Murray), Rye Meads 19th May 2001 (Colin Plant), Datchworth 22nd April 2003 (Steve Palmer) and Balls Park, Hertford 26th April 2003 (Andrew Wood). My own record from Rye Meads and that by Steve Palmer from Datchworth have been critically examined to eliminate the possibility that they are *Elachista nobilella* (see Collins & Porter, 2005), although that is a much smaller species and perhaps unlikely to be confused; the others have probably not been so treated.

0603 *Elachista subnigrella* Douglas

Recorded: 1901 only
Distribution / Status: Extinct resident
Caterpillar food plants: Not recorded. Elsewhere, Upright Brome
Records in database: 1

Our only report is from the Cheshunt area a century ago (Boyd, 1901).

0606 *Elachista humilis* Zell.

Recorded: 2003 – 2003
Distribution / Status: Local / Resident
Conservation status: No perceived threats
Caterpillar food plants: Not recorded. Elsewhere, Tufted Hair-grass
Records in database: 2

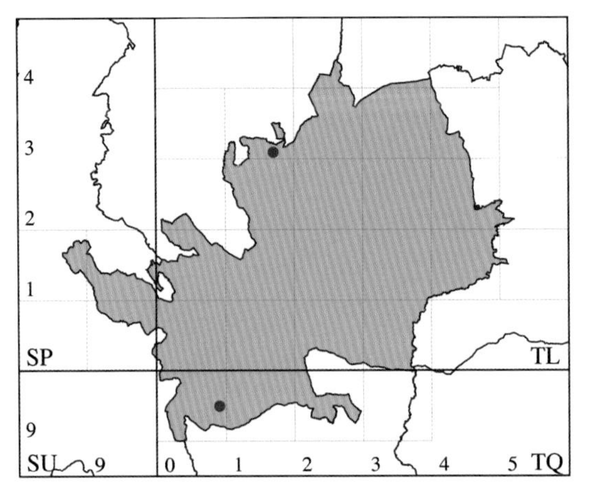

Our two records are both mine – from Croxley Common Moor on 17th May 2003 and Oughtonhead Common on 12th June 2003.

0607 *Elachista canapennella* (Hb.)

Recorded: 1890 – 2006
Distribution / Status: Widespread / Resident
Conservation status: No perceived threats
Caterpillar food plants: Not recorded. Elsewhere, various grasses
Records in database: 28

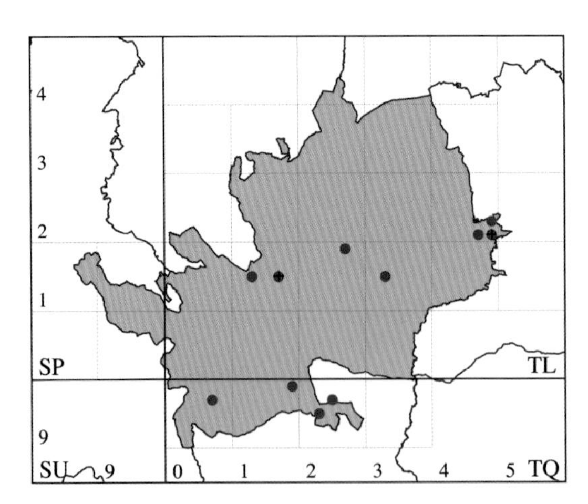

This is one of the few species in this family that can confidently be treated as widespread – if somewhat under-recorded.

0608 *Elachista rufocinerea* (Haw.)

Recorded:	1834 – 2006
Distribution / Status:	Widespread / Resident
Conservation status:	No perceived threats
Caterpillar food plants:	Not recorded. Elsewhere, various grasses
Records in database:	30

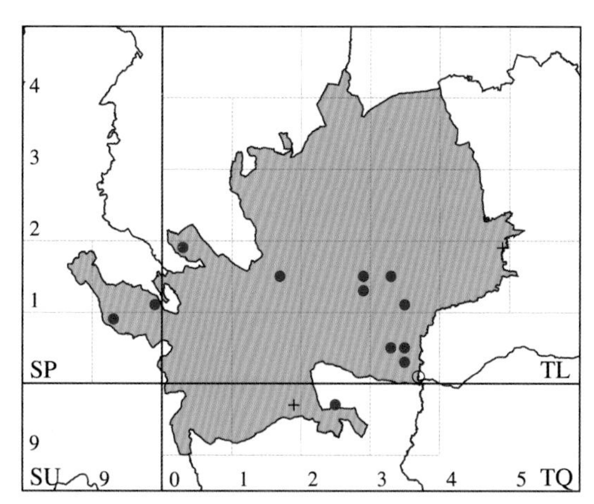

This is probably a widespread and common species.

0609 *Elachista maculicerusella* Bruand = *cerusella* (Hb.)

Recorded:	1890 – 2006
Distribution / Status:	Widespread / Resident
Conservation status:	No perceived threats
Caterpillar food plants:	Not recorded. Elsewhere, Reed and Reed-grass
Records in database:	20

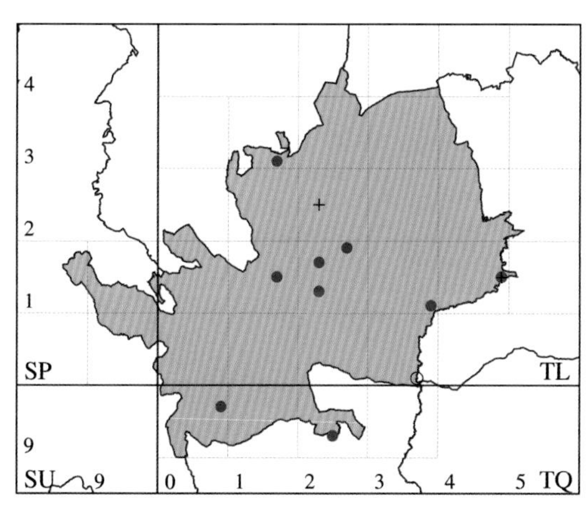

The records indicate this species to be fairly frequent in the county.

0610 *Elachista argentella* (Cl.)

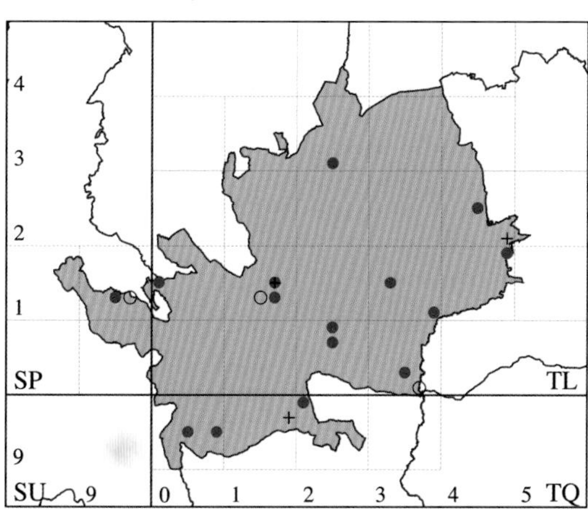

Recorded:	1887 – 2006
Distribution / Status:	Widespread / Resident
Conservation status:	No perceived threats
Caterpillar food plants:	Not recorded. Elsewhere, various grasses
Records in database:	32

Most rank grassland habitats will produce this species. Though certainly widespread and common, care should be taken not to overlook the only other completely white and unmarked member of the family, 591: *Mendesia farinella* (Thunb.), which is not yet recorded in Hertfordshire and which is slightly larger with ciliate antennae.

0611 *Elachista triatomea* (Haw.)

Recorded:	1890 – 2003
Distribution / Status:	Resident
Conservation status:	No perceived threats
Caterpillar food plants:	Not recorded. Elsewhere, Fescue grasses
Records in database:	6

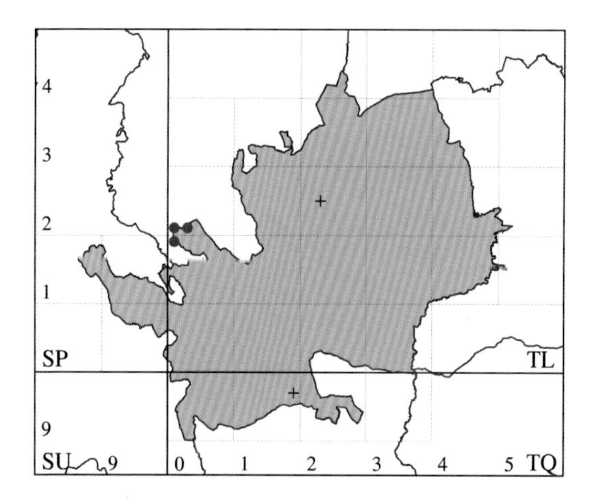

Recorded from 1890 in the Sandridge area (Griffith) to 2003 at Knebworth Quary, this must surely be an overlooked moth in Hertfordshire?

0617 *Elachista obliquella* Stt. = *megerlella* (Hb.)

Recorded:	2004 only
Distribution / Status:	Local / Resident
Conservation status:	No perceived threats
Caterpillar food plants:	Not recorded. Elsewhere, various grasses, especially False-brome
Records in database:	1

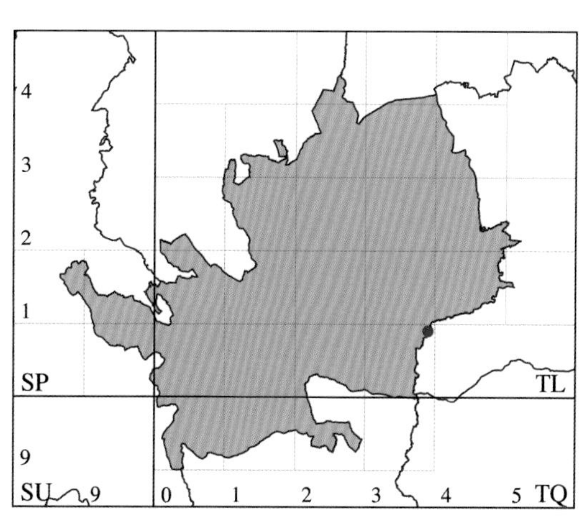

Rye Meads RSPB nature reserve provides our only record, where Joan Childs caught an example on 6th August 2004.

0620 *Elachista gangabella* Zell.

Recorded: 1991 only
Distribution / Status: Resident
Caterpillar food plants: False-brome. Elsewhere, Cock's-foot Grass
Records in database: 1

Therfield Heath gives us the only Hertfordshire record, with mines on False Brome on 14th October 1991 (John Langmaid).

0623 *Elachista bisulcella* (Dup.)

Recorded: Pre-1890 only
Distribution / Status: Extinct resident
Caterpillar food plants: Not recorded. Elsewhere, Tufted Hair-grass; Tall Fescue
Records in database: 1

Our only report is that from the Sandridge area at least a century ago (Griffith, 1890).

0625 *Biselachista cinereopunctella* (Haw.)

Recorded: Pre-1890 only
Distribution / Status: Extinct resident
Caterpillar food plants: Not recorded. Elsewhere, Carnation-grass
Records in database: 1

As with the previous species, our only report is that from the Sandridge area (Griffith, 1890).

0630 *Biselachista albidella* (Nyl.)

Recorded: Pre-1901 only
Distribution / Status: Extinct resident
Caterpillar food plants: Not recorded. Elsewhere, sedges and Cotton-grass
Records in database: 1

Cheshunt (Boyd, 1901) provides the only record for this species. Habitat loss may dictate that this species is now extinct in the county?

0631 *Cosmiotes freyerella* (Hb.)

Recorded: 1890 – 2003
Distribution / Status: Local / Resident
Conservation status: No perceived threats
Caterpillar food plants: Not recorded. Elsewhere, grasses, especially *Poa* species
Records in database: 7

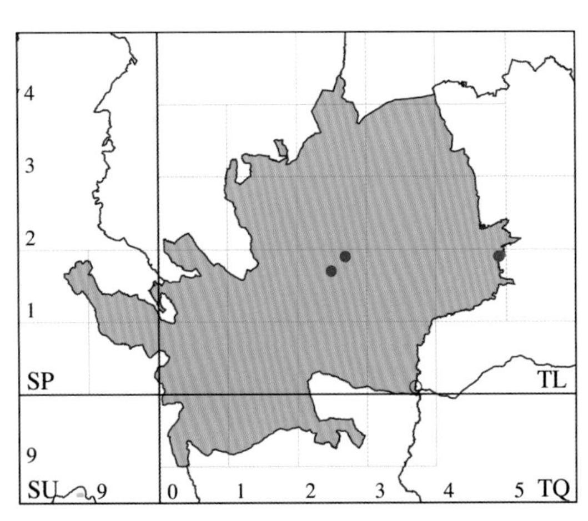

Recent records are from Welwyn, 26th July 1995 (Raymond Uffen), Bishops Stortford, 1st August 2002 (Andrew Palmer) and Datchworth, 22nd April 2003 (Steve Palmer).

0633 *Cosmiotes stabilella* (Stt.)

Recorded: 2002 – 2002
Distribution / Status: Local / Resident
Conservation status: No perceived threats
Caterpillar food plants: Not recorded. Elsewhere, grasses
Records in database: 1

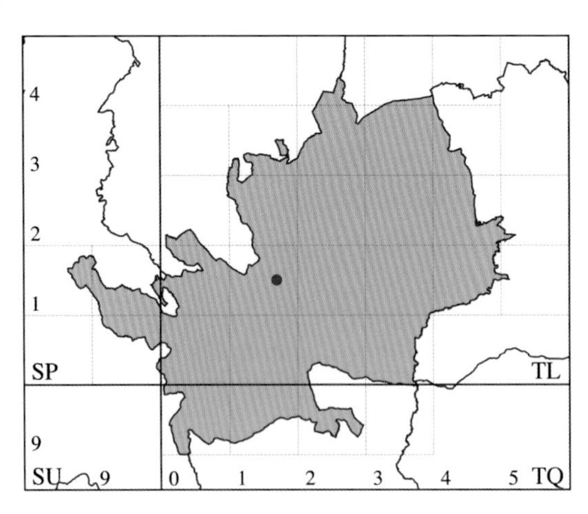

Our single record is from Marshall's Heath on 26th July 2002 (John Murray).

OECOPHORIDAE *sensu lato*

Opinions vary on the characters that define a moth as belonging to the Oecophoridae. Many European authors treat the subfamilies Oecophorinae, Amphisbatinae, Stathmopodinae, Chimabacinae and Depressariinae as full families; the authors of volume 4 (part 1) of *Moths and butterflies of Great Britain and Ireland* (published in 2002) cautiously retained the names as subfamilies, but I think that enough evidence has emerged in the intervening years to support the raising, by others, of these groups to family level. In Hertfordshire we have 15 Oecophoridae *sensu stricto*, 1 in Stathmopodidae, 3 in Amphisbatidae, 3 in Chimabacidae and 30 in Depressariidae, giving an overall total of 52 species of oecophorid in the wider sense; this latter figure compares with 86 species in Britain.

OECOPHORIDAE sensu stricto

0637 *Crassa tinctella* (Hb.)

Recorded: 1901 only
Distribution / Status: Absent / Extinct resident
Conservation status: Herts Extinct
Caterpillar food plants: Not recorded. Elsewhere, under decaying bark
Flight period: Not recorded. Elsewhere, May/June
Records in database: 1

Our only record is that from Cheshunt, published in 1901 by Boyd; it may have been made at any period within the preceding forty years. The moth is an extremely local resident of ancient woodland in southern England.

0638a *Denisia albimaculea* (Haw.)

Recorded: 1901 only
Distribution / Status: Absent / Extinct resident
Conservation status: Herts Extinct
Caterpillar food plants: Not recorded. Elsewhere, on lichens on dead wood
Flight period: Not recorded. Elsewhere, June
Records in database: 1

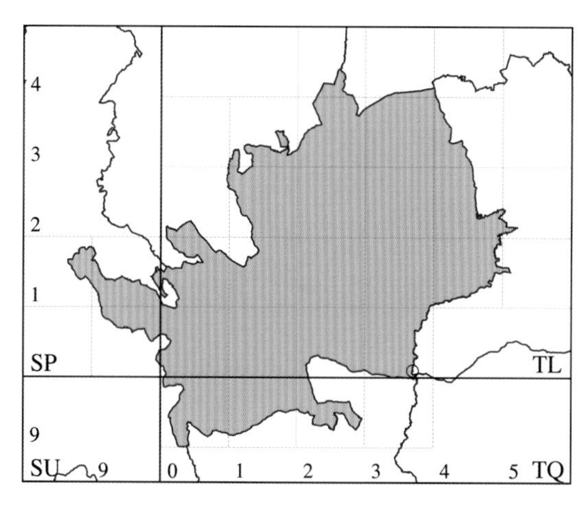

Cheshunt (Boyd, 1901) is the only Hertfordshire record. I have not seen any specimens and consequently am unable to completely rule out the unlikely possibility that this might be *Denisia augustella* (Hb.).

0640 *Batia lunaris* (Haw.)

Recorded:	1834 – 2006
Distribution / Status:	Widespread / Common resident
Conservation status:	No perceived threats
Caterpillar food plants:	Not recorded. Elsewhere, on lichens on dead wood and in plant galls
Flight period:	June to September
Records in database:	140

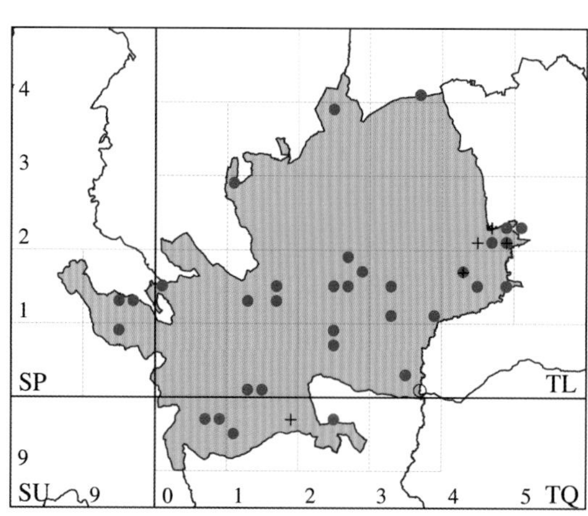

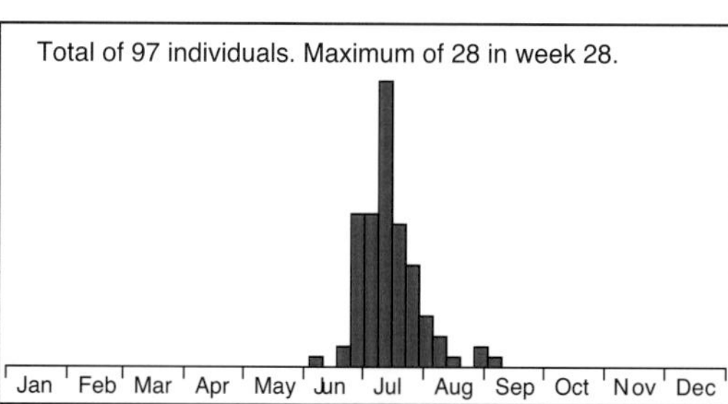

This is a common species that comes readily to light. We have very slender evidence of a second generation of adults in late August/September, but numbers are too low to be statistically significant. Some of the specimens collected by Griffith (1890) are in fact the next species, 640a: *Batia internella*.

0640a *Batia internella* (Jäckh)

Recorded:	Pre-1890 only
Distribution / Status:	Absent / Extinct resident
Conservation status:	Herts Extinct
Caterpillar food plants:	Not recorded. Elsewhere, on powdery lichens on tree trunks
Flight period:	Not recorded
Records in database:	2

This species was not recognised as British until as recently as 1990 (Harper, 1990). Five Hertfordshire specimens, one from Sandridge, three from Wheathampstead and one unlabelled, all under the label *Batia lunaris*, in the Griffiths collection at Cardiff Museum were sent to Dr John Langmaid by Mike Wilson. Two were dissected and proved to be *B. internella*. Griffiths was collecting in the county in the last forty years of the nineteenth century.

0642 *Batia unitella* (Hb.)

Recorded:	1965 – 2006
Distribution / Status:	Widespread / Common resident
Conservation status:	No perceived threats
Caterpillar food plants:	Fungi under loose tree bark
Flight period:	Mid-June to mid-August
Records in database:	154

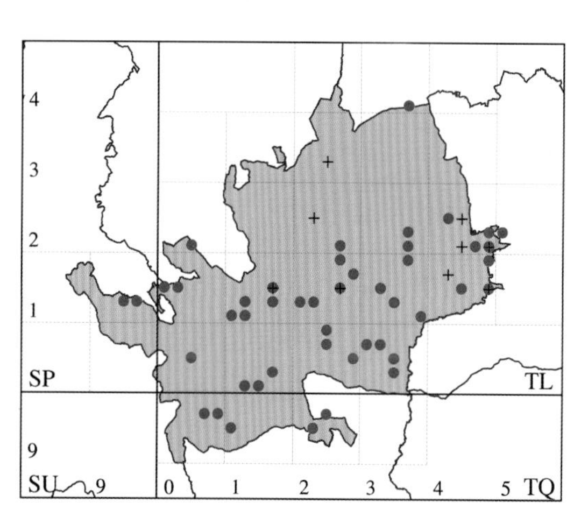

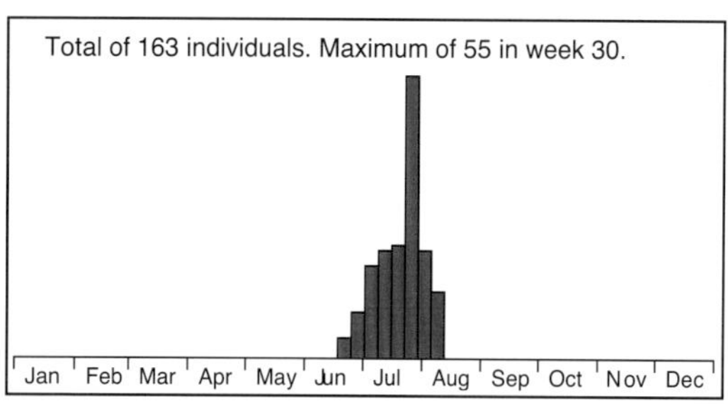

A frequent visitor to light traps, likely to be present in most areas of the county.

0642a *Metalampra italica* Baldizzone

Recorded:	2004 – 2006
Distribution / Status:	Local / Rare resident
Conservation status:	No perceived threats
Caterpillar food plants:	Under the bark of oak logs
Flight period:	June to August
Records in database:	4

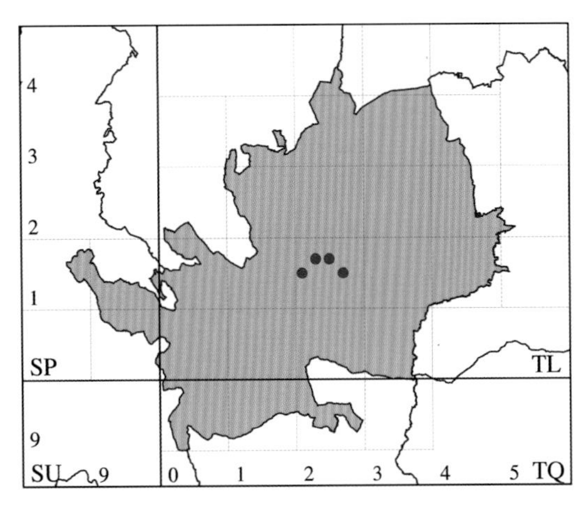

This attractive species was described as new to science as recently as 1977. Thought to be endemic to Italy, it was recorded in Britain from Devon in 2003, when Bob Heckford found specimens at Plympton on 16th August. On 7th August 2004 he found another in his light trap and in the same year, Raymond Uffen recorded two in his kitchen and two more outside the open door of his home in Welwyn on 28th July. The Hertfordshire moths may have emerged from an oak log imported to Ray's garden from Patmore Heath, but the source of the logs cannot be tied down because it is not known with certainty from which logs the moths may have emerged. In 2005, a log was enclosed and further moths subsequently emerged. Raymond also found an adult at the margin of Dowdells Wood on 18th June 2005 and another adult at rest on *Ganoderma* bracket fungus on the upturned root plate of an ash tree at Danesbury Park, Welwyn. Finally, although the cut-off date for this review of Hertfordshire moths is theoretically the end of December 2006, it seems worth recording here the four adults caught at light on a Herts Moth Group recording trip to Tewin Orchard Nature Reserve on 4th August 2007. All were slightly worn. It is probable that *Metalampra italica* is resident in central Hertfordshire, though the source of the population is obscure; the moth is still known only from Italy and England.

0644 *Borkhausenia fuscescens* (Haw.)

Recorded: 1890 – 2006
Distribution / Status: Local / Uncommon resident
Conservation status: No perceived threats
Caterpillar food plants: Not recorded. Elsewhere, on dead leaves
Flight period: July and early August
Records in database: 31

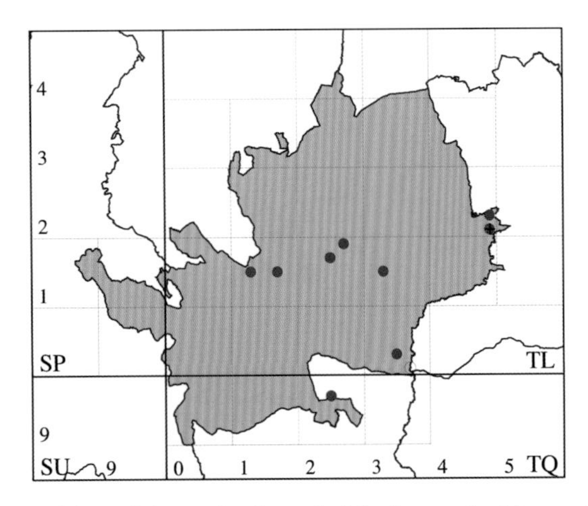

The adult moth is over by the end of the first week of August in most years, though there is a single late record from 5th September during 2006. The caterpillars spin a silk tube on the dead leaf they intend to eat and cover it with frass. Adults have been reared from bird nests in other parts of the country.

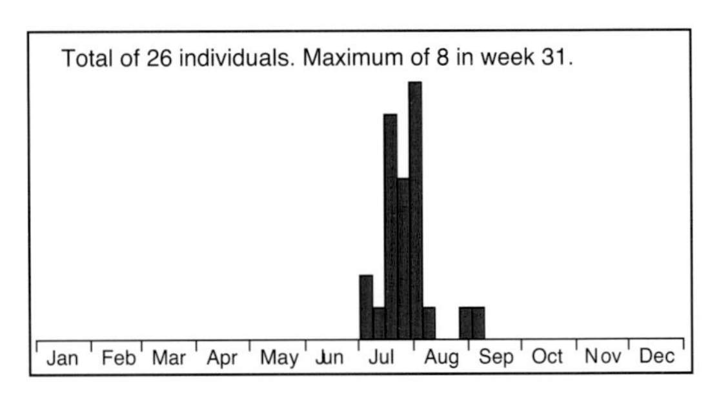

0645 *Borkhausenia minutella* (L.)

Recorded: Pre-1901 only
Distribution / Status: Absent / Extinct resident
Conservation status: Herts Extinct
Caterpillar food plants: Not recorded
Flight period: Not recorded
Records in database: 1

There is a single Hertfordshire record, from Cheshunt in the years prior to 1901 (Boyd). This moth was formally regarded as extinct in the British Isles, but during 2002 David Agassiz found examples in Kent; on this basis it may yet be re-found in our county. The caterpillar feeds on dry, dead vegetable matter such as leaves or piles of cut reeds.

0646 *Telechrysis tripuncta* (Haw.)

Recorded: 1992 – 2004
Distribution / Status: Local / Rare resident
Conservation status: Herts Rare
Caterpillar food plants: Not recorded. Elsewhere, inside dead stems of bramble
Flight period: May/June
Records in database: 3

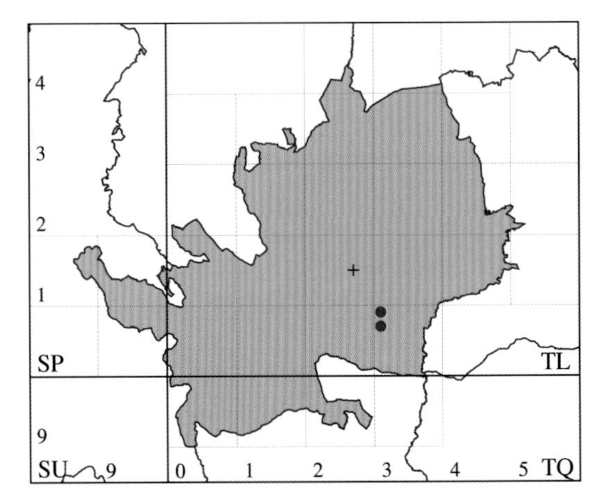

Very little is known about this moth in Britain. In Hertfordshire we have just three records, from Tewinbury on 4th June 1992 and Great Grove Wood, Bayford on 31st May 1998 (Raymond Uffen) and Wormley Wood during 2004 (Mark Cooper).

0647 *Hofmannophila pseudospretella* (Stt.) Brown House Moth

Recorded: 1888 – 2006
Distribution / Status: Ubiquitous / Abundant resident
Conservation status: Pest species when indoors
Caterpillar food plants: Dry, dead animal and plant matter
Flight period: March to October
Records in database: 439

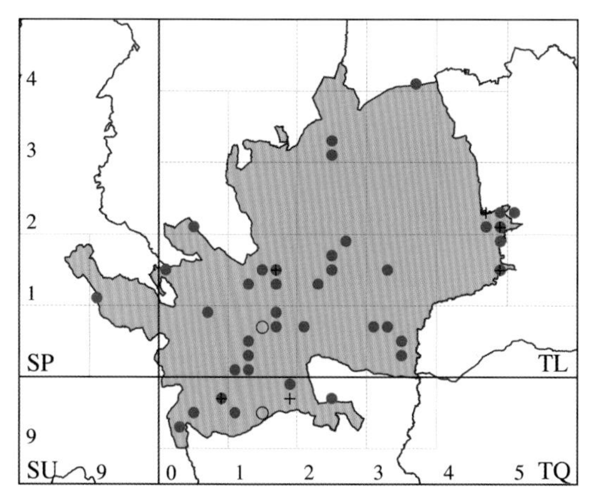

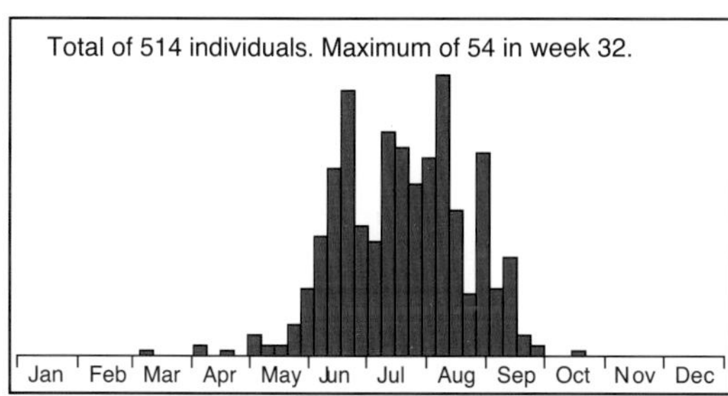

In the great outdoors this moth performs a useful function as one of nature's 'tidiers', feeding on all manner of dry animal and plant debris from birds' nests through fox droppings to the fur and feather of dead animals. Indoors it is a pest species. The chart shows that it can be found in the adult state from March to October and, whilst certainly continuously brooded with four or five generations per year in warm environments, it is not to be found during the winter.

0648 *Endrosis sarcitrella* (L.) White-shouldered House Moth

Recorded: 1888 – 2006
Distribution / Status: Ubiquitous / Abundant resident
Conservation status: Pest species when indoors
Caterpillar food plants: Dry, dead animal and plant matter
Flight period: February to November
Records in database: 218

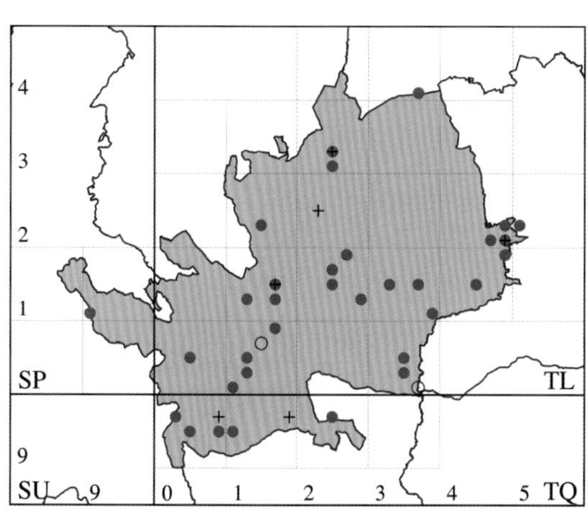

Like the previous species, the White-shouldered House Moth is a pest that is more or less omnivorous on dead animal and plant matter. For many years, the wicker basket that I keep in my bathroom to house dirty linen was infested about its base

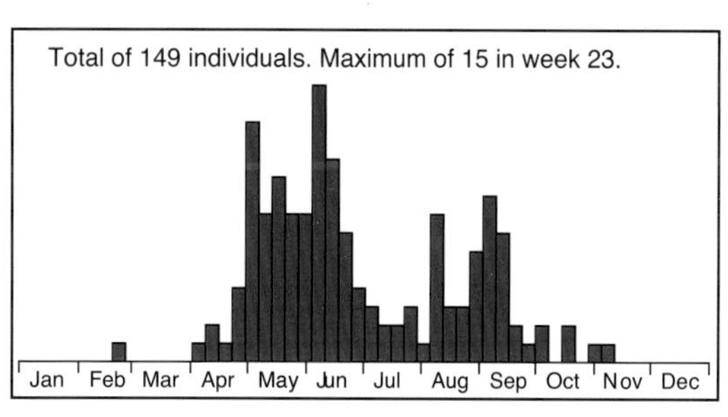

with the larvae of this moth. In spite of many attempts to eradicate it, the moth continued to thrive and during 2003 I recorded five successive generations.

0649 *Esperia sulphurella* (Fabr.)

Recorded: 1887 – 2006
Distribution / Status: Widespread / Common resident
Conservation status: No perceived threats
Caterpillar food plants: Under loose bark. Elsewhere, also in fungus *Daldinia concentrica*
Flight period: April to June
Records in database: 95

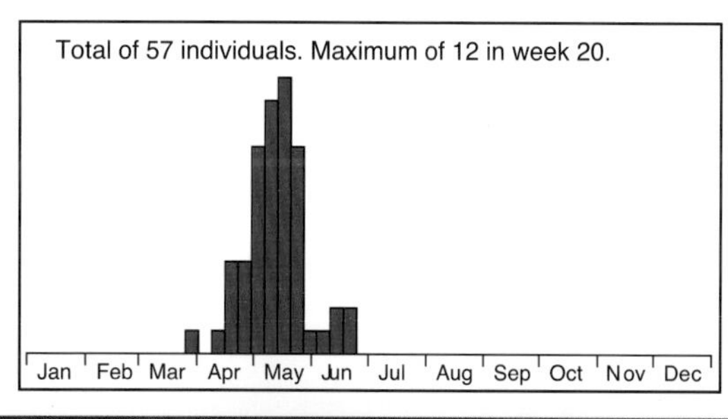

This is another species that has always been common in Hertfordshire; our earliest record appears to be from Aldbury on 11th June 1887, when adults were beaten from hedges (field meeting report by A. E. Gibbs in *Transactions of the Hertfordshire Natural History Society and Field Club* **4**). Adults often fly in sunshine, never far from the food source, when the yellow hind wings are obvious and betray its identity.

0650 *Esperia oliviella* (Fabr.)

Recorded:	1834 – 1901
Distribution / Status:	Absent / Extinct
Conservation status:	Herts Extinct
Caterpillar food plants:	Not recorded. Elsewhere, under bark and in dead wood
Flight period:	Not recorded. Elsewhere, June and July
Records in database:	2

This species is illustrated by J. F. Stephens from a Hertford specimen in *Illustrations of British Entomology* **4**: 228 (published in 1834). There is also a record from Cheshunt (Boyd, 1901). These are our only Hertfordshire records.

0652 *Alabonia geoffrella* (L.)

Recorded:	1888 – 2003
Distribution / Status:	Extremely local / Rare resident
Conservation status:	Herts Vulnerable
Caterpillar food plants:	Unknown
Flight period:	May/June
Records in database:	18

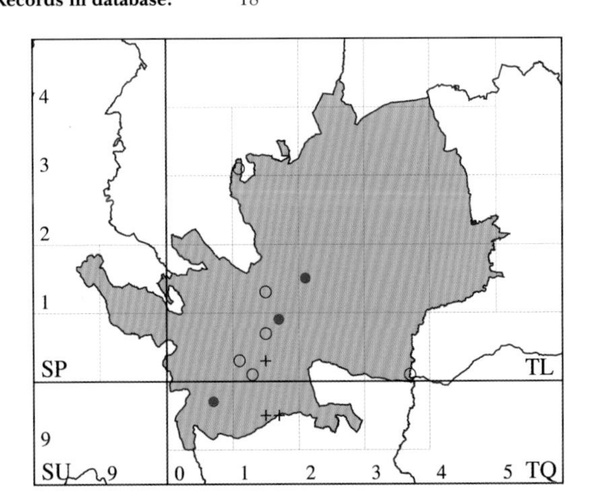

The cluster of records is interesting, but care should be taken not to overlook the open circles in the south-east at Cheshunt (Boyd, 1901) and in the north-west at Hexton (Foster, 1937). Nevertheless, the three modern records fall within the general cluster, at Stocking Springs in 1998 (C. R. Smith), Belsize Close, St Albans in 2001 (Wendy Hatton) and Whippendell Wood on 24th May 2003 (myself). Overall, the map suggests a declining species.

0658 *Carcina quercana* (Fabr.) The Flat Cooper

Recorded:	1888 – 2006
Distribution / Status:	Ubiquitous / Abundant resident
Conservation status:	No perceived threats
Caterpillar food plants:	Leaves of Hornbeam and oak. Elsewhere, on other tree species
Flight period:	June to October
Records in database:	477

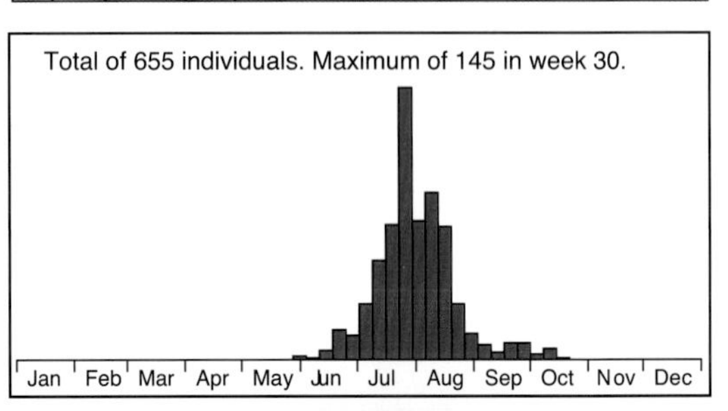

This is probably one of our most familiar micro moths, even if the uninitiated misidentify it as a tortricid and then inevitably fail to arrive at a name. During a light-hearted discussion with Mark Cooper on the usefulness or otherwise of English names for micro-moths, *Carcina quercana* was jokingly given the name of 'The Flat Cooper', for reasons which are wholly flippant. Mention is made here only because the name was picked up on by a European entomologist whilst I was collecting in Hungary and used in a publication; the origin of this entirely 'spoof' name, and its author, is therefore placed on record!

STATHMOPODIDAE

0877 *Stathmopoda pedella* (L.)

Recorded:	2004 – 2006
Distribution / Status:	Local / Uncommon resident
Conservation status:	Herts Rare
Caterpillar food plants:	Not recorded. Elsewhere, on the fruit of Alder
Flight period:	July to early August
Records in database:	3

There are just three records, all of individual examples, of this strikingly distinctive moth. The light trap in the adjoining gardens of James Fish and Julian Reeves in Bishops Stortford produced moths on 8th August 2004 and 9th July 2005; my

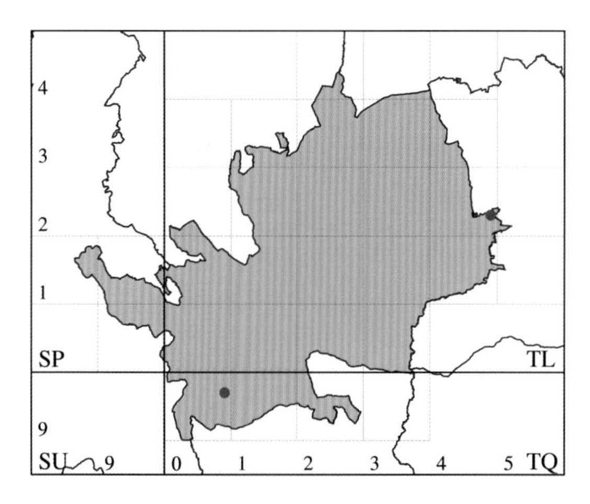

own lights produced another at Casiobury Park Nature Reserve, Watford on 1st July 2006. Alder grows nearby at the latter site whilst the Bishops Stortford trap is in the valley bottom and Alder grows at intervals along the length of the River Stort. In spite of its striking appearance, this moth is probably an overlooked resident in Hertfordshire.

AMPHISBATIDAE

0660 *Pseudatemelia josephinae* (Toll)

Recorded: 1980 – 2002
Distribution / Status: Local / Rare resident
Conservation status: Herts Rare
Caterpillar food plants: Not recorded. Elsewhere, on dead leaves
Flight period: June. Elsewhere, June to August
Records in database: 2

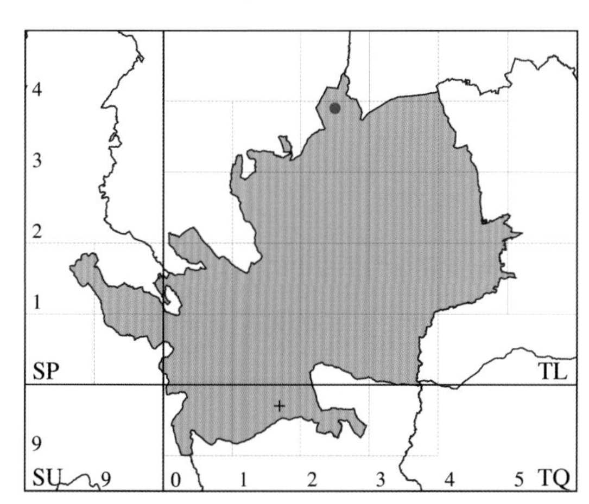

There are two valid Hertfordshire records, from Elstree in 1980 (Barry Goater) and from Ashwell Quarry on 8th June 2002 by myself. Boyd (1901) record *Oecophora flavifrontella* from Dark Lane, Cheshunt. Annoyingly, he fails to cite the authors of the names he uses. Foster (1937) interpreted the intended species as '*flavifrontella* Hb. (*nec* Hein.)', but this synonymy is absent from the 1972 checklist by Kloet & Hincks and is also not mentioned in *MBGBI* volume 4 part 1. It is perhaps of relevance that the name of *flavifrontella* was also applied to 660: *Pseudatemelia josephinae* by Meyrick in 1928. It is not at all clear which species is actually intended by Boyd, though in 1937 Foster would almost certainly have followed Meyrick. *MBGBI* records Hertfordshire for *Pseudatemelia josephinae*, but not for *P. flavifrontella*. On balance, this record probably relates to *josephinae*, but I have not mapped it for either species.

0661 *Pseudatemelia flavifrontella* ([[D.& S.]])

Recorded: 1968 – 2002
Distribution / Status: Local / Rare resident
Conservation status: Herts Rare
Caterpillar food plants: Not recorded. Elsewhere, on dead leaves
Flight period: June
Records in database: 2

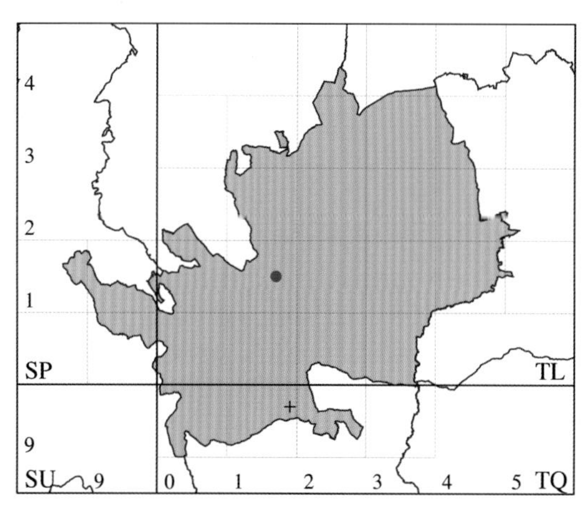

As with the last species we have two valid records, from Borehamwood on 5th June 1968 (Eric Bradford) and from Marshall's Heath on 1st June 2002 (John Murray), but see also the comments under 660: *Pseudatemelia josephinae*.

662 *Pseudatemelia subochreella* (Doubl.)

A specimen labelled '*Barnet/ Middlesex /27.5.44/ S Wakely/Ex coll S Wakely*' is in the University Museum of Zoology, Cambridge, and is the source of the Middlesex 'dot' in *Moths and Butterflies of Great Britain and Ireland* volume 4. Barnet is, of course, partly in Middlesex and partly in Hertfordshire; it is my understanding that the moth was actually captured in VC 20 and so I include it here.

CHIMABACHIDAE

0663 *Diurnea fagella* ([D.& S.])

Recorded: 1890 – 2006
Distribution / Status: Widespread / Abundant resident
Conservation status: No perceived threats
Caterpillar food plants: Hornbeam. Elsewhere, also on other trees
Flight period: March/April
Records in database: 168

This is one of our commonest early spring moths, with males coming to light often in large numbers and in a range of colour forms that broadly group into a lighter grey group and a far darker black group. The black group seem to represent about 25 per cent of the total population. Females, which have wings of a different shape, are very easily found at rest on tree trunks

in woodlands during the early part of the night. Unlike the next species, *fagella* is frequent in gardens, presumably reflecting its ability to feed on a variety of deciduous trees.

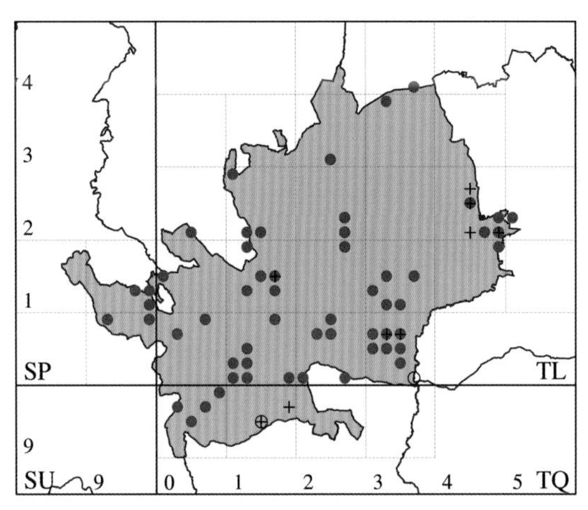

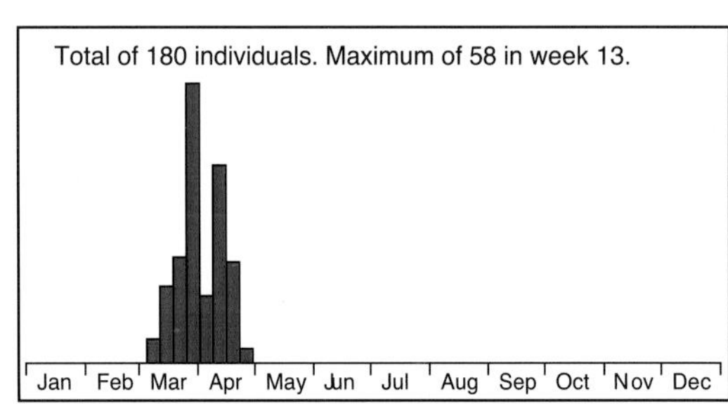

0664 *Diurnea lipsiella* ([D.& S.]) = *phryganella* (Hb.)

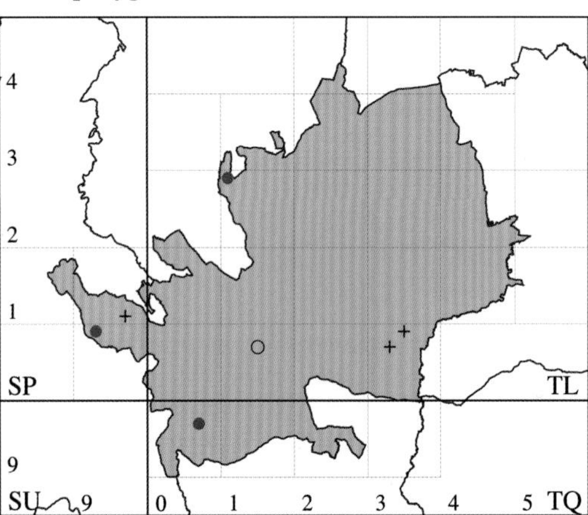

Recorded:	1888 – 2004
Distribution / Status:	Loca / Uncommon resident
Conservation status:	Herts Scarce
Caterpillar food plants:	Not recorded. Elsewhere, on oak
Flight period:	October/November
Records in database:	10

This is the autumn counterpart of 663: *Diurnea fagella*, but the records indicate that it is far less frequent in Hertfordshire and always in low numbers. It appears likely to be confined to woodlands with mature oak trees and is absent from garden moth trap lists.

0665 *Dasystoma salicella* (Hb.)

Recorded:	Pre-1890 only
Distribution / Status:	Absent / Extinct
Conservation status:	Herts Extinct
Caterpillar food plants:	Black Poplar; Aspen
Flight period:	Not recorded. Elsewhere, March/April
Records in database:	1

The only available Hertfordshire record is from the Sandridge area, where larvae were found on Black Poplar and Aspen (Griffith, 1890).

DEPRESSARIIDAE

0666 *Semioscopis avellanella* (Hb.)

Recorded:	1969 only
Distribution / Status:	Absent / Extinct resident
Conservation status:	Herts Extinct
Caterpillar food plants:	Not recorded. Elsewhere, on lime, birch and Hornbeam
Flight period:	Not recorded. Elsewhere, March/April
Records in database:	1

The only Hertfordshire record seems to be that made by Barry Goater of one 'at rest on trunk of *Betula*, Whippendell Wood, Watford' on 24th April 1969. Volume 4 of *Moths and Butterflies of Great Britain and Ireland* states that it is associated with mature birch woodland in the north and with ancient small-leaved lime woodland in the south; neither is a habitat which abounds in Hertfordshire. This work seems to either ignore or overlook the mention of Hornbeam in Maitland Emmet's 'Chart' in *MBGBI* volume 7 part 2 which, given that the first-mentioned work shows records all over south-east England, seems a far more likely foodplant. However, in adjacent Bedfordshire there is only a single record, made in the north of that county in 1990 whilst for Essex, Goodey (2002) lists it as Extinct. This seems very likely to be the case in Hertfordshire.

0667 *Semioscopis steinkellneriana* ([D.& S.])

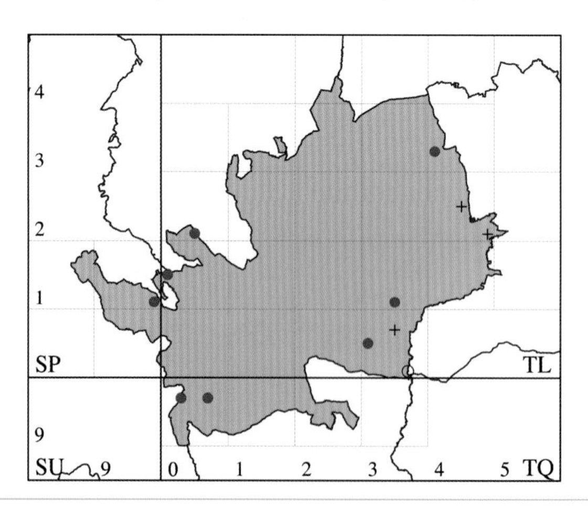

Recorded:	1901 – 2006
Distribution / Status:	Local / Uncommon resident
Conservation status:	Insufficiently known
Caterpillar food plants:	Not recorded. Elsewhere, on Blackthorn, Rowan and hawthorn
Flight period:	April to early May
Records in database:	14

The preferred habitat is blackthorn thickets and this may explain its absence from garden lists. Although attracted to light it is primarily a dawn species, flying from first light to sunrise, which explains its absence from lists made on trips to other sites as most are ended well before dawn breaks. Where lights are left until daybreak near blackthorn, the moth is caught – hence the 1988 record from my garden trap.

0668 *Luquetia lobella* ([D.& S.])

Recorded:	1890 – 2005
Distribution / Status:	Local / Uncommon resident
Conservation status:	Herts Scarce
Caterpillar food plants:	Not recorded. Elsewhere, on Blackthorn
Flight period:	May/June
Records in database:	8

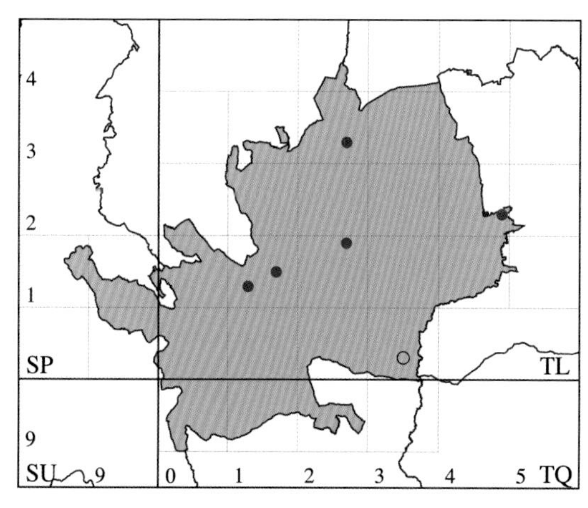

The preferred habitat is low growing stems of Blackthorn suckers in the base of mixed ancient hedges; hedges with dense Blackthorn are said to be shunned. Larvae spin webs under leaves less than a metre above ground. It comes sparingly to light, but is otherwise rarely seen so is likely to be very much under-recorded.

0670 *Depresssaria daucella* ([D.& S.])

Recorded:	2000 – 2005
Distribution / Status:	Local / Rare resident
Conservation status:	Herts Rare
Caterpillar food plants:	Not recorded. Elsewhere, on water dropworts (flowers)
Flight period:	August & March. Elsewhere, September to April
Records in database:	4

We have four records from three localities: my own garden in Bishops Stortford on 9th March 2000 and 9th March 2002, northern Bishops Stortford on 19th March 2005 (James Fish & Julian Reeves) and Hexton Chalk Pit on the Herts Moth Group outing of 18th August 2001. Various species of water dropwort grow along the River Stort and presumably are the source of the Bishops Stortford records, but there scarcely seems much of the foodplant at Hexton, which is a chalk grassland site; an alternative food plant may be indicated. All of the identifications are supported by genitalia dissection.

0671 *Depressaria ultimella* Stt.

Recorded:	Pre-1901 only
Distribution / Status:	Absent / Extinct resident
Conservation status:	Herts Extinct
Caterpillar food plants:	Not recorded. Elsewhere, on Fool's Water-cress
Flight period:	Not recorded. Elsewhere, September to April
Records in database:	1

Our only record is that from Cheshunt given by Boyd (1901); at that date the Lea Valley at Cheshunt Marsh would have been admirably suitable for this moth. There is, no apparent reason why this species should not still be present in Hertfordshire.

0672 *Depressaria heraclei* Retz. = *pastinacella* (Dup.)

Recorded:	1890 – 2002
Distribution / Status:	Local / Uncommon resident
Conservation status:	Herts Scarce
Caterpillar food plants:	Hogweed. Elsewhere, also on Wild Parsnip
Flight period:	August to mid-May
Records in database:	14

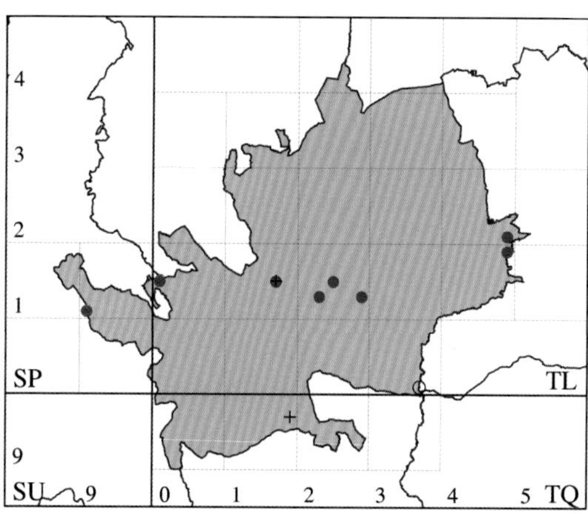

Although regularly encountered in Hertfordshire, the map shows that it is actually recorded from rather few sites.

0674 *Depressaria badiella* (Hb.)

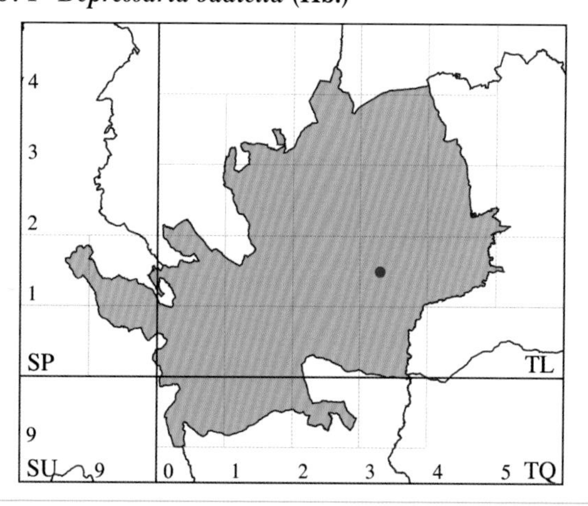

Recorded: 1834 – 2003
Distribution / Status: Local / Rare resident
Conservation status: Herts Rare
Caterpillar food plants: Not recorded. Elsewhere, on Cat's-ear, Perennial Sow-thistle and other composites
Flight period: August. Elsewhere, July to October
Records in database: 2

Originally recorded from Hertford in *Illustrations of British Entomology* (Stephens, 1834) our only other record was made in Hertford again by Andrew Wood, in his garden at Bengeo, on 20th August 2003.

0676 *Depressaria pulcherrimella* Stt.

Recorded: 1901 – 1995
Distribution / Status: Local / Rare resident
Conservation status: Herts Rare
Caterpillar food plants: Not recorded. Elsewhere, on Pignut, Wild Carrot and perhaps other related plants
Flight period: August. Elsewhere, July to September
Records in database: 3

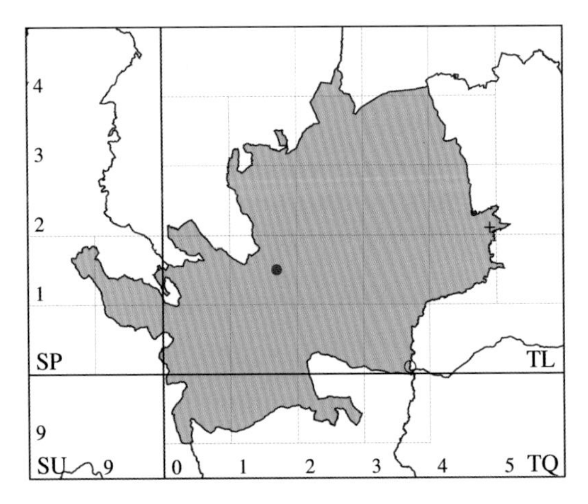

Cheshunt (Boyd, 1901), my garden in Bishops Stortford on 7th August 1987 and Marshall's Heath in 1995 (John Murray) are the only Hertfordshire records.

0677 *Depressaria douglasella* Stt.

Recorded: 1917 only
Distribution / Status: Absent / Extinct resident
Conservation status: Herts Extinct
Caterpillar food plants: Not recorded. Elsewhere, on Wild Carrot
Flight period: August
Records in database: 1

A specimen taken by G.H. Heath at Boxmoor on 16th August 1917 is now in the collections of the National Museums of Scotland in Edinburgh and is the source of the Hertfordshire dot on the map in *Moths and Butterflies of Great Britain and Ireland* volume 4(1). It is our only record.

0682 *Depressaria chaerophylli* Zell.

Recorded: 1890 – 2004
Distribution / Status: Local / Rare resident
Conservation status: Herts Rare
Caterpillar food plants: Not recorded. Elsewhere, on Rough Chervil
Flight period: January/February. Elsewhere, August to April
Records in database: 5

Modern records are from Marshall's Heath in 2002 (John Murray) and from Ware on two dates in 2004; the latter at least have been dissected, though there is no reason to doubt the first. This is yet another under-recorded moth with us.

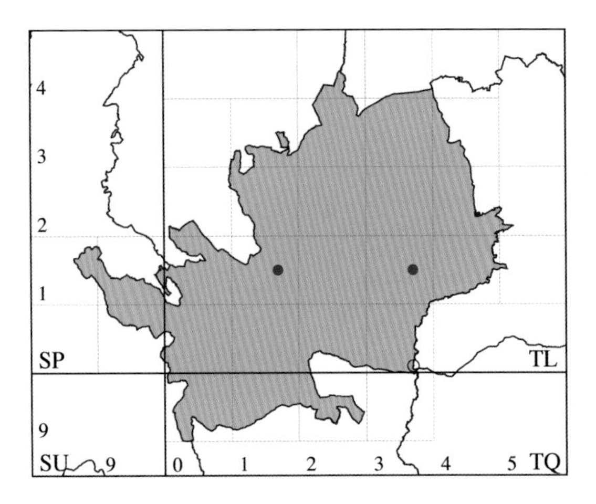

0688 *Agonopterix heracliana* (L.)

Recorded: 1888 – 2006
Distribution / Status: Widespread / Abundant resident
Conservation status: No perceived threats
Caterpillar food plants: Not recorded. Elsewhere, on various Apiaceae
Flight period: July to May
Records in database: 123

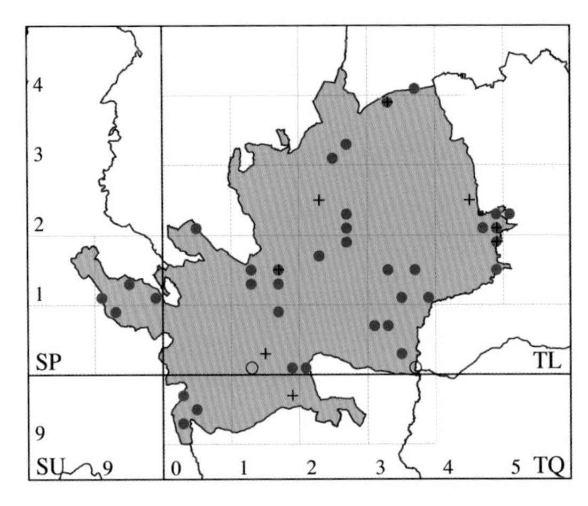

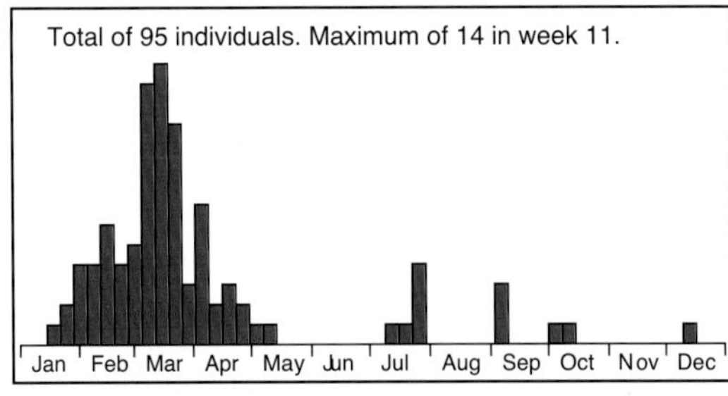

It would be a surprise if this familiar hibernator did not turn up at all well-recorded sites in the county. The peak of adults observed in the spring represents adults awakening from hibernation at a period when macro-lepidopterists are still determined to 'do the micros this year' and the number of moths in the trap is still low enough for them to act on this plan!

0689 *Agonopterix ciliella* (Stt.)

Recorded:	1890 – 2004
Distribution / Status:	Local / Uncommon resident
Conservation status:	Herts Scarce
Caterpillar food plants:	Not recorded. Elsewhere, on various Apiaceae
Flight period:	July. Elsewhere, July to May
Records in database:	11

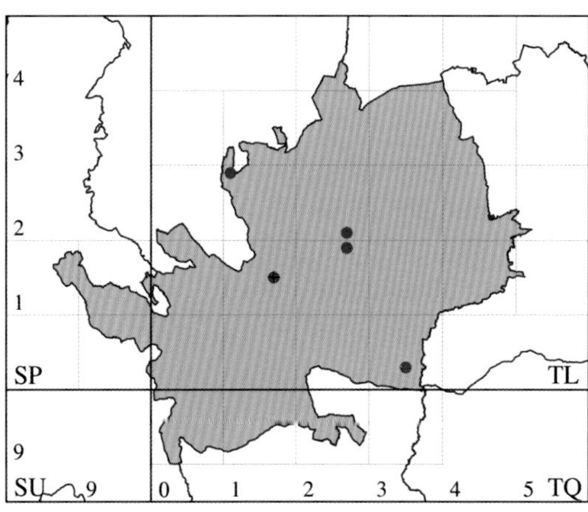

In spite of its ability to thrive on several umbelliferous plants, including Hogweed, Angelica and Wild Carrot, there are rather few records of this moth in Hertfordshire. It is very easily confused with 688: *Agonopterix heracliana*; all recent records of *ciliella* are confirmed by genitalia dissection, but not all *heracliana* are so validated and there is a possibility, though very small, that some of the latter are misidentified *ciliella*.

0691 *Agonopterix purpurea* (Haw.)

Recorded:	1834 – 1925
Distribution / Status:	Absent / Extinct resident
Conservation status:	Herts Extinct
Caterpillar food plants:	Not recorded. Elsewhere, on various Apiaceae
Flight period:	Elsewhere, August to May
Records in database:	4

Our records are from the Hertford area in 1834 (Stephens), the Sandridge area prior to 1890 (Griffith), Cheshunt prior to 1901 (Boyd) and Hitchin in 1925 (Foster). The preferred habitat is dry grassland, especially downland.

0692 *Agonopterix subpropinquella* (Stt.)

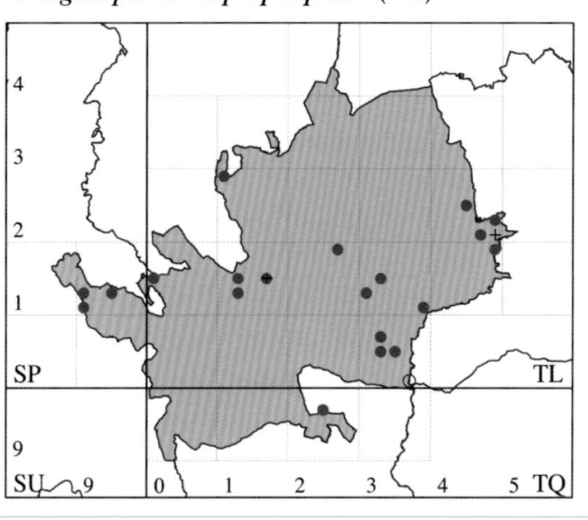

Recorded:	1890 – 2004
Distribution / Status:	Widespread / Common resident
Conservation status:	No perceived threats
Caterpillar food plants:	Not recorded. Elsewhere, on knapweeds, thistles and burdocks
Flight period:	August to April
Records in database:	31

Although overwintering as an adult, this moth is more usually reported in the autumn, especially August, than in the spring. This perhaps reflects the wanderings of entomologists since, although evidently widespread, the moth's foodplant requirements suggest that gardens, the source of most spring records of moths in the county, are probably not the preferred habitat.

0694 *Agonopterix nanatella* (Stt.)

Volume 4, part 1 of the series *Moths and butterflies of Great Britain and Ireland*, published in 2002, shows that this moth is reported from Hertfordshire, but without details.

0695 *Agonopterix alstromeriana* (Cl.)

Recorded:	1890 – 2006
Distribution / Status:	Widespread / Common resident
Conservation status:	No perceived threats
Caterpillar food plants:	Hemlock
Flight period:	July to early May
Records in database:	50

Given that the foodplant is not especially common in the Hertfordshire countryside it is interesting to discover just how widespread the moth actually is.

0696 *Agonopterix propinquella* (Tr.)

Recorded: 1890 – 2003
Distribution / Status: Local / Uncommon resident
Conservation status: Herts Scarce
Caterpillar food plants: Not recorded. Elsewhere, on thistles and perhaps burdocks
Flight period: August. Elsewhere, September to June
Records in database: 8

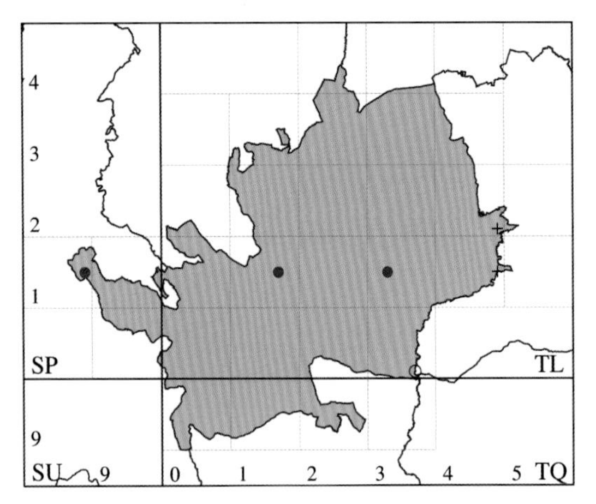

Somewhat perversely, whilst the last species is widespread in the face of an apparent scarcity of foodplant, this present species is scarce in the face of an undoubted surfeit of its pabulum! The reasons for this apparent anomaly are not at all clear.

0697 *Agonopterix arenella* ([D.& S.])

Recorded: 1834 – 2006
Distribution / Status: Widespread / Common resident
Conservation status: No perceived threats
Caterpillar food plants: Not recorded. Elsewhere, on thistles, knapweed and burdocks
Flight period: August to June
Records in database: 87

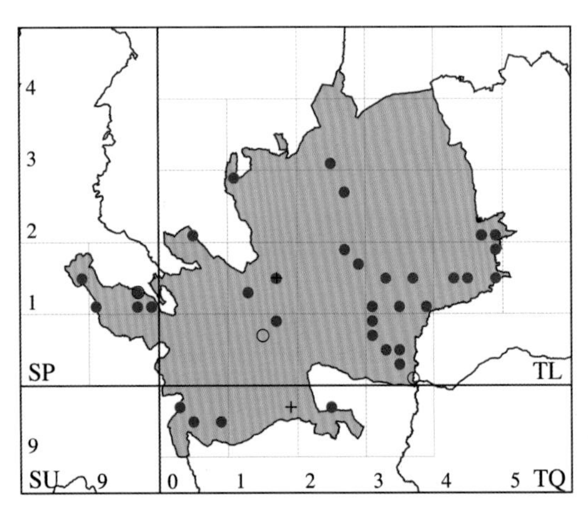

This is one of the most frequently encountered of the *Agonopterix* in Hertfordshire and July is the only month when it is unlikely that it can be found. In warm spells in the early spring it can be beaten out of old, untidy hedges in which it hibernates.

0698 *Agonopterix kaekeritziana* (L.) = *liturella* ([D.& S.])

Recorded: 1890 – 2003
Distribution / Status: Local / Uncommon resident
Conservation status: Herts Scarce
Caterpillar food plants: Not recorded. Elsewhere, on knapweeds
Flight period: July/August. Elsewhere, July to September
Records in database: 8

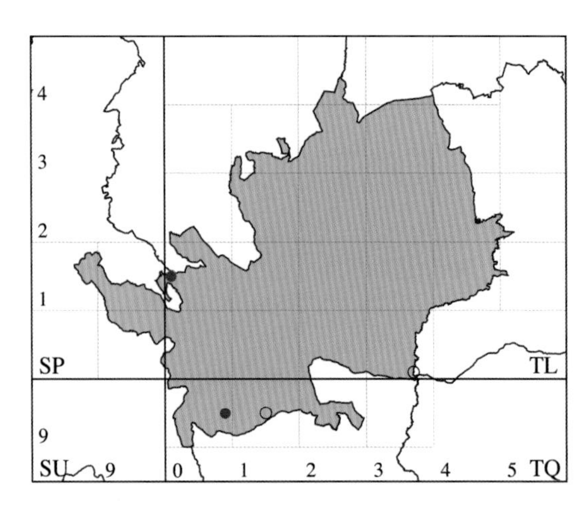

Although the distribution map suggests a rare species, the adult only rarely comes to light and so the moth is simply not recorded. The best way to find it is to search knapweed flowers on balmy nights during the summer when adults might be found feeding on the nectar. It is apparently unknown exactly where the moth lays its eggs, and so there is some scope for original observations to be made by those who have both the enthusiasm and patience.

0700 *Agonopterix pallorella* (Zell.)

Recorded: 2001 only
Distribution / Status: Local / Rare resident
Conservation status: Herts Rare
Caterpillar food plants: Not recorded. Elsewhere, on Greater Knapweed, less often on Hardheads and Saw-wort
Flight period: June, August & October. Elsewhere, August to April
Records in database: 3

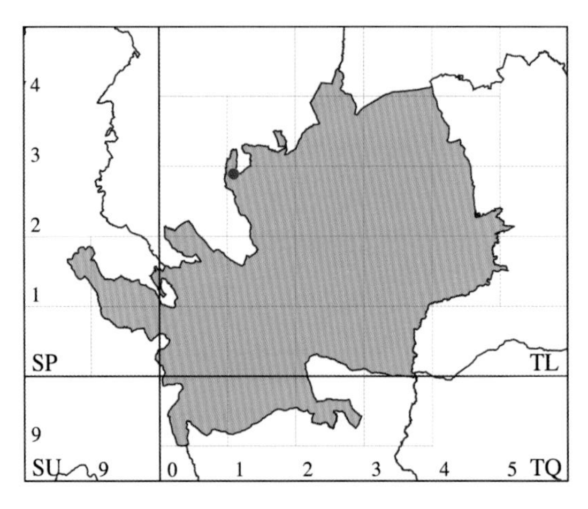

Our only records are my own from Hexton Chalk Pit on 16th June, 18th August and 20th October, all in 2001. The October specimen is diminutive; that from 16th June is out of season, but the weather during 2001 slowed the seasons and is probably the explanation for this.

0701 *Agonopterix ocellana* (Fabr.)

Recorded: 1901 – 2004
Distribution / Status: Local / Uncommon resident
Conservation status: Herts Scarce
Caterpillar food plants: Not recorded. Elsewhere, on willows and sallows
Flight period: March and July. Elsewhere, September to April
Records in database: 6

There is a concentration of records in the south-east of the county, all in or around the Broxbourne Woods complex. The

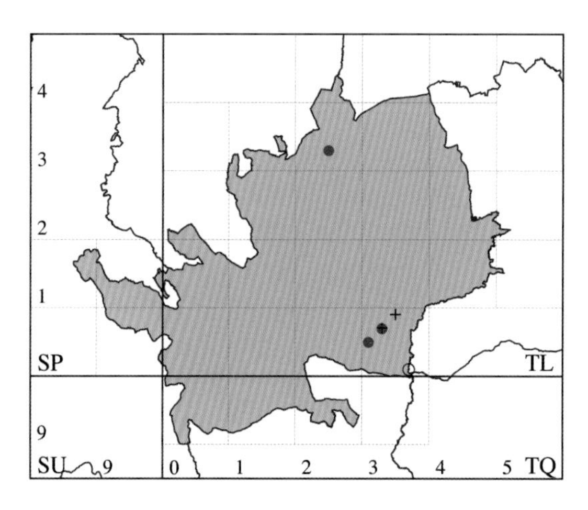

single north-westerly record is from Baldock on 4th July 1995 (Kerry Robinson); the specimen was named by myself.

0702 *Agonopterix assimilella* (Tr.)

Recorded: 1890 – 1997
Distribution / Status: Local / Uncommon resident
Conservation status: Herts Scarce
Caterpillar food plants: Not recorded. Elsewhere, on Broom
Flight period: Not recorded. Elsewhere, June to August
Records in database: 7

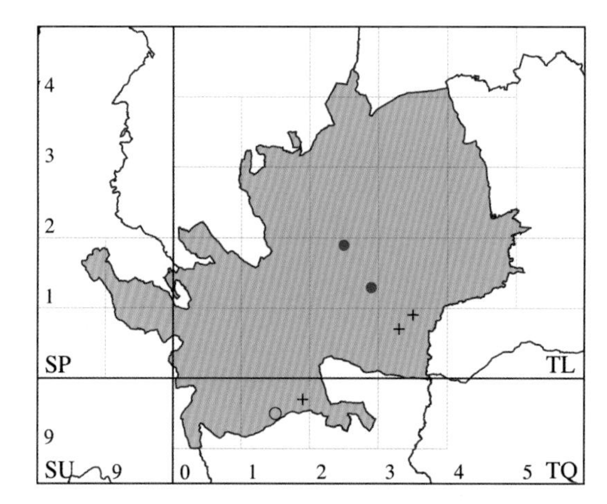

Unlike most other *Agonopterix* this species spends the winter in the larval stage, inside a stem of Broom. In the spring it feeds from within stems spun together with silk. The only recent record is from Panshanger Park in 1997 (Tom Gladwin) but there is no voucher specimen; all the records known are concentrated in the south-east sector of the county.

0704 *Agonopterix scopariella* (Hein.)

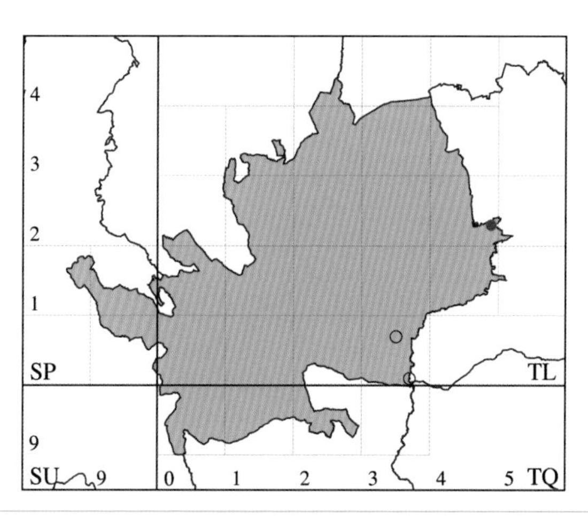

Recorded: 1901 – 2005
Distribution / Status: Local / Rare resident
Conservation status: Herts Rare
Caterpillar food plants: Not recorded. Elsewhere, on Broom
Flight period: April. Elsewhere, August to April
Records in database: 3

The discovery of this species by Rachel Terry, amongst the micros from the Bishops Stortford light trap run by James Fish and Julian Reeves on the night of 3rd April 2005, creates the first record since those listed for the Cheshunt area by Boyd (1901). Broom is a fairly prevalent garden plant and also forms a large patch on the Bishops Stortford ring road as it enters Birchanger Wood, not too far from the trap site.

0706 *Agonopterix nervosa* (Haw.)

Recorded: 1890 – 2006
Distribution / Status: Widespread / Common resident
Conservation status: No perceived threats
Caterpillar food plants: Not recorded. Elsewhere, on Gorse, Broom, Dyer's Greenweed, Petty Whin
Flight period: August to April
Records in database: 24

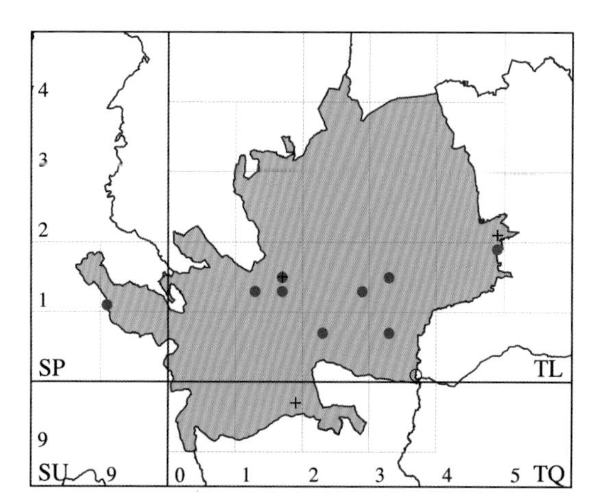

The map suggests a species that is likely to be widespread and it is odd that the other Broom-feeding species, 704: *Agonopterix scopariella* and 702: *Agonopterix assimilella*, are apparently so scarce whilst *nervosa* is more frequently encountered. In Europe *Laburnum* is also noted as a foodplant; this tree thrives in some of the county's larger gardens although there is no evidence at present of it being utilised in Britain.

0709 *Agonopterix liturosa* (Haw.)

Recorded: 1890 - 2003
Distribution / Status: Local / Uncommon resident
Conservation status: Herts Rare
Caterpillar food plants: Not recorded. Elsewhere, on St John's-worts
Flight period: July/August
Records in database: 6

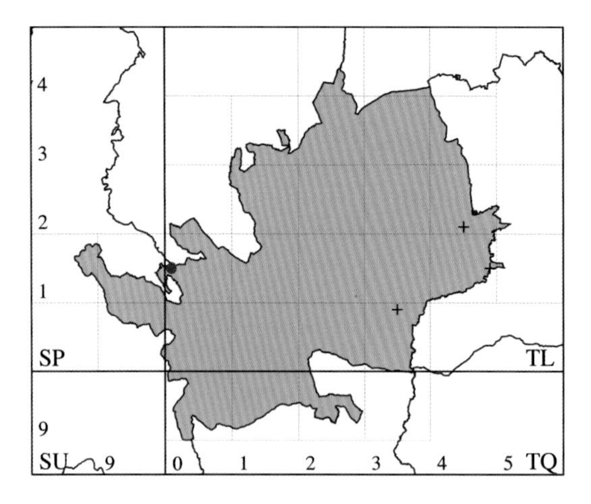

It is unclear how this species spends the winter - a fact that should tell the reader that it has not been knowingly found from the end of autumn until about May, when larvae are evident. This in turn suggests a great measure of under-recording.

0710 *Agonopterix conterminella* (Zell.)

Recorded: 1890 - 1901
Distribution / Status: Absent / Extinct resident
Conservation status: Herts Extinct
Caterpillar food plants: Not recorded. Elsewhere, on willows and sallows
Flight period: Elsewhere, August/September
Records in database: 2

Our two records are from the Sandridge area (Griffith, 1890) and the Cheshunt area (Boyd, 1901) and neither can be mapped reliably.

0711 *Agonopterix curvipunctosa* (Haw.) = *zephyrella* (Hb.)

Recorded: pre-1890 only
Distribution / Status: Absent / Extinct resident
Conservation status: Herts Extinct
Caterpillar food plants: Not recorded. Elsewhere, on Cow Parsley, Chervil and related plants
Flight period: Elsewhere, August to April
Records in database: 1

Our only available record is from Sandridge in the period prior to the year 1890 (Griffith) and cannot be accurately mapped.

0713 *Agonopterix angelicella* (Hb.)

Recorded: 1890 - 1995
Distribution / Status: Local / Rare resident
Conservation status: Herts Rare
Caterpillar food plants: Not recorded. Elsewhere, on Angelica and Hogweed
Flight period: July/August
Records in database: 5

Apart from the un-mappable record from the Sandridge area made prior to 1890 (Griffith) and that which is arbitrarily assigned to the most likely tetrad from Bricket Wood in 1931 (Fryer) our only records are from Sawbridgeworth Marsh,

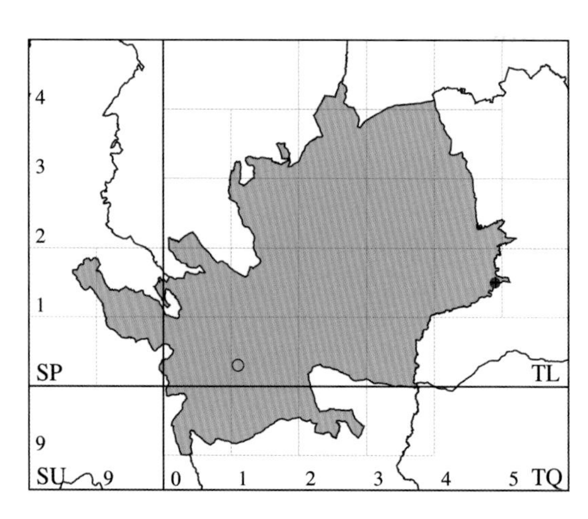

where myself and the late Charles Watson caught examples at mv light on 12th August 1987, 27th July 1990 and 29th July 1995.

0714 *Agonopterix yeatiana* (Fabr.)

Recorded: 1834 - 2004
Distribution / Status: Local / Rare resident
Conservation status: Herts Rare
Caterpillar food plants: Not recorded. Elsewhere, on various white-flowering Apiaceae
Flight period: May. Elsewhere, August to June
Records in database: 2

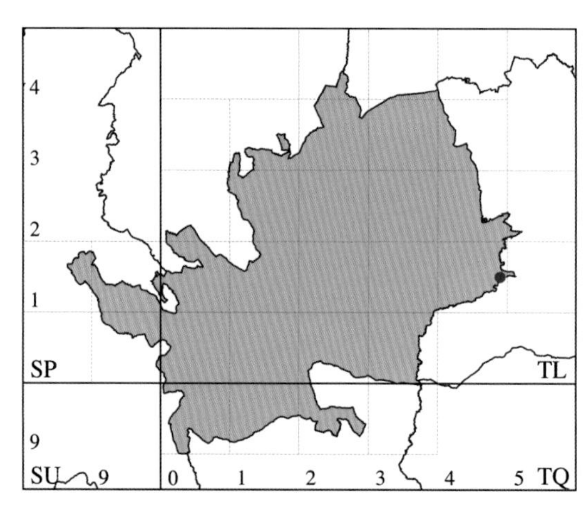

This moth is illustrated by J. F. Stephens in his 1834 publication *Illustrations of British Entomology* **4**: 200 from a specimen collected near Hertford. The only other county record is one that I caught at Sawbridgeworth Marsh on 29th May 2004. To the south of Hertfordshire, Rachel Terry has caught it a few hundred metres over the border into Middlesex at Barnet on 27th June 2004 and Marcel Ashby also caught one in his north London garden in Hornsey on 17th June 2004. It is evident that 2004 was a good year for this moth.

0715 *Agonopterix capreolella* (Zell.)

Recorded: 1868 only
Distribution / Status: Absent / Extinct resident
Conservation status: UK BAP Priority Species. Herts Extinct
Caterpillar food plants: Not recorded. Elsewhere, on Burnet Saxifrage
Flight period: Elsewhere, September to April
Records in database: 1

Hertfordshire's only claim to this species is the report of one from Cheshunt, caught by W. C. Boyd in 1868 (*Entomologist's Monthly Magazine* **5**: 147).

ETHMIIDAE

With only six British species, one of which is extinct, this is a small family of moths composed of just a single genus. It has been variously lumped with the oecophorids and the yponomeutids in the past, but various physical characters place it in a family on its own.

0718 *Ethmia dodecea* (Haw.)

Recorded:	2002 only
Distribution / Status:	Random / Vagrant
Conservation status:	Insufficiently known
Caterpillar food plants:	No data. Elsewhere, on Common Gromwell
Flight period:	July. Elsewhere, May to August in a single protracted brood
Records in database:	1

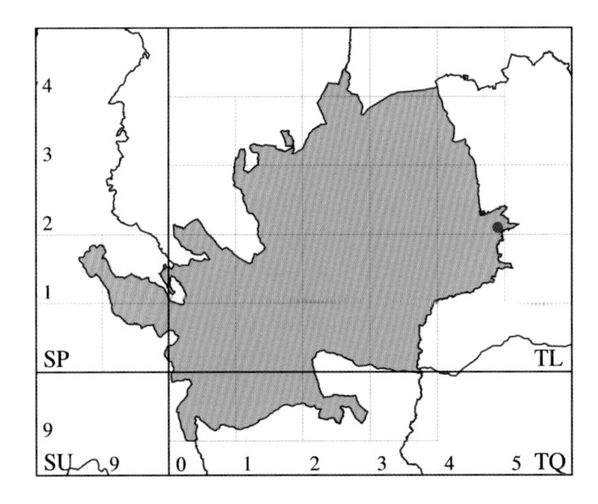

We have only a single report from Hertfordshire – an adult was taken by me in my garden light trap in Bishops Stortford on 18th July 2002. Although recorded in most south-east counties in England, it appears that this is an uncommon species. For the counties adjacent, Arnold *et al.* (1997) lists only a single record for Bedfordshire, on 27th June 1987, and Goodey (2002) categorises it as a Rare Vagrant in Essex, citing only a single record, from the east coast on 1st July 1986. I did not catch any migrants or any other 'unusual' moths either on that night or in the periods before and after, though I note that the trap was brought in at first light – something I am not always that good at!

GELECHIIDAE

Moths in the family Gelechiidae include many whose wild-caught adults can only be separated at all reliably by dissection though membership of the family is easy since all species have the characteristic hook-shaped hind wing (in some it is less marked than in others). Whilst many are attracted to light, an equal number either are not or only attend the light trap on rare occasions, so that recording these species involves seeking out and rearing the early stages. Although seemingly a rather specialist activity this is not always as difficult as it seems at first thought and there is considerable scope for new discoveries to be made by the fresh eye and mind of the amateur. British gelechiids number 162 of which we have valid records of 84 in Hertfordshire, though 22 may be absent today. I have followed the sequence of species used in volume 4, part 2, of the work *Moths and butterflies of Great Britain and Ireland*, which places several species in different subfamilies to those indicated by the Bradley (2000) checklist. As a result, several species are out of numerical sequence.

ANOMOLOGINAE

0724 *Metzneria lappella* (L.)

Recorded:	1991 – 2006
Distribution / Status:	Local / Common resident
Conservation status:	Herts Scarce
Caterpillar food plants:	Elsewhere, on burdock seeds
Flight period:	Mid-June to end of July
Records in database:	6

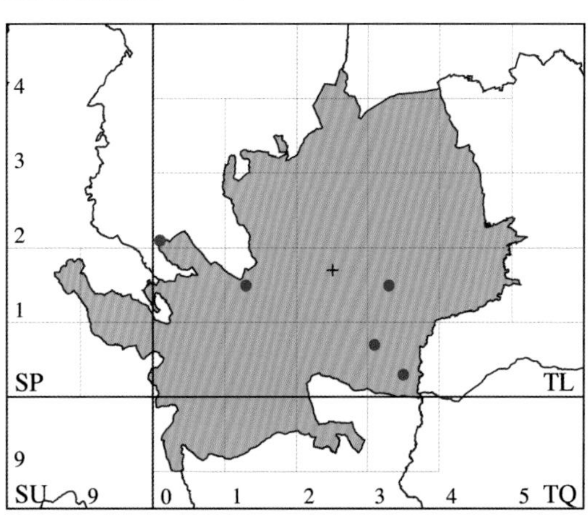

Almost certainly grossly under-recorded and likely to be rather more widespread than the map currently indicates, though perhaps still Local. Burdock heads collected in winter may contain larvae; if so, these should pupate in May and generate adults a few weeks later.

0726 *Metzneria metzneriella* (Stt.)

Recorded:	1962 – 2006
Distribution / Status:	Widespread / Common resident
Conservation status:	Insufficiently known
Caterpillar food plants:	Elsewhere, knapweeds and Saw-wort (seeds)
Flight period:	June/July.
Records in database:	39

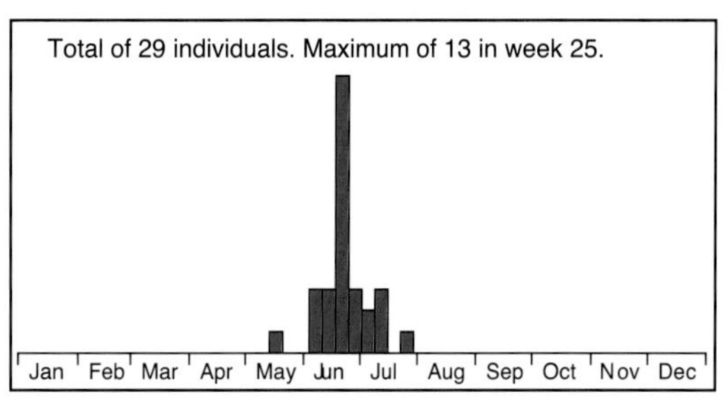

Seed capsules of 'Hardheads' collected over winter will generate adults in the spring if larvae are present. Although various books suggest a flight period extending into August, the Hertfordshire data contradicts this.

0727a *Metzneria aprilella* (H.- S.)

Recorded: 1983 only
Distribution / Status: Extremely local / Rare resident
Conservation status: Herts Rare
Caterpillar food plants: Elsewhere, on Greater Knapweed
Flight period: Elsewhere, May to August
Records in database: 1

Our only record is from Welwyn on 22nd June 1983 (Raymond Uffen). The larvae over-winter in the stem just below the dead flower head and if stems are cut, adults will emerge in June if they are present.

0728 *Monochroa cytisella* (Curtis)

Recorded: 1901 - 2006
Distribution / Status: Local / Uncommon resident
Conservation status: Herts Scarce
Caterpillar food plants: Elsewhere, on bracken
Flight period: July
Records in database: 5

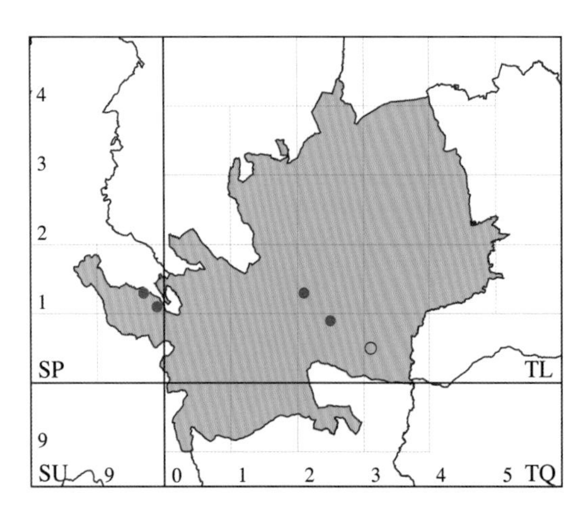

Although we have no larval records, all adult captures are associated with the known foodplant. The moth is probably very much under-recorded.

0729 *Isophrictis striatella* ([D.& S.])

Recorded: 2004 only
Distribution / Status: Local / Uncommon resident
Conservation status: Herts Scarce
Caterpillar food plants: Elsewhere, on Tansy or Sneezewort
Flight period: Elsewhere, July/August
Records in database: 5

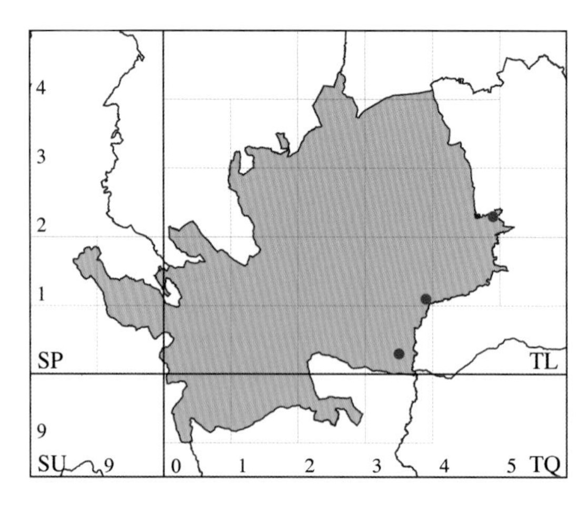

All of our recent records are from the vicinity of the Lea and Stort Valleys, but there is no apparent reason for this. Another surprise is that all of our records are from the year 2004. Larvae feed in the upper stem and flower head of the foodplant and over-winter here, pupating in the stem or amongst debris on the ground.

0730 *Apodia bifractella* (Dup.)

Recorded: 1890 - 2006
Distribution / Status: Local / Uncommon resident
Conservation status: Herts Scarce
Caterpillar food plants: Ploughman's Spikenard (seeds). Elsewhere, also on Fleabane
Flight period: July/August
Records in database: 7

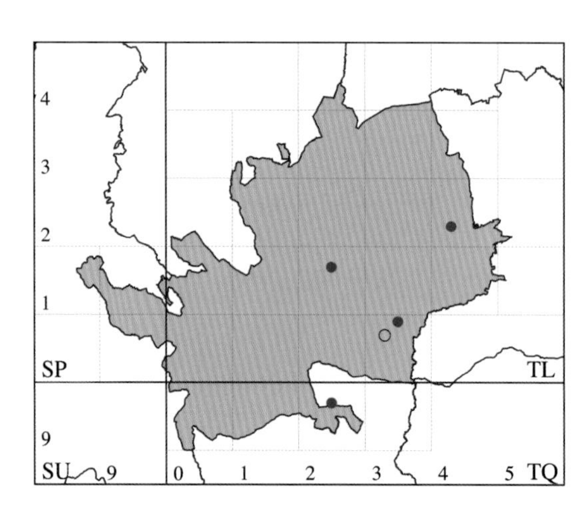

Our only breeding record is of adults reared by myself from dead flower heads of Ploughman's Spikenard collected at Westland Green in 1st November 2001 by Charles Watson. All other mapped records are of adults

0731 *Eulamprotes atrella* ([D.& S.])

Recorded: 1890 - 2004
Distribution / Status: Local / Uncommon resident
Conservation status: Herts Scarce
Caterpillar food plants: St John's-wort
Flight period: July/August
Records in database: 5

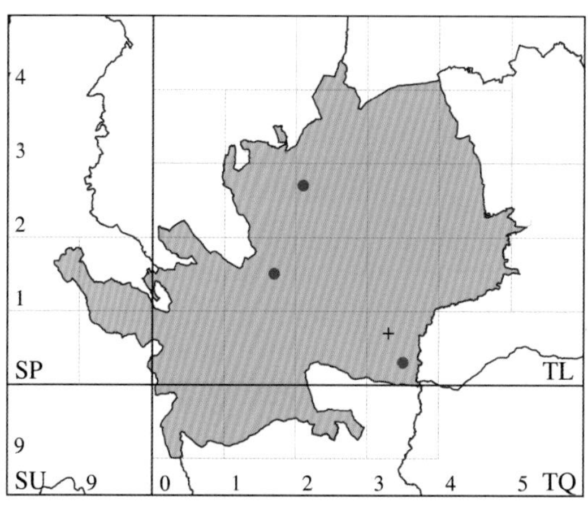

Most records are from light traps and suggest a widespread, but rather localised species.

0735 *Monochroa tenebrella* (Hb.)

Recorded: 1890 – 2004
Distribution / Status: Local / Uncommon resident
Conservation status: Herts Threatened
Caterpillar food plants: Elsewhere, on Sheep's Sorrel
Flight period: June, Elsewhere, into July
Records in database: 6

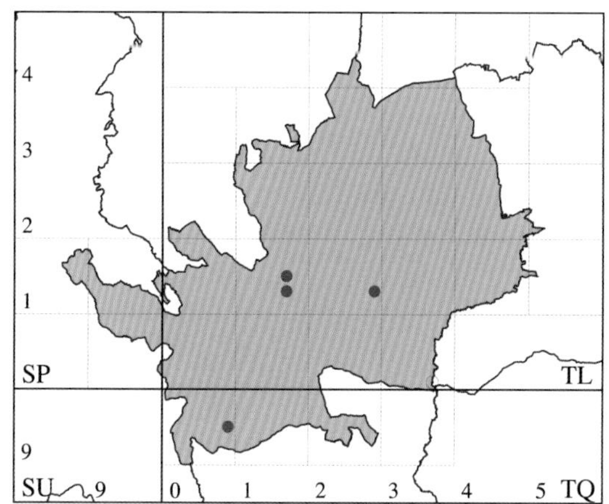

Our records reflect the distribution of acid grasslands in the county, at Marshalls Heath, Croxley Common Moor, Nomansland Common and Tewin. This habitat restriction renders the species Threatened in the county.

0736 *Monochroa lucidella* (Steph.)

Recorded: 1998 only
Distribution / Status: Local / Uncommon resident
Conservation status: Herts Rare
Caterpillar food plants: Common Spike-rush
Flight period: Elsewhere,
Records in database: 1

Our only record was made by Raymond Uffen at Aldenham Golf Course on 10th July 1998. The moth must surely be present elsewhere?

0737 *Monochroa palustrella* (Douglas)

Recorded: 1987 – 2006
Distribution / Status: Local / Uncommon resident
Conservation status: No perceived threats
Caterpillar food plants: Elsewhere, on Curled Dock in the rootstock
Flight period: July/August
Records in database: 15

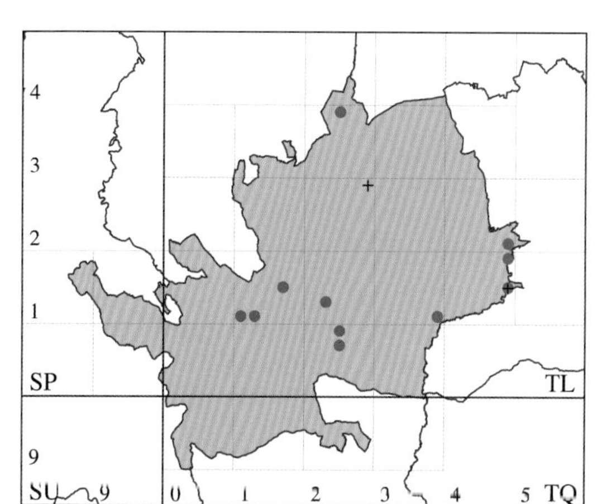

The records suggest that this may be a widespread and not uncommon species; as more moth enthusiasts start to look at their micros, the map is likely to fill with dots.

0740 *Monochroa hornigi* (Stdgr.)

Recorded: 1973 only
Distribution / Status: Very Local or absent / Rare resident or extinct
Conservation status: Herts Extinct
Caterpillar food plants: Elsewhere, *Persicaria* – mining the stems
Flight period: Elsewhere, July/August
Records in database: 2

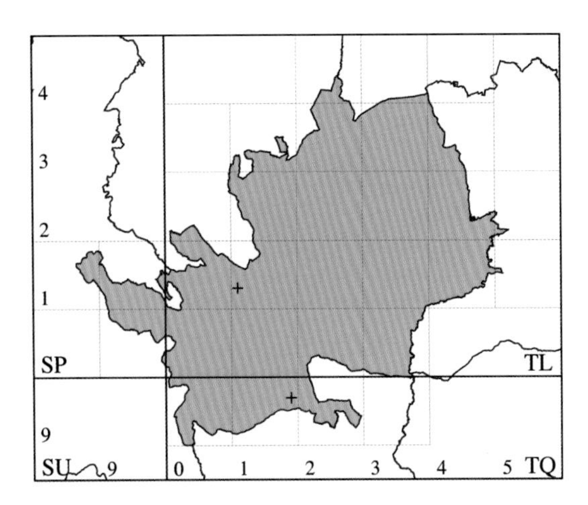

In 1978, Eric Bradford (*Entomologist's Record* **90**: 189) reported this species from his garden 'several years ago'. In the same article he refers to a report of this species in the Barnfield light trap on the Rothamsted Estate at Harpenden. No date is given, but Bradford reports that '... it must be recent, as Mr Karsholt mentions it as being the second specimen to be taken in Britain'. Subsequent research indicates that it was captured on 5th July 1973.

0742 *Monochroa lutulentella* (Zell.)

Recorded: 1868 – 2004
Distribution / Status: Local / Uncommon resident
Conservation status: Herts Scarce
Caterpillar food plants: Elsewhere, in the rootstock of Meadowsweet
Flight period: Elsewhere, June to August
Records in database: 2

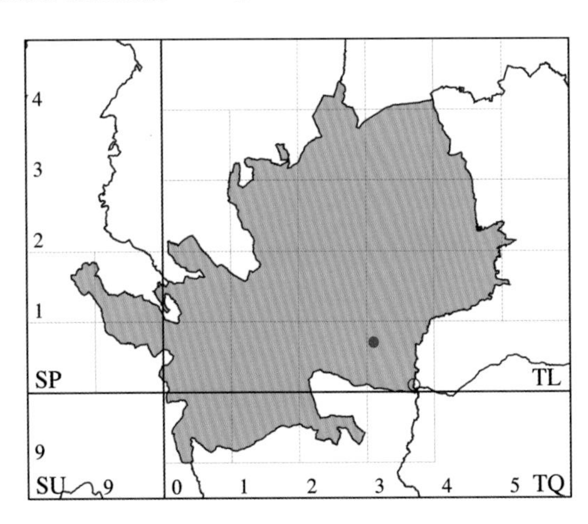

The separation of our two records, from Cheshunt in 1868 (Boyd) and Wormley Wood in 2004 (Mark Cooper), by 136 years is strong support for the notion that many micro moths are simply under-recorded in the county and will be found if looked for in the right habitat.

0744 *Monochroa arundinetella* (Stt.)

Recorded: Pre-1901 only
Distribution / Status: Absent or extremely local / Extinct or rare resident
Conservation status: Herts Extinct
Caterpillar food plants: Elsewhere, Greater Pond Sedge – mining the leaves
Flight period: Elsewhere, June/July
Records in database: 1

Our only report is from Cheshunt Marsh prior to 1901 (Boyd). It may be overlooked, but good quality wetlands are rare in Hertfordshire.

0746 *Chrysoesthia drurella* (Fabr.)

Recorded: 1901 – 2006
Distribution / Status: Local / Uncommon resident
Conservation status: Herts Scarce
Caterpillar food plants: oraches and goosefoots, mining the leaves
Flight period: Elsewhere, June then August/September
Records in database: 7

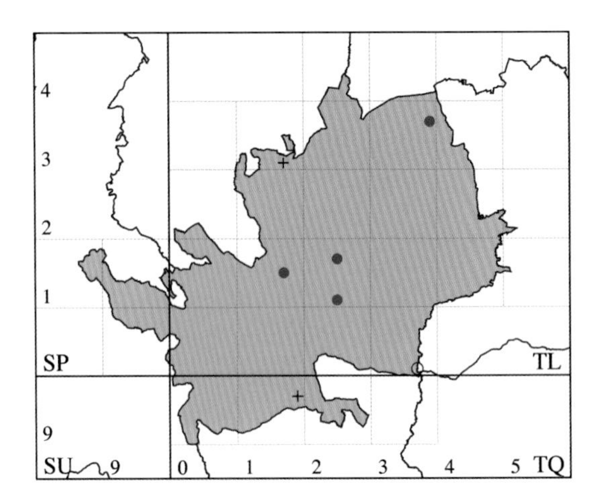

The very distinctive mines on the foodplant are illustrated in volume 4 (part 2) of *Moths and butterflies of Great Britain and Ireland*; if more people were aware of the form of the mines, which are evident in July/August and then again from September to May, the moth might well be found in many more places.

0747 *Chrysoesthia sexguttella* (Thunb.)

Recorded: 1901 – 2005
Distribution / Status: Loca / Uncommon resident
Conservation status: Herts Scarce
Caterpillar food plants: Orache. Elsewhere, also on goosefoots
Flight period: Elsewhere, June then September/October
Records in database: 12

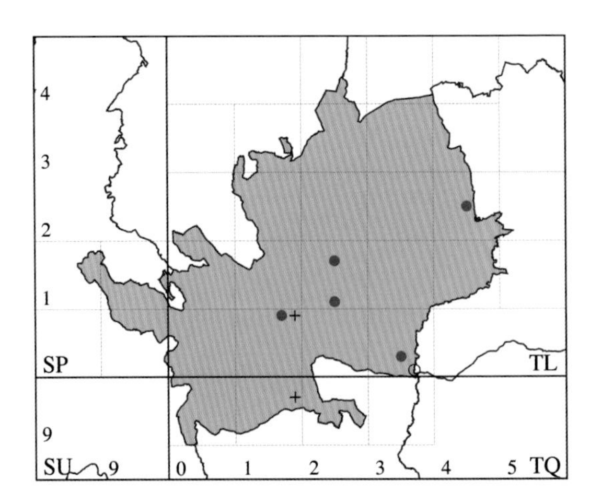

This is another leaf-mining species that is probably under-recorded. Mines are evident in June and then September/ October.

0748 *Ptocheuusa paupella* (Zell.)

Recorded: 1901 – 2001
Distribution / Status: Local / Rare resident
Conservation status: Herts Rare
Caterpillar food plants: Elsewhere, on Common Fleabane and Golden Samphire
Flight period: Elsewhere, August/September
Records in database: 2

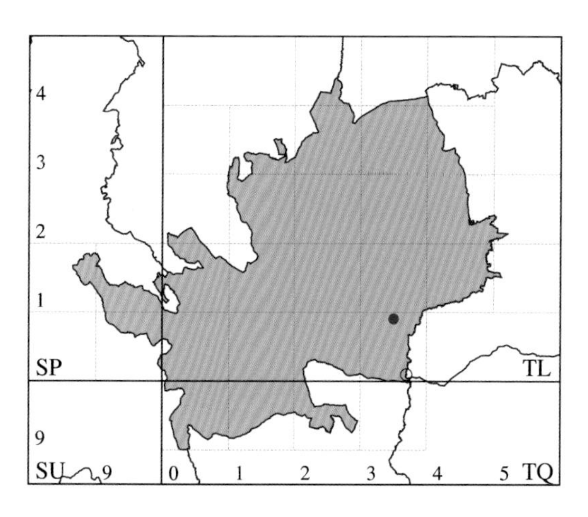

Apart from Cheshunt prior to 1901 our only record is from the same general south-eastern area of the county along Ermine Street (Roman Road) on 17th August 2001 (Raymond Uffen). The great separation of the dates suggests that it is under-recorded.

0752 *Aristotelia ericinella* (Zell.)

Recorded: 1890 – 1999
Distribution / Status: Local / Rare resident
Conservation status: Herts Endangered
Caterpillar food plants: Elsewhere, on Heather
Flight period: Elsewhere, in August
Records in database: 3

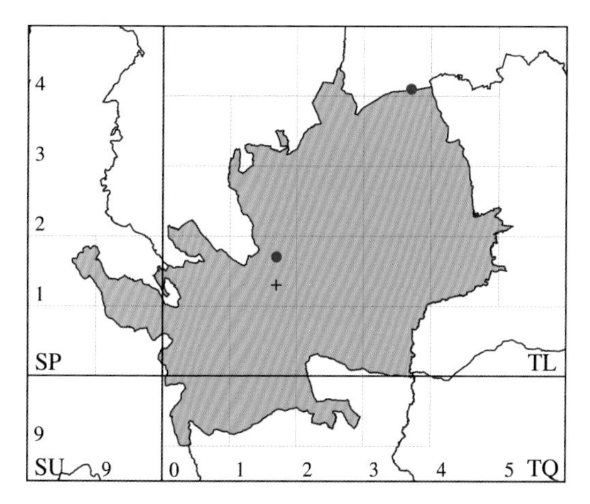

Our two old records, from the Sandridge area prior to 1890 (Griffith) and Cheshunt prior to 1901 (Boyd) are not unexpected, but the 1999 report from Royston by John Chainey (whose identification skills are not questioned) is a surprise as the site is calcareous and the foodplant likes acid soils.

0777 *Bryotropha basaltinella* (Zell.)

Volume 4, part 2, of *Moths and Butterflies of Great Britain and Ireland* published in 2002 shows a record for Hertfordshire, but details of the record are not available.

0779 *Bryotropha affinis* (Haw.)

Recorded: 1890 – 2006
Distribution / Status: Widespread / Common resident
Conservation status: No perceived threats
Caterpillar food plants: Elsewhere, on mosses
Flight period: May to August
Records in database: 52

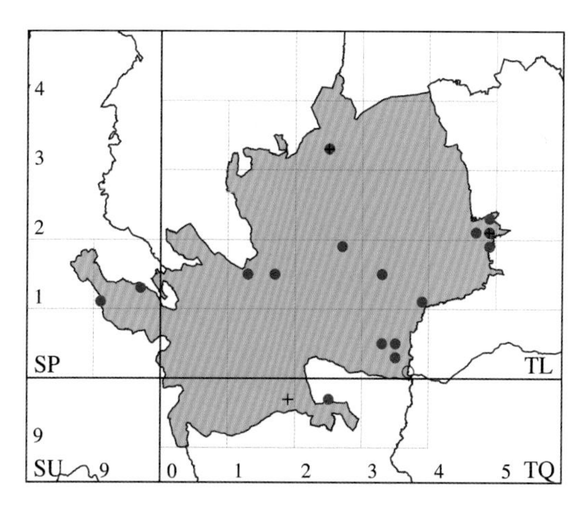

Most garden moth traps will turn up this 'little brown job' if people actually bother to collect the micros.

0780 *Bryotropha similis* ([D.& S.])

Recorded: 1890 – 2006
Distribution / Status: Local / Uncommon resident
Conservation status: No perceived threats
Caterpillar food plants: Elsewhere, on mosses
Flight period: July to early August
Records in database: 9

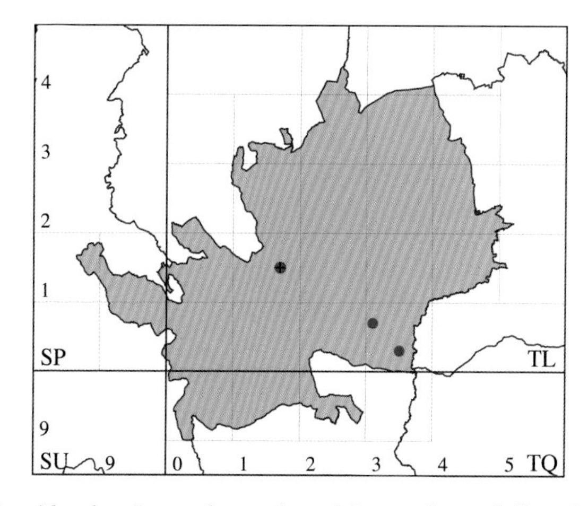

As with other *Bryotropha* species, adults mostly need dissection for correct identification.

0782 *Bryotropha senectella* (Zell.)

Recorded: 1890 – 2006
Distribution / Status: Local / Uncommon resident
Conservation status: No perceived threats
Caterpillar food plants: Elsewhere, on mosses
Flight period: July/August
Records in database: 12

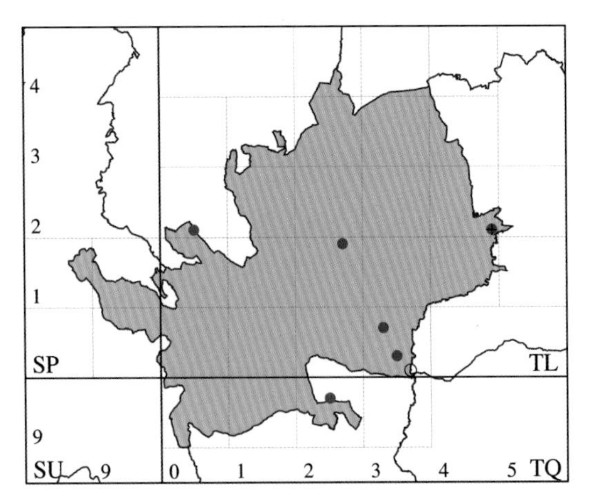

The 'cheek' colour character in the identification is unreliable for worn specimens and so dissection is essential to confirm records of this species.

0787 *Bryotropha terrella* ([D.& S.])

Recorded: 1886 – 2006
Distribution / Status: Widespread / Common resident
Conservation status: No perceived threats
Caterpillar food plants: Elsewhere, on mosses
Flight period: May to August
Records in database: 99

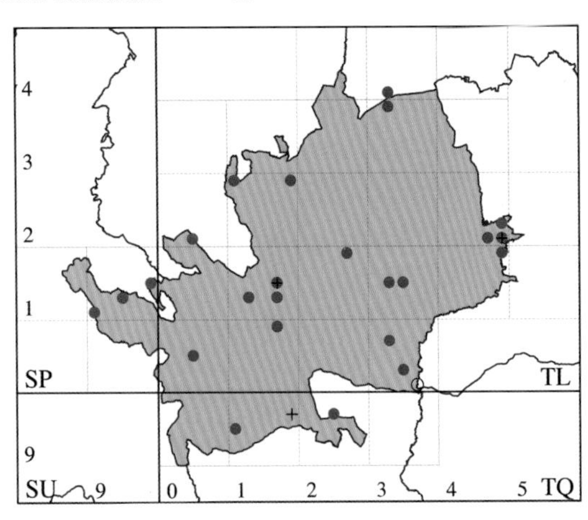

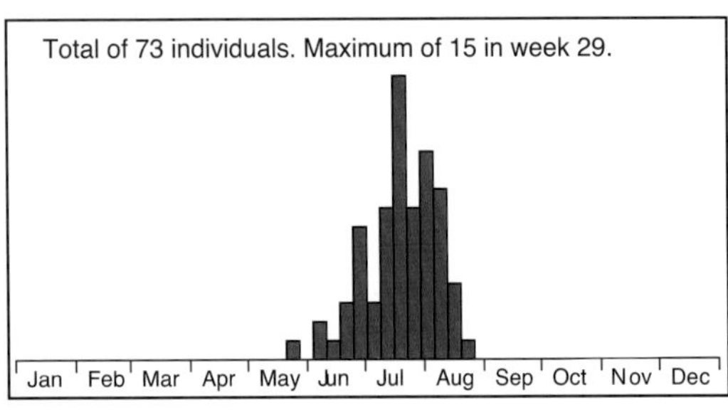

In spite of this being a common moth in the county, we have no breeding records. Adults are regarded as distinctive by some, but failure to verify names by dissection might cause some examples of 788: *Bryotropha politella* to be missed.

0788 *Bryotropha politella* (Stt.)

Recorded: 1890 – 1901
Distribution / Status: Probably absent / Probably extinct
Conservation status: Herts Extinct
Caterpillar food plants: Unknown
Flight period: Elsewhere, June
Records in database: 2

Our two records are from the Sandridge area prior to 1890 and from Turnford Lock, in the Lea Valley, prior to 1901 (Boyd). Separation from 787: *B. terrella* requires examination of the genitalia and if all examples of this more common species are not dissected it is possible that records of *politella* may be missed.

0789 *Bryotropha domestica* (Haw.)

Recorded: 1886 – 2006
Distribution / Status: Widespread / Common resident
Conservation status: No perceived threats
Caterpillar food plants: Elsewhere, on mosses
Flight period: June to August
Records in database: 39

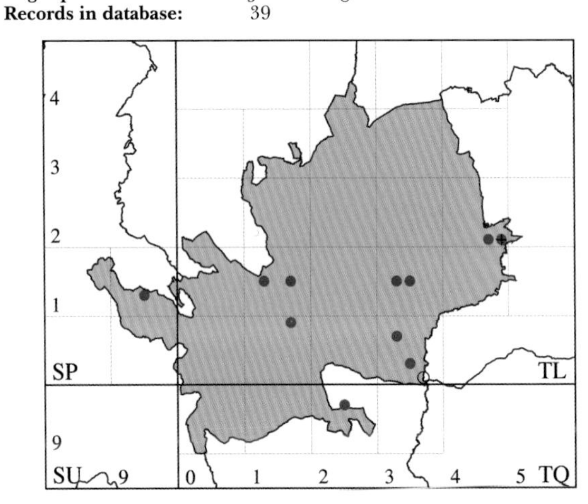

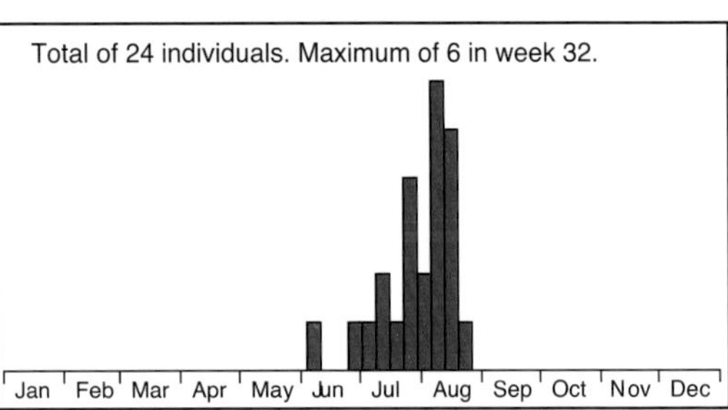

Our first report is from Hitchin on 10th July 1886; the moth appears always to have been common in the county.

GELECHIINAE

0755 *Stenolechia gemmella* (L.)

Recorded: 1890 – 2003
Distribution / Status: Local / Uncommon resident
Conservation status: No perceived threats
Caterpillar food plants: Elsewhere, on oak
Flight period: August/September.
Records in database: 7

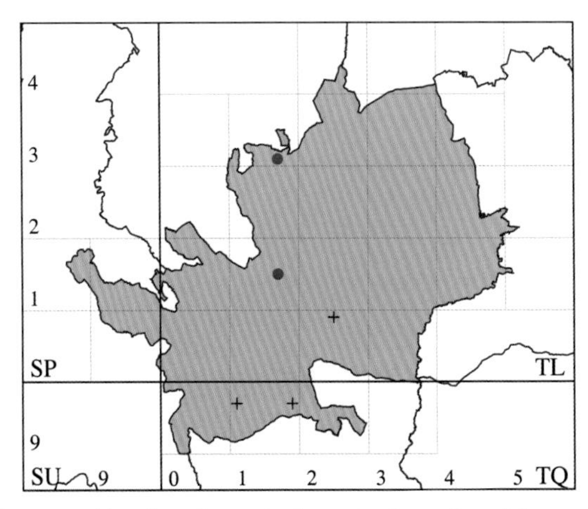

The caterpillars bore into a bud causing it to die; adults can be found at rest in crevices on oak trunks by day.

0756 *Parachronistis albiceps* (Zell.)

Recorded: 1901 – 2006
Distribution / Status: Widespread / Common resident
Conservation status: No perceived threats
Caterpillar food plants: Hazel
Flight period: July. Elsewhere, into August
Records in database: 8

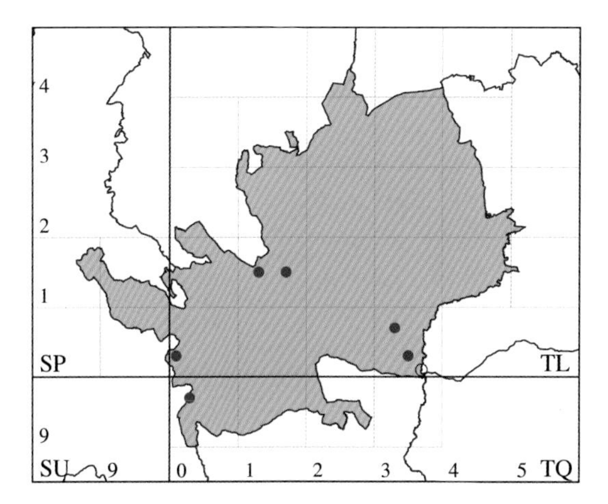

The larva feeds in the bud of the tree in May and apparently is undescribed. The species is predicted to be widespread in the county.

0757 *Recurvaria nanella* ([D.& S.])

Recorded: 1901 - 2000
Distribution / Status: Local / Uncommon resident
Conservation status: Herts Rare
Caterpillar food plants: Elsewhere, on apple, plum and Blackthorn
Flight period: Elsewhere,
Records in database: 2

This is another example of a species whose under-recorded status is emphasised by the widely-spaced dates of the first two records: Cheshunt prior to 1901 (Boyd) and Bishops Stortford, 28th July 2000 (by myself). A subsequent record, made on a Herts Moth Group field trip to Tewin Orchard on 4th August 2007, after the December 2006 cut-off date, supports this and is mapped in order to emphasise that point.

0758 *Recurvaria leucatella* (Cl.)

Recorded: 1834 – 2005
Distribution / Status: Local / Uncommon resident
Conservation status: No perceived threats
Caterpillar food plants: Elsewhere, hawthorn and apple
Flight period: July/August
Records in database: 11

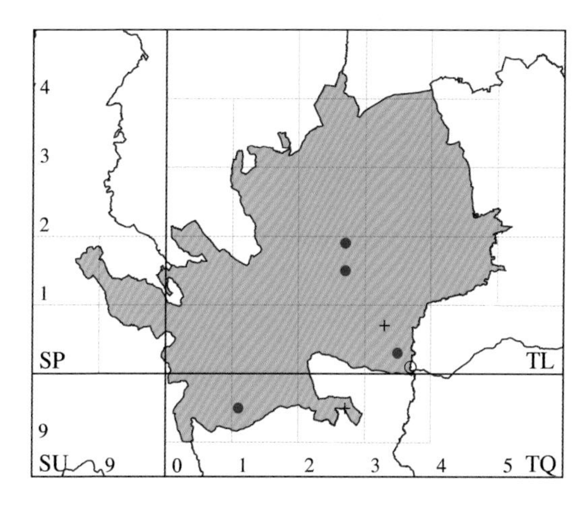

First reported for our county from the Hertford area as *Telea leucatella* L. J. F. Stephens *Illustrations of British Entomology*, published in 1834. The caterpillar spins leaves of the foodplant together and feeds within.

0759 *Coleotechnites piceaella* (Kearfott)

Recorded: 1968 only
Distribution / Status: Absent or extremely local / Extinct or rare resident
Conservation status: Herts Extinct
Caterpillar food plants: Elsewhere, on Norway Spruce, mining the needles
Flight period: Elsewhere, July
Records in database: 1

Norway Spruce is uncommon in Hertfordshire and this will limit the range of the moth, which is reported only once, from Borehamwood on 13th July 1968. It was first found in Britain at Pinner, Middlesex in June 1952, by the late Bill Minnion, but that record appears to have been missed by the compilers of the maps for *Moths and Butterflies of Great Britain and Ireland* volume 4, part 2. The moth is extremely local and reported Elsewhere, from South Essex, West Kent and South Hampshire only.

0760 *Exoteleia dodecella* (L.)

Recorded: 1890 – 2005
Distribution / Status: Local / Uncommon resident
Conservation status: Herts Scarce
Caterpillar food plants: Elsewhere, Scots Pine and Larch
Flight period: June/July
Records in database: 4

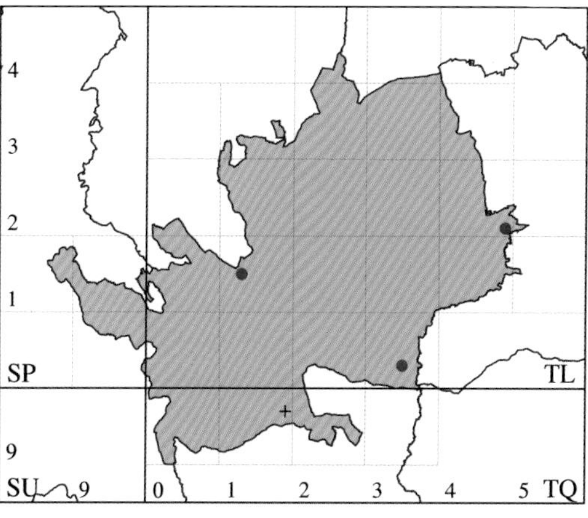

The records reflect the garden light traps of micro-lepidopterists rather than the true distribution pattern. It is also recorded over the border in Barnet, Middlesex.

0762 *Athrips mouffetella* (L.)

Recorded: 1890 – 2006
Distribution / Status: Widespread / Common resident
Conservation status: No perceived threats
Caterpillar food plants: Elsewhere, honeysuckles and Snowberry
Flight period: Late June to early August
Records in database: 27

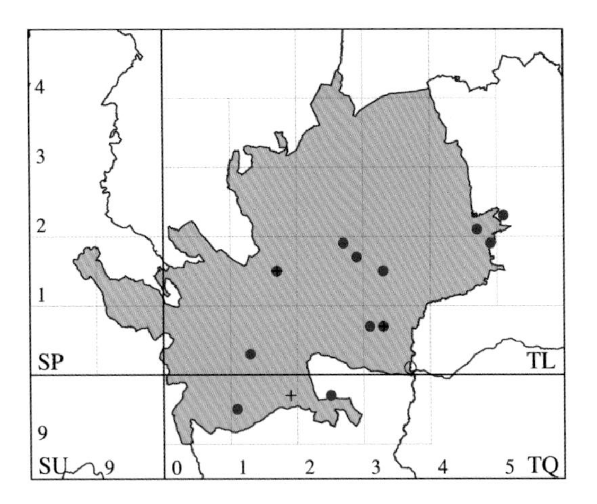

This is a moth that is likely to be found in a great many additional sites where the foodplant grows.

0764 *Pseudotelphusa scalella* (Scop.)

Recorded: 1937 – 1977
Distribution / Status: Local or absent / Rare resident or extinct
Conservation status: Herts Extinct
Caterpillar food plants: Mosses
Flight period: Elsewhere, May/June
Records in database: 2

Broxbourne Wood (G. V. Bull, undated record given in Foster, 1937) and nearby Hoddesdonpark Wood (David Agassiz) in 1977, provide our only records.

0773 *Pseudotelphusa paripunctella* (Thunb.)

Recorded: 1890 – 2004
Distribution / Status: Local / Uncommon resident
Conservation status: Herts Rare
Caterpillar food plants: Elsewhere, on oaks
Flight period: June. Elsewhere, May/June
Records in database: 2

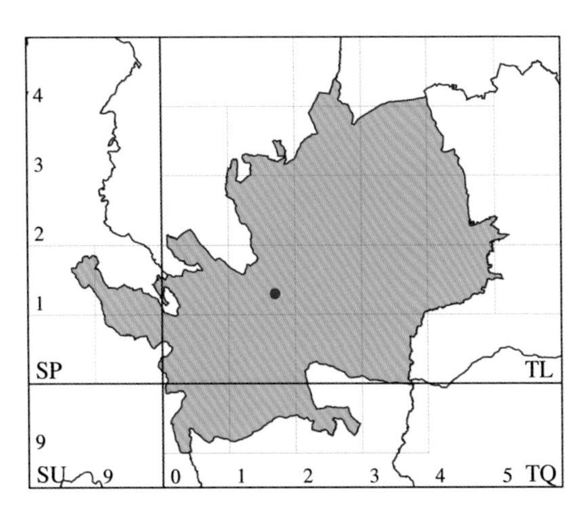

Apart from a 1890 record from the Sandridge area, this moth is known in Hertfordshire only from Nomansland Common, where I caught it at light on 12th June 2004.

0766 *Altenia scriptella* (Hb.) = *Teleiodes scriptella* (Hb.)

Recorded: 1834 only
Distribution / Status: Absent / Extinct
Conservation status: Herts Extinct
Caterpillar food plants: Elsewhere, on Field Maple
Flight period: Elsewhere, June/July
Records in database: 1

Illustrated by J. F. Stephens from a Hertford specimen in *Illustrations of British Entomology* **4**: 215 (1834). This is our only record.

0765 *Teleiodes vulgella* ([D.& S.])

Recorded: 1890 – 2006
Distribution / Status: Widespread / Common resident
Conservation status: No perceived threats
Caterpillar food plants: Elsewhere, on hawthorns and Blackthorn, rarely *Cotoneaster*
Flight period: Late-May to mid-August
Records in database: 89

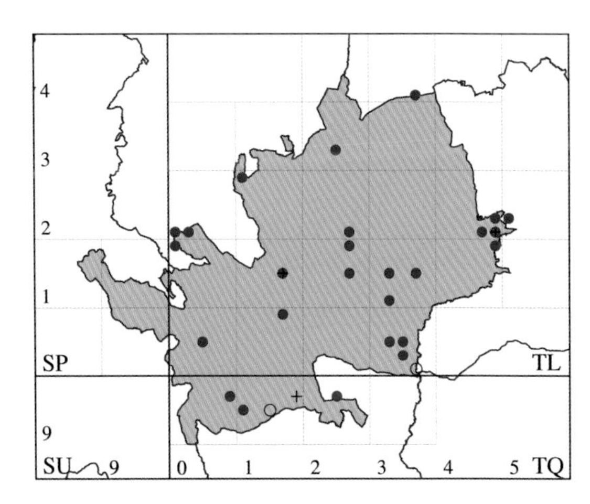

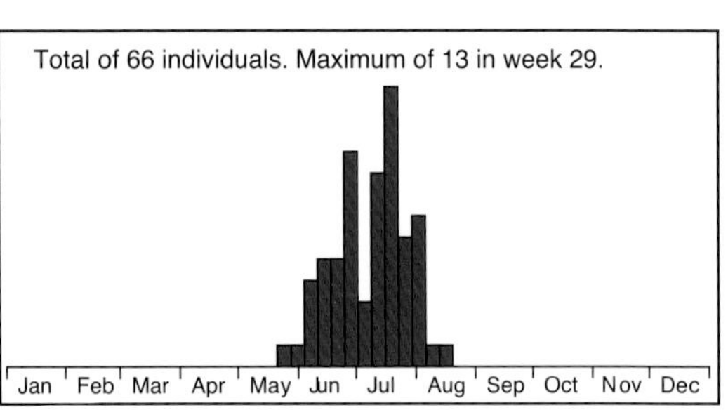

This is a numerically common species in most light traps in the county.

0774 *Teleiodes luculella* (Hb.)

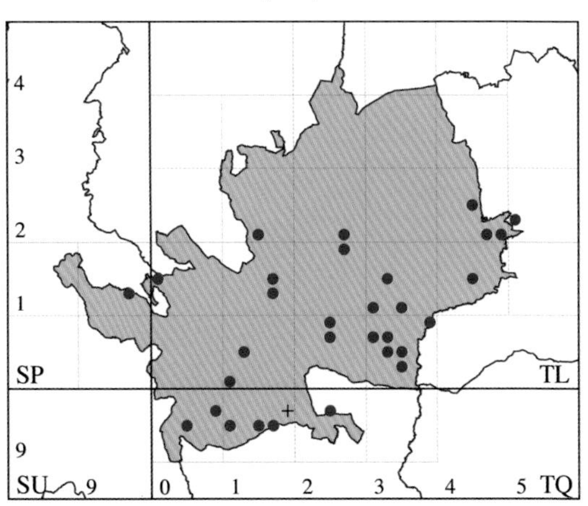

Recorded: 1834 – 2006
Distribution / Status: Widespread / Uncommon resident
Conservation status: No perceived threats
Caterpillar food plants: Elsewhere, on oaks
Flight period: May to July
Records in database: 46

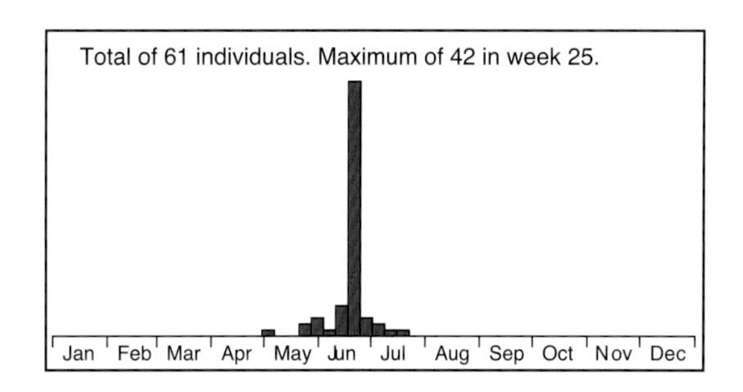

The larvae feed between spun leaves of oak trees and the adults can be found resting on oak trunks by day in the flight period.

0775 *Teleiodes sequax* (Haw.)

Recorded: 2000 only
Distribution / Status: Local / Rare resident
Conservation status: Herts Endangered
Caterpillar food plants: Elsewhere, on Common Rock Rose and Hoary Rock Rose
Flight period: Elsewhere, June to July
Records in database: 1

Rock rose is a scarce and threatened plant in Hertfordshire and it is no surprise that our only record of the moth, from Hexton Chalk Pit on 31st May 2000 (Raymond Uffen) relates to the chalky landscape of the north-west boundary. It may be present at other chalk downland sites and should be looked for at Aldbury Nowers, Therfield Heath and elsewhere.

0768 *Carpatolechia notatella* (Hb.)

Recorded: 1890 – 1978
Distribution / Status: Local or absent / Rare resident or extinct
Conservation status: Insufficient data
Caterpillar food plants: Common Sallow
Flight period: July
Records in database: 3

Our records are from the Sandridge area prior to 1890 (Griffith) and then Borehamwood on 7th July 1970 and 14th July 1978 (Eric Bradford). In recent years it has been found in Barnet (Middlesex) by Rachel Terry and is surely overlooked in our county?

0770 *Carpatolechia proximella* (Hb.)

Recorded: 1890 – 2004
Distribution / Status: Local / Uncommon resident
Conservation status: No perceived threats
Caterpillar food plants: Birch and Alder
Flight period: June. Elsewhere, May/June
Records in database: 3

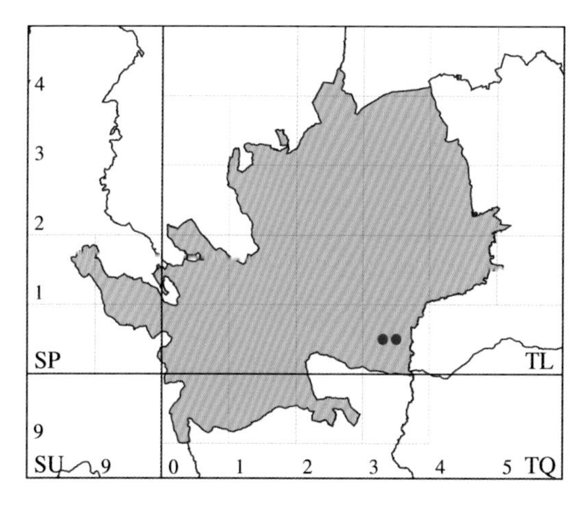

The two adjacent tetrads containing Thunderfield Grove both generated this species on 5th June 2004 (Mark Cooper); it will surely be present in several woodland areas of Hertfordshire.

0771 *Carpatolechia alburnella* (Zell.)

Recorded: 1970 – 1995
Distribution / Status: Local / Uncommon resident
Conservation status: No perceived threats
Caterpillar food plants: Elsewhere, on birch
Flight period: Elsewhere, June to September
Records in database: 3

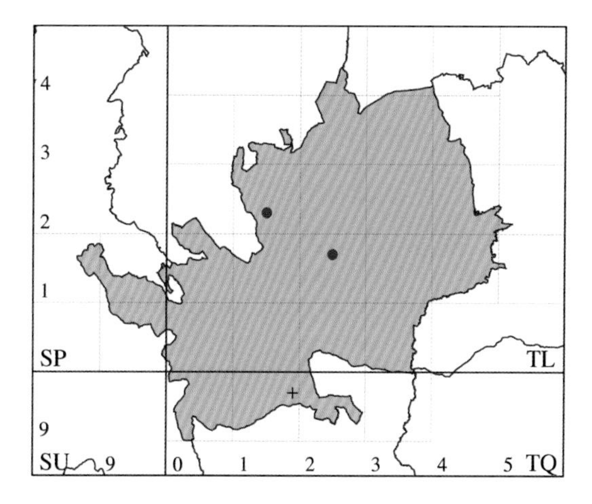

Our three records are from Borehamwood on 27th June 1970 (Eric Bradford), Breachwood Green in 1995 (Peter Alton) and Welwyn on 20th July 1995 (Raymond Uffen).

0772 *Carpatolechia fugitivella* (Zell.)

Recorded: 1901 – 2006
Distribution / Status: Local / Uncommon resident
Conservation status: No perceived threats
Caterpillar food plants: elm
Flight period: Elsewhere,
Records in database: 11

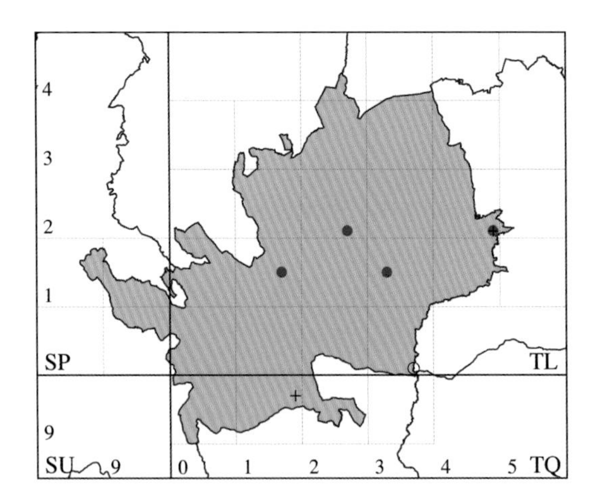

Repeated records year after year in my garden at Bishops Stortford suggest that the moth is not uncommon and, therefore, probably overlooked. The hedge that borders my garden contains Wych Elm.

0776 *Teleiopsis diffinis* (Haw.)

Recorded: 1906 – 2004
Distribution / Status: Local / Uncommon resident
Conservation status: Herts Vulnerable
Caterpillar food plants: Sheep's Sorrel
Flight period: Elsewhere,
Records in database: 4

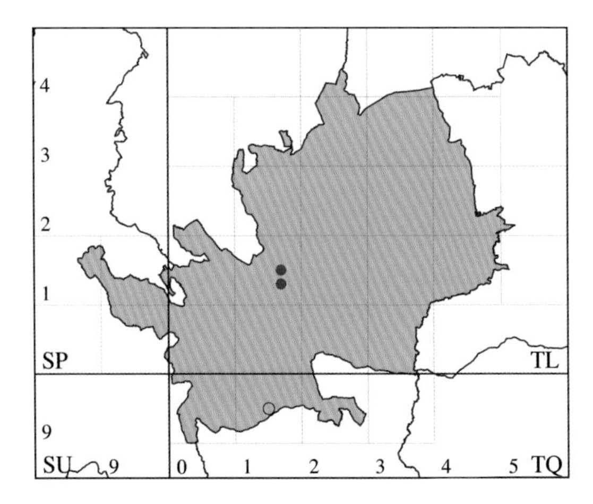

An example taken at light at Bushey Heath in 1906 by P. J. Barraud, was reported as new to Hertfordshire (Gibbs, 1907). More recently we have found it at Marshall's Heath in 1997 (John Murray) and Nomansland Common on 29th June 2004 (Raymond Uffen) and 28th August 2004 (myself) – the latter two in association with the foodplant.

0790 *Chionodes fumatella* (Douglas)

Recorded: 1974 only
Distribution / Status: Local or absent / Rare resident or extinct
Conservation status: Herts Extinct
Caterpillar food plants: Elsewhere, on Bird's-foot Trefoil
Flight period: No data. Elsewhere, July/August
Records in database: 1

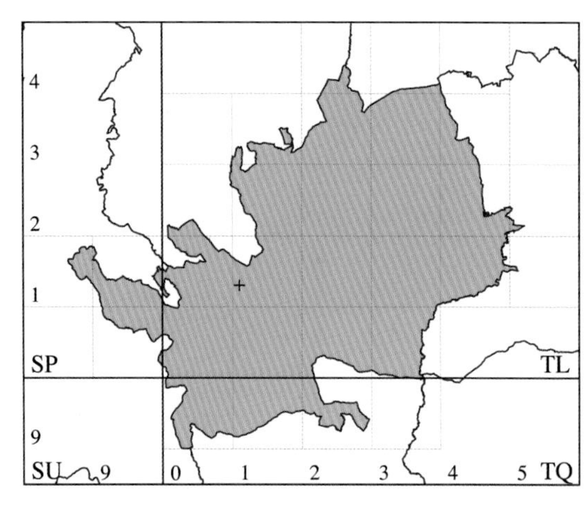

An example at the light trap on the Rothamsted Estate at Harpenden in 1974 (R. Fairclough) provides the only Hertfordshire record.

0791 *Chionodes distinctella* (Zell.)

Our only record is the mention of Hertfordshire on the distribution map in volume 4, part 2, of *Moths and Butterflies of Great Britain and Ireland*. The source of that record is a handwritten note by the late Maitland Emmet that reads 'Fairclough, 1974'. The name of the locality is indecipherable, but is a short word beginning with the letter B – it may well be Barnfield on the Rothamsted Estate at Harpendon.

0859 *Psoricoptera gibbosella* (Zell.)

Recorded: 1890 - 2004
Distribution / Status: Local / Uncommon resident
Conservation status: No perceived threats
Caterpillar food plants: oak
Flight period: Elsewhere, July to early October
Records in database: 4

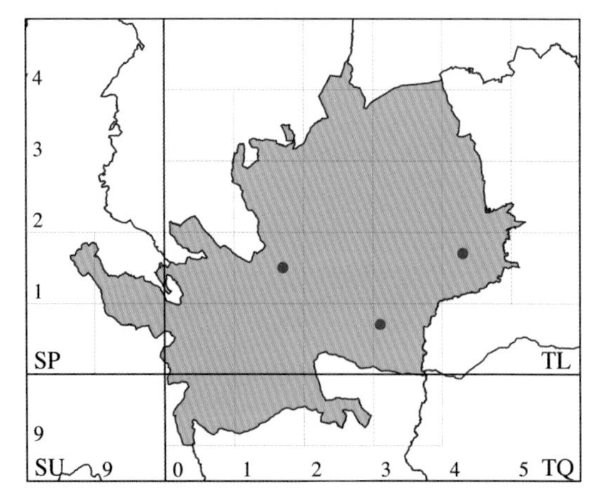

Likely to be under-recorded, in the southern half of the county at least where there are many suitable habitats.

0792 *Mirificarma mulinella* (Zell.)

Recorded: 1890 – 1969
Distribution / Status: Local / Uncommon resident
Conservation status: Insufficient data
Caterpillar food plants: Elsewhere, Gorse and Broom flowers
Flight period: Elsewhere,
Records in database: 4

Old records are from the Sandridge area (Griffith, 1890) and Broxbourne Wood (Boyd, 1901). Recent records are from Borehamwood on 24th and 29th August 1969 (Eric Bradford). The species is likely to be overlooked as it is not uncommon in the south-east of England.

0793 *Mirificarma lentiginosella* (Zell.)

Recorded: Pre-1890 only
Distribution / Status: Absent / Extinct
Conservation status: Herts Extinct
Caterpillar food plants: Not recorded. Elsewhere, on Dyer's Greenweed
Flight period: Not recorded. Elsewhere, July/August
Records in database: 1

Our only record is that given for the Sandridge area by Griffith (1890); there is insufficient detail to map the record. This is the source of the record in the distribution map in volume 4, part 2, of *Moths and Butterflies of Great Britain and Ireland*.

0796 *Aroga velocella* (Zell.)

Recorded: 2000 only
Distribution / Status: Local / Uncommon resident
Conservation status: Herts Vulnerable
Caterpillar food plants: Sheep's Sorrel
Flight period: Elsewhere, May and August
Records in database: 1

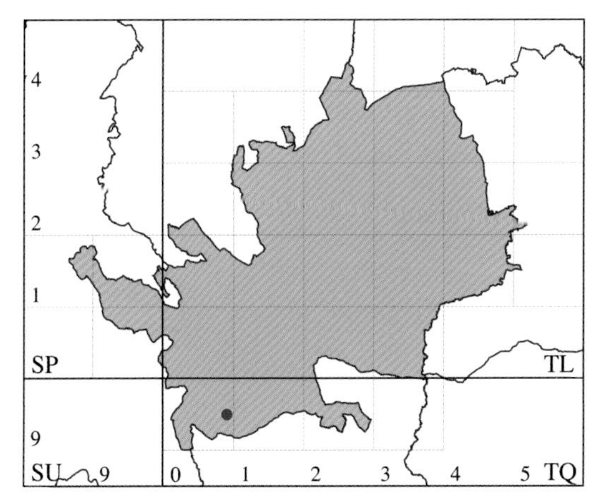

Larvae were found on Croxley Common Moor on 27th June 2000 (Raymond Uffen). Other acid grasslands in the county are quite likely to support this species, but the habitat is rare and so the survival of the moth here is threatened.

0799 *Neofriseria singula* (Stdgr.)

Recorded: 1980 – 2005
Distribution / Status: Extremely local / Rare resident
Conservation status: Herts Vulnerable
Caterpillar food plants: Sheep's Sorrel
Flight period: July. Elsewhere, June/July
Records in database: 3

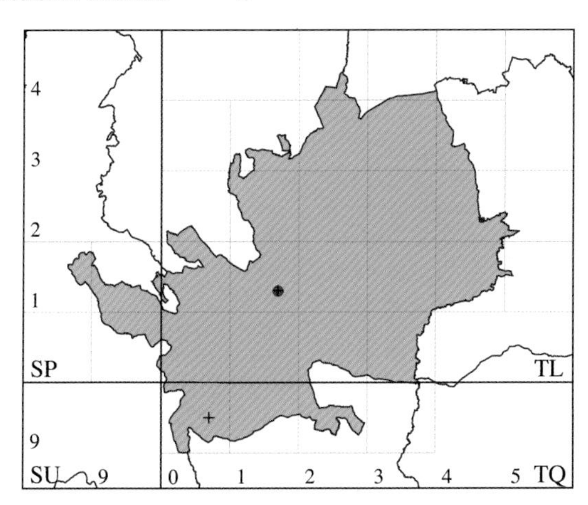

This is another species of acid grasslands, recorded at Nomansland Common and Croxley Common Moor (Raymond Uffen). The moths are easily disturbed at dusk by waving a net over the foodplant.

0800 *Gelechia rhombella* ([D.& S.])

Recorded: 1868 – 2003
Distribution / Status: Local / Uncommon resident
Conservation status: No perceived threats
Caterpillar food plants: Elsewhere, on apple and Pear
Flight period: July/August
Records in database: 8

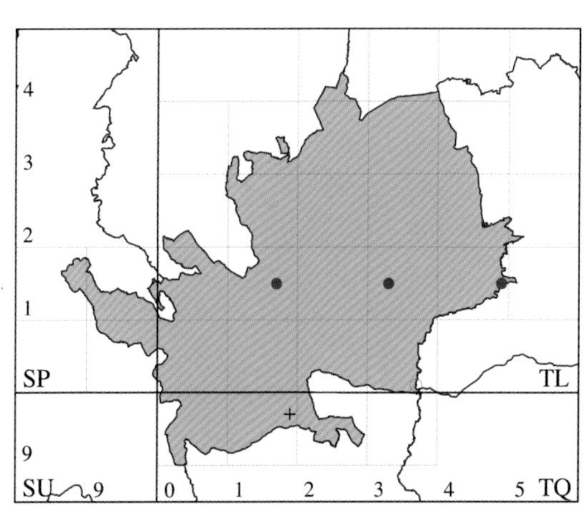

There is no real reason, other than under-recording, why this moth appears absent from large areas of Hertfordshire.

0801 *Gelechia scotinella* H.- S.

Recorded: 1971 – 2002
Distribution / Status: Local / Uncommon resident
Conservation status: No perceived threats
Caterpillar food plants: Elsewhere, on Blackthorn
Flight period: July/August
Records in database: 2

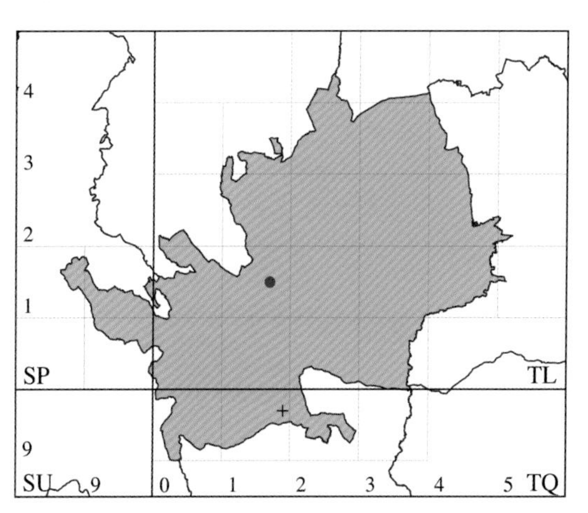

Our two records are from Borehamwood on 18th August 1971 (Eric Bradford) and Marshall's Heath on 20th July 2002 (John Murray).

0801a *Gelechia senticetella* Stdgr.

Recorded: 2000 – 2006
Distribution / Status: Local / Uncommon resident – spreading
Conservation status: No perceived threats
Caterpillar food plants: Elsewhere, on Juniper and cupressaceous trees
Flight period: July/August
Records in database: 18

This is an adventive species, probably having arrived with imported cypress and similar trees. It had arrived in Hertfordshire by 31st July 2000, when Steve Palmer recorded the first example in a light trap at Datchworth. Repeat catches in several garden traps indicate that the moth is now established here.

0802a *Gelechia sororculella* (Hb.)

Recorded: 1890 – 1966
Distribution / Status: Local or absent / Rare resident or extinct
Conservation status: Herts Extinct
Caterpillar food plants: Elsewhere, Goat Willow and Grey Willow
Flight period: Elsewhere, July/August
Records in database: 2

Apart from an example in the Sandridge area prior to 1890 (Griffith) we have a single record – from Stevenage on 6th August 1966 (Jack Newton).

0806 *Gelechia nigra* (Haw.)

Recorded: Pre-1890 only
Distribution / Status: Absent / Extinct
Conservation status: Herts Extinct
Caterpillar food plants: Elsewhere, on Aspen, White and Grey Poplar
Flight period: Elsewhere, June/July
Records in database: 1

Our only record is from the Sandridge area prior to 1890 (Griffith). There is insufficient detail to map the record.

0807 *Gelechia turpella* ([D.& S.])

Recorded: 1890 – 1900
Distribution / Status: Absent / Extinct
Conservation status: Herts Extinct
Caterpillar food plants: Elsewhere, Black and Lombardy Poplars
Flight period: Elsewhere, July
Records in database: 2

A rare and rather local species in south-east England, recorded from Hertfordshire in the Sandridge area prior to 1890 (Griffith) and the Cheshunt area prior to 1901 (Boyd).

0816 *Scrobipalpa obsoletella* (F. v. R.)

Recorded: 1970 – 2004
Distribution / Status: Local / Uncommon resident
Conservation status: Herts Vulnerable
Caterpillar food plants: Elsewhere, on Orache (and perhaps goosefoots)
Flight period: May to September in two generations
Records in database: 2

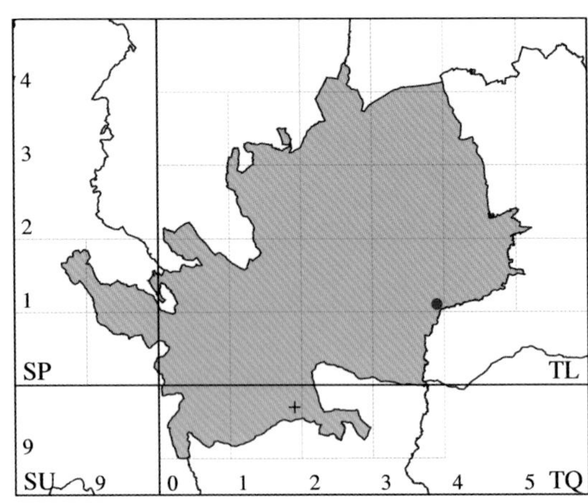

Old records may not be distinguishable from those of *Scrobipalpa nitentella*, but our two, from Borehamwood on 17th July 1970 (Eric Bradford) and Rye Meads on 5th August 2004 (Joan Childs) are reliable. *Scrobipalpa nitentella* is not, so far, recorded from the county.

0818 *Scrobipalpa atriplicella* (F. v. R.)

Recorded: 1901 – 1999
Distribution / Status: Local / Uncommon resident
Conservation status: Herts Vulnerable
Caterpillar food plants: Elsewhere, oraches and goosefoots
Flight period: Elsewhere, May then July/August
Records in database: 3

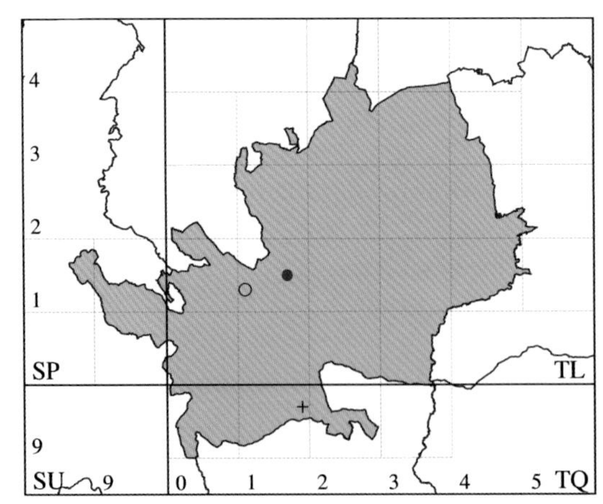

As with 816: *Scrobipalpa obsoletella*, this species can be confused with the as yet unrecorded (in Hertfordshire) *Scrobipalpa nitentella*. Our records from Borehamwood on 2nd August 1970 (Eric Bradford) and Marshall's Heath on 16th July 1999 are correct; I take the record from Harpenden in 1900 on trust since it has been accepted by the editors of *Moths and Butterflies of Great Britain and Ireland* and is the source of the Hertfordshire map dot for this species in volume 4, part 2.

0819 *Scrobipalpa costella* (H.& W.)

Recorded: 1969 – 2006
Distribution / Status: Widespread / Common resident
Conservation status: No perceived threats
Caterpillar food plants: Woody Nightshade
Flight period: March to November
Records in database: 109

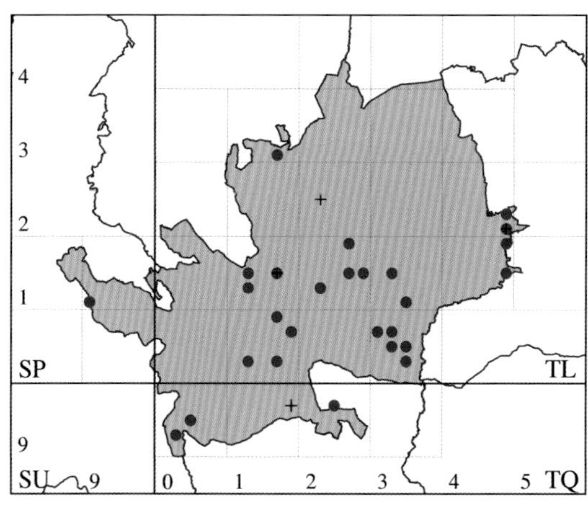

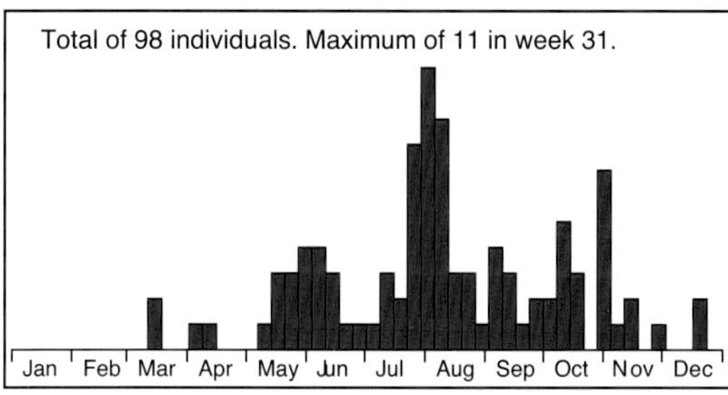

The caterpillar makes distinctive mines on the leaves of the foodplant. National texts suggest that there may be more than one generation per year over a protracted period; the Hertfordshire data seem to be suggesting that there are in fact three generations per year here.

0822 *Scrobipalpa acuminatella* (Sircom)

Recorded:	1890 – 2005
Distribution / Status:	Widespread / Uncommon resident
Conservation status:	No perceived threats
Caterpillar food plants:	Creeping thistle. Elsewhere, also on other thistles and Knapweed
Flight period:	Elsewhere, May/June
Records in database:	10

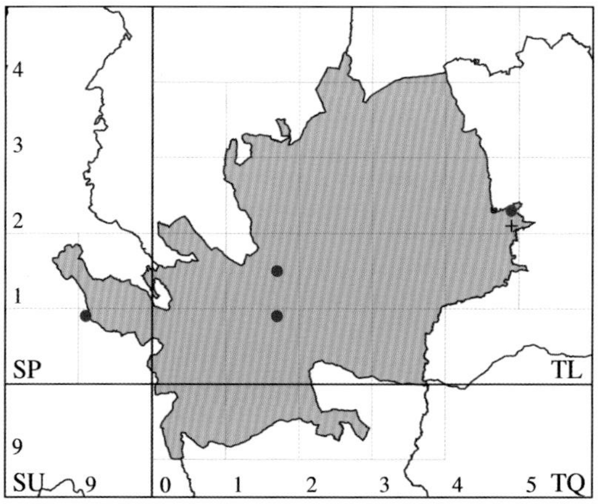

Caterpillars mine the leaves of thistles and are fairly easy to find. The species is regarded as very much under-recorded because few people engage in careful searching for mines; it is likely to be widespread.

0825 *Phthorimaea operculella* (Zell.) Potato Tuber Moth

Recorded:	1970 only
Distribution / Status:	Local / Rare adventive or perhaps immigrant
Conservation status:	Herts Extinct
Caterpillar food plants:	Potato (imported)
Flight period:	No data
Records in database:	1

Our only record is from Eric Bradford's former garden at Borehamwood on 24th April 1970. Wild-caught adults require dissection for correct identification.

0830 *Caryocolum fraternella* (Douglas)

Recorded:	1890 – 2004
Distribution / Status:	Local / Uncommon resident
Conservation status:	No perceived threats
Caterpillar food plants:	Elsewhere, stitchworts and mouse-ears
Flight period:	Elsewhere, July/August
Records in database:	5

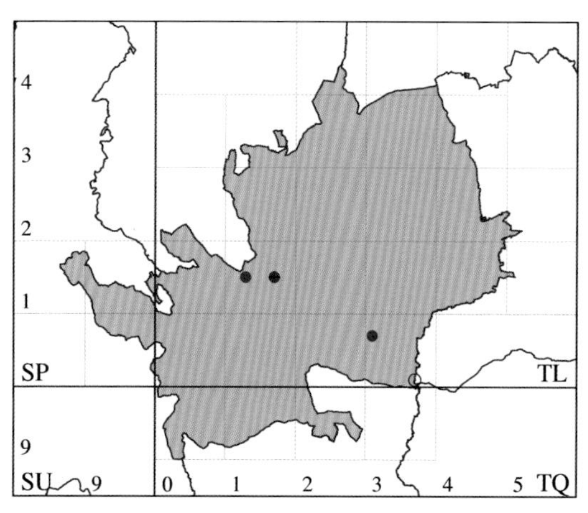

A damp grassland species, this moth is likely to be overlooked in many places in the county.

0831 *Caryocolum proximum* (Haw.)

Recorded:	1890 – 1963
Distribution / Status:	Local / Uncommon resident
Conservation status:	Herts Extinct
Caterpillar food plants:	Elsewhere, stitchworts and mouse-ears
Flight period:	Elsewhere, July/August
Records in database:	2

Our only relatively recent record is from Borehamwood in 1963 (Eric Bradford); an older record heralds from Sandridge area (Griffith, 1890). It is a widespread but local grassland species in southern Britain and is probably overlooked in Hertfordshire.

0832 *Caryocolum blandella* (Douglas)

Recorded:	1890 – 2004
Distribution / Status:	Local / Uncommon resident
Conservation status:	No perceived threats
Caterpillar food plants:	Elsewhere, on Greater Stitchwort
Flight period:	Mid-June to August
Records in database:	9

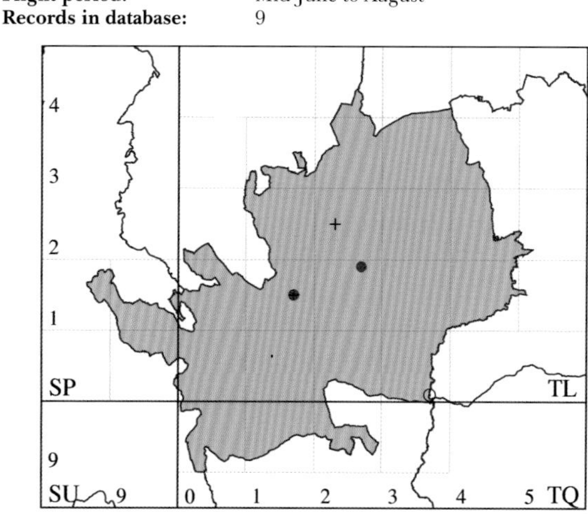

Careful searching in the southern Hertfordshire woodlands is likely to turn up this species.

0834 *Caryocolum tricolorella* (Haw.)

Recorded:	1890 – 1977
Distribution / Status:	Local / Uncommon resident
Conservation status:	Insufficient data
Caterpillar food plants:	Elsewhere, Greater Stitchwort
Flight period:	Elsewhere, July to September
Records in database:	5

Apart from the Sandridge area prior to 1890 (Griffith) and Stevenage on 21 June 1966 (Jack Newton), the only other area of the county to support this species at the moment seems to be the Broxbourne complex of woodlands, where it was last seen in 1977.

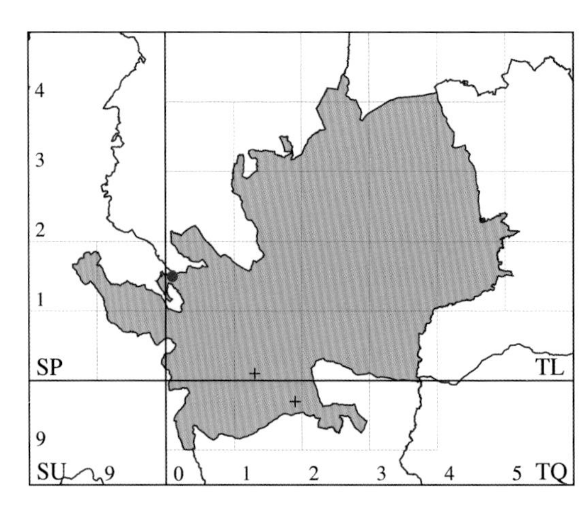

The only record since the 1960s was made at Ravensdell Wood on 23rd July 1997 by David Manning.

0836 *Caryocolum kroesmanniella* (H.- S.) = *huebneri* auctorum

Recorded:	1966 only
Distribution / Status:	Absent / Extinct
Conservation status:	Herts Extinct
Caterpillar food plants:	Elsewhere, Greater and Bog Stitchworts
Flight period:	Elsewhere, July/August
Records in database:	1

An entry stating 'Stevenage – larva on 16 April 1966, adult on 14 June 1966' is present in a hand written list of moths from an unknown address in Stevenage by Jack Newton, where it was listed as '*huebneri*'. *Caryocolum huebneri* is now very probably extinct in Britain, although many old records are misidentified *kroesmanniella*. The adult specimen is in the Natural History Museum in London and was examined by David Agassiz and Klaus Sattler in March 2005 who state that the identification as *kroesmanniella* is correct.

ANACAMPSINAE

0841 *Sophronia semicostella* (Hb.)

Recorded:	1890 – 2003
Distribution / Status:	Local / Uncommon resident
Conservation status:	Herts Rare
Caterpillar food plants:	No data. In Europe on Sweet Vernal Grass
Flight period:	June/July
Records in database:	5

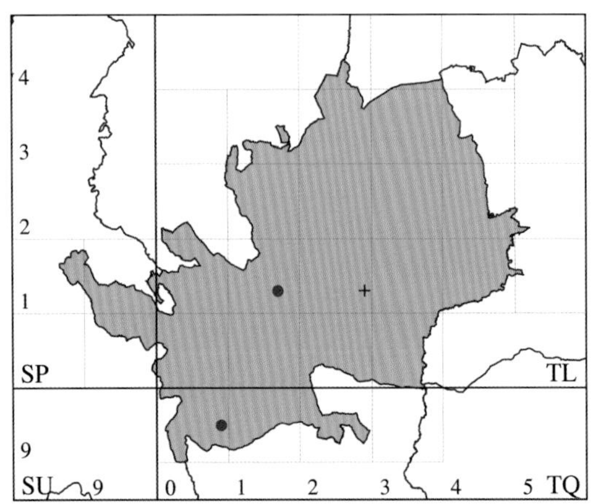

Sandridge prior to 1890 (Griffith), Panshanger Park in 1994 and Nomansland Common in 1999 and 2000 (Raymond Uffen) and Croxley Common Moor in 2003 (myself) are the only reports.

0843 *Aproaerema anthyllidella* (Hb.)

Recorded:	1890 – 1997
Distribution / Status:	Local / Uncommon resident
Conservation status:	Herts Rare
Caterpillar food plants:	Elsewhere, mainly on Kidney Vetch and also other herbaceous Fabaceae
Flight period:	Elsewhere, May/June and August/September
Records in database:	4

0844 *Syncopacma larseniella* (Gozm.)

Recorded:	1970 – 2006
Distribution / Status:	Local / Uncommon resident
Conservation status:	Insufficiently known
Caterpillar food plants:	Elsewhere, on Greater and Common Bird's-foot Trefoils
Flight period:	June/July
Records in database:	7

Separation from 849: *Syncopacma cinctella* requires dissection of genitalia and so an old record listed as *larseniella* from Beaumont Green, near Wormley, prior to 1901 cannot be accepted and is not mapped. The first confirmed record is from Borehamwood in 1970 (Eric Bradford).

0847 *Syncopacma taeniolella* (Zell.)

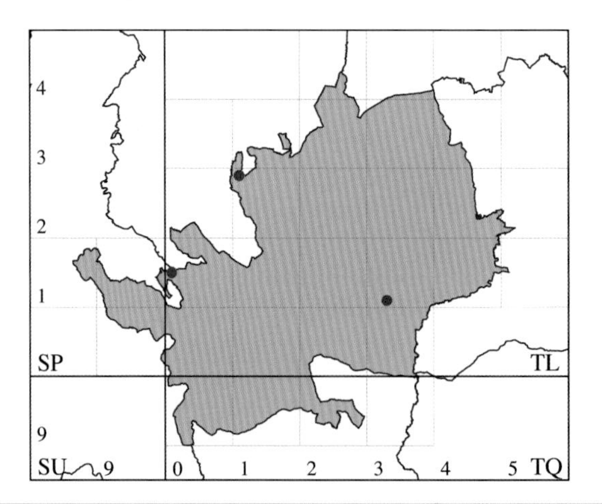

Recorded: 1890 – 2001
Distribution / Status: Local / Uncommon resident
Conservation status: Insufficiently known
Caterpillar food plants: Elsewhere, on Greater and Common Bird's-foot Trefoils
Flight period: July
Records in database: 4

The continuous white band on the underside of the forewing allows this species to be separated from the others in the genus.

0848 *Syncopacma albipalpella* (H.- S.)

Recorded: 1985 – 2003
Distribution / Status: Extremely local / Rare resident
Conservation status: UK BAP Priority Species
Herts Endangered
Caterpillar food plants: Petty Whin
Flight period: July
Records in database: 2

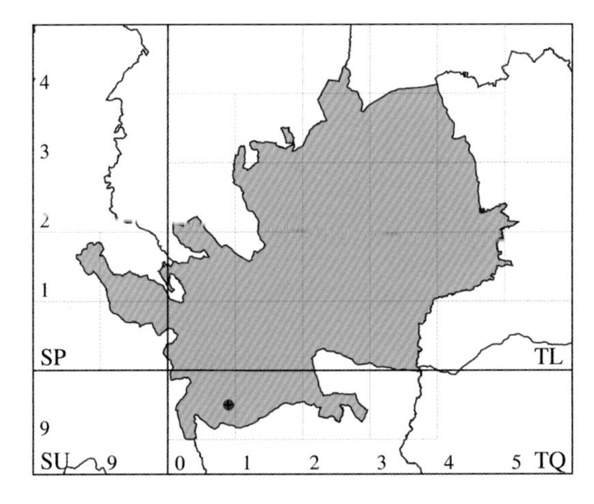

The only site in Britain for this species is near Watford, in Hertfordshire; elsewhere in the country the last reliable record was made in 1973. The foodplant appears to be on the decline at the Hertfordshire site, a process that probably began with cessation of grazing during a foot and mouth disease epidemic, and in 2002 Raymond Uffen found just three larval spinnings on plants on drier ground. During 2003 he found just two larval spinnings, both either damaged or parasitised, and commented that the moth seems unlikely to survive on this site. The moth is protected at the site, but we are aware of specific trips being made to collect this species here; we can only assume that the people concerned were not aware of its extremely precarious nature. There is no doubt that collecting the larval spinnings of this species at its Hertfordshire site is likely to cause the species to become extinct in the British Isles and it is hoped that entomologists will respect this fact. There is urgent need for funding to undertake autecological studies on this Priority Species within the UK Biodiversity Action Plan.

0849 *Syncopacma cinctella* (Cl.)

Recorded: 1972 only
Distribution / Status: Local / Uncommon resident
Conservation status: Herts Extinct
Caterpillar food plants: Elsewhere, on Greater and Common Bird's-foot Trefoils
Flight period: Elsewhere, July
Records in database: 1

Confusion with 844: *Syncopacma larseniella* has been discussed under that species. Our only record of *cinctella* is from Wormley Wood in 1972 (David Agassiz).

0853 *Anacampsis populella* (Cl.)

Recorded: 1995 – 2006
Distribution / Status: Local / Common resident
Conservation status: No perceived threats
Caterpillar food plants: Poplar, Aspen and willow
Flight period: July to mid September
Records in database: 12

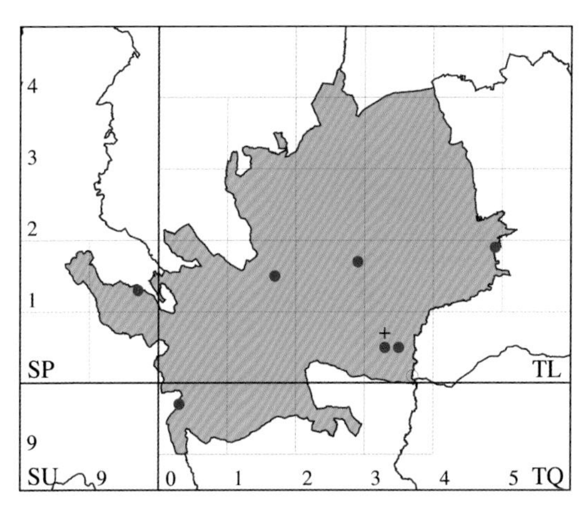

Dissection of a large number of 'identified' specimens has shown clearly that both this species and the next, 854: *Anacampsis blattariella* are not separable in any of their allegedly distinctive forms without genitalia examination. For this reason all old records of adults are omitted from the map unless specimens have been dissected.

0854 *Anacampsis blattariella* (Hb.)

Recorded: 1969 – 2006
Distribution / Status: Local / Common resident
Conservation status: No perceived threats
Caterpillar food plants: Birch
Flight period: July to mid September
Records in database: 8

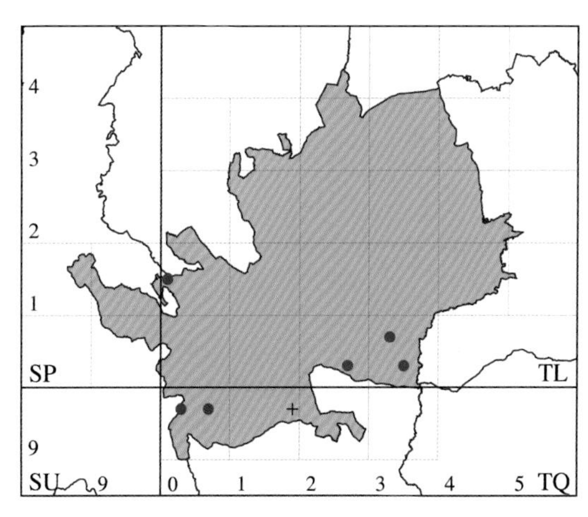

Confusion with 853: *Anacampsis populella* has been mentioned under that heading and old records of adults of the present species are not mapped here. The larvae feed on a different foodplant.

CHELARIINAE

0797 *Neofaculta ericetella* (Geyer)

Recorded: 1890 - 2000
Distribution / Status: Very local / Herts Uncommon resident
Conservation status: Vulnerable
Caterpillar food plants: Elsewhere, Heather, Bell Heather and Cross-leaved Heath
Flight period: May/June
Records in database: 4

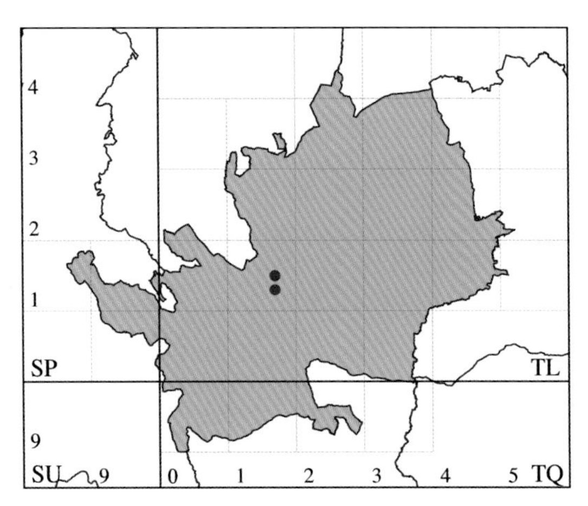

The scarcity of the foodplant will be an important factor in the distribution of this species in Hertfordshire.

0855 *Acompsia cinerella* (Cl.)

Recorded: 1834 – 2000
Distribution / Status: Local / Uncommon resident
Conservation status: Herts Scarce
Caterpillar food plants: Elsewhere, on mosses
Flight period: June/July
Records in database: 6

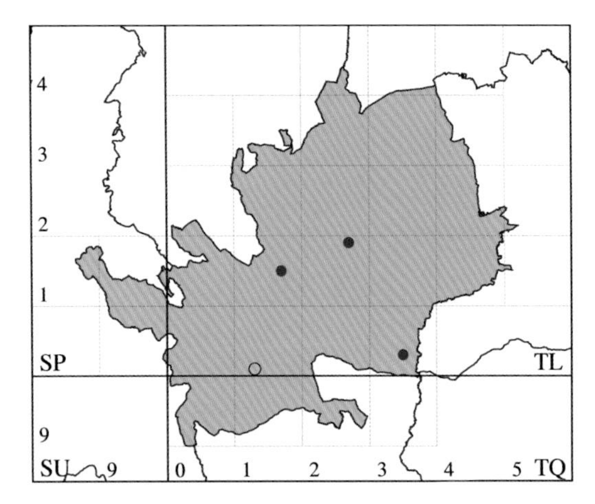

Most records are from light traps and as more people take up the study of micros the number of records is likely to increase.

0856 *Anarsia spartiella* (Schrank)

Recorded: 1890 – 1901
Distribution / Status: Absent / Extinct
Conservation status: Unknown
Caterpillar food plants: Elsewhere, on Gorse, Broom and Dyer's Greenweed
Flight period: Elsewhere, June to August
Records in database: 2

The Sandridge area, prior to 1890 (Griffith) and the Cheshunt area prior to 1901 (Boyd) provide our only records.

0858 *Hypatima rhomboidella* (L.)

Recorded: 1834 – 2006
Distribution / Status: Widespread / Common resident
Conservation status: No perceived threats
Caterpillar food plants: Hornbeam. Elsewhere, on birch and Hazel
Flight period: June to October
Records in database: 30

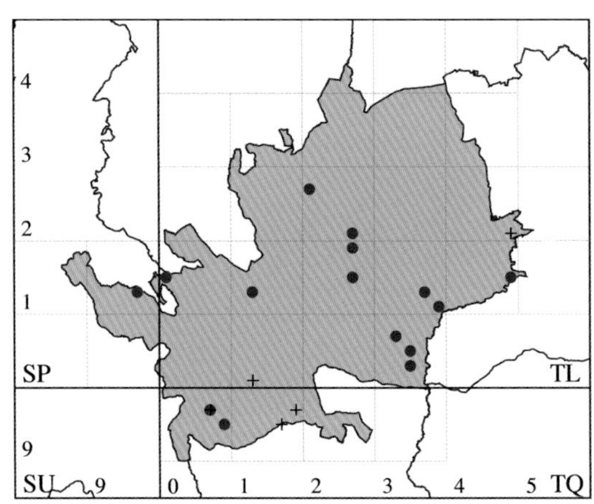

An unusually early adult was taken at light in Astonbury Wood on 16th June 2003; otherwise the expected flight period of August and September is observed, occasionally drifting into October. Hornbeam appears to be a previously unreported foodplant.

DICHOMERIDINAE

0861 *Acompsia schmidtiellus* (Heyd.)

Recorded: 1953 only
Distribution / Status: Extremely local or absent / Rare resident or extinct
Conservation status: Herts Extinct
Caterpillar food plants: Elsewhere, on Marjoram
Flight period: Elsewhere, July/August
Records in database: 1

Although our only record is from Welwyn, in 1953, the moth may be locally resident on the chalk grassland in the north-west of the county along the border with Bedfordshire and Buckinghamshire and should be searched for there.

0862 *Dichomeris marginella* (Fabr.)

Recorded: 1890 – 2006
Distribution / Status: Local / Common resident
Conservation status: No perceived threats
Caterpillar food plants: Juniper
Flight period: June to August
Records in database: 46

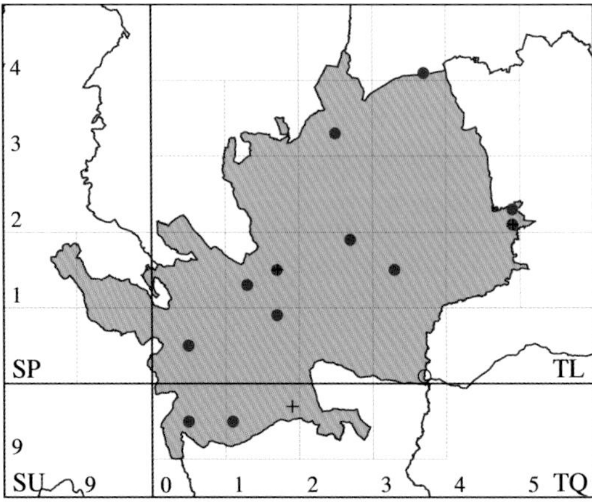

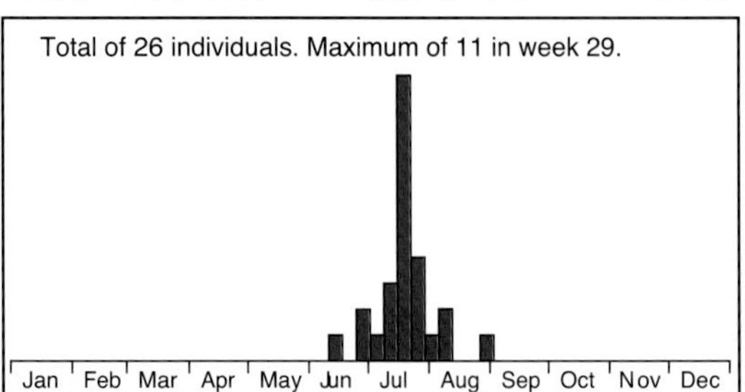

The ability of the caterpillar to thrive on garden cultivars of Juniper probably allows this moth to spread across the county; native Juniper is restricted to a few places in the west. The possibility that the moth may have adapted to feeding on imported Cupressaceae should not be overlooked.

0866 *Brachmia blandella* (Fabr.)

Recorded: 1973 – 2006
Distribution / Status: Local / Common resident
Conservation status: No perceived threats
Caterpillar food plants: Unknown.
Flight period: Late June to early August
Records in database: 20

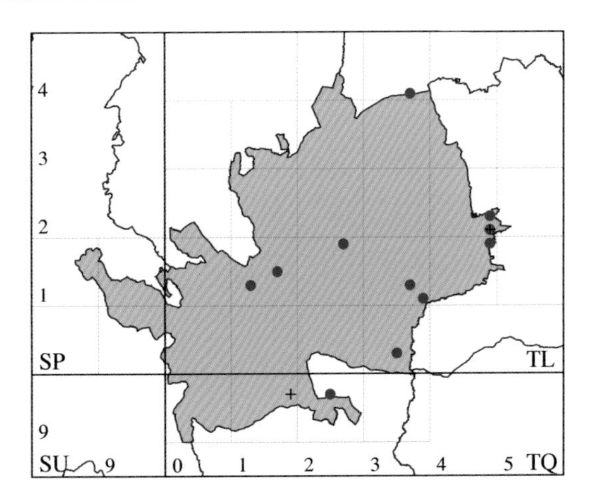

This is a common moth in Hertfordshire, but confusion exists over the true nature of its foodplant in Britain.

0868 *Helcystogramma rufescens* (Haw.)

Recorded: 1890 – 2006
Distribution / Status: Widespread / Common resident
Conservation status: No perceived threats
Caterpillar food plants: Elsewhere, on grasses
Flight period: Mid-june to mid-August
Records in database: 62

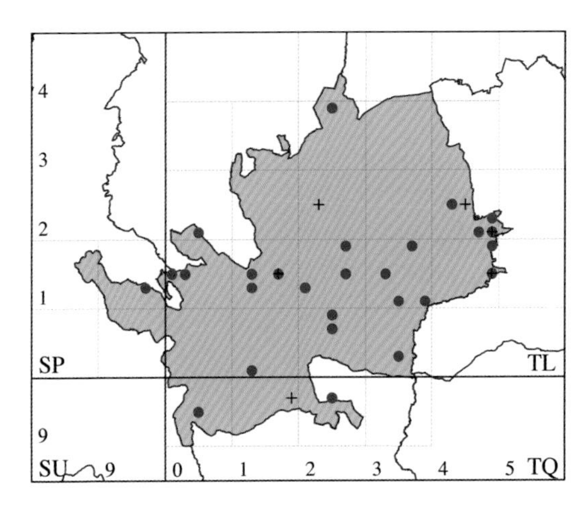

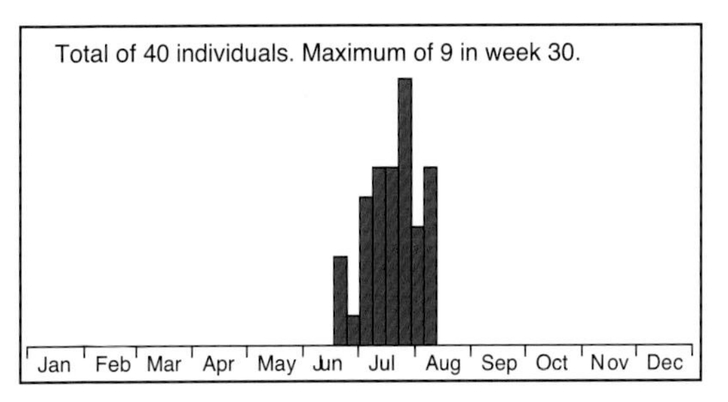

Adults are attracted easily to light and most records emanate from this source.

PEXICOPIINAE

0808 *Platyedra subcinerea* (Haw.)

Recorded: 1994 – 2004
Distribution / Status: Local / Uncommon resident
Conservation status: Herts Scarce
Caterpillar food plants: Elsewhere, on Mallow and Garden Hollyhock
Flight period: No data. Elsewhere, August to June
Records in database: 4

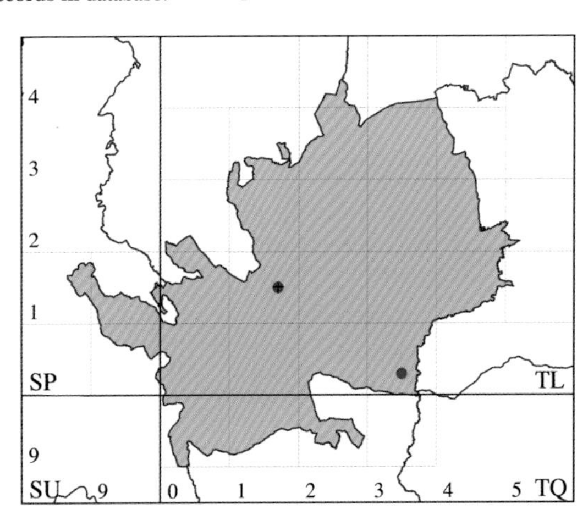

The adults overwinter in thatch where available, but in substitutes such as birds' nests where it is not.

0809 *Pexicopia malvella* (Hb.)

Recorded: 1900 – 2006
Distribution / Status: Local / Uncommon resident
Conservation status: Herts Rare
Caterpillar food plants: Elsewhere, on Mallow and Garden Hollyhock
Flight period: Elsewhere, June to August
Records in database: 2

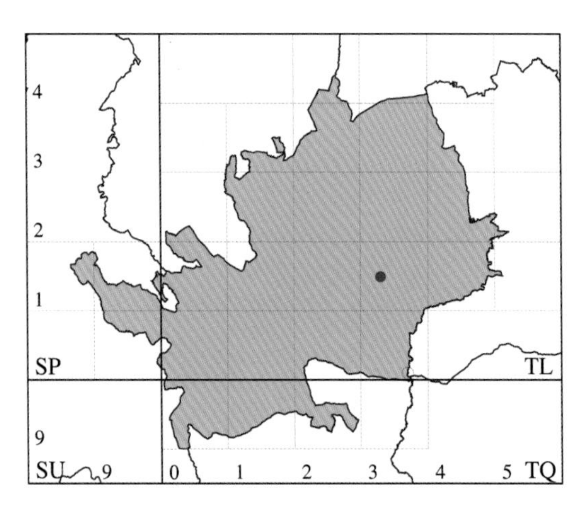

A record from Andrew Wood's garden moth trap in the Bengeo district of Hertford on 28th June 2006 demonstrates the under-recorded nature of many micro moths in the county – the only other record was made prior to 1901, at Cheshunt.

0840 *Thiotricha subocellea* (Steph.) = *Reuttia subocellea* (Steph.)

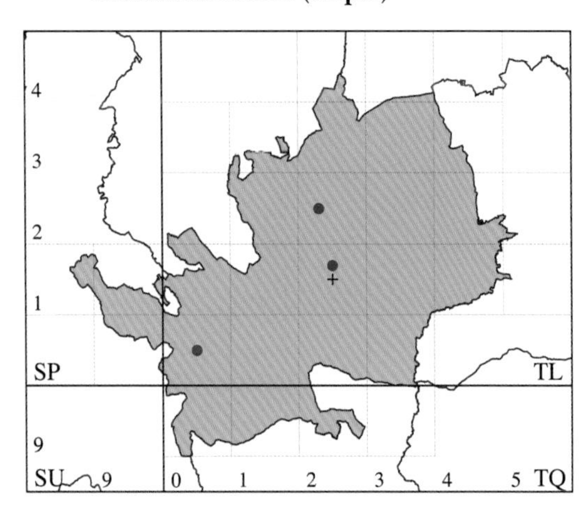

Recorded:	1985 - 2004
Distribution / Status:	Local / Uncommon resident
Conservation status:	Herts Scarce
Caterpillar food plants:	Marjoram.
Flight period:	July. Elsewhere, also August
Records in database:	5

A female was observed egg-laying on Marjoram at Digswell in July 1985 (Raymond Uffen). Adults are reputedly most easily recorded by gently using a sweep net on the food plant.

AUTOSTICHIDAE

Originally included in the family Gelechiidae, these few species are now treated separately. One obvious difference is their lack of a falcate hind wing. Three of the four British species are recorded for Hertfordshire, all in genus *Oegoconia*. Positive separation of the adults requires examination of the genitalia in both sexes and my insistence on this accounts for the quite recent 'first year' given for each species.

0870 *Oegoconia quadripuncta* (Haw.)

Recorded:	1997 - 2006
Distribution / Status:	Widespread / Common resident
Conservation status:	No perceived threats
Caterpillar food plants:	Not recorded. Elsewhere, on dead and decaying plant and animal matter
Flight period:	Late June to early September
Records in database:	24

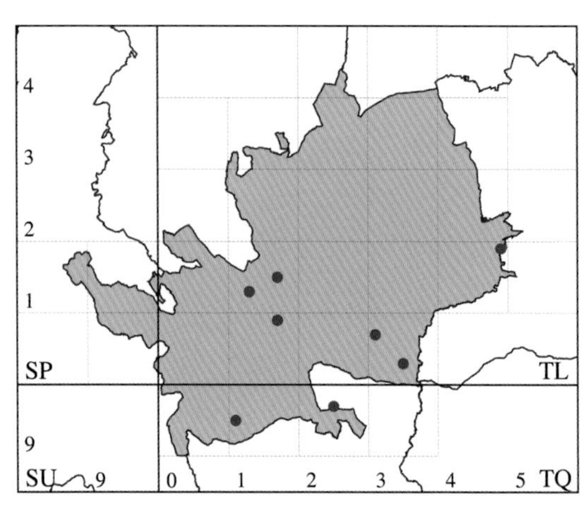

All of the records for Hertfordshire are from light traps and most reports are of single examples.

0871 *Oegoconia deauratella* (H.- S.)

Recorded:	1997 - 2006
Distribution / Status:	Widespread / Common resident
Conservation status:	No perceived threats
Caterpillar food plants:	Not recorded. Elsewhere, on dead and decaying plant and animal matter
Flight period:	Late June to end of July
Records in database:	46

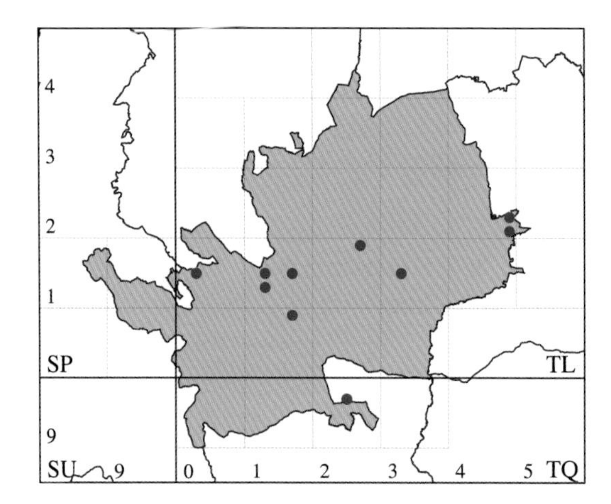

Most records are from light traps and this appears to be, numerically, the more common of the three species.

0871a *Oegoconia caradjai* Popescu-Gorj & Căpuşe

Recorded:	2000 - 2004
Distribution / Status:	Local / Uncommon resident
Conservation status:	Herts Scarce
Caterpillar food plants:	Not recorded. Elsewhere, on dead and decaying plant and animal matter
Flight period:	Late June to mid-August
Records in database:	7

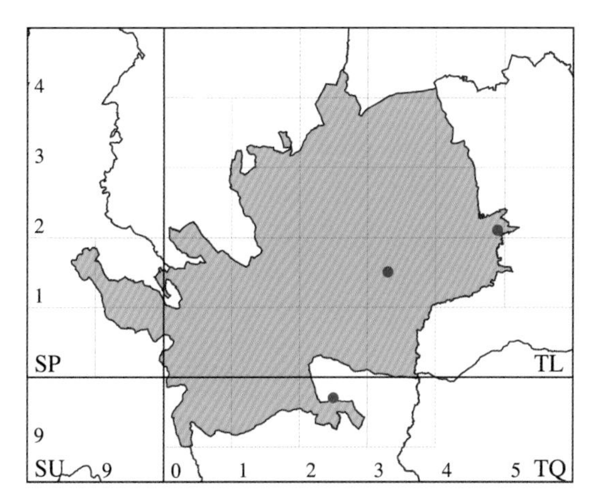

Clearly the least encountered of this trio of species and, so far, never in numbers greater than one. This species was only recently recognized as being British (Agassiz, 1982), emphasising the need to dissect all adults in order to identify them properly.

BLASTOBASIDAE

This is a much under-studied group of moths, treated by past authors as a subfamily within the Coleophoridae (the abdominal segments supports combs of bristles – something that will be familiar to anyone who has ever dissected a *Coleophora*). Because they are under-studied it will come as no surprise to learn that the names with which many of us have become familiar (*lignea* and *decolorella*) are incorrectly applied and have been replaced. Two of the three British species are found in Hertfordshire – both as quite recent colonists.

0873 *Blastobasis adustella* Walsingham
= *lignea* Walsingham

Recorded:	1966 – 2006
Distribution / Status:	Ubiquitous / Abundant resident
Conservation status:	No perceived threats
Caterpillar food plants:	Holm Oak leaves; 'dry, dead leaves'
Flight period:	July to September
Records in database:	368

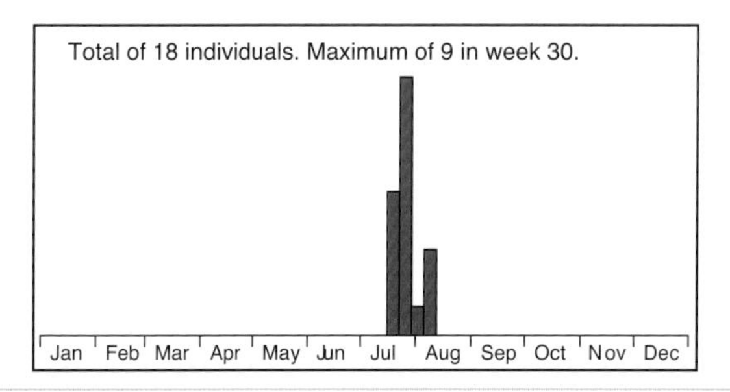

The geographical origin of the British population is unclear, though the species is absent from Europe and the nearest other population is on Madeira. In the British Isles it was found in Ireland in 1902 and Lancashire in 1917 (Agassiz, 1996). It did not reach the south-east until later, but by the 1970s appears to have become well-established there. The first Hertfordshire record was at Borehamwood in 1966 (Eric Bradford), but a lack of active moth recorders in the county in the 1960s, 1970s an early 1980s means that we are not able to understand the speed or direction of its spread. Live leaves of Holm Oak containing nepticulid mines, picked by me in April 2007 at Bricketwood Common and immediately sealed in a plastic 'food container' produced two adult *B. lignea* in July 2007. The pupal cases were later found spun up between two layers of tissue.

0874 *Blastobasis lacticolella* Rebel
= *decolorella* (Woll.)

Recorded:	1987 – 2006
Distribution / Status:	Ubiquitous / Abundant resident
Conservation status:	No perceived threats
Caterpillar food plants:	Dried vegetable matter
Flight period:	Late May to November
Records in database:	144

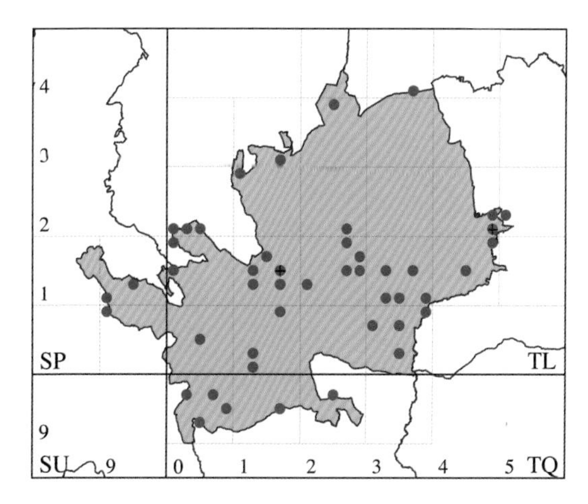

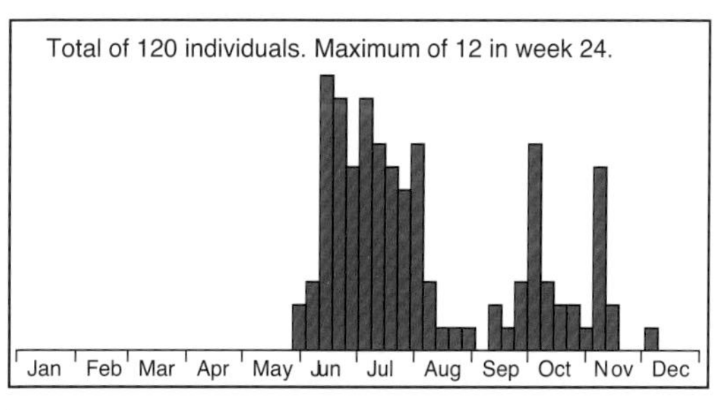

As with the last species, the source of British individuals is probably the island of Madeira, but *lacticolella* did not reach Britain until 1946, when it was found in south-east London

(Wakely, 1947). Our first Hertfordshire record was not until 1987 when I found it in my garden light trap in Bishops Stortford, but it was probably established earlier, because that was my first full year in residence in the county and apart from Raymond Uffen, whose stalwart efforts have produced many new species for the county list, it appears that there were no other microlepidopterists in the county since the departure of Eric Bradford in the late 1960s. We were able to define the species as 'expected everywhere' by the year 2002, but in truth it had probably reached this abundance by about 2000.

BATRACHEDRIDAE

The family was originally included within the Momphidae and comprises mainly tropical species with only six in the Palaearctic Region. Of these, three are found in Britain and two of these are recorded in Hertfordshire. The third is known from a single specimen in Cornwall during 1991. The long, pointed and very narrow wings are a diagnostic feature of the group.

0878 *Batrachedra praeangusta* (Haw.)

Recorded:	1890 – 2006
Distribution / Status:	Local / Common resident
Conservation status:	No perceived threats
Caterpillar food plants:	Not recorded. Elsewhere, on willow, sallow and poplar
Flight period:	July/ August. Elsewhere early June to September
Records in database:	15

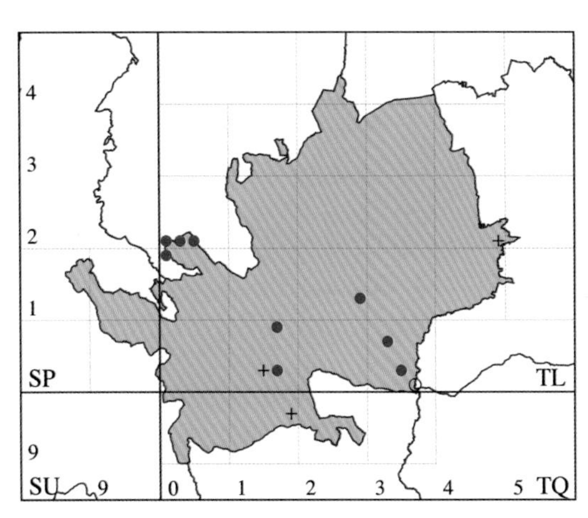

The caterpillar feeds inside the catkins earlier in the year and adults can be shaken out of the foodplant, although all of the Hertfordshire records are of adults, mainly from light traps.

0879 *Batrachedra pinicolella* (Zell.)

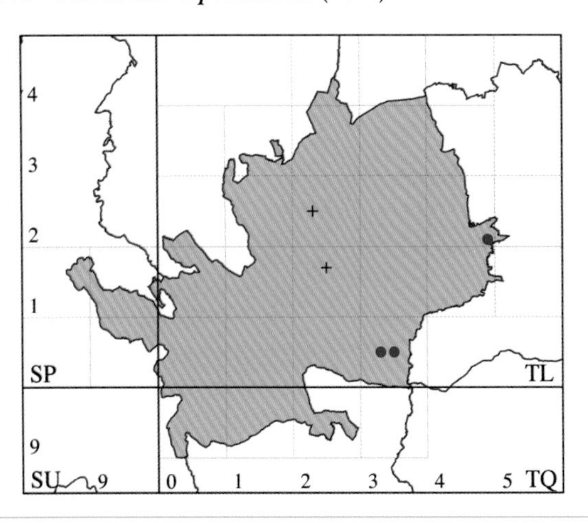

Recorded:	1965 – 2004
Distribution / Status:	Local / Uncommon resident
Conservation status:	Herts Rare
Caterpillar food plants:	Not recorded. Elsewhere, on Norway Spruce
Flight period:	Mid-June to August
Records in database:	6

This seems to be a far less frequent moth than the previous species, though both come readily to light. The distribution reflects a marked absence of the foodplant from much of the county.

MOMPHIDAE

In the strict sense, the family Momphidae contains in Britain only those species in the genus *Mompha*, whilst others formerly included are now housed in the families Batrachedridae and Cosmopterigidae. Of the fifteen British species of *Mompha* we have eleven confirmed as having occurred in Hertfordshire, and a twelfth that requires confirmation. Of the three that are missing, two are less frequent in the south-east but one is probably overlooked and awaits discovery here. Adult momphids have a characteristic shape when at rest, which immediately gives them away, but specific identification of some requires dissection. Rearing from the early stages is relatively easy to achieve. The larval mines and galls are accurately drawn in volume 4 (part 1) of *Moths and butterflies of Great Britain and Ireland*, which also illustrates the adults, and there are larger pictures of the adults in volume 5 of *Microlepidoptera of Europe* (Koster & Sinev, 2003).

0880 *Mompha langiella* (Hb.)

Recorded:	1868 – 1994
Distribution / Status:	Local / Rare resident
Conservation status:	Herts Extinct
Caterpillar food plants:	Enchanter's Nightshade. Elsewhere, also on Greater and Broad-leaved Willowherbs
Flight period:	July. Elsewhere, August to April/May
Records in database:	4

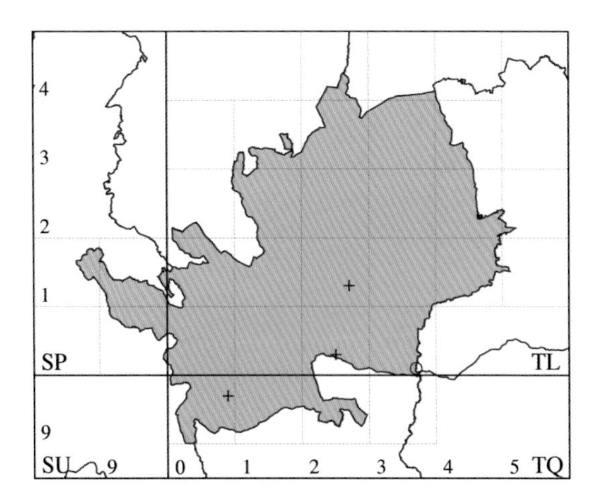

Our earliest record is from Cheshunt in 1868 recorded by W. C. Boyd in *Entomologist's Monthly Magazine* **5**: 147. Our latest is from Tewin Mill on 21st July 1994 by Raymond Uffen. In between there are reports of mines in Enchanter's Nightshade at Casiobury Park and Gobions Wood in Brookmans Park.

0883 *Mompha raschkiella* (Zell.)

Recorded:	1890 – 2006
Distribution / Status:	Widespread / Common resident
Conservation status:	No perceived threats
Caterpillar food plants:	Rosebay Willow-herb
Flight period:	May and August
Records in database:	31

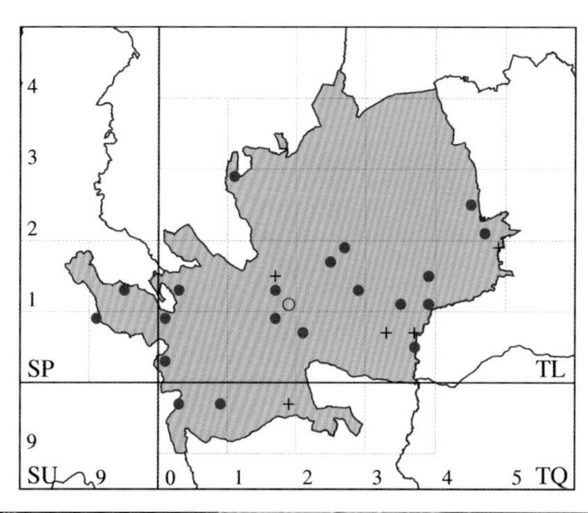

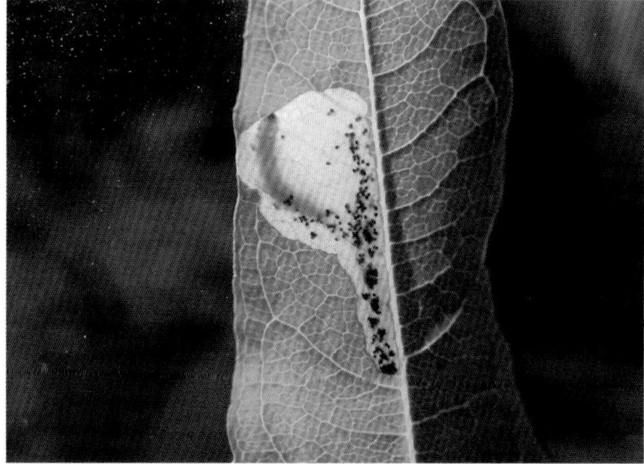

The distinctive mines made by the larvae of this moth in the leaves of Rosebay Willowherb account for most of the county's records of this rather attractive little moth.

0884 *Mompha miscella* ([D.& S.])

Recorded:	1902 – 2006
Distribution / Status:	Extremely local / Rare resident
Conservation status:	Herts Endangered
Caterpillar food plants:	Rock-rose
Flight period:	June. Elsewhere, May/June and August
Records in database:	3

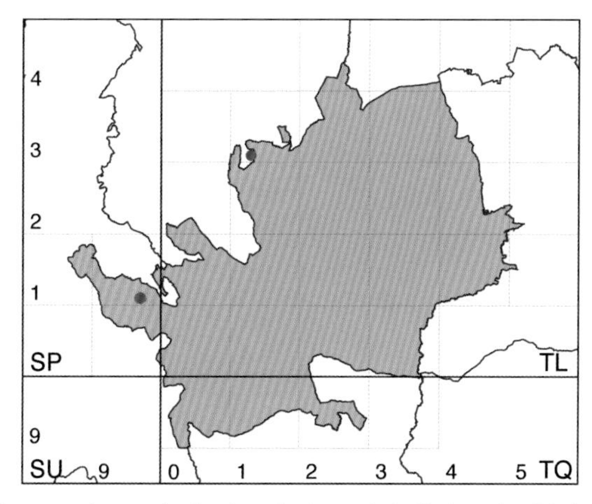

There can be no doubt that the loss of chalk downland habitat in Hertfordshire is responsible for the very restricted distribution of this moth in Hertfordshire. It was added to the county fauna by A. E. Gibbs from Aldbury, in September 1902 (Barraud, 1903) and was found there again on a Herts Moth Group recording trip in June 2007 – there can be no doubt that it has maintained a continuous presence, but the current scarcity of Rock-rose places it under considerable threat. Our other report is from Tingley Wood at Pirton, where it was recorded recently by Raymond Uffen.

0885 *Mompha conturbatella* (Hb.)

Recorded:	1998 only
Distribution / Status:	Local / Rare resident
Conservation status:	Herts Rare
Caterpillar food plants:	Rosebay Willowherb
Flight period:	July. Elsewhere, June/July
Records in database:	1

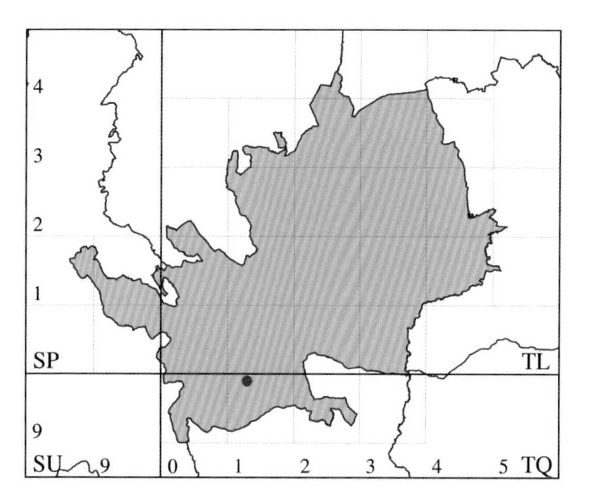

Our only record is of an example taken at Aldenham on 10th July 1998 by Raymond Uffen.

0886 *Mompha ochraceella* (Curtis)

Recorded:	1890 – 2006
Distribution / Status:	Widespread / Common resident
Conservation status:	No perceived threats
Caterpillar food plants:	Great Willowherb
Flight period:	June/July
Records in database:	18

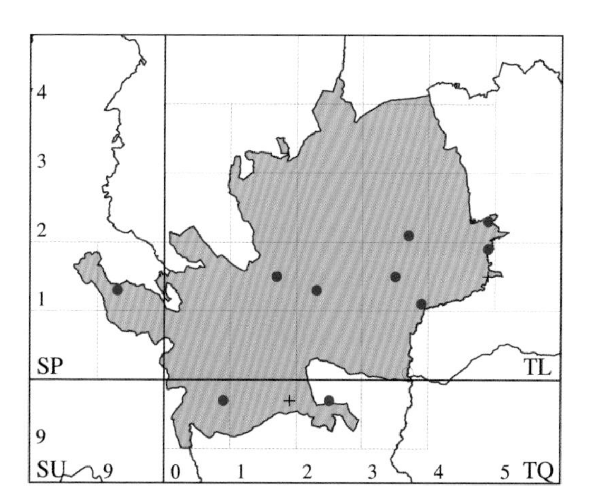

To the inexperienced observer, adults may superficially resemble those of 893: *Mompha epilobiella*, but the latter species has grey hind wings whilst *ochraceella* has them strikingly white. There is also a size difference and the two do not seem to overlap. Caterpillars mine under the 'bark' of the lower stem and into the roots, in the spring sometimes, but not always, mining into a lower leaf. The species is likely to be under-recorded in Hertfordshire.

0888 *Mompha propinquella* (Stt.)

Recorded:	1968 – 2005
Distribution / Status:	Local / Uncommon resident
Conservation status:	No perceived threats
Caterpillar food plants:	No data. Elsewhere, Great and Broad-leaved Willow-herb
Flight period:	June to August
Records in database:	9

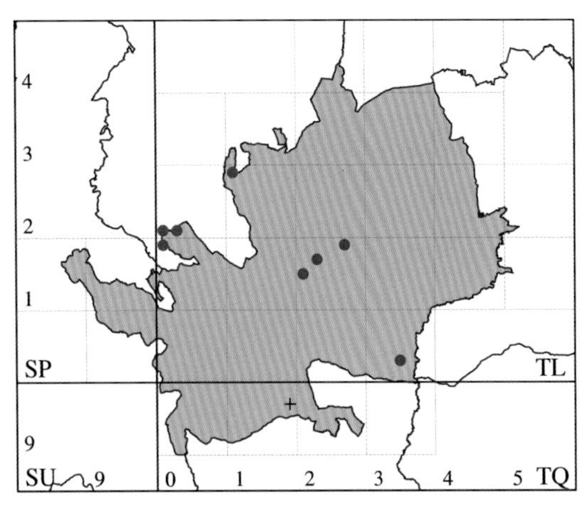

Our earliest record is as recent as 1968, when Eric Bradford noted it at Borehamwood. Although all our records are confirmed, this species can be confused with *Mompha lacteella* (Stephens) which, strangely, is not recorded from Hertfordshire.

[0889 *Mompha divisella* H.- S.

The only Hertfordshire record is from Cheshunt in 1868 by W. C. Boyd (*Entomologist's Monthly Magazine* **5**: 147). Unfortunately, at that time 889a: *Mompha bradleyi* had not been recognised in Britain and so it is unclear in the absence of a voucher specimen to which of the two species this record relates. For the time being, therefore, *Mompha divisella* cannot be accepted onto the county list.]

0889a *Mompha bradleyi* Riedl

Recorded: 1993 – 2005
Distribution / Status: Local / Uncommon resident
Conservation status: Herts Rare
Caterpillar food plants: No data. Elsewhere, on Great Willow-herb.
Flight period: October/November. Elsewhere, September to May
Records in database: 3

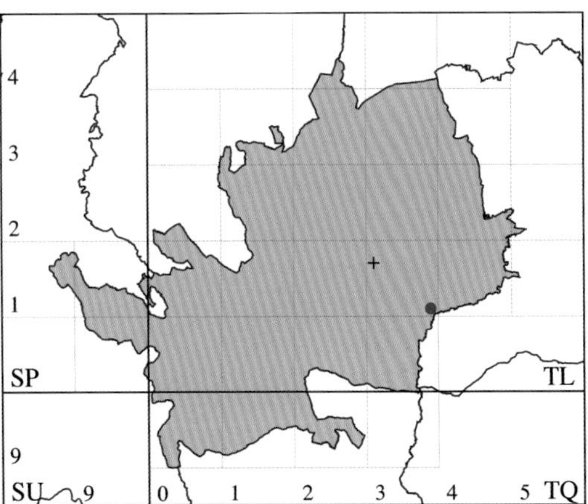

Positive separation of wild-caught adults of this species from 889: *Mompha divisella* requires genitalia dissection in both sexes. We have two confirmed modern records of adults from Stapleford in October 1993 (Mark Sterling) and from Rye House RSPB nature reserve on 15th November 2005 (Joan Childs) whilst Brian Elliott has reared adults from larvae collected on the common at Letchworth, in an area which has now been 'tidied' and is no longer suitable.

0890 *Mompha jurassicella* (Frey) = *subdivisella* Bradley

Recorded: 1989 – 2003
Distribution / Status: Under-recorded, probably Local / Uncommon resident
Conservation status: Herts Rare
Caterpillar food plants: Great Willowherb
Flight period: Elsewhere, September to April
Records in database: 2

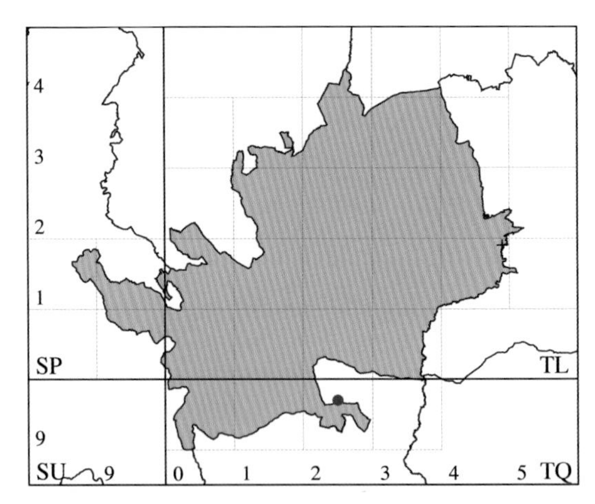

The late John Bradley described *Mompha subdivisella* as a new species in 1951 (Bradley, 1951), but it was subsequently shown by others that this was in fact *jurassicella* – a species already described by Frey in 1881 from Europe. Our two records are my own from Twyford Bury, on the River Stort, on 7th September 1989 and from High Barnet on 16th March 2003 (Rachel Terry).

0891 *Mompha sturnipennella* (Tr.) = *nodicolella* Fuchs

Recorded: 1993 – 2004
Distribution / Status: Local / Rare resident
Conservation status: Herts Rare
Caterpillar food plants: Rosebay Willowherb
Flight period: Elsewhere, July to April
Records in database: 3

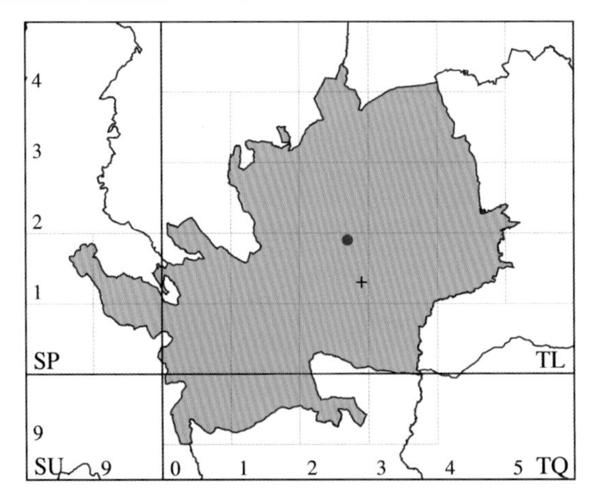

This is a generally scarce and local moth in Britain, with just three records from Hertfordshire, of larval galls at Panshanger Park in 1993 and 1994 (Raymond Uffen) and an adult at Datchworth on 1st August 2004 (Steve Palmer). The caterpillars make distinctive galls in the flowering region of the stem of the food plant; these persist long after the plant has died and render recording easy, so that we can be certain that the moth is absent from the very many places where we have specifically searched for it.

0892 *Mompha subbistrigella* (Haw.)

Recorded: 1890 – 2006
Distribution / Status: Local / Common resident
Conservation status: No perceived threats
Caterpillar food plants: Broad-leaved Willowherb (seed pods)
Flight period: September to May
Records in database: 149

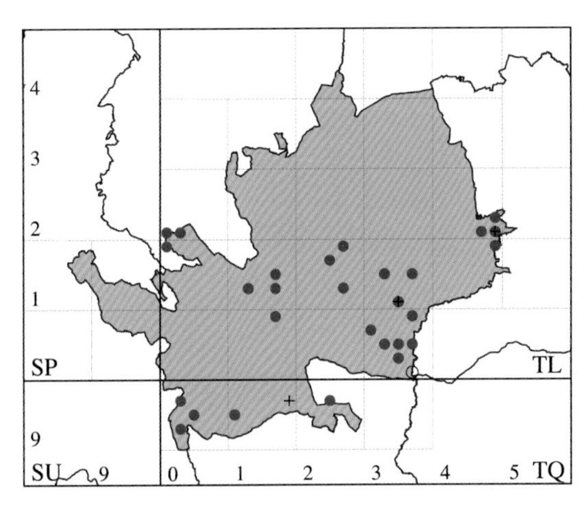

Examples of this moth frequently appear indoors during the winter months and many others are found dead on the inside of windows. This might explain the lack of records in the north of the county (where rather few Herts Moth Group members live), although adults are also taken in light traps away from gardens.

0893 *Mompha epilobiella* ([D.& S.])

Recorded:	1890 – 2006
Distribution / Status:	Local / Common resident
Conservation status:	No perceived threats
Caterpillar food plants:	Great Willowherb, amongst spun shoots
Flight period:	September to May
Records in database:	34

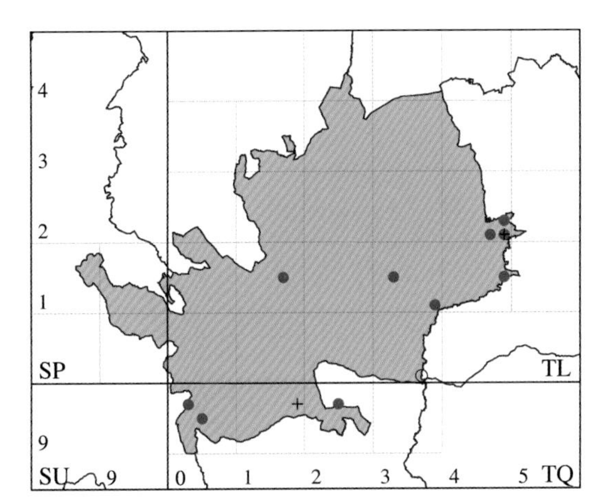

This is probably an over-looked species since adults at rest in the bottom of moth traps are rather nondescript brown and small, so consequently ignored by 'macro' specialists: It is likely to be overlooked in most, if not all, garden light traps.

COSMOPTERIGIDAE

My definition of Cosmopterigidae here follows that of Koster (2002), in volume 4, part 2, of *Moths and Butterflies of Great Britain and Ireland*, with the species of subfamily Blastodacninae being removed to family Agonoxenidae. The checklist numbers are retained throughout to avoid any possible confusion. Four of the twelve British members of the newly defined family are found in Hertfordshire.

0894 *Cosmopterix zieglerella* (Hb.)

Recorded:	2005 only
Distribution / Status:	Local / Rare resident
Conservation status:	Herts Rare
Caterpillar food plants:	Hop
Flight period:	No data. Elsewhere, June/July
Records in database:	1

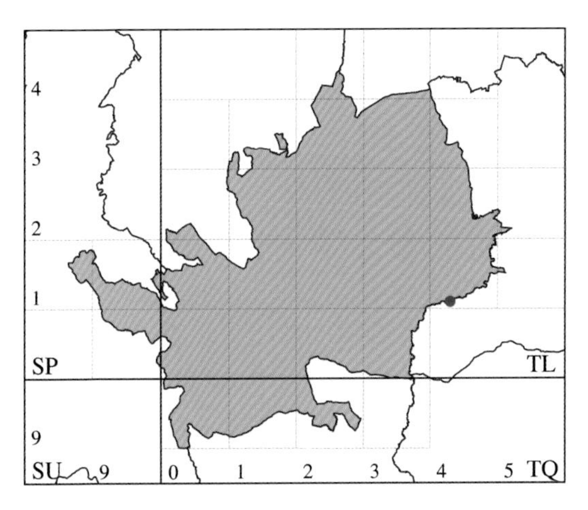

This has been a decidedly rare species in the past, but from 2003 to 2005 it started to suddenly appear, as larval mines on Hop leaves, at various places in the south-east. In Hertfordshire, Hop is a very local plant indeed and the moth is not expected to be present in much of the county. We seem to have only one record, from the valley of the River Stort at Parndon Mead, where Marcel Ashby found mines in 2005.

0898 *Limnaecia phragmitella* Stt.

Recorded:	1901 – 2006
Distribution / Status:	Common / Abundant resident
Conservation status:	No perceived threats
Caterpillar food plants:	Greater Reedmace
Flight period:	July to August
Records in database:	33

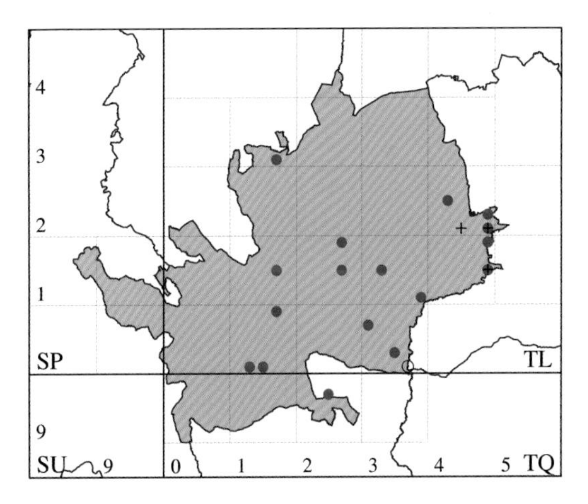

If seed heads of reedmace start to disintegrate so that the normally smooth, brown sausage-shaped heads begin to sprout white fluffy tufts, then this is a sign that larvae of this moth are probably eating the seeds. To confirm, lay the seed head flat on your joined hands and use your two thumbs to prise the seeds and associated fluff away from the stem; it should 'unroll' to reveal the pinkish larvae. These feed from about September/October to May.

0899 *Pancalia leuwenhoekella* (L.)

Recorded:	1937 – 2000
Distribution / Status:	Local / Rare resident
Conservation status:	Herts Rare
Caterpillar food plants:	No data. Elsewhere on Hairy Violet and Dog Violet
Flight period:	May/June – in sunshine over foodplants
Records in database:	5

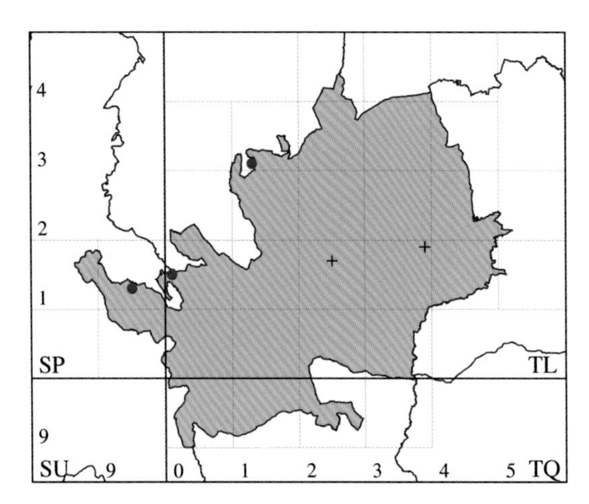

The caterpillar of this species feeds first as a leaf miner and then later on the bark of the roots. Adults fly in sunshine and probably do not come to light traps; the moth is, therefore, likely to be under-recorded. Our records are from the Ashridge Estate by J. A. K. Hervey (Foster, 1937), Harmer Green Wood and Barwick Wood in 1991 (Raymond Uffen), Ravensdell Wood in 1997 (David Manning) and Tingley Wood Down, Pirton in 2000 (Raymond Uffen). The very similar *Pancalia schwarzella* (Fabr.) is not yet recorded in the county and could be confused with *leuwenhoekella*.

0908 *Sorhagenia rhamniella* (Zell.)

Recorded:	2004 only
Distribution / Status:	Local / Rare resident
Conservation status:	Herts Rare
Caterpillar food plants:	No data. Elsewhere on Buckthorn
Flight period:	July. Elsewhere, July/August
Records in database:	2

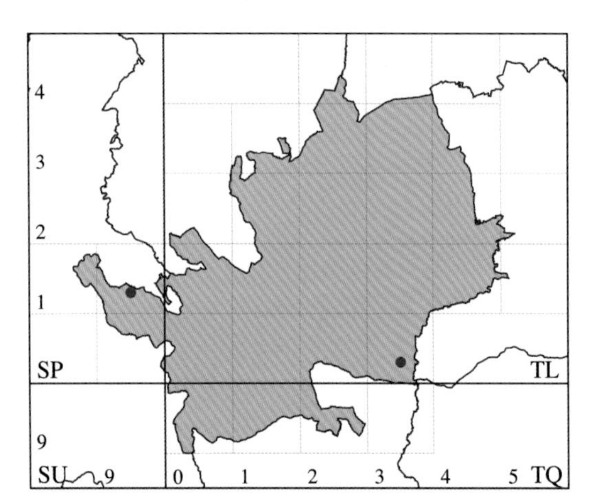

The three British species of *Sorhagenia* can only be separated by genitalia inspection and, though not yet recorded, the other two are likely to be present. As they may all fly together, it is essential that several examples are collected and dissected from each place where they are found. For the present species we have records from Aldbury Nowers, with several attracted to light traps on the Herts Moth Group field trip of 24th July 2004 and from Cheshunt in the same year in Mark Cooper's garden.

AGONOXENIDAE

My definition of Agonoxenidae follows that of Koster (2002), in volume 4, part 2, of the series *Moths and Butterflies of Great Britain and Ireland*, and is essentially the species of subfamily Blastodacninae which are removed from the Cosmopterigidae. The checklist numbers are retained throughout to avoid any possible confusion. There are six British species, of which all are recorded in Hertfordshire.

0902 *Chrysoclista lathamella* Fletcher

Recorded:	2006 only
Distribution / Status:	Extremely local / Rare resident
Conservation status:	Nationally Rare Herts Vulnerable
Caterpillar food plants:	Not recorded. Thought to be associated with sallow or willow.
Flight period:	June. Elsewhere, June to August
Records in database:	1

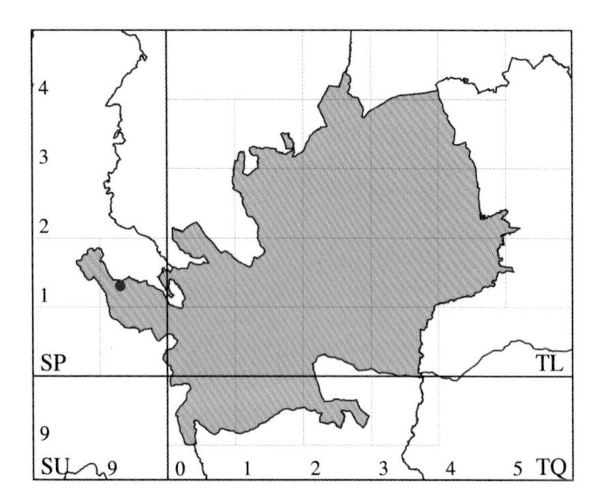

One caught in my light trap at Tring Sewage Works, in the company of several other Herts Moth Group members, on the night of 9th June 2007, technically falls outside the cut-off date of 31st December 2006 for this review. However, as a resident, its larvae must have been present in 2006 for it to be here as an adult in 2007. This is a nationally rare species about which rather little is known.

0903 *Chrysoclista linneella* (Cl.)

Recorded:	1901 - 2001
Distribution / Status:	Local / Rare resident
Conservation status:	Insufficiently known
Caterpillar food plants:	Not recorded. Elsewhere in the bark of lime trees
Flight period:	July. Elsewhere, June to August
Records in database:	3

The adults are bright orange with silver/grey spots and may be seen at rest in the trunks of lime trees; apparently they also come to light. Our few records are from Waltham Cross (Boyd, 1901), Tewin on 19th July 1997 (Raymond Uffen) and Garston on 29th July 2001 (Colin Everett), but I suspect that if people bothered to examine lime trunks in the summer the moth might prove rather more widespread than the map currently indicates it to be.

0904 *Spuleria flavicaput* (Haw.)

Recorded: 1888 – 2006
Distribution / Status: Local / Uncommon resident
Conservation status: Herts Scarce
Caterpillar food plants: Not recorded. Elsewhere, on Common-Hawthorn
Flight period: May/June
Records in database: 18

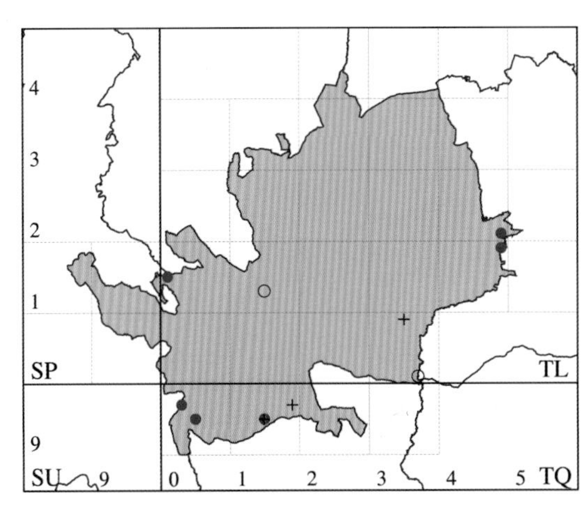

Essentially a black moth with a yellow head, this is a species that can be confused with little else. The caterpillar mines a twig of hawthorn, typically about the thickness of a knitting-needle. The map shows that records are rather sparse; the earliest is from near Bamville Wood Farm (Harpenden Common), in the years before 1889, by A. E. Gibbs.

0905 *Blastodacna hellerella* (Dup.)

Recorded: 1901 – 2006
Distribution / Status: Widespread / Common resident
Conservation status: No perceived threats
Caterpillar food plants: Not recorded. Elsewhere on Common-Hawthorn
Flight period: June/July to early August
Records in database: 89

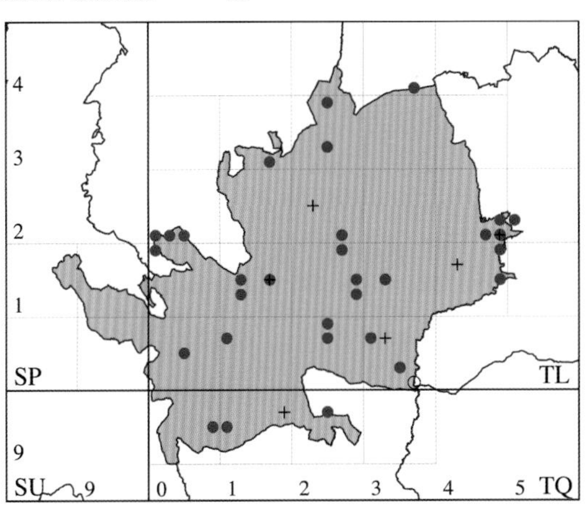

A long and narrow moth at rest that can only really be confused with the apparently quite rare 906: *Blastodacna atra*. The caterpillar feeds inside hawthorn berries, often spinning berries together but, unlike the larvae of some flies (Diptera) that feed in the same location, without frass exuding from the berry.

0906 *Blastodacna atra* (Haw.) Apple Pith Moth

Recorded: 1901 – 2005
Distribution / Status: Local / Rare resident
Conservation status: Herts Rare
Caterpillar food plants: Not recorded. Elsewhere on Domestic Apple
Flight period: July.
Records in database: 4

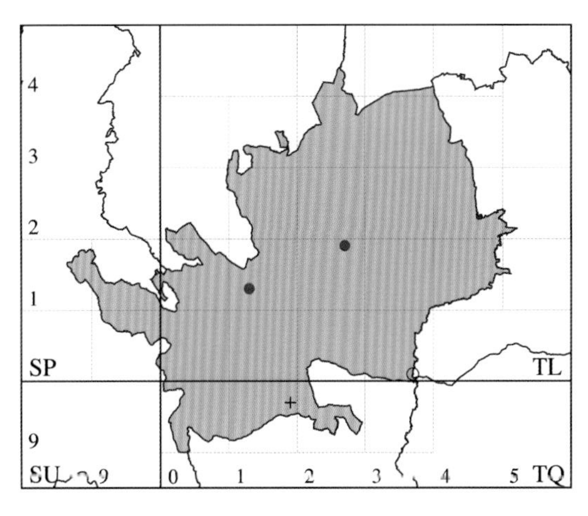

In view of the 'pest' status of this species, it is interesting to discover that apart from one historic record from Cheshunt (Boyd, 1901) and one from 1969 at Borehamwood (Eric Bradford) there are only two other records: from the Rothamsted Estate at Harpenden on 19th July 2002 (Gould, 2007) and from Datchworth 18th July 2005. The caterpillar mines inside a twig of an apple tree causing blossom on that twig to die.

0907 *Dystebenna stephensi* (Stt.)

Recorded: 1965 – 2004
Distribution / Status: Local / Uncommon resident
Conservation status: Herts Scarce
Caterpillar food plants: In the bark of mature oak trees
Flight period: July to August, elsewhere to September
Records in database: 8

Traditionally, the caterpillars are said to be easy to detect as they exude bright orange frass from the bark of mature (especially veteran) oak trees. However, identical feeding signs are produced by larvae of 416: *Argyresthia glaucinella* and so there is scope for confusion between the two species. Larvae should be collected and reared wherever possible. Adults may also be found sitting very low down on the same trees in the flight period and this is perhaps a more effortless method of recording than extracting the larvae from oak bark. At Moor Park, on 19th July 2004, Raymond Uffen recorded adults as 'frequent on veteran oaks having complete canopies' and at Danesbury Park, Welwyn, on 22nd July 2004 he found adults on the trunks of oaks of 2.64 to 3.30 metres girth. This is unlikely to be a common species, but may well be found wherever there are very large oak trees.

SCYTHRIDIDAE

Scythridids are typically found in open exposed habitats and shun dense vegetation areas such as scrub and woodland. Their life histories are not fully known, but most larvae spin a silk web on the foodplant and feed from within this. Though there are around 250 European representatives of the family there are only twelve in Britain, of which four are recorded for Hertfordshire.

0911 *Scythris grandipennis* (Haw.)

Recorded: Pre-1890 only
Distribution / Status: Absent / Extinct
Conservation status: Herts Extinct
Caterpillar food plants: No data. Elsewhere on Dwarf Gorse
Flight period: Elsewhere, June
Records in database: 1

Our only Hertfordshire record is that from the Sandridge area given by Griffith (1890); this cannot be mapped as the precise location is not known.

0914 *Scythris crassiuscula* (H.- S.)

Recorded: 1834 – 1999
Distribution / Status: Extremely local / Rare resident
Conservation status: Herts Endangered
Caterpillar food plants: Rock-rose
Flight period: Not recorded. Elsewhere, July
Records in database: 4

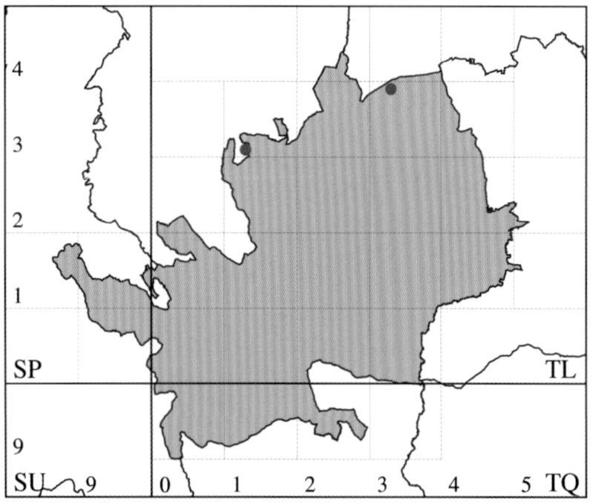

This is a chalk downland species and so the historical records from Hertford (Stephens, 1834) and St Albans in 1901 (Gibbs) are a little surprising, though not impossible. More expected are the two recent reports from Church Hill, at Therfield Heath on 29th June 1995 and Tingley Wood, Pirton on 5th September 1999, both courtesy of Raymond Uffen. Chalk downland sites that support the foodplant are rare and mostly degraded and whilst Rock-rose itself is absent from many; for this reason, the moth is regarded as Endangered in Hertfordshire.

0918 *Scythris limbella* (Fabr.) = *quadriguttella* (Thunb.)

Recorded: 1901 – 1965
Distribution / Status: Extremely local or absent / Rare resident or extinct
Conservation status: Herts Extinct
Caterpillar food plants: Not recorded. Elsewhere on goosefoots and oraches
Flight period: No data. Elsewhere June to September
Records in database: 3

Though both food plant groups are prevalent in the county it looks as if we have lost the moth, which is rather localized in terms of its overall British distribution. Our records are from St Albans (Gibbs) and Waltham Cross (Boyd), both prior to 1901, then from Borehamwood on 16th May 1965 (Eric Bradford). However, although we have not seen it in the county for some 41 years, it was taken as recently as 18th August 2005 in Barnet, just across our border to the south in Middlesex, by Rachel Terry. It may yet be refound in Hertfordshire.

0920 *Scythris potentillella* (Zell.)

Recorded: 2005 – 2006
Distribution / Status: Extremely local / Abundant resident
Conservation status: Herts Endangered
Caterpillar food plants: Common Sorrel and Sheep's Sorrel
Flight period: June to September
Records in database: 2

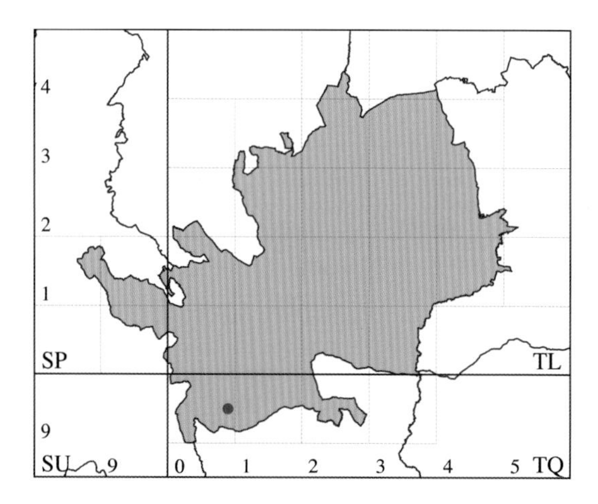

The discovery of large numbers of this nationally rare species in a very restricted area of Croxley Common Moor in August and September of 2005 by David and Conall Murray (Murray, 2007), was as unexpected as it was pleasing. Several specimens have been dissected to confirm the identification. Frequent visits to the moor during 2006 produced the first *potentillella* on 10th June, but then no more until 1st July, when two were found; the last sighting was on 23rd September.

TORTRICOIDEA
TORTRICIDAE
TORTRICINAE

The tortricoids, or tortricids, or even 'deltoids' in some older books' are familiar to most people with an interest in moths – even to those who profess to be interested only in the 'macros'. This is scarcely surprising since, as the moth family containing the second largest number of European species (after the Noctuidae), its members are regular attendees at light traps. Modern thinking incorporates the formerly separate family of Cochylidae within subfamily Tortricinae; this, together with the Chlidanotinae and the Olethreutinae, forms our modern-day Tortricidae, with a European total of 937 species. In recent years several new species have been discovered in Britain and the current fauna is around 390 species. In Hertfordshire we have acceptable records for 235 but of these 30 are either extinct or possibly so; almost all the remainder are under-recorded and our knowledge of the early stages within our county is embarrassingly minimal. In general, older records are difficult, if not impossible, to locate to a particular tetrad; I have only mapped those which can, which means that most maps may depict only modern records.

0924 *Hysterophora maculosana* (Haw.)

Recorded: 1888 – 2004
Distribution / Status: Local / Resident
Conservation status: Insufficiently known
Caterpillar food plants: Not recorded. Elsewhere, in seed capsule of Bluebell
Flight period: May. Elsewhere, May/June
Records in database: 9

Almost certainly under-recorded and likely to be in most woods that have a carpet of bluebells.

0921 *Phtheochroa inopiana* (Haw.)

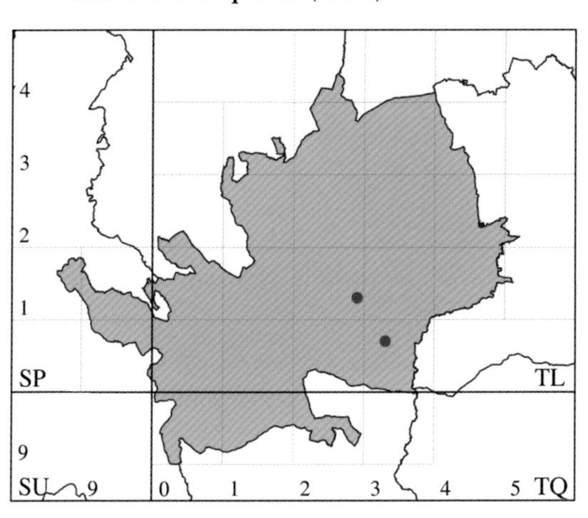

Recorded: 1997 - 2004
Distribution / Status: Local / Resident
Conservation status: Insufficiently known
Caterpillar food plants: Not recorded. Elsewhere, on Fleabane
Flight period: July. Elsewhere, June to August
Records in database: 4

One at Panshanger Park in 1997 (Tom Gladwin) and a male caught by me at Broxbourne Woods on 15th July 2004 are our only records

0923 *Phtheochroa sodaliana* (Haw.)

Recorded: 2002 – 2003
Distribution / Status: Local / Resident
Conservation status: Insufficiently known
Caterpillar food plants: Not recorded. Elsewhere, on Buckthorn
Flight period: June. Elsewhere, May/June
Records in database: 3

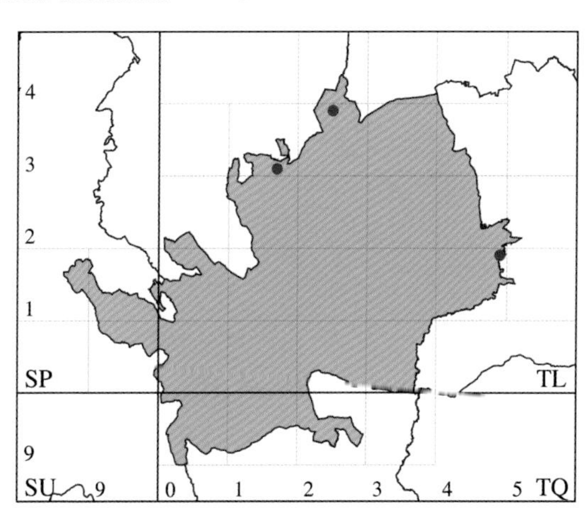

The two northerly records, from Ashwell Quarry in 2002 and Oughtonhead Common in 2003, are on the chalk and thus expected. The third record, from Andrew Palmer's garden light trap in the newly built Bishops Park area of Bishops Stortford in 2003 must surely suggest that the moth has either colonised, or been introduced with, buckthorns that have been planted amongst the thousands of other trees on the new ring road that passes very close to Andrew's house.

0925 *Phtheochroa rugosana* (Hb.)

Recorded: 1890 – 2006
Distribution / Status: Widespread / Resident
Conservation status: No perceived threats
Caterpillar food plants: White Bryony (berries)
Flight period: May to July
Records in database: 79

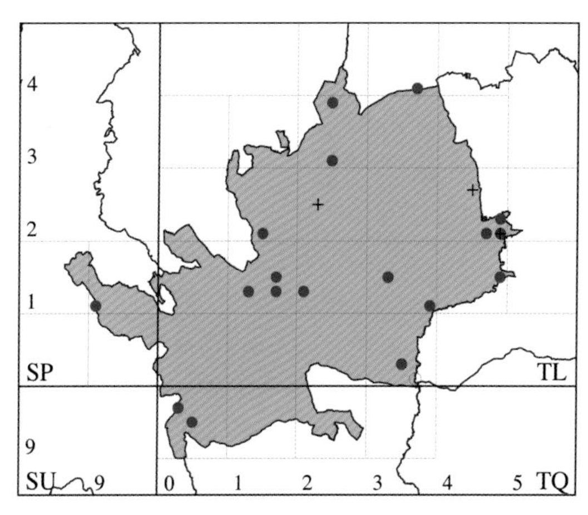

White Bryony seems to be a widespread plant in hedges and the moth is likely to be equally well distributed. Larvae were found on berries in Stevenage on 7th August 1966 (Jack Newton).

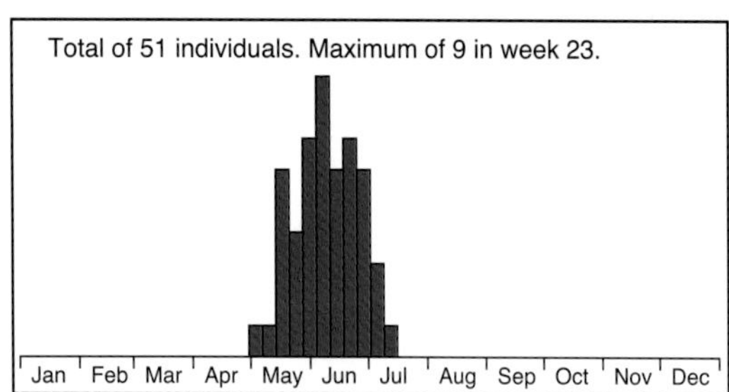

0926 *Phalonidia manniana* (F. v. R.)

Recorded: 1979 – 2004
Distribution / Status: Local / Resident
Conservation status: Insufficiently known
Caterpillar food plants: Elsewhere, Water Mint and Gipsy-wort
Flight period: June. Elsewhere, June/July
Records in database: 6

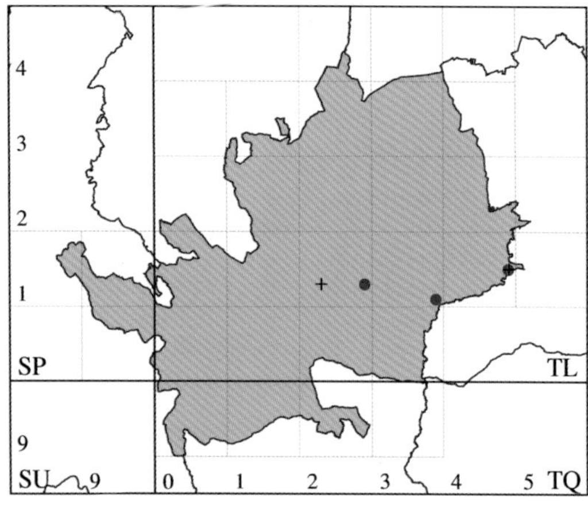

Our records are from Sawbridgeworth Marsh, Rye Meads, Lemsford Springs and Panshanger Park – all wetland sites. The requirement for wetland habitat probably means that the moth will only be locally distributed in Hertfordshire.

0930 *Gynnidomorpha alismana* (Rag.)

One at Bishops Stortford, 13th July 2007 (James Fish & Julian Reeves), postdates the survey and is omitted from totals, analyses, etc.

0936 *Cochylimorpha straminea* (Haw.)

Recorded: 1900 – 2006
Distribution / Status: Local / Common resident
Conservation status: No perceived threats
Caterpillar food plants: Not recorded. Elsewhere, Lesser Knapweed
Flight period: May/June and late July/August
Records in database: 25

The records are scattered and the moth may well be found widely across the county where the foodplant grows. The moth is noticeably more numerous at sites on calcareous soils, but is apparently not confined to such places. Road verges and other habitats could be usefully searched.

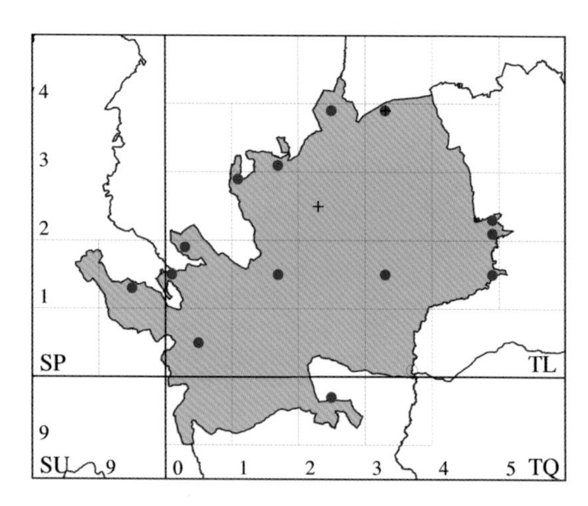

0937 *Agapeta hamana* (L.)

Recorded: 1890 – 2006
Distribution / Status: Ubiquitous / Common resident
Conservation status: No perceived threats
Caterpillar food plants: Not recorded. Elsewhere, thistles of genus *Carduus*, possibly also *Cirsium*
Flight period: June to August
Records in database: 353

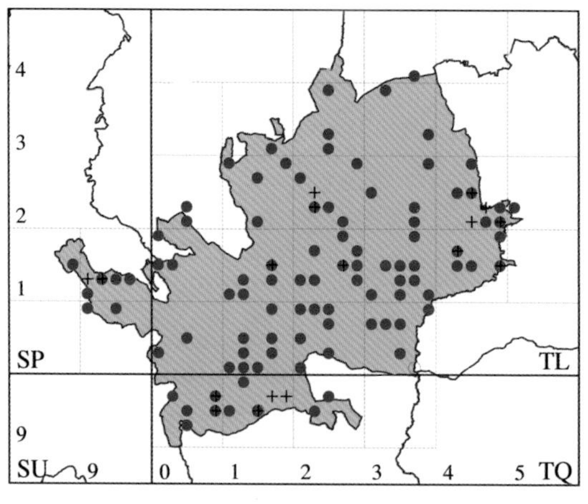

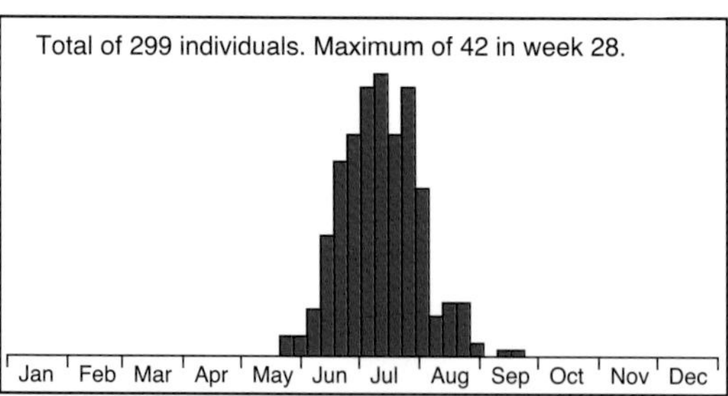

Almost every patch of rough grassland, from fields to road verges, will support this species in Hertfordshire as long as the foodplant is present. First-generation larvae feed in the flower head, but those of the second generation feed in the stems and roots.

0938 *Agapeta zoegana* (L.)

Recorded: 1834 – 2006
Distribution / Status: Local / Uncommon resident
Conservation status: No perceived threats
Caterpillar food plants: Not recorded. Elsewhere, in rootstock of Lesser Knapweed and Small Scabious
Flight period: June to August
Records in database: 60

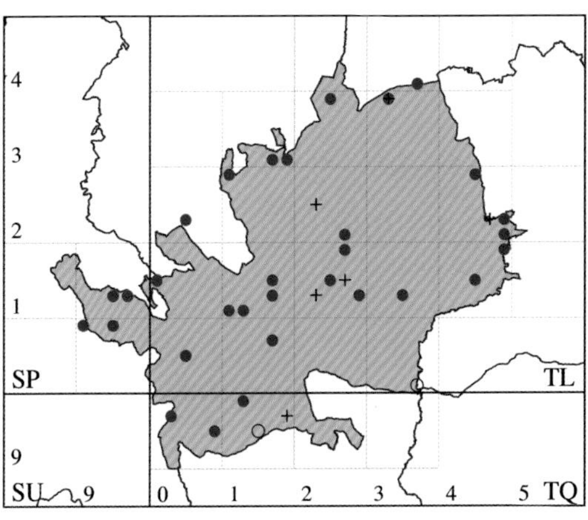

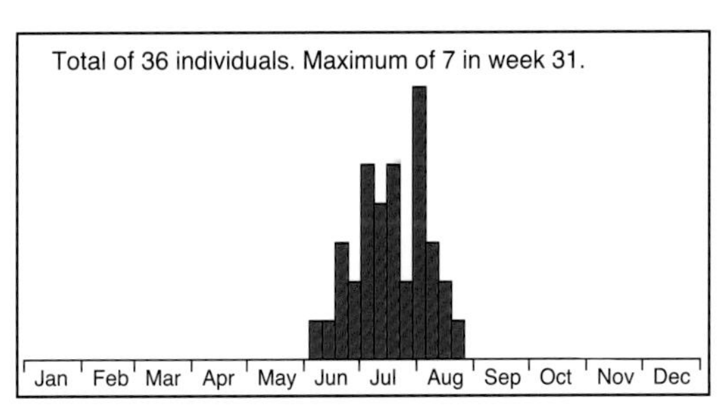

Far less numerically common than 938: *Agapeta hamana*, and single brooded, it almost as widespread but seems to be absent from the arable area of the north-east.

0939 *Aethes tesserana* ([D.& S.])

Recorded: 1834 – 2000
Distribution / Status: Probably very local / Uncommon resident
Conservation status: Insufficiently known
Caterpillar food plants: Not recorded. Elsewhere, in the roots of many species of yellow-flowering members of the Compositae
Flight period: July. Elsewhere, May to August
Records in database: 7

Our earliest record is that illustrated by J. F. Stephens from Hertford in his *Illustrations of British Entomology* 4: 189 (published in 1834); our latest is from Bishops Stortford, June 2000, by Charles Watson. In between, it was noted in the Sandridge area before 1890, the Cheshunt area before 1901, at Harpenden in 1926, near Hitchin in the 1920s and at Tewin, on 27th July 1991 (Raymond Uffen).

0941 *Aethes hartmanniana* (Cl.)

Recorded: 1886– 2005
Distribution / Status: Local / Resident
Conservation status: Insufficiently known
Caterpillar food plants: Not recorded. Elsewhere, in the rootstock of Field and Small Scabious
Flight period: July. Elsewhere, June to August
Records in database: 6

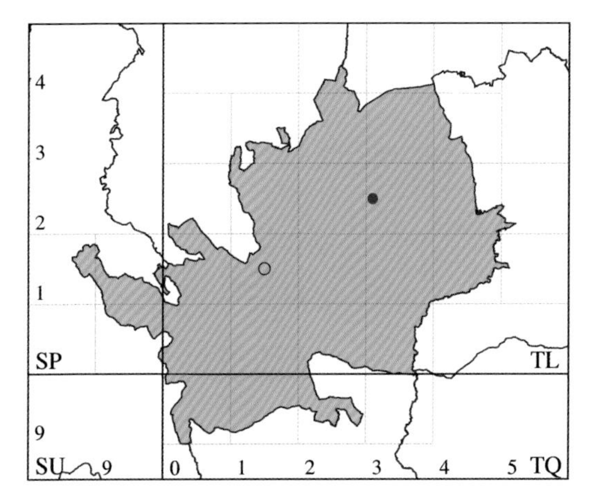

The only modern record is my own from Wood End, on 22nd July 2005. The open circle on the map represents one at Mackerye End (Griffith, 1890) and is the 'Sandridge area' record noted by Foster (1937). Old records from Broxbourne and the Hitchin area cannot mapped accurately.

0942 *Aethes piercei* (Obr.)

Recorded: 1884 – 2006
Distribution / Status: Extremely Local / Rare resident
Conservation status: Herts Rare
Caterpillar food plants: Not recorded. Elsewhere, in the rootstock of Devil's-bit Scabious
Flight period: Not recorded. Elsewhere, May to July
Records in database: 4

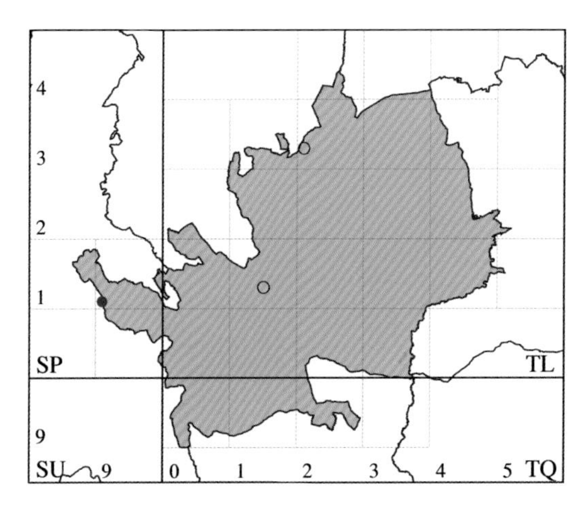

There are three old records, for the Sandridge area in 1884 (Griffith), from Wilbury Hill, near Hitchin in 1886 (Durrant) and the area east of Bamville Wood Farm (near Harpenden Common) prior to 1889 (Gibbs). The only other record is of a male amongst scale-less moths collected at Tring by Ian Burrus during 2006 and put into a tube with other unidentified micros for me to dissect the following winter. The moth may be overlooked, but the foodplant is scarce and the combination of foodplant with appropriate habitat even less frequent and so the moth is regarded as rare in the county.

0944 *Aethes williana* (Brahm)

Recorded: 1890 – 1909
Distribution / Status: Absent / Former resident
Conservation status: Insufficiently known
Caterpillar food plants: Not recorded. Elsewhere, in the root and stem of Wild Carrot
Flight period: Elsewhere, May to August
Records in database: 3

There are three Hertfordshire records – from the Sandridge area at Mackerye End (Griffith, 1890), from the Wheathampstead area in 1909 (Gibbs) and from Ashridge, approximately 1909 (Hervey); none can be accurately mapped. It should be searched for where the foodplant grows on chalk grassland sites.

0945 *Aethes cnicana* (Westwood)

Recorded: 1890 – 2003
Distribution / Status: Local / Uncommon resident
Conservation status: Insufficiently known
Caterpillar food plants: Not recorded. Elsewhere, in thistle stems
Flight period: June/July
Records in database: 16

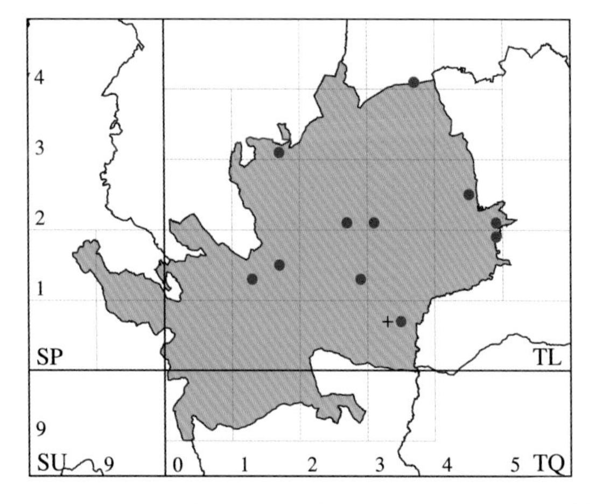

Separation from 946: *Aethes rubigana* is best confirmed by dissection of the genitalia in most cases.

0946 *Aethes rubigana* (Tr.)

Recorded: 1890 – 2005
Distribution / Status: Local / Common resident
Conservation status: No perceived threats
Caterpillar food plants: Not recorded. Elsewhere, in the seed heads of Great Burdock
Flight period: June to August
Records in database: 22

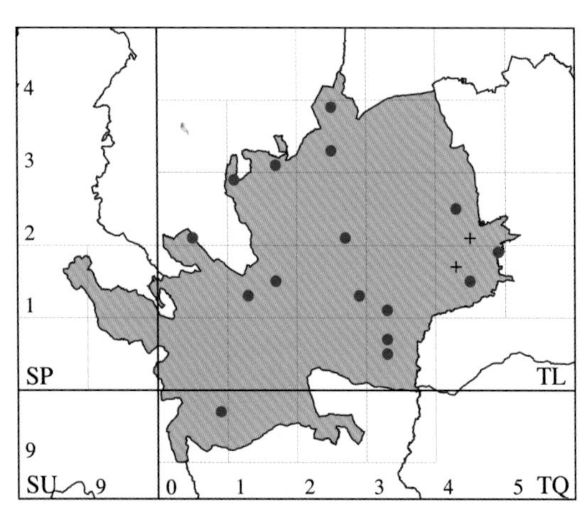

Separation from 945: *Aethes cnicana* is mentioned under that species; both are probably under-recorded.

0947 *Aethes smeathmanniana* (Fabr.)

Recorded: 1834 – 2005
Distribution / Status: Local / Resident
Conservation status: No perceived threats
Caterpillar food plants: Not recorded. Elsewhere, on Yarrow and Lesser Knapweed
Flight period: May/early June and July to early September
Records in database: 41

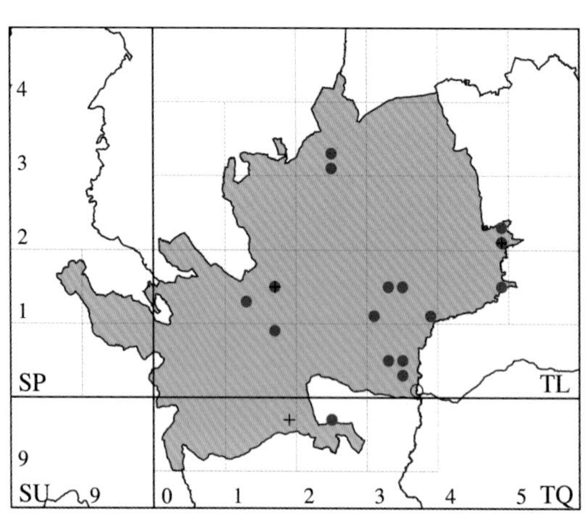

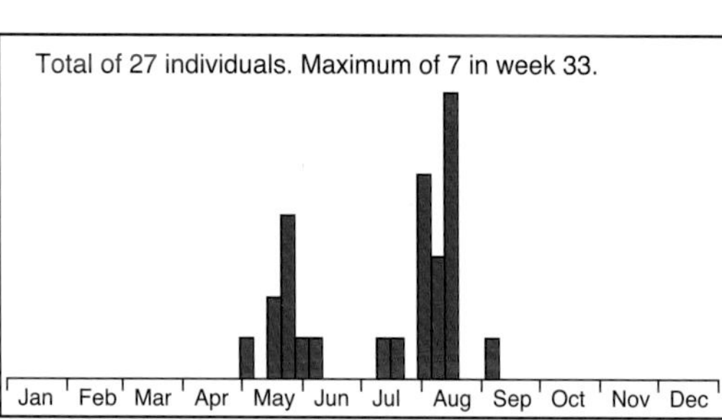

The adult flies from the start of May to early September in Hertfordshire. Nationally it is said to fly from late May to August in a single protracted emergence; the apparent gap of records in June/July is, therefore, interesting.

0949 *Aethes dilucidana* (Steph.)

Recorded: 1926 – 1991
Distribution / Status: Extremely local or absent / Rare resident or extinct
Conservation status: Herts Rare
Caterpillar food plants: Not recorded. Elsewhere, on Wild Parsnip
Flight period: July. Elsewhere, July/August
Records in database: 2

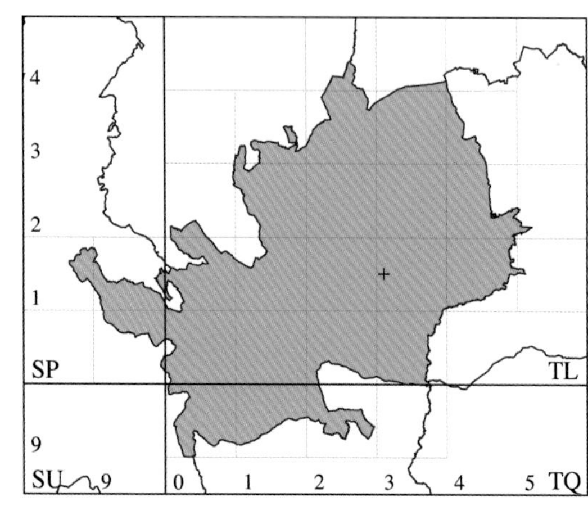

Our two records are from near Knebworth in 1926 (Fryer, given in Foster, 1937) and Waterford Sand Pit, where Raymond Uffen found it on 28th July 1991. It is probably still present in the county where the foodplant grows.

[0950 *Aethes francillana* (Fabr.)

The record given by Gibbs (1902) in the *Victoria County History* was later withdrawn by the same author (see Foster, 1937: 159). Foster (1937) also records 'Royston' in 1926 (Fryer) and Harpenden [presumed to be in the 1930s] by C. B. Williams. It is typically a coastal species, where it feeds on Wild Carrot and, unfortunately, there has been considerable confusion in the past of this species with 949: *Aethes dilucidana*. Old records cannot be relied upon and I am not able to admit this species to the Hertfordshire list in the absence of a dissected specimen.]

0951 *Aethes beatricella* (Wals.)

Recorded: 1996 – 2005
Distribution / Status: Local / Resident
Conservation status: Insufficiently known
Caterpillar food plants: Not recorded. Elsewhere, on Hemlock
Flight period: June/July
Records in database: 4

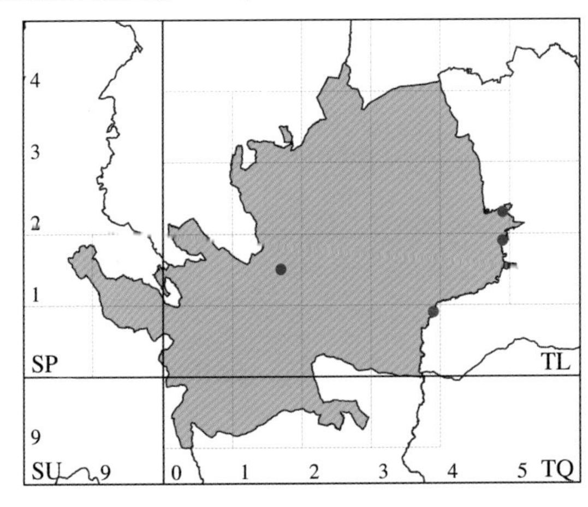

The foodplant is scarce, but where it grows the moth is likely to be found (see, also, the map for 0695: *Agonopterix alstromeriana,* which also feeds on Hemlock). The caterpillar feeds on the seeds at first then later burrows into the upper stem where it hibernates before pupating in the spring. Hemlock stems brought indoors in the spring may well yield adult moths in due course.

0952 *Commophila aeneana* (Hb.)

Recorded: 1962 – 2006
Distribution / Status: Local / Rare resident
Conservation status: Herts Rare
Caterpillar food plants: Not recorded. Elsewhere, in the rootstock of Common Ragwort
Flight period: June. Elsewhere, late May to July
Records in database: 4

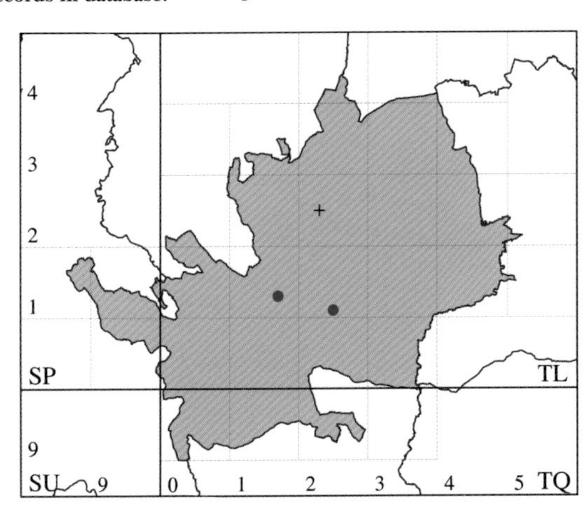

This striking and attractive moth is evidently scarce in Hertfordshire and is probably threatened by ragwort control. Although ragwort regenerates from seed the rootstock is destroyed before larval development is completed; established areas of ragwort are more likely to generate this species. However, much searching has mostly failed to find what is a distinctive species and so we must assume that its scarcity is genuine.

0954 *Eupoecilia angustana* (Hb.)

Recorded: 1890 – 2004
Distribution / Status: Local / Resident
Conservation status: Insufficiently known
Caterpillar food plants: Not recorded. Elsewhere, noted on flowers and seeds of plantains, Yarrow, Marjoram, Wild Thyme and Golden Rod
Flight period: June. Elsewhere, June to September
Records in database: 5

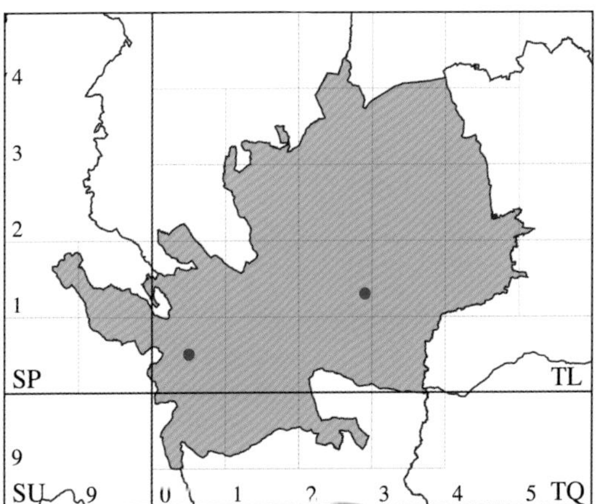

Old records from the Sandridge area (1890) and Ashridge (1934) cannot be mapped. Recent reports are from Panshanger Park in 1997 (Tom Gladwin) and Roughdown Common, where I took it at light on both 8th and 25th June 2004.

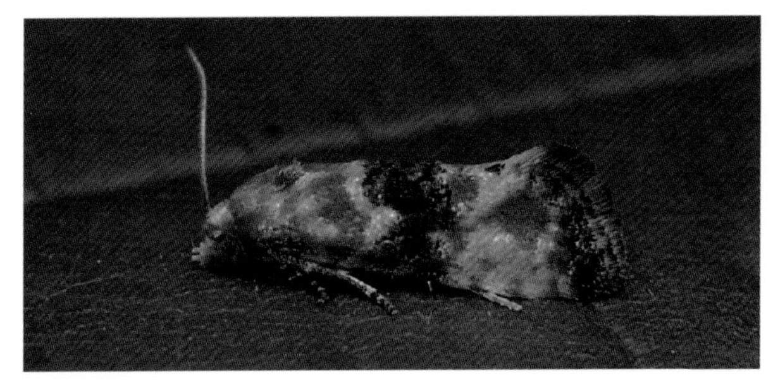

0956 *Cochylidia implicitana* (Wocke)

Recorded: 1941 – 2003
Distribution / Status: Local / Resident
Conservation status: Insufficiently known
Caterpillar food plants: Not recorded. Elsewhere, on Chamomile, Scentless Mayweed, Stinking Mayweed and Golden Rod
Flight period: Late May/June. Elsewhere, June to August
Records in database: 5

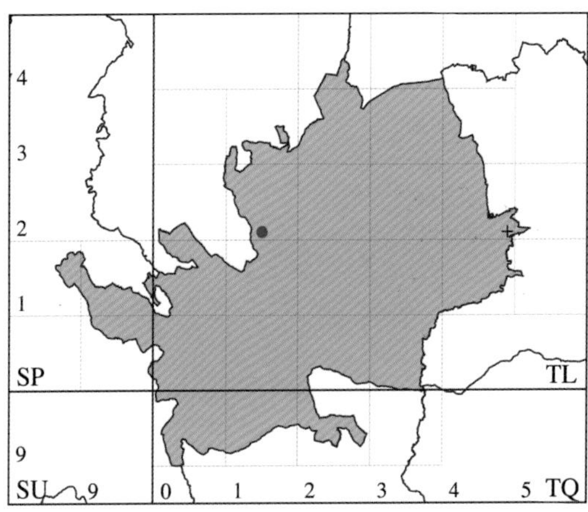

Harpenden, 1941 (J. C. F. Fryer) seems to be the first report for the county. The species was again recorded from the same locality in 1947 (Fryer, 1950). Since then, I have found adults at light in my garden in Bishops Stortford in 1988 and 1990 and at Hurst Wood, near Luton, on 30th May 2003.

0959 *Cochylidia rupicola* (Curt.)

Recorded:	1901 only
Distribution / Status:	Absent / Extinct
Conservation status:	Herts Extinct
Caterpillar food plants:	Not recorded. Elsewhere, Hemp Agrimony
Flight period:	Elsewhere, June/July
Records in database:	1

Our only record is of one in the St Albans area in 1901, recorded by A. E. Gibbs.

0960 *Falseuncaria ruficiliana* (Haw.)

Recorded:	1934 – 1934
Distribution / Status:	Absent / Extinct
Conservation status:	Herts Extinct
Caterpillar food plants:	Not recorded. Elsewhere, on seeds of Cowslip and Lousewort
Flight period:	Elsewhere, May to August
Records in database:	1

Foster (1937) records it from Ashridge in 1934 by Hervey, who noted that it was 'common'. There are no other records for the county.

0962 *Cochylis roseana* (Haw.)

Recorded:	1966 – 2006
Distribution / Status:	Local / Common resident
Conservation status:	No perceived threats
Caterpillar food plants:	Developing seeds of Teasel
Flight period:	June/July. Elsewhere, May to August
Records in database:	24

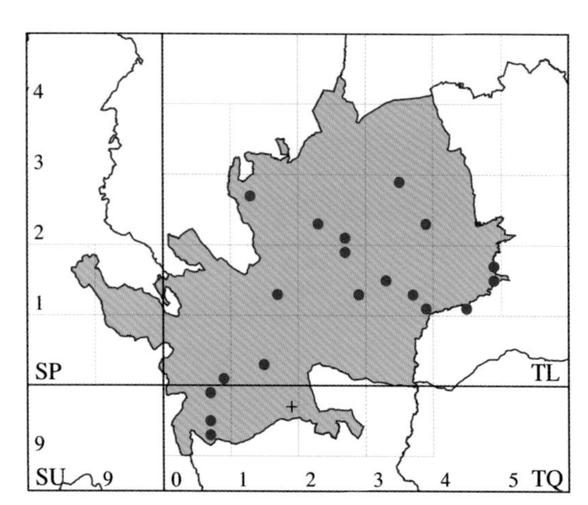

The caterpillar tunnels through the seeds laterally, spiralling around the seed head to do so, with the result that an affected teasel head, when split vertically, reveals a row of holes in the seeds on each side of the central cavity. The map should be compared with that for 1097: *Endothenia gentianaeana*, which feeds in the stem and central cavity of the seed head. The technique of searching for these two species is identical – so it is clear that the present species is far less frequently encountered than is *gentianaeana*, which was found in almost every teasel head split open from 2000 to 2006.

0963 *Cochylis flaviciliana* (Westwood)

Recorded:	1937 – 1965
Distribution / Status:	Absent / Former resident
Conservation status:	Insufficiently known
Caterpillar food plants:	Not recorded. Elsewhere, on the seeds of Field Scabious
Flight period:	Early August. Elsewhere, June to August
Records in database:	2

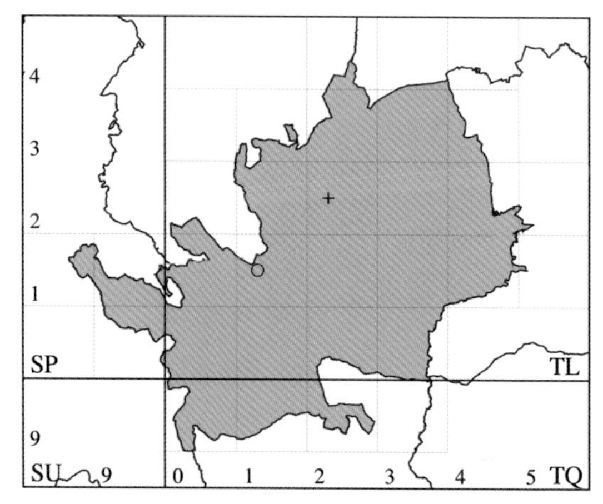

One was taken in the light trap at Harpenden in the 1930s by C. B. Williams (Foster, 1937) and one was caught in Stevenage, at mv light on 3 August 1965 (Jack Newton).

0964 *Cochylis dubitana* (Hb.)

Recorded:	1901 – 2005
Distribution / Status:	Local / Uncommon resident
Conservation status:	No perceived threats
Caterpillar food plants:	Not recorded. Elsewhere, on flowers and seeds of various Compositae
Flight period:	May (Elsewhere, June) and then July August
Records in database:	21

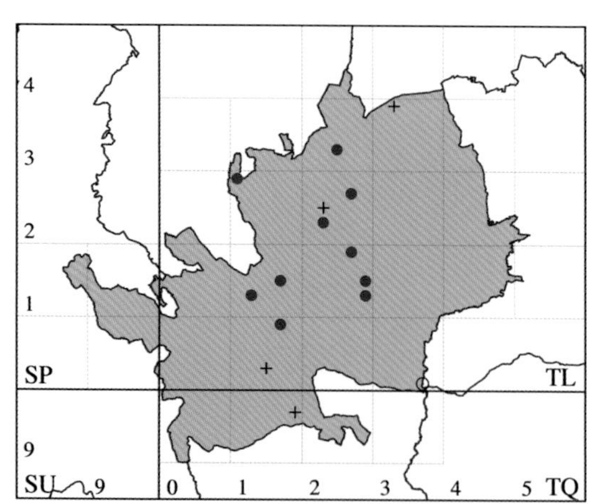

Though the text books tell us that the colour combination of head and thorax enable separation of this species from 965: *Cochylis hybridella* and 966: *Cochylis atricapitana* the reality is that separation from *hybridella* requires genitalia examination for absolute certainty. Records of first-generation adults from

Baldock on 15th May 2002 (K. Robinson) and from Pryors Wood, Stevenage on 18th May 2002 (A. Wood) are both about a week earlier than expected.

0964a *Cochylis molliculana* Zell.

Recorded:	2006 only
Distribution / Status:	Extremely local / Recent colonist
Conservation status:	Likely to spread
Caterpillar food plants:	Not recorded. Elsewhere, on Bristly Ox-tongue
Flight period:	August.
Records in database:	1

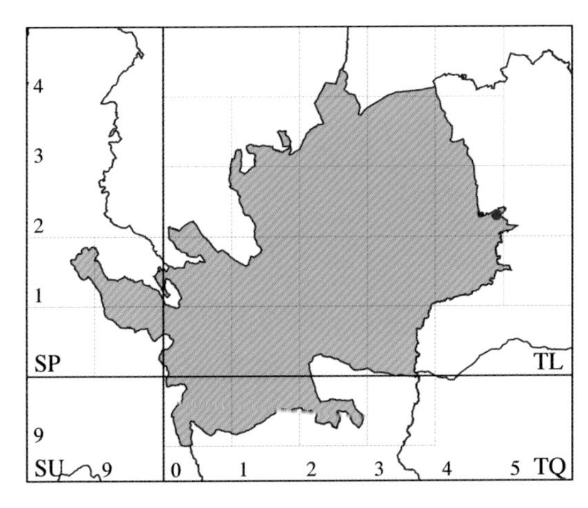

This is a recent colonist of Britain, first noted in Dorset in 1993. It has since spread to affect Middlesex, Essex and Hertfordshire at around the same time, with our first, and so far only, record made at Bishops Stortford on 23rd August 2006, when Rachel Terry found a single example whilst dissecting micros collected at the trap run by Julian Reeves and James Fish.

0965 *Cochylis hybridella* (Hb.)

Recorded:	1966 – 2006
Distribution / Status:	Widespread / Common resident
Conservation status:	No perceived threats
Caterpillar food plants:	Not recorded. Elsewhere, on seeds of Ox-tongues and Hawk's-beards
Flight period:	June to early September with a partial second generation in October
Records in database:	45

Late examples, certainly of this species, are recorded by me at Bishops Stortford on 14th October 2000 and at Cheshunt by Mark Cooper, on 11th October 2005. The moth is normally single-brooded.

0966 *Cochylis atricapitana* (Steph.)

Recorded:	1997 – 2006
Distribution / Status:	Widespread / Common resident
Conservation status:	No perceived threats
Caterpillar food plants:	Not recorded. Elsewhere, on Common Ragwort
Flight period:	Mid-May to mid-September
Records in database:	42

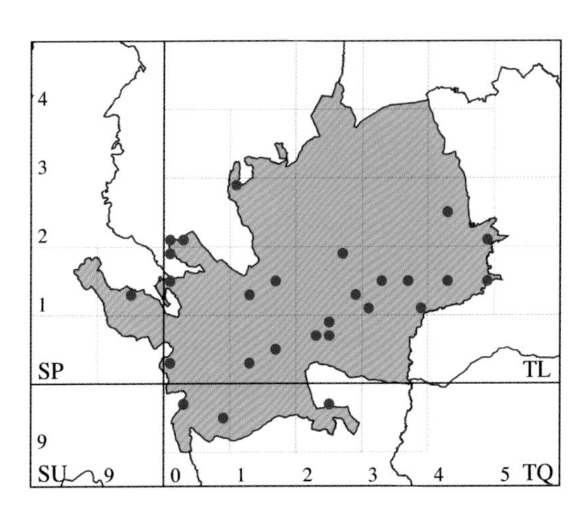

This is normally a double-brooded species, with adults in May/June then late July/August. Our data does not disagree with this, though Hertfordshire records extend to early September.

0968 *Cochylis nana* (Haw.)

Recorded:	1890 – 2006
Distribution / Status:	Local / Uncommon resident
Conservation status:	Insufficiently known
Caterpillar food plants:	Not recorded. Elsewhere, on birch catkins
Flight period:	June
Records in database:	11

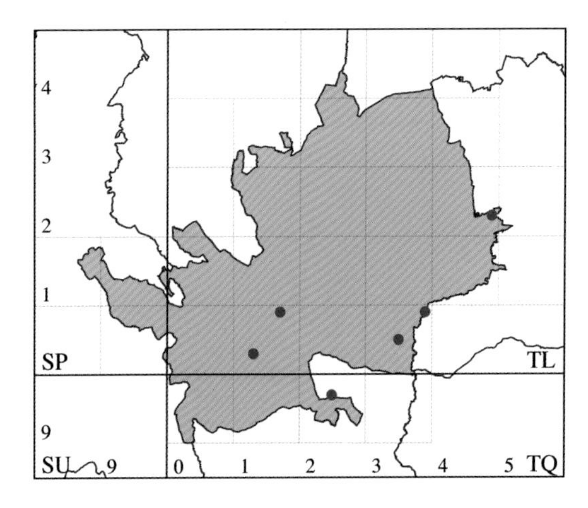

In spite of the fact that birch trees affect most of the county, this small moth is unrecorded in much of Hertfordshire.

0969 *Pandemis corylana* (Fabr.) Chequered Fruit-tree Tortrix

Recorded:	1890 – 2006
Distribution / Status:	Widespread / Common resident
Conservation status:	No perceived threats.
Caterpillar food plants:	Hazel. Elsewhere, on many other trees and shrubs
Flight period:	July to mid-September,
Records in database:	242

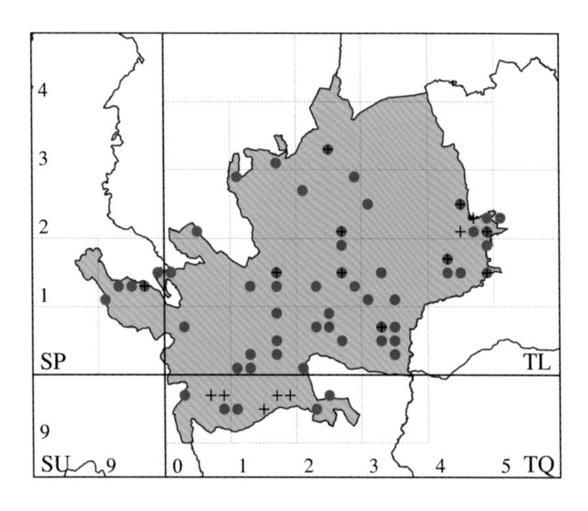

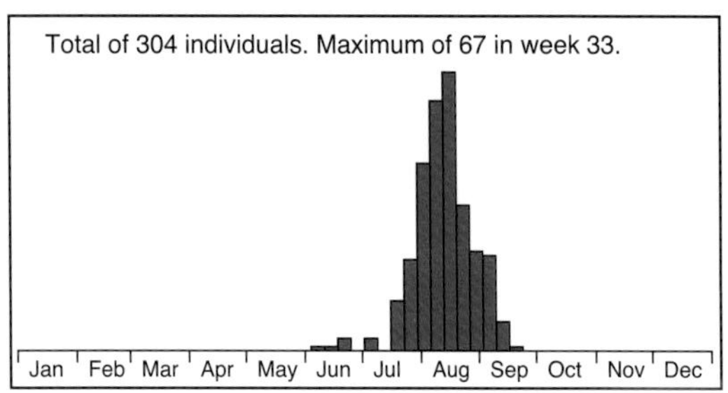

A few correctly identified adults are occasionally caught at light in June, though the main emergence takes place in July. Confusion is possible during June with forms of 970: *Pandemis cerasana*, but our few Hertfordshire June records of *corylana* are known to be correct.

0970 *Pandemis cerasana* (Hb.) Barred Fruit-tree Tortrix

Recorded:	1889 – 2006
Distribution / Status:	Ubiquitous / Common resident
Conservation status:	No perceived threats.
Caterpillar food plants:	Hornbeam, oak, Hazel. Elsewhere, on leaves of trees and shrubs
Flight period:	June to mid-August
Records in database:	267

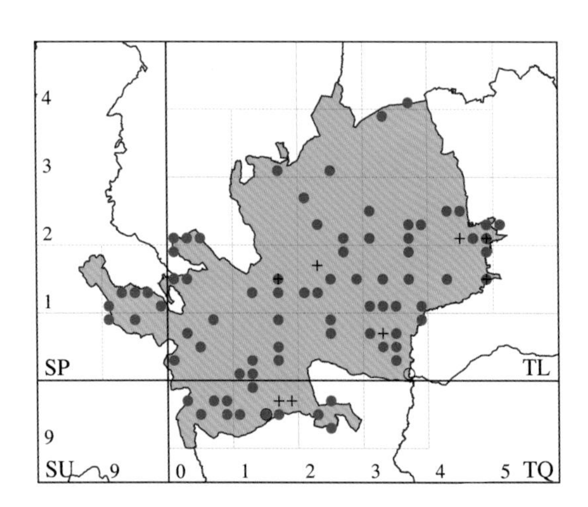

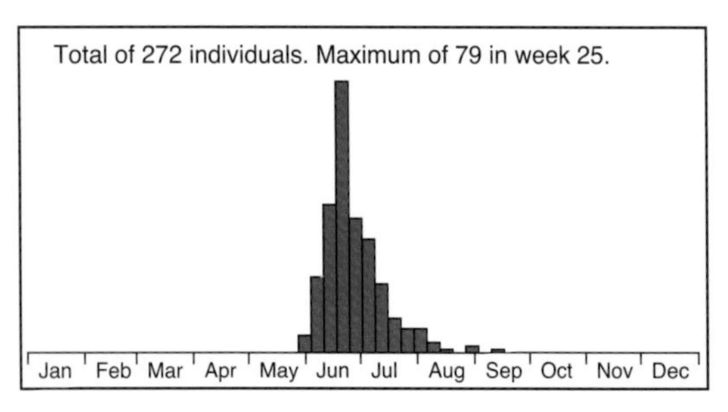

Adults appear, in general, a month before 969: *Pandemis corylana*, but the two overlap in late July and August, so may be caught together. During 2006, a few late examples were noted in September, but this does not seem to be typical behaviour.

[0971 *Pandemis cinnamomeana* (Tr.)

One taken in a garden in Watford in 1956 (Penrose, 1980) is our only record. The species is associated with larger, mature woodlands and is rare in the south-east. A voucher specimen was not retained and it is likely that this records results from a misidentification of another species of *Pandemis*.]

0972 *Pandemis heparana* ([D.& S.]) Dark Fruit-tree Tortrix

Recorded:	1889 – 2006
Distribution / Status:	Ubiquitous / Common resident
Conservation status:	No perceived threats.
Caterpillar food plants:	Not recorded. Elsewhere, on leaves of trees and shrubs
Flight period:	June to August
Records in database:	320

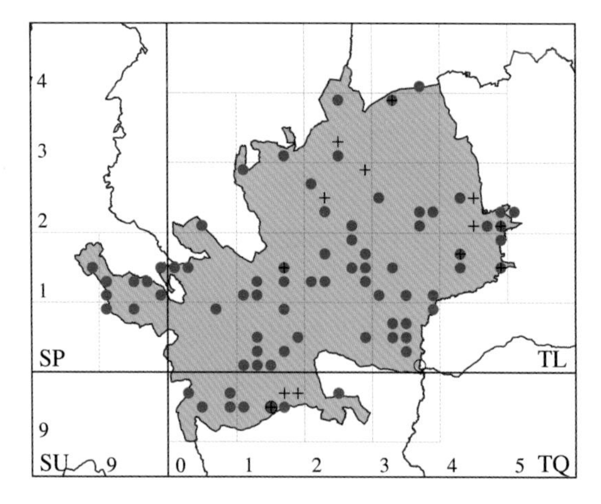

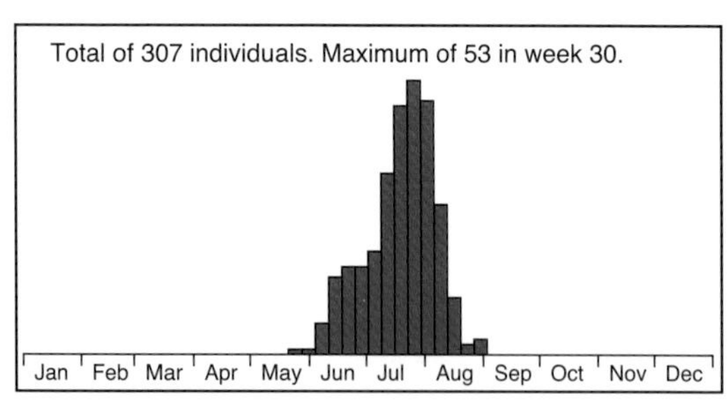

0974 *Argyrotaenia ljungiana* (Thunb.) = *pulchellana* (Haw.)

Recorded:	1890 – 2006
Distribution / Status:	Widespread / Common resident
Conservation status:	No perceived threats
Caterpillar food plants:	Not recorded. Elsewhere, polyphagous
Flight period:	Late April/May then July/August
Records in database:	347

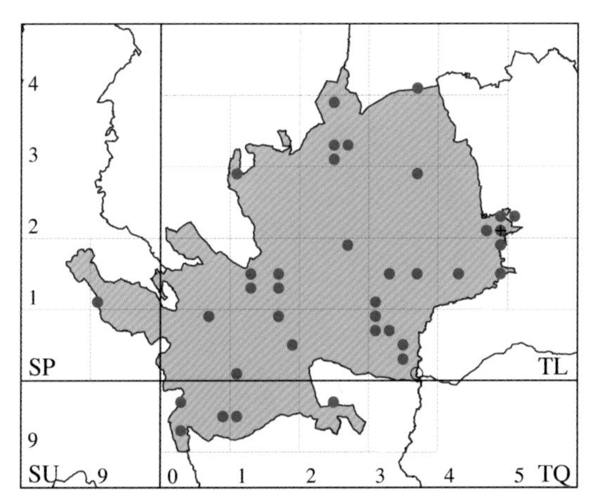

Though recorded on several occasions in the nineteenth century (Sandridge, Hitchin, Northwood, Rickmansworth and Cheshunt are listed in Foster, 1937) this moth seems to have become scarce during the first sixty or seventy years of the twentieth. It extended its range again from the mid-1980s onwards and is probably still doing so. Adults were recorded on the two unseasonally early dates of 1st February 2004 at Bengeo (Andrew Wood) and 17th March 2000 in my garden in Bishops Stortford.

0977 *Archips podana* (Scop.) Large Fruit-tree Tortrix

Recorded:	1890 – 2006
Distribution / Status:	Ubiquitous / Common resident
Conservation status:	No perceived threats.
Caterpillar food plants:	Not recorded. Elsewhere, on leaves of trees and shrubs
Flight period:	June to early October in two generations
Records in database:	350

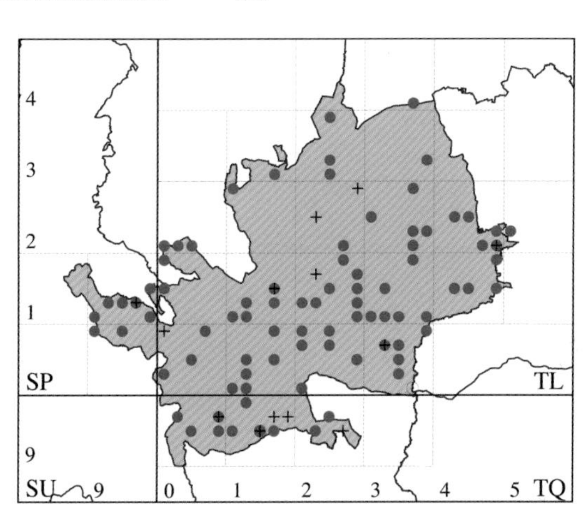

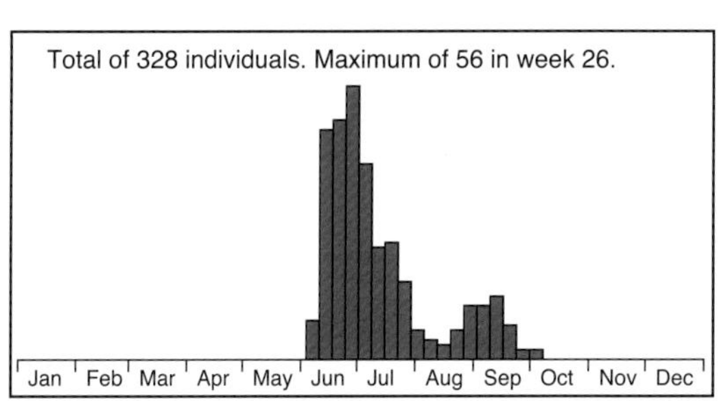

Almost all woodland, scrub and hedgerow habitat will support this moth in Hertfordshire and it is equally frequent in most garden light traps.

0979 *Archips crataegana* (Hb.)

Recorded:	1890 – 2006
Distribution / Status:	Local / Uncommon resident
Conservation status:	No perceived threats
Caterpillar food plants:	Not recorded. Elsewhere, on leaves of trees and shrubs
Flight period:	Mid-June to mid-July
Records in database:	25

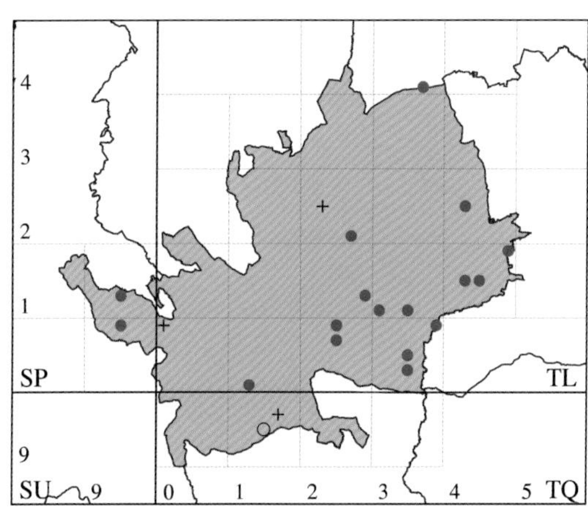

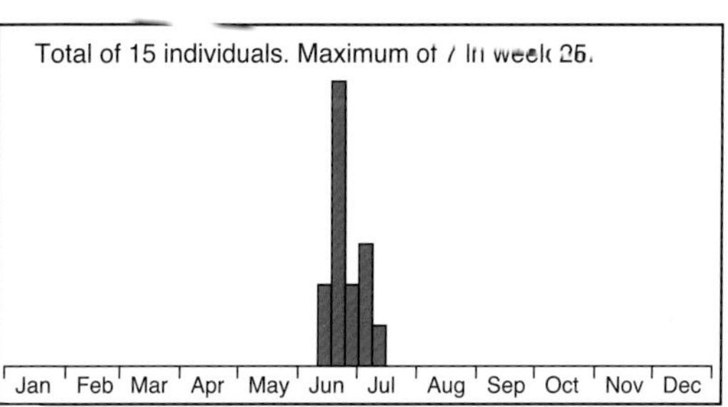

Though it must be remembered that the number of individuals used to create the graph is small, the flight period nevertheless appears contracted in comparison with 977: *Archips podana* and 980: *Archips xylosteana*. This species is seemingly rather local and rarely found away from oak trees, which are perhaps the preferred larval food source in Hertfordshire.

0980 *Archips xylosteana* (L.) Brown Oak Tortrix

Recorded:	1834 – 2006
Distribution / Status:	Widespread / Common resident
Conservation status:	No perceived threats.
Caterpillar food plants:	Beech. Elsewhere, on leaves of many trees and shrubs
Flight period:	Mid-June to August
Records in database:	133

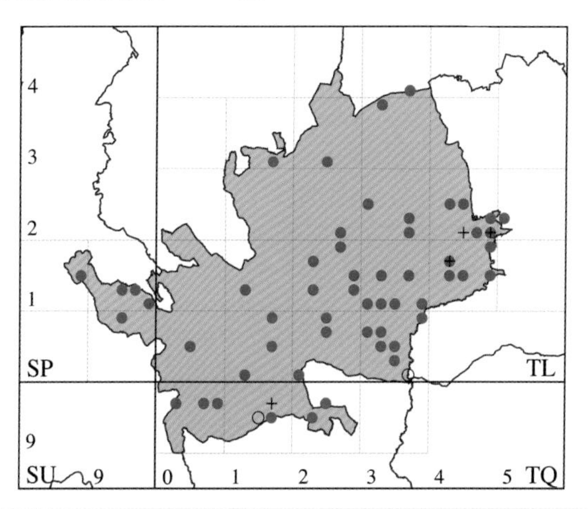

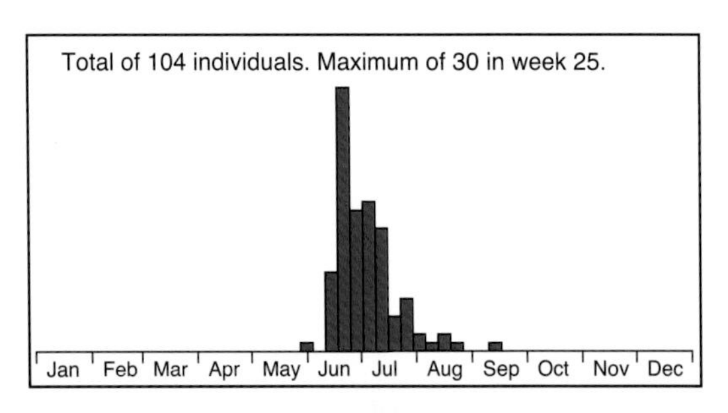

This has always been a frequent moth in the county, and was first recorded as long ago as 1834, in Hertford, from where we also record an unusually late example of an adult in the Bengeo district on 11th September 2006 (Andrew Wood). At the other end of the year our earliest extreme was on 1st June 2003 at Ware (Elizabeth Goodyear).

0981 *Archips rosana* (L.) Rose Tortrix

Recorded:	1890 – 1999
Distribution / Status:	Local / Rare resident
Conservation status:	Herts Rare
Caterpillar food plants:	Not recorded. Elsewhere, on leaves, buds and flowers of trees and shrubs
Flight period:	July to early October
Records in database:	10

Although it can apparently sometimes be a pest on apple trees in southern England, this species seems to be a rarity in Hertfordshire. Old records are from Sandridge (Griffith, 1890), the Cheshunt area (Boyd, 1901), St Albans (Gibbs, 1902) and Hitchin (Foster, 1934) with Foster (1937) adding Letchworth and Bushey Heath without any indication of year. A record from Watford in 1956 (Penrose, 1980) is unconfirmed and probably incorrect. It was noted in Stevenage on 15th June 1966 (Jack Newton). Recent records are from Panshanger Park in 1997 and Digswell village in 1999 (Tom Gladwin), Croxley Common Moor on 1st July 2004 (Alan Outen). Further records from a garden in Bricketwood on 22nd June 2005 and 15th & 16th October 2006 (Henry Ellis) are, with the consent of the captor, treated as unconfirmed since there are no voucher specimens.

0982 *Choristoneura diversana* (Hb.)

Recorded:	1889 – 2004
Distribution / Status:	Local / Rare resident
Conservation status:	Herts Rare
Caterpillar food plants:	Not recorded. Elsewhere, on leaves of trees and shrubs
Flight period:	Not recorded. Elsewhere, June/July
Records in database:	5

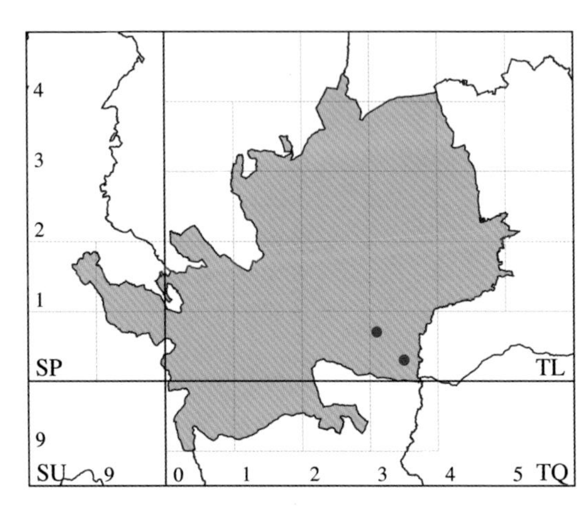

Our only recent records are from Cheshunt and Wormley Wood in the south-east. It was also recorded from the Cheshunt area by Boyd (1901) as well as from the St Albans area (Gibbs, 1889) and the Sandridge area (Griffith, 1890). This is a large species that is unlikely to have been overlooked to any significant degree and so its rarity appears to be genuine.

0983 *Choristoneura hebenstreitella* (Mull.)

Recorded:	1834 – 2006
Distribution / Status:	Local / Common resident
Conservation status:	No perceived threats
Caterpillar food plants:	Not recorded. Elsewhere, on leaves of trees and shrubs
Flight period:	Mid-June to August
Records in database:	27

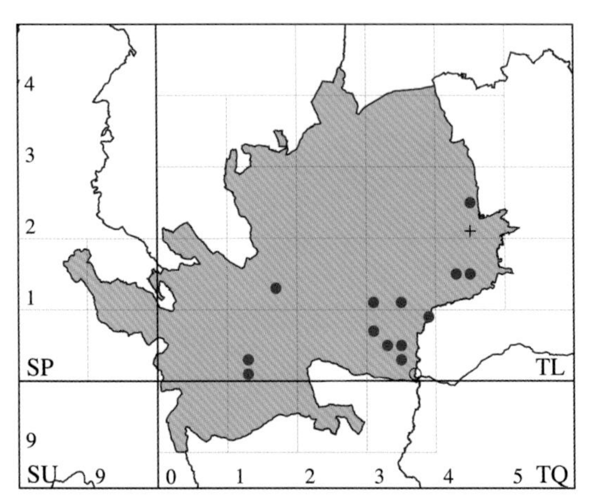

The spread of records in the south-east may reflect the 'better' woodlands in this region or it may reflect the greater number of visits to these woodlands by microlepidopterists. The moth is likely to be more widespread, but perhaps not excessively so.

0985 *Cacoecimorpha pronubana* (Hb.) Carnation Tortrix

Recorded: 1964 – 2006
Distribution / Status: Widespread / Common resident
Conservation status: No perceived threats
Caterpillar food plants: Garden carnations, potted Geranium in a greenhouse, Lemon Geranium, Tomato, Strawberry and Hornbeam. Elsewhere, widely polyphagous
Flight period: May to October
Records in database: 109

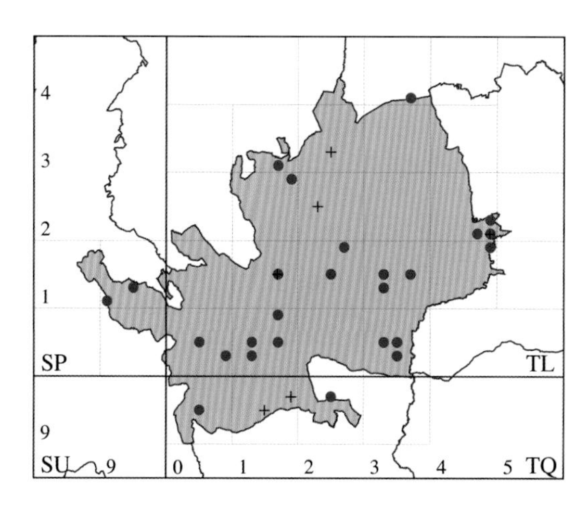

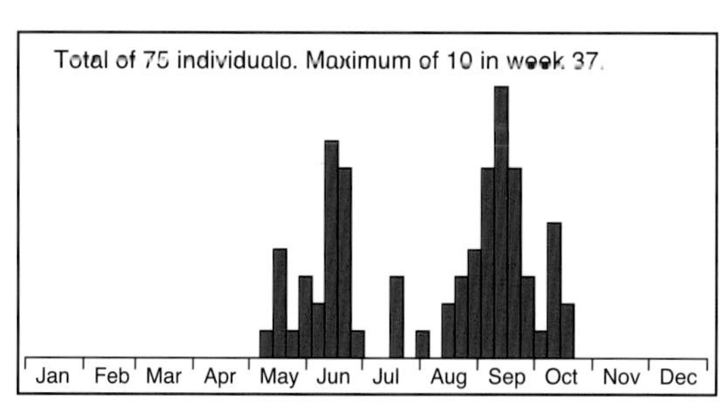

In the wild, the Carnation Tortrix is apparently double-brooded with adults in May June and again in September. Indoors, where it can be a pest of potted plants, it is continuously brooded.

0986 *Syndemis musculana* (Hb.)

Recorded: 1890 – 2006
Distribution / Status: Widespread / Common resident
Conservation status: No perceived threats.
Caterpillar food plants: Not recorded. Elsewhere, on leaves of trees and shrubs including conifers
Flight period: Late April to early June
Records in database: 143

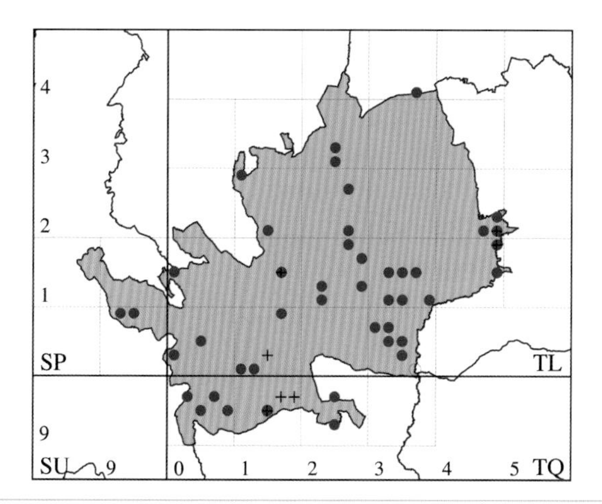

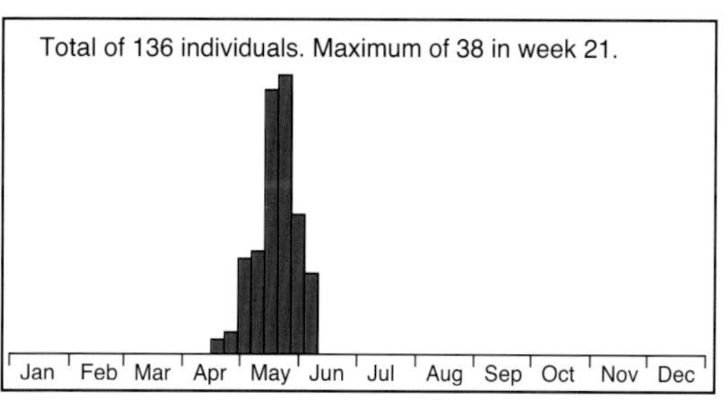

This is a familiar sight in most moth traps and is often the first tortricid to be caught in the year.

0987 *Ptycholomoides aeriferanus* (H.- S.)

Recorded: 1969 – 2006
Distribution / Status: Local / Common resident
Conservation status: No perceived threats
Caterpillar food plants: Larch – between spun needles
Flight period: Late June to early August
Records in database: 27

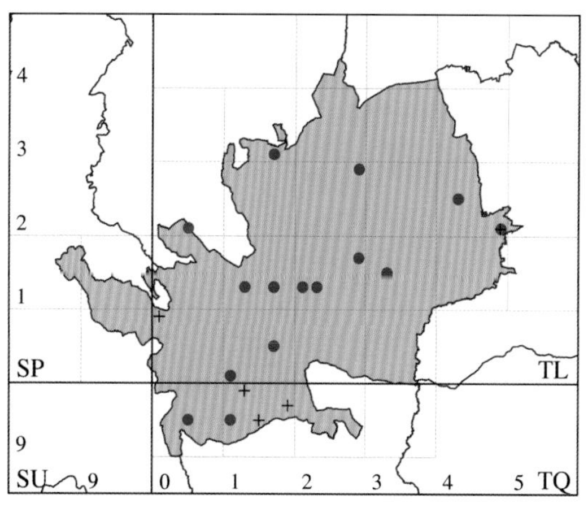

The distribution of larch trees restricts the distribution of the moth, but adults come readily to light traps and should be found in areas where the trees grow, including larger gardens.

0989 *Aphelia paleana* (Hb.) Timothy Tortrix

Recorded: 1900 – 2006
Distribution / Status: Local / Common resident
Conservation status: No perceived threats.
Caterpillar food plants: Not recorded. Elsewhere, mostly on grasses but also on herbaceous plants and trees
Flight period: June/July
Records in database: 55

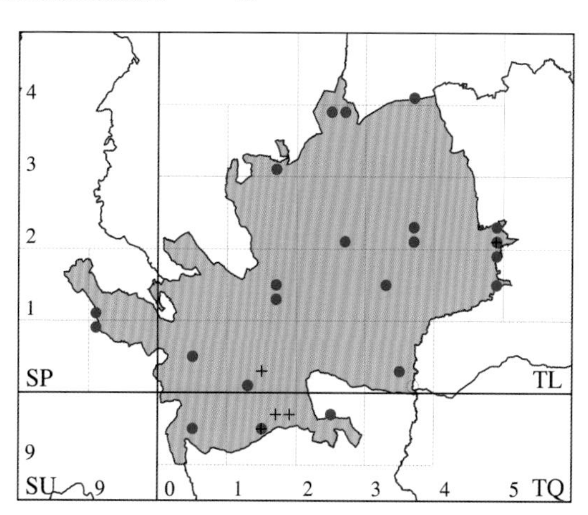

In spite of the colloquial name the moth is not confined to Timothy Grass nor to grasslands. However, it is certainly more numerous in unimproved and semi-improved leys than elsewhere.

0993 *Clepsis spectrana* (Tr.) Cyclamen Tortrix

Recorded: 1890 – 2006
Distribution / Status: Widespread / Common resident
Conservation status: No perceived threats.
Caterpillar food plants: Not recorded. Elsewhere, polyphagous on herbaceous plants
Flight period: Late May to early September
Records in database: 53

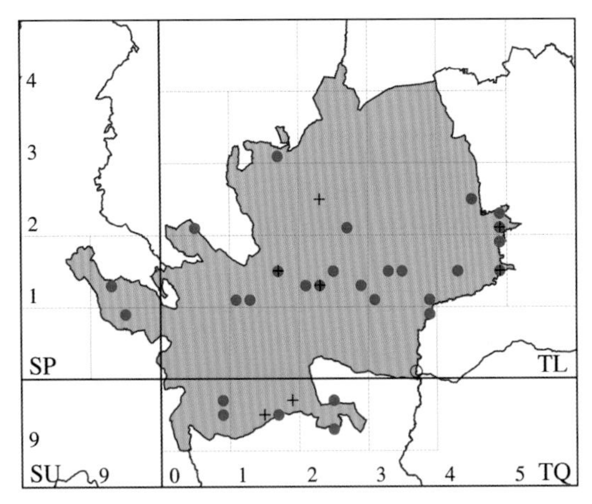

An under-recorded species, likely to be common in most parts of Hertfordshire. A late adult was caught by me at Rye Meads on 14th October 2000.

0994 *Clepsis consimilana* (Hb.)

Recorded: 1890 – 2006
Distribution / Status: Ubiquitous / Common resident
Conservation status: No perceived threats
Caterpillar food plants: Hornbeam. Elsewhere, widely polyphagous
Flight period: Late May to August then September to November
Records in database: 267

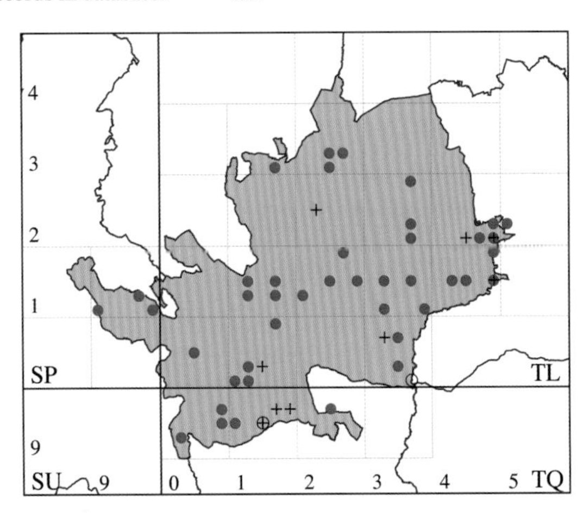

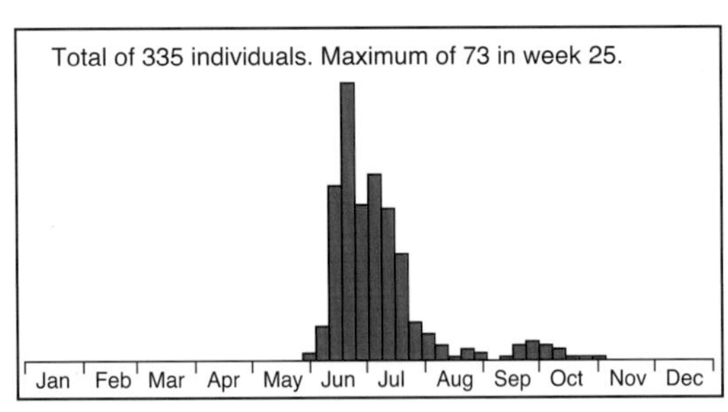

This species is much under-recorded, probably because it is small and brown with scarcely any discernible markings. The larvae are said to prefer feeding on withered leaves. In Hertfordshire, there has been a small second generation of adults from 2003 to 2006, but prior to that period records beyond the end of August are exceptional.

0998 *Epiphyas postvittana* (Walker) Light-brown Apple Moth

Recorded: 2000 – 2006
Distribution / Status: Widespread / Common resident
Conservation status: No perceived threats.
Caterpillar food plants: Not recorded. Elsewhere, widely polyphagous.
Flight period: January to December
Records in database: 784

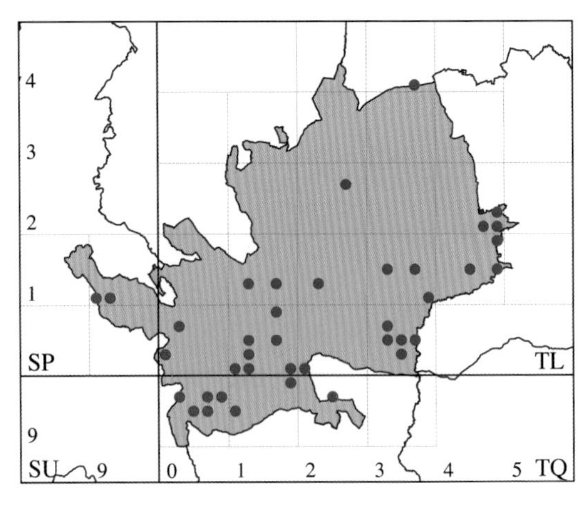

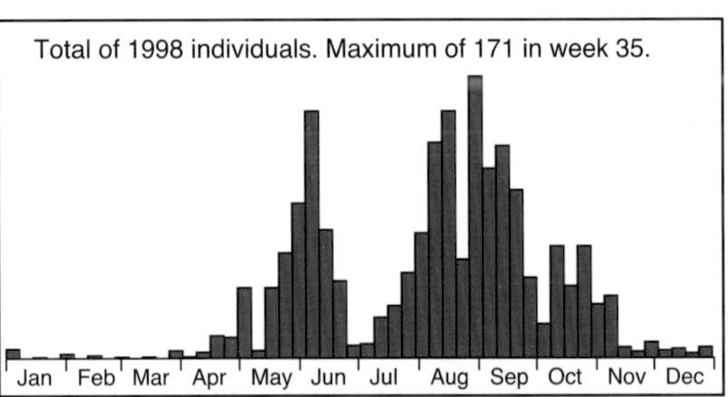

A native of Australia this pest of apple trees was first found in Britain in Cornwall, during 1936, where it remained for many years. In the early 1980s it started to spread and in 1983 was recorded for the first time in both Kent and Essex. The first Hertfordshire records were apparently those relating to the two adults taken in my Bishops Stortford garden on 2nd June and 19th August 2000. Though some earlier county records may have gone unreported, my trap had run almost nightly from 1987 onwards yet these were both my first records and the only Hertfordshire records for 2000. In 2001, it was recorded at Rickmansworth (Paul Clack), Garston (Colin Everett) and in my garden again. In 2002, it was reported from all over the southern part of the county – mostly from sites where traps had been run the previous year without finding it. The sudden nature of the spread is emphasised, given that this moth was unknown in our county prior to 2000, by the large number of records in the database. The northern map dot is at Royston where the moth appeared first in 2002; the absence of records from much of the north of the county is surprising as the species has already penetrated much further north in the rest of Britain.

1000 *Ptycholoma lecheana* (L.)

Recorded: 1834 – 2006
Distribution / Status: Widespread / Common resident
Conservation status: No perceived threats
Caterpillar food plants: Downy Birch. Elsewhere, on various trees and shrubs
Flight period: May/June
Records in database: 32

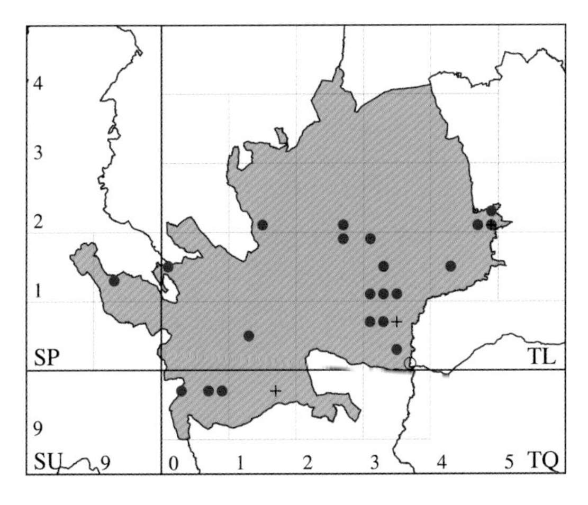

The records indicate a common moth that is under-recorded.

1001 *Lozotaeniodes formosanus* (Geyer)

Recorded: 1967 – 2006
Distribution / Status: Widespread / Common resident
Conservation status: No perceived threats
Caterpillar food plants: Not recorded. Elsewhere, on Scots Pine
Flight period: Mid-June to August, occasionally later
Records in database: 198

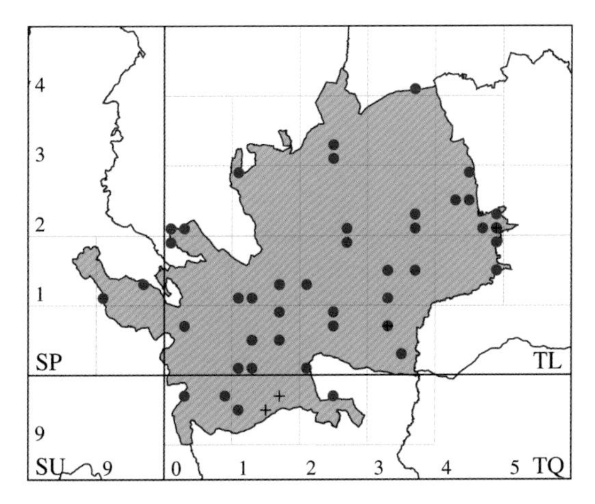

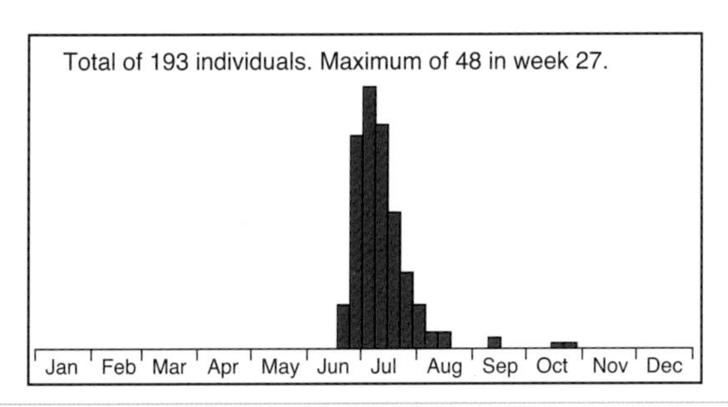

Unknown in Britain prior to 1945, when it was found in Surrey, *Lozotaeniodes formosanus* has spread to reach Hertfordshire by 1967, when Barry Goater caught an example at the Haberdasher's Aske's School at Aldenham on 15th July. It seems to have been slow to spread and Barry did not catch the first in his garden until 1976; that year was exceptionally hot and the moth could simply have been a vagrant. There are no more records until the mid 1980s, but there were almost no microlepidopterists in the county in the intervening years and in my first full year of trapping here, at Bishops Stortford, it was a regular visitor to the trap. A line of Scots Pine trees ('The Firs') was then present about a hundred yards from my house (though few of these trees now remain having been replaced with 'more appropriate' species). Late adults in September and October, perhaps representing a partial second generation, were noted in the extreme east (Bishops Stortford) and extreme west (Chorleywood) of the county in 2001, 2005 and 2006.

1002 *Lozotaenia forsterana* (Fabr.)

Recorded: 1890 – 2006
Distribution / Status: Widespread / Common resident
Conservation status: No perceived threats
Caterpillar food plants: Ivy. Elsewhere, polyphagous, but most frequent on Ivy
Flight period: Late May to mid-July
Records in database: 265

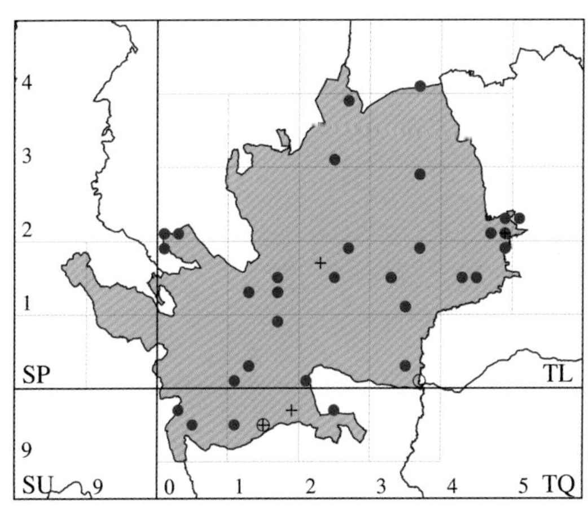

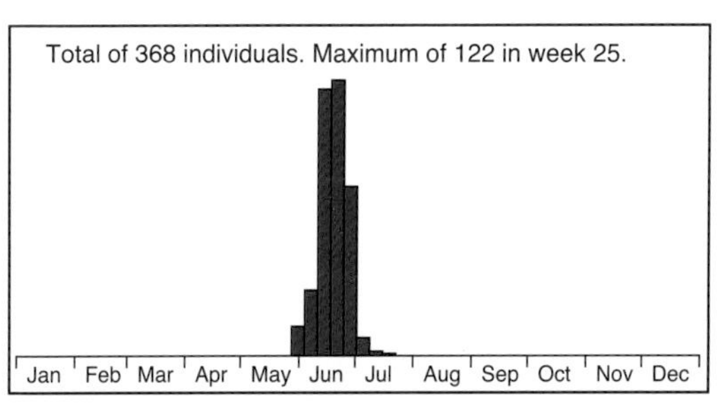

This species is likely to be found in most places where ivy is established.

1006 *Epagoge grotiana* (Fabr.)

Recorded: 1889 – 2006
Distribution / Status: Local / Common resident
Conservation status: No perceived threats
Caterpillar food plants: Not recorded. Elsewhere, on oak, hawthorn and bramble
Flight period: Mid-June to early August
Records in database: 46

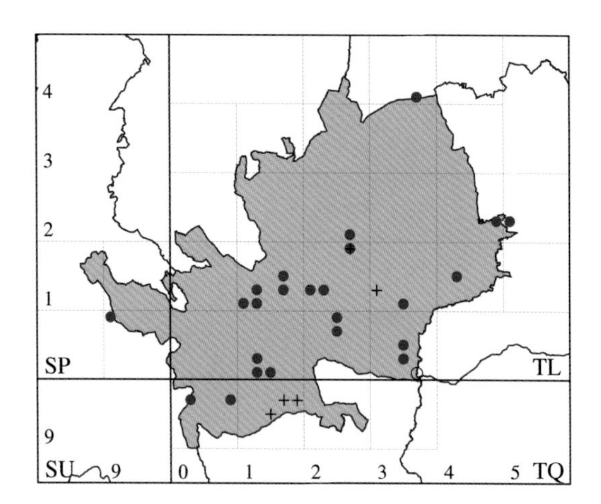

The habit of flying at dusk, before traps are put out, and at dawn, after most of those not set in gardens have been taken in, undoubtedly makes this an under-recorded species.

1007 *Capua vulgana* (Fr.)

Recorded: 1882 – 2006
Distribution / Status: Local / Uncommon resident
Conservation status: No perceived threats
Caterpillar food plants: Hornbeam. Elsewhere, on various trees and bushes
Flight period: Late May/June
Records in database: 18

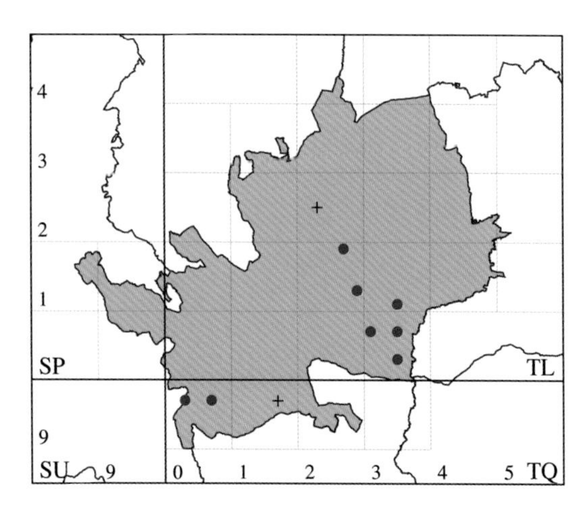

This is another crepuscular species and few of our records are from individuals attracted to light, though they do come occasionally.

1010 *Ditula angustiorana* (Haw.) Red-barred Fruit Tortrix

Recorded: 1890 – 2006
Distribution / Status: Widespread / Common resident
Conservation status: No perceived threats.
Caterpillar food plants: Not recorded. Elsewhere, on various trees and bushes
Flight period: June to early August
Records in database: 248

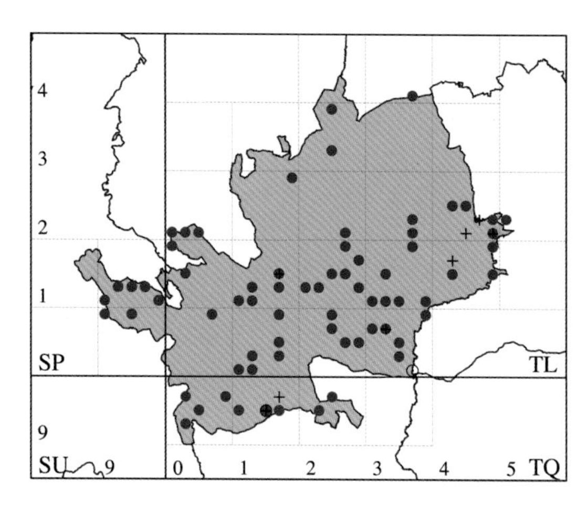

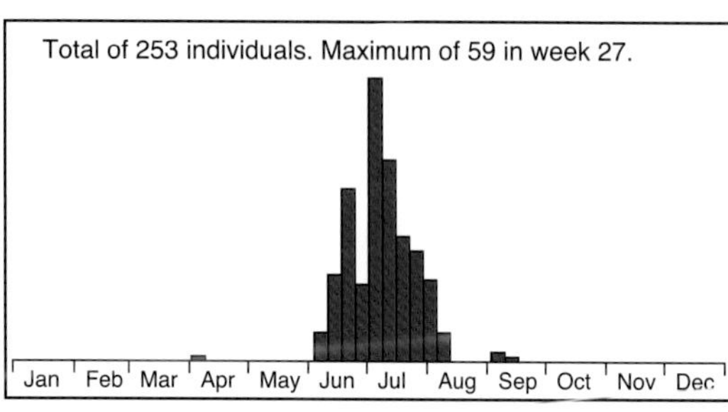

This is a distinctive species that is, as with others, under-recorded. Occasional late examples are noted in September; our earliest report is from Bishops Stortford on 5th April 2003 (James Fish & Julian Reeves).

1011 *Pseudargyrotoza conwagana* (Fabr.)

Recorded: 1888 – 2006
Distribution / Status: Widespread / Common resident
Conservation status: No perceived threats
Caterpillar food plants: Not recorded. Elsewhere, Ash (seeds) and privet (berries)
Flight period: Late May to August
Records in database: 162

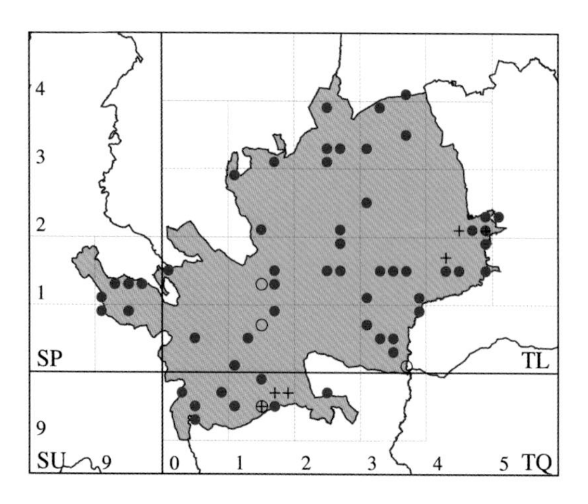

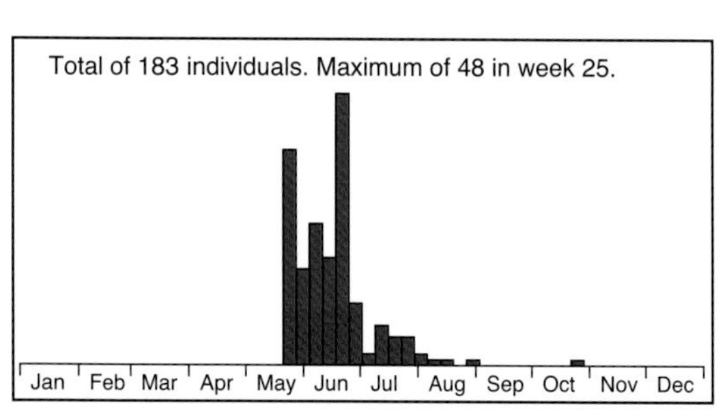

The appearance of large numbers of fresh examples in May and early June and the preponderance of worn examples thereafter suggests a species that is rather long-lived in the adult stage rather than one with a protracted emergence period, although small numbers of fresh-looking individuals do sometimes attend light traps throughout June.

1013 *Olindia schumacherana* (Fabr.) after 1062

1014 *Isotrias rectifasciana* (Haw.) after 1062

1015 *Eulia ministrana* (L.)

Recorded: 1888 – 2006
Distribution / Status: Local / Common resident
Conservation status: No perceived threats
Caterpillar food plants: Not recorded. Elsewhere, on the leaves of various trees
Flight period: Late April to June
Records in database: 40

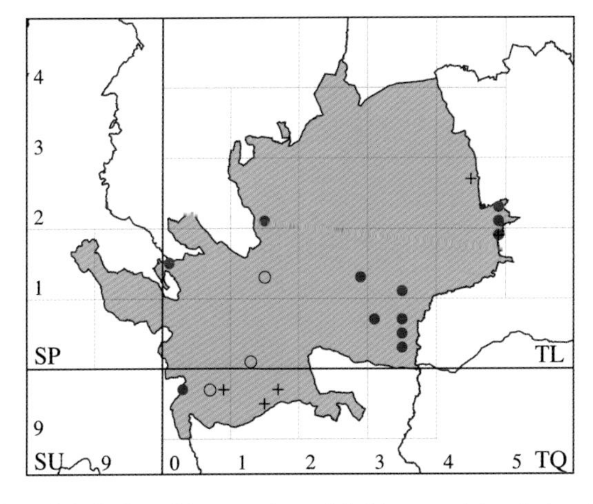

The adult is found in a variety of habitats and its distinctive appearance means that it is unlikely to be overlooked or wrongly identified. Thus, it may be genuinely local with us.

The genus *Cnephasia*

With the exception of *Cnephasia longana*, which can usually be recognised, and *Cnephasia incertana* females, which can be separated from other *Cnephasia* species of the same sex by the elongated ovipositor which protrudes from the abdomen, all specimens will require dissection to allow correct identification. The following species accounts dismiss **all** records where the genitalia have not been examined and, where the recorder is inexperienced, a slide made available for examination.

1016 *Cnephasia longana* (Haw.)

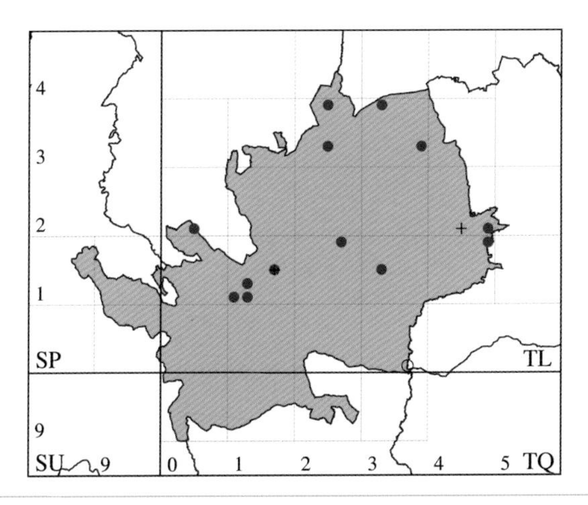

Recorded: 1900 – 2006
Distribution / Status: Local / Common resident
Conservation status: No perceived threats.
Caterpillar food plants: Not recorded. Elsewhere, on various herbaceous plants
Flight period: July to the first half of August
Records in database: 23

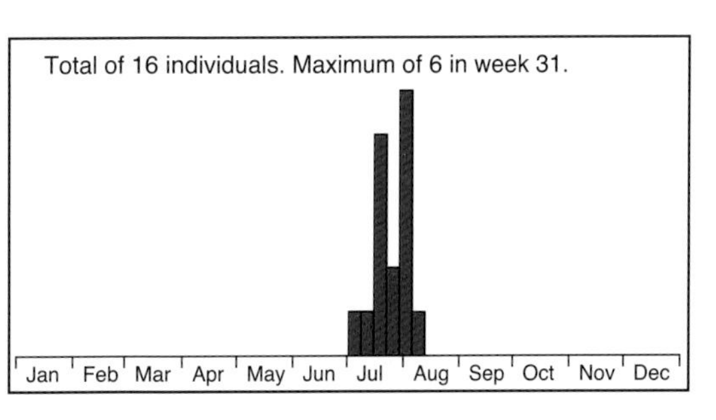

It is odd that most records are from the north; most under-recorded moths show a southern bias. Confusion is possible with 1029: *Eana osseana*, which appears rare in Hertfordshire.

1018 *Cnephasia communana* (H.- S.)

Recorded: 1890 – 2005
Distribution / Status: Widespread / Common resident
Conservation status: No perceived threats
Caterpillar food plants: Apparently unknown in Britain
Flight period: Mid-May to July
Records in database: 45

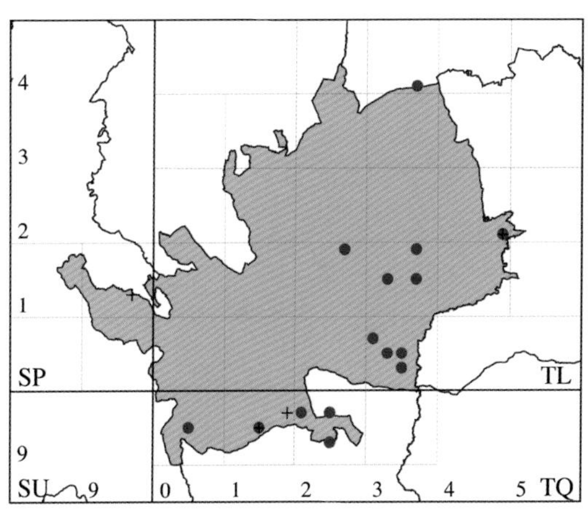

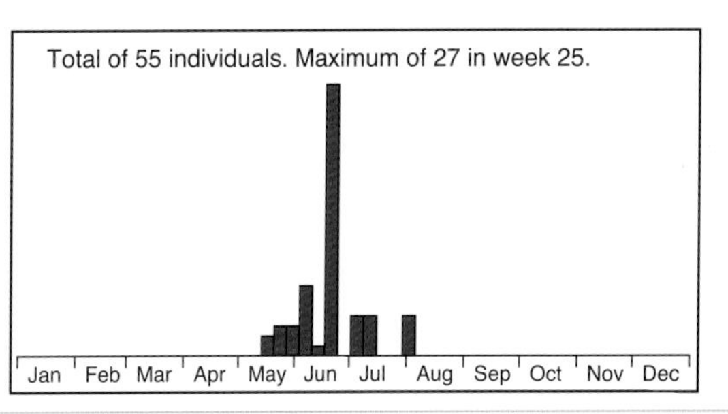

This species is most often encountered near to north London and is numerically scarce away from here. The distribution is almost the exact opposite of that for 1016: *Cnephasia longana* showing, if nothing else, that our coverage of dissected specimens is geographically even.

1020 *Cnephasia stephensiana* (Doubl.) Grey Tortrix

Recorded: 1890 – 2006
Distribution / Status: Ubiquitous / Common resident
Conservation status: No perceived threats .
Caterpillar food plants: Not recorded. Elsewhere, polyphagous on herbaceous plants
Flight period: Mid-June to early August, occasionally in May
Records in database: 141

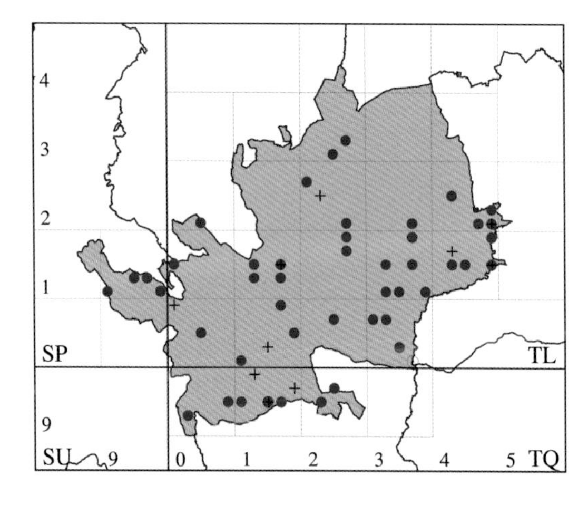

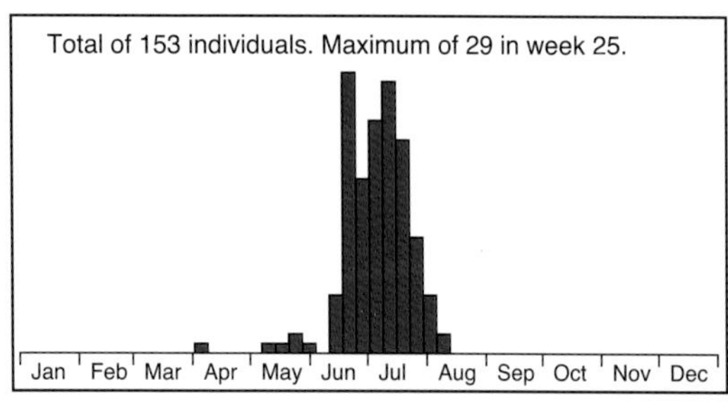

Large examples of *Cnephasia* are probably this species if they are male (though large females may be *asseclana*). Nevertheless, I require dissection for inclusion here. The presence of several examples in May, and one as early as 3rd April 2003 at Bishops Stortford, is rather surprising, but the main flight period is in keeping with the national situation.

1021 *Cnephasia asseclana* ([D.& S.]) Flax Tortrix = *interjectana* (Haw.)

Recorded: 1890 – 2006
Distribution / Status: Ubiquitous / Common resident
Conservation status: No perceived threats .
Caterpillar food plants: Not recorded. Elsewhere, polyphagous on herbaceous plants
Flight period: Mid-June to mid-August
Records in database: 86

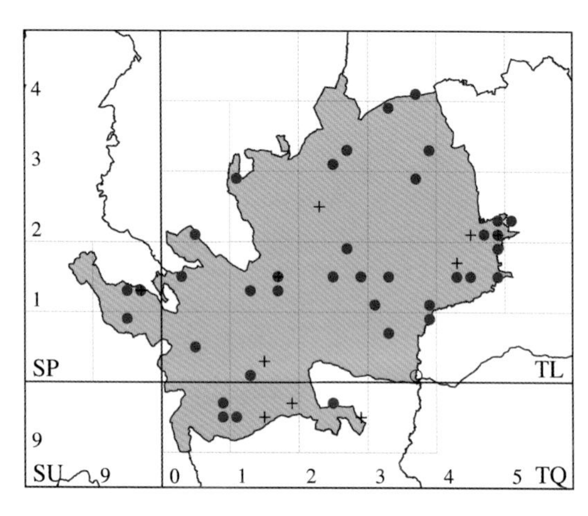

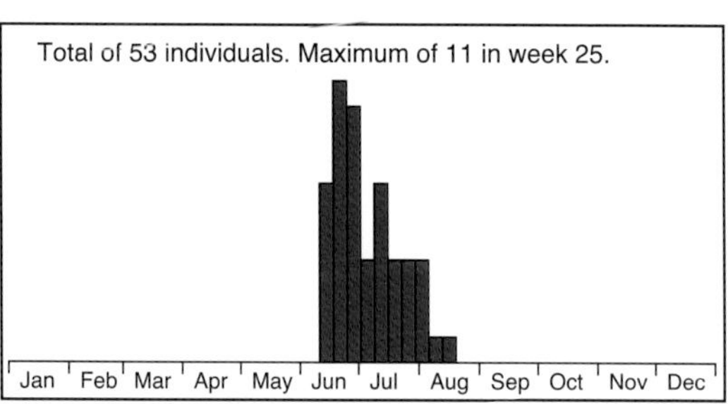

Numerically, this is the commonest *Cnephasia* species in Hertfordshire.

1022 *Cnephasia pasiuana* (Hb.)

Recorded: 1890 – 2006
Distribution / Status: Local / Uncommon resident
Conservation status: No perceived threats
Caterpillar food plants: Not recorded. Elsewhere, polyphagous on flowers of the Compositae
Flight period: Late June to early August
Records in database: 13

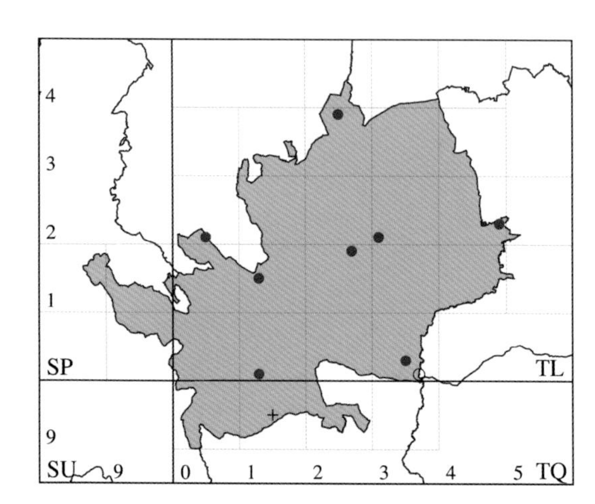

Small, plain grey *Cnephasia* specimens will probably be either this species or *genitalana*. The records are scattered across the whole county, but the species is rarely encountered.

1023 *Cnephasia genitalana* Pierce & Metcalfe

Recorded: 2001 – 2006
Distribution / Status: Local / Uncommon resident
Conservation status: No perceived threats
Caterpillar food plants: Not recorded. Elsewhere, polyphagous on herbaceous plants, especially Compositae
Flight period: July/August
Records in database: 23

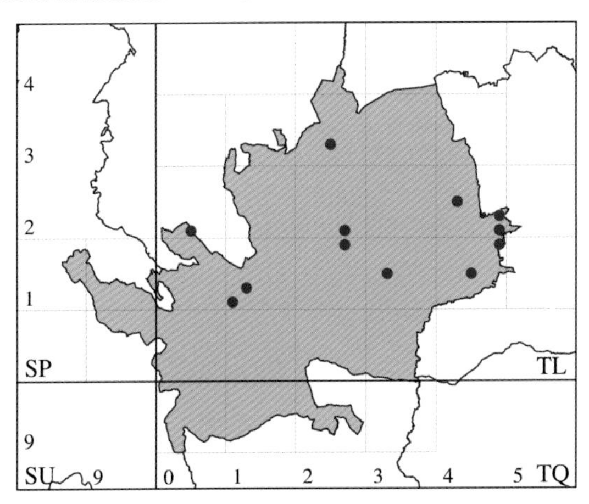

In contrast with the superficially similar *pasiuana* this species is absent from the south of the county – perhaps genuinely so.

1024 *Cnephasia incertana* (Tr.) Light Grey Tortrix

Recorded: 1888 – 2005
Distribution / Status: Widespread / Uncommon resident
Conservation status: Stable
Caterpillar food plants: Not recorded. Elsewhere, polyphagous on herbaceous plants
Flight period: Late May to early August
Records in database: 49

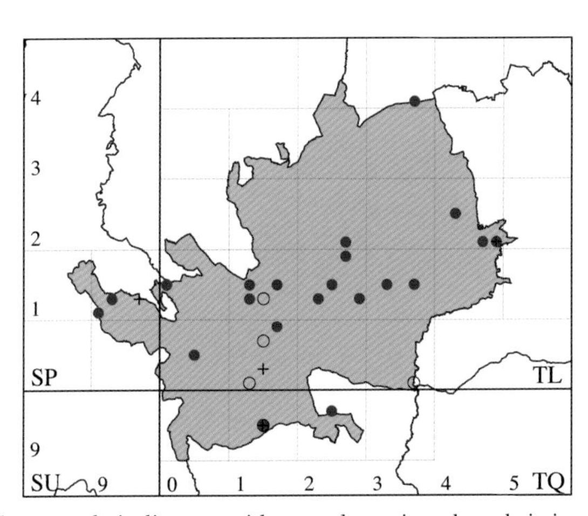

The records indicate a widespread species, though it is not numerically common at any recorded site.

1025 *Tortricodes alternella* ([D.& S.])

Recorded: 1834 – 2006
Distribution / Status: Widespread / Common resident
Conservation status: No perceived threats
Caterpillar food plants: Not recorded. Elsewhere, polyphagous on trees and shrubs
Flight period: Mid-January to May
Records in database: 75

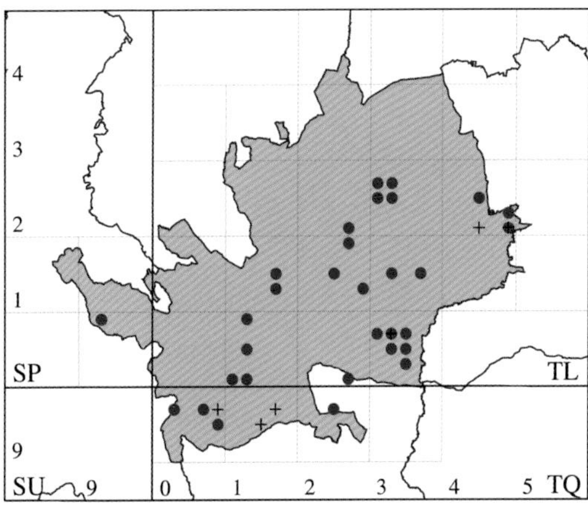

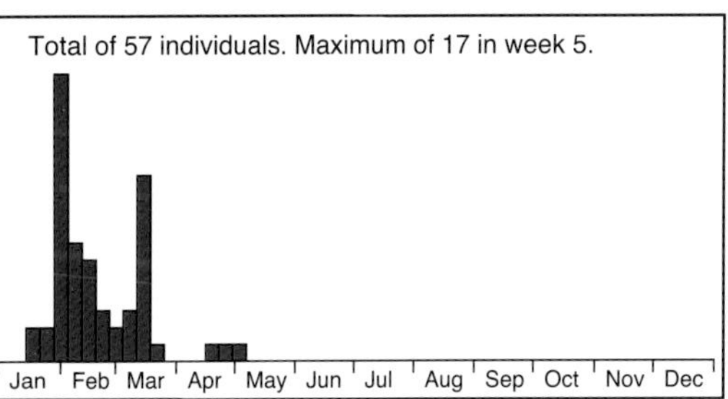

Adults are amongst the first moths in the trap at the start of the year, but the exact emergence date varies with season. Thus, the double peak in the flight chart represents weather patterns in the 2000 to 2006 period covered, not separate broods of adults.

1026 *Exapate congelatella* (Cl.)

Recorded: 1822 – 2006
Distribution / Status: Extremely local / Rare resident
Conservation status: Herts Rare
Caterpillar food plants: Not recorded. Elsewhere, widely polyphagous
Flight period: October to December
Records in database: 6

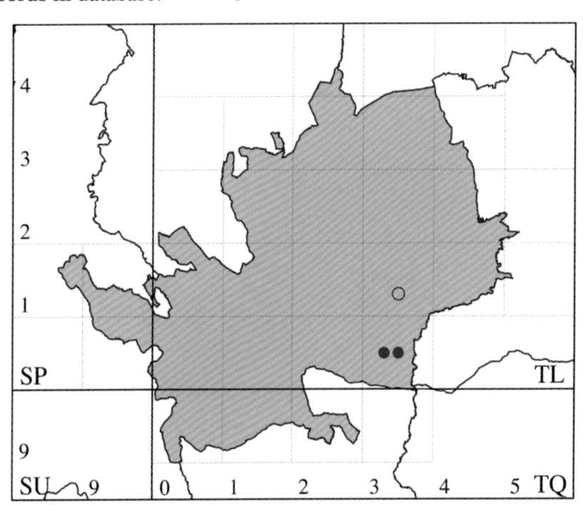

There are three old Hertfordshire records: It is listed by J. F. Stephens (1824) as 'abundant in all Saints Churchyard, Hertford, 27th Dec 1822' in *Illustrations of British Entomology* **4**: 235. Griffith (1890) includes it in his list for the Sandridge area and Boyd (1901) mentions it in his list for the Cheshunt area. Since then, Mark Cooper has found adults at Thunderfield

Grove on 24th October 2004 (1) and 27th December 2006 (8) and in Wormley Wood on 29th October 2004 (10). It is quite likely that Mark has refound the moth in the same locality where it was recorded by Boyd. The late date in the year when adult moths are active may suggest a degree of under-recording, though I have failed to find it in several places. It is evidently quite rare in Essex to the east and is apparently absent from Middlesex to the south. [One at mv light, Bishops Stortford, 2nd November 2007 (James Fish & Julian Reeve) is beyond the period covered by this book and is not mapped, but may indicate a degree of under-recording.]

1027 *Neosphaleroptera nubilana* (Hb.)

Recorded:	1890 - 2005
Distribution / Status:	Extremely local / Rare resident
Conservation status:	Herts Rare
Caterpillar food plants:	Common Hawthorn. Elsewhere, also on Blackthorn
Flight period:	Elsewhere, June/July
Records in database:	8

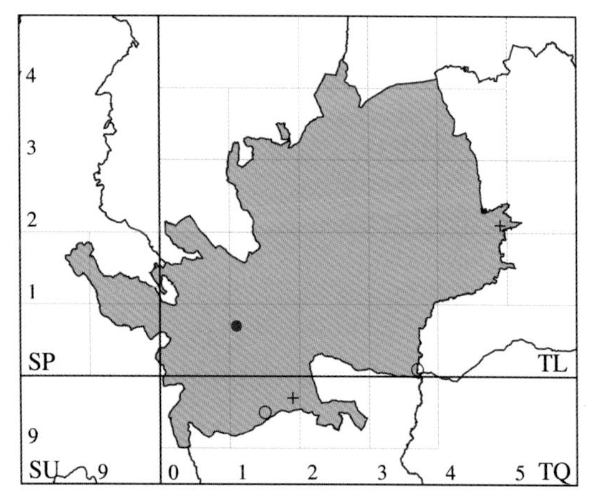

Our only recent record is of a male taken at Gorehambury on 27th June 2005 by Wendy Hatton, identified from a genitalia slide. During 1987, I reared adults from larvae found on a hawthorn hedge in Apton Road, Bishops Stortford and in the same year I caught adults in the garden light trap a few hundred yards away, but I have not seen it here since. The most recent record prior to that was at Drayton Road, Borehamwood, where Eric Bradford recorded it at light on 24th June 1967. All other reports are from the 1937 county list or earlier. It seems genuinely rare in Hertfordshire. People who use commercially available pheromone lures to attract clearwings (Sesiidae) may wish to be aware that I inadvertently attracted this species to the combination MYO-TIP-VES at a site in Middlesex in 2002 (see Plant, 2003).

1029 *Eana osseana* (Scop.)

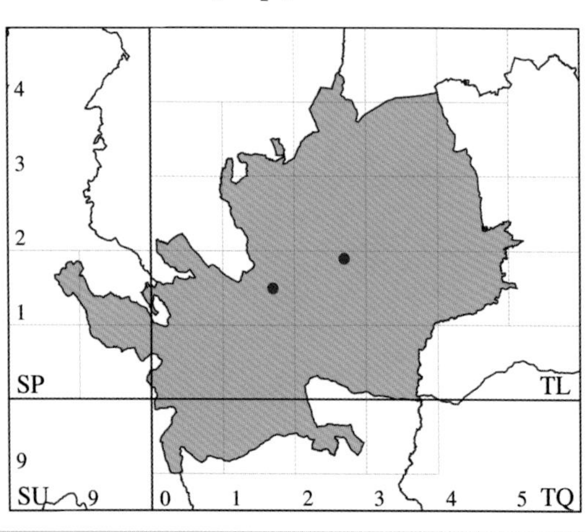

Recorded:	1916 - 2002
Distribution / Status:	Extremely local / Rare resident
Conservation status:	Herts Rare
Caterpillar food plants:	Not recorded. Elsewhere, on the fibrous roots of grasses and herbaceous plants
Flight period:	Elsewhere, July/August
Records in database:	4

Our four records are from Royston in 1916 and Hitchin in 1934 (both in the 1937 county list, but neither of which can be mapped accurately), from Datchworth on 3rd August 1999 (Steve Palmer) and Marshal's Heath in 2002 (John Murray). Separation from 1016: *Cnephasia longana* can be difficult and may require dissection of voucher specimens.

1030 *Eana incanana* (Steph.)

Recorded:	1991 - 2006
Distribution / Status:	Local / Uncommon resident
Conservation status:	No perceived threats
Caterpillar food plants:	Not recorded. Elsewhere, in flowers and buds of Bluebell and Ox-eye Daisy
Flight period:	Late May to early August
Records in database:	26

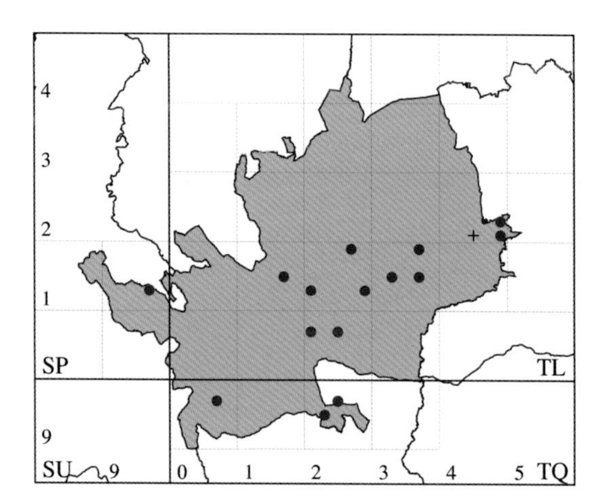

The distribution of the two foodplants will limit the range of the moth. Habitat data from capture sites suggests (though does not prove), that bluebells are utilised in Hertfordshire; the moth may just be under-recorded in areas where that plant is absent.

1032 *Aleimma loeflingiana* (L.)

Recorded:	1885 - 2006
Distribution / Status:	Ubiquitous / Common resident
Conservation status:	No perceived threats
Caterpillar food plants:	Not recorded. Elsewhere, oak, Hornbeam and Field Maple
Flight period:	June to mid-August
Records in database:	150

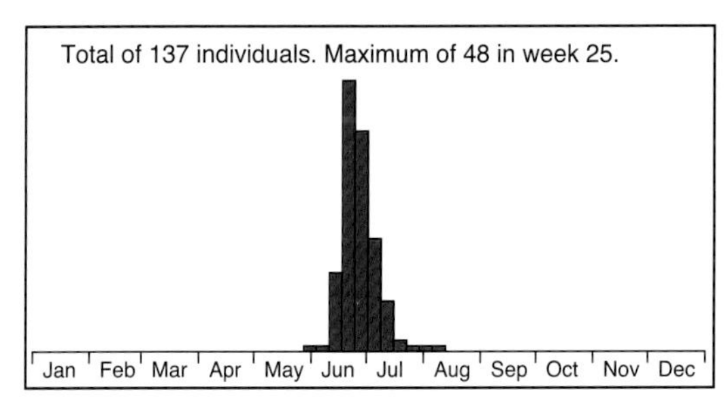

This is a familiar species in most garden light traps and is also frequent in woodland habitats.

1033 *Tortrix viridana* (L.) Green Oak Tortrix

Recorded: 1888 – 2006
Distribution / Status: Widespread / Common resident
Conservation status: No perceived threats.
Caterpillar food plants: English Oak, Sessile Oak, Turkey Oak, Hornbeam. Elsewhere, also on Beech, poplar and other trees
Flight period: June to mid-July
Records in database: 404

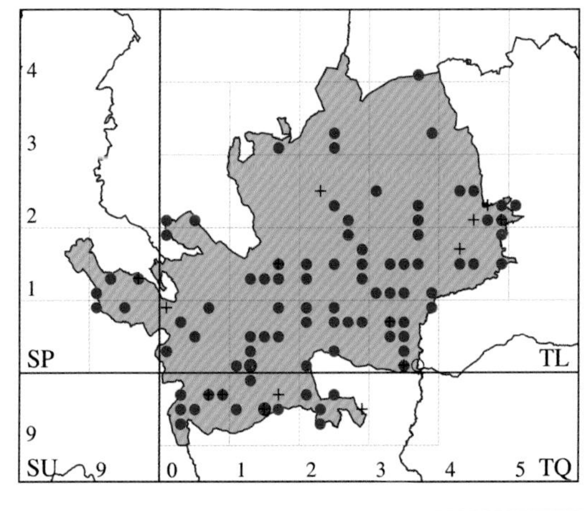

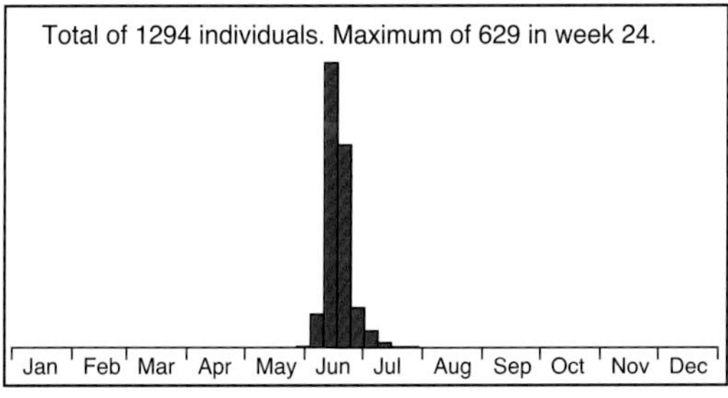

Perhaps the most familiar of all tortrix moths, this green insect is likely to be discovered at almost every Hertfordshire site surveyed. Oak is certainly the favoured foodplant and it is not uncommon for the canopy of really rather large trees to be completely defoliated by the larvae in May/June; the noise produced by, literally, millions of particles of caterpillar 'frass' falling from the canopy sounds like rainfall. The oak trees invariably recover within a few weeks and since the moth is in the egg stage from July through to the following April they suffer no further damage until the following year. Large examples can be confused by the inexperienced with 2418: Cream-bordered Green Pea, which has white, rather than grey, hind wings

1034 *Spatalistis bifasciana* (Hb.)

Recorded: 1890 – 2006
Distribution / Status: Extremely local / Rare resident
Conservation status: Herts Rare
Caterpillar food plants: Not recorded. Elsewhere, on berries of Buckthorn, Alder Buckthorn and Dogwood
Flight period: Elsewhere, late May to July
Records in database: 3

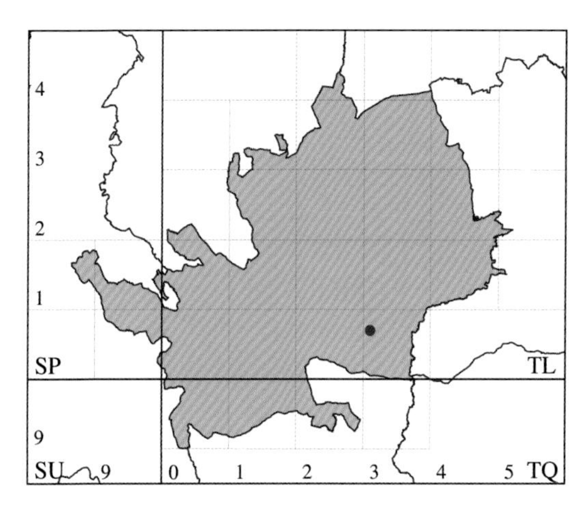

Our three records are from the Sandridge area (Griffith, 1890) and from Old Grove, where it was recorded by Mark Cooper, with one on 24th June 2005 and four on 9th June 2006. Neither buckthorn species was present in the area, though small quantities of Dogwood were evident.

1035 *Acleris bergmanniana* (L.)

Recorded: 1890 – 2005
Distribution / Status: Local / Resident
Conservation status: No perceived threats
Caterpillar food plants: Not recorded. Elsewhere, on rose
Flight period: June and July
Records in database: 20

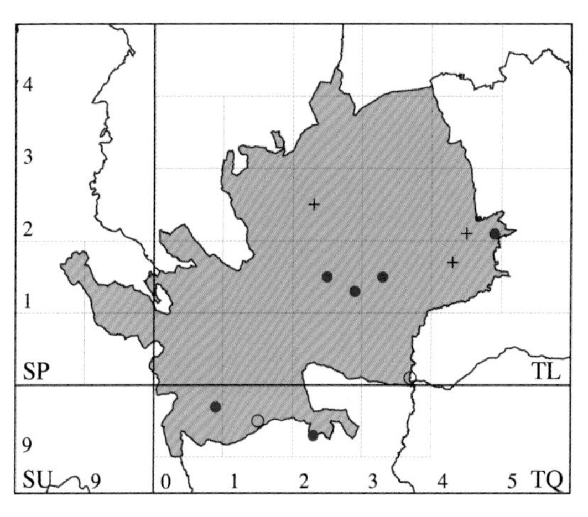

This is a common species in Britain; its local distribution and low population density, at least as measured in light traps, in Hertfordshire is surprising.

1036 *Acleris forsskaleana* (L.)

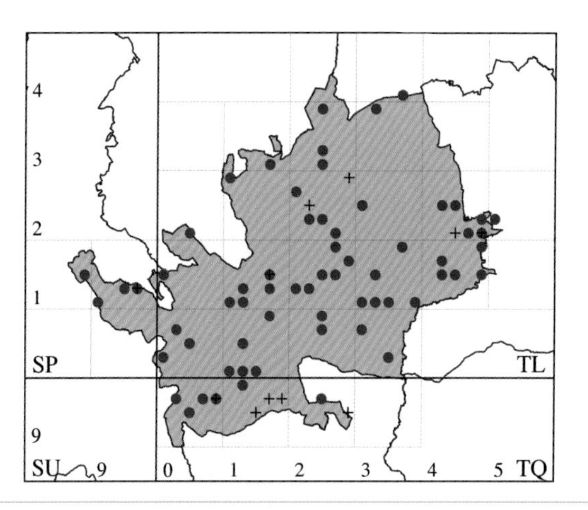

Recorded:	1890 – 2006
Distribution / Status:	Ubiquitous / Common resident
Conservation status:	No perceived threats
Caterpillar food plants:	Not recorded. Elsewhere, on Sycamore and Field Maple
Flight period:	June to September
Records in database:	178

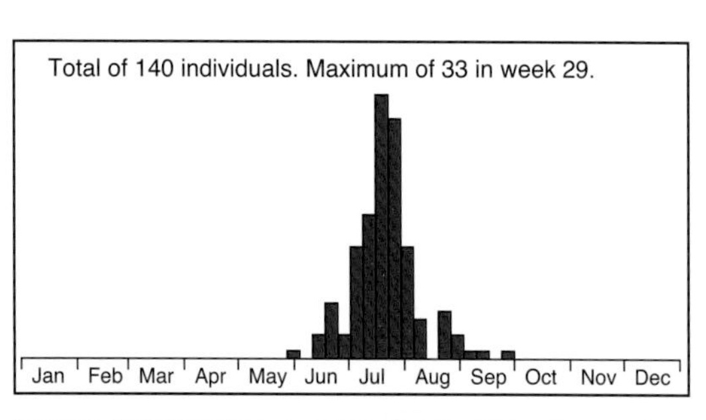

This species is likely to be present on lists obtained at all sites surveyed in the appropriate season.

1037 *Acleris holmiana* (L.)

Recorded:	1934 – 2004
Distribution / Status:	Local / Resident
Conservation status:	Insufficiently known
Caterpillar food plants:	Not recorded. Elsewhere, on rosaceous trees and shrubs
Flight period:	July/August
Records in database:	19

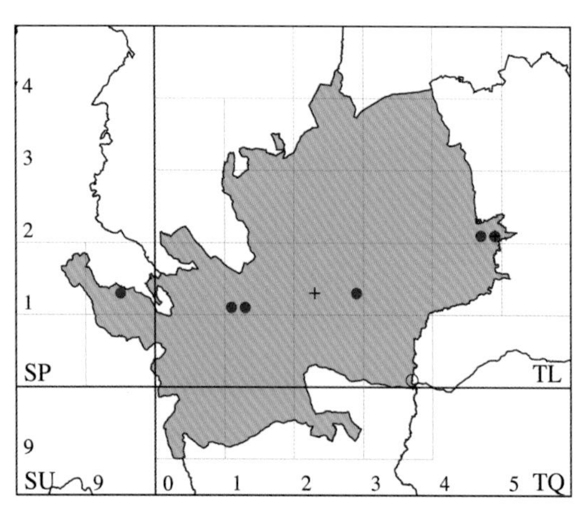

The adult moth is distinctive and can scarcely be overlooked by microlepidopterists. It therefore appears likely to have a genuinely local distribution.

1038 *Acleris laterana* (Fabr.)

Recorded:	1890 – 2005
Distribution / Status:	Local / Common resident
Conservation status:	No perceived threats
Caterpillar food plants:	Not recorded. Elsewhere, on rosaceous trees and shrubs
Flight period:	Mid-July to September
Records in database:	39

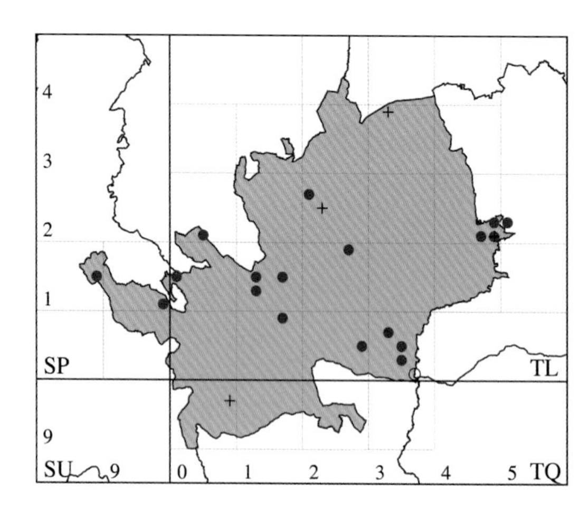

Almost all our records support the text book position that *Acleris laterana* flies in August and September in a single generation, rendering separation from *Acleris comariana* (which looks identical) easy as this latter species flies in two generations, in June/July then late August to early October. In August any remaining *comariana* should be worn whilst *laterana* should be fresh. However, a series of six (5 males and one female) taken by me at Zouches Farm near Dunstable on 17th July 2003, on the basis that they might be the first county record for *comariana* all transpired to be *laterana* upon dissection. This emphasises the need to dissect specimens of this species pair for satisfactory identification and I have, therefore, revisited all available material.

[1039 *Acleris comariana* (Lienig & Zeller) Strawberry Tortrix

Acleris comariana is recorded at Bricket Wood (Gibbs, 1889) and from the Sandridge area (Griffith, 1890), but unfortunately, the name *comariana* has also been used in the past for 1038: *Acleris laterana* (Fabricius), though the name is absent from the Doubleday checklist of 1862, in which *latifasciana* (the old name for *laterana* Haworth) is treated as a variety of *schalleriana* Linnaeus. *Acleris laterana* is common and widespread in Hertfordshire (now) whilst there are no other records at all of *comariana* – which itself perhaps casts suspicion on the two earlier records? The separation of the two requires examination of the genitalia as discussed under the other species. *Acleris comariana* seems to be more associated with damp ground than is *laterana* (David Agassiz, personal communication). With all this in mind, it seems unwise to admit *comariana* to the Hertfordshire fauna unless a specimen is located and dissected or new, confirmed records become available.]

1041 *Acleris sparsana* ([D.& S.])

Recorded:	1888 – 2006
Distribution / Status:	Widespread / Common resident
Conservation status:	No perceived threats
Caterpillar food plants:	Guelder Rose. Elsewhere, on Beech, Hornbeam and Field Maple
Flight period:	September to November, overwintering to March
Records in database:	130

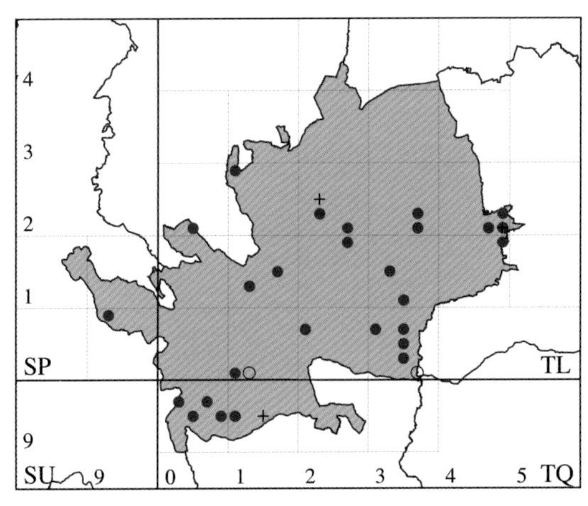

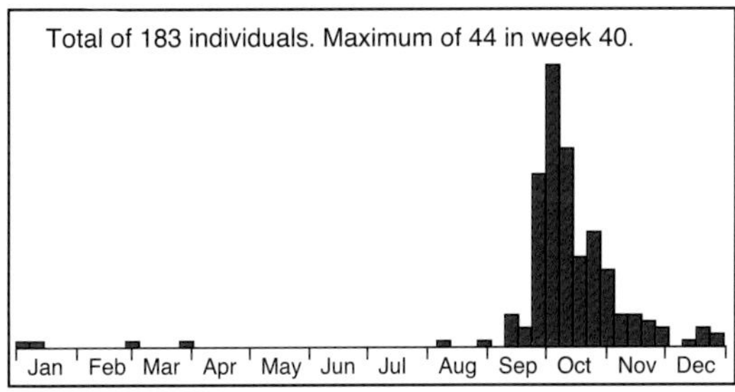

Most individuals are recorded in the autumn with very few noted after hibernation. It is not clear when eggs are laid, but our data suggest that the bulk of adults appear unable to survive a Hertfordshire winter, so that eggs must surely be laid in the autumn? Our unusual foodplant record is provided from Bricket Wood in 1890 'where the larva of *Peronoa tristana* is common, feeding on *Viburnum opulus*, a rather unusual food-plant' (Griffith, 1890).

1042 *Acleris rhombana* ([D.& S.]) Rhomboid Tortrix

Recorded:	1888 – 2005
Distribution / Status:	Widespread / Common resident
Conservation status:	No perceived threats.
Caterpillar food plants:	Not recorded. Elsewhere, polyphagous on deciduous trees
Flight period:	Late August to November
Records in database:	77

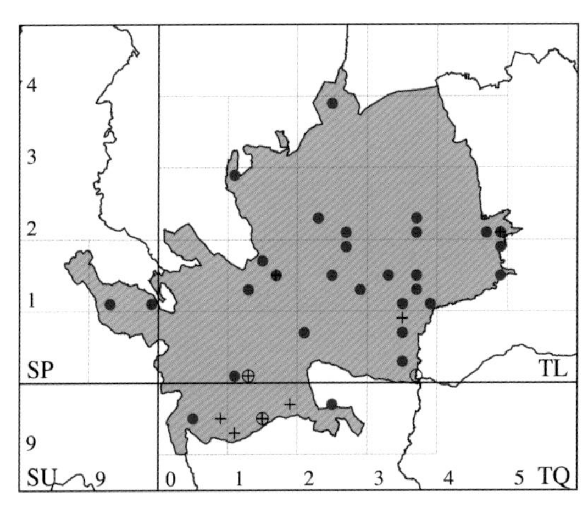

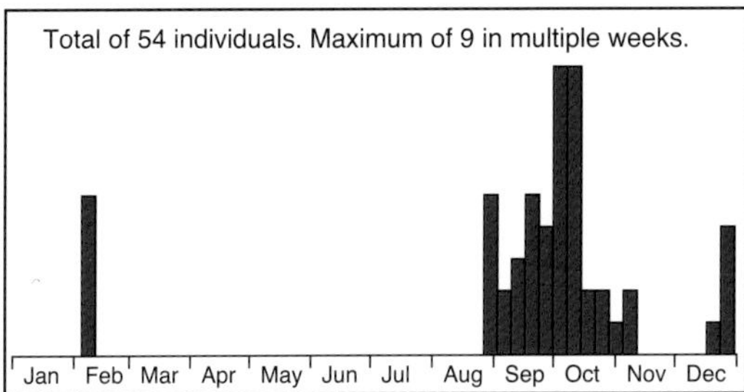

In general, this species does not overwinter as an adult; the unexpected winter records on the chart are all from the light trap on the Rothamsted Estate at Harpenden, on 23rd and 24th December 2002 and 7th February 2003. There are no such records outside the 2002/2003 winter.

1043 *Acleris aspersana* (Hb.)

Recorded:	1890 – 2003
Distribution / Status:	Local / Uncommon resident
Conservation status:	Herts Scarce
Caterpillar food plants:	Not recorded. Elsewhere, polyphagous on herbaceous plants
Flight period:	July. Elsewhere, July/August
Records in database:	16

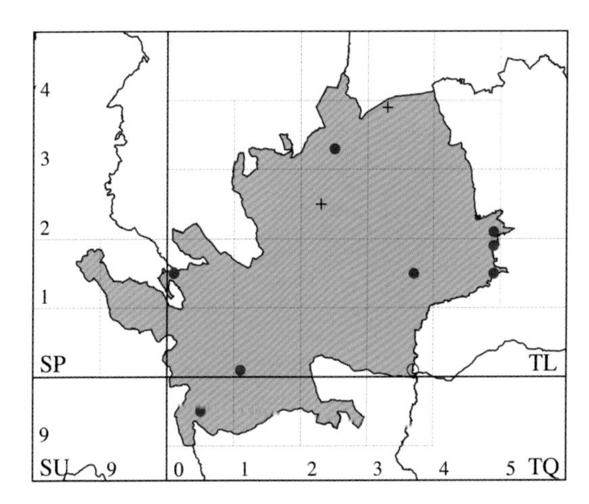

We have not recorded this species in the last three years of the survey and overall the reports are somewhat sparse, albeit widespread. This appears to be a scarce moth at Hertfordshire light traps.

1044 *Acleris ferrugana* ([D.& S.])

Recorded:	1927 – 2006
Distribution / Status:	Widespread / Common resident
Conservation status:	No perceived threats
Caterpillar food plants:	Not recorded. Elsewhere, on oak and sallow
Flight period:	January to November
Records in database:	37

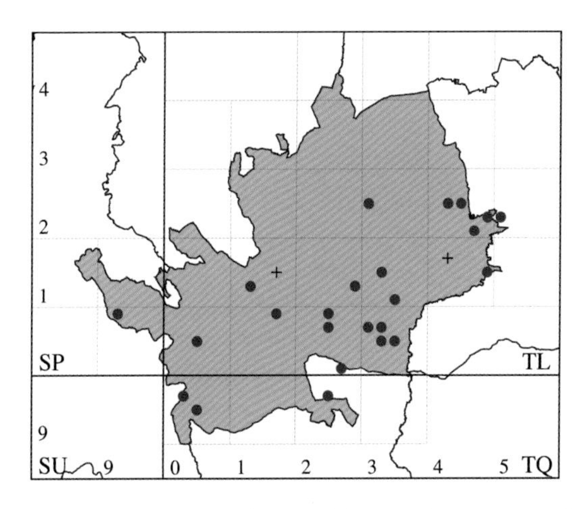

Separation of this species in the adult stage from 1045: *Acleris notana* requires genitalia examination for absolute certainty and the distribution map reflects only confirmed reports. The presence of adults in all months except December emphasises that our resident population is boosted by primary immigration from overseas in most years.

1045 *Acleris notana* (Donovan) = *tripunctana* (Hb.)

Recorded:	1968 – 2006
Distribution / Status:	Widespread / Common resident
Conservation status:	No perceived threats
Caterpillar food plants:	Not recorded. Elsewhere, on birch and alder
Flight period:	Mid-June to mid-August then a second generation in October overwintering to March
Records in database:	20

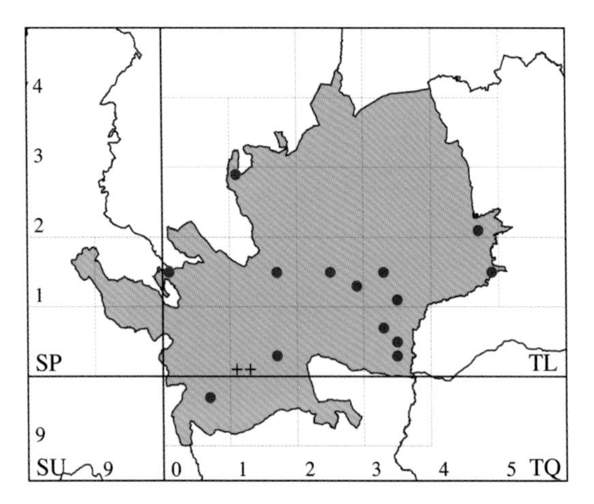

Separation of this species in the adult stage from 1044: *Acleris ferrugana* requires genitalia examination for absolute certainty and the distribution map shows confirmed reports only.

1046 *Acleris shepherdana* (Steph.)

Recorded:	1883 only
Distribution / Status:	Absent / Former resident
Conservation status:	Herts Extinct
Caterpillar food plants:	Not recorded. Elsewhere, on Meadowsweet
Flight period:	Not recorded. Elsewhere, August/ September
Records in database:	1

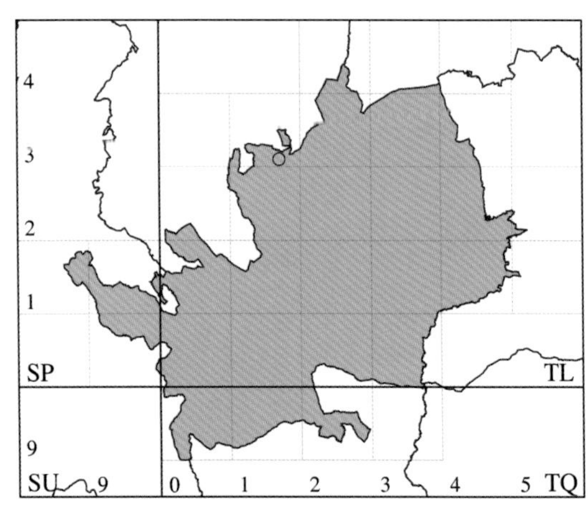

Our only report of this fenland/marshland moth is of one at Ickleford, near Hitchin in 1883 (Durrant), repeated as 'Herts' in Meyrick's 1928 *Revised Handbook*.

1047 *Acleris schalleriana* (L.)

Recorded:	1890 – 2006
Distribution / Status:	Local / Uncommon resident
Conservation status:	Insufficiently known
Caterpillar food plants:	Not recorded. Elsewhere, on Wayfaring Tree (rarely on Guelder Rose)
Flight period:	Late May to July then November to February, in two generations
Records in database:	25

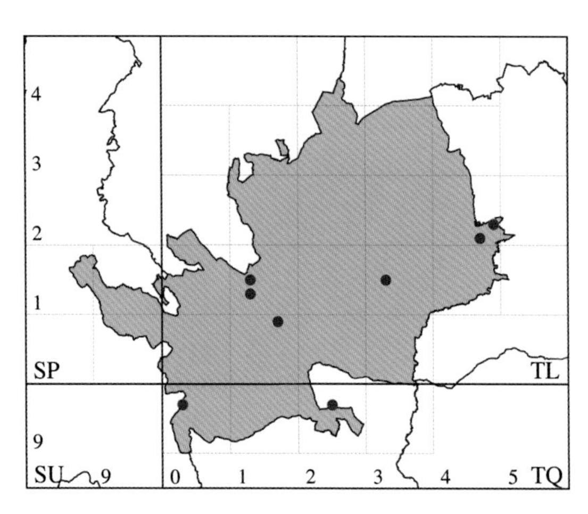

This rather locally distributed species is expected on chalky soils, but may have adapted to the increasingly popular plantings of the foodplant on the verges and embankments associated with new roads.

1048 *Acleris variegana* ([D.& S.]) Garden Rose Tortrix

Recorded:	1888 – 2006
Distribution / Status:	Ubiquitous / Common resident
Conservation status:	No perceived threats.
Caterpillar food plants:	Not recorded. Elsewhere, widely polyphagous
Flight period:	Late June to mid-November
Records in database:	625

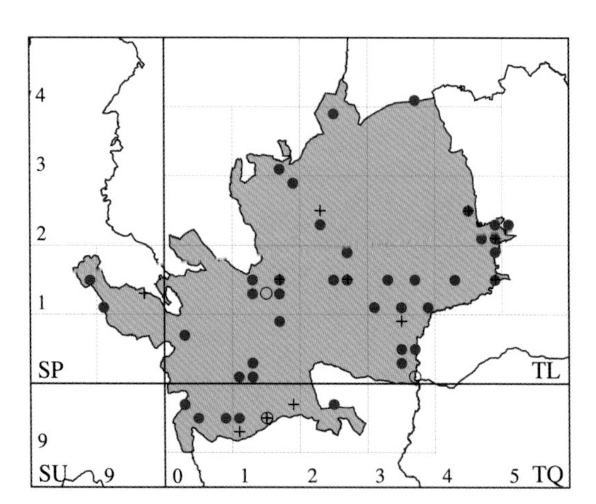

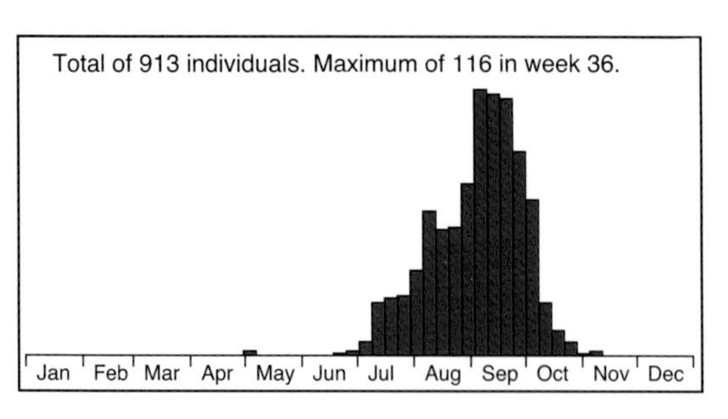

The Garden Rose Tortrix is amongst the most frequent "micros" at garden light traps and is likely to be common everywhere. It has a number of colour forms and in my garden in Bishops Stortford I have recorded f. *aspersana* Fabricius, f. *cirrana* Curtis and the melanic f. *caeruleoatrana* Strand as well as the 'typical' form, but we do not have any numerical data on the frequency of any of the forms in Hertfordshire.

1050 *Acleris kochiella* (Goeze) = *boscana* (Fabr.)

Recorded:	1998 – 2002
Distribution / Status:	Local / Uncommon resident
Conservation status:	Herts Vulnerable
Caterpillar food plants:	Not recorded. Elsewhere, on elms
Flight period:	Elsewhere, June/July then September to March in two generations
Records in database:	16

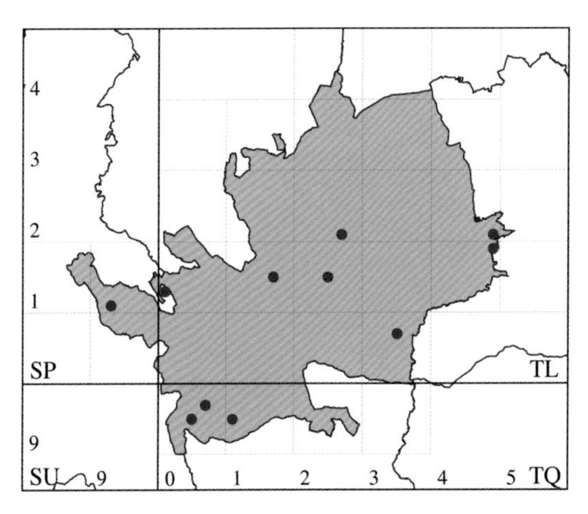

Although recorded in 2006 a few yards inside Buckinghamshire at Chorleywood by Richard Ellis, there are no Hertfordshire records since 2002. Though older records with which comparison can be made are few, the moth appears likely to have declined as a consequence of the 1970s epidemic of Dutch Elm Disease.

1051 *Acleris logiana* (Cl.)

Recorded:	2005 only
Distribution / Status:	Extremely local / Vagrant
Conservation status:	-
Caterpillar food plants:	Not recorded. Elsewhere, on birch
Flight period:	Elsewhere, September to April
Records in database:	1

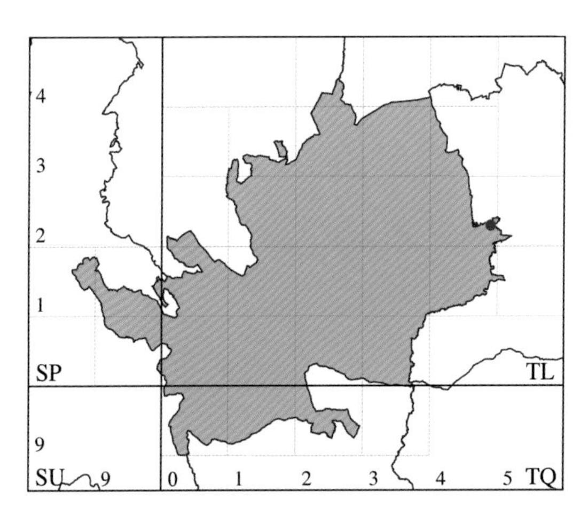

Our single record was made by Rachel Terry who recognised a male amongst the micros saved from the Bishops Stortford light trap of James Fish and Julian Reeves. Formerly restricted to Scottish birch woods, it was recorded in the south first in Hampshire in 1991. It was noted on the Isle of Wight in 1997, and turned up in East Suffolk in 2000, East Norfolk and Berkshire in 2004 and North Essex and West Suffolk in 2005. In the latter year, it was also recorded for the first time in the Channel Islands. It remains to be seen if it becomes established in Hertfordshire.

1053 *Acleris hastiana* (L.)

Recorded:	1890 – 2006
Distribution / Status:	Local / Common resident
Conservation status:	No perceived threats
Caterpillar food plants:	Common Sallow
Flight period:	June/July then October to March in two generations
Records in database:	38

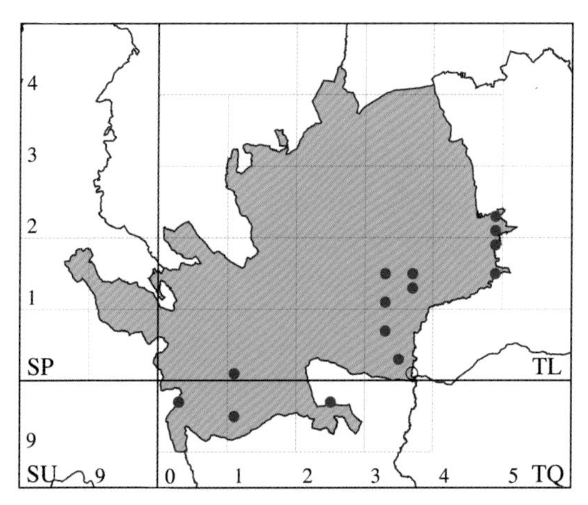

The distribution of this moth is curious when compared to that of 1054: *Acleris cristana*, with which it may be confused.

1054 *Acleris cristana* ([D.& S.])

Recorded:	1973 – 2006
Distribution / Status:	Widespread / Common resident
Conservation status:	No perceived threats
Caterpillar food plants:	Domestic Apple and Blackthorn. Elsewhere, various rosaceous trees and bushes
Flight period:	Mid-July to mid-May, hibernating as an adult
Records in database:	105

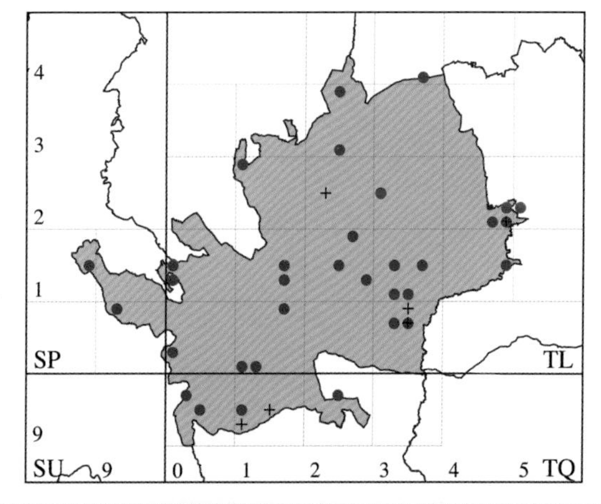

There are more post-hibernation records than there are records from the autumn. Both this species and the last occur is a huge variety of colour forms.

1061 *Acleris literana* (L.)

Recorded: 1890 – 2006
Distribution / Status: Extremely local / Uncommon resident
Conservation status: Herts Rare
Caterpillar food plants: Not recorded. Elsewhere, on oak
Flight period: Elsewhere, August to May
Records in database: 7

Recent reports are from Welwyn on 31st March 1995 (Raymond Uffen), Digswell on 7th May 2003 and Bishops Stortford on 15th April 2004 (James Fish & Julian Reeves). Oddly, the moth is not recorded from the various oak woodlands in the county; perhaps it is not especially attracted to light. Equally interesting is that our recent records disagree with what we are told by the text books, that beating the lichen-covered boughs of oak branches in late summer and autumn is the best way of recording this moth whilst it is seldom seen in spring after hibernation.

1062 *Acleris emargana* (Fabr.)

Recorded: 1890 – 2006
Distribution / Status: Local / Common resident
Conservation status: No perceived threats
Caterpillar food plants: Not recorded. Elsewhere, on sallows, poplars and birches
Flight period: Late July to October
Records in database: 28

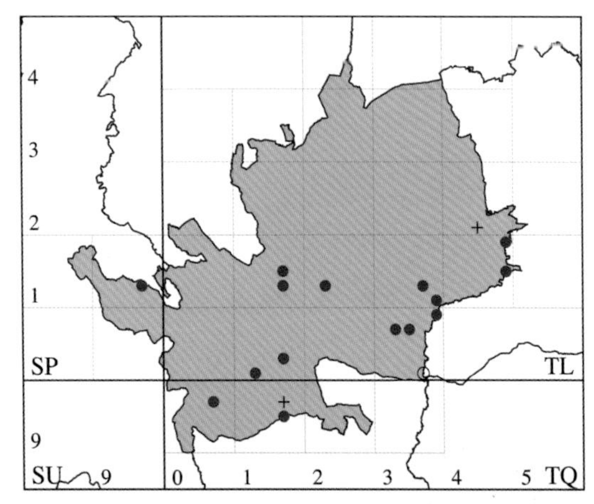

The recent split of *Acleris effractana* from this species (see Karsholt et al, 2005) does not appear to affect southern Britain, although the reader is referred to the unexpected arrival in the south of 1051: *Acleris logiana* and the clear need to check carefully any specimen of any species that does not look 'quite right'.

CHLIDANOTINAE

1013 *Olindia schumacherana* (Fabr.)

Recorded: 1990 – 2003
Distribution / Status: Extremely local / Uncommon resident
Conservation status: Insufficiently known
Caterpillar food plants: Not recorded. Elsewhere, on a variety of herbaceous plants
Flight period: June/July
Records in database: 4

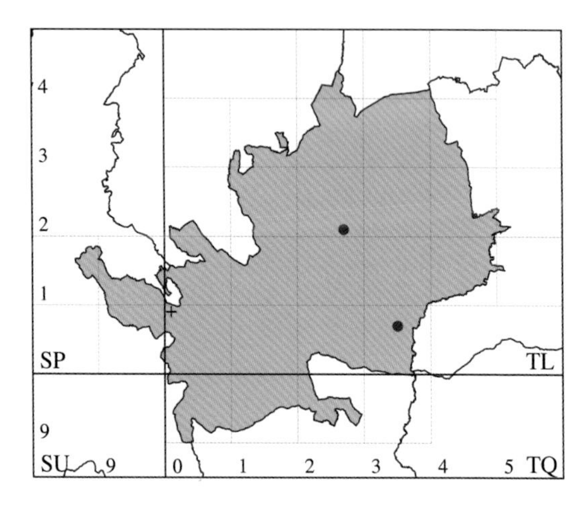

Martin Albertini found this species at Frithsden Beeches in the west of the county on 29th June 1999 and since then I have found it at Danemead Wood in the east on 15th June 2000 and in the centre of the county at Astonbury Wood on 6th July 2002 and 16th June 2003. There do not appear to be any other records.

1014 *Isotrias rectifasciana* (Haw.)

Recorded: 1888 – 2005
Distribution / Status: Very local / Uncommon resident
Conservation status: Insufficiently known
Caterpillar food plants: Not recorded. Elsewhere, associated with hawthorn
Flight period: May/June
Records in database: 14

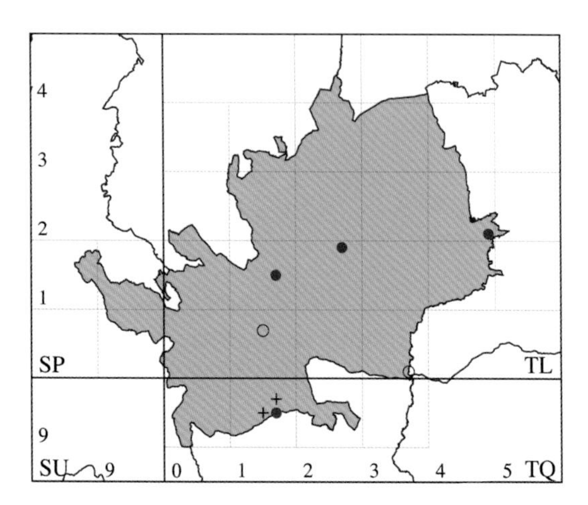

The records are scattered and may suggest an under-recorded species.

1063 *Celypha striana* ([D.& S.])

Recorded: 1890 – 2006
Distribution / Status: Widespread / Common resident
Conservation status: No perceived threats
Caterpillar food plants: Not recorded. Elsewhere, in the rootstock of Dandelion
Flight period: June to early September
Records in database: 381

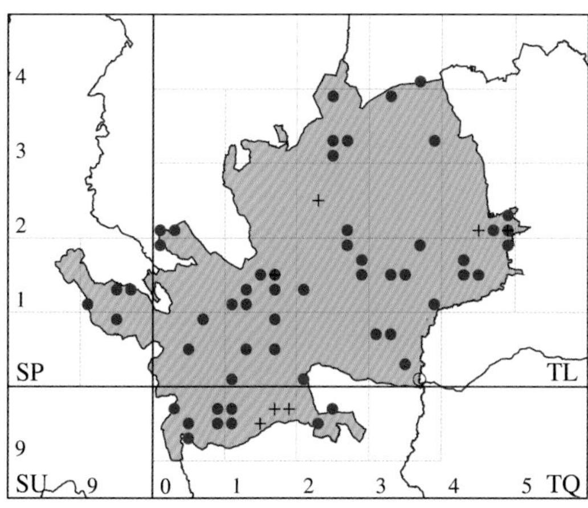

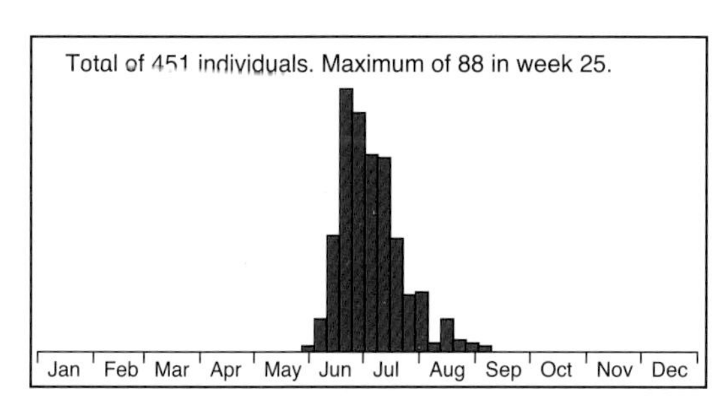

In the arable areas of the north-east, the moth may be less common because of the use of weed-killers that eliminate the dandelions needed by the caterpillars.

1064 *Celypha rosaceana* (Schl.)

Recorded: 1890 – 2006
Distribution / Status: Local / Uncommon resident
Conservation status: Insufficiently known
Caterpillar food plants: Not recorded. Elsewhere, in the rootstock of Field Milk-thistle and Dandelion
Flight period: Elsewhere, June and July
Records in database: 8

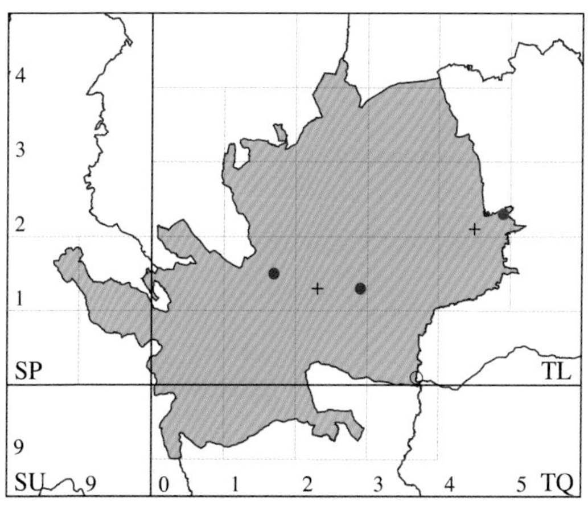

This is a fairly distinctive species and both sexes come to light traps, so the conclusion that can be drawn from the data is that it is probably rather locally distributed in addition to being under-recorded.

1067 *Celypha cespitana* (Hb.)

Recorded: 1890 – 2001
Distribution / Status: Local / Uncommon resident,
Conservation status: Insufficiently known
Caterpillar food plants: Not recorded. Elsewhere, on various low-growing plants
Flight period: Elsewhere, June to August
Records in database: 3

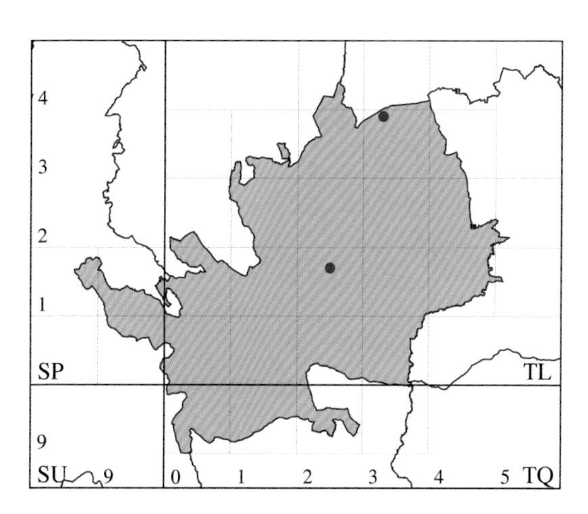

The two recent records are widely spaced and this species is probably overlooked. It is of interest that during 2006 Richard Ellis caught an adult in his garden at Chorleywood, not mapped here because his garden is in Buckinghamshire even though the map tetrad is mostly in Hertfordshire. Although differing from 1076: *Celypha lacunana* in several respects, the two are superficially similar and few people examine every individual of the latter species encountered from June to August.

1068 *Celypha rivulana* (Scop.)

Recorded: Pre-1890 only
Distribution / Status: Absent / Former resident
Conservation status: Herts Extinct
Caterpillar food plants: Not recorded. Elsewhere, polyphagous on herbaceous plants
Flight period: Elsewhere, July and August
Records in database: 1

Our only record is in Griffith's list for the Sandridge area in the years to 1890. It is an inhabitant of marshes, damp woodland and other wet habitats.

1076 *Celypha lacunana* ([D.& S.])

Recorded: 1888 – 2006
Distribution / Status: Ubiquitous / Abundant resident
Conservation status: No perceived threats
Caterpillar food plants: Stinging Nettle. Elsewhere, polyphagous on herbaceous plants
Flight period: May to July then August to September in two generations
Records in database: 786

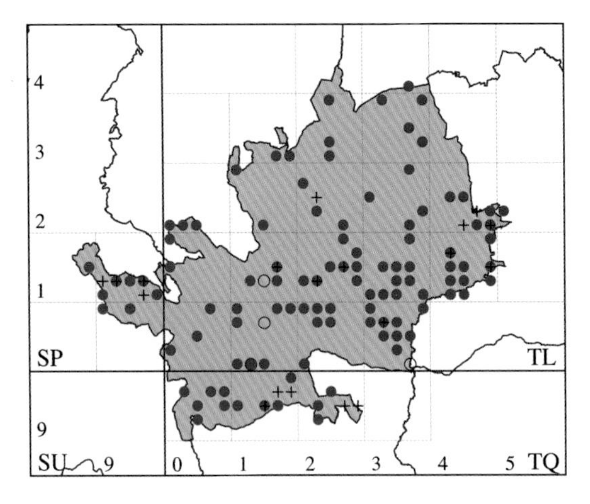

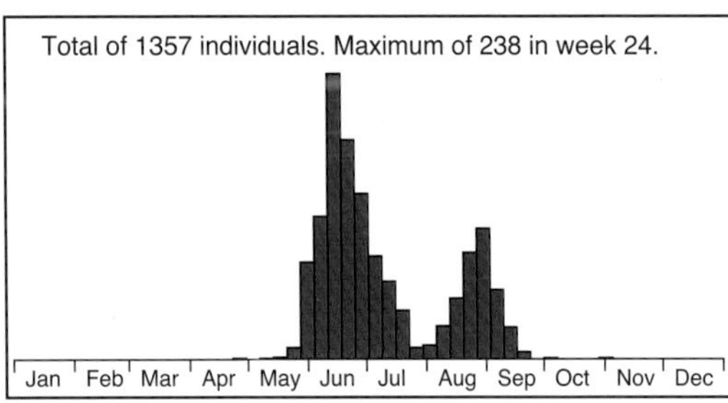

This species has the distinction of being the only micro moth recorded from *every* vice-county of Britain and Ireland. In Hertfordshire, it is found everywhere in high number.

1079 *Piniphila bifasciana* (Haw.)

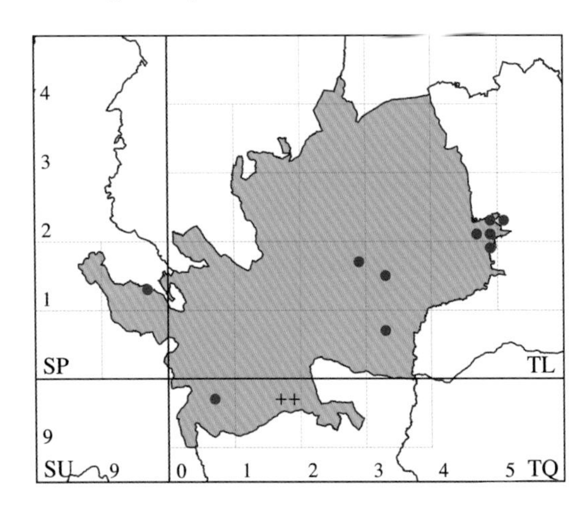

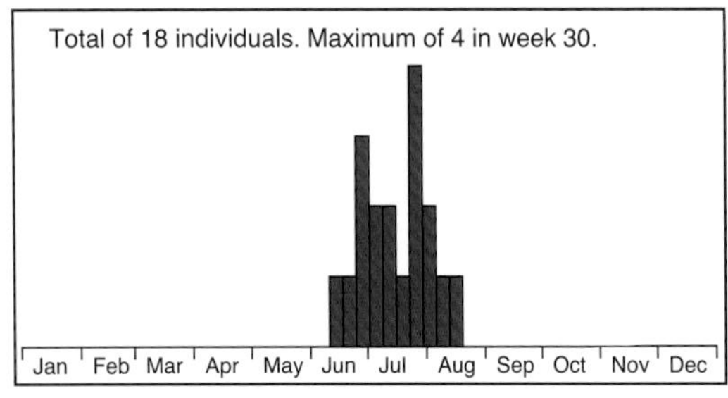

Recorded: 1934 – 2006
Distribution / Status: Local / Common resident
Conservation status: Insufficiently known
Caterpillar food plants: Not recorded. Elsewhere, on young shoots and male flowers of Scots Pine
Flight period: Mid-June to mid-August
Records in database: 27

Apparently scarce in the past, with only a single record given in the 1937 county list (From Hitchin, in 1934), this species has certainly become more numerous in the years since about 2000. I failed to find it in my garden light trap from 1987 to 1999 and caught my first in 2000; it has been a regular visitor in each year since then. Throughout the entire period, there has been no apparent change to the mature Scots Pine trees a hundred yards or so away from my garden – except that some were felled.

1082 *Hedya pruniana* (Hb.) Plum Tortrix

Recorded: 1888 – 2006
Distribution / Status: Ubiquitous / Common resident
Conservation status: No perceived threats.
Caterpillar food plants: Blackthorn. Elsewhere, leaves of fruit trees
Flight period: Mid-May to July
Records in database: 159

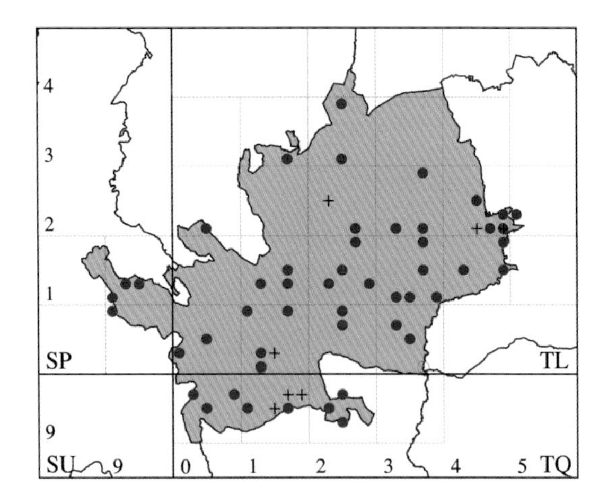

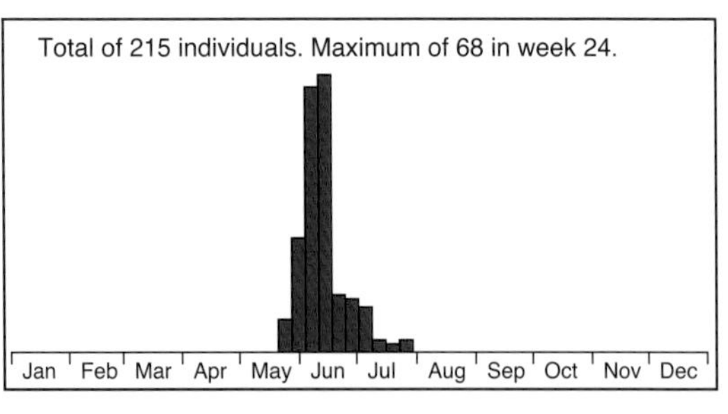

A widespread and common species often confused with 1083: *Hedya nubiferana*.

1083 *Hedya nubiferana* (Haw.)

Recorded: 1890 – 2006
Distribution / Status: Ubiquitous / Common resident
Conservation status: No perceived threats.
Caterpillar food plants: Blackthorn. Elsewhere, on leaves of fruit trees
Flight period: Mid-May to early August
Records in database: 188

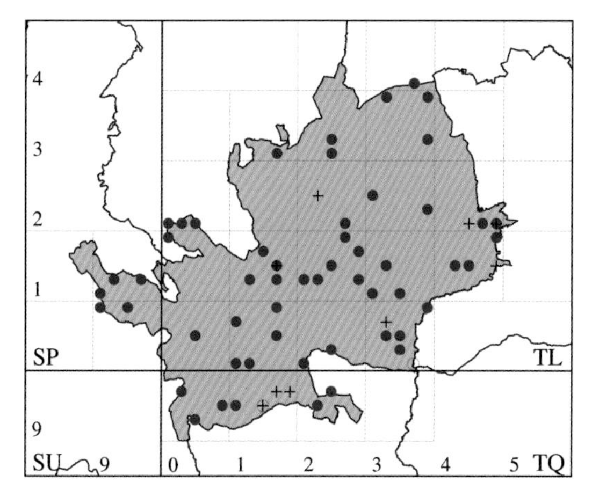

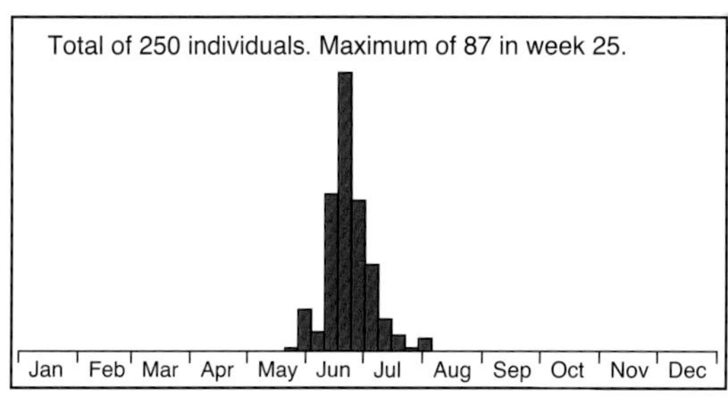

A familiar species in all light traps, peaking slightly later than 1082: *Hedya pruniana*, in most years.

1084 *Hedya ochroleucana* (Fr.)

Recorded: 1890 – 2003
Distribution / Status: Local / Uncommon resident
Conservation status: Insufficiently known
Caterpillar food plants: Not recorded. Elsewhere, on roses, occasionally apple
Flight period: June/July
Records in database: 11

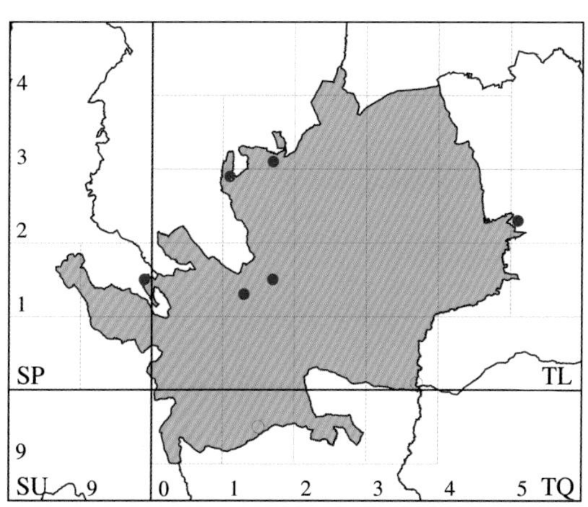

A distinctive species, unlikely to be overlooked, so perhaps genuinely local in its distribution.

1086 *Hedya salicella* (L.)

Recorded: 1899 – 2006
Distribution / Status: Local / Common resident
Conservation status: No perceived threats
Caterpillar food plants: Not recorded. Elsewhere, various species of willow and sallow, especially White Willow
Flight period: Mid-June to early August
Records in database: 29

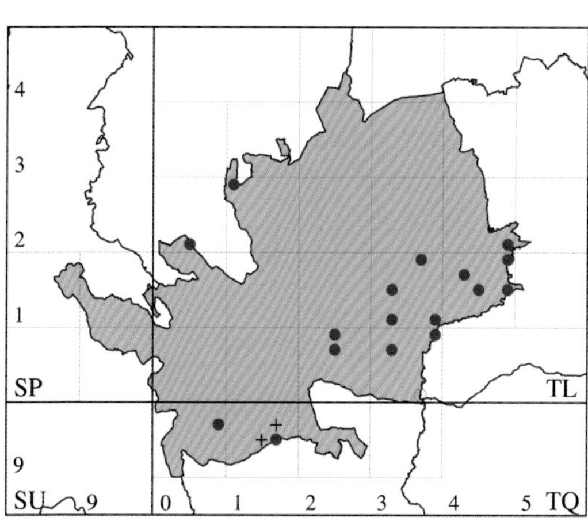

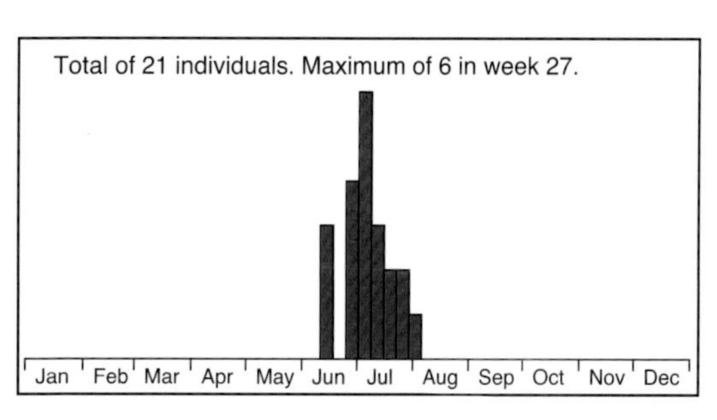

The peculiar distribution in a belt across the south-east of the county is interesting and unexplained, but is unlikely to represent recording bias.

1087 *Orthotaenia undulana* ([D.& S.])

Recorded: 1890 – 1934
Distribution / Status: Absent / Former resident
Conservation status: Herts Extinct
Caterpillar food plants: Not recorded. Elsewhere, polyphagous on leaves of shrubs and trees
Flight period: Elsewhere, mid-May to July
Records in database: 4

Our only records are from the Sandridge area (Griffith, 1890), the Cheshunt area (Boyd, 1901), Bricket Wood in 1931 (Fryer) and Bushey Heath in 1934 (Hervey), the last two in Foster (1937).

1088 *Pseudosciaphila branderiana* (L.)

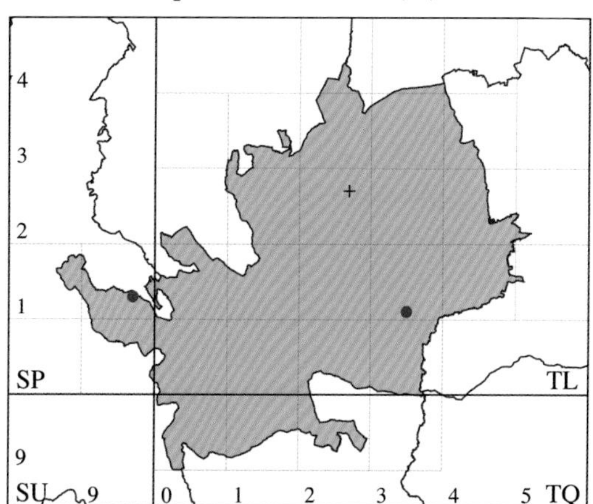

Recorded:	1890 – 2003
Distribution / Status:	Extremely local / Rare resident
Conservation status:	Herts Scarce
Caterpillar food plants:	Not recorded. Elsewhere, on leaves of Aspen
Flight period:	Elsewhere, late June to August
Records in database:	5

Recent records are all my own from Aldbury Common on the Ashridge Estate on 4th July 2000 and 30th June 2001 and Balls Wood, within the Broxbourne Woods National Nature Reserve, on 24th June 2003. It is probably under-recorded. Though it does come to light, it might be more easily recorded by collecting larvae in the rolled leaves of Aspen trees (and rearing through to eliminate species with similar habits).

1089 *Apotomis semifasciana* (Haw.)

Recorded:	1890 – 2003
Distribution / Status:	Extremely local / Rare resident
Conservation status:	Herts Rare
Caterpillar food plants:	Not recorded. Elsewhere, on leaves of sallows and willows
Flight period:	Elsewhere, July
Records in database:	4

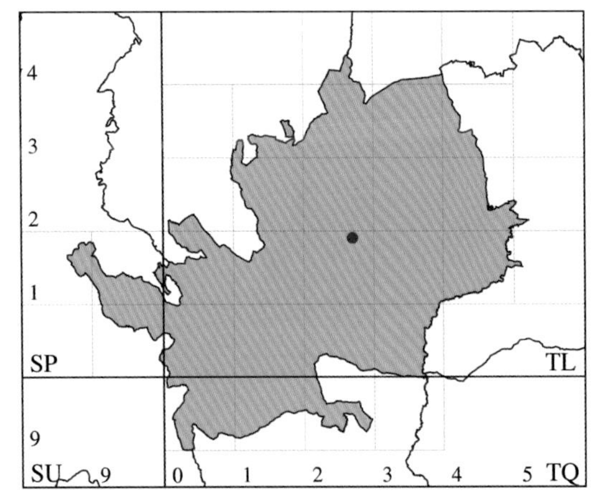

Our only recent record was made by Steve Palmer at Datchworth on 23rd June 2003.

1091 *Apotomis lineana* ([D.& S.])

Recorded:	1900 – 2004
Distribution / Status:	Local / Uncommon resident
Conservation status:	No perceived threats
Caterpillar food plants:	Not recorded. Elsewhere, leaves of White Willow and Crack Willow
Flight period:	Late June to early August
Records in database:	12

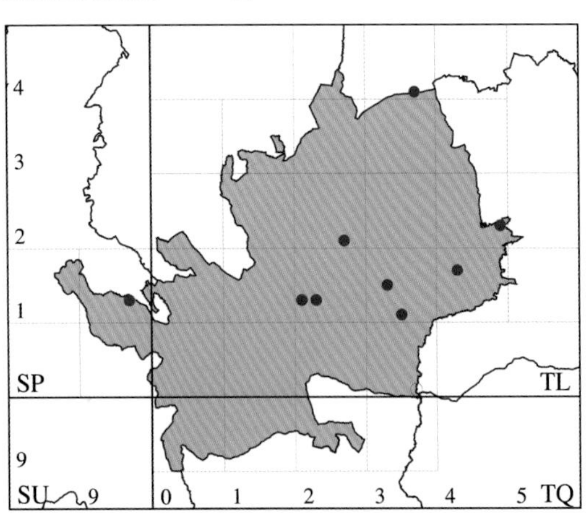

Apart from the records made in the Cheshunt area (Boyd, 1901) and at Harpenden in the early 1930s (C. B. Williams) all our records have been made since January 2000.

1092 *Apotomis turbidana* (Hb.)

Recorded:	1934 – 2006
Distribution / Status:	Local / Uncommon resident
Conservation status:	No perceived threats
Caterpillar food plants:	Not recorded. Elsewhere, on leaves of birch
Flight period:	June and July
Records in database:	21

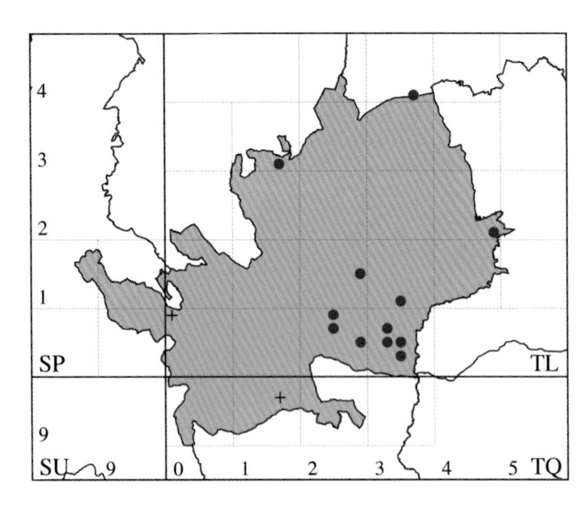

This fairly widespread but local moth rests by day on birch trunks and is very hard to spot. It is almost certainly under-recorded in Hertfordshire.

1093 *Apotomis betuletana* (Haw.)

Recorded:	1890 – 2006
Distribution / Status:	Widespread / Common resident
Conservation status:	No perceived threats
Caterpillar food plants:	Downy Birch
Flight period:	Mid-June to September
Records in database:	80

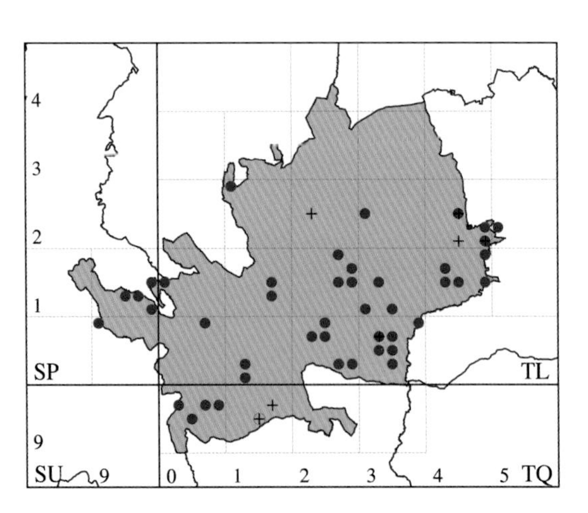

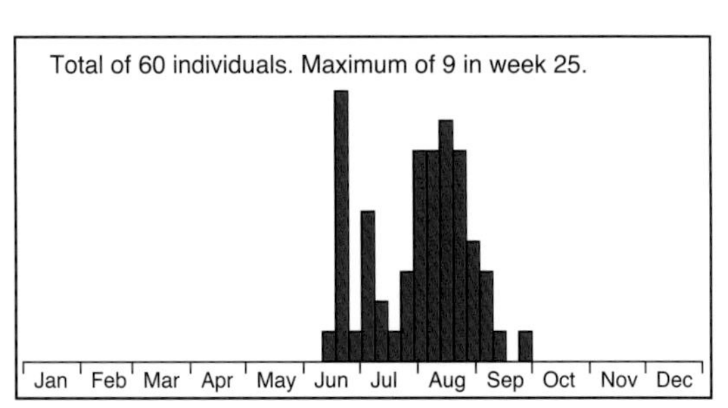

Adults are likely to be found wherever birch trees grow, which means pretty much all of the county; both Silver Birch and Downy Birch are likely to be suitable for the larvae.

1094 *Apotomis capreana* (Hb.)

Recorded: 1890 – 2005
Distribution / Status: Extremely local / Rare resident
Conservation status: Herts Rare
Caterpillar food plants: Not recorded. Elsewhere, on leaves of Goat Willow
Flight period: Elsewhere, June and July/August
Records in database: 3

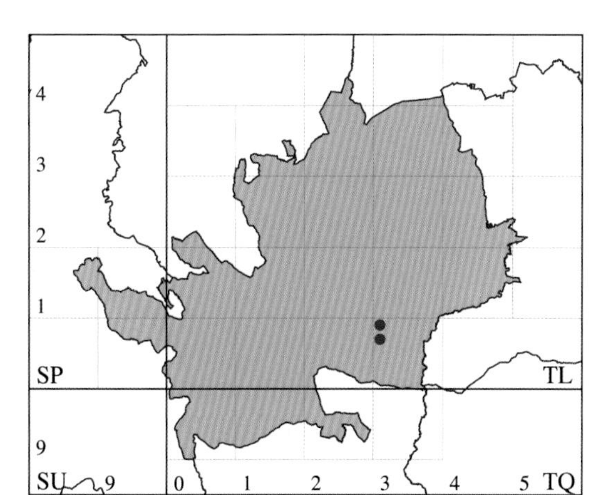

Sandridge (Griffith, 1890) then Great Groves Wood, 13th July 2002 (Kerry Robinson) and Old Grove, 29th July 2005 (Mark Cooper) are our only records.

1097 *Endothenia gentianaeana* (Hb.)

Recorded: 1900 – 2006
Distribution / Status: Widespread / Common resident
Conservation status: No perceived threats
Caterpillar food plants: In the seed heads of Teasel
Flight period: July
Records in database: 126

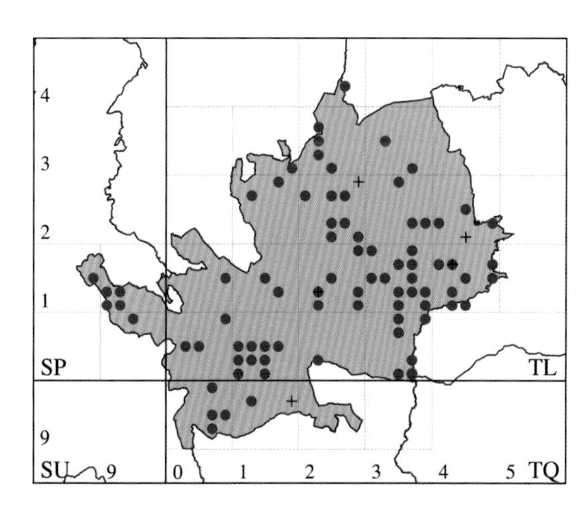

Almost all records are of larvae. It is important to note that the head and prothoracic plate of the caterpillar of this species are dark brown; this separates them from the larvae of 1099: *Endothenia marginana*, in which they are black. The latter are less frequently encountered in teasel heads and have an alternative food plant.

1098 *Endothenia oblongana* (Haw.)

Recorded: 1926 only
Distribution / Status: Absent / Former resident
Conservation status: Herts Extinct
Caterpillar food plants: Not recorded. Elsewhere, probably on Lesser Knapweed
Flight period: Elsewhere, June and July
Records in database: 1

There has been confusion over the use of the names *oblongana*, *sellana* and others for both the present species and the next, 1099: *Endothenia marginana*. Old records summarised by Foster (1937) fall under the two headings of first '*Endothenia oblongana*, Haw. (*marginana*, Haw.) (*similana*, Wilk. *nec* Hübn.)' - which I interpret as 1098: *E. oblongana* and then '*E. sellana* Hübn.' which I interpret as 1099: *E. marginana*. On this basis our only record of the present species is from Harpenden, taken in 1926 (Fryer).

1099 *Endothenia marginana* (Haw.)

Recorded: 1890 – 2006
Distribution / Status: Widespread / Common resident
Conservation status: No perceived threats
Caterpillar food plants: In seed heads of Teasel. Elsewhere, also in Betony and hemp-nettles
Flight period: June to August
Records in database: 19

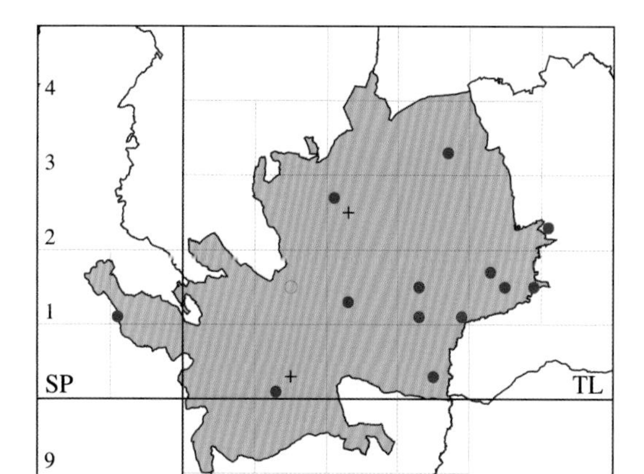

Refer to the discussion of larval recognition under 1097: *Endothenia gentianaeana*. This species is likely to be much under-recorded.

[1100 *Endothenia pullana* (Haw.)

Originally added to the list by Griffith (1884) from the area centred upon Sandridge, this record is corrected by Griffith (1890) as being 1101: *Endothenia ustulana* (Haw.). There are no other records and so this species is not recorded for Hertfordshire.]

1101 *Endothenia ustulana* (Haw.)

Recorded: 1884 only
Distribution / Status: Absent / Former resident
Conservation status: Herts Extinct
Caterpillar food plants: Not recorded. Elsewhere, in rootstock and lower stem of Bugle
Flight period: Elsewhere, June and July
Records in database: 2

Griffith (1884) records *Penthina carbonana* (= *Endothenia pullana*) from the Sandridge area, but later corrects this to *ustulana* in his 1890 paper, where he also notes that there were actually two examples taken, from Symondshyde Great Wood and 'near St Albans. Although it is clear that both were taken prior to 1884 no specific year is given. There do not appear to be any other Hertfordshire records and so we must probably regard it as extinct here.

1102 *Endothenia nigricostana* (Haw.)

Recorded: 1834 – 2005
Distribution / Status: Extremely local / Rare resident
Conservation status: Herts Vulnerable
Caterpillar food plants: Not recorded. Elsewhere, Hedge Woundwort, mining the stem and roots
Flight period: Elsewhere, June
Records in database: 5

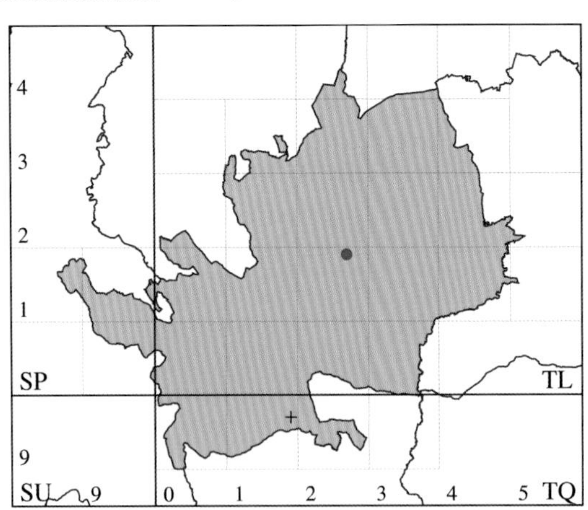

Our earliest record is from Hertford in 1834 (J. F. Stephens), our latest is from Datchworth on 21st June 2005 (Steve Palmer). The moth is scarce nationally and so qualifies for the Herts Vulnerable status category.

1103 *Endothenia ericetana* (H. & W.)

Recorded: Pre-1937 only
Distribution / Status: Absent / Former resident
Conservation status: Herts Extinct
Caterpillar food plants: Not recorded. Elsewhere, Marsh Woundwort
Flight period: Elsewhere, late June to August
Records in database: 1

Our single record is from Harpenden, where it was recorded by Fryer in the early 1930s and included by Foster in his 1937 county list.

1104 *Endothenia quadrimaculana* (Haw.)

Recorded: 1968 only
Distribution / Status: Absent / Former resident
Conservation status: Herts Extinct
Caterpillar food plants: Not recorded. Elsewhere, mining roots and stems of Marsh Woundwort
Flight period: Elsewhere, June and July
Records in database: 2

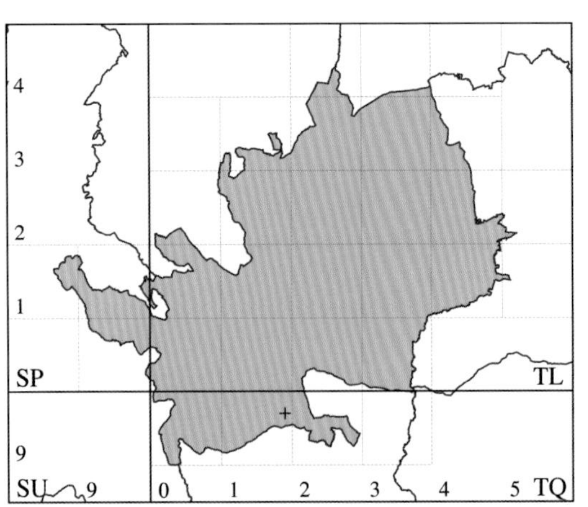

Two examples taken by Eric Bradford at Borehamwood, one on each of 13th July and 12th August 1968, are our only records.

1106 *Lobesia reliquana* (Hb.)

Recorded: 1890 – 2004
Distribution / Status: Extremely local / Rare resident
Conservation status: Insufficiently known
Caterpillar food plants: Not recorded. Elsewhere, on oak, Blackthorn and birch
Flight period: Elsewhere, May and early June
Records in database: 4

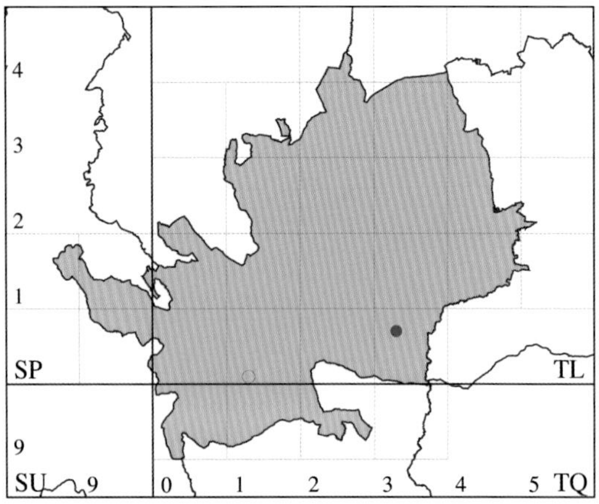

In spite of there being apparently suitable habitat, at least in the south of the county, there are very few records of the moth and the only recent report is my own from Broxbourne Wood, near the west car park, on 15th May 2004.

1108 *Lobesia abscisana* (Doubl.)

Recorded: 1890 – 2006
Distribution / Status: Widespread / Common resident
Conservation status: No perceived threats
Caterpillar food plants: Not recorded. Elsewhere, in the shoots of Creeping Thistle
Flight period: Late June to August
Records in database: 41

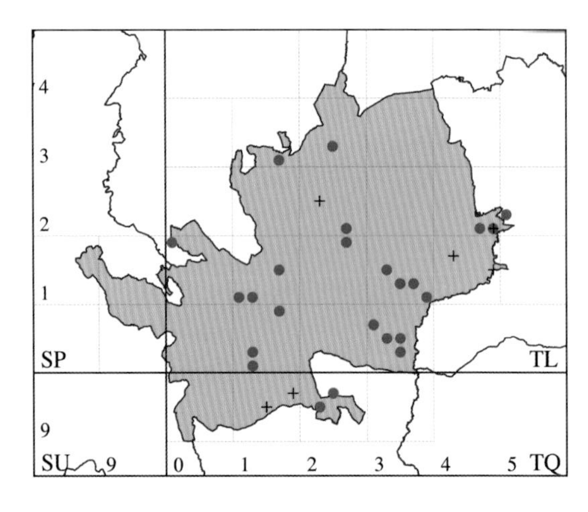

Elsewhere, this species has two generations per year, but the May emergence of adults is as yet unreported in Hertfordshire.

1109 *Lobesia littoralis* (H. & W.)

Recorded: 1937 – 2006
Distribution / Status: Local / Common resident
Conservation status: Insufficiently known
Caterpillar food plants: Thrift. Elsewhere also on Bird's-foot Trefoil
Flight period: June/July then August/September
Records in database: 20

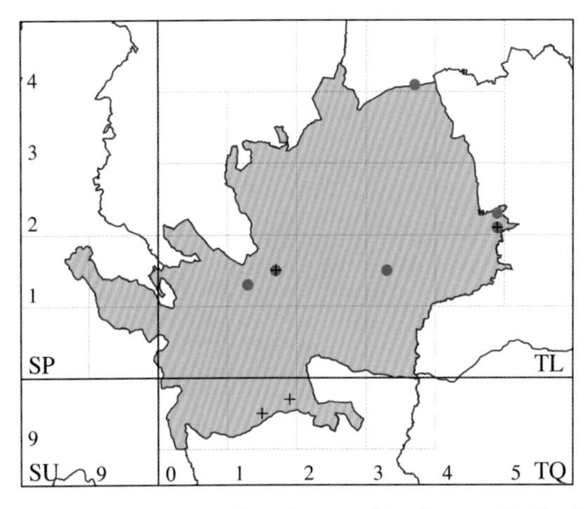

An empty pupa case was found protruding from a Thrift plant in a garden in Bushey on 21st June 1979 (Barry Goater). All our other reports are of adults.

1110 *Bactra furfurana* (Haw.)

Recorded:	2003 only
Distribution / Status:	Extremely local / Rare resident
Conservation status:	Herts Rare
Caterpillar food plants:	Not recorded. Elsewhere, Conglomerate Rush and Common Club Rush
Flight period:	Elsewhere, June and July
Records in database:	1

One at the King's Meads, Hertford, on 19th July 2003 (Andrew Wood) is our only record. It is probably awaiting discovery elsewhere in the Lea and Stort river valleys – perhaps at Rye Meads and Sawbridgeworth Marsh in particular. However, as a wetland species its distribution will be severely restricted – perhaps only to these two rivers.

1111 *Bactra lancealana* (Hb.)

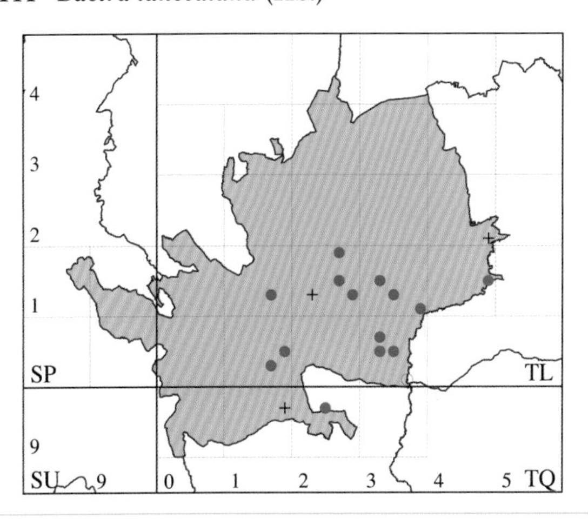

Recorded:	1890 – 2006
Distribution / Status:	Local / Common resident
Conservation status:	No perceived threats
Caterpillar food plants:	Not recorded. Elsewhere, on various rushes, club rushes and Gallingale
Flight period:	May to early October, in two generations
Records in database:	25

Although there will be areas of the county where this species is absent, most wetland sites are likely to support populations.

1113 *Eudemis profundana* ([D.& S.])

Recorded:	1890 – 2006
Distribution / Status:	Widespread / Common resident
Conservation status:	No perceived threats
Caterpillar food plants:	Not recorded. Elsewhere, on oak leaves
Flight period:	July/August
Records in database:	60

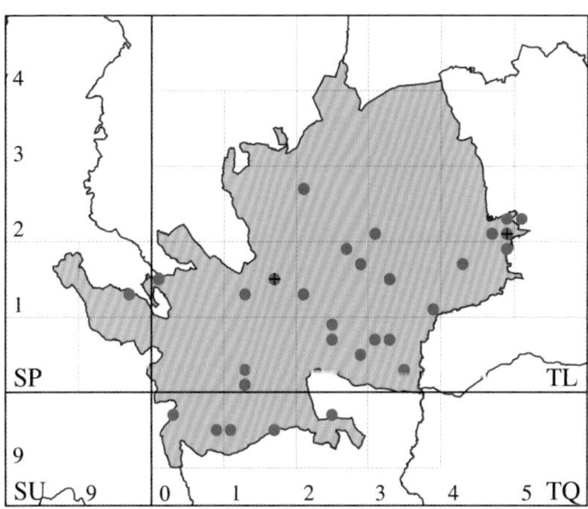

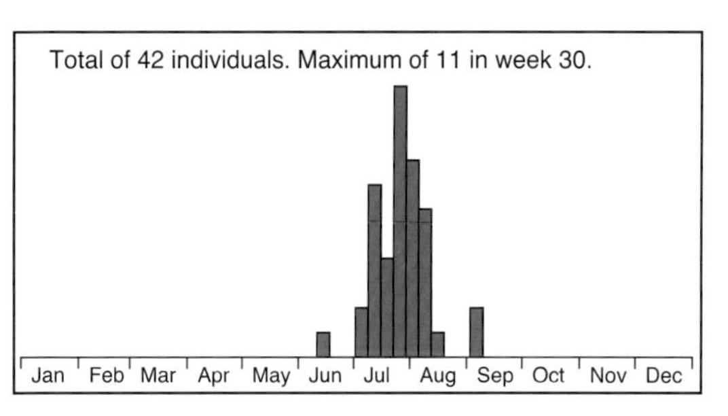

This is a common and expected species in most areas. Surprisingly, the rather similar 1114: Eudemis *porphyrana* (Hb.) is not yet recorded in Hertfordshire.

1115 *Ancylis achatana* ([D.& S.])

Recorded: 1900 – 2006
Distribution / Status: Widespread / Common resident
Conservation status: No perceived threats
Caterpillar food plants: Not recorded. Elsewhere, on hawthorns, Blackthorns and *Cotoneaster*
Flight period: June/July
Records in database: 121

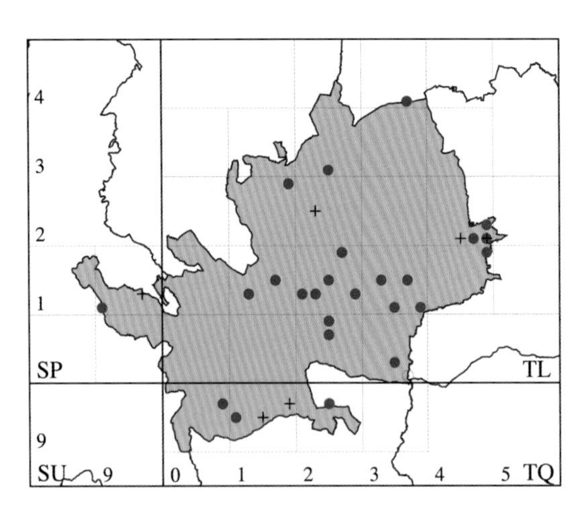

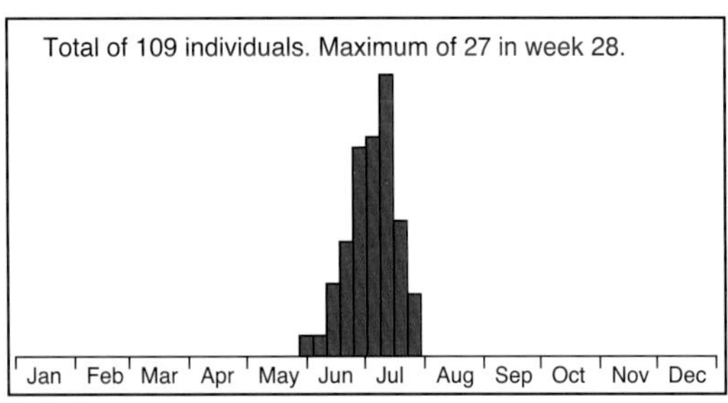

The records indicate a widespread and common species that is likely to be under-recorded in the county.

1116 *Ancylis comptana* (Fr.)

Recorded: 1934 – 1994
Distribution / Status: Absent or extremely local / Rare resident
Conservation status: Herts Endangered
Caterpillar food plants: Not recorded. Elsewhere, on burnets, cinquefoils and strawberries
Flight period: Elsewhere, April/May then July
Records in database: 4

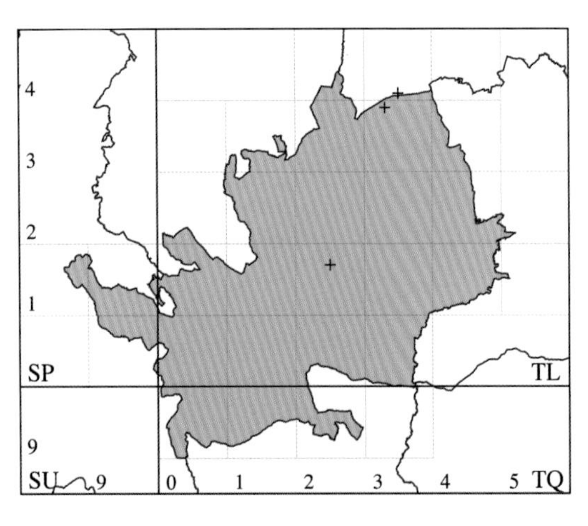

Ashridge 'common' in 1934 (Hervey), Royston (= Therfield) Heath in 1977 (David Agassiz) and 15th May 1979 (Barry Goater) then Welwyn, 12th July 1994 (Raymond Uffen) are our only records of this primarily chalk/limestone grassland species. It is surely still present?

1118 *Ancylis uncella* ([D.& S.])

Recorded: Pre-1900 only
Distribution / Status: Absent / Probable former resident
Conservation status: Herts Extinct
Caterpillar food plants: Not recorded. Elsewhere, on birch
Flight period: Elsewhere, May/June
Records in database: 1

Provisional distributions maps prepared by the late Maitland Emmet showed a Hertfordshire dot for this species '*teste Ted Hancock*'. No details are available except that the record appears to have been made prior to 1900.

[1119 *Ancylis geminana* (Donovan)

Provisional distributions maps prepared by the late Maitland Emmet showed a Hertfordshire dot for this species '*teste Ted Hancock*'. No details are available except that the record appears to have been made prior to 1900. Three 'forms' of this taxon have now been elevated to full species rank, namely *A. geminana* sensu stricto, *A. diminutana* and *A. subarcuana*. The form of the specimen on Emmet's maps is not noted and so cannot be positively related to this species, though it very probably relates to the record of 1119a, below, as that is the only Hertfordshire record known of any of these three species. Either way, it is not possible to admit *geminana* to the Hertfordshire list unless more detail of the record emerges.]

1119a *Ancylis diminutana* (Haw.)

Recorded: Pre-1890 only
Distribution / Status: Absent / Probable former resident
Conservation status: Herts Extinct
Caterpillar food plants: Not recorded. Elsewhere, on various sallows
Flight period: Elsewhere, May to August
Records in database: 1

Our only record is that from the Sandridge area in Griffith (1890).

1120 *Ancylis mitterbacheriana* ([D.& S.])

Recorded: 1890 – 2006
Distribution / Status: Local / Common resident
Conservation status: No perceived threats
Caterpillar food plants: Not recorded. Elsewhere, on oak and Beech
Flight period: May/June
Records in database: 21

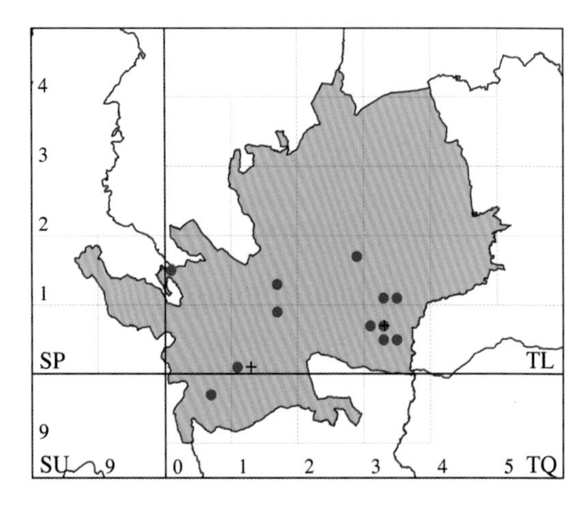

A distinctive species, unlikely to be misidentified and probably under-recorded.

1121 *Ancylis upupana* (Tr.)

Recorded: 1927 only
Distribution / Status: Absent / Probable former resident
Conservation status: Herts Extinct
Caterpillar food plants: Not recorded. Elsewhere, on birch and elm
Flight period: Elsewhere, May/June
Records in database: 1

Our only report is from Broxbourne in 1927 by Fryer (Foster, 1937).

1122 *Ancylis obtusana* (Haw.)

Recorded: 1994 only
Distribution / Status: Absent or extremely local / Rare resident
Conservation status: Herts Endangered
Caterpillar food plants: Not recorded. Elsewhere, on leaves of Buckthorn and Alder Buckthorn
Flight period: Elsewhere, late May to early July
Records in database: 1

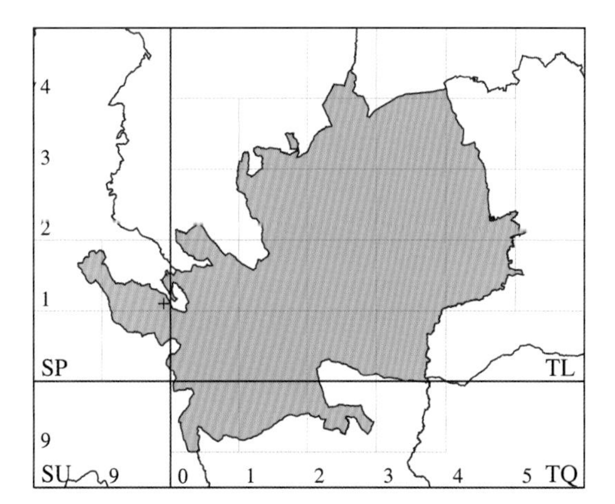

One caught at Frithsden Beeches on 11th June 1994 by Gavin Boyd is the only Hertfordshire record of this species.

1123 *Ancylis laetana* (Fabr.)

Recorded: 1890 – 2003
Distribution / Status: Local / Uncommon resident
Conservation status: Insufficiently known
Caterpillar food plants: Not recorded. Elsewhere, on Aspen
Flight period: Elsewhere, May/June
Records in database: 7

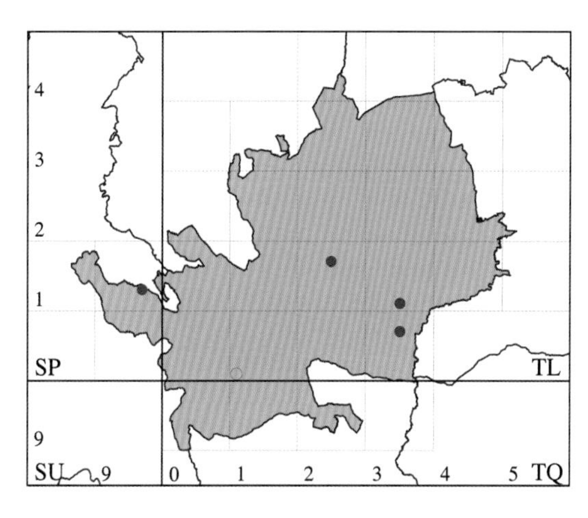

Primarily a woodland species that flies at sunset and after dark, we have recent records from Aldbury Common, Danemead Wood, Balls Wood and Welwyn.

1125 *Ancylis unculana* (Haw.)

Recorded: Pre-1900 only
Distribution / Status: Absent / Probable rare resident
Conservation status: Herts Extinct
Caterpillar food plants: Not recorded. Elsewhere, on leaves of Buckthorn and Alder Buckthorn
Flight period: Elsewhere, June/July
Records in database: 1

Provisional distributions maps prepared by the late Maitland Emmet showed a Hertfordshire dot for this species '*teste Ted Hancock*'. No details are available except that the record appears to have been made prior to 1900.

1126 *Ancylis badiana* ([D.& S.])

Recorded: 1888 – 2006
Distribution / Status: Widespread / Common resident
Conservation status: No perceived threats
Caterpillar food plants: Not recorded. Elsewhere, on leaves of vetches and clovers
Flight period: May to mid-June
Records in database: 34

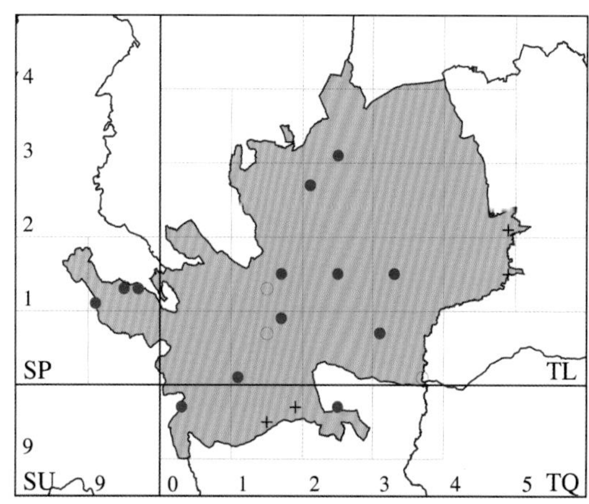

Likely to be found in many parts of the county wherever the foodplant is able to grow.

1129 *Ancylis apicella* ([D.& S.])

Recorded: 1884 only
Distribution / Status: Absent / Former resident
Conservation status: Herts Extinct
Caterpillar food plants: Not recorded. Elsewhere, on leaves of Alder Buckthorn and Buckthorn
Flight period: Elsewhere, May/June then July/August
Records in database: 1

The Sandridge area (Griffith, 1884) is the location of our only record.

1130 *Epinotia pygmaeana* (Hb.)

Recorded:	1925 – 1980
Distribution / Status:	Absent or extremely local / Extinct or rare resident
Conservation status:	Herts Rare
Caterpillar food plants:	Not recorded. Elsewhere, on Norway and Sitka Spruce and on Firs
Flight period:	Elsewhere, April to early June
Records in database:	4

'Highdown', Hitchin 1925 (Foster), Ashridge, 1934 (Hervey), Hilfield Reservoir, 4th April 1980 and Reddings Avenue, Bushey, 16th June 1980 (Barry Goater) are our only records. It may persist in the county, perhaps limiting its activities to the canopy of suitable trees, although Hertfordshire is not blessed with all that many woodlands containing spruce.

1132 *Epinotia subocellana* (Donovan)

Recorded:	1889 – 2000
Distribution / Status:	Extremely local / Rare resident
Conservation status:	Insufficiently known
Caterpillar food plants:	Not recorded. Elsewhere, on sallows
Flight period:	Elsewhere, late May to early August
Records in database:	7

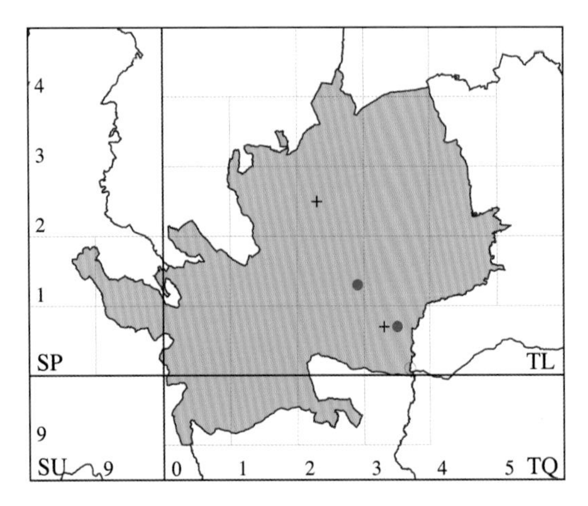

Our two most recent records are from Panshanger Park in 1997 (Tom Gladwin) and my own from Danemead Wood on 20th July 2000.

1133 *Epinotia bilunana* (Haw.)

Recorded:	1890 – 2006
Distribution / Status:	Widespread / Common resident
Conservation status:	No perceived threats
Caterpillar food plants:	Not recorded. Elsewhere, in the catkins of birch
Flight period:	June to early July
Records in database:	30

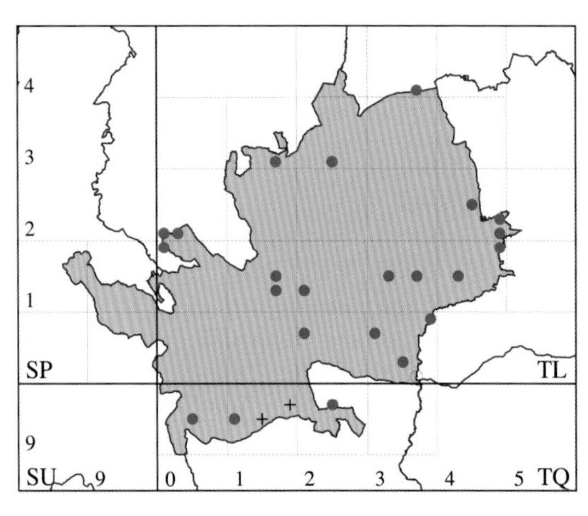

Confusion with the evidently less common 1134: *Epinotia ramella* is discussed under that species.

1134 *Epinotia ramella* (L.)

Recorded:	1890 – 2005
Distribution / Status:	Local / Common resident
Conservation status:	No perceived threats
Caterpillar food plants:	Not recorded. Elsewhere, in twigs and catkins of birch
Flight period:	Late July to October
Records in database:	33

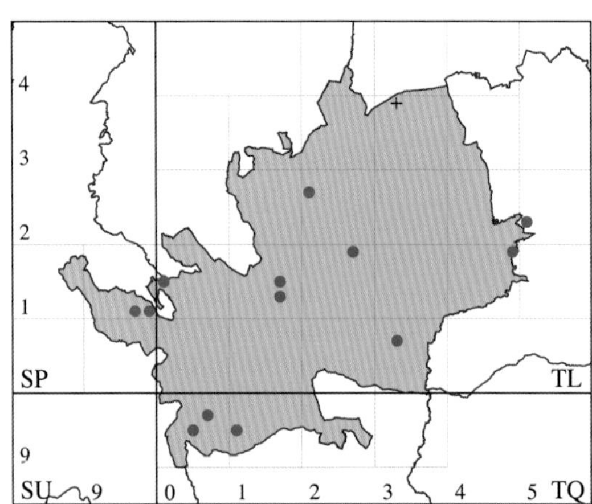

This species flies later than 1133: *Epinotia bilunana* and this makes easy the separation of an otherwise difficult species pair that both depend on the same food source and which are expected to occur together. There is potential for overlap in July, when males of *bilunana* are recognised by the presence of a basal fold on the costa of the fore wing – a feature absent from males of *ramella*.

1135 *Epinotia demarniana* (F. von Ros.)

Recorded: 1934 – 2006
Distribution / Status: Local / Common resident
Conservation status: Insufficiently known
Caterpillar food plants: Not recorded. Elsewhere, in catkins of birch, Alder and Goat Willow
Flight period: June/July
Records in database: 11

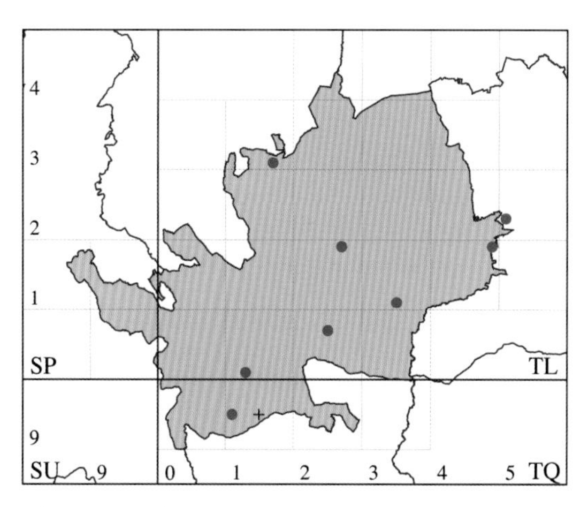

Usually thought of as a scarce species, the number of records of *demarniana* actually exceeds that of some allegedly more frequent species.

1136 *Epinotia immundana* (F. von Ros.)

Recorded: 1890 – 2006
Distribution / Status: Local / Common resident
Conservation status: Insufficiently known
Caterpillar food plants: Not recorded. Elsewhere, in catkins of birch and Alder
Flight period: April/June then August
Records in database: 23

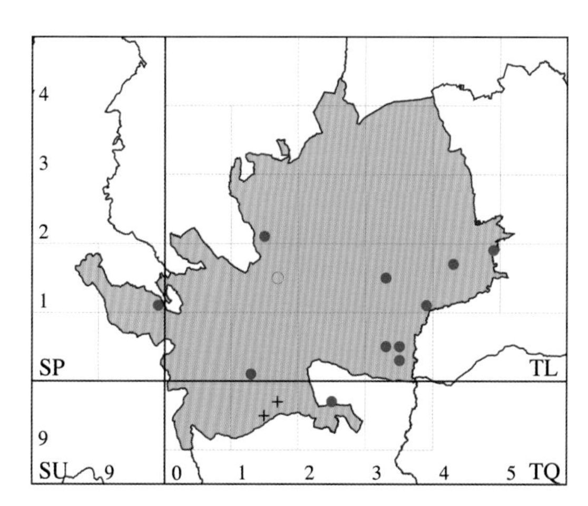

As elsewhere in Britain, we have a small second generation of adults in Hertfordshire. Griffith (1890) records this species 'on the banks of the Lea, near Wheathampstead, where they abound on the alders'; the lack of suitable riverside alders in 2006 is probably responsible in no small part for the moth's present status of Local.

1137 *Epinotia tetraquetrana* (Haw.)

Recorded: 1890 – 2004
Distribution / Status: Local / Common resident
Conservation status: Insufficiently known
Caterpillar food plants: Not recorded. Elsewhere, on birch and Alder
Flight period: Elsewhere, April/May
Records in database: 8

The spread of records and the fact that the species is numerically common in sites where it is found suggests an under-recorded species.

1138 *Epinotia nisella* (Cl.)

Recorded: 1890 – 2006
Distribution / Status: Widespread / Common resident
Conservation status: No perceived threats
Caterpillar food plants: Not recorded. Elsewhere, on sallows and poplars
Flight period: July to October
Records in database: 40

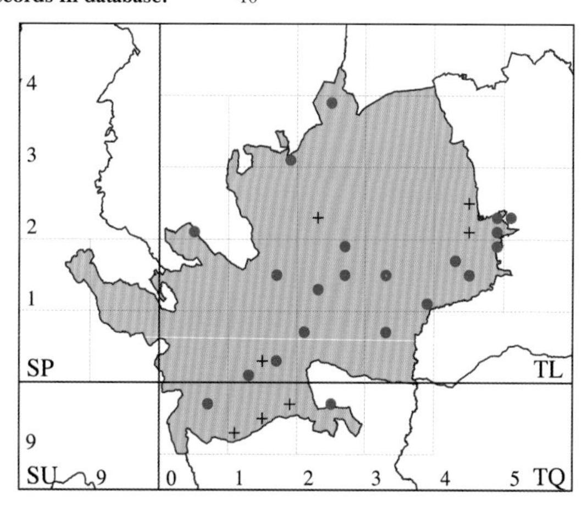

Many different colour forms of this moth are evident. In Hertfordshire, the majority conform to f. *decorana* Hb., but several others can be encountered, though we have no numerical data on these. The grey form *cinereana* Haworth appears to be restricted to Aspen and is regarded as a full species by some authors and for this reason the records are now listed separately, as follows: Sandridge area (Griffith, 1884), Hitchin area (Foster, 1916), Harpenden, early 1930s (C. B. Williams), Broxbourne, 1934 (in Foster, 1937) and Broxbourne Wood, 3rd August 2003 (Colin Plant).

1139 *Epinotia tenerana* ([D.& S.]) Nut Bud Moth

Recorded: 1888 – 2003
Distribution / Status: Local / Common resident
Conservation status: Insufficiently known.
Caterpillar food plants: Not recorded. Elsewhere, in catkins and buds of Hazel
Flight period: July to September
Records in database: 19

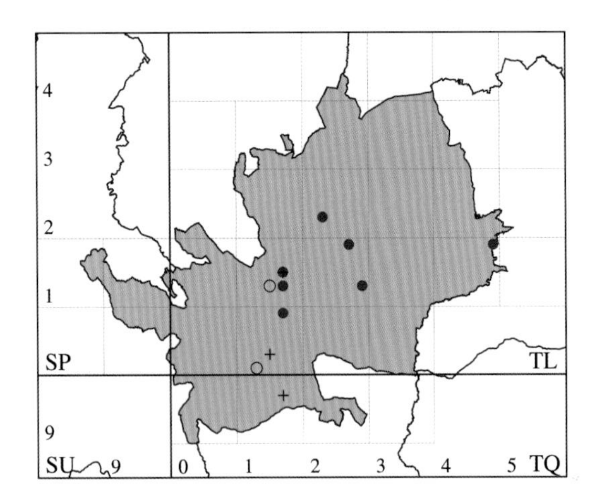

The records are few but widespread and the moth is probably overlooked.

1142 *Epinotia tedella* (Cl.)

Recorded: 1890 – 2003
Distribution / Status: Extremely Local / Uncommon resident
Conservation status: Insufficiently known
Caterpillar food plants: Not recorded. Elsewhere, on Norway Spruce
Flight period: Elsewhere, May/June
Records in database: 7

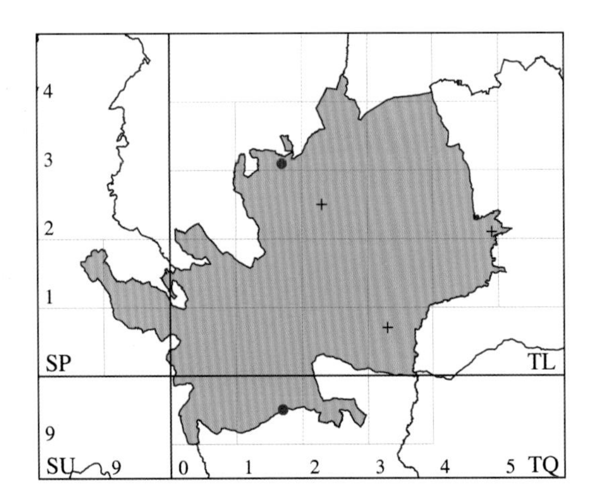

The lack of spruce plantations in Hertfordshire will doubtless limit the distribution of this species, which is recorded most recently from Aldenham Country Park on 15th June 2002 and Oughtonhead Common on 7th June 2003, where examples entered my light traps.

1144 *Epinotia signatana* (Douglas)

Recorded: 2000 – 2003
Distribution / Status: Extremely local / Rare resident
Conservation status: Herts Rare
Caterpillar food plants: Not recorded. Elsewhere, on Blackthorn, Wild Cherry and Bird-cherry
Flight period: Elsewhere, June/July
Records in database: 2

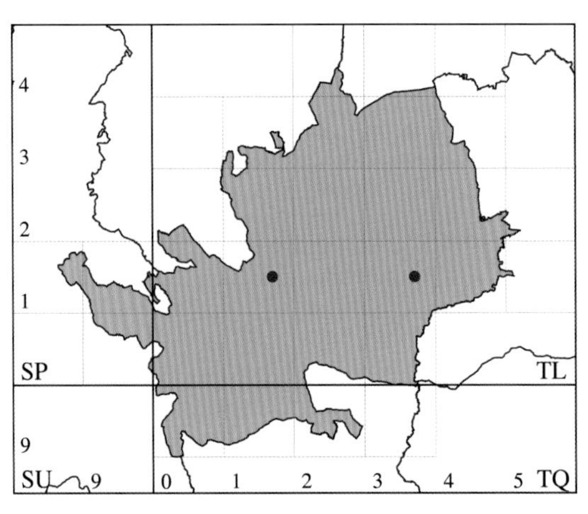

Our two records are both recent – from Marshall's Heath on 13th July 2000 and Ware on 1st June 2003 (Elizabeth Goodyear). There are no earlier records available.

1145 *Epinotia nanana* (Tr.)

Recorded: 1886 – 1966
Distribution / Status: Absent or extremely local / Former resident
Conservation status: Herts Extinct
Caterpillar food plants: Not recorded. Elsewhere, on Norway and Sitka Spruce
Flight period: Elsewhere, June to August
Records in database: 4

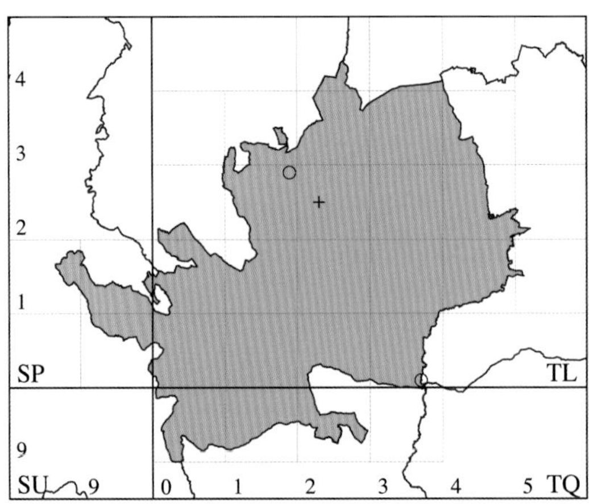

Our records are from Wilbury Hill, Hitchin, on 10th July 1886 during a field meeting of the Hertfordshire Natural History Society and Field Club, the Sandridge area (Griffith, 1890), the Cheshunt area (Boyd, 1901) and Stevenage, 2nd July 1966 (Jack Newton). The lack of spruce plantations in the county probably indicates that this moth is now absent?

1146 *Epinotia rubiginosana* (H. – S.)

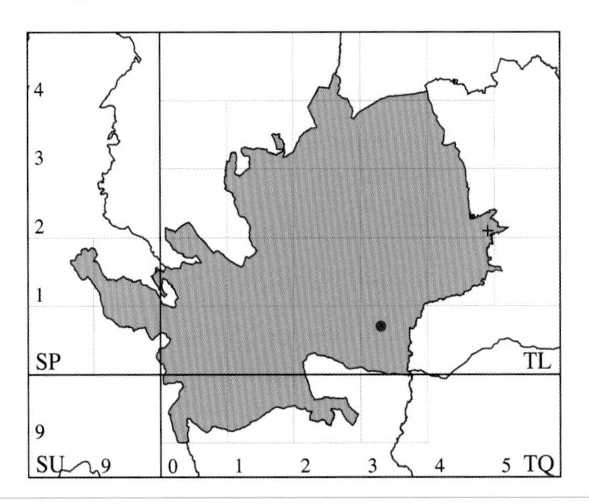

Recorded:	1988 – 2003
Distribution / Status:	Local / Rare resident
Conservation status:	Insufficiently known
Caterpillar food plants:	Not recorded. Elsewhere, on Scots Pine
Flight period:	Elsewhere, June
Records in database:	2

The only Hertfordshire records are my own from Brickendon Village Green, on 27th May 2003 and from my garden in Bishops Stortford on 19th July 1988. Scots Pine trees grow in the vicinity of both trap positions and the moth is likely to be found elsewhere in the county.

1147 *Epinotia cruciana* (L.) Willow Tortrix

Recorded:	1890 – 2003
Distribution / Status:	Local / Common resident
Conservation status:	Insufficiently known.
Caterpillar food plants:	Not recorded. Elsewhere, on the terminal leaves of Osier
Flight period:	Elsewhere June to early August
Records in database:	5

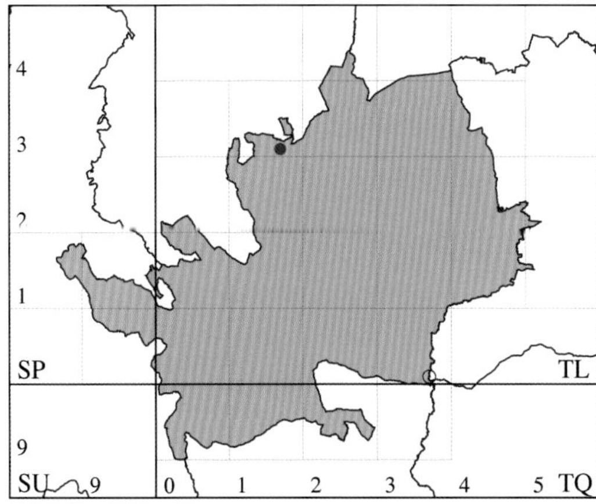

This species was expected, and found, at Oughtonhead Common on 12th July 2003 and it is likely that more will be found in other suitable habitat areas, perhaps in the Stort and Lea river valleys.

1150 *Epinotia abbreviana* (Fabr.)

Recorded:	1968 – 2006
Distribution / Status:	Widespread / Common resident
Conservation status:	No perceived threats
Caterpillar food plants:	In the leaf buds of elm. Stinging Nettle
Flight period:	June/July
Records in database:	24

Mined leaf buds display characteristic pattern of holes when the leaf later opens and this is sufficient evidence to record the moth in spring. A larva collected from Stinging Nettle at Batch Wood on 17th April 2004, and fed to maturity on this plant by Rachel Terry yielded a male *E. abbreviana* (identified from examination of genitalia) later in the year. This is an extremely unusual foodplant. Perhaps it fell from overhanging trees and had no alternative food source; certainly it is an unusual example of xenophagy.

1151 *Epinotia trigonella* (L.) = *stroemiana* (Fabr.)

Recorded:	1888 – 2004
Distribution / Status:	Local / Uncommon resident
Conservation status:	Insufficiently known
Caterpillar food plants:	Not recorded. Elsewhere, on leaves of birch
Flight period:	August/September
Records in database:	12

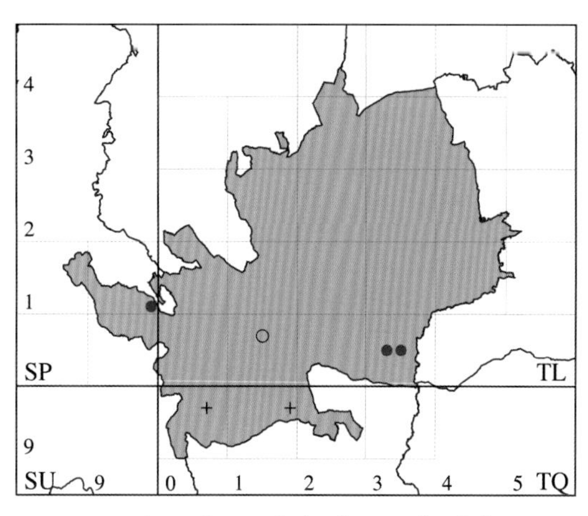

The concentration of records in the south of the county is unexpected, as birch is not confined to this region.

1152 *Epinotia maculana* (Fabr.)

Recorded:	1884 – 1889
Distribution / Status:	Absent / Former resident
Conservation status:	Herts Extinct
Caterpillar food plants:	Not recorded. Elsewhere, on Aspen
Flight period:	Elsewhere, August to October
Records in database:	2

Our two records are from the Sandridge area (Gibbs, 1884) and Bricket Wood (Gibbs, 1889).

1153 *Epinotia sordidana* (Hb.)

Recorded:	1890 – 2004
Distribution / Status:	Extremely local / Uncommon resident
Conservation status:	Insufficiently known
Caterpillar food plants:	Alder
Flight period:	Elsewhere, August to October
Records in database:	5

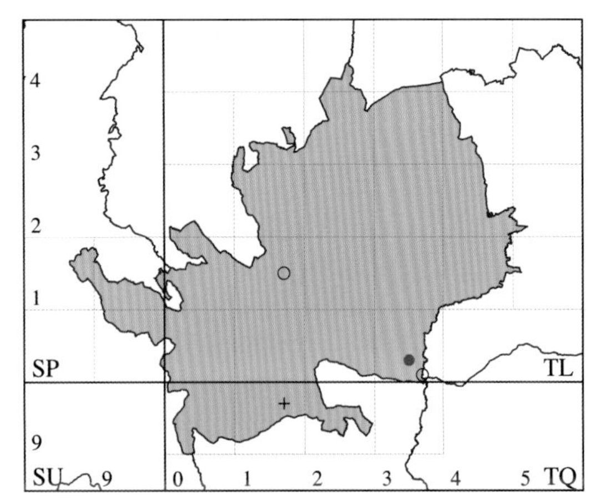

Griffith (1890) records this species 'on the banks of the Lea, near Wheathampstead, where they abound on the alders' and on 3rd and 4th June 1979 Barry Goater found twenty larvae in pods on Alder leaves at the Haberdasher's Aske's School. More recently, adults were caught at light in Cheshunt in 2002 and 2003 by Mark Cooper. It is surely under-recorded in Hertfordshire.

1154 *Epinotia caprana* (Fabr.)

Recorded:	Pre-1884 only
Distribution / Status:	Absent / Former resident
Conservation status:	Herts Extinct
Caterpillar food plants:	Not recorded. Elsewhere, on sallows
Flight period:	Elsewhere, late July and August
Records in database:	1

Listed for the Sandridge area (as *semifuscana*) by Griffith (1884). There are no other records.

1155 *Epinotia brunnichana* (L.)

Recorded:	1888 – 2006
Distribution / Status:	Widespread / Common resident
Conservation status:	No perceived threats
Caterpillar food plants:	Not recorded. Elsewhere, on birches, Hazel and sallows
Flight period:	July/August
Records in database:	31

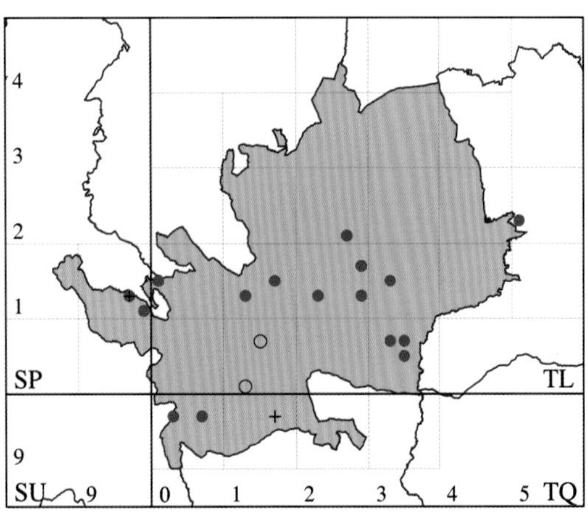

Apparently widespread in the south of the county, there are no reports from the north.

1156 *Epinotia solandriana* (L.)

Recorded:	1890 – 2006
Distribution / Status:	Local / Uncommon resident
Conservation status:	Insufficiently known
Caterpillar food plants:	Not recorded. Elsewhere, on birch, Hazel and Goat Willow leaves
Flight period:	July/August
Records in database:	12

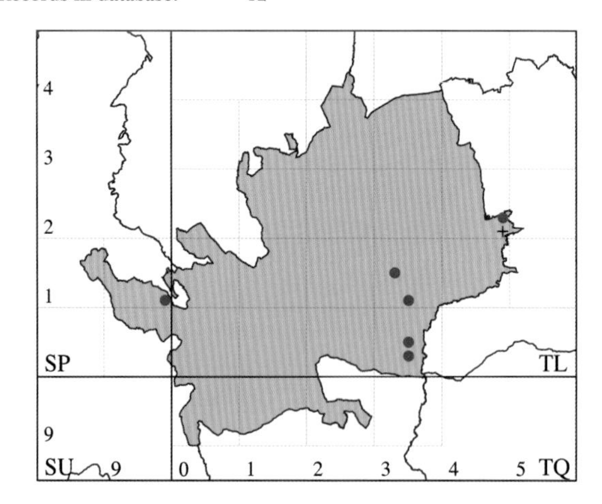

Many candidate specimens of this species turn out to be 1155: *Epinotia brunnichana* on close examination. It is only reported as single individuals.

1157 *Crocidosema plebejana* Zell.

Recorded:	2005 only
Distribution / Status:	Absent / Vagrant
Conservation status:	-
Caterpillar food plants:	Not recorded. Elsewhere, Tree Mallow
Flight period:	Elsewhere July to October
Records in database:	1

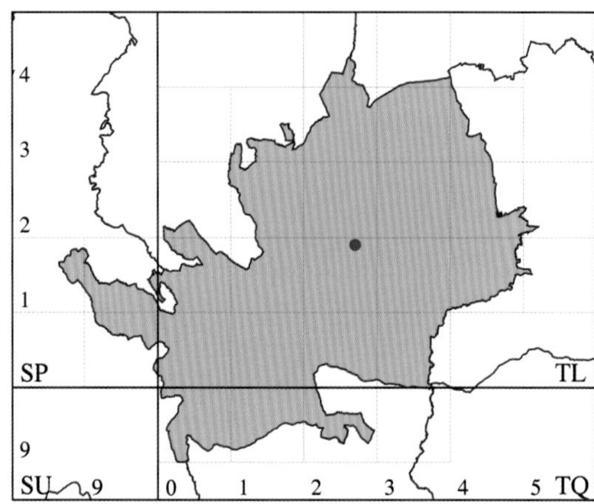

One at Datchworth on 21st June 2005 (Steve Palmer) must have been a wanderer and is our only record of this usually coastal species.

1159 *Rhopobota naevana* (Hb.) Holly Tortrix

Recorded: 1890 – 2006
Distribution / Status: Widespread / Common resident
Conservation status: No perceived threats.
Caterpillar food plants: Poplar. Elsewhere, on the leaves of Holly and fruit trees
Flight period: Mid-June to mid-August
Records in database: 78

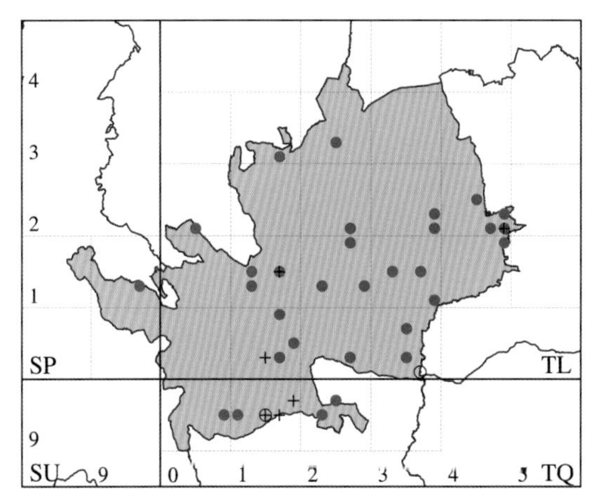

Larvae were found and reared on poplar at Hilfield Reservoir, Aldenham on 26th May 1980 (Barry Goater).

1161 *Rhopobota stagnana* ([D.& S.])

Recorded: 1903 – 2002
Distribution / Status: Extremely local / Uncommon resident
Conservation status: Herts Threatened
Caterpillar food plants: Not recorded. Elsewhere, on Small Scabious
Flight period: Elsewhere, April to June then August/ September
Records in database: 8

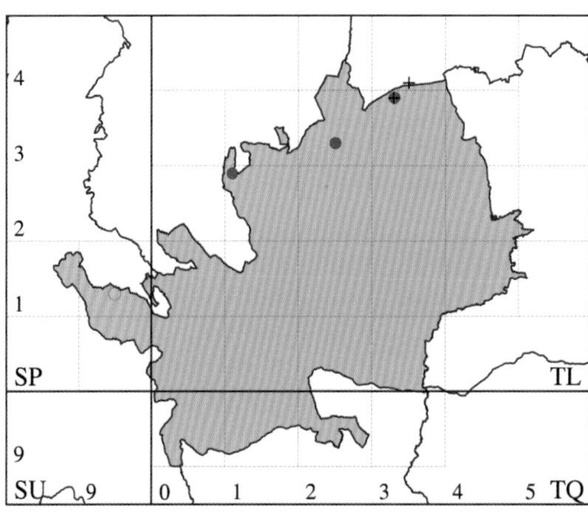

This is a chalk downland species, first recorded in the county at Aldbury Nowers in 1903. Good chalk downland with a supply of the foodplant is rare in the county, placing the moth into the lower category of threat.

1163 *Zeiraphera ratzeburgiana* (Ratz.)

Recorded: 1890 – 2005
Distribution / Status: Local / Uncommon resident
Conservation status: Insufficiently known
Caterpillar food plants: Not recorded. Elsewhere, spruce
Flight period: July/August
Records in database: 10

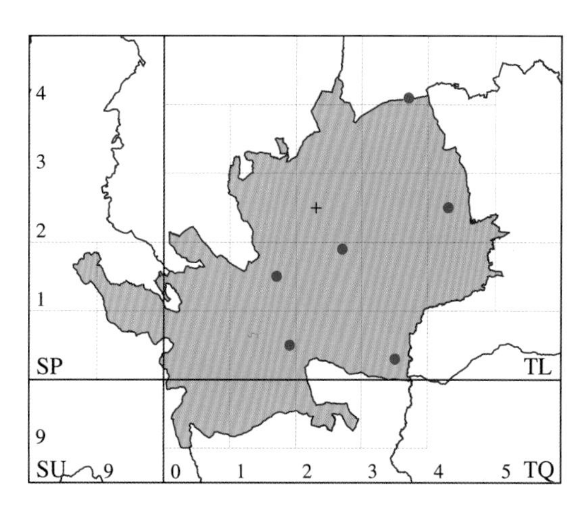

The scarcity of spruce trees in the county will render this moth a rather local species.

1165 *Zeiraphera isertana* (Fabr.)

Recorded: 1890 – 2006
Distribution / Status: Local / Common resident
Conservation status: No perceived threats
Caterpillar food plants: oak
Flight period: Late June to early September
Records in database: 56

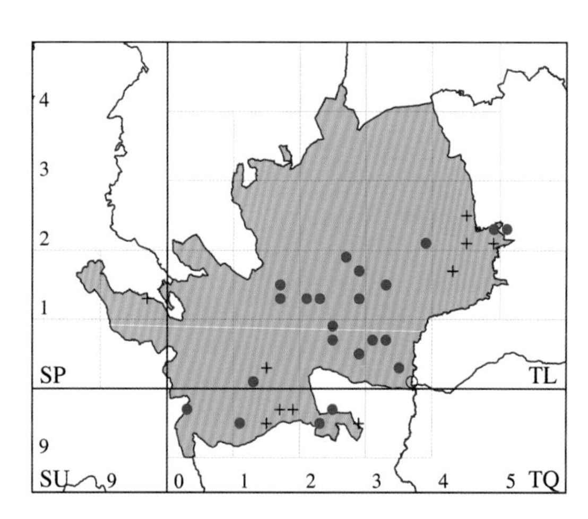

The apparent lack of records in the north of the county reflects the larval requirement for oak woodland, rather than isolated oak trees.

1166 *Zeiraphera griseana* (Hb.) Larch Tortrix
= *diniana* (Guen.)

Recorded: 1890 – 2003
Distribution / Status: Widespread / Common resident
Conservation status: Insufficiently known.
Caterpillar food plants: Not recorded. Elsewhere, on Larch
Flight period: July
Records in database: 9

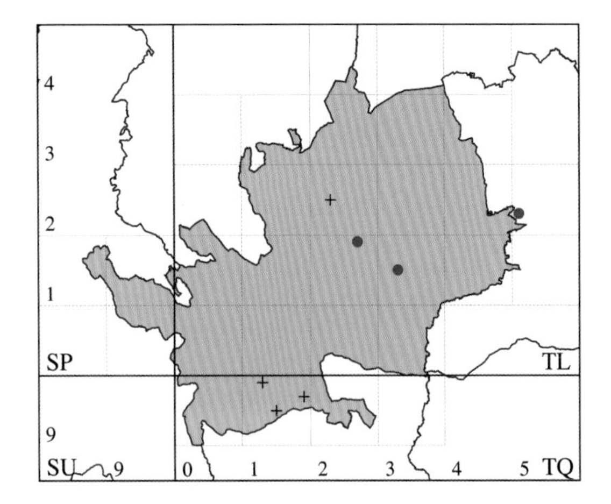

The scarcity of Larch trees in the county will render this moth a rather local species.

1167 *Gypsonoma aceriana* (Dup.)

Recorded: 1900 – 2004
Distribution / Status: Very local / Uncommon resident
Conservation status: No perceived threats
Caterpillar food plants: Lombardy Poplar. Elsewhere, also on other poplars
Flight period: July
Records in database: 10

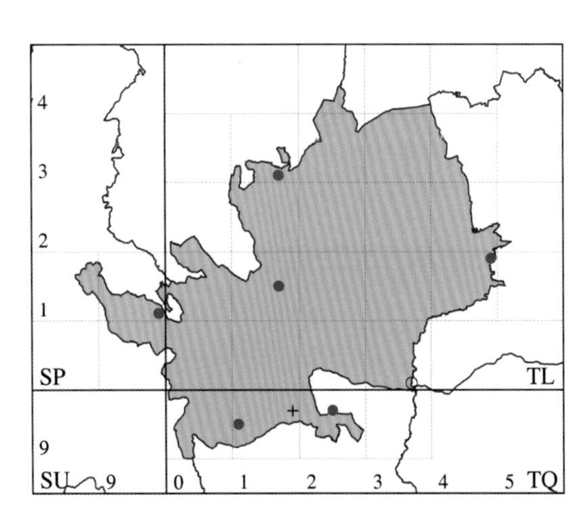

The larvae feed internally in shoots and leaf stalks, its presence usually betrayed by frass exuding between bud scale and petiole during May. It is probably under-recorded, though Larch is a scarce tree in the county.

1168 *Gypsonoma sociana* (Haw.)

Recorded: 1890 – 2006
Distribution / Status: Local / Common resident
Conservation status: No perceived threats
Caterpillar food plants: Not recorded. Elsewhere, in stems of Black Poplar, Aspen and sometimes willows
Flight period: July
Records in database: 23

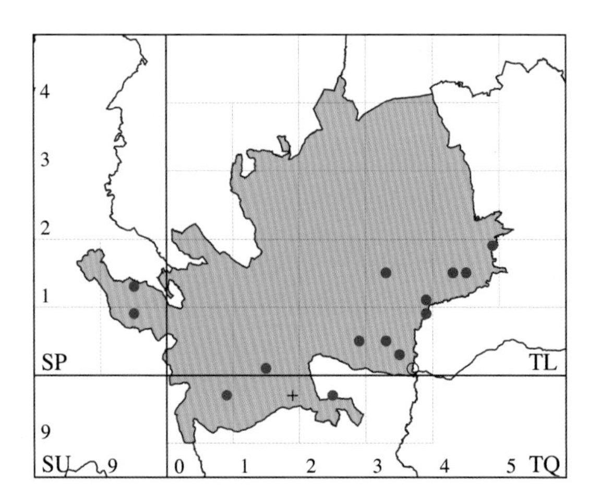

We have no larval records – all our reports are of adults and almost all confirmed by dissection. Black Poplar is unlikely to be the main host in Hertfordshire. The south-eastern distribution is interesting and contrasts with both 1167: *Gypsonoma aceriana* and 1169: *Gypsonoma dealbana*.

1169 *Gypsonoma dealbana* (Fr.)

Recorded: 1890 – 2006
Distribution / Status: Widespread / Common resident
Conservation status: No perceived threats
Caterpillar food plants: Oak, Sallow, Hazel, and Goat Willow
Flight period: June to early August
Records in database: 128

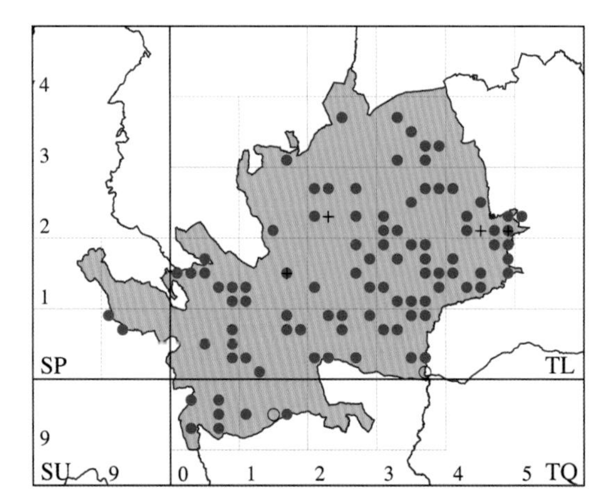

The caterpillar spins an elongate tube of silk and frass, which becomes progressively wider as the larva develops, on the underside of a leaf. This cannot be confused with any other species.

1170 *Gymnosoma oppressana* (Tr.)

Recorded: 1900 – 2006
Distribution / Status: Local / Uncommon resident
Conservation status: Insufficiently known
Caterpillar food plants: Not recorded. Elsewhere, on poplars
Flight period: June/July
Records in database: 8

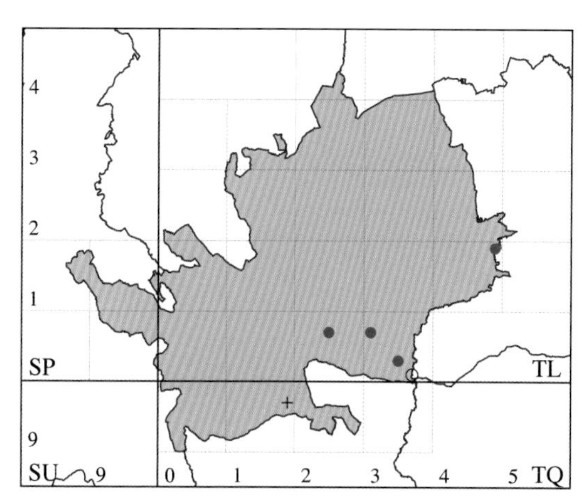

Although certainly under-recorded, this is probably a rather local moth in Hertfordshire.

1171 *Gypsonoma minutana* (Hb.)

Recorded: 2003 – 2006
Distribution / Status: Extremely local / Uncommon resident
Conservation status: Insufficiently known
Caterpillar food plants: Not recorded. Elsewhere,
Flight period: July to early August
Records in database: 2

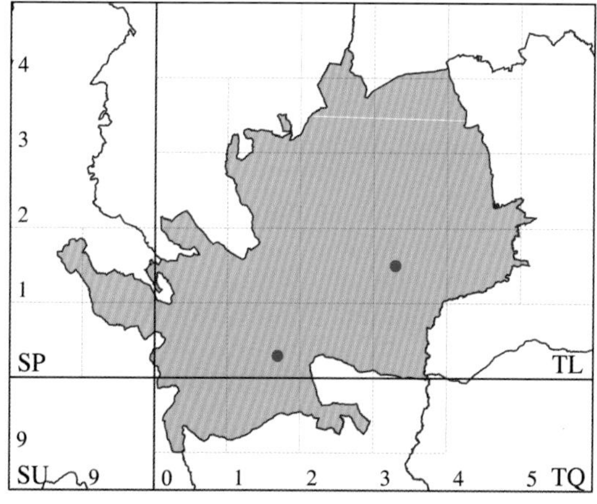

Our two records are from Bengeo, Hertford, in July 2003 (Andrew Wood) and one on a Herts Moth Group recording trip to Broad Colney Lakes, on 5th August 2006.

1174 *Epiblema cynosbatella* (L.)

Recorded: 1888 – 2006
Distribution / Status: Ubiquitous / Common resident
Conservation status: No perceived threats.
Caterpillar food plants: Not recorded. Elsewhere, on the leaves of roses
Flight period: May/June
Records in database: 188

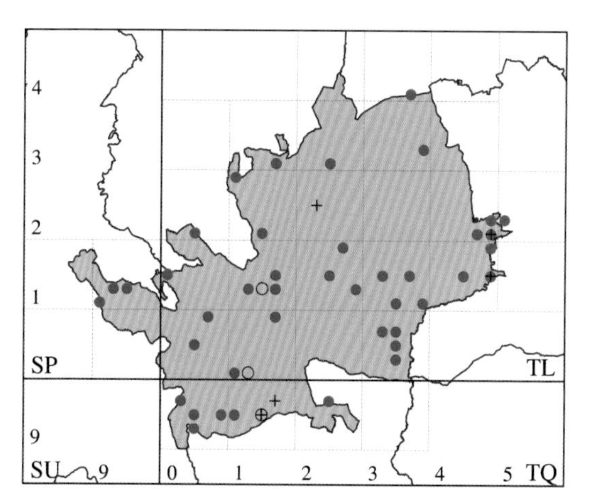

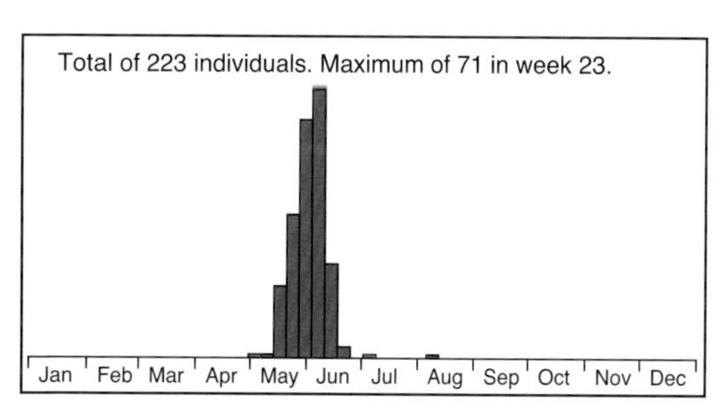

Amongst the black and white tortrix moths that appear in the spring, this is the only one with yellow palps, making it easy to identify. Two unusually late records were made during 2005 – at Bishops Stortford on 2nd July (James Fish & Julian Reeves) and at Royston on 9th August (John Chainey).

1175 *Epiblema uddmanniana* (L.) Bramble Shoot Moth

Recorded: 1834 – 2006
Distribution / Status: Ubiquitous / Abundant resident
Conservation status: No perceived threats.
Caterpillar food plants: Terminal leaves of Bramble and Raspberry. Elsewhere also on Loganberry
Flight period: Mid-May to early August, but see text
Records in database: 231

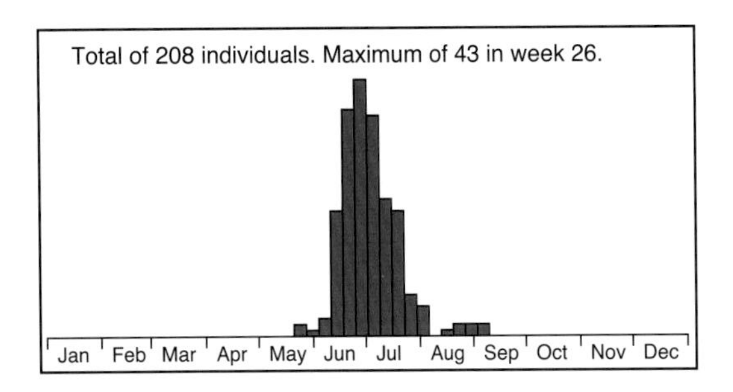

The normal June/July flight period for this species is extended on each side in Hertfordshire and during 2003 and 2005 there was a small second generation of adults from mid-August to early September. The adult moth is distinctive.

1176 *Epiblema trimaculana* (Haw.)

Recorded: 1890 – 2005
Distribution / Status: Widespread / Common resident
Conservation status: No perceived threats
Caterpillar food plants: Common Hawthorn
Flight period: Late May to early July
Records in database: 36

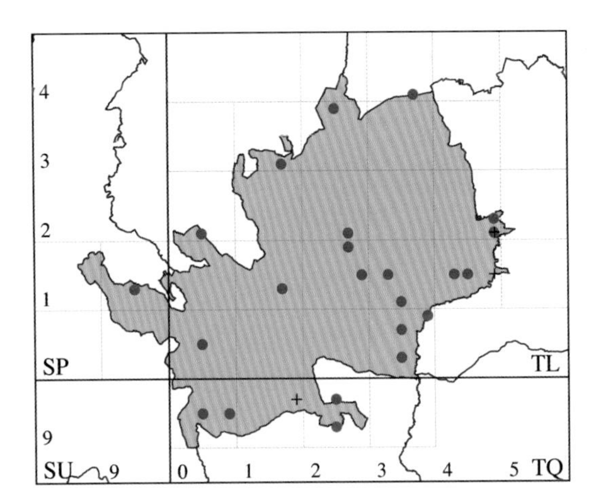

This species and the next, 1177: *Epiblema rosaecolana* are best separated by examination of the genitalia, as they look similar and fly together. Both are equally likely to be encountered in the county.

1177 *Epiblema rosaecolana* (Doubl.)

Recorded: 1890 – 2006
Distribution / Status: Widespread / Common resident
Conservation status: No perceived threats
Caterpillar food plants: Not recorded. Elsewhere, on the leaves of various species of rose
Flight period: Late May to early July
Records in database: 47

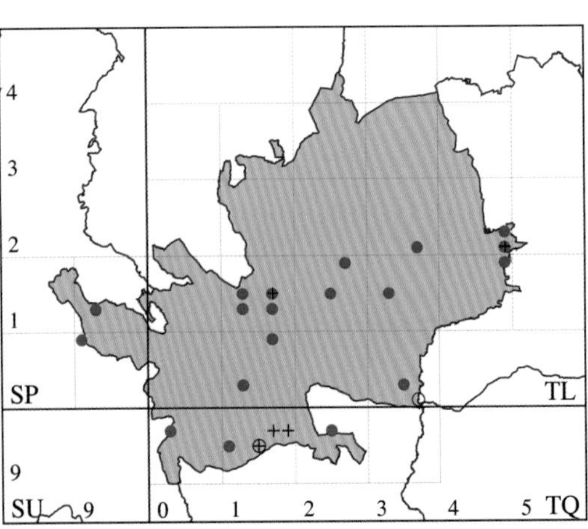

See comments under the last species, above. The map includes only those records that have been properly verified.

1178 *Epiblema roborana* ([D.& S.])

Recorded: 1890 – 2006
Distribution / Status: Local / Uncommon resident
Conservation status: Insufficiently known
Caterpillar food plants: Not recorded. Elsewhere, on the leaves of various species of rose
Flight period: July and early August
Records in database: 23

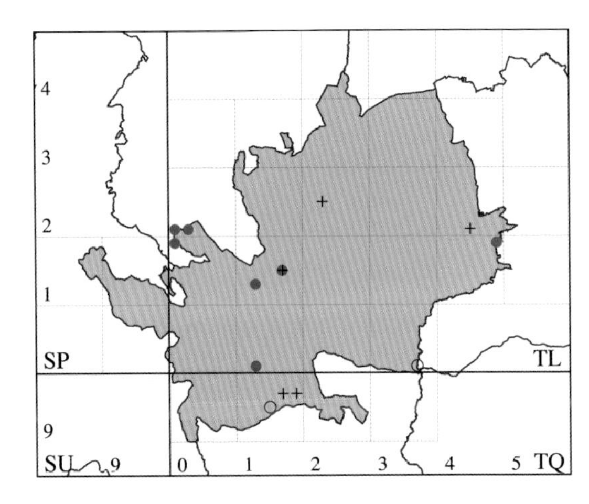

The adults fly slightly later than 1176: *Epiblema trimaculana* and 1177: *Epiblema rosaecolana* so confusion is unlikely to occur, though any mid-July examples ought to be checked carefully. This seems to be the least common of the trio.

1180 *Epiblema tetragonana* (Steph.)

Recorded: 1890 – 1909
Distribution / Status: Absent / Former resident
Conservation status: Herts Extinct
Caterpillar food plants: Not recorded. Elsewhere, on leaves of rose
Flight period: Elsewhere, July
Records in database: 2

Our only records are from the Sandridge area (Griffith, 1890) and from Wheathampstead in 1909, so it is possible that we have lost this species from the Hertfordshire fauna.

1183 *Epiblema foenella* (L.)

Recorded: 1890 – 2006
Distribution / Status: Local / Common resident
Conservation status: No perceived threats
Caterpillar food plants: Mugwort
Flight period: July
Records in database: 39

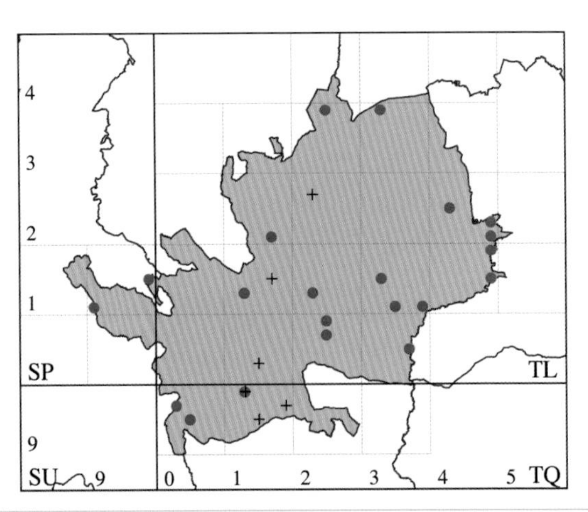

Though local, the distribution is limited by the foodplant and where that is present the moth is likely to be found. The caterpillar feeds in the root then mines up the stem and into side branches.

1184 *Epiblema scutulana* ([D.& S.])

Recorded: 1967 – 2005
Distribution / Status: Local / Common resident
Conservation status: No perceived threats
Caterpillar food plants: Not recorded. Elsewhere, Musk Thistle and Spear Thistle
Flight period: May/June
Records in database: 11

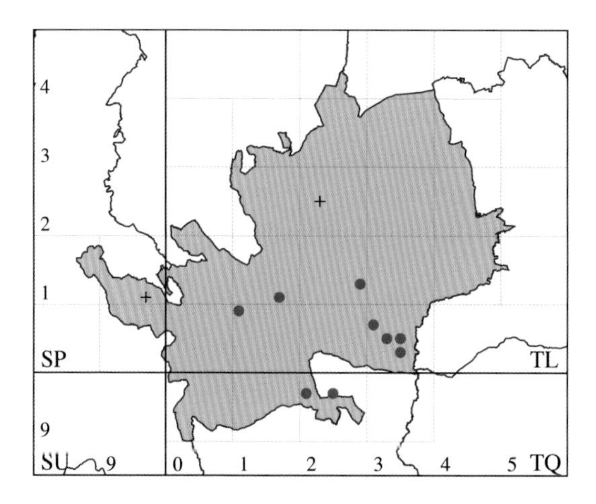

This species and the next have been treated as a single species in the past, and old records that did not specify f. *cirsiana* and for which we have not been able to examine a specimen have had to be disregarded in the interests of accuracy.

1184a *Epiblema cirsiana* (Zell.)

Recorded: 1890 – 2005
Distribution / Status: Very local / Uncommon resident
Conservation status: Insufficiently known
Caterpillar food plants: Not recorded. Elsewhere, Marsh Thistle and Knapweed
Flight period: Elsewhere, May/June
Records in database: 3

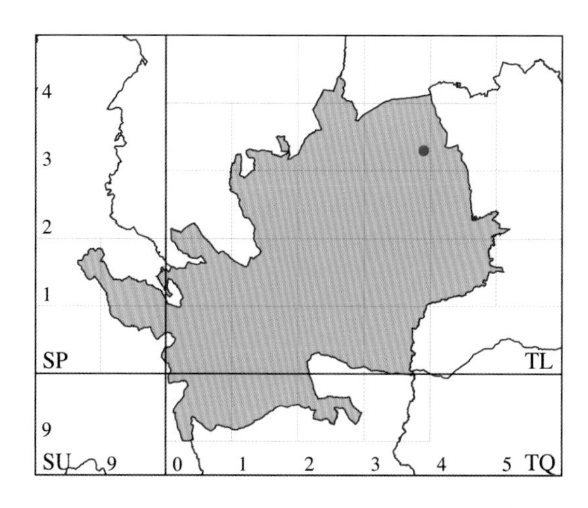

Two old records are from the Sandridge area (Griffith, 1890) and the Hitchin area (Foster, 1934); neither is mapped. The recent report is from Wyddial on 27th May 2005 (Tom Casey). The moth is probably under-recorded. Confusion is possible between this species and 1186: *Epiblema cnicicolana* (Zell.), which feeds on Fleabane and which is not yet reliably recorded from Hertfordshire.

1186 *Epiblema sticticana* (Fabr.) = *farfarae* (Fletcher)

Recorded: 1966 – 2000
Distribution / Status: Very local / Uncommon resident
Conservation status: Insufficiently known
Caterpillar food plants: Not recorded. Elsewhere, on Coltsfoot
Flight period: May/June
Records in database: 9

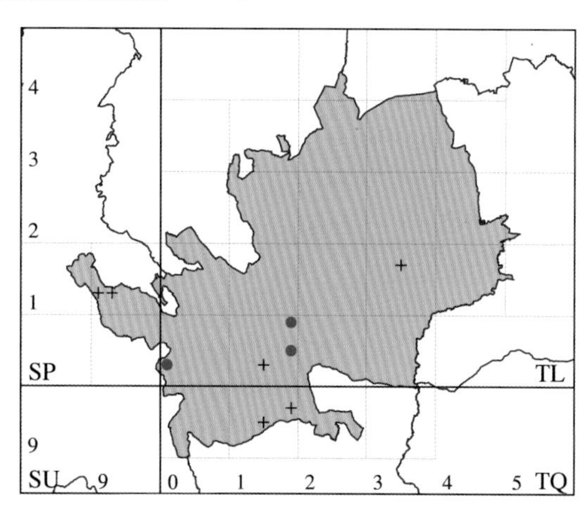

Records are few and very localised and perhaps reflect the 'tidy' nature of much of Hertfordshire. However, the moth is probably present wherever there are established plants of Coltsfoot and if entomologists break their winter diapause a little earlier they might find it to be rather more widespread than the map indicates.

1187 *Epiblema costipunctana* (Haw.)

Recorded: 1890 – 1999
Distribution / Status: Very local / Rare resident
Conservation status: Herts Rare
Caterpillar food plants: Not recorded. Elsewhere, on Common Ragwort
Flight period: Elsewhere, May to early July then late July to August in two generations
Records in database: 7

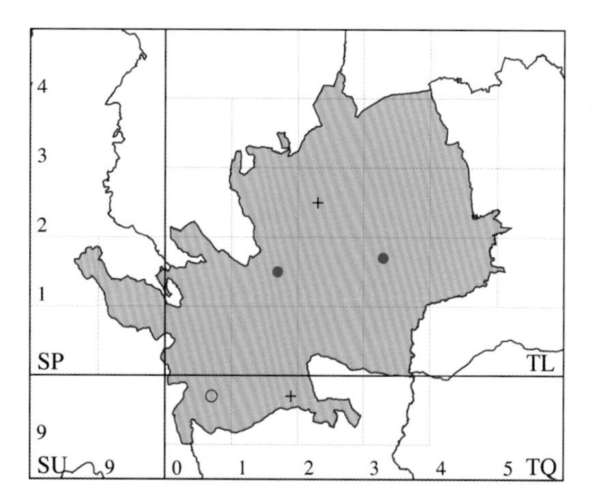

In spite of the abundance of Common Ragwort, this moth is hard to find and may, like 952: *Commophila aeneana*, be genuinely scarce in Hertfordshire.

1192 *Eucosma conterminana* (Guen.)

Recorded: 1994 – 2006
Distribution / Status: Very local / Uncommon resident
Conservation status: Insufficiently known
Caterpillar food plants: Not recorded. Elsewhere, on Great, Prickly and Garden Lettuce (flowers and seeds)
Flight period: July to mid-August
Records in database: 10

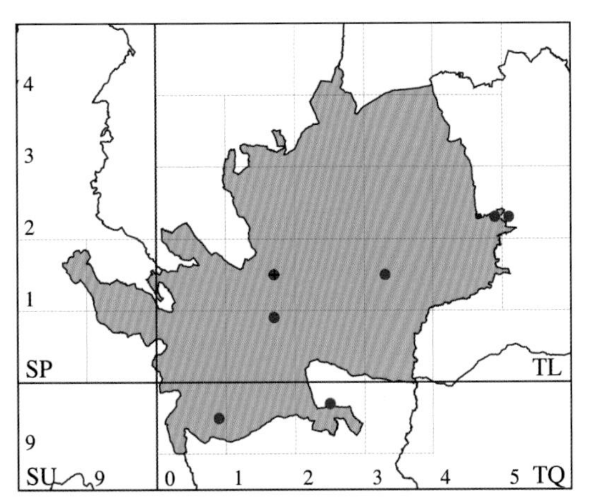

This is a rather scarce species of south-east Britain and its distribution in Hertfordshire will be limited by foodplant availability.

1197 *Eucosma campoliliana* ([D.& S.])

Recorded: 1890 – 2006
Distribution / Status: Widespread / Common resident
Conservation status: No perceived threats
Caterpillar food plants: On the seeds and stems of Common Ragwort
Flight period: Mid-June to mid-August
Records in database: 30

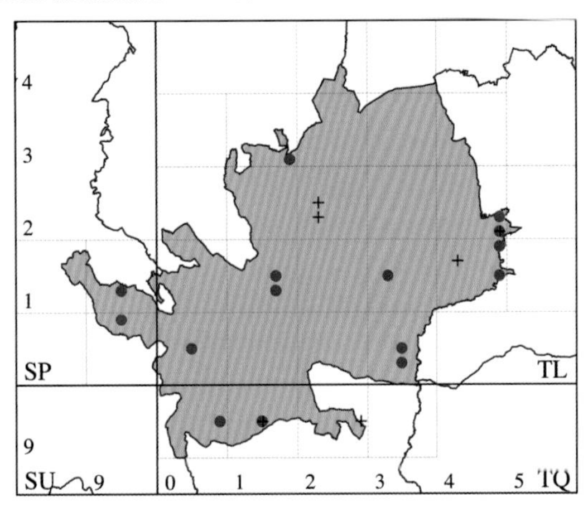

There is no shortage of Ragwort and the moth can be found easily if looked for. Unlike some other ragwort-feeders, such as 952: *Commophila aeneana* or 1187: *Epiblema costipunctana* it is probably widespread across the county.

1198 *Eucosma pauperana* (Dup.)

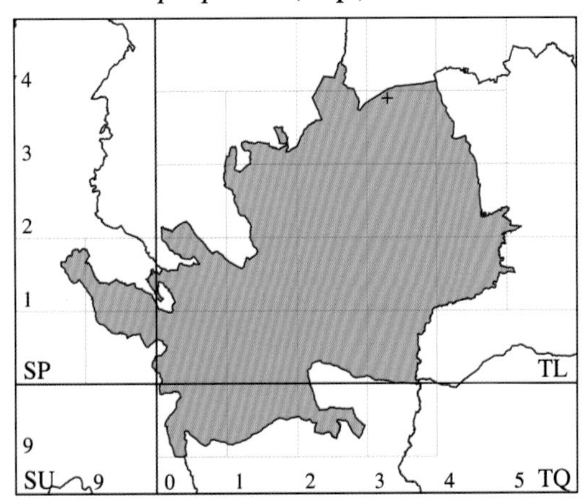

Recorded: 1979 only
Distribution / Status: Extremely local / Rare resident
Conservation status: Herts Endangered
Caterpillar food plants: Not recorded. Elsewhere, on hips of Dog Rose
Flight period: Elsewhere, April/May
Records in database: 1

Our one record is from Therfield Heath on 15th May 1979 (Barry Goater & Rob Dyke). The popular collecting locality at a lay-by in Meldreth is in the Cambridgeshire vice-county, not in Hertfordshire. Chalk downs are the favoured locality of this species and these are scarce in Hertfordshire, so if the moth is rediscovered it should certainly be regarded as Endangered.

1200 *Eucosma hohenwartiana* ([D.& S.])

Recorded: 1988 – 2006
Distribution / Status: Widespread / Common resident
Conservation status: No perceived threats
Caterpillar food plants: Not recorded. Elsewhere, on flowers and seeds of Lesser Knapweed
Flight period: Mid-June to mid-August
Records in database: 36

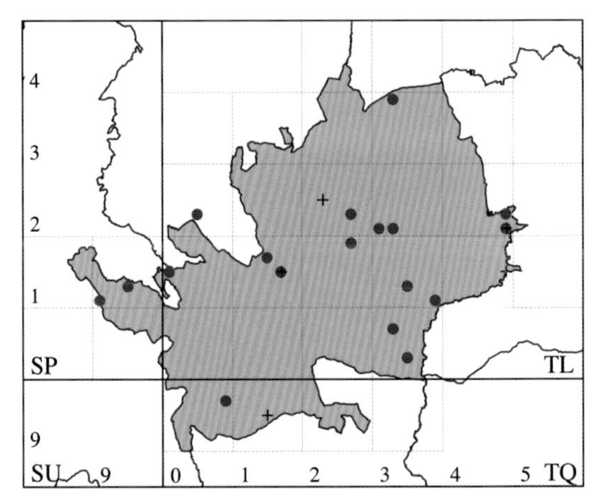

Agassiz & Langmaid (2004) showed that the form *fulvana* of this species is a species in its own right; consequently, early records not supported by a specimen have been disregarded as they could refer to either species. The true *hohenwartiana* is restricted to Lesser Knapweed.

1200b *Eucosma fulvana* Steph.

Recorded: 1926 – 2004
Distribution / Status: Local / Common resident
Conservation status: Insufficiently known
Caterpillar food plants: Not recorded. Elsewhere, on flowers and seeds of Greater Knapweed
Flight period: July to first week of August
Records in database: 8

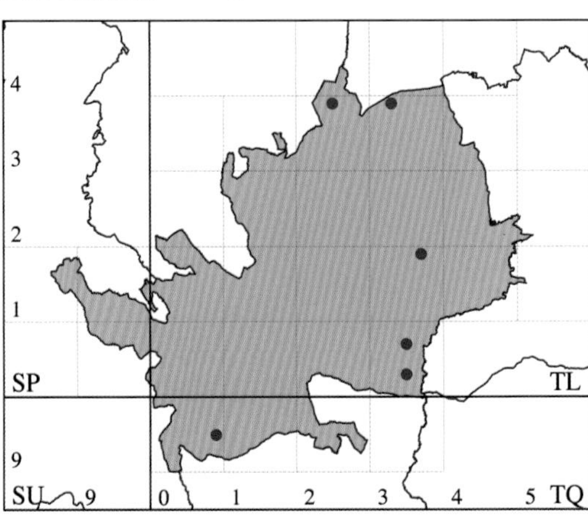

Agassiz & Langmaid (2004) showed this is a species in its own right and so early reports of form *fulvana* of the last species are gathered under the present heading. *Eucosma fulvana* is restricted to Greater Knapweed.

1201 *Eucosma cana* (Haw.)

Recorded: 1834 – 2006
Distribution / Status: Ubiquitous / Common resident
Conservation status: No perceived threats
Caterpillar food plants: Creeping Thistle. Elsewhere, on various thistles and Lesser Knapweed
Flight period: Late May to early August
Records in database: 152

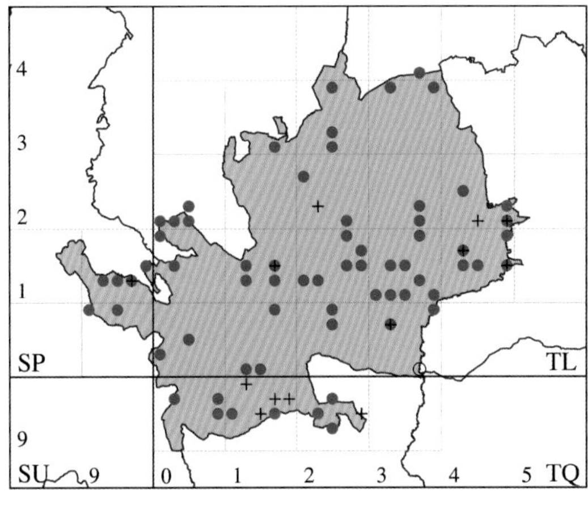

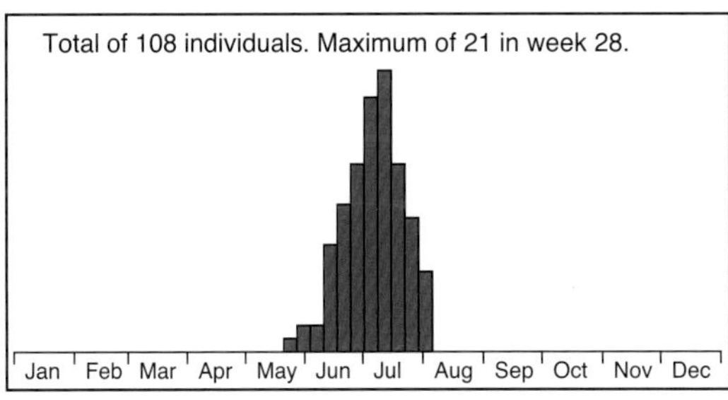

This is a distinctive species that is likely to be found almost everywhere it is looked for.

1202 *Eucosma obumbratana* (Lien.& Zell.)

Recorded: 1900 – 2004
Distribution / Status: Local / Uncommon resident
Conservation status: No perceived threats
Caterpillar food plants: Not recorded. Elsewhere, on Field Milk-thistle
Flight period: Late June to July. Elsewhere, also August
Records in database: 14

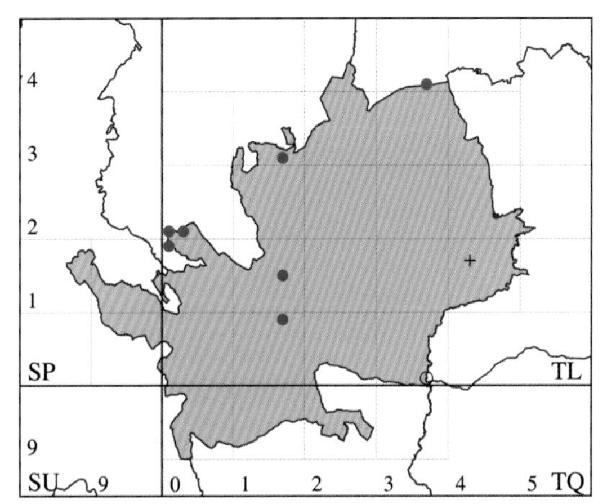

In keeping with the national position, this is a moth that in Hertfordshire is widely distributed, but always scarce.

1204 *Thiodia citrana* (Hb.)

One was caught at Weston on 20th May 2007 by Alan Cockburn and named in 2008 by Brian Goodey. This is the only county record and so is worth recording here, but is after the cut-off date of 31st December; this species is, threfore, omitted from the totals, analysis and discussion.

1205 *Spilonota ocellana* ([D.& S.]) Bud Moth

Recorded: 1962 – 2006
Distribution / Status: Ubiquitous / Common resident
Conservation status: No perceived threats.
Caterpillar food plants: Apple and Common Hawthorn. Elsewhere, buds and leaves of fruit trees
Flight period: Late May to early September
Records in database: 171

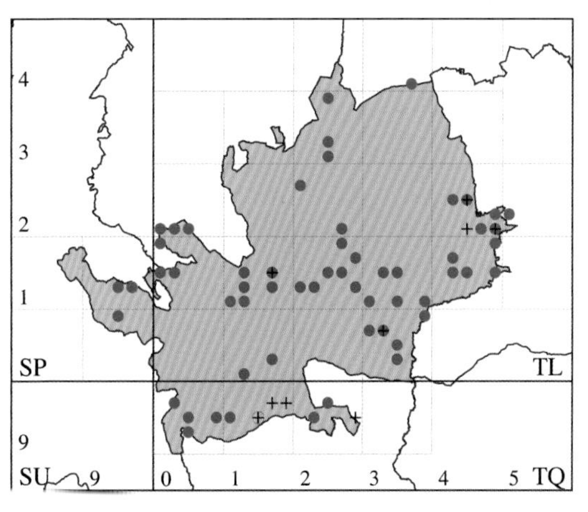

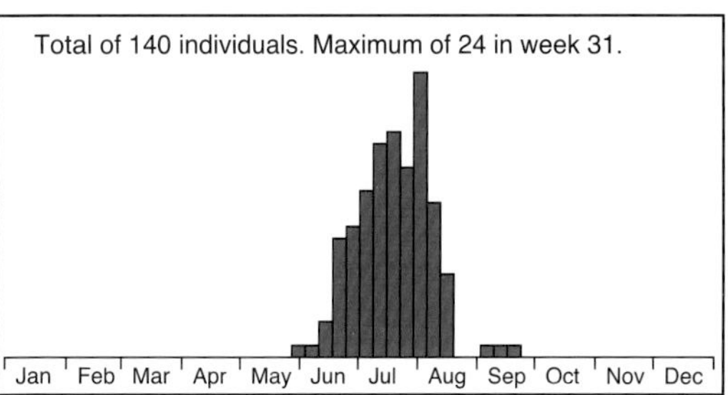

This usually numerous moth is widespread across the county. The greyish form *laricana* is now regarded as a full species (see 1205a, next), but true *ocellana* nevertheless has a grey form that can be difficult to distinguish from *laricana*. Foster (1937) lumps both species together so that old records cannot be separated in the absence of specimens.

1205a *Spilonota laricana* (Hein.)

Recorded: 1967 – 2005
Distribution / Status: Local / Uncommon resident
Conservation status: Insufficiently known
Caterpillar food plants: Not recorded. Elsewhere, on Larch
Flight period: Late June to mid-August
Records in database: 15

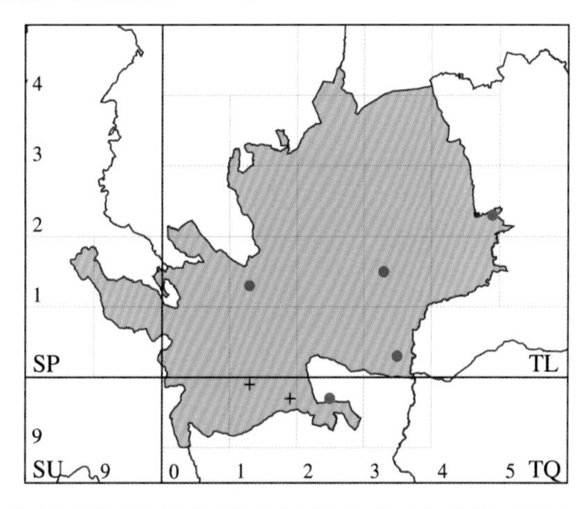

Until recently this species was regarded as a larch-feeding form of 1205: *Spilonota ocellana* and so old records are partly obscured. Our earliest confirmed record is from Borehamwood on 6th June 1967 (Eric Bradford).

1207 *Clavigesta purdeyi* (Durrant) Pine Leaf-mining Moth

Recorded:	1971 – 2006
Distribution / Status:	Local / Common resident
Conservation status:	Insufficiently known.
Caterpillar food plants:	Not recorded. Elsewhere, mines the needles of Scots Pine and Corsican Pine
Flight period:	Late July to August, elsewhere also September
Records in database:	17

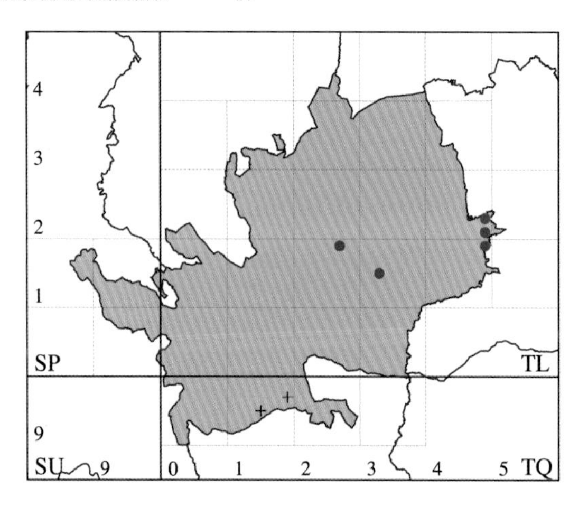

The majority of records come from my garden light traps in Bishops Stortford, but there are also reports from gardens in Hertford (Andrew Wood) and Datchworth (Steve Palmer). The older records are from Bushey (Barry Goater) and Borehamwood (Eric Bradford). Mature Scots Pine trees are more or less confined to gardens and parks within Hertfordshire and these areas are often hard to access or record in.

[1208 *Pseudococcyx posticana* (Zett.)

The late Maitland Emmet noted this species as recorded in Hertfordshire in the draft maps for the as yet unpublished Tortricidae volume of *Moths and Butterflies of Great Britain and Ireland,* but the record was not supported by data. There is, however, no published literature reference to this species, whose larvae feed on Scots Pine. It seems possible that the record was sent to Emmet in error.]

1209 *Pseudococcyx turionella* (L.) Pine Bud Moth

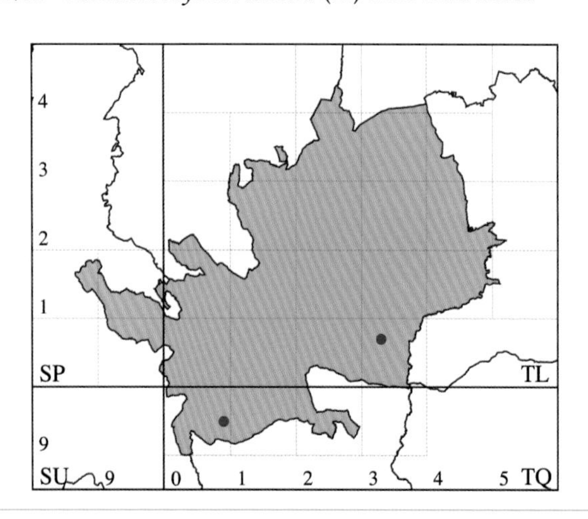

Recorded:	2003 – 2004
Distribution / Status:	Very local / Uncommon resident
Conservation status:	Insufficiently known
Caterpillar food plants:	Not recorded. Elsewhere, buds and shoots of Scots Pine
Flight period:	Elsewhere, May/June
Records in database:	2

Our two records are both from light traps operated by me at Croxley Common Moor on 17th May 2003 and Broxbourne Wood on 15th May 2004.

1210 *Rhyacionia buoliana* ([D.& S.]) Pine Shoot Moth

Recorded:	1900 – 2006
Distribution / Status:	Local / Uncommon resident
Conservation status:	Insufficiently known.
Caterpillar food plants:	Not recorded. Elsewhere, on the shoots of various pine trees
Flight period:	July. Elsewhere, late June to mid-August
Records in database:	10

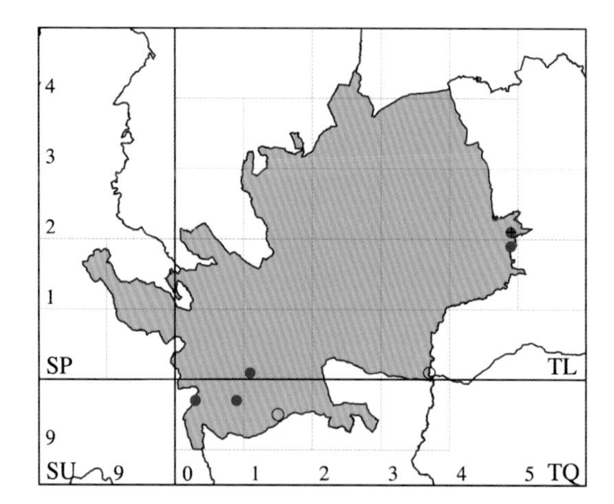

Probably under-recorded, though the lack of pine plantations in the county will probably not permit this to become a common moth here.

1211 *Rhyacionia pinicolana* (Doubl.)

Recorded:	1885 – 2006
Distribution / Status:	Local / Uncommon resident
Conservation status:	No perceived threats.
Caterpillar food plants:	Not recorded. Elsewhere, on the shoots of Scots Pine
Flight period:	Late June to mid-August
Records in database:	42

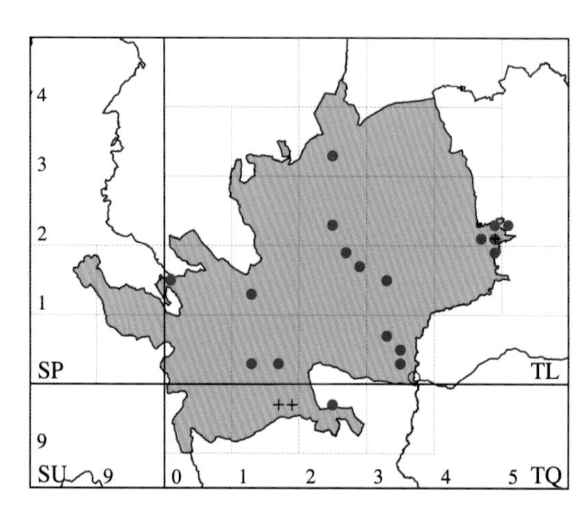

Evidently a more frequent species with us than 1210: *Rhyacionia buoliana* which, interestingly, does not appear to be as dependant upon Scots Pine as is the present species.

1212 *Rhyacionia pinivorana* (Lien.& Zell.) Spotted Shoot Moth

Recorded: 1883 – 2006
Distribution / Status: Local / Common resident
Conservation status: No perceived threats.
Caterpillar food plants: Not recorded. Elsewhere, on the shoots of Scots Pine
Flight period: Late May to June
Records in database: 27

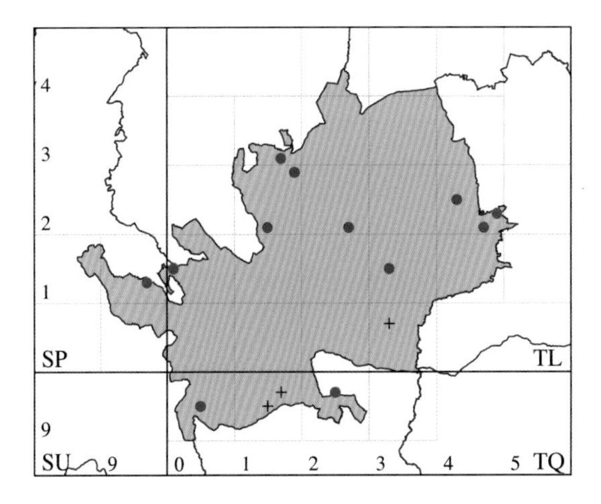

Though fairly widespread, the restrictions imposed by the distribution of the larval foodplant will act on this species as much as on the last species.

1216 *Enarmonia formosana* (Scop.) Cherry Bark Tortrix

Recorded: 1888 – 2006
Distribution / Status: Local / Uncommon resident
Conservation status: Insufficiently known.
Caterpillar food plants: Not recorded. Elsewhere, tunnelling in the bark of cherry trees and other fruit trees
Flight period: Later May to early August
Records in database: 25

Though the adult is distinctive, the species is more easily recorded from the tell-tale larval sign of frass mixed with sap exuding from the fissures in the bark of older cherry trees.

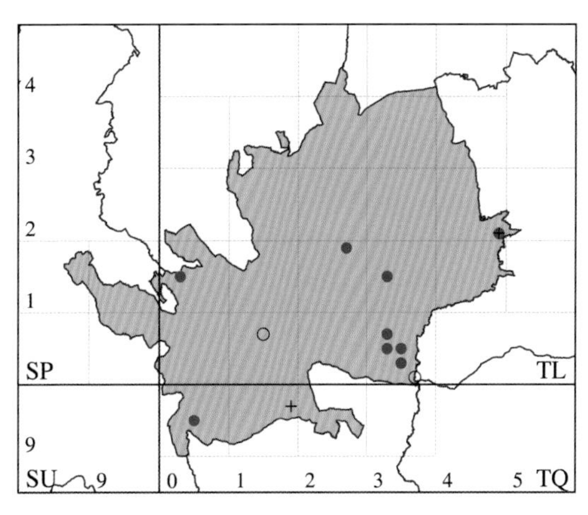

1217 *Eucosmomorpha albersana* (Hb.)

Recorded: 1890 – 1937
Distribution / Status: Absent / Former resident
Conservation status: Herts Extinct
Caterpillar food plants: Not recorded. Elsewhere, on honeysuckles
Flight period: Elsewhere, May/June
Records in database: 3

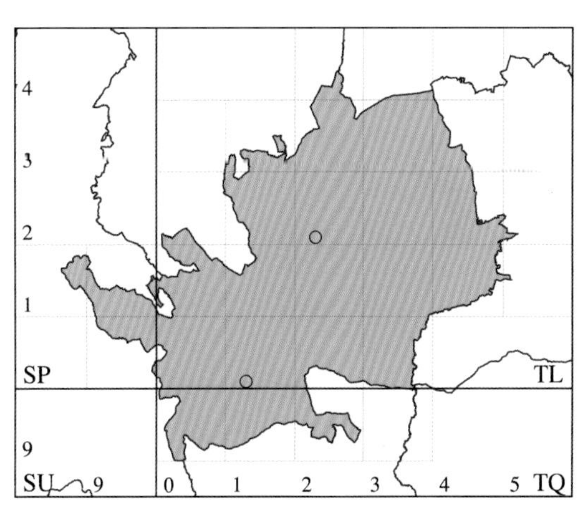

Our only records are for the Sandridge area (Griffith, 1890), Knebworth Great Wood in 1923 (Edwards) and Bricket Wood (Fryer) in Foster (1937). At the end of the nineteenth century it was apparently common; today it appears to be scarce and is apparently absent from Hertfordshire.

1219 *Lathronympha strigana* (Fabr.)

Recorded: 1886 – 2006
Distribution / Status: Widespread / Common resident
Conservation status: No perceived threats
Caterpillar food plants: Not recorded. Elsewhere, on various St John's-worts
Flight period: June to August
Records in database: 35

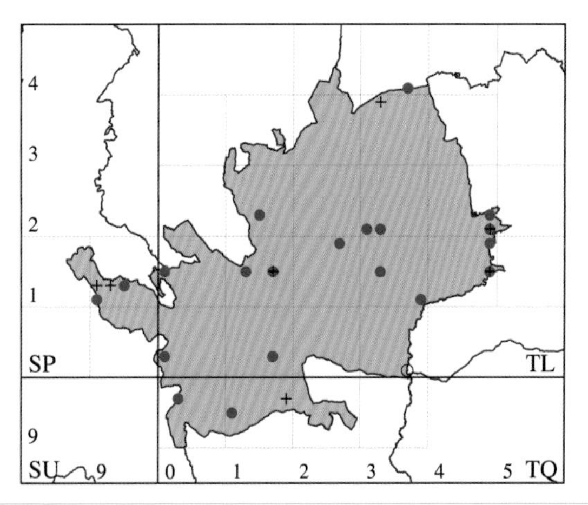

This is a familiar species on brownfield and similar sites where the foodplant, especially Perforate St. John's-wort, grows in profusion.

1221 *Strophedra weirana* (Douglas)

Recorded:	1890 – 2005
Distribution / Status:	Local / Uncommon resident
Conservation status:	No perceived threats
Caterpillar food plants:	Beech
Flight period:	June to mid-July
Records in database:	13

This rather small moth is easily overlooked, but is not uncommon in mature Beech woodland in the west of the county and is probably under-recorded elsewhere.

1222 *Strophedra nitidana* (Fabr.)

Recorded:	1890 – 2004
Distribution / Status:	Very local / Rare resident
Conservation status:	Herts Scarce
Caterpillar food plants:	English Oak
Flight period:	June
Records in database:	5

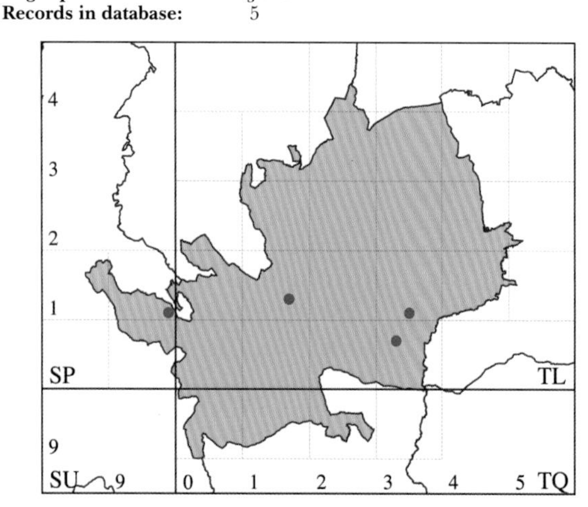

Although likely to be present in most oak woodland in the south of the county, this species remains under-recorded.

1223 *Pammene splendidulana* (Guen.)

Recorded:	1890 – 1997
Distribution / Status:	Very local / Rare resident
Conservation status:	Herts Scarce
Caterpillar food plants:	Not recorded. Elsewhere, on oak
Flight period:	Elsewhere, April to early June
Records in database:	4

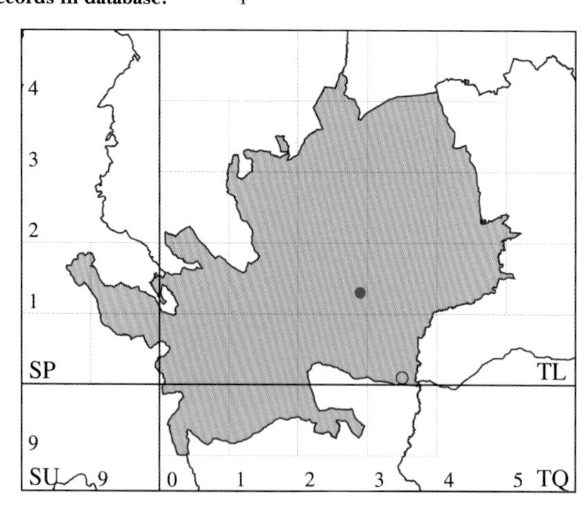

This is a species of oak woods, though it may also occur in parkland where there are mature oaks present. Our records are from Sandridge (Griffith, 1890), Bricket Wood in 1929 and Theobalds Park in an unknown year (Foster, 1937) and Panshanger Park in 1997 (Tom Gladwin).

1227 *Pammene giganteana* (Peyer.) = *inquilina* Fletcher

Recorded:	1890 – 2002
Distribution / Status:	Very local / Rare resident
Conservation status:	Herts Scarce
Caterpillar food plants:	Not recorded. Elsewhere, inside apple (*Andricus*) and spongy (*Biorhiza*) galls on oak
Flight period:	Late March to May
Records in database:	3

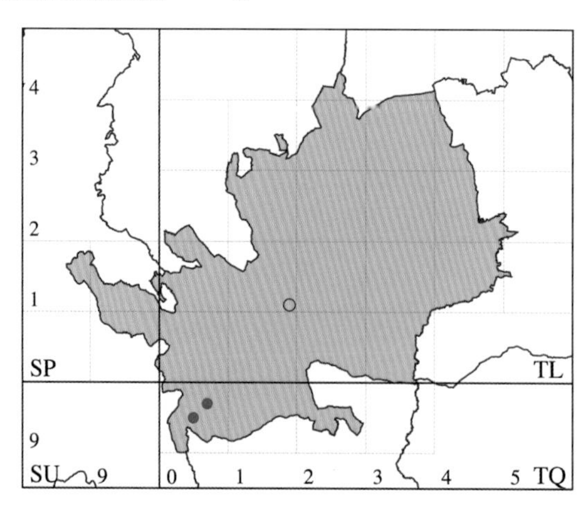

We have one old record, from 'Symmonds Hyde' (Griffith, 1890) and two more recent, both made in 2002 – my own from Whippendell Wood on 26th March 2002 and at Rickmansworth on 1st April 2002 (Paul Clack). The moth rarely leaves the cover of the oak and is probably under-recorded for this reason and because of its early flight period.

1228 *Pammene argyrana* (Hb.)

Recorded:	1834 – 2005
Distribution / Status:	Very local / Rare resident
Conservation status:	Herts Scarce
Caterpillar food plants:	Not recorded. Elsewhere, inside spongy galls (*Biorhiza*) on oak
Flight period:	April/May
Records in database:	8

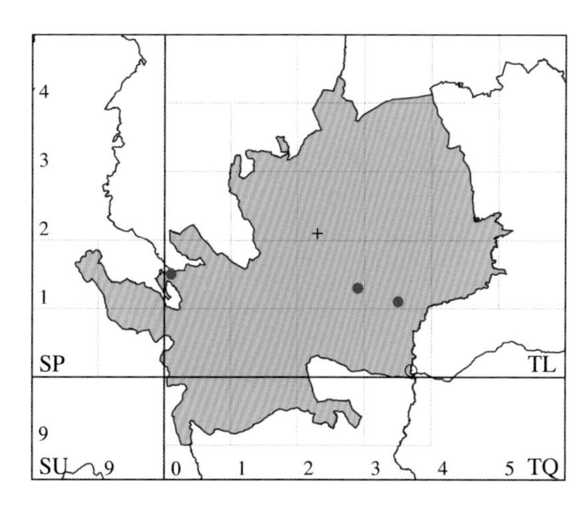

The moth is probably restricted to oak woodlands and appears to be numerically uncommon in Hertfordshire. The early flight period may render it under-recorded.

1229 *Pammene albuginana* Guen.)

Recorded: 2000 – 2005
Distribution / Status: Local / Rare resident
Conservation status: Herts Scarce
Caterpillar food plants: Not recorded. Elsewhere, inside apple (*Andricus*) and spongy (*Biorhiza*) galls on oak
Flight period: Elsewhere, June
Records in database: 2

The record in for the Sandridge area given, as *Ephippiphora gallicolana*, in Griffith (1884), was in error – corrected in Griffith (1890). The only other Hertfordshire records are of a male taken at light on 16th June 2000 at Danemead Wood, a part of the Broxbourne Woods complex, by myself and another at Hobbs Close, Cheshunt on 27th July 2005 taken by Mark Cooper.

1231 *Pammene spiniana* (Dup.)

Recorded: 1890 – 1901
Distribution / Status: Absent / Former resident
Conservation status: Herts Extinct
Caterpillar food plants: Not recorded. Elsewhere, on flowers of Blackthorn and hawthorn
Flight period: Elsewhere, August/September
Records in database: 2

Our only records are from the Sandridge area (Griffith, 1890) and the Cheshunt area (Boyd, 1901); neither can be accurately mapped.

1232 *Pammene populana* (Fabr.)

Recorded: 1890 – 1964
Distribution / Status: Absent / Former resident
Conservation status: Herts Extinct
Caterpillar food plants: Not recorded. Elsewhere, on sallows and osiers
Flight period: Elsewhere, July
Records in database: 5

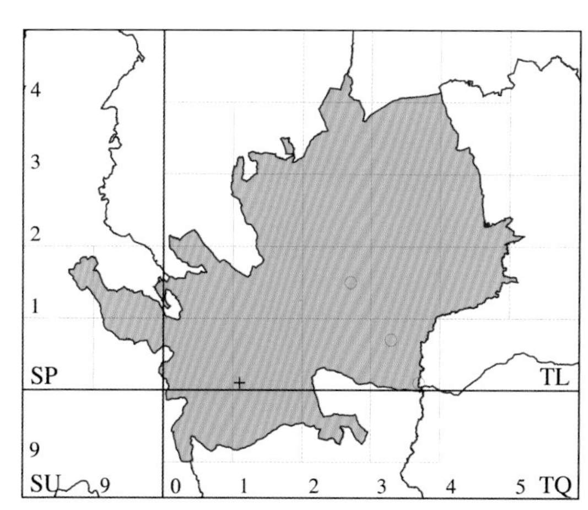

Our most recent report is from Bricketwood Common, where Eric Bradford recorded an adult on 29th August 1964. Cheshunt (Boyd, 1901) Broxbourne and Tewin (Foster, 1937) provide the two earlier sightings.

1233 *Pammene aurita* Razowski = *aurantiana* (Stdgr.)

Recorded: 1995 – 2003
Distribution / Status: Local / Common resident
Conservation status: No perceived threats
Caterpillar food plants: Not recorded. Elsewhere, on the seeds of Sycamore
Flight period: July/August
Records in database: 5

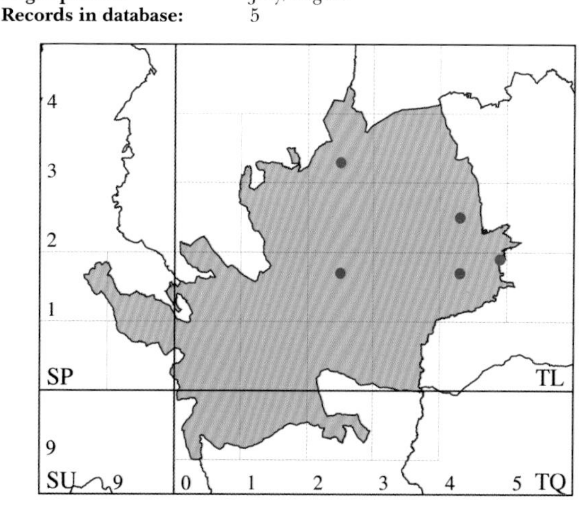

This is a fairly recent arrival in Britain, having been first recorded in Kent in 1943. All Hertfordshire records are given: Bishops Stortford, 2000 (Charles Watson), Welwyn, 20th July 1995 (Raymond Uffen), Baldock, 11th August 1998 (Kerry Robinson) and my own from Much Hadham, 1st August 2000 and Albury, 10th July 2003.

1234 *Pammene regiana* (Zell.)

Recorded: 1918 – 2005
Distribution / Status: Widespread / Common resident
Conservation status: No perceived threats
Caterpillar food plants: Not recorded. Elsewhere, on the seeds of Sycamore, Norway Maple and perhaps Field Maple
Flight period: June/July. Elsewhere, May to July
Records in database: 18

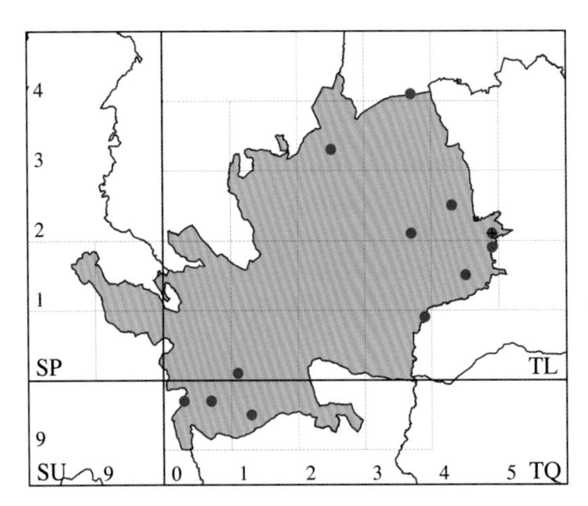

The moth is common where it is found and it is probably overlooked in many parts of the county.

1236 *Pammene fasciana* (L.)

Recorded: 1970 – 2006
Distribution / Status: Widespread / Common resident
Conservation status: No perceived threats
Caterpillar food plants: Internally in acorns
Flight period: Late June
Records in database: 54

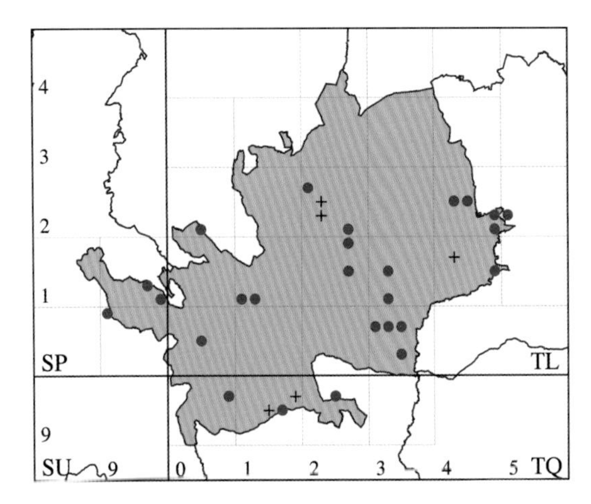

Past confusion with 1236a: *Pammene herrichiana*, which was regarded as a Beech-feeding form of *fasciana* has confused the records so that only those where it is clear which form was recorded can be included here.

1236a *Pammene herrichiana* (Hein.)

Recorded: 1997 only
Distribution / Status: Extremely local / Rare resident
Conservation status: Herts Rare
Caterpillar food plants: Not recorded. Elsewhere, on Beech mast
Flight period: Elsewhere, May/June
Records in database: 1

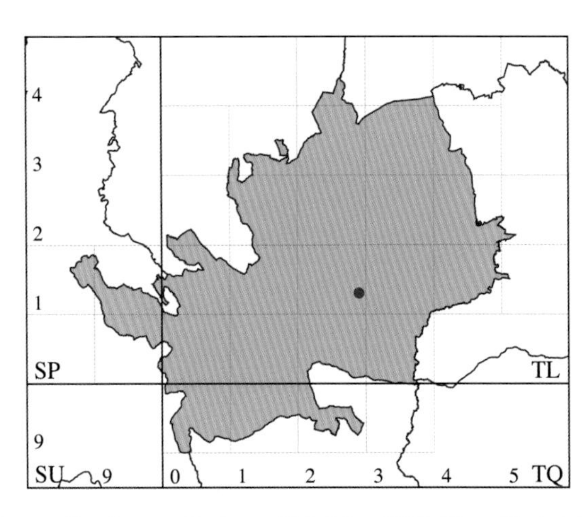

One at Panshanger Park on 25th May 1997 (Tom Gladwin) is our only record.

1237 *Pammene germmana* (Hb.)

Recorded: 1890 – 2004
Distribution / Status: Local / Uncommon resident
Conservation status: Herts Rare
Caterpillar food plants: Unknown in Britain
Flight period: May/June
Records in database: 5

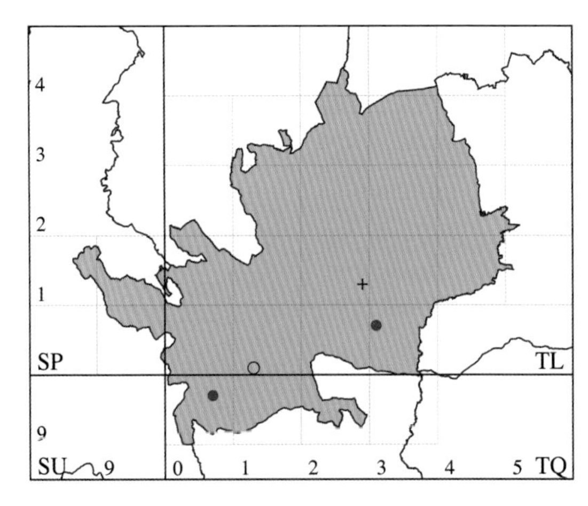

The theory that the larval foodplant in Britain may be oak is not contradicted by our localities for this moth, which are Bricket Wood, Knebworth Great Wood, Whippendell Wood, Wormley Wood and Panshanger Park.

1238 *Pammene ochsenheimeriana* (Lien. & Zell.)

Recorded: Pre-1901 only
Distribution / Status: Absent / Former resident
Conservation status: Herts Extinct
Caterpillar food plants: Not recorded. Elsewhere, on fir, perhaps also spruce and pine
Flight period: Elsewhere, May/June
Records in database: 1

Our only record is from Waltham Cross, reported in Boyd (1901).

1239 *Pammene rhediella* (Cl.) Fruitlet Mining Tortrix

Recorded: 1890 – 1999
Distribution / Status: Local / Rare resident
Conservation status: Herts Scarce
Caterpillar food plants: Not recorded. Elsewhere, inside the fruit of hawthorn and fruit trees
Flight period: Elsewhere, May/June
Records in database: 8

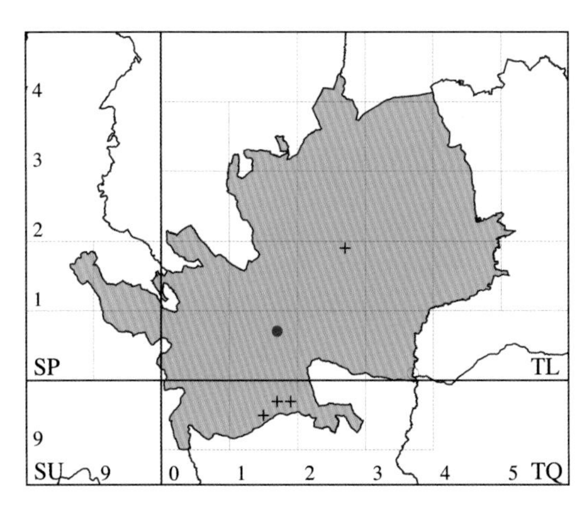

Our most recent record is from Highfield Park, St Albans on 5th May 1999 (Raymond Uffen), but the moth is likely to be elsewhere in the county awaiting rediscovery.

1241 *Grapholita compositella* (Fabr.)

Recorded:	1890 – 2005
Distribution / Status:	Widespread / Common resident
Conservation status:	No perceived threats
Caterpillar food plants:	Not recorded. Elsewhere, on clovers
Flight period:	May/June and August in two generations
Records in database:	10

The widespread nature of the few recent records suggest a species that is probably greatly under-recorded. It is widespread and common in grasslands and ruderal habitats in the south-east of England.

1242 *Grapholita internana* (Guen.)

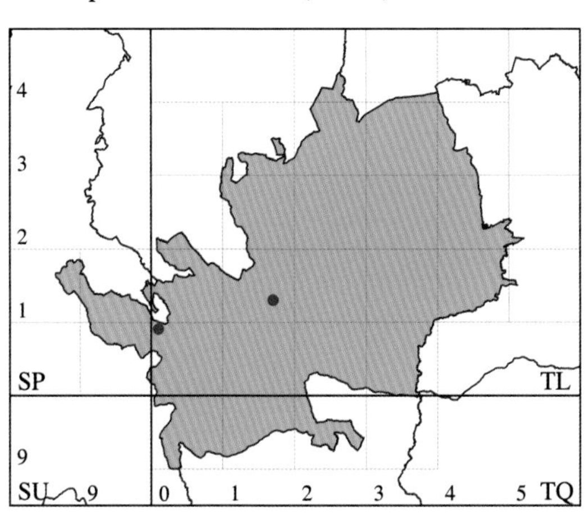

Recorded:	1887 – 2003
Distribution / Status:	Local / Uncommon resident
Conservation status:	Herts Scarce
Caterpillar food plants:	Not recorded. Elsewhere, on Gorse
Flight period:	May. Elsewhere, April to June
Records in database:	5

Recent records are from Berkhamsted Common and Nomansland Common, in May 2003 (Raymond Uffen). It was from the former locality that the first county record was made by A. E. Gibbs on 11th June 1887. It is likely to be under-recorded, but appropriate sites are few in number.

1245 *Grapholita janthinana* (Dup.)

Recorded:	1890 – 2005
Distribution / Status:	Widespread / Common resident
Conservation status:	Insufficiently known
Caterpillar food plants:	Not recorded. Elsewhere, on hawthorn berries
Flight period:	End of June to early August
Records in database:	19

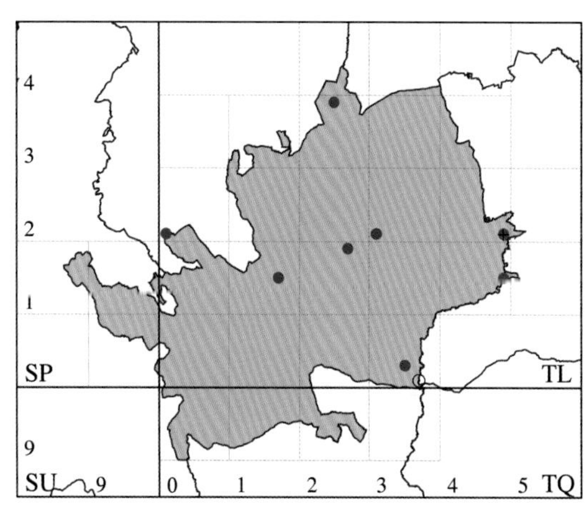

The records suggest that this moth is widespread in the county, but it certainly prefers old, established hawthorn in hedges that are left uncut and is rarely, if ever, found in hedges that are regularly pruned.

1246 *Grapholita tenebrosana* (Dup.)

Recorded:	1890 – 2000
Distribution / Status:	Local / Rare resident
Conservation status:	Insufficiently known
Caterpillar food plants:	Not recorded. Elsewhere, within rose hips, especially of Dog Rose
Flight period:	Elsewhere, mid-June to July
Records in database:	4

Old records are from the Sandridge area prior to 1890, Lilley in July 1931 and from Harpenden and Bricketwood Common prior to 1937. Our only recent record was a male (named by genitalia dissection) from the garden light trap run by Charles Watson in Bishops Stortford during June 2000.

1247 *Grapholita funebrana* (Tr.) Plum Fruit Moth

Recorded: 1900 – 2006
Distribution / Status: Widespread / Common resident
Conservation status: No perceived threats.
Caterpillar food plants: Not recorded. Elsewhere, inside plums and Damson
Flight period: Late June/July
Records in database: 21

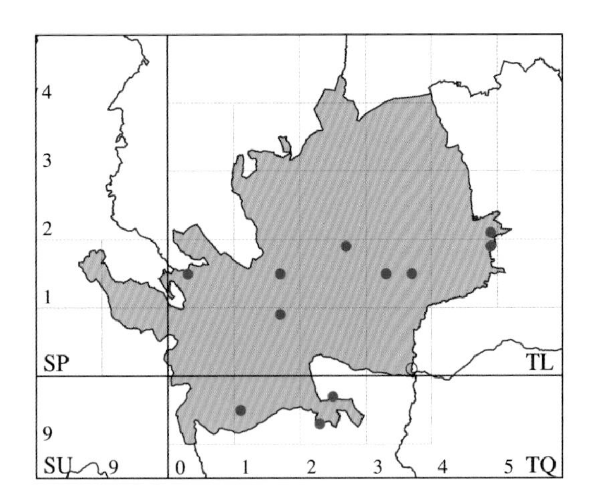

Most records are confirmed by dissection of genitalia and the moth is probably widespread, at least in the south of the county.

1248 *Grapholita molesta* (Busck) Oriental Fruit Moth

Recorded: 1966 only
Distribution / Status: Absent / Accidental importation
Conservation status: -
Caterpillar food plants: Not recorded. Elsewhere, in fruit of plums, apples, Pears and Apricots
Flight period: Elsewhere, March to September in three generations
Records in database: 1

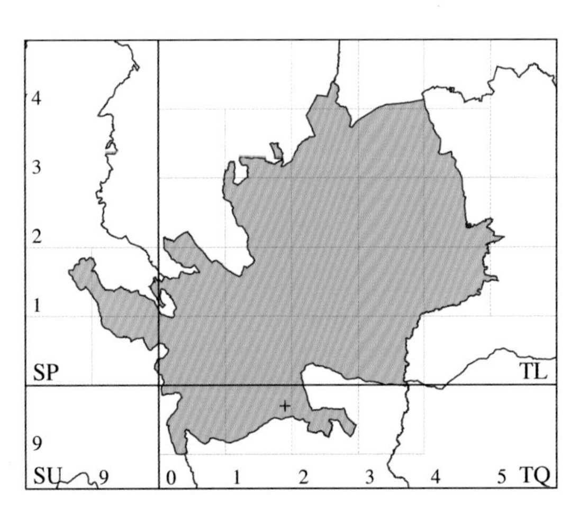

One example taken at Borehamwood on 23rd April 1966 by Eric Bradford is our only county record. The larvae are occasionally imported with peaches and adults are sometimes reared, but evidently cannot survive in the British climate – so far.

1251 *Grapholita jungiella* (Cl.)

Recorded: 1890 – 2005
Distribution / Status: Widespread / Common resident
Conservation status: Insufficiently known
Caterpillar food plants: Not recorded. Elsewhere, on peas and vetches
Flight period: Late April/May/ Elsewhere, a second generation in late July/August
Records in database: 10

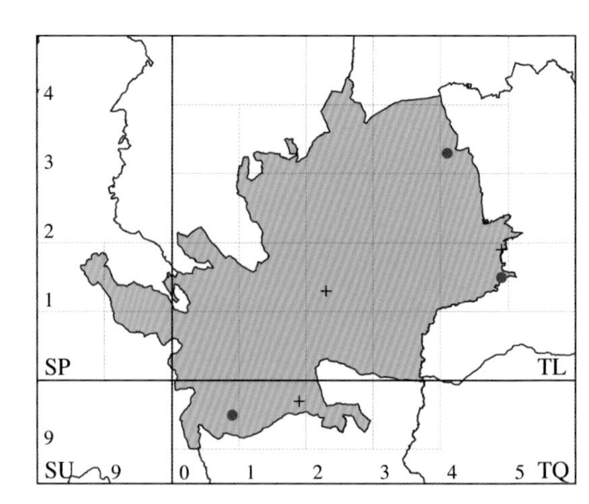

The foodplants suggest that this is likely to be a moth of disturbed and ruderal habitats. If so, it is likely to be widespread but very local in Hertfordshire.

1254 *Cydia strobilella* (L.) Spruce Seed Moth

Recorded: 1899 only
Distribution / Status: Absent / Former resident
Conservation status: Herts Extinct
Caterpillar food plants: Not recorded. Elsewhere, on Norway Spruce
Flight period: Elsewhere, May
Records in database: 1

One in Hertford during 1899 is the only available record and the absence of spruce plantations in the county suggests that the moth is unlikely still to be present here.

1255 *Cydia ulicetana* (Haw.)

Recorded: 1834 – 2005
Distribution / Status: Widespread / Common resident
Conservation status: No perceived threats
Caterpillar food plants: Gorse. Elsewhere, also on Petty Whin and Broom
Flight period: Late April/May then late July to September in two generations
Records in database: 29

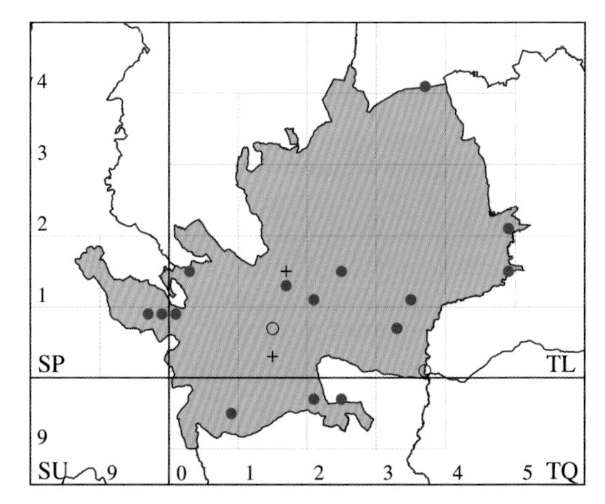

This is *succedana* of most British authors. Razowski (2003) illustrates *ulicetana* from Britain and notes that the taxon which Bradley (2000 checklist) and others refer to as *succedana* ([D.& S.]) does not occur in our country. It is widespread and common and expected wherever there are gorse bushes.

1256 *Cydia servillana* (Dup.)

Recorded: 1929 – 1991
Distribution / Status: Extremely local or absent / Rare resident
Conservation status: Herts Rare
Caterpillar food plants: Not recorded. Elsewhere, on Common Sallow and Great Sallow in galls on the stems
Flight period: Elsewhere, May/June
Records in database: 2

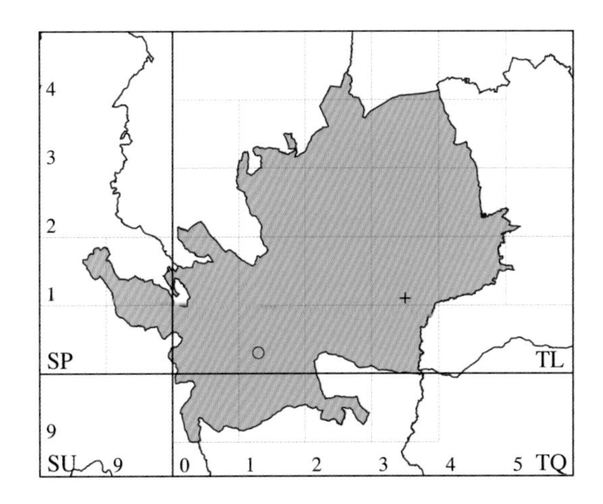

Our two records are from Bricket Wood in 1929 (Foster, 1937) and from Balls Wood, 9th April 1991 (Raymond Uffen).

1257 *Cydia nigricana* (Fabr.) Pea Moth

Recorded: 1890 – 2005
Distribution / Status: Widespread / Common resident
Conservation status: Insufficiently known.
Caterpillar food plants: Not recorded. Elsewhere, on developing seeds inside the pod of various legumes, including cultivated peas
Flight period: May to August
Records in database: 9

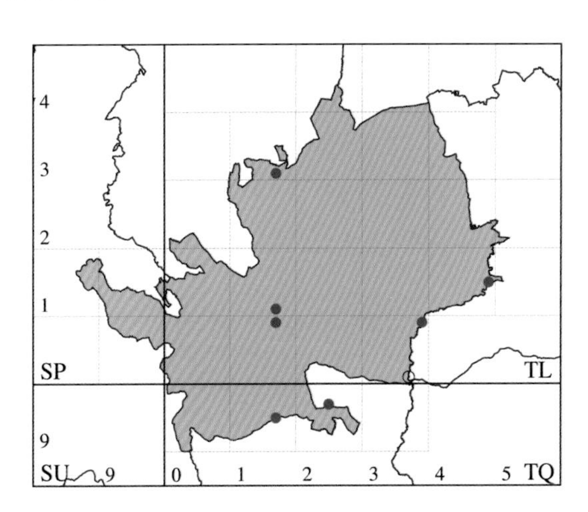

Peas are not a common commercial crop in Hertfordshire where the larvae evidently thrive in the seed pods of native legumes instead. The moth is widespread in the county, but apparently nowhere common.

1259 *Cydia fagiglandana* (Zell.)

Recorded: 1890 – 2006
Distribution / Status: Widespread / Common resident
Conservation status: No perceived threats
Caterpillar food plants: Not recorded. Elsewhere, in Beech mast
Flight period: Late June to early August
Records in database: 28

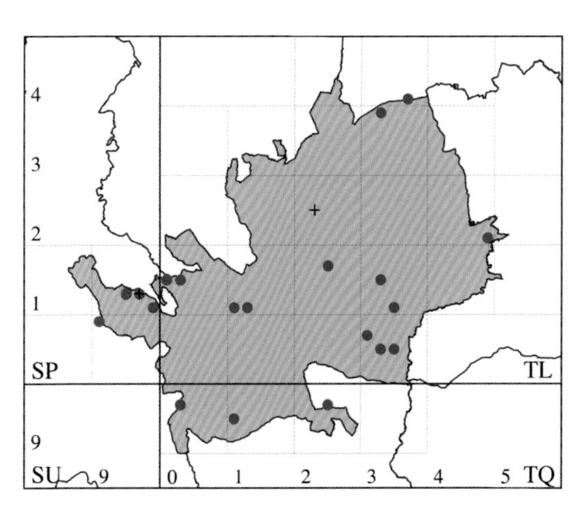

Almost all our adult records are in July; the moth is to be found wherever a mast-producing beech tree is within easy reach.

1260 *Cydia splendana* (Hb.)

Recorded: 1890 – 2006
Distribution / Status: Widespread / Common resident
Conservation status: No perceived threats.
Caterpillar food plants: Not recorded. Elsewhere, in acorns and Sweet Chestnuts
Flight period: Mid-June to mid-September
Records in database: 156

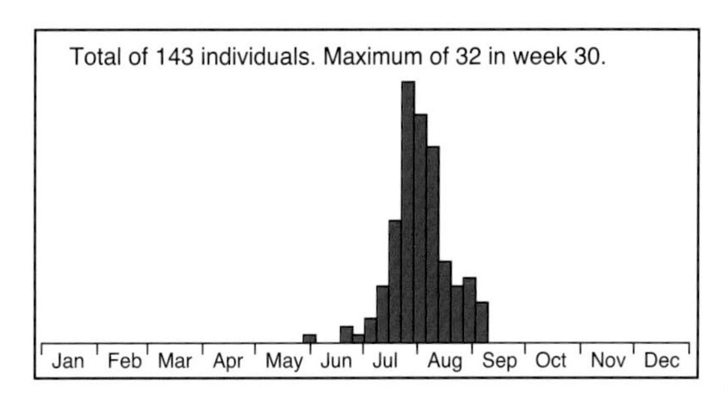

This is one of the more familiar tortricid moths in Hertfordshire and is often found in garden light traps if there are suitable host trees nearby.

1261 *Cydia pomonella* (L.) Codling Moth

Recorded:	1885 – 2006
Distribution / Status:	Ubiquitous / Common resident
Conservation status:	No perceived threats.
Caterpillar food plants:	In the core of apples, elsewhere, also in pears
Flight period:	Late May to early September
Records in database:	381

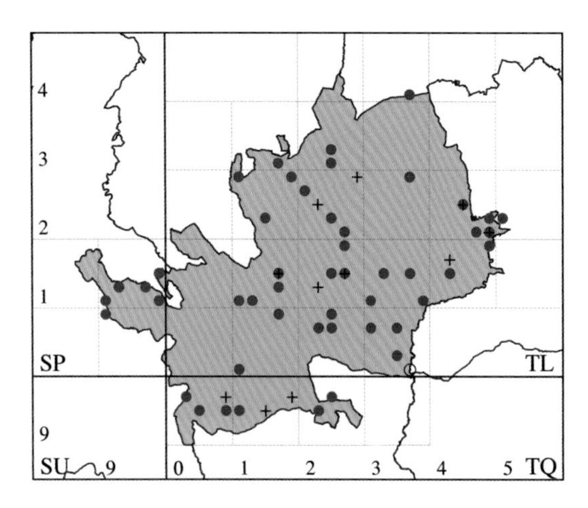

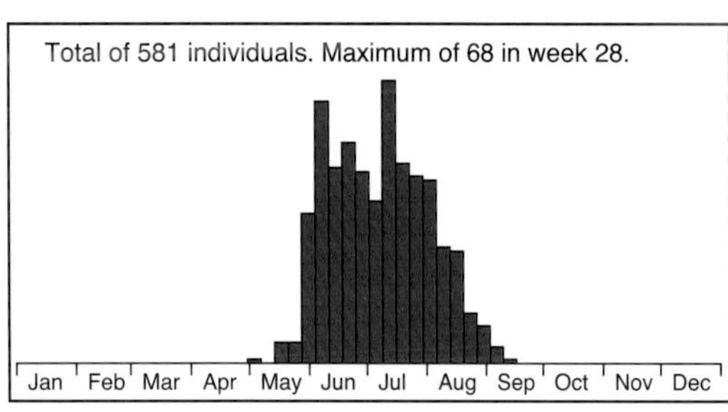

The chart shows that the moth is on the wing throughout the summer in Hertfordshire; it is expected everywhere.

1267 *Cydia cosmophorana* (Tr.)

Recorded:	2003 – 2007
Distribution / Status:	Extremely local / Rare resident
Conservation status:	Herts Scarce
Caterpillar food plants:	Not recorded. Elsewhere, on Scots Pine
Flight period:	Elsewhere, May/June
Records in database:	2

One was taken by me at light in Hurst Wood on 30th May 2003 and another, a female, came to Alan Cockburn's light at Weston, on 24th May 2007.

1268 *Cydia coniferana* (Ratz.)

Recorded:	1999 – 2005
Distribution / Status:	Local / Uncommon resident
Conservation status:	Herts Scarce
Caterpillar food plants:	Not recorded. Elsewhere, under the bark of Scots Pine
Flight period:	Elsewhere, Mid-May to August in two generations
Records in database:	3

Our three reports are from Datchworth, 3rd August 1999 (Steve Palmer), Hertford, 9th June 2005 (Andrew Wood) and Cheshunt, 27th July 2005 (Mark Cooper). There are no historic records.

1269 *Cydia conicolana* (Heylaerts)

Recorded:	2002 only
Distribution / Status:	Local / Uncommon resident
Conservation status:	Herts Scarce
Caterpillar food plants:	Not recorded. Elsewhere, in cones of Scots Pine and Corsican Pine
Flight period:	May. Elsewhere, late May/June
Records in database:	3

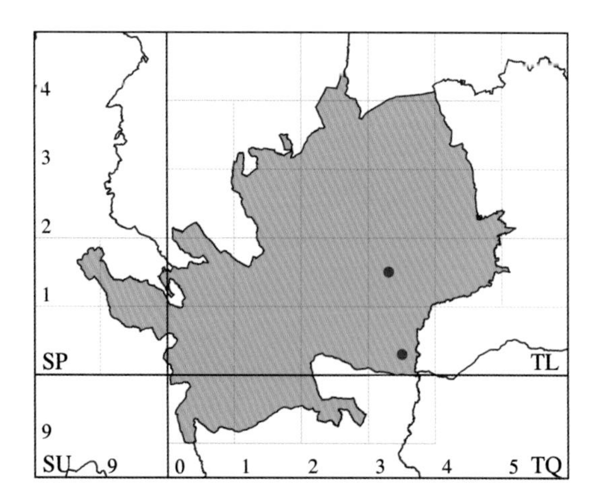

The only acceptable records available are from Cheshunt on 10th May 2002 and 25th May 2005 (Mark Cooper) and Hertford on 27th May 2005 (Andrew Wood).

1271 *Pammene gallicana* (Guen.)

Recorded:	1890 – 1999
Distribution / Status:	Widespread / Common resident
Conservation status:	No perceived threats
Caterpillar food plants:	Not recorded. Elsewhere, on seeds of wild carrot and perhaps other umbellifers
Flight period:	Elsewhere, July/August
Records in database:	3

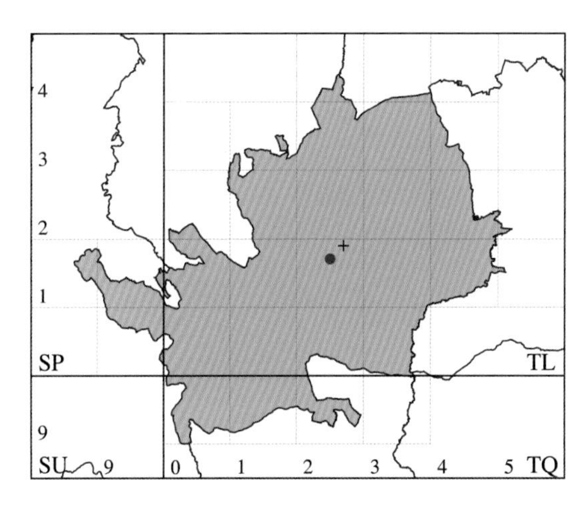

An old record from the Sandridge area (Griffith, 1890) cannot be mapped. More recent reports are from Datchworth on 2nd July 1982 (Steve Palmer) and from Welwyn on 12th August 1999 (Raymond Uffen).

1272 *Pammene aurana* (Fabr.)

Recorded: 1890 – 2004
Distribution / Status: Local / Uncommon resident
Conservation status: Insufficiently known
Caterpillar food plants: Hogweed – on the seeds
Flight period: June/July
Records in database: 10

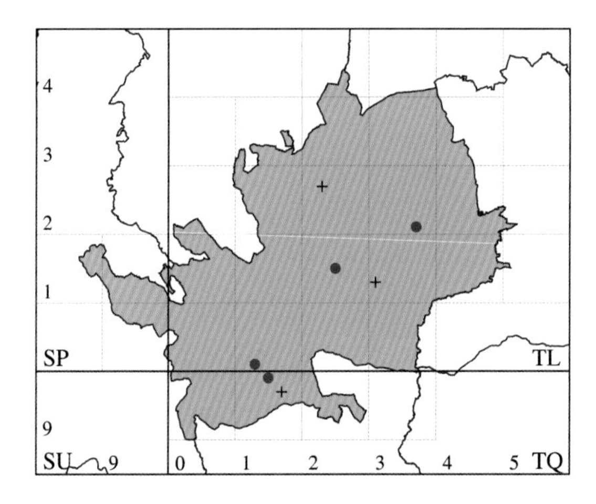

Though the records are few this is likely to be a widespread and common moth in the county if looked for properly.

1273 *Dichrorampha petiverella* (L.)

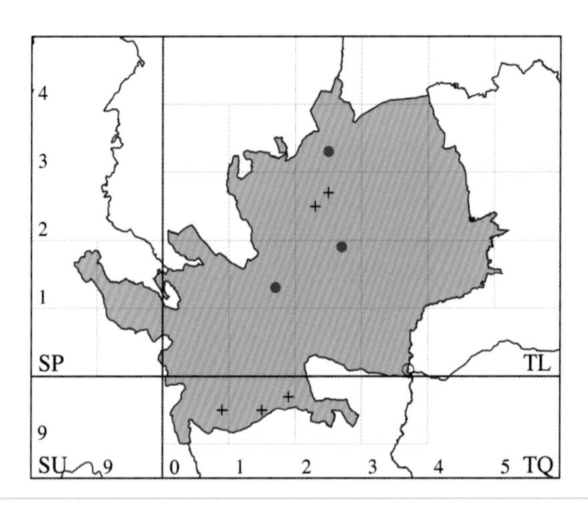

Recorded: 1890 – 2005
Distribution / Status: Widespread / Common resident
Conservation status: No perceived threats
Caterpillar food plants: Not recorded. Elsewhere, in the roots of Yarrow, Sneezewort and Tansy
Flight period: Mid-June to early August
Records in database: 16

As with the last species, this is likely to be a widespread and common moth in the county if looked for properly. However, it may be less frequently encountered than it was in the past.

1274 *Dichrorampha alpinana* (Tr.)

Recorded: 1998 – 2006
Distribution / Status: Local / Uncommon resident
Conservation status: Insufficiently known
Caterpillar food plants: Not recorded. Elsewhere, in the roots of Tansy
Flight period: Elsewhere, June to August
Records in database: 12

There has been much confusion in the past between this species and 1275: *Dichrorampha flavidorsana*. The records of *alpinana* from Hertford (Stephens, 1834) and the Sandridge area (Griffith, 1890) given in Foster (1937) are deleted by Foster (1945) who then adds 'bred from ox-eye daisy, 1944 (Fryer and Edelsten)'. However, Bradley, Tremewan & Smith (1979) consider that records of moths from this foodplant are referable to 1275: *Dichrorampha flavidorsana* Knaggs. Foster (1945) next makes a separate entry in his list for *flavidorsana* stating that this had been 'bred from ox-eye daisy and *Chrysanthemum uliginosum* 1944 (Fryer and Edelsten)'. In the absence of specimens to dissect these old records are excluded from the map and our earliest reliable record was that from my garden in Bishops Stortford in 1998, when several were noted at rest on Tansy flowers on 5th July and identified by genitalia examination – the only means by which this species may be separated from the next.

1275 *Dichrorampha flavidorsana* Knaggs

Recorded:	1999 only
Distribution / Status:	Local / Rare resident
Conservation status:	Insufficiently known
Caterpillar food plants:	Not recorded. Elsewhere, in the roots of Tansy
Flight period:	Elsewhere, July/August
Records in database:	1

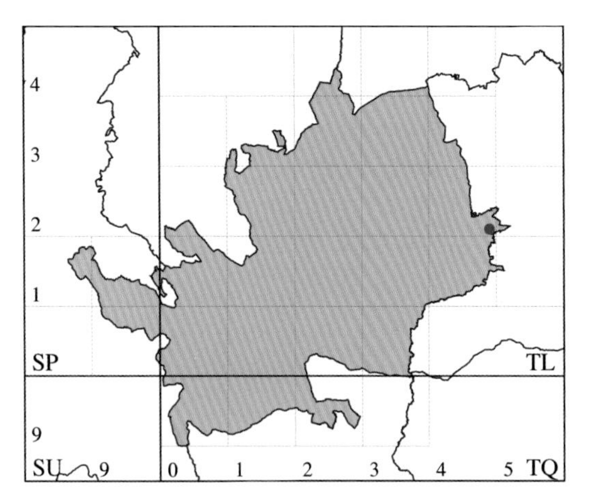

See the discussion under 1274: *Dichrorampha alpinana*. Our only valid record is of males around Tansy plants in my garden at Bishops Stortford on 13th July 1999, identified by genitalia examination.

1276 *Dichrorampha plumbagana* (Tr.)

Recorded:	1888 – 2005
Distribution / Status:	Local / Uncommon resident
Conservation status:	Insufficiently known
Caterpillar food plants:	Not recorded. Elsewhere, in the rootstock of Yarrow
Flight period:	June
Records in database:	10

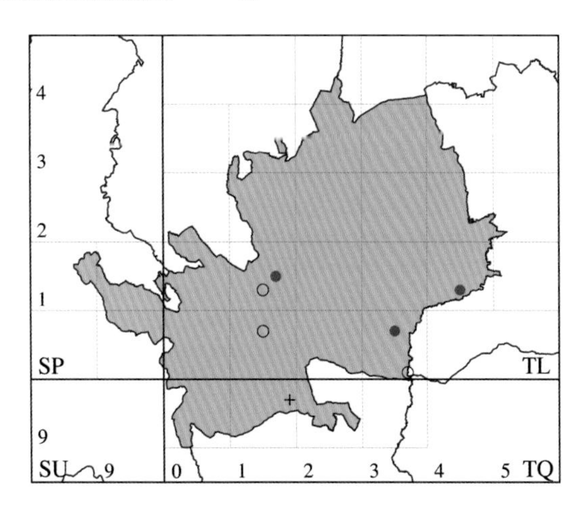

There is no reason why this moth should be as scarce as it appears to be and if candidate examples are collected in association with the correct foodplant dissection is likely to confirm the identification.

1278 *Dichrorampha sequana* (Hb.)

Recorded:	1890 – 1966
Distribution / Status:	Absent extremely local / Former resident
Conservation status:	Herts Extinct
Caterpillar food plants:	Not recorded. Elsewhere, in the rootstock of Yarrow and Tansy
Flight period:	Elsewhere, June
Records in database:	6

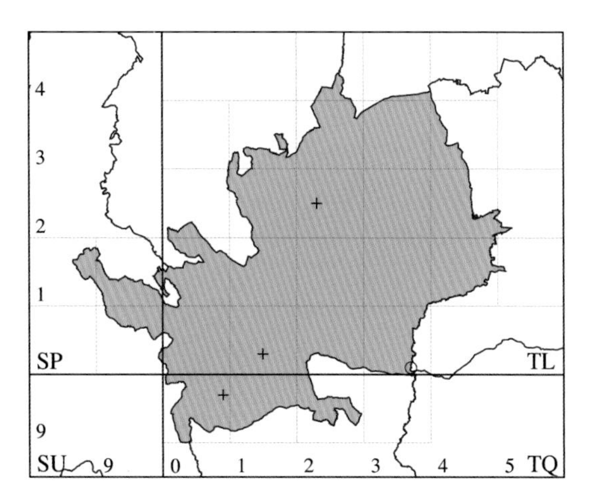

One at Frogmore on 15th June 1966 (Eric Bradford) is the last report from our county.

1279 *Dichrorampha acuminatana* (Lien. & Zell.)

Recorded:	1885 – 2006
Distribution / Status:	Local / Uncommon resident
Conservation status:	Insufficiently known
Caterpillar food plants:	Not recorded. Elsewhere, in the rootstock of Tansy and Ox-eye Daisy
Flight period:	May (elsewhere to June) and then August/September in two generations
Records in database:	12

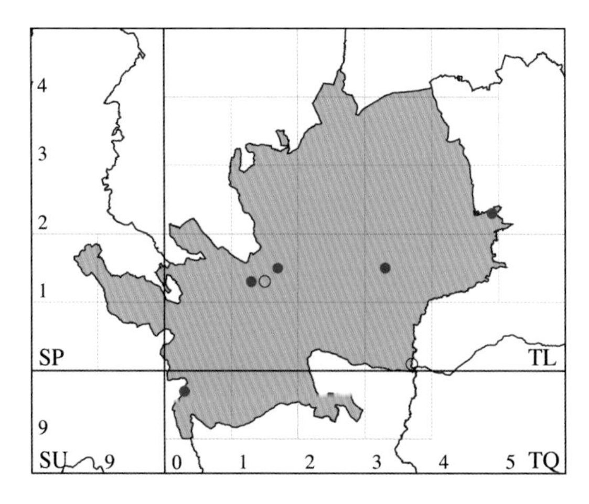

As with others in this neglected group, dissection is the only really accurate means of identifying wild-caught adults. An example at Harpenden on 11th July 2003 falls between the expected dates for the two generations of adults, though summer 2003 was an unusually hot and rainless period.

1280 *Dichrorampha consortana* Stephens

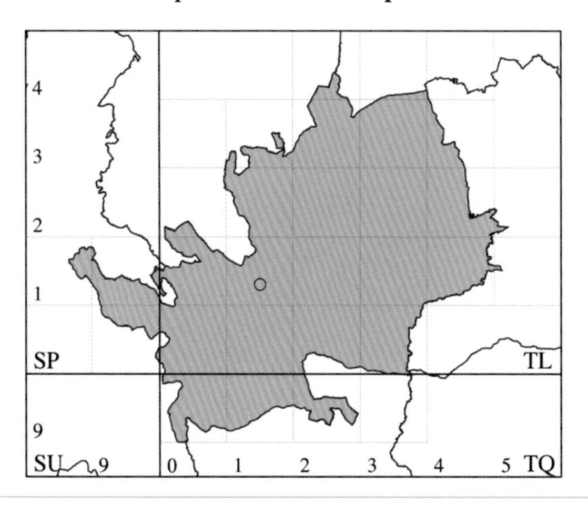

Recorded: 1944 only
Distribution / Status: Absent / Former resident
Conservation status: Herts Extinct
Caterpillar food plants: Ox-eye Daisy
Flight period: Elsewhere, July/August
Records in database: 1

Our only record is from Harpenden, when adults were reared from Ox-eye Daisy in 1944 by Fryer and Edelsten (Foster, 1945).

1281 *Dichrorampha simpliciana* (Haw.)

Recorded: 1890 – 2005
Distribution / Status: Widespread / Common resident
Conservation status: No perceived threats
Caterpillar food plants: Not recorded. Elsewhere, in the rootstock of Mugwort
Flight period: June to mid-August. Elsewhere, July to September
Records in database: 14

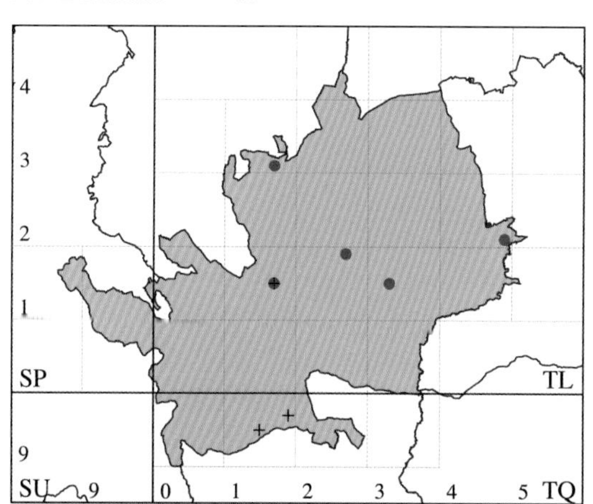

Adults were bred from Mugwort collected at Bushey, in 1974 (Barry Goater). The moth is surely under-recorded in Hertfordshire.

1284 *Dichrorampha vancouverana* McDunnough = *gueneeana* (Obr.)

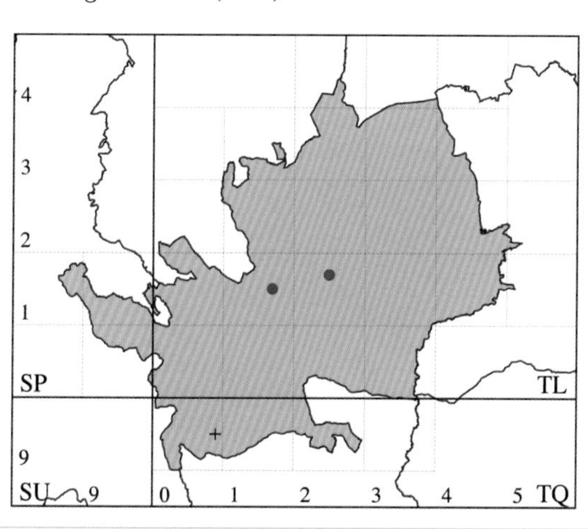

Recorded: 1992 – 2002
Distribution / Status: Local / Uncommon resident
Conservation status: Insufficiently known
Caterpillar food plants: In the rootstock of Yarrow and elsewhere, Tansy
Flight period: Elsewhere, June/July
Records in database: 3

Adults were bred by Fryer and Edelsten from Yarrow, on Harpenden Common during 1944 (Foster, 1945). This is another species that is probably overlooked in Hertfordshire.

1285 *Dichrorampha plumbana* (Scop.)

Recorded: 1890 – 1998
Distribution / Status: Local / Uncommon resident
Conservation status: Insufficiently known
Caterpillar food plants: Not recorded. Elsewhere, in the rootstock of Ox-eye Daisy and Yarrow
Flight period: Elsewhere, May/June
Records in database: 6

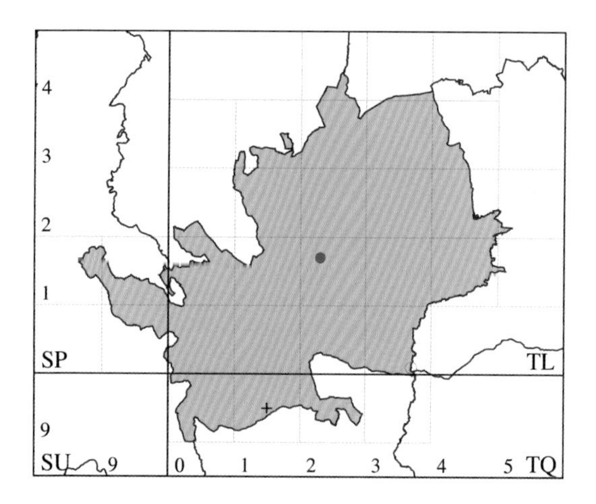

The only record from our 'recent' period is from Welwyn on 29th May 1998 (Raymond Uffen).

1287 *Dichrorampha aeratana* (Pierce & Metc.)

Recorded: 1944 – 2005
Distribution / Status: Local / Rare resident
Conservation status: Insufficiently known
Caterpillar food plants: In the rootstock of Ox-eye Daisy
Flight period: Elsewhere, May/June
Records in database: 2

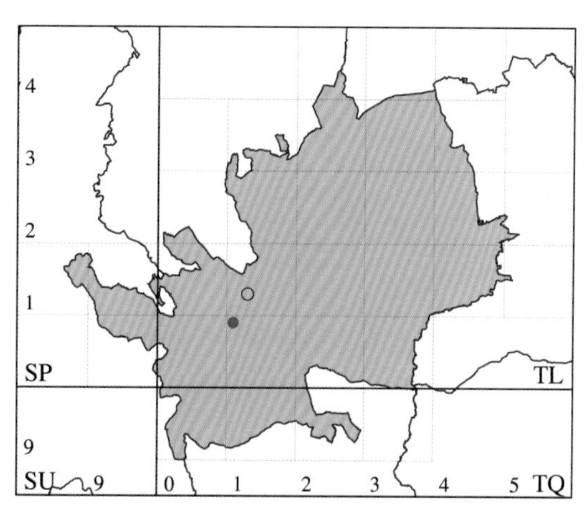

Adults were bred by Fryer and Edelsten from ox-eye daisy collected on Harpenden Common in 1944 (Foster, 1945). The only recent record is from nearby Redbourne, where Wendy Hatton caught a male on 26th June 2005.

EPERMENIOIDEA
EPERMENIIDAE

Until recently, members of this family were treated as members of the Yponomeutidae, but this idea is not supported by recent research. Of the eight British species, four are reported in Hertfordshire. Two have not been seen for a few years and regarded as in danger of extinction here.

0478 *Phaulernis fulviguttella* (Zell.)

Recorded: 1890-1980
Distribution / Status: Extremely local or absent / Rare resident
Conservation status: Herts Endangered
Caterpillar food plants: Not recorded. Elsewhere, on seeds of Hogweed and Wild Angelica
Flight period: Not recorded. Elsewhere, July/August
Records in database: 4

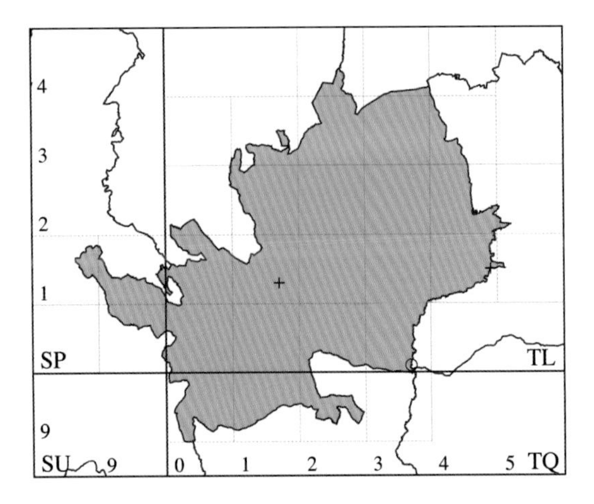

It is surprising to learn that this moth is absent from the county; we have not seen it for 26 years. It is widespread and locally common throughout Britain.

0481 *Epermenia falciformis* (Haw.)
= *illigerella* auctorum

Recorded: 1890 – 2004
Distribution / Status: Local / Common resident
Conservation status: No perceived threats
Caterpillar food plants: No data. Elsewhere, on Wild Angelica and Ground Elder
Flight period: May to August. Elsewhere, in two generations
Records in database: 11

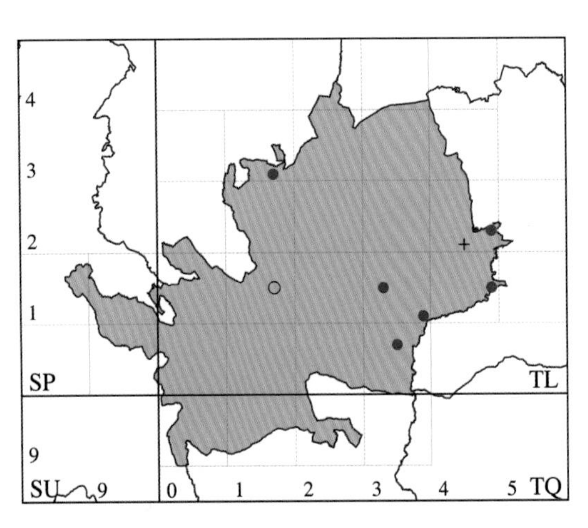

A fairly distinctive species whose distribution partly reflects the places where people interested in micro moths have operated light traps.

0482 *Epermenia insecurella* (Stt.)

Recorded: 1987 – 1987
Distribution / Status: Local / Extremely rare resident
Conservation status: UK BAP Priority Species / Herts Endangered
Caterpillar food plants: Bastard Toadflax
Flight period: Not recorded.
Records in database: 1

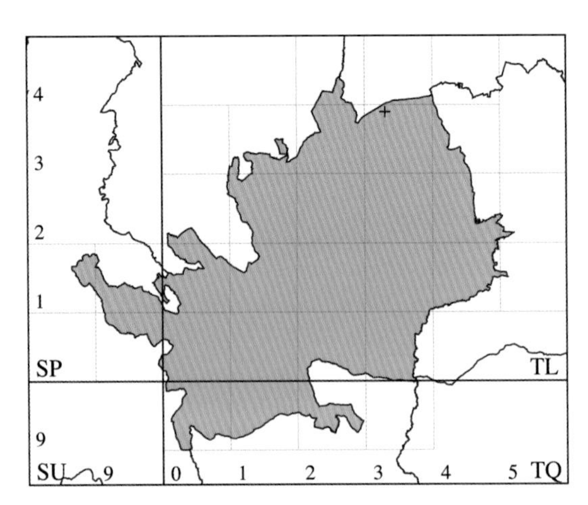

The only site known to support this moth in Hertfordshire is Church Hill at Therfield Heath, from where we have a positive report of larvae in 1987, courtesy of the late Maitland Emmet. Adults are said to fly in afternoon sunshine in May/June and then July/August. It is a nationally rare species of chalk downland and is often absent from areas where the foodplant is frequent. Refinding this species at Church Hill, a Site of Special Scientific Interest, and mapping the areas where it survives should be amongst the highest conservation priorities within the county. The site is managed at present for a specific floral interest and it is unclear how this management fits with the conservation requirements of the moth.

0483 *Epermenia chaerophyllella* (Goeze)

Recorded: 1901 – 2006
Distribution / Status: Local / Common resident
Conservation status: No perceived threats
Caterpillar food plants: Not recorded. Elsewhere, on Hogweed, Wild Parsnip, Wild Carrot and others
Flight period: April to August. Elsewhere, all year in two or three generations
Records in database: 20

This is a distinctive moth – readily recognised by the striking scale tufts on its 'back'. It is probably resident in many more places than those few from which we currently have records.

SCHRECKENSTEINIOIDEA

SCHRECKENSTEINIIDAE

The editors of volume 3 of *Moths and Butterflies of Britain and Ireland* placed the Schreckensteiniidae after the Yponomeutidae and the Epermeniidae; at various dates these species have been included in the Elachistidae, the Heliodinidae and, surprisingly, the Pterophoridae. Here I follow the later checklist of Bradley (2000) in positioning them somewhere between the Tortricidae and the Pyralidae. The single European species is widespread in Britain, but very scarce in Hertfordshire.

0485 *Schreckensteinia festaliella* (Hb.)

Recorded: 1890 – 1999
Distribution / Status: Local / Rare resident
Conservation status: Insufficient data
Caterpillar food plants: No data. Elsewhere on bramble
Flight period: April. Elsewhere March to September
Records in database: 4

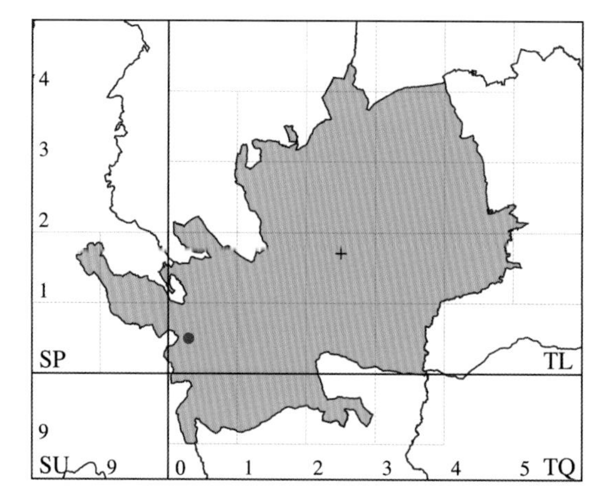

Old records are from the Sandridge area prior to 1890 (Griffith, and the Ashridge Estate prior to 1937 (Hervey), neither of which can be mapped. More recently, Raymond Uffen recorded it at Harmer Green Wood, Welwyn on 20th April 1992 and at Sheethanger Common on 30th April 1999. There are said to be three generations of adults per year in Britain, but we have no data for Hertfordshire. There is no shortage of foodplant so the lack of the moth is surprising.

ALUCITOIDEA

ALUCITIDAE

It may come as a surprise to some that there are 16 'many-plumed moths' on the European list, separation of which usually involves examination of the internal genital structure. Fortunately, we have just the one in both Britain and Hertfordshire.

1288 *Alucita hexadactyla* L. Twenty-plume Moth

Recorded: 1888 – 2006
Distribution / Status: Widespread / Common resident
Conservation status: No perceived threats
Caterpillar food plants: Garden and Wild Honeysuckles
Flight period: January to November
Records in database: 346

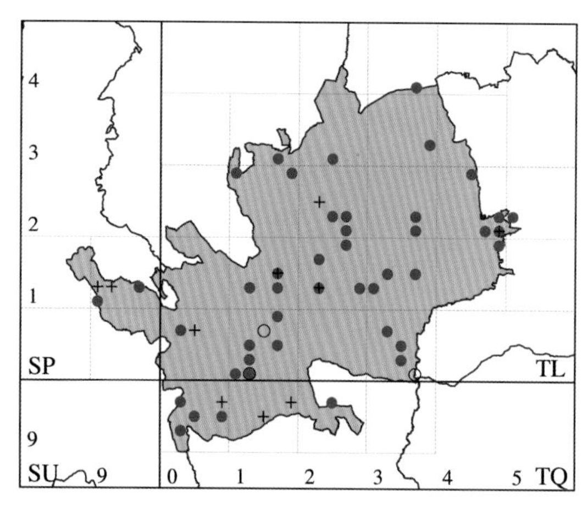

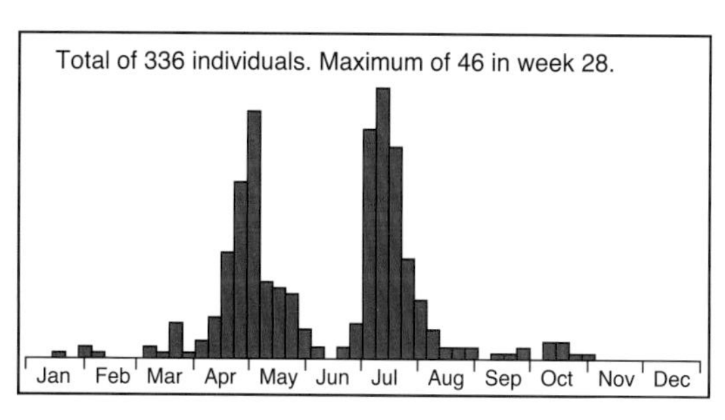

This is a widespread and very common resident of gardens, woodlands, hedgerows and other habitats where honeysuckle grows. Adults are often found hibernating in sheds and greenhouses etc, but the main flight period shows that there are two generations per year, peaking in the April/May and again and in July.

PYRALOIDEA

Bradley (2000) divided the British pyralid moths into ten subfamilies, namely Crambinae, Schoenobiinae, Scopariinae, Nymphulinae, Evergestinae, Glaphyriinae, Pyraustinae, Pyralinae, Galleriinae and Phycitinae. However, recent researches (for example, Goater, Nuss & Speidel, 2005), show that we must split off the first seven of these to a new family – the Crambidae, retaining only the last three in a much reduced, but far more consistent, Pyralidae. Within each of the two newly defined families several names have been changed in recent years and, as relationships between species have become better understood, the positions of species within the list have altered. As elsewhere in this list, I have retained the original Bradley & Fletcher Log Book numbers so that there is no confusion over which species is implied. Worldwide, the pyralids form a huge group of over 16,000 species and it is not beyond the bounds of possibility that future researches may necessitate a split of the Phycitinae away from the remaining groups to form a family in its own right. Overall, the Crambidae and Pyralidae form a very diverse group. The larvae of the Acentropinae (which includes the old Nymphulinae) are adapted to life under water whilst our Galleriinae are parasites in the nests of bees. The Phycitinae contain species adapted to excessively dry conditions and many are pests of stored food and other dried materials; other Phycitinae are predatory on aphids whilst many of the non-British Wurthiinae are associated with ants' nests. There are approximately 139 species of Crambidae in Britain, of which we have recorded 67 in Hertfordshire. In the newly defined Pyralidae there are around 85 species with 48 in Hertfordshire.

CRAMBIDAE

CRAMBINAE

1290 *Chilo phragmitella* (Hb.)

Recorded: 1900 – 2006
Distribution / Status: Very local / Uncommon resident
Conservation status: Herts Vulnerable
Caterpillar food plants: In the stem and rootstock of Reed and Reed Sweet-grass
Flight period: June/July
Records in database: 7

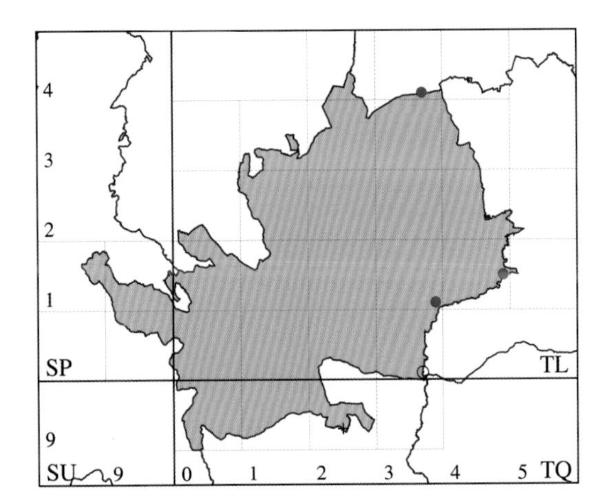

The 1901 record from Cheshunt Marsh (Boyd) and the presence of currently resident colonies at both Sawbridgeworth Marsh and Rye Meads is indicative of the likely presence of this species throughout the Stort Valley and along the Lea at least as far upstream as Hertford. The older record from Totteridge on 23rd July 1977 (Ian Lorimer) and the modern one from Royston on 30th July 2006 (John Chainey) both probably relate to vagrants. As a breeding species, the moth is extremely vulnerable to the cutting (and especially burning) of reeds. Although traditional reed management involves regular cutting, this must surely be modified where sites are very small and physically isolated; burning of cut reeds has no place whatsoever in the ecological management of wetland – its only value is to satisfy the base instincts of conservation volunteers.

1292 *Calamotropha paludella* (Hb.)

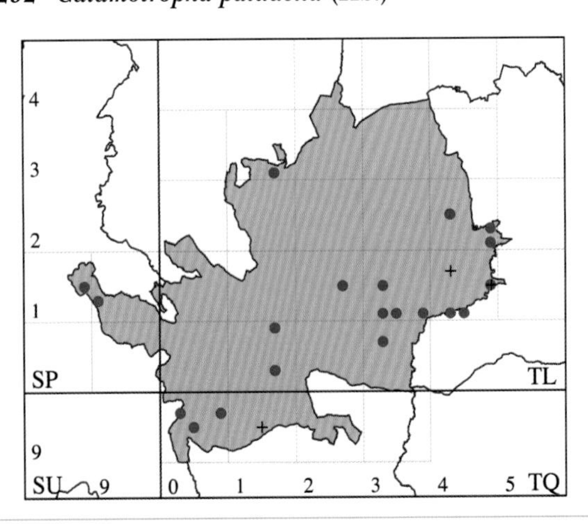

Recorded: 1969 – 2006
Distribution / Status: Local / Common resident
Conservation status: No perceived threats
Caterpillar food plants: Greater Reedmace
Flight period: Mid-June to late August
Records in database: 43

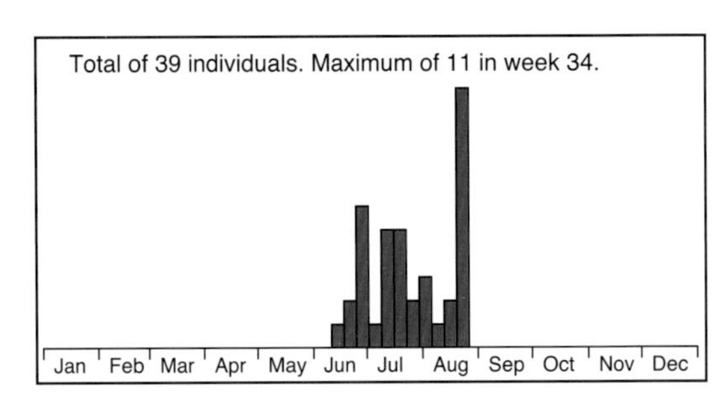

Formerly restricted to large fens and marshes in the East Anglian fenland district and in central southern England, individual adults occasionally wandered to other areas and were recorded as 'vagrants'. This was undoubtedly the source of the first Hertfordshire example at Bushey on 16th July 1969 (Barry Goater). During the 1980s, the number of such vagrants increased and it became clear that the species was becoming resident in other parts of the country. After the Bushey example, there were none reported in Hertfordshire until I found it at Sawbridgeworth Marsh on 27th July 1990. Whether or not it was resident on the marsh at that date is unclear, though my gut feeling is that it was and it was certainly established by 1995 when I caught several freshly emerged examples on 29th July. Occasional wanderers appeared in various new localities, including garden light traps, for the next few years and by 2000 it was clearly resident across most of southern and eastern Hertfordshire.

1293 *Chrysoteuchia culmella* (L.)

Recorded: 1888 – 2006
Distribution / Status: Ubiquitous / Abundant resident
Conservation status: No perceived threats
Caterpillar food plants: Elsewhere, in the base of grass stems
Flight period: June to mid-August.
Records in database: 982

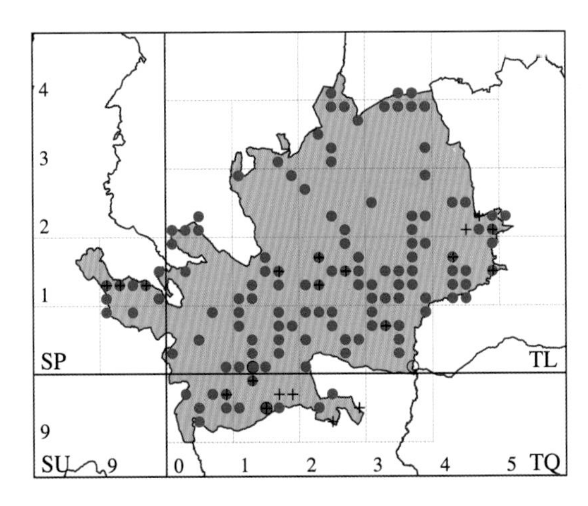

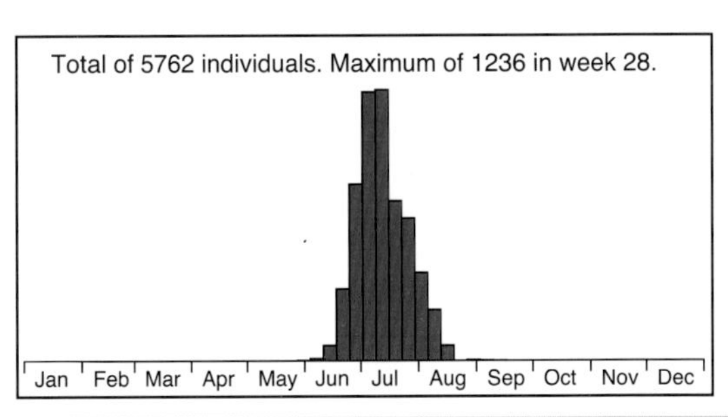

This is probably one of the most abundant of our summer moths and there can be few traps that do not catch it. Seasonally late records were made at Harpenden on 3rd September 2005 (Phil Gould) and Bishops Stortford on 10th September 2000 by myself. The latter could have been an immigrant example (Plant, 2000), but Gould (2006) suggests that these late individuals might reflect a partial second generation. An earlier review of unusually late records in Bedfordshire (Manning, 2001), suggests a third possibility – that of a single, extended emergence.

1294 *Crambus pascuella* (L.)

Recorded:	1885 – 2006
Distribution / Status:	Ubiquitous / Abundant resident
Conservation status:	No perceived threats
Caterpillar food plants:	Not recorded. Elsewhere, on grasses
Flight period:	June to early September
Records in database:	690

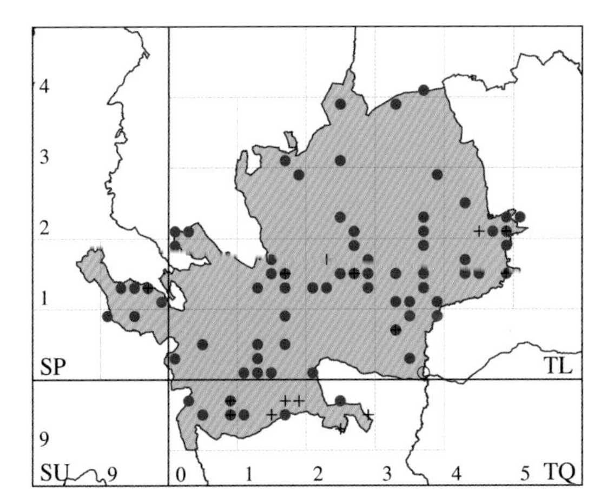

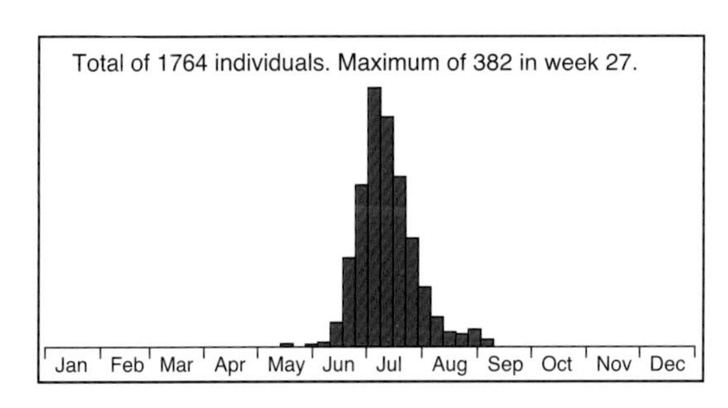

This is another abundant member of the group referred to as 'grass moths'. Earlier than expected adults visited light traps at Harpenden on 15th May 2001 (Phil Gould) and at Nomansland Common on 28th May 2001 (Trevor Chapman).

[1296 *Crambus silvella* (Hb.)

The record from Watford in July 1957 (Penrose, 1980) is an error of identification.]

[1298 *Crambus ericella* (Hb.)

The record from Watford in July 1957 (Penrose, 1980) is an error of identification.]

[1299 *Crambus hamella* (Thunb.)

Listed in error by Penrose (1980). This is perhaps the source of the 1970 listing for Herts in Parsons (1993). The species has never been reliably recorded in Hertfordshire.]

1301 *Crambus lathoniellus* (Zinck.)

Recorded:	1887 – 2006
Distribution / Status:	Ubiquitous / Abundant resident
Conservation status:	No perceived threats
Caterpillar food plants:	Not recorded. Elsewhere, on grasses
Flight period:	Mid-May to mid-August
Records in database:	346

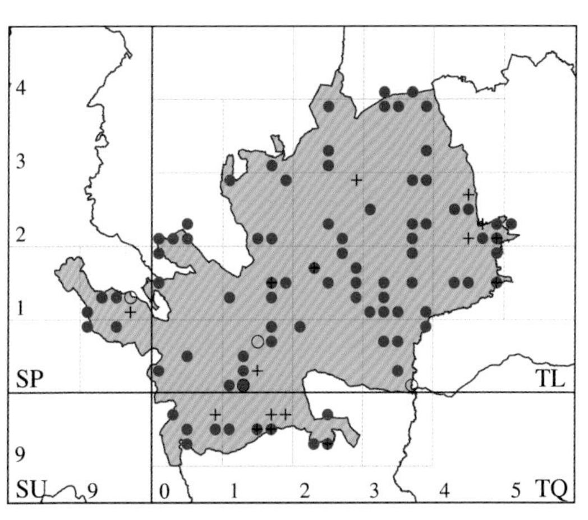

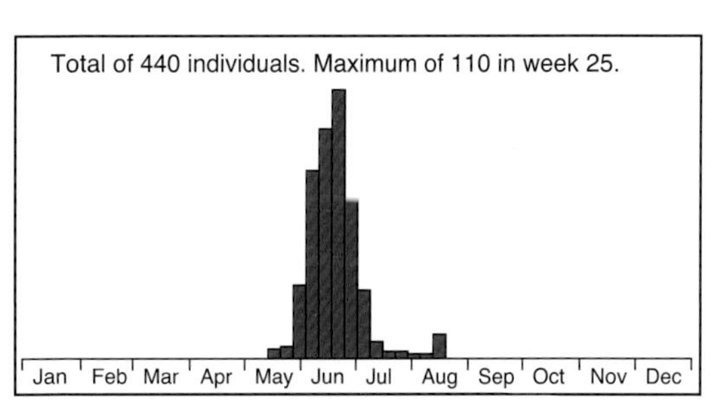

In the past, some works have referred to this species as *Crambus pratellus* and so there may have been some past confusion between this and 1300: *Crambus pratella* (L.). This scarcely seems to matter since the present species is widespread and common whilst *Crambus pratella* (L.), does not occur in Hertfordshire, as far as we are aware.

1302 *Crambus perlella* (Scop.)

Recorded:	1834 – 2006
Distribution / Status:	Ubiquitous / Common resident
Conservation status:	No perceived threats
Caterpillar food plants:	Not recorded. Elsewhere, on various grasses
Flight period:	June to August
Records in database:	361

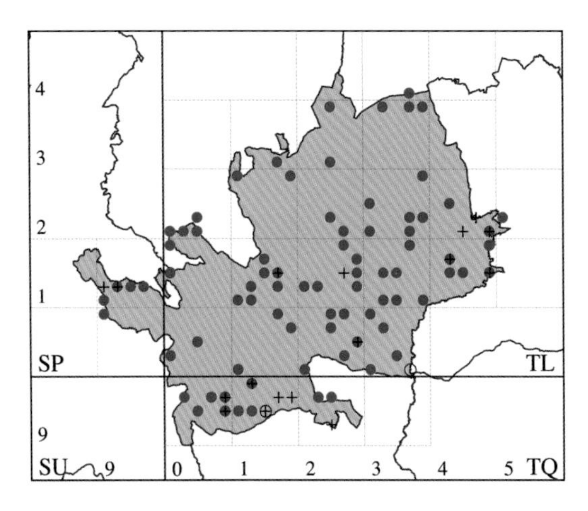

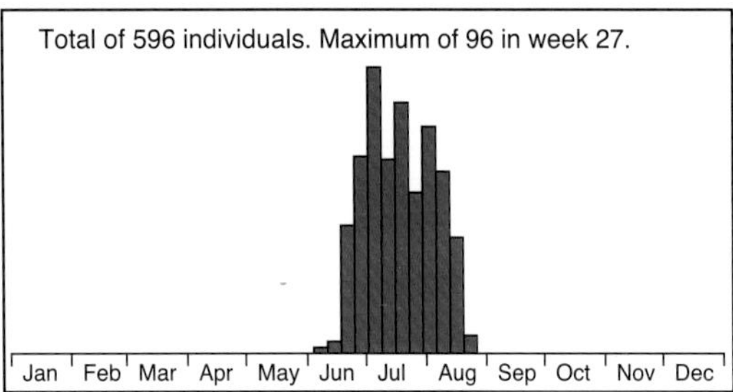

As with the other Hertfordshire representatives of the genus *Crambus* this is a species that is expected in almost all sites where moth traps are operated.

1303 *Agriphila selasella* (Hb.)

Recorded: 1901 – 2005
Distribution / Status: Very local / Rare – probably vagrant
Conservation status: Insufficiently known
Caterpillar food plants: Not recorded. Elsewhere, on various grasses
Flight period: July/August
Records in database: 15

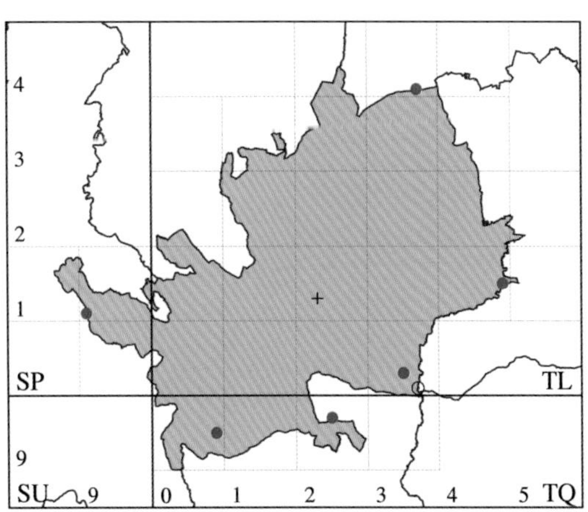

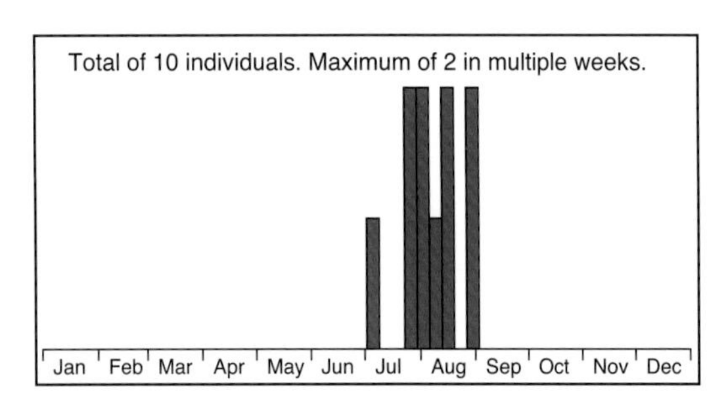

This moth is frequently reported, but almost always in error for the ubiquitous 1305: *Agriphila tristella*. Examples with the long pale streak along the forewing pure white are *selasella*, but those with the streak yellowish brown could be either species. However, wing-tips of *selasella* are more rounded (rather pointed in *tristella*). Once candidate *selasella* are selected it is necessary to look at the head in side view; in *tristella* it is strongly and obviously produced forwards and slightly upwards to form what some books refer to as a 'cone'; in *selasella* the head is only slightly produced and the projection is rounded in profile – not conical. Beginners should look for the feature on *tristella* first before trying to prove it absent on the other species. *Agriphila selasella* is rare in Hertfordshire and probably only occurs as a vagrant from the Thames area and elsewhere. The mid-county record is from Lemsford Springs in 1979 and is apparently unsupported by a voucher specimen.

1304 *Agriphila straminella* ([D.& S.])

Recorded: 1962 – 2006
Distribution / Status: Ubiquitous / Abundant resident
Conservation status: No perceived threats
Caterpillar food plants: Not recorded. Elsewhere, on various grasses
Flight period: July/August
Records in database: 462

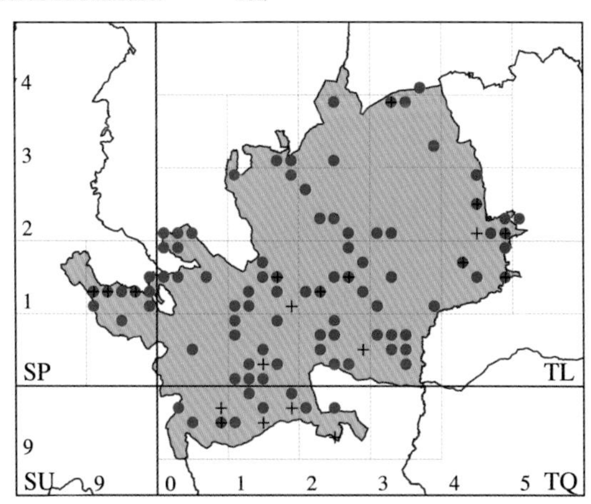

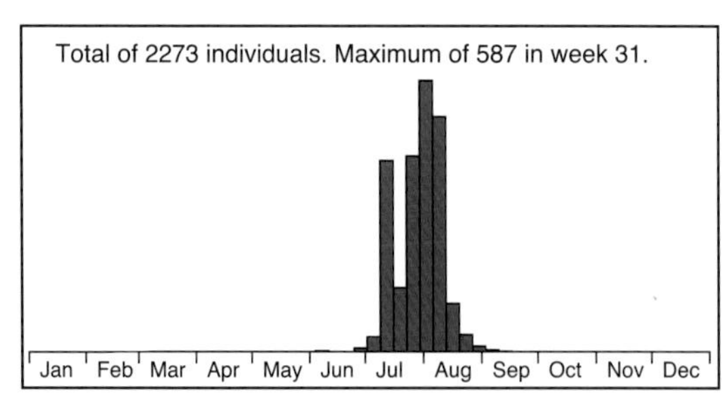

This is a super-abundant moth that will be found in every grassy corner of the county.

1305 *Agriphila tristella* ([D.& S.])

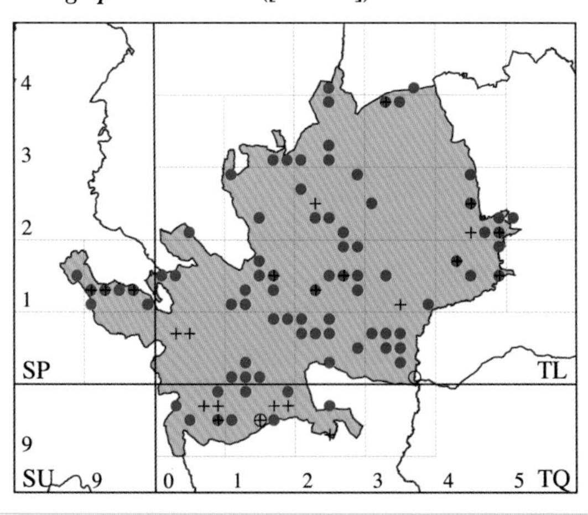

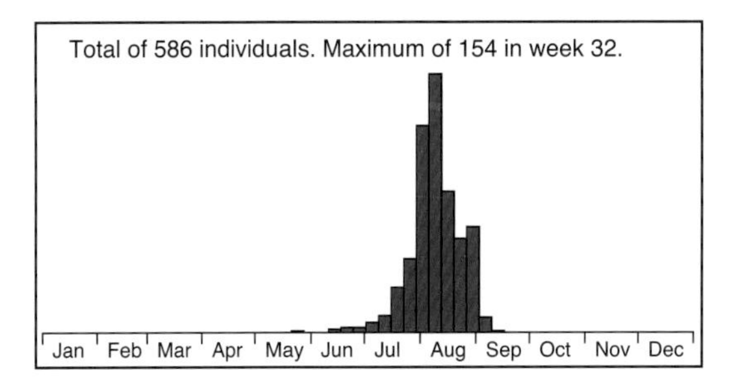

Recorded: 1890 – 2006
Distribution / Status: Ubiquitous / Abundant resident
Conservation status: No perceived threats
Caterpillar food plants: Not recorded. Elsewhere, on various grasses
Flight period: Late June to early September
Records in database: 373

This is another grass moth that is found everywhere in the county. Separation from the much rarer 1303: *Agriphila selasella* is mentioned under that species.

1306 *Agriphila inquinatella* ([D.& S.])

Recorded: 1890 – 2006
Distribution / Status: Local / Common resident
Conservation status: Herts Scarce
Caterpillar food plants: Not recorded. Elsewhere, on various grasses
Flight period: July to early September
Records in database: 142

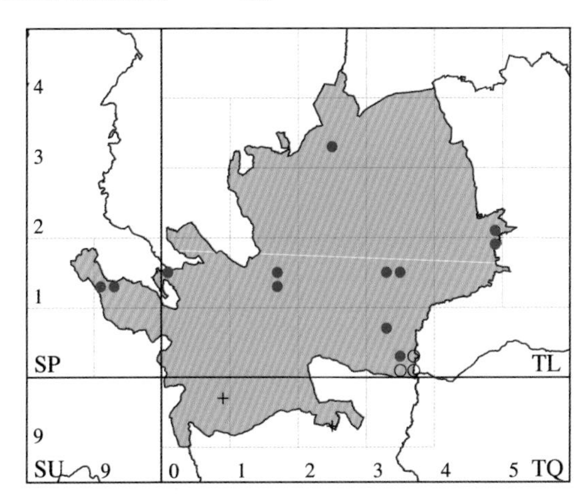

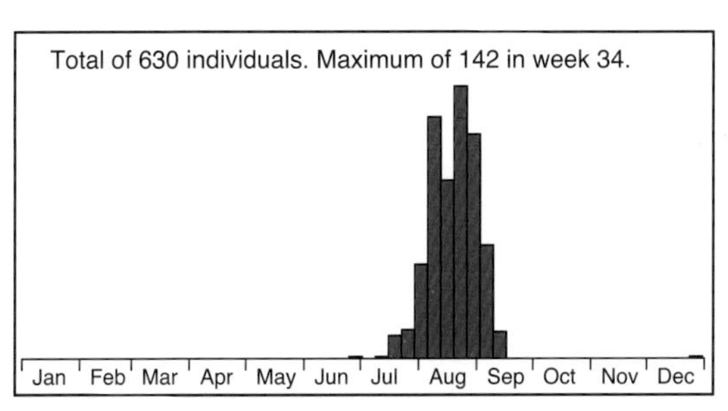

It comes as a surprise to discover that this is a rather localised moth in Hertfordshire, particularly in comparison with 1309: *Agriphila geniculea* with which it is confused by many people. The south of the county is well-recorded, so the absence of the moth in an area where it formerly occurred is worrying.

1309 *Agriphila geniculea* (Haw.)

Recorded: 1834 – 2006
Distribution / Status: Ubiquitous / Common resident
Conservation status: No perceived threats
Caterpillar food plants: Not recorded. Elsewhere, on various grasses
Flight period: August to mid-September
Records in database: 332

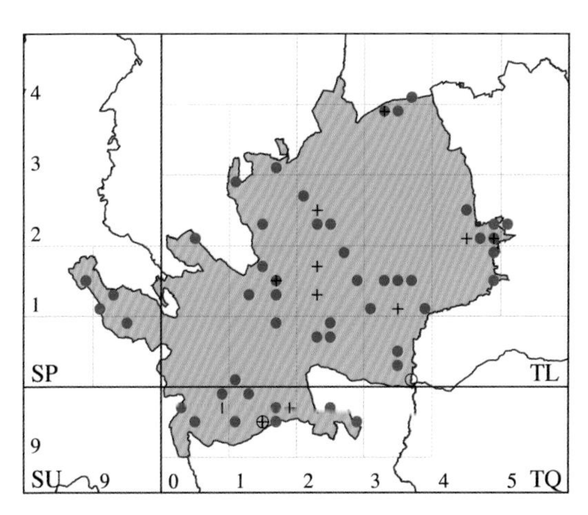

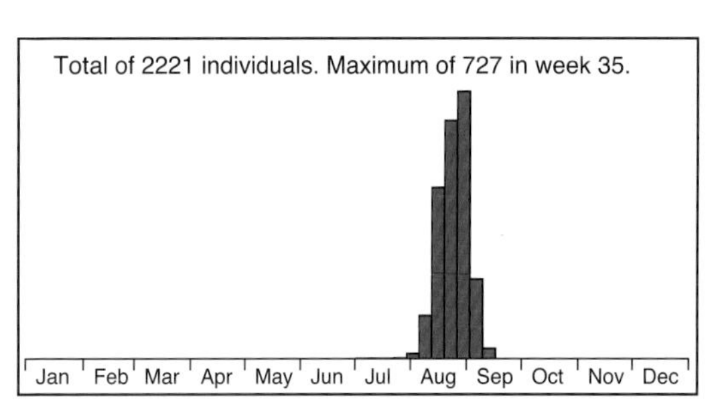

J. F. Stephens lists *geniculea* Haw. for Hertford in *Illustrations of British Entomology*, published in 1834. Durrant (1888) interprets this as the *inquinatella* of Humphreys & Westwood, but the illustration appears to be of what we today regard as the *geniculea* of Haworth. The moth is widespread across the county, but never in the numbers that some of the other 'grass moths' present and not at every site recorded.

1313 *Catoptria pinella* (L.)

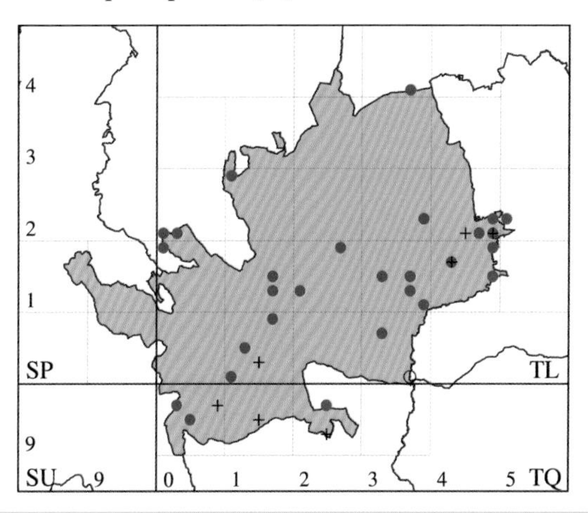

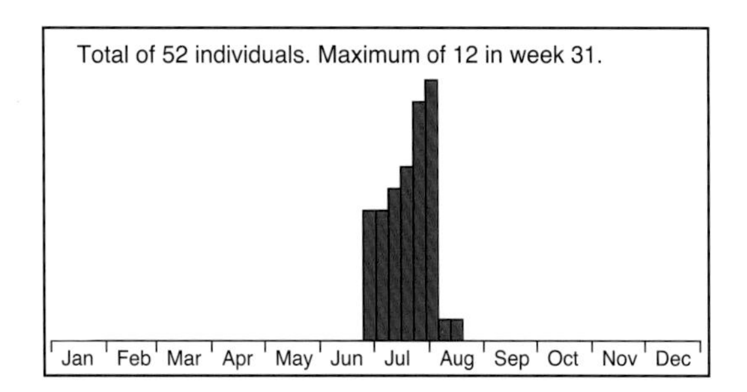

Recorded:	1885 – 2006
Distribution / Status:	Widespread / Common resident
Conservation status:	No perceived threats
Caterpillar food plants:	Not recorded. Elsewhere, on various grasses and sedges
Flight period:	Late June to mid-August
Records in database:	84

Although by no means as common as some of the other grass moths this distinctive species is nevertheless likely to be found in most parts of Hertfordshire.

1316 *Catoptria falsella* ([D.& S.])

Recorded:	1900 – 2006
Distribution / Status:	Widespread / Common resident
Conservation status:	No perceived threats
Caterpillar food plants:	Not recorded. Elsewhere, on mosses, including *Tortula muralis*
Flight period:	July/August
Records in database:	87

This rather small crambid is surprisingly well-distributed in the county; though older records are rather sparse, it appears likely always have been so. The adult has usually finished by the end of August, but we have three September reports, on 9th September 2005 at Ware (Liz Goodyear), on 11th September 2006 at Royston (John Chainey & Jenny Spence) and my own on 19th September 1987 at Patmore Hall Wood near Bishops Stortford.

1321 *Thisanotia chrysonuchella* (Scop.)

Recorded:	1834 – 1937
Distribution / Status:	Absent / Former resident
Conservation status:	Herts Extinct
Caterpillar food plants:	Not recorded. Elsewhere, on various grasses
Flight period:	Elsewhere, May/June
Records in database:	3

We have just three Hertfordshire records for this species of chalk downland and the Breckland. These are from Hertford (Stephens, 1834), Aldbury in 1900 (Nathaniel Rothschild) and Ashridge in 1937 (J. K. Hervey). These are the sources of the pre-1970 records reported in Parsons (1993) without detail. It is extremely unlikely that this species still thrives in the county, though a thorough search of the chalk grasslands between Tring and Dunstable in late May or early June has probably never been undertaken.

1323 *Pediasia contaminella* (Hb.)

Recorded:	1976 – 2005
Distribution / Status:	Local / Rare resident
Conservation status:	Herts Scarce
Caterpillar food plants:	Not recorded. Elsewhere, on various grasses
Flight period:	July/August
Records in database:	10

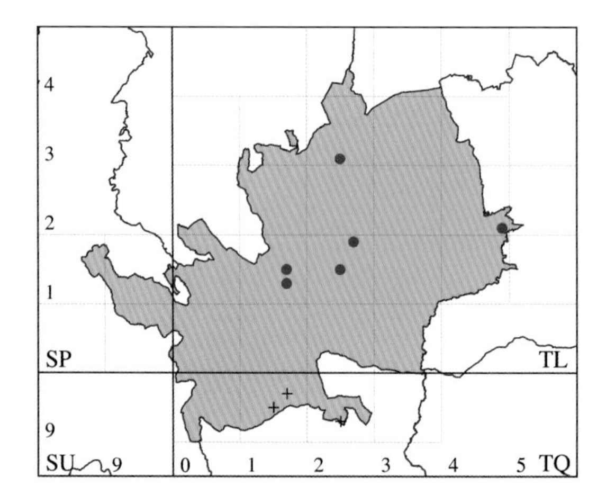

Goater (1986) describes the British distribution of this species as being 'local in dry grassland, on golf courses and playing fields in Essex, Kent, Middlesex and Hertfordshire and extending at least as far as east Hampshire'. It is interesting to note that our first county record was made by Barry Goater himself, at the Haberdasher's Aske's School in Aldenham as recently as 6th July 1976 and he caught it again in his garden at Bushey on 20th September of the same year which, as those old enough will recall, was the exceptionally hot drought year. Ian Lorimer took the next at Totteridge in 1979, but there are no more reports until 29th July 1997 at Datchworth (Steve

Palmer) and 17th July 1999 at Digswell (Tom Gladwin). More recent records are in my garden at Bishops Stortford in 2001 (and again in June 2007 – beyond the period covered by this review), Marshall's Heath (John Murray) and Wheathampstead (Trevor Chapman) in 2002, Nomansland Common on 13th July 2004 (Raymond Uffen) and Weston on 1st August 2005 (Alan Cockburn).

SCHOENOBIINAE

1328 *Schoenobius gigantella* ([D.& S.])

Recorded: 1890 – 2006
Distribution / Status: Extremely local / Uncommon resident
Conservation status: Herts Vulnerable
Caterpillar food plants: Not recorded. Elsewhere, shoots and stems of Reed and Reed Sweet-grass
Flight period: Mid-June to late August
Records in database: 7

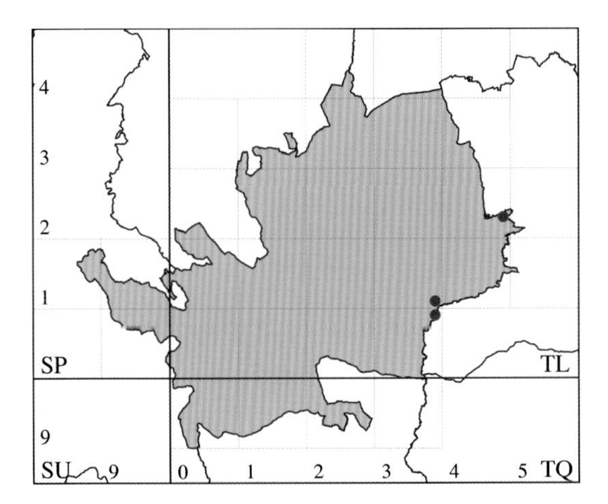

The most northerly map dot is from the adjoining gardens of James Fish and Julian Reeves in Bishops Stortford, where an adult caught by them on 20th June 2005 was likely a wanderer from somewhere further south in the Stort Valley. As a breeding species this moth has only been found at Rye Meads and in spite of many trap nights in the correct season has not yet turned up at Sawbridgeworth Marsh. It seems to require larger reed beds and so its presence might be predicted at Amwell, in the Lea Valley, which site is less well-recorded than some others. Comments about management made under 1290: *Chilo phragmitella* apply here equally.

1329 *Donacaula forficella* (Thunb.)

Recorded: 1890 – 2006
Distribution / Status: Local / Common resident
Conservation status: Herts Threatened
Caterpillar food plants: Not recorded. Elsewhere, Reed, Reed Sweet-grass and sedges
Flight period: Mid-June to late August
Records in database: 29

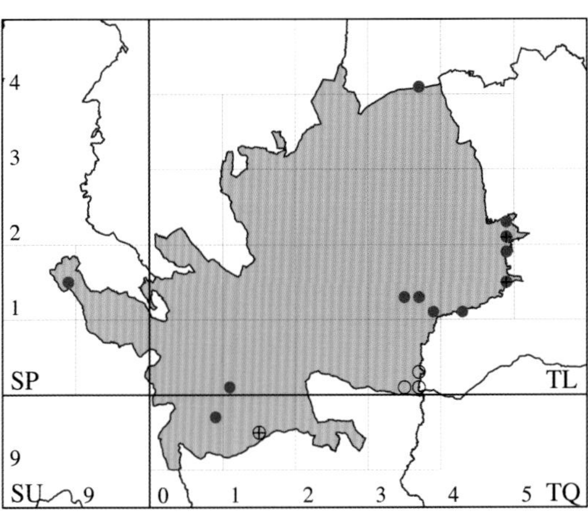

This species appears to be far more widespread than 1328: *Schoenobius gigantella* and is evidently able to thrive in wetlands with quite small areas of reed bed, though at Sawbridgeworth Marsh it is probably associated with the sedges, as indeed it is at Rushey Mead Nature Reserve in Bishops Stortford (which is on the North Essex side of the river). Nevertheless, it is very local and confined to wetland habitats, which are themselves considerably threatened in our county.

1330 *Donacaula mucronellus* ([D.& S.])

Recorded: 1901 – 2006
Distribution / Status: Local / Uncommon resident
Conservation status: Herts Threatened
Caterpillar food plants: Not recorded. Elsewhere, Reed, Reed Sweet-grass and sedges
Flight period: Mid-June/July, elsewhere into August
Records in database: 10

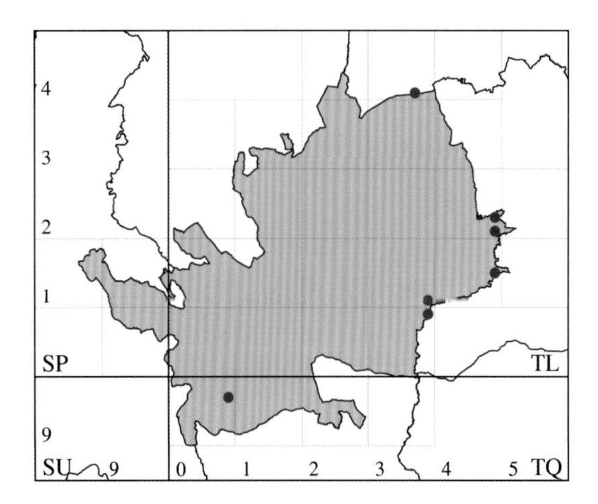

The comments made under 1329: *Donacaula forficella* apply equally well to this species which will have an identical distribution pattern in the county.

ACENTROPINAE

1331 *Acentria ephemerella* ([D.& S.]) Water Veneer

Recorded: 1868 – 2006
Distribution / Status: Ubiquitous / Abundant resident
Conservation status: No perceived threats
Caterpillar food plants: On unrecorded species of pondweed below the water surface, elsewhere including *Elodea, Potamogeton* and *Chara*
Flight period: July to early September, probably in two generations
Records in database: 289

4
3
2
1
SP
TL
9
SU
9
0 1 2 3 4 5 TQ

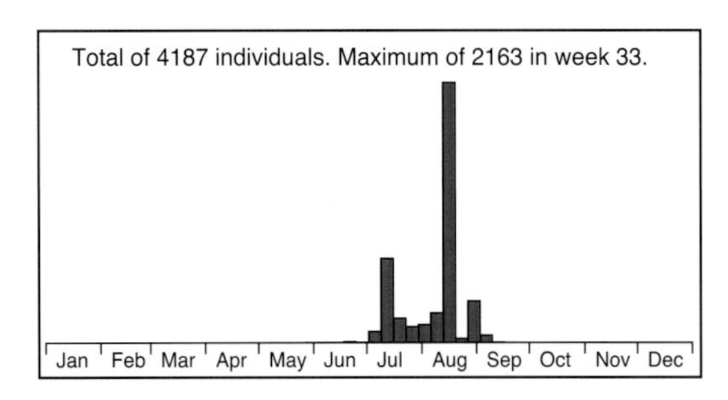

The female Water Veneer has two forms – one with practically no wings and one with wings fully developed. The female has long fringes of 'hairs' on its legs and swims vigorously under water. The larvae feed under water on various plants, apparently 'breathing' through the skin (Agassiz, 1996b) and pupate attached to underwater vegetation. Upon emergence, the males and the fully-winged form of the female disperse over a wide area and it is not uncommon to find several hundreds of males in the moth trap in the morning. The normal life span of these adults is said to be about two days, but I have attracted males to a vertical sheet only to find that all are dead three or four hours later; two days might be an over-estimate. In Hertfordshire, almost all July swarms are comprised of males, which presumably find wingless females as a result of this dispersal. The fully winged form of the female is often caught in Hertfordshire light traps, but not until mid-August in most years, when it may be found alongside several hundreds of males. These females are presumably mated in flight or soon after and will establish new breeding populations; this seems to be a logical adaptation to ponds drying out in the late summer and suggests two generations, in contradiction to the established view that there is a single protracted emergence. Unfortunately, the distribution of our breeding populations is masked by the dispersal flights of this fully aquatic moth, but there is no reason to suppose that the species is under any particular threat.

1345 *Elophila nymphaeata* (L.) Brown China-mark

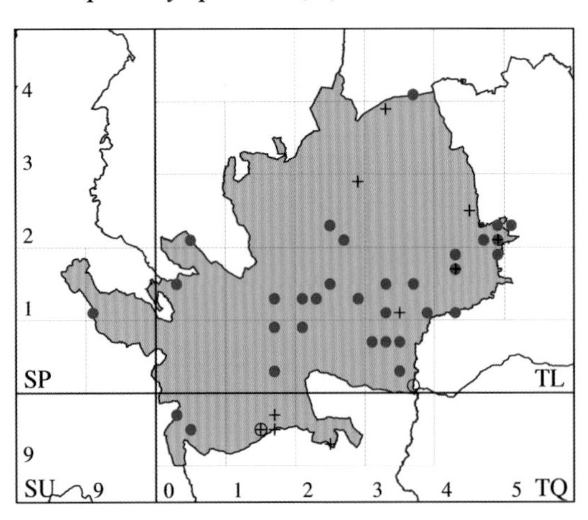

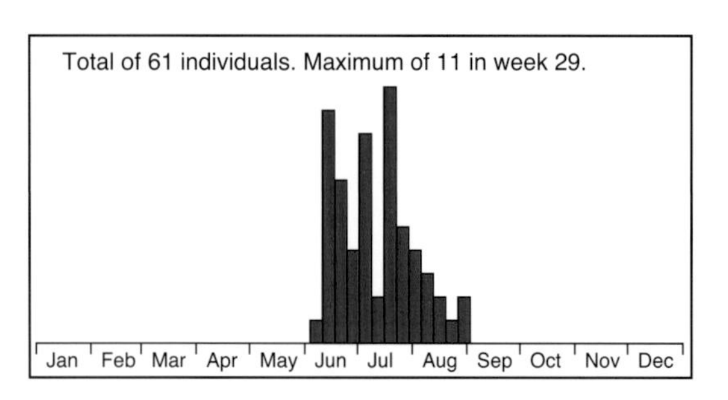

Recorded: 1885 – 2006
Distribution / Status: Widespread / Common resident
Conservation status: No perceived threats
Caterpillar food plants: Not recorded. Elsewhere, on pondweeds including *Elodea*, *Potamogeton* and *Chara* below the water surface
Flight period: June to August
Records in database: 93

The aquatic larvae at first mine leaves of water plants and later feed externally from a case constructed of cut sections of leaves. Almost any well-vegetated static water body will suffice, including garden ponds and though some adults may disperse, the distribution map is probably a close representation of the breeding distribution in the county.

1348 *Parapoynx stratiotata* (L.) Ringed China-mark

Recorded: 1901 – 2006
Distribution / Status: Widespread / Common resident
Conservation status: No perceived threats
Caterpillar food plants: Not recorded. Elsewhere, on pondweeds below the water surface
Flight period: June to early September
Records in database: 127

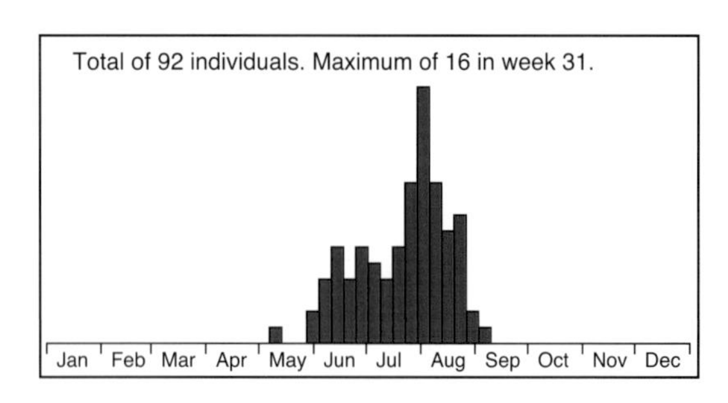

The caterpillar spins together leaves of water plants to create a protective tent in which it lives and feeds. The adults are regular at light and though they may disperse, the map probably reflects the breeding distribution fairly well.

1349 *Parapoynx obscuralis* (Grote)

Examples of this American species were found amongst imported water plants at a nursery in Hemel Hempstead during 1967 (Goater, 1986). Further examples were noted at glasshouses in Enfield, Middlesex in 1984.

1350 *Nymphula stagnata* (Donovan) Beautiful China-mark

Recorded: 1890 – 2006
Distribution / Status: Local / Uncommon resident
Conservation status: Herts Scarce
Caterpillar food plants: Yellow Water-lily, within the stem. Elsewhere, also on bur-reed
Flight period: Late June to early September
Records in database: 30

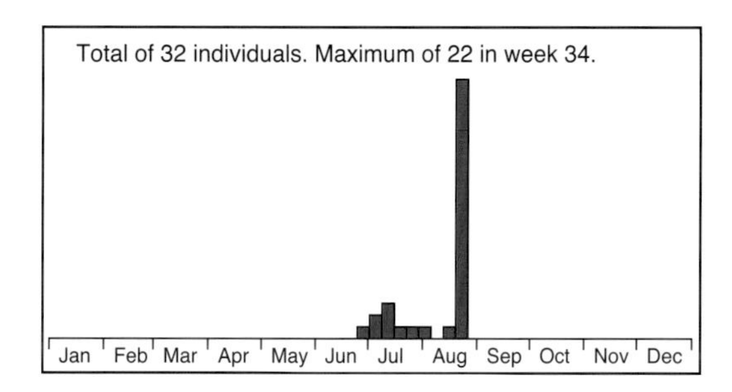

This is by far the most local of the china-mark moths in Hertfordshire and rarely do catches exceed more than one or two individuals. The larvae mine the pith in bur-reed stems and overwinter in the stems making them vulnerable to winter 'conservation management'.

1354 *Cataclysta lemnata* (L.)

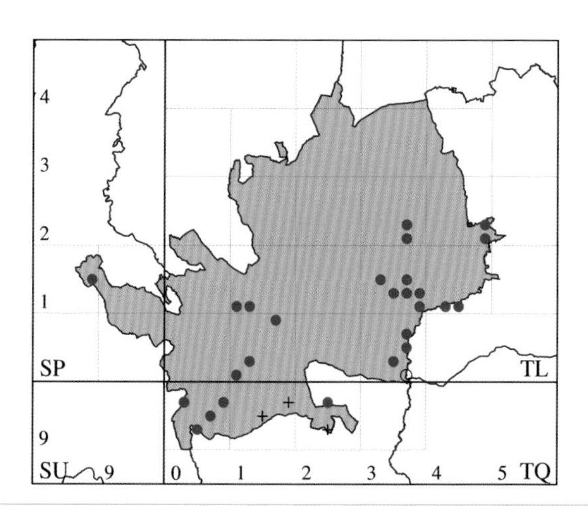

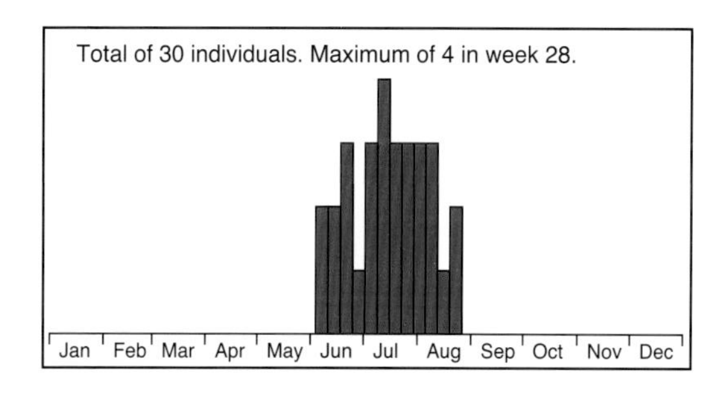

Recorded: 1885 – 2006
Distribution / Status: Widespread / Common resident
Conservation status: No perceived threats
Caterpillar food plants: Not recorded. Elsewhere, duckweed, below the water surface
Flight period: June to August
Records in database: 55

The distinctive males are easily disturbed from waterside vegetation though females are seldom recorded other than at light. The caterpillar is air-breathing and feeds from within a case made of overlapping duckweed 'leaves' in which an air bubble is trapped. The absence of records from the north of the county (in comparison with the other aquatic china-mark moths) is interesting and unexplained.

SCOPARIINAE

The arrival a small grey pyralid at the sheet, usually greeted with a cry of 'it's a scop', strikes dread fear in the heart of many an amateur moth enthusiast – and some experts! With the exception of 1332: *Scoparia subfusca*, some well-marked 1333: *Scoparia pyralella* in which the reniform stigma is clearly yellow, 1338: *Dipleurina lacustrata*, 1336: *Eudonia pallida*, some 1342: *Eudonia angustea* (by date) and most 1344: *Eudonia mercurella* reliable identification must be based on genitalia dissection. For this reason, most historic records have been ignored in the following species accounts.

1332 *Scoparia subfusca* Haw.

Recorded: 1890 – 2006
Distribution / Status: Widespread / Common resident
Conservation status: No perceived threats
Caterpillar food plants: Not recorded. Elsewhere, in the roots of Coltsfoot and Hawkweed Ox-tongue
Flight period: June to August
Records in database: 63

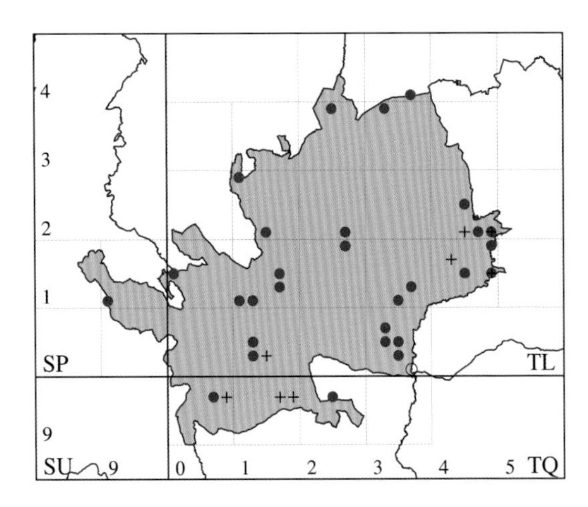

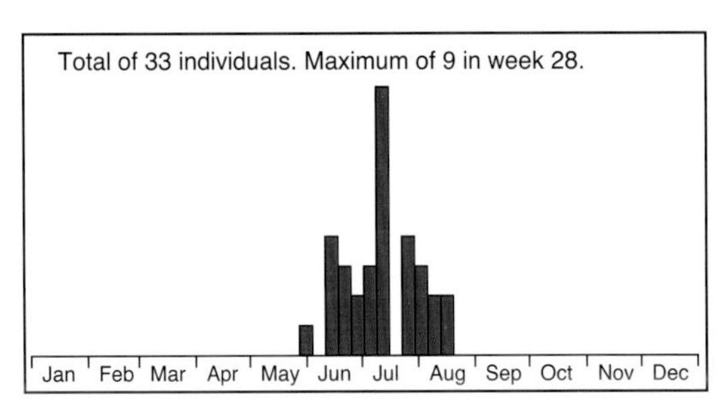

This large *Scoparia* is distinctive, at least within the known British fauna and dissection is not required for a record to be accepted. It appears to be a widespread and fairly common species in Hertfordshire.

1333 *Scoparia pyralella* ([D.& S.])

Recorded: 1890 – 2006
Distribution / Status: Widespread / Common resident
Conservation status: No perceived threats
Caterpillar food plants: Not recorded. Elsewhere, perhaps on decaying plant matter
Flight period: Mid-May to mid-August
Records in database: 186

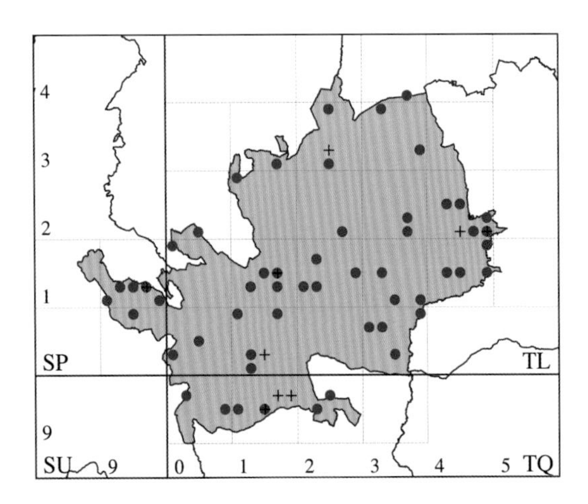

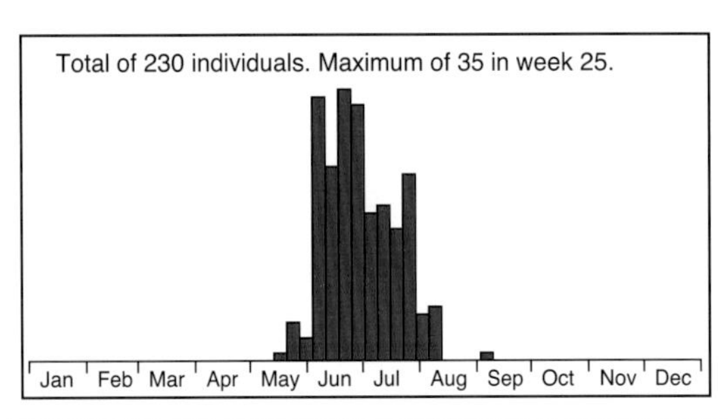

Considerable confusion exists between this species and the far more numerically common 1334: *Scoparia ambigualis* in particular; date is no guide. Most specimens have been dissected, but moths with numerous obvious yellow scales in the forewing reniform stigma are usually this species. The moth illustrated has not been dissected.

1334 *Scoparia ambigualis* (Tr.)

Recorded: 1979 – 2006
Distribution / Status: Ubiquitous / Abundant resident
Conservation status: No perceived threats
Caterpillar food plants: Not recorded. Elsewhere, apparently unknown, perhaps mosses
Flight period: May to August
Records in database: 607

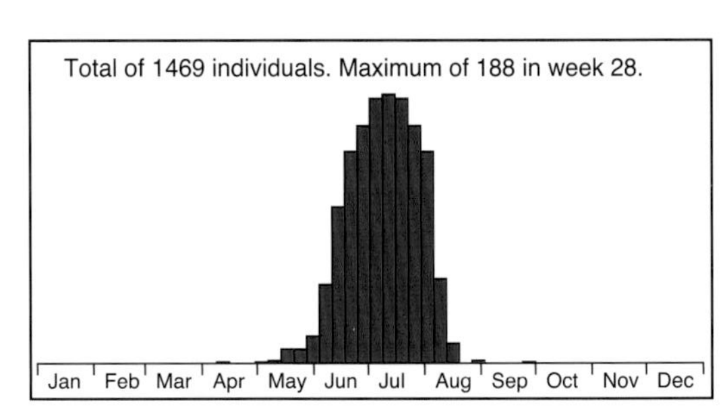

Confirmed records show this to be a widespread and abundant resident. Separation of most specimens from 1333: *Scoparia pyralella* is impossible without genital examination. The two fly together and the notion that *ambigualis* appears earlier in the year than *pyralella* is without foundation in Hertfordshire.

1334a *Scoparia basistrigalis* Knaggs

Recorded: 1988 – 2005
Distribution / Status: Extremely local / Rare resident
Conservation status: Herts Scarce
Caterpillar food plants: Not recorded. Elsewhere, apparently unknown
Flight period: June/July
Records in database: 8

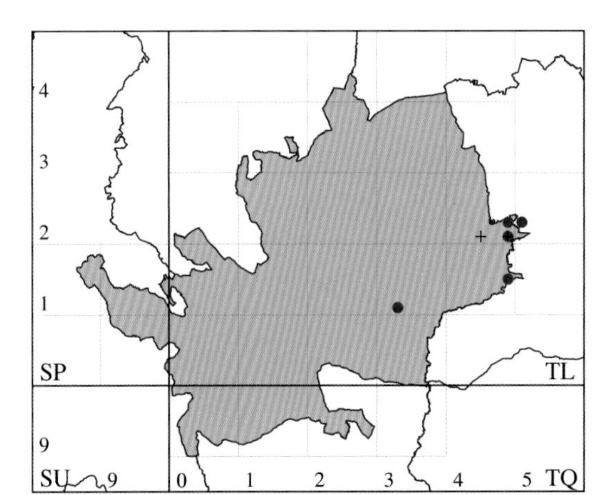

Confirmed records show a bias towards my home area of the county, but since my efforts in both catching and dissecting moths are spread further afield this is probably not recorder-bias. The moth is apparently resident in this eastern area having been caught at Birchanger Wood, Stocking Wood, woodland at Sawbridgeworth Marsh and in two gardens in Bishops Stortford. The western outlier is from Balls Park, Hertford, where I caught it in 2001. Though undoubtedly overlooked it is generally not expected outside woodland and is probably extremely local in distribution here.

[1335 *Scoparia ancipitella* (La Harpe)

This species was listed, without data, by Parsons (1993) for Hertfordshire in the period since 1970. The source of this record is unclear and it is entirely possible that Herefordshire may have been intended? The moth is quite unexpected in the south-east of England and the record cannot be accepted.]

1336 *Eudonia pallida* (Curtis)

Recorded: 1890 – 2006
Distribution / Status: Local / Rare resident
Conservation status: Herts Scarce
Caterpillar food plants: Not recorded. Elsewhere, perhaps mosses or lichens on the ground?
Flight period: July
Records in database: 12

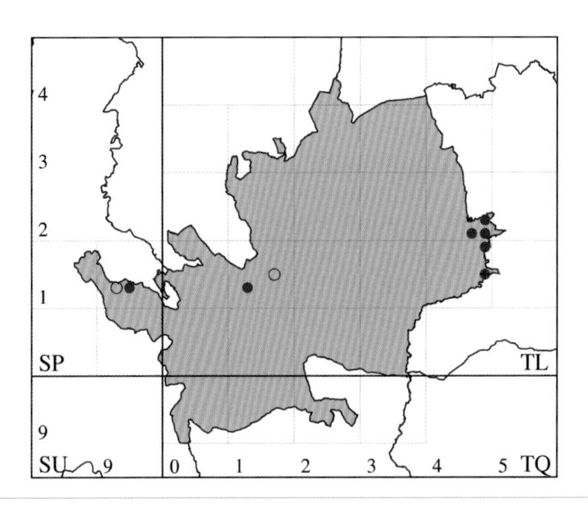

Griffith (1890) lists this species for the Sandridge area and Gibbs (1906) records Dundale, near Tring, 1905 (A. T. Goodson) 'an insect which previously had only been recorded for Sandridge'. The appearance of this species is distinctive and so these old records are accepted. More recent records suggest that the moth is quite scarce and localised in Hertfordshire. Because of this, a representative selection of examples from my garden in Bishops Stortford was dissected and the identifications thus confirmed; it is surely overlooked elsewhere in the county?

1338 *Eudonia (Dipleurina) lacustrata* (Panzer)

Recorded: 1890 – 2006
Distribution / Status: Widespread / Common resident
Conservation status: No perceived threats
Caterpillar food plants: Not recorded. Elsewhere, moss growing on trees and walls
Flight period: June to early August
Records in database: 192

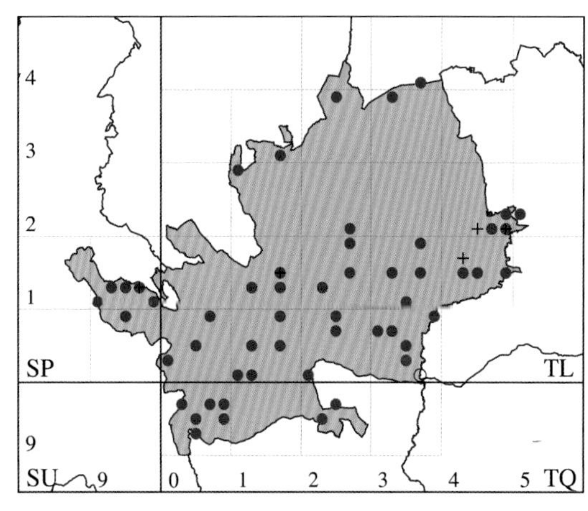

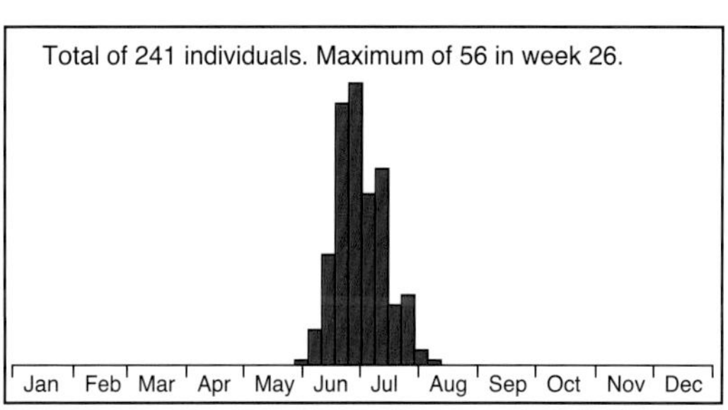

This is usually an easy species to recognise from the presence of a white patch on the forewing – easily visible from a distance, but far less obvious in close view and downright difficult under a hand lens! The moth is common throughout the county.

1340 *Eudonia truncicolella* (Stt.)

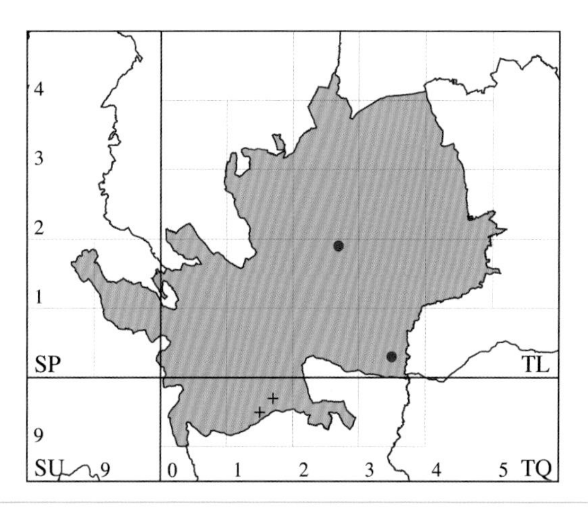

Recorded:	1976 – 2004
Distribution / Status:	Extremely local / Rare – perhaps a vagrant
Conservation status:	Herts Rare
Caterpillar food plants:	Not recorded. Elsewhere, mosses on the ground
Flight period:	July to early September
Records in database:	4

Acceptable records are from the Haberdasher's Aske's School, 6th July 1976 (Barry Goater), Bushey, 3rd September 1981 (Barry Goater), Datchworth, 19th August 2001 (Steve Palmer) and Cheshunt, 2004 (Mark Cooper).

1342 *Eudonia angustea* (Curtis)

Recorded:	1900 – 2006
Distribution / Status:	Local / Common resident
Conservation status:	No perceived threats
Caterpillar food plants:	Not recorded. Elsewhere, mosses and lichens on vertical surfaces
Flight period:	March to November
Records in database:	154

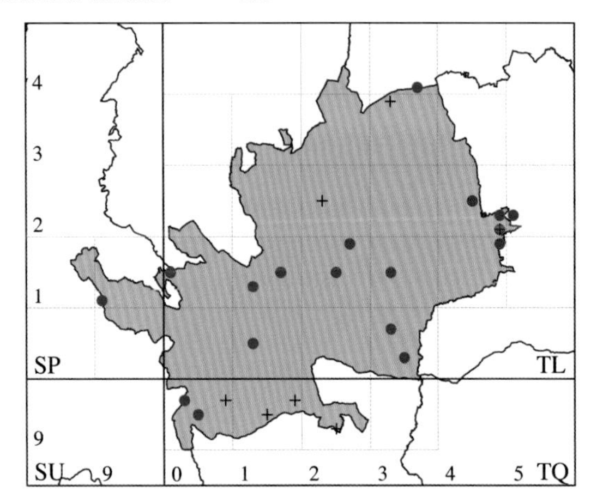

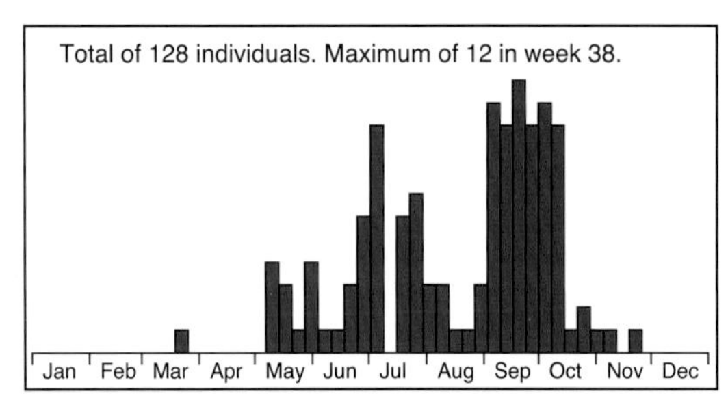

Gibbs (1905) lists the first county record from Watford – 'by Mr. Kitchin in 1900'. Recent reports show it to be a widespread but local species in Hertfordshire and one that can be found for an extended period across the year. There are at least two, perhaps three peaks in the adult flight chart.

1343 *Eudonia delunella* (Stt.)

Recorded:	1890 – 1901
Distribution / Status:	Absent / Extinct
Conservation status:	Herts Extinct
Caterpillar food plants:	Not recorded. Elsewhere, mosses and lichens on vertical surfaces
Flight period:	Elsewhere, July/August
Records in database:	5

Griffith (1890) lists this species for the Sandridge area and Boyd (1901) states 'Bayford'. These are repeated in Foster (1937) under the name of *Scoparia resinea* Haw. The species is listed subsequently by Parsons (1993) for the pre-1970 period on the basis of these records given by Foster (Parsons, pers. comm., 2007) and there are no other valid Hertfordshire records. Published records from Watford in June 1955, July 1957, 1958 and August 1961 (Penrose, 1980) are incorrect. In Britain, recent records are given for the New Forest, Faringdon in Berkshire and from Camarthenshire, Dumfriesshire and South Devon by Goater (1986).

1344 *Eudonia mercurella* (L.)

Recorded:	1890 – 2006
Distribution / Status:	Ubiquitous / Abundant resident
Conservation status:	No perceived threats
Caterpillar food plants:	Not recorded. Elsewhere, mosses on trees, walls, rocks etc
Flight period:	June to August
Records in database:	389

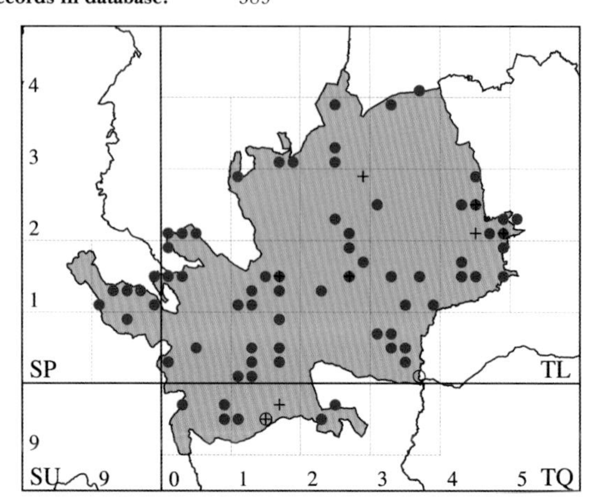

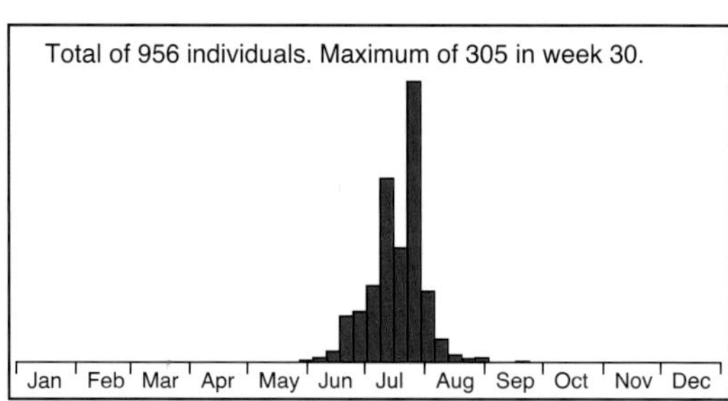

This is a very common species in the county. It takes several forms, but the majority of Hertfordshire examples are light and the really dark forms appear quite uncommon.

EVERGESTINAE

1356 *Evergestis forficalis* (L.) Garden Pebble

Recorded:	1885 – 2006
Distribution / Status:	Widespread / Common resident
Conservation status:	No perceived threats
Caterpillar food plants:	Not recorded. Elsewhere, on various Cruciferae
Flight period:	May/June then late July to early September, in two generations
Records in database:	346

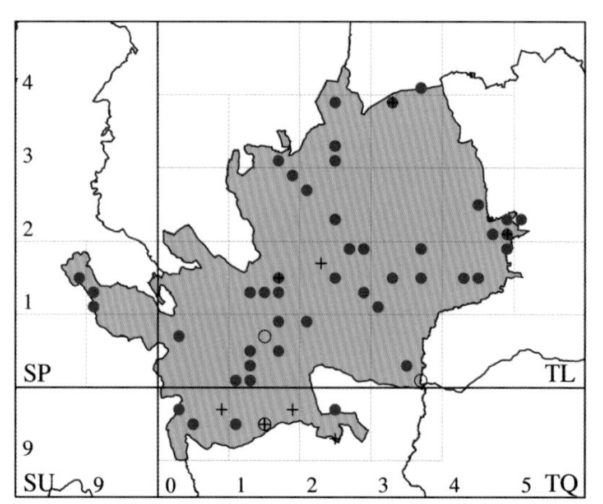

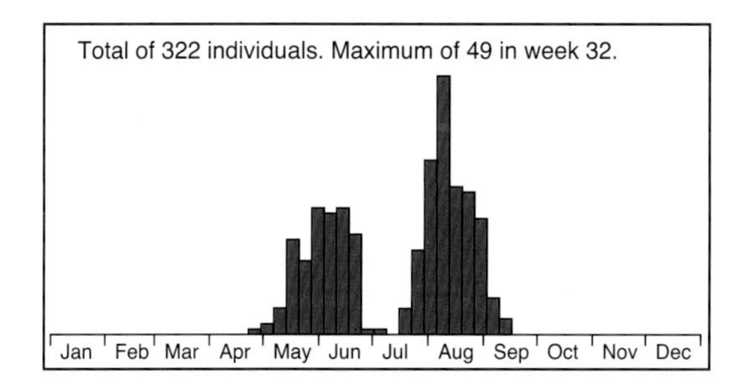

The Garden Pebble is a familiar micro, but often goes unidentified by beginners who, on account of its size, search for it in books covering 'macro' moths only. The separation of the two generations of adults is clear from the flight chart, above.

1357 *Evergestis extimalis* (Scop.)

Recorded:	1901 – 2003
Distribution / Status:	Random / Vagrant or immigrant
Conservation status:	-
Caterpillar food plants:	Not recorded. Elsewhere, various Cruciferae
Flight period:	July
Records in database:	3

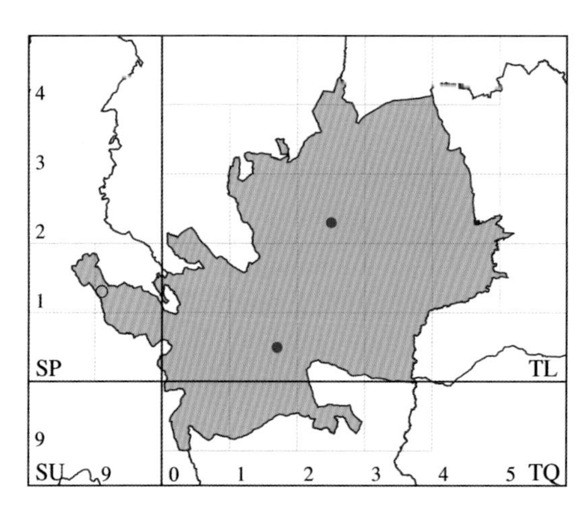

Valid Hertfordshire records are from Tring, 1900 (Goodson), Stevenage, 2000 (Mark Gurney) and London Colney, 23rd July 2003 (Bill and Pearl Page). The species breeds along the Thames Estuary throughout South Essex, extending westwards into east London where it is an expected species on most post-industrial sites, and this may be the source of Hertfordshire individuals.

1358 *Evergestis pallidata* (Hufn.)

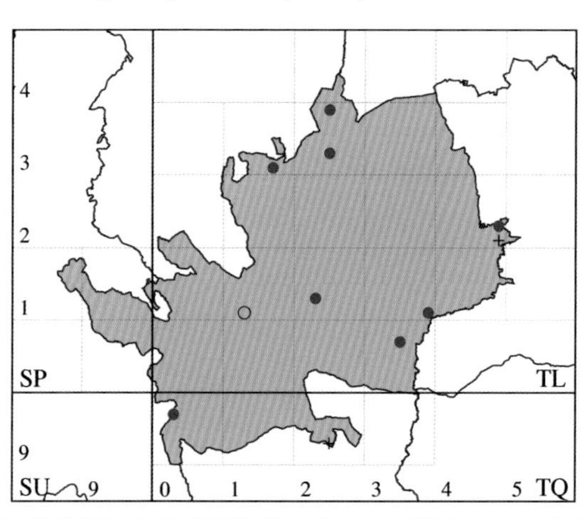

Recorded:	1941 – 2006
Distribution / Status:	Local / Uncommon resident and vagrant
Conservation status:	Herts Scarce
Caterpillar food plants:	Not recorded. Elsewhere, various Cruciferae
Flight period:	Mid-July to early August
Records in database:	11

Foster (1941) reports this as new to the county 'Between Redbourn and St Albans, on the River Ver, not common (Fryer)'; no year is given. This is the basis for the inclusion of this species in the review by Parsons (1993). The next record was made when Ian Lorimer caught one at Totteridge in 1979 and there are no more until 17th July 1991 (in my garden at Bishops Stortford). These last two, as well as one at Baldock on 21st July 1999 (Kerry Robinson), one at Ashwell Quarry on 27th July 2002 (myself) and another at Bishops Stortford on 29th July 2006 (James Fish & Julian Reeves) were probably wanderers. Records from wet areas at Danemead Wood and Rye Meads (2000), Lemsford Springs (2001) and Oughtonhead Common (2003), all in my own collection, are more likely to represent breeding populations.

PYRAUSTINAE

1361 *Pyrausta aurata* (Scop.)

Recorded:	1900 – 2006
Distribution / Status:	Widespread / Common resident
Conservation status:	No perceived threats
Caterpillar food plants:	Garden Mint, Water Mint. Elsewhere on various other labiates
Flight period:	May to September in two generations
Records in database:	483

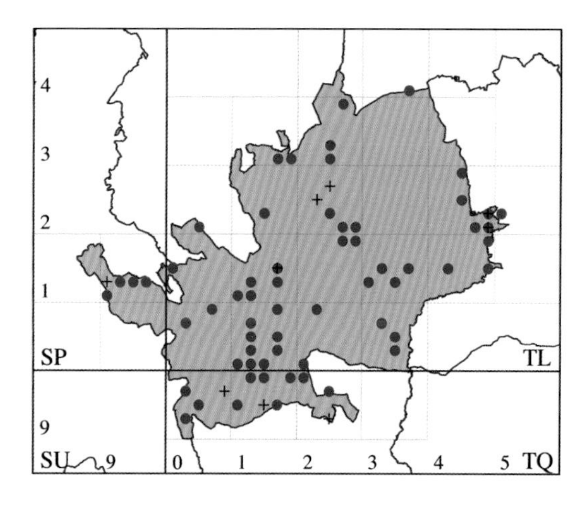

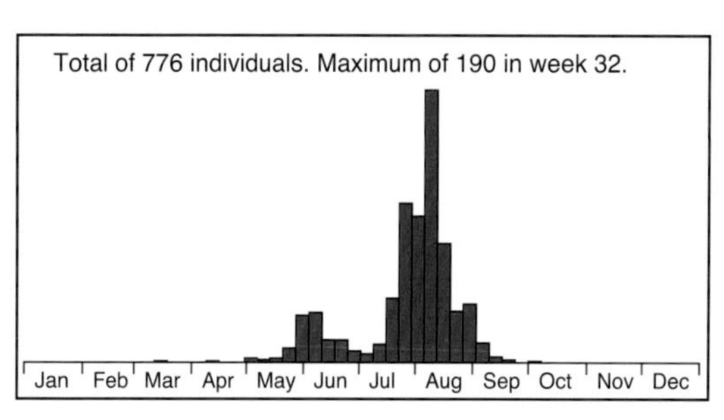

The first county record purports to be from 'the *lucina* ground at Dancers End on the Bucks border' (Gibbs, 1904a), but this site is actually in Buckinghamshire so our first record for VC 20 becomes that from Tring, made in 1900 by A. L. Goodson. Today it is numerous wherever mint, of any variety, grows. In gardens it frequents Spearmint, but in the river valleys of the Stort and Lea it uses the more abundant Water Mint. In woodlands and lanes it probably uses other labiate plants.

1362 *Pyrausta purpuralis* (L.)

Recorded: 1834 – 2006
Distribution / Status: Local / Uncommon resident
Conservation status: No perceived threats
Caterpillar food plants: Not recorded. Elsewhere, Corn Mint and Wild Thyme
Flight period: May to September
Records in database: 63

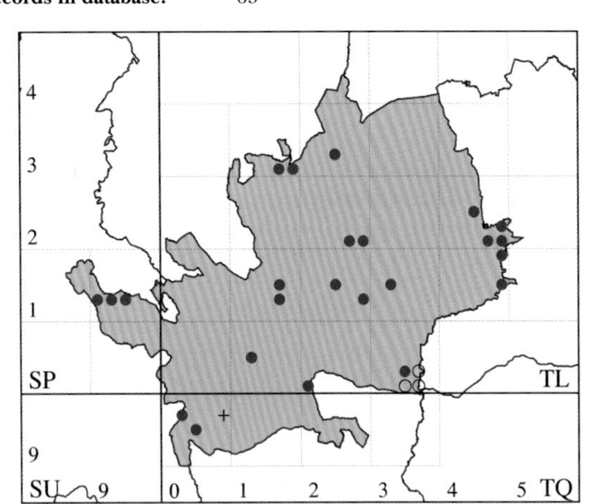

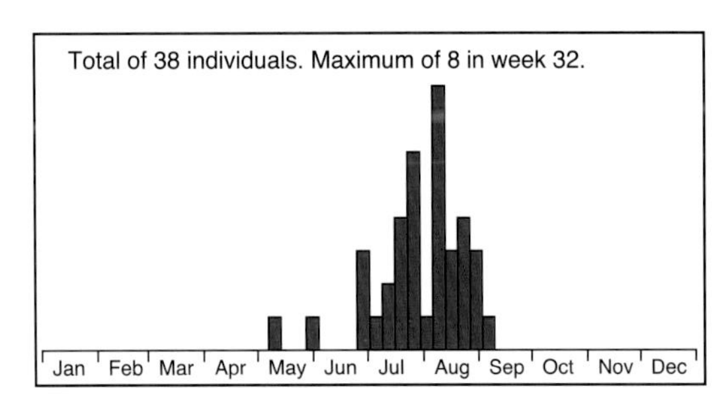

If the moth is caught and examined it is easy to separate from 1361: *Pyrausta aurata* by the presence of yellow areas in the dark basal part of the upper surface of the hind wing. It should be noted that *purpuralis* can be of the same brown colour as typical *aurata*. Separation from *Pyrausta ostrinalis*, which is so far not recorded in Hertfordshire, requires examination of the underside. Some records supported only by photographs are omitted from the map, though these are rather few. It is likely that garden Thyme is also used as a foodplant in some areas.

1365 *Pyrausta despicata* (Scop.) = *cespitalis* ([D.& S.])

Recorded: 1834 – 2004
Distribution / Status: Very local / Uncommon resident
Conservation status: Herts Scarce
Caterpillar food plants: Not recorded. Elsewhere, Rat-tail Plantain and Ribwort Plantain
Flight period: Late May and July. Elsewhere, May to August
Records in database: 16

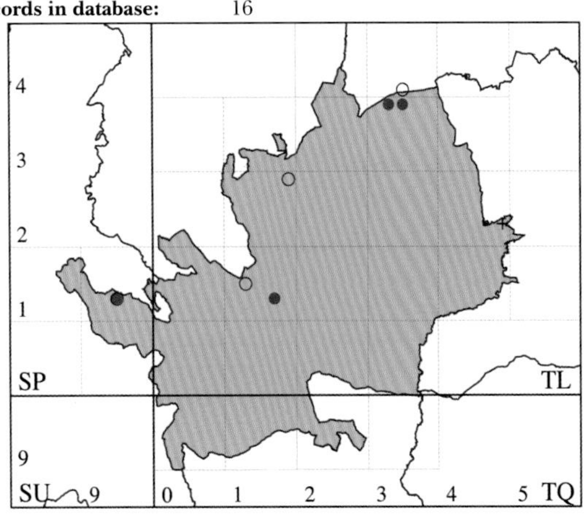

A record from Nomansland Common (an acid grassland site) in 2001 (C. Smith) is out of character with all the other reports, which are from chalkland sites, including that in the east, made by me at Bishops Stortford Lime Pit on 27th May 1991.

1366 *Pyrausta nigrata* (Scop.)

Recorded: 1900 – 2006
Distribution / Status: Very local / Common resident
Conservation status: Herts Rare
Caterpillar food plants: Not recorded. Elsewhere, Marjoram and thyme, especially *Thymus praecox*
Flight period: May/June
Records in database: 5

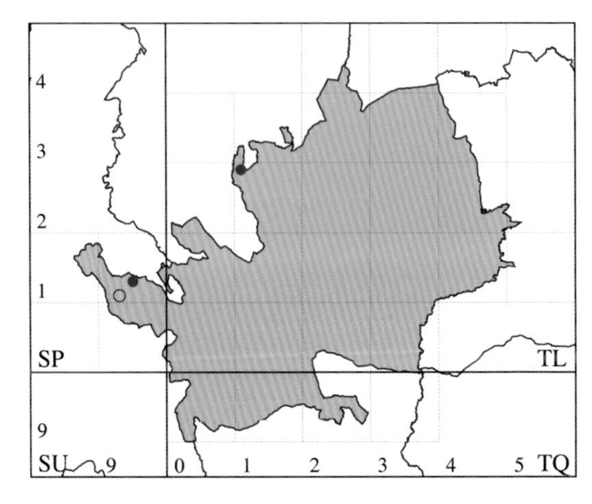

Old records are from Tring Park (1900) and Aldbury Nowers (1902); current sites are Aldbury Nowers, Hexton Chalk Pit and Telegraph Hill – the latter two sites occupying the same map tetrad. This attractive, day-flying moth is surely overlooked at Therfield Heath, Blows Down and other chalkland sites along the north-west frontier?

1368 *Loxostege sticticalis* (L.)

Recorded: 1900 – 2001
Distribution / Status: Random / Immigrant
Conservation status: -
Caterpillar food plants: Not recorded. Elsewhere, Mugwort and Wormwood
Flight period: August/September
Records in database: 3

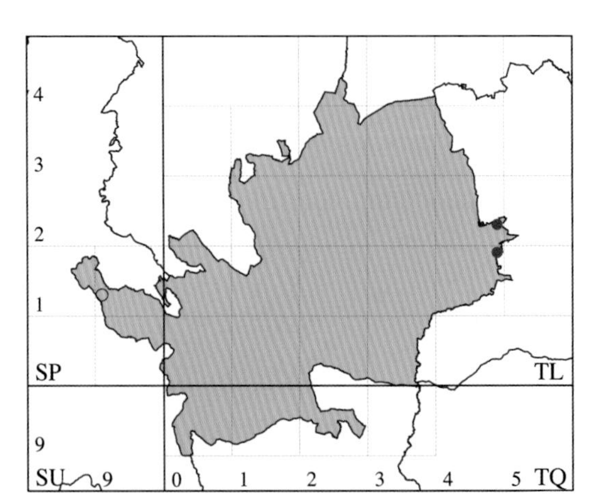

Our three Hertfordshire records are from Tring in 1900 (A. L. Goodson), northern Bishops Stortford, 2 males and a female on 3rd August 1995 (James Fish & Julian Reeves) and southern Bishops Stortford on 27th September 2001 (Charles Watson). There is no doubt that these records relate to primary immigrants.

1370 *Sitochroa palealis* ([D.& S.])

Recorded:	1901 – 2006
Distribution / Status:	Local / Uncommon resident and perhaps immigrant or vagrant
Conservation status:	Herts Scarce
Caterpillar food plants:	Wild Carrot
Flight period:	Mid-July/August
Records in database:	15

In recording this species from Harpenden in 1947, Fryer (1950) notes that there had been only two previous Hertfordshire records, in 1901 and 1944. The former was at Bushey Heath (P. J. Barraud), but details of the latter are not immediately apparent. There are no further records until 1997 at Marshall's Heath (John Murray), 6th August 1997 at Ravensdell Wood (David Manning) and 17th August 1998 at Patmore Heath by me. Eleven further records emanate from the years 2000 to 2006 but breeding has only been confirmed at the two tetrads of Therfield Heath; at least the central Hertfordshire records – those away from the chalk – may relate to immigrant or vagrant examples.

1371 *Sitochroa verticalis* (L.)

Recorded:	1888 – 2006
Distribution / Status:	Local / Uncommon resident and perhaps immigrant
Conservation status:	No perceived threats
Caterpillar food plants:	Not recorded. Elsewhere, on a wide variety of plants
Flight period:	June to August
Records in database:	39

There is a clear bias of records towards the chalk on the northern edge of the county, where the species is certainly resident, though interestingly there are no records from the equally calcareous border area further south-west; perhaps this is under-recording. Away from the chalk, some records are

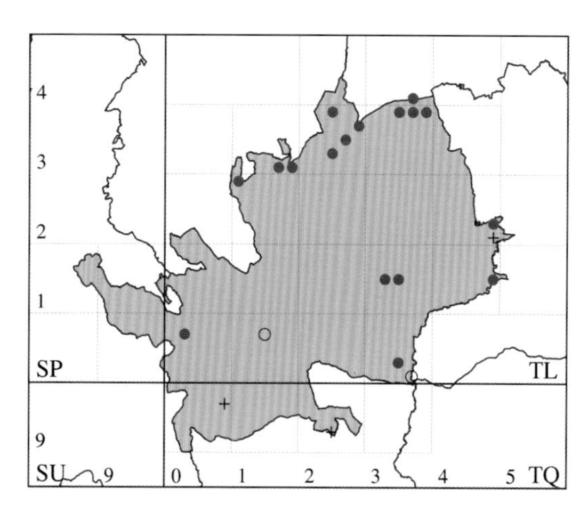

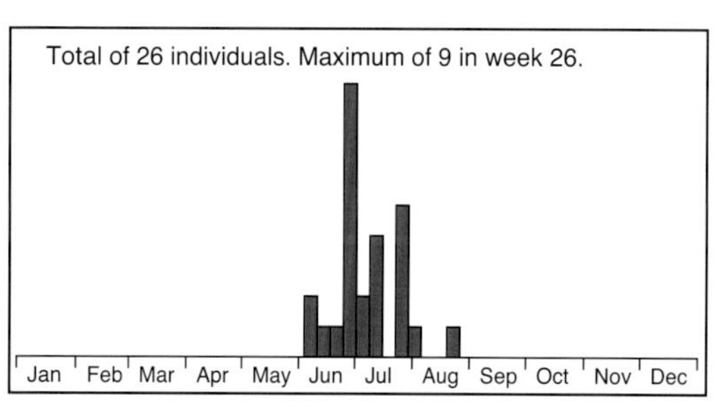

likely to relate to immigrant examples, though discerning these is likely to prove impossible. During the 1970s and 1980s the moth was tolerably widespread and common in suitable habitat in parts of northern London and so the lack of records from southern Hertfordshire during that period is rather surprising; it may be that this species has declined as the various brownfield sites in that area have been developed over the last thirty years.

1373 *Paratalanta pandalis* (Hb.)

Recorded:	1916 – 1993
Distribution / Status:	Absent / Former resident
Conservation status:	Herts Extinct
Caterpillar food plants:	Not recorded. Elsewhere, Wood Sage, Marjoram and Golden Rod
Flight period:	Elsewhere, June
Records in database:	4

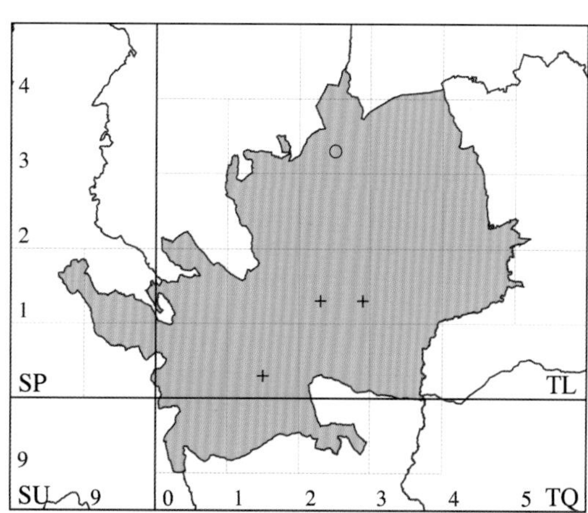

Our four records are from Baldock in 1916 (A. H. Foster), Frogmore on 25th June 1966 (Eric Bradford), Lemsford Springs in 1979 (Tom Gladwin) and Panshanger Park on 14th June 1993 (Tom Gladwin). The species does not appear ever to have been recorded in Bedfordshire, to our north, and to the east the last Essex record was made in 1980 (Goodey, 2004). If this moth was ever resident in Hertfordshire it is certainly no longer so; these four old records are perhaps more likely to refer to immigrant examples.

1374 *Paratalanta hyalinalis* (Hb.)

Recorded: 1901 – 1937
Distribution / Status: Absent / Former resident
Conservation status: Herts Extinct
Caterpillar food plants: Not recorded. Elsewhere, Lesser Knapweed
Flight period: Elsewhere, June/July
Records in database: 6

Goater (1986) regards this as a local species of chalk downland and clearings in Beech woods. Foster (1937) lists Hertfordshire records from Bushey Heath (Barraud), Hemel Hempstead (Piffard), St Albans (Gibbs, Dickson) and Tring (Goodson, Gibbs). All relate to the late nineteenth century apart from the Tring record by Goodson, which was certainly made between 1904 and 1937. There are no other records.

1375 *Ostrinia nubilalis* (Hb.) European Corn-borer

Recorded: 1966 – 2006
Distribution / Status: Local / Immigrant and vagrant
Conservation status: -
Caterpillar food plants: Not recorded. Elsewhere, in the lower stem of Mugwort
Flight period: Late June to early August
Records in database: 18

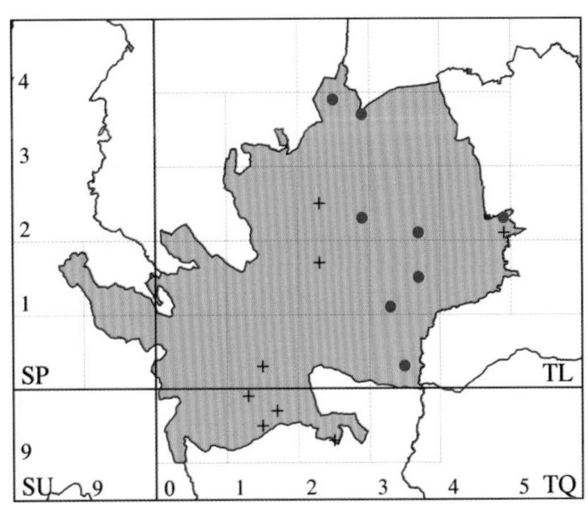

Up to the 1930s this species was known in Britain only as a very rare immigrant, but since then it has established itself in coastal areas. It was certainly established along the Essex side of the Thames Estuary by the late 1970s and it is a very common moth there today. It is difficult, therefore, to know the source of most of the recent Hertfordshire records since they may be immigrants from overseas, vagrants from the Thames or both. Our first records are from Frogmore on 25th June 1966 (Eric Bradford) and Bushey on 9th July 1966 (Barry Goater); these and possibly the next, at Stevenage on 11th June 1970 (Jack Newton), were probably immigrant examples. Moths at Welwyn in 1974 (Peter Waterton), Wall Hall on 1st July 1974 and Aldenham on 16th July 1976 (Barry Goater) and Totteridge in 1979 (Ian Lorimer) may also have originated overseas, but the 1976 record at least may have been a wanderer from the Thames (this was the hot summer). To date, we have no evidence of this species breeding in the county, though it is likely to do so.

1376 *Eurrhypara hortulata* (L.) Small Magpie

Recorded: 1888 – 2006
Distribution / Status: Ubiquitous / Abundant resident
Conservation status: No perceived threats
Caterpillar food plants: Stinging Nettle. Elsewhere, occasionally on woundwort, mint and similar plants
Flight period: Mid-May to mid-August
Records in database: 889

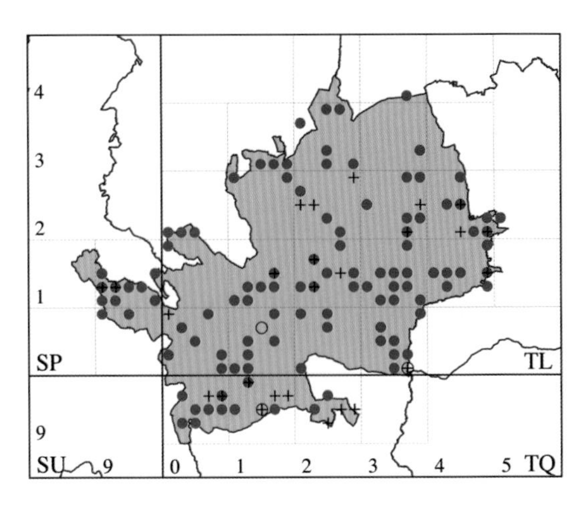

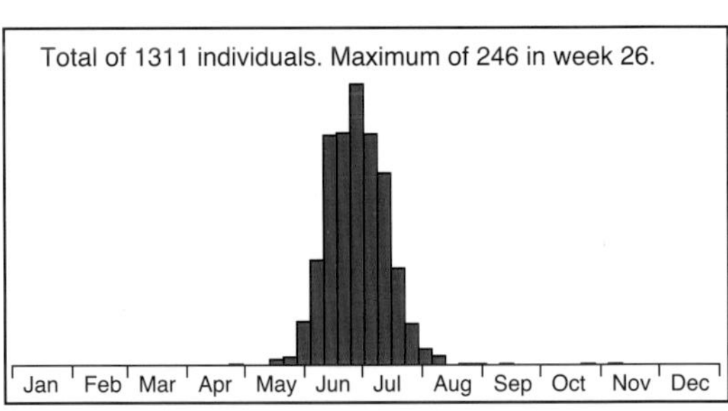

The Small Magpie is amongst the most common of Hertfordshire's moths and almost any nettle patch will support it. Seasonally late examples have appeared in the last few years, the latest being one at Baldock, found by Kerry Robinson on 8th November 1996, but these are exceptional and there is no perceptible lengthening of the flight period.

1377 *Perinephela lancealis* ([D.& S.])

Recorded: 1997 – 2006
Distribution / Status: Local / Common resident
Conservation status: Herts Scarce
Caterpillar food plants: Not recorded. Elsewhere, Wood Sage and Hemp Agrimony
Flight period: June to early August
Records in database: 20

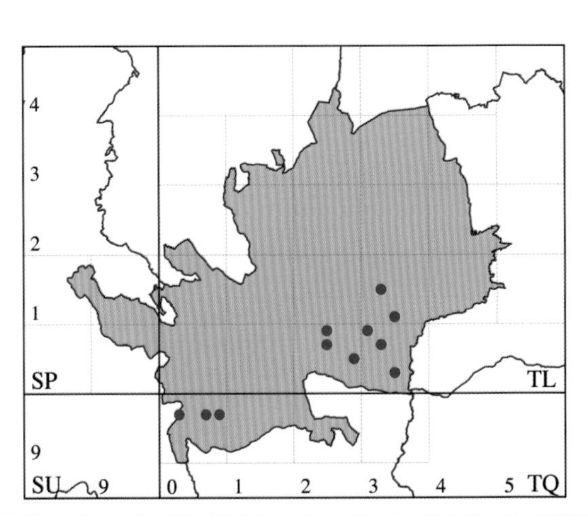

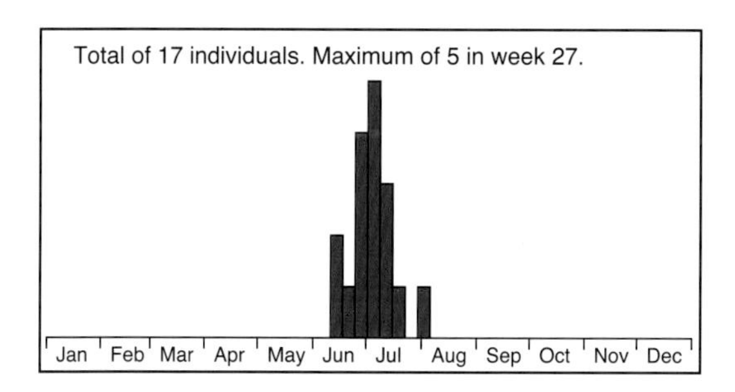

The southern woodlands of the county are the home of this moth, which is a sort of narrow-winged version of 1405: Mother of Pearl. In this habitat it is expected; elsewhere it is not, though occasional wanderers turn up in gardens near these woodland sites.

1378 *Phlyctaenia coronata* (Hufn.)

Recorded: 1890 – 2006
Distribution / Status: Widespread / Common resident
Conservation status: No perceived threats
Caterpillar food plants: Not recorded. Elsewhere, Elder, Lilac and Privet.
Flight period: Late May to mid-August
Records in database: 425

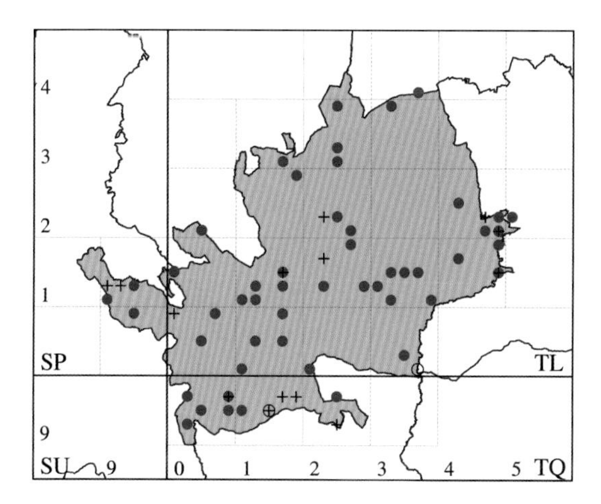

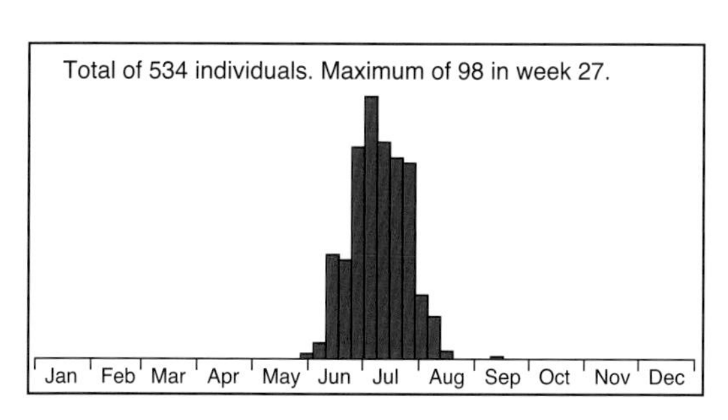

This is one of rather few insects that are able to feed on Elder, where it lives as a caterpillar in a web on the underside of a young leaf. To the uninitiated, confusion of the adult moth is possible with *Phlyctaenia stachydalis*, but this latter species is not recorded in Hertfordshire and unlikely to be present.

1380 *Phlyctaenia perlucidalis* (Hb.)

Recorded: 1990 – 2006
Distribution / Status: Local / Uncommon resident
Conservation status: No perceived threats
Caterpillar food plants: Not recorded. Elsewhere, various thistles
Flight period: June to early August
Records in database: 38

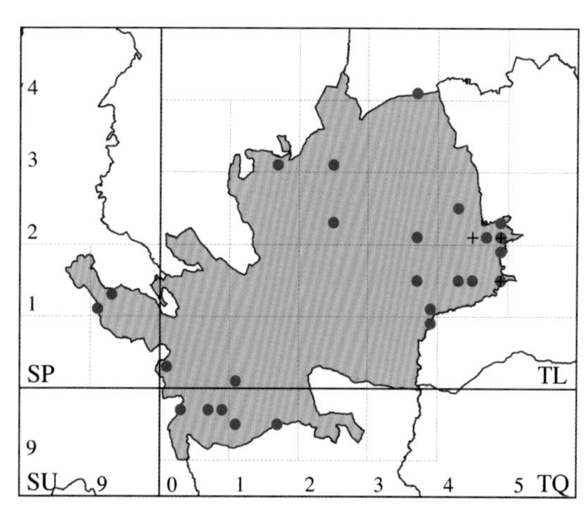

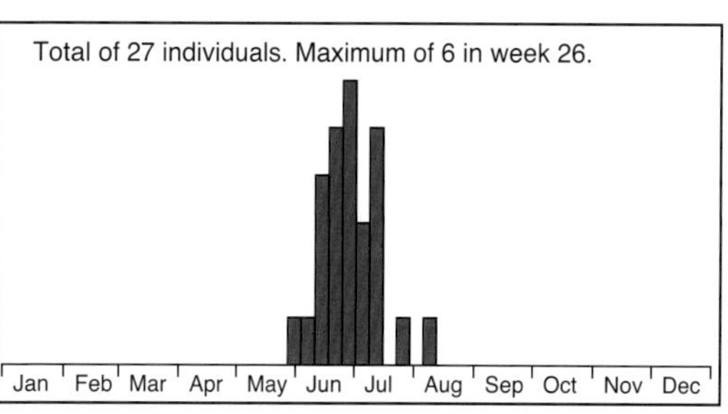

Unknown as a British species until 1951, when it was discovered at Wood Walton Fen in Huntingdonshire (Mere & Bradley, 1957), this moth was initially confined to the fens, but subsequently has spread from this focus. It was first noted in Hertfordshire by myself and Charles Watson at Stocking Wood, near Bishops Stortford, on 25th June 1990, but I also caught it in my garden in the town on 11th July 1990 and at Sawbridgeworth Marsh on 17th July 1990. At the latter site I caught several examples both then and on several later dates that year –strong evidence of a resident population that was already established. Today it is certainly resident here and since it is by no means confined to wetlands it is probably using one or more unknown foodplants. The peculiar gap in the records for central Hertfordshire, a well-recorded area, cannot yet be explained. The records in the north-east fit nicely with a range expansion that started in Fenland; it is tempting to suggest that the south-western block of map dots indicates a quite separate invasion from that direction.

1381 *Anania funebris* (Strom)

Recorded: 1901 – 1931
Distribution / Status: Absent / Former resident
Conservation status: UK BAP Priority Species. Herts Extinct
Caterpillar food plants: Not recorded. Elsewhere, on Golden Rod
Flight period: Elsewhere, June/July
Records in database: 3

(Gibbs, 1904a) lists two records of this quite unmistakeable species, from 'St Albans, 1901, new to the county, specimen now in the county museum' and 'seen but not taken in the scrub at Bricket Wood in 1903'; both records were made by Miss Alice Dickinson. Foster (1937) repeats these and adds 'Tring (Goodson)' without date; Goodson's record was probably made in the 1920s or early 1930s. There are no other records of this woodland moth in our county.

1382 *Anania verbascalis* ([D.& S.])

Recorded: 1834 – 2004
Distribution / Status: Extremely local / Rare resident
Conservation status: Herts Vulnerable
Caterpillar food plants: Not recorded. Elsewhere, Wood Sage and Mullein
Flight period: July. Elsewhere, June/July
Records in database: 2

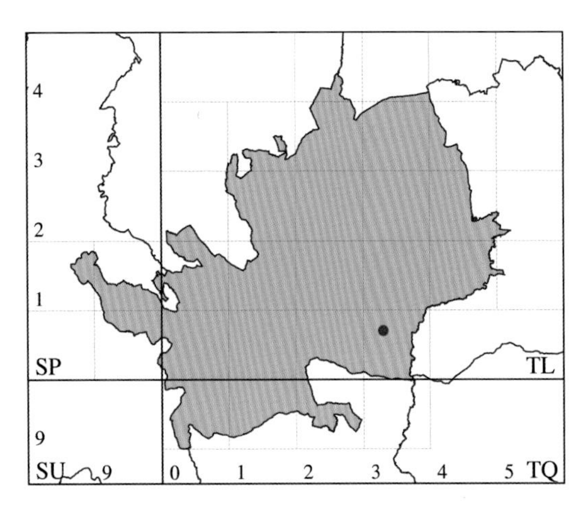

This moth was illustrated by a specimen from 'Hertford' by J. F. Stephens in his *Illustrations of British Entomology*, published in 1834. Stephens' definition of Hertford was a wide one and it is tempting to think that the actual site may have been Broxbourne Wood, where I made the only other county record of an adult at light on 15th July 2004. Wood Sage abounds in Broxbourne Wood, and throughout the entire Broxbourne Woods complex and it is probable that this moth will be found elsewhere in these woodlands. However, specific searching has failed to find it.

1385 *Ebulea crocealis* (Hb.)

Recorded:	1834 – 1989
Distribution / Status:	Extremely local or absent / Rare resident or Extinct
Conservation status:	Herts Endangered
Caterpillar food plants:	Not recorded. Elsewhere, Ploughman's Spikenard and Fleabane
Flight period:	Not recorded. Elsewhere, July/August
Records in database:	6

There are three nineteenth-century records: Stephens (1834) lists 'Hertford'; Griffith (1890) reports it from the Sandridge area and Boyd (1901) lists the Cheshunt area. None of these can be mapped accurately. More recently, we have two twentieth-century reports, from Northaw Great Wood on 17th July 1966 (Barry Goater) and my own record from Broxbourne Wood on 24th June 1989. Goater (1986) suggests that the moth prefers marshy habitats.

1386 *Opsibotys fuscalis* ([D.& S.])

Recorded:	1834 – 1834
Distribution / Status:	Absent / Former resident
Conservation status:	Herts Extinct
Caterpillar food plants:	Not recorded. Elsewhere, Yellow-rattle and Common Cow-wheat
Flight period:	Elsewhere, June
Records in database:	1

Our only record is that for 'Hertford' in J. F. Stephens *Illustrations of British Entomology* **4**: 56 (1834).

1387 *Nascia cilialis* (Hb.)

Recorded:	1976 – 2006
Distribution / Status:	Extremely local / Common resident
Conservation status:	Herts Vulnerable
Caterpillar food plants:	Not recorded. Elsewhere, Great Pond-sedge and other sedges
Flight period:	Late May to August. Elsewhere, June/July
Records in database:	11

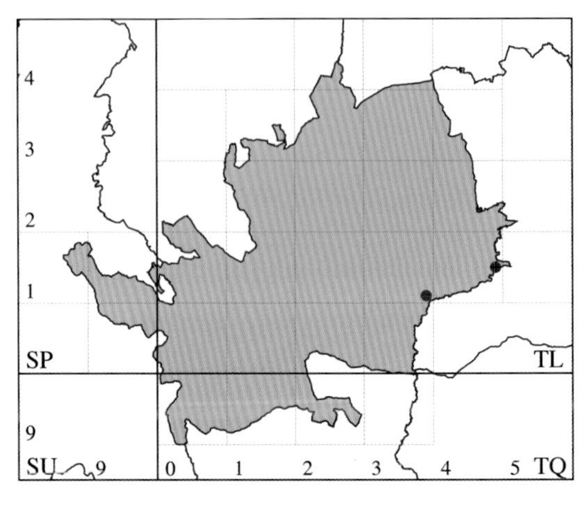

Sawbridgeworth Marsh, on the border of Hertfordshire and North Essex, supports a nationally important population of this rare moth, which until recently was confined to the fens of Cambridgeshire and Huntingdonshire; it was first found here in 1976 by David Agassiz. Rye Meads, situated where the Rivers Lea and Stort join each other, has also produced adults, though in far lower number and it is without doubt the combination of both sedge and reed beds at Sawbridgeworth Marsh that permit this species to thrive. However the population of the moth at Sawbridgeworth has certainly declined; during 1989 I caught over 300 examples in a single trap on 14th June (all released), but in subsequent years numbers overall have fallen and from 2001 to 2006 only single figures were caught on each visit. Although the caterpillar feeds on sedges, it hibernates in a papery cocoon on or within a dead reed stem and here it also pupates; there is, as a result, an obvious need for sedges and reeds not to be physically separated and although rotational cutting of reeds is perceived as an essential part of reed bed management, this is a small site and the moth is clearly at risk if the wrong patch of reed is cut during the wrong time of year. At all times, it is seen as important to retain areas where sedges and reeds adjoin or intermingle. It is also clear that burning of arisings from vegetation cutting is also a damaging activity that is likely to hasten extinction. The Essex Wildlife Trust, who are responsible for the management of Sawbridgeworth Marsh, have recently devised a cutting regime that is specifically designed to encourage the recovery of the population of this moth. The Herts Moth Group hopes to be able to continue the long-term monitoring of the population and offer advice as appropriate.

1388 *Udea lutealis* (Hb.)

Recorded:	1834 – 2005
Distribution / Status:	Local / Rare resident
Conservation status:	Herts Vulnerable
Caterpillar food plants:	Not recorded. Elsewhere, polyphagous on herbaceous plants
Flight period:	Mid-July to mid-August
Records in database:	44

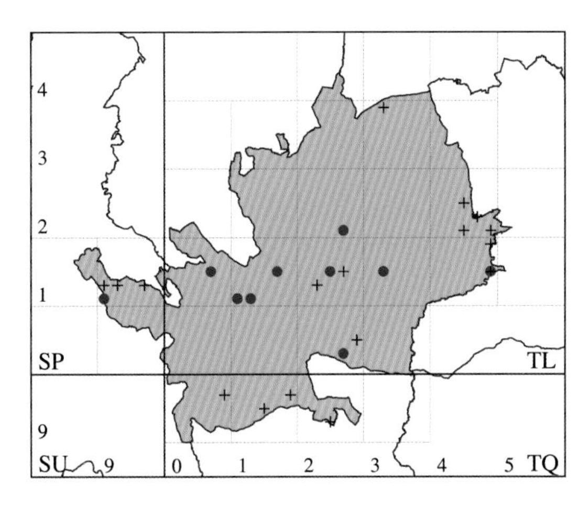

The pattern of distribution shows an apparent loss from areas where this species was formerly found; this loss is regarded as real. Taken with a marked decrease in numbers since the 1980s it is clear that this species is in decline in Hertfordshire. It used to be found on brownfield sites, field edges and other ruderal habitats.

1390 *Udea prunalis* ([D.& S.])

Recorded: 1901 – 2006
Distribution / Status: Widespread / Common resident
Conservation status: No perceived threats
Caterpillar food plants: Not recorded. Elsewhere, polyphagous on herbaceous plants, trees and bushes
Flight period: Mid-June to early August
Records in database: 292

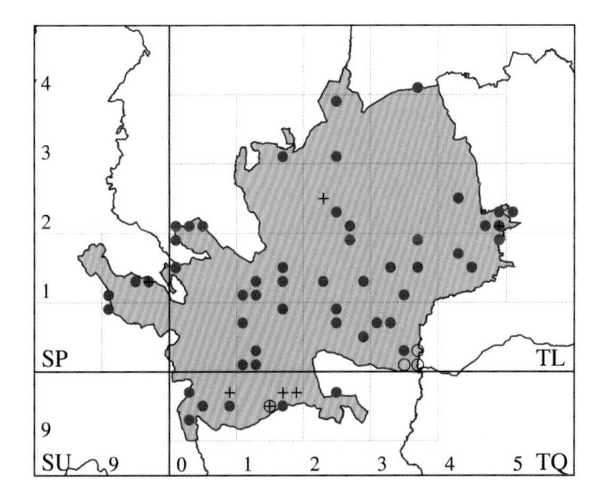

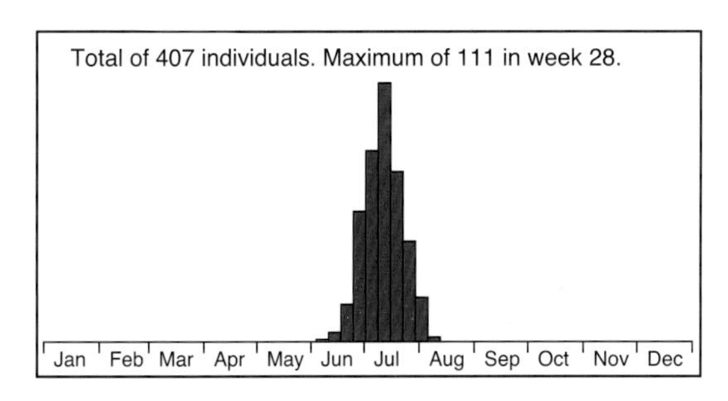

This moth starts to peak in numbers as 1392: *Udea olivalis* is mid-way through its decline and though there is an overlap zone, in most individual years this is very narrow. In spite of being a common species we have no breeding records for the county.

1392 *Udea olivalis* ([D.& S.])

Recorded: 1885 – 2006
Distribution / Status: Ubiquitous / Abundant resident
Conservation status: No perceived threats
Caterpillar food plants: Not recorded. Elsewhere, polyphagous on herbaceous plants
Flight period: Later May to July
Records in database: 604

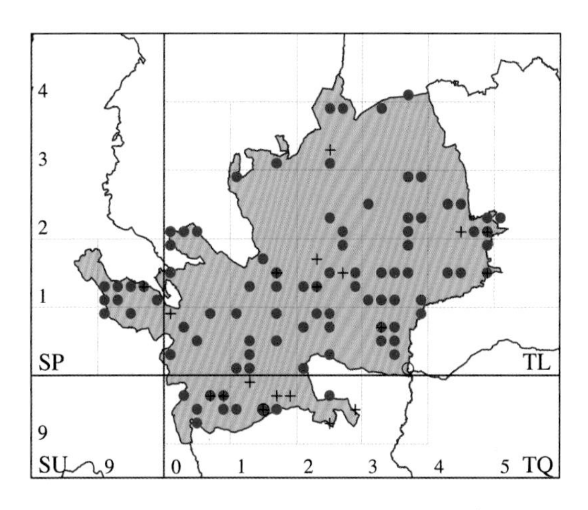

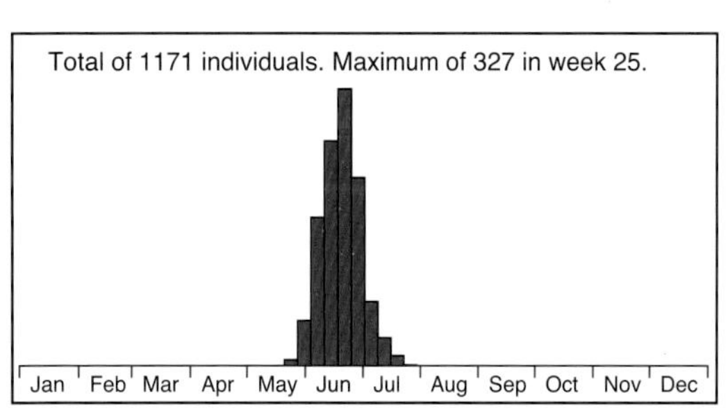

There can be few gardens that do not boast this very common moth on their lists, but as for the previous species we seem to have no data on Hertfordshire foodplants.

1395 *Udea ferrugalis* (Hb.) Rusty-dot Pearl

Recorded: 1890 – 2006
Distribution / Status: Local / Immigrant. Perhaps temporary resident
Conservation status: No perceived threats
Caterpillar food plants: Not recorded. Elsewhere, polyphagous on herbaceous plants
Flight period: May/June; August/September; October/November in three distinct 'generations'
Records in database: 106

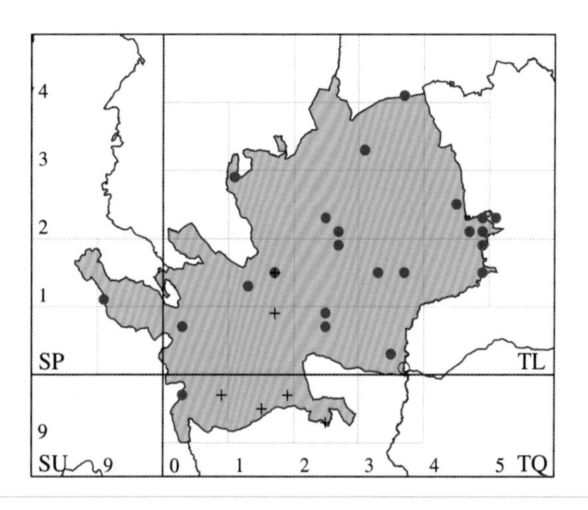

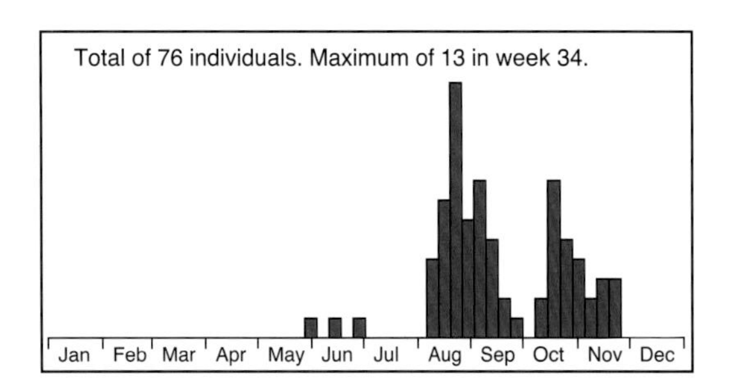

Gibbs (1904a) lists one on the window of the taxidermist's room [at Tring Museum] on 10th November 1903, collected by A. L. Goodson, and adds that it has only previously been taken at Sandridge [Griffith] and Cheshunt [Boyd]. Foster (1937) lists only these three records and there are no more until one at Watford in November 1956 (Ray Penrose). In recent years we record small numbers in almost every year and these are presumed to be immigrants from overseas, though there is some evidence nationally that it has become resident and is perhaps on the way to becoming established. The Hertfordshire records are all of adults and larvae have not been found. These adults form two distinct peaks in August/September and October/November as the chart shows clearly and there are three records in earlier months, at Bushey on 26th May 1966 (Barry Goater), at Friars Wood, on 28th May 2005 (John Chainey) and my own from Astonbury Wood, on 16th June 2003.

1398 *Nomophila noctuella* ([D.& S.]) Rush Veneer

Recorded:	1867 – 2006
Distribution / Status:	Random / Immigrant
Conservation status:	-
Caterpillar food plants:	Not recorded. Elsewhere, on clovers and grasses
Flight period:	June to November
Records in database:	378

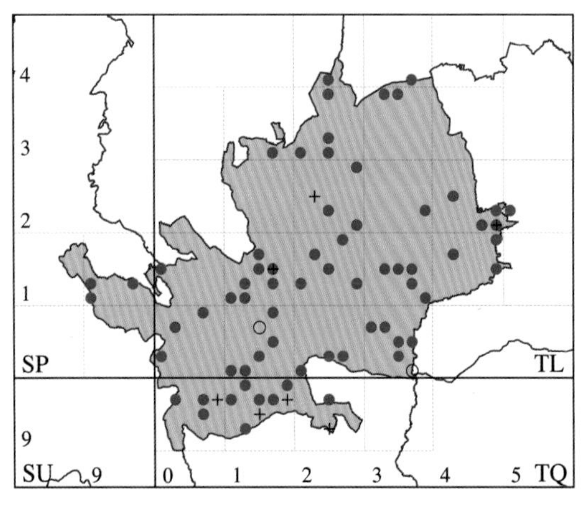

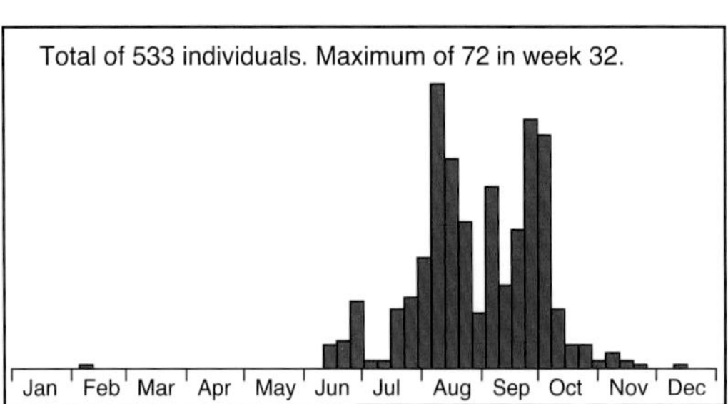

Our earliest report is from Cheshunt in 1867 (Boyd, *Entomologist's Monthly Magazine* **4**: 286). At this date, the concept of migration in insects was unheard of, but we now know that this species is present almost exclusively as a primary immigrant. The chart shows three peaks, in late June, in mid-August and in early October. The latter peak is likely to be formed entirely by immigrant moths, but those arriving earlier in the year might produce larvae and a second generation of adults to help create the August peak. One at light in Hertford on 6th February 2003 (Andrew Wood) is especially early/late, but coincides with local sightings of Silver Y and a Humming-bird Hawk moth at the same general time – all part of a massive winter immigration of moths to the south of Britain. There is no evidence to date of Rush Veneer moths surviving the winter in Hertfordshire.

1400 *Antigastra catalaunalis* (Dup.)

Recorded:	1867 only
Distribution / Status:	Random / Former immigrant
Conservation status:	-
Caterpillar food plants:	Not recorded in Britain
Flight period:	Elsewhere, August to October
Records in database:	1

One captured by W. C. Boyd at Cheshunt on 18th September 1867 was the first British record of this species (see Stainton, 1867: *Entomologist's Monthly Magazine* **4**: 152). The record is repeated in Knaggs (*Ent. Annual* **1868**: 108 – 109). There are no other Hertfordshire records of what is a very rare immigrant nationally.

1401 *Maruca vitrata* (Fabr.) Mung Moth = *testulalis* (Geyer)

Recorded:	2003 only
Distribution / Status:	Local / Accidental import
Conservation status:	-
Caterpillar food plants:	Imported French Beans
Flight period:	-
Records in database:	1

A larva was found by John Webb in imported pods of French Beans at his Hitchin greengrocery shop during late May 2003. The beans had been 'topped and tailed' before importation. The adult was reared on 26th June 2003 after pupating between sheets of tissue and is now preserved in my own collection.

1403 *Diasemiopsis ramburialis* (Dup.)

Recorded:	1963 only
Distribution / Status:	Random / Extremely rare immigrant
Conservation status:	-
Caterpillar food plants:	Not recorded in Britain
Flight period:	Elsewhere, June to October
Records in database:	1

This rare moth is known in Britain only as an immigrant and there is no evidence of it breeding here. One was captured at Arkley by T. G. Howarth on 21st September 1961 (*Entomologist's Record* **73**: 241); the same record was reported for the wrong date in *Entomologist* **96**: 38, where it is given as 22nd – the morning after. This is our only record.

1403a *Duponchelia fovealis* Zell.

Recorded:	2001 – 2006
Distribution / Status:	Random / -
Conservation status:	No perceived threats
Caterpillar food plants:	Not recorded in Britain
Flight period:	July and October
Records in database:	3

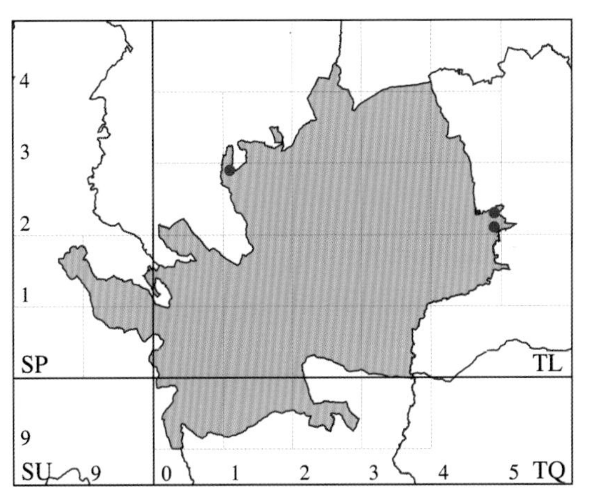

We have three records of this rare immigrant. It was added to the county list by me at Hexton Chalk Pit on 20th October 2001 and subsequently I caught a second example in my garden in Bishops Stortford on 31st July 2004. Elsewhere in the same town, James Fish and Julian Reeves mustered a third at their shared garden trap on 21st October 2006.

1405 *Pleuroptya ruralis* (Scop.) Mother of Pearl

Recorded: 1890 – 2006
Distribution / Status: Ubiquitous / Abundant resident
Conservation status: No perceived threats
Caterpillar food plants: Stinging Nettle
Flight period: Late June to early September
Records in database: 944

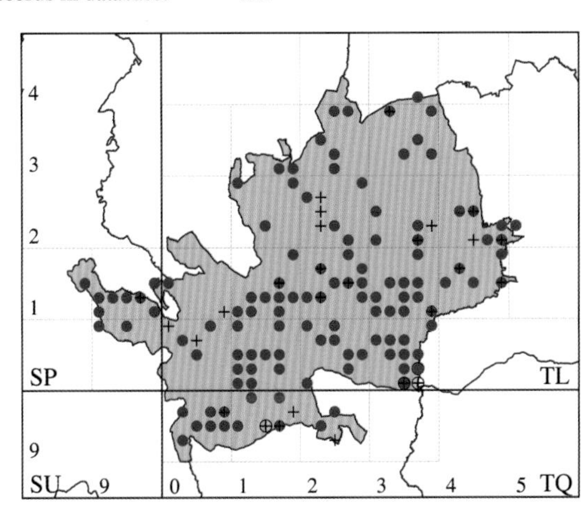

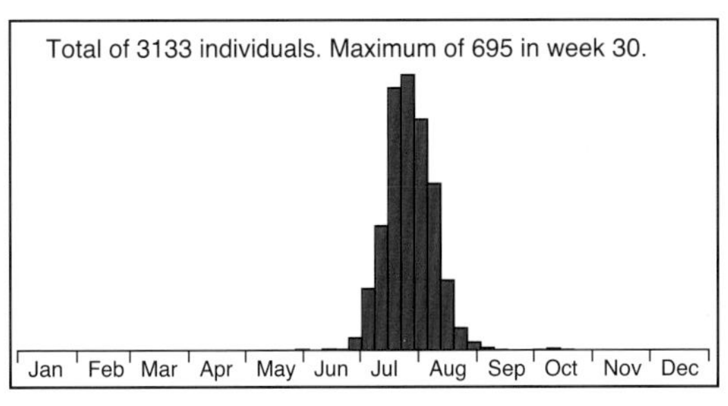

There can be few places in Hertfordshire that do not support this abundant moth, whose colloquial name derives from the reflective pattern of the upper surface of the wings.

1408 *Palpita vitrealis* (Rossi) = *unionalis* (Hb.)

Recorded: 1959 – 2006
Distribution / Status: Random / Rare immigrant
Conservation status: -
Caterpillar food plants: Not recorded in Britain
Flight period: August to October
Records in database: 4

One was taken at light in Arkley by T. G. Howarth, on 11th October 1959 (Bell, 1961) at a time of much migrant activity. Subsequently, Raymond Uffen caught one at light in Welwyn on 6th August 1982, Andrew Wood caught another in Bengeo, Hertford, on 3rd September 2006 and James Fish and Julian Reeves trapped another in their shared garden trap in Bishops Stortford on 10th October 2006. Most British examples probably originate in Spain or North Africa.

PYRALIDAE

PYRALINAE

1413 *Hypsopygia costalis* (Fabr.) Gold Triangle

Recorded: 1834 – 2006
Distribution / Status: Ubiquitous / Common resident
Conservation status: No perceived threats
Caterpillar food plants: Not recorded. Elsewhere, dry vegetable matter
Flight period: June to October in two generations
Records in database: 414

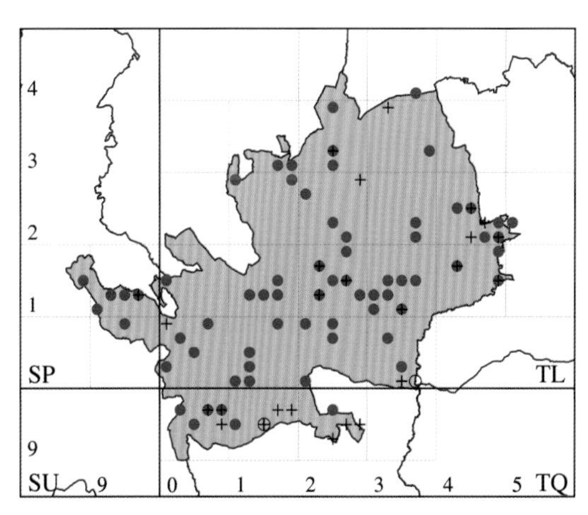

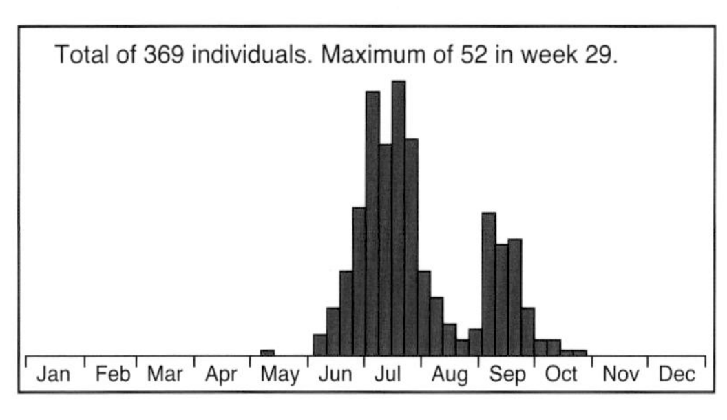

From 1834 to the present day this has been a common Hertfordshire moth. In contrast to the statement in the standard work of Goater (1986) that it is single-brooded, it is evident that it is now double-brooded in Hertfordshire.

1414 *Synaphe punctalis* (Fabr.)

Recorded: 1997 only
Distribution / Status: Local / Vagrant
Conservation status: -
Caterpillar food plants: Not recorded. Elsewhere, on mosses, including *Hypnum cupressiforme*
Flight period: Elsewhere, July/August
Records in database: 1

Our only record is from Marshall's Heath in 1997 (John Murray); the moth was presumably a vagrant from Breckland or some other area of East Anglia where there are resident populations.

1415 *Orthopygia glaucinalis* (L.)

Recorded: 1834 - 2006
Distribution / Status: Widespread / Common resident
Conservation status: No perceived threats
Caterpillar food plants: Not recorded. Elsewhere, dead and decaying vegetable matter
Flight period: June to mid-August then September to early November in two generations
Records in database: 206

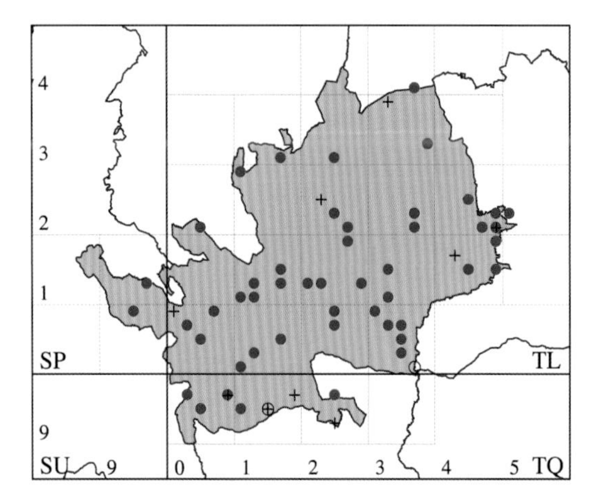

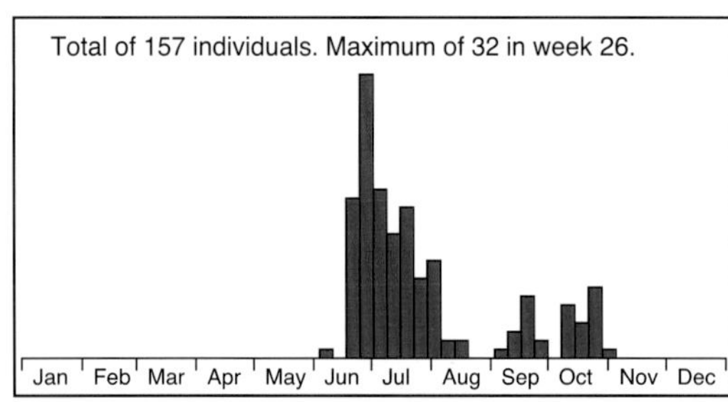

As with 1413: Gold Triangle, this species now shows two clear generations of adults each year rather than the one which it has traditionally produced.

1417 *Pyralis farinalis* (L.)

Recorded: 1885 - 2006
Distribution / Status: Local / Common resident
Conservation status: No perceived threats
Caterpillar food plants: Not recorded. Elsewhere, stored cereals, often feeding for two years
Flight period: Late May to October
Records in database: 139

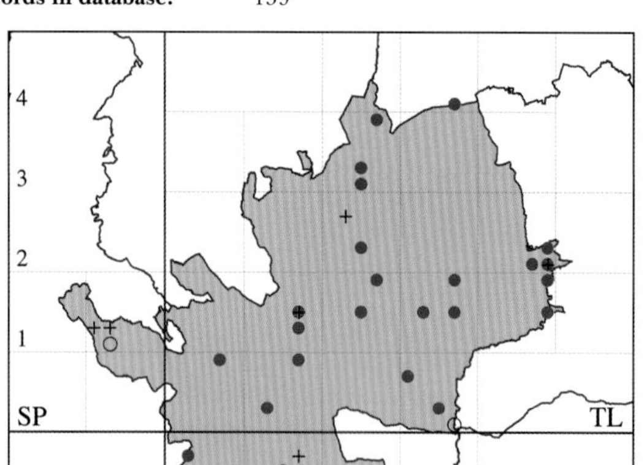

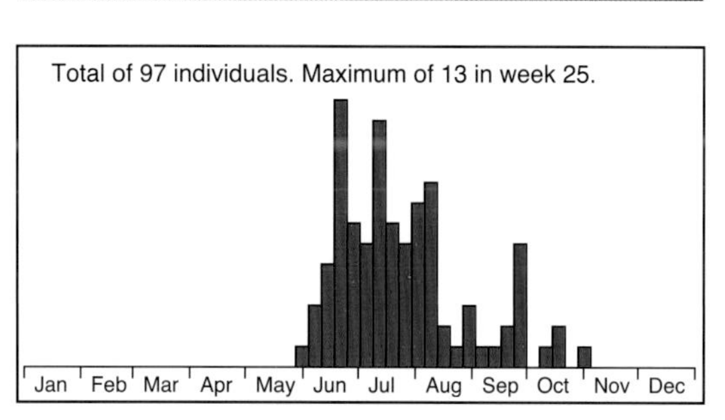

Most reports of adults relate in some way to individuals that were probably reared indoors, in which category I include records from domestic gardens in towns; this probably accounts for the long adult flight period. As a wild insect, the moth has declined considerably as a result of modern farming methods in relation to grain production and also, undoubtedly, to the great reduction in the number of fields still actually in grain production.

1420 *Aglossa caprealis* (Hb.) Small Tabby

Recorded: 1834 - 1937
Distribution / Status: Absent / Former resident
Conservation status: Herts Extinct
Caterpillar food plants: Not recorded. Elsewhere, dried grasses (hay, chaff etc) and grass seed – often feeding for two years
Flight period: Elsewhere, July
Records in database: 5

Our records are from the Hertford area (Stephens, 1834), the Sandridge area (Griffith, 1890), the Cheshunt area (Boyd, 1901) and East Barnet (Gillum, in Foster, 1937); none can be mapped accurately. Bernard Skinner has one further record included in the card-index of immigrant moths that he maintains for the national record, from St. Albans 'under straw litter in a box' on 31st July 1934 (reported by Mark Parsons). Modern farming methods and the lack of poorly-maintained thatched roofs are probably the two main reasons for the decline and loss of this moth from the Hertfordshire fauna.

1421 *Aglossa pinguinalis* (L.) Large Tabby

Recorded: 1885 - 2006
Distribution / Status: Local / Uncommon resident
Conservation status: Insufficiently known
Caterpillar food plants: Not recorded. Elsewhere, vegetable refuse and animal dung
Flight period: June/July
Records in database: 47

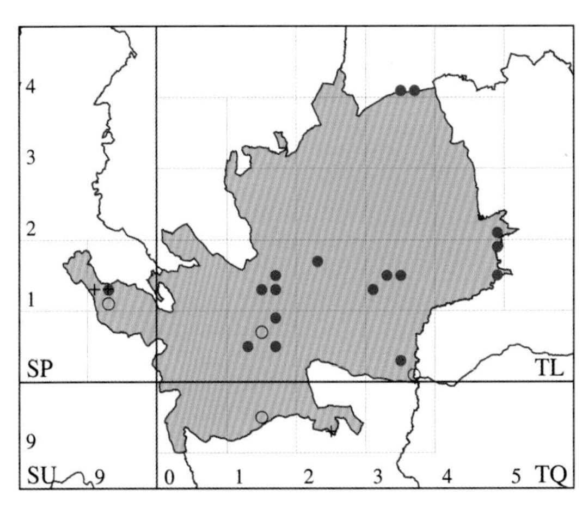

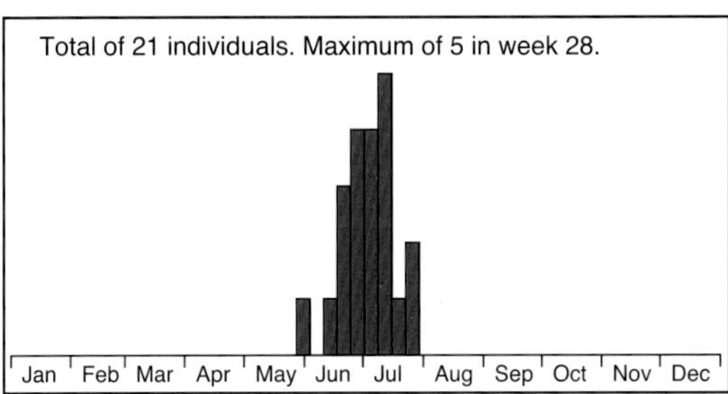

Usually, this moth is rather scarce and very local in its distribution, but during 2005 and 2006 there was an unexpected flurry of reliable records backed by specimens or photographs. Thirty-five of the 47 county records have been made during the period 2000 to 2006 and the moth is evidently increasing at the moment.

1424 *Endotricha flammealis* ([D.& S.])

Recorded:	1890 – 2006
Distribution / Status:	Ubiquitous / Abundant resident
Conservation status:	No perceived threats
Caterpillar food plants:	Not recorded. Elsewhere, polyphagous on herbaceous plants and trees
Flight period:	Mid-June to mid-August
Records in database:	675

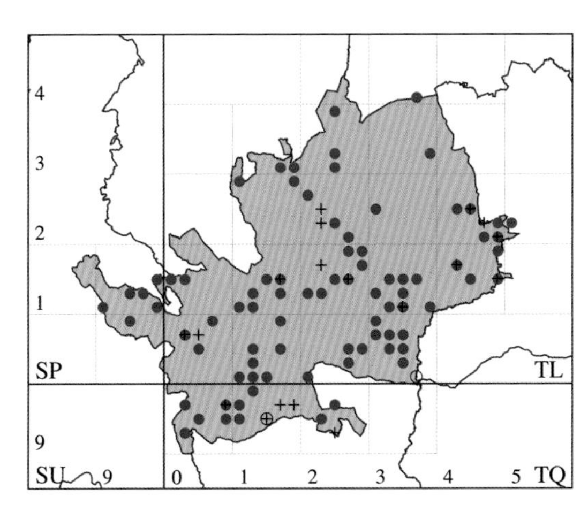

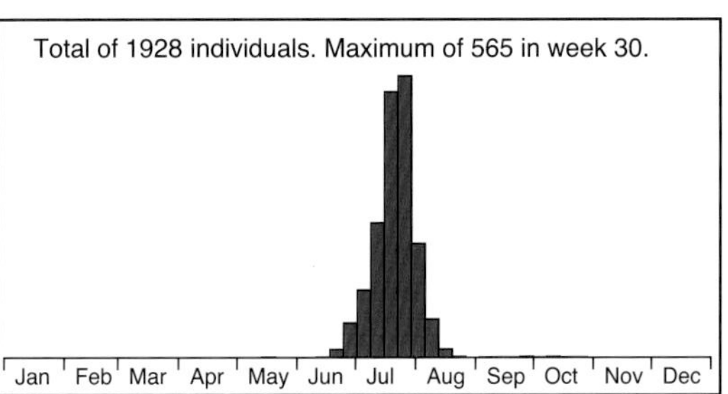

This is another common and widespread moth for which we have absolutely no information on foodplant or other larval requirements in Hertfordshire.

GALLERIINAE

1425 *Galleria mellonella* (L.) Wax Moth

Recorded:	1885 – 2006
Distribution / Status:	Widespread / Common resident
Conservation status:	Pest species
Caterpillar food plants:	Honeycomb – in wild bee nests and bee-hives
Flight period:	June to October
Records in database:	131

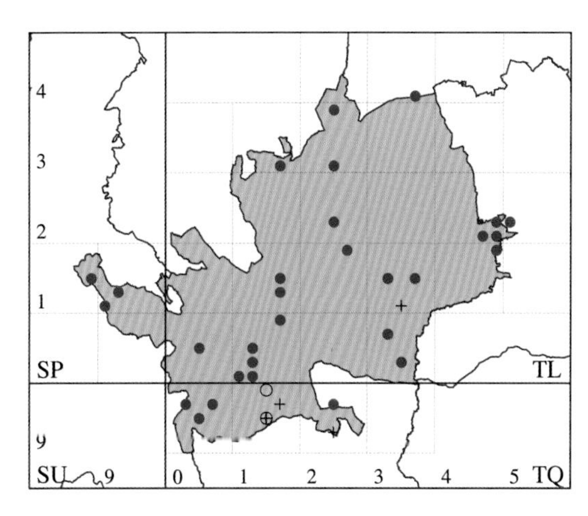

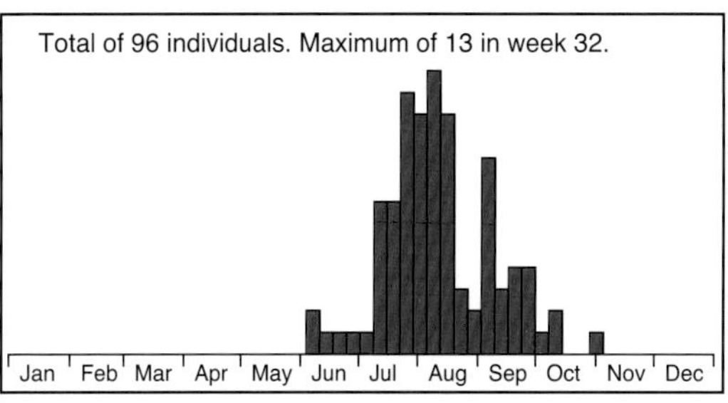

Though rather widespread, the moth is nevertheless somewhat local in its distribution in the county. A good many records are made in areas devoid of bee hives and there can be so doubt that either the moth is surviving on feral Honey Bee nests or else it is invading the nests of one or more species of bumble bee.

1426 *Achroia grisella* (Fabr.) Lesser Wax Moth

Recorded:	1868 – 2006
Distribution / Status:	Widespread / Common resident
Conservation status:	No perceived threats
Caterpillar food plants:	Honeycomb – in wild bee nests and bee-hives
Flight period:	July/August
Records in database:	23

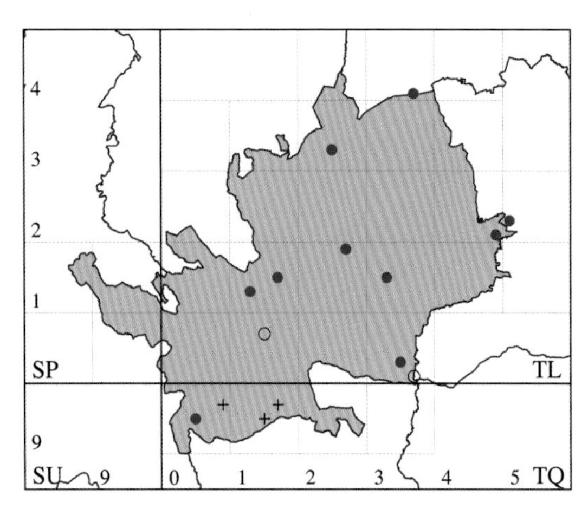

First recorded in the county at Cheshunt in 1868 (Boyd, *Entomologist's Monthly Magazine* **5**: 147) this rather uninteresting looking little moth wreaks havoc in bee hives and is perhaps not able to adapt to wild bees. If this is so, it may account for its scarcity, as bee-keepers tend to destroy it on sight. Slender evidence for this is the greater abundance of 1428: Bee Moth, whose preferences are exactly the reverse.

1428 *Aphomia sociella* (L.) Bee Moth

Recorded:	1885 – 2006
Distribution / Status:	Widespread / Common resident
Conservation status:	No perceived threats
Caterpillar food plants:	On the comb of bumble bee *Bombus terrestris*. Elsewhere, apparently preferring bumble bees over hive bees
Flight period:	May to July
Records in database:	649

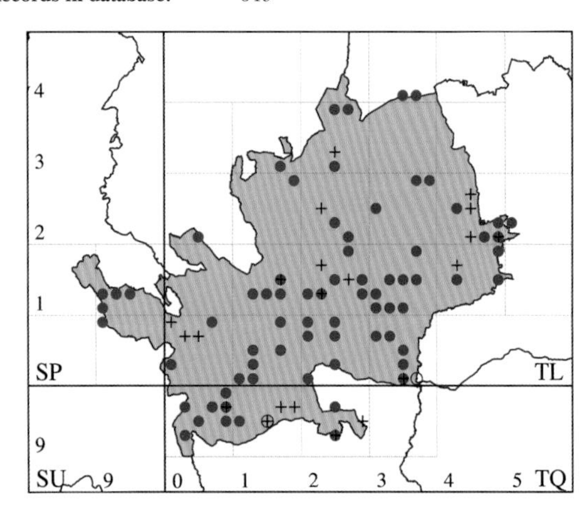

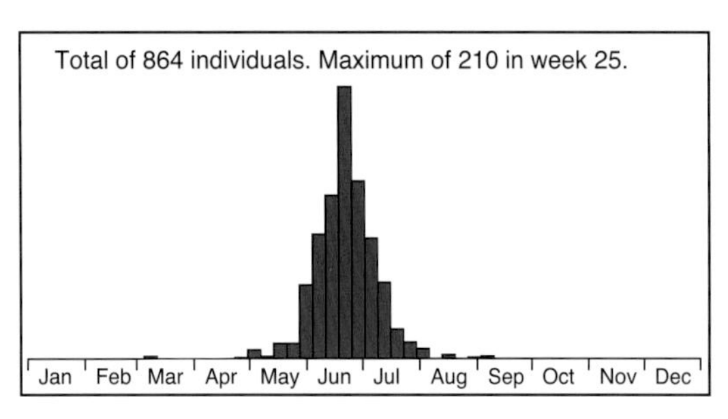

The fact that this species prefers nests of bumble bees over hive bee nests as a breeding place probably accounts for its comparative success as it is not usually in a position to be eradicated by bee-keepers.

[1430 *Paralipsa gularis* (Zell.) Stored Nut Moth

A record for Watford in August 1962 is considered to result from an identification error.]

PHYCITINAE

1433 *Cryptoblabes bistriga* (Haw.)

Recorded:	1931 – 2004
Distribution / Status:	Local / Uncommon resident
Conservation status:	Herts Scarce
Caterpillar food plants:	Not recorded. Elsewhere, oak
Flight period:	June/July
Records in database:	9

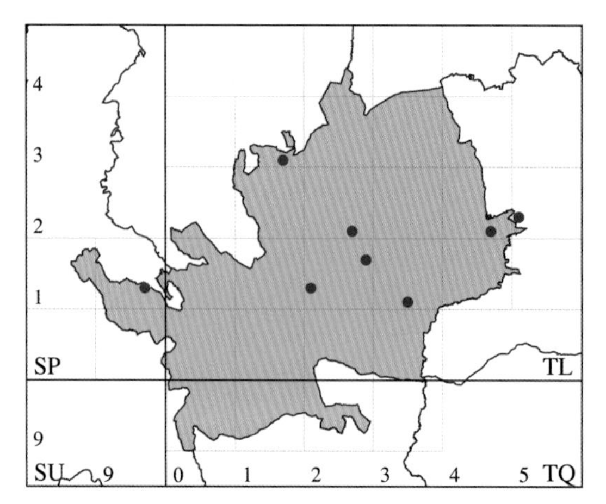

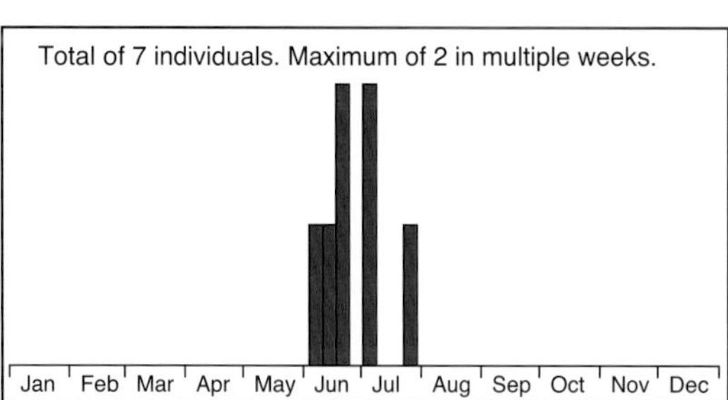

The distribution pattern of this moth is surprising. It is a rather local species of oak woodland, but the best oak woods in Hertfordshire lie in the south of the county where the moth appears to be absent; a distribution more like that of 1449: *Elegia similella* was expected. I have seen many of the moths and so misidentification can be ruled out, at least in most cases. Beginners may perhaps confuse worn examples with some of the *Ephestia* species, but this does not seem to be the case here.

1434 *Cryptoblabes gnidiella* (Mill.)

Recorded:	1968 – 1972
Distribution / Status:	Random / Introduced with produce
Conservation status:	-
Caterpillar food plants:	Imported Pomegranate
Flight period:	-
Records in database:	2

Our two records are both from Borehamwood, in 1968 and 1972 (Eric Bradford) the latter bred from a Pomegranate.

1436 *Conobathra repandana* (Fabr.)

Recorded: 1890 – 2006
Distribution / Status: Widespread / Common resident
Conservation status: No perceived threats
Caterpillar food plants: Not recorded. Elsewhere, oak, usually high up
Flight period: Mid-June to early September
Records in database: 156

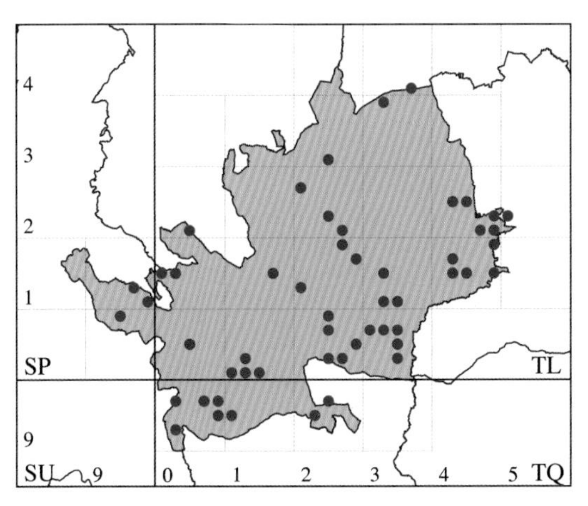

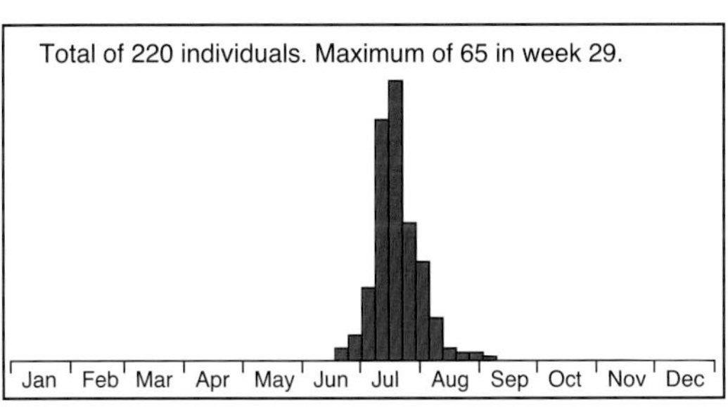

This is one of the most frequent phycitine pyralids in Hertfordshire moth traps and is usually numerically common. Apart from being attracted to light it is easily disturbed from oak branches by day.

1437 *Acrobasis consociella* (Hb.)

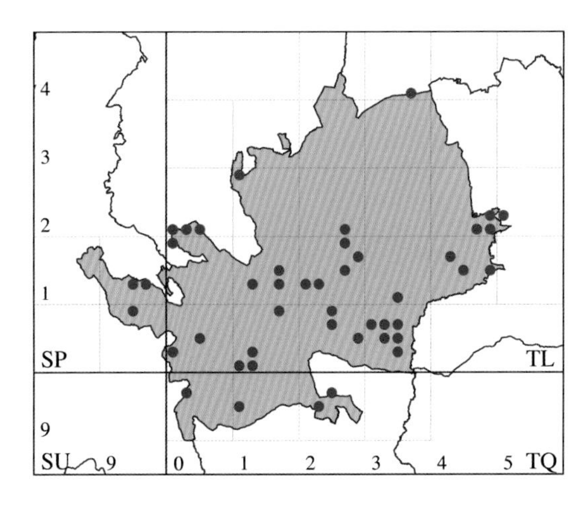

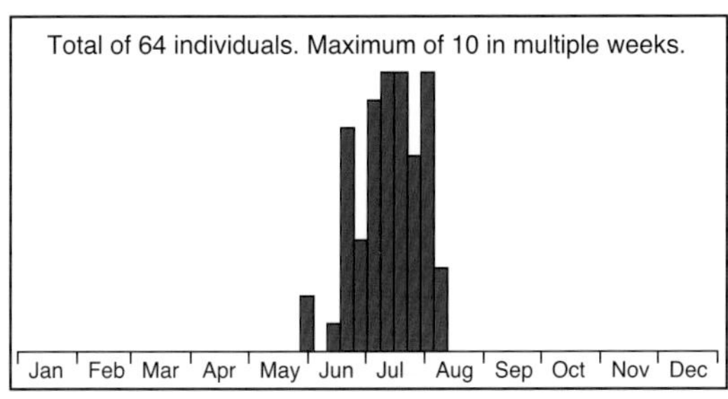

Recorded: 1890 – 2006
Distribution / Status: Widespread / Common resident
Conservation status: No perceived threats
Caterpillar food plants: Hornbeam. Elsewhere, oak, preferring saplings
Flight period: Mid-June to mid-August
Records in database: 79

The early peak in the flight chart relates to one in Mark Cooper's garden light trap at Cheshunt on 31st May 2005; Mark was also responsible for the rearing record on Hornbeam. The moth is widespread and common, but less often seen than the last species.

1438 *Trachycera suavella* (Zinck.)

Recorded: 1901 – 2006
Distribution / Status: Widespread / Uncommon resident
Conservation status: No perceived threats
Caterpillar food plants: Not recorded. Elsewhere, Blackthorn
Flight period: July/August
Records in database: 18

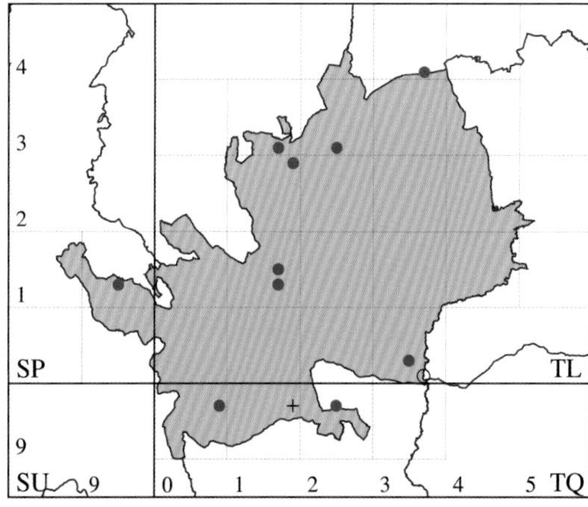

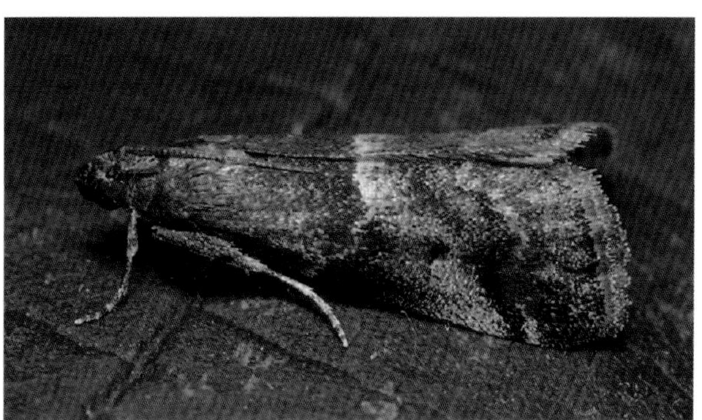

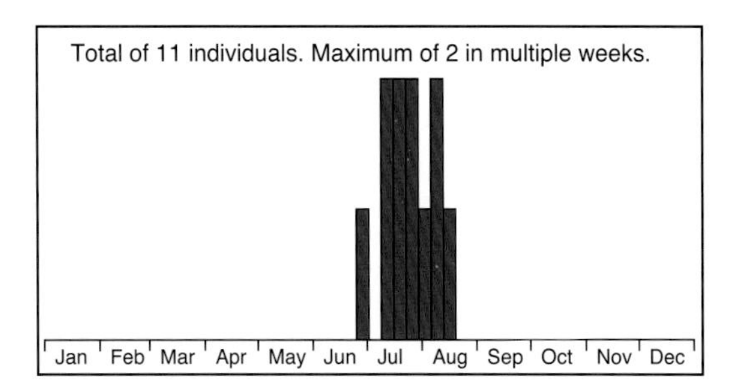

The three *Trachycera* species (called *Numonia* species in older books), often present difficulty to the inexperienced observer, though with care all can be separated confidently in the field. Compared with 1439: *Trachycera advenella* this species is rather local and uncommon here, though it is perhaps under-recorded.

1439 *Trachycera advenella* (Zinck.)

Recorded:	1890 – 2006
Distribution / Status:	Widespread / Common resident
Conservation status:	No perceived threats
Caterpillar food plants:	Common Hawthorn
Flight period:	Late June to early September
Records in database:	197

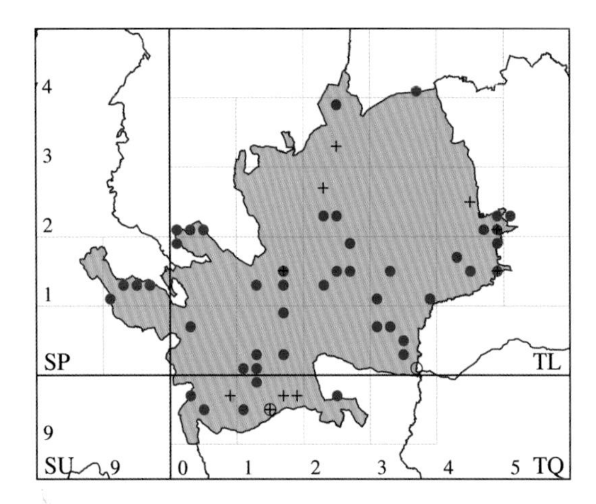

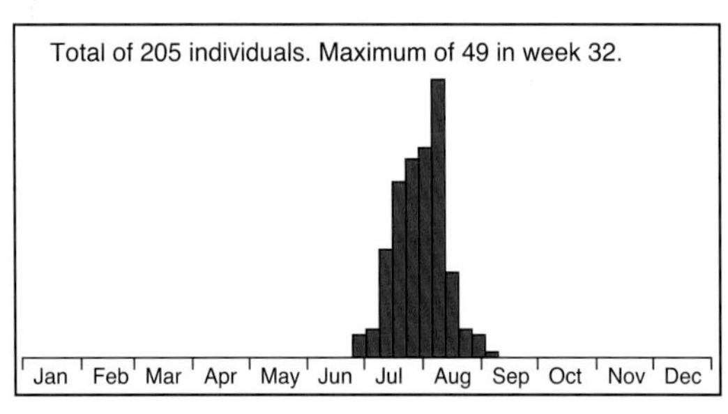

This is amongst the commonest pyralid moths in Hertfordshire, but it often arrives in a worn state and is either not recognised or ignored by those who only look at 'macros'. Larvae were found on a hawthorn hedge in Bishops Stortford in 2002, spinning flowers together in a loose mass and feeding from within; adults were later reared.

1440 *Trachycera marmorea* (Haw.)

Recorded:	1890 – 2005
Distribution / Status:	Local / Uncommon resident
Conservation status:	Herts Scarce
Caterpillar food plants:	Not recorded. Elsewhere, Blackthorn, occasionally hawthorn
Flight period:	Late June to early September
Records in database:	11

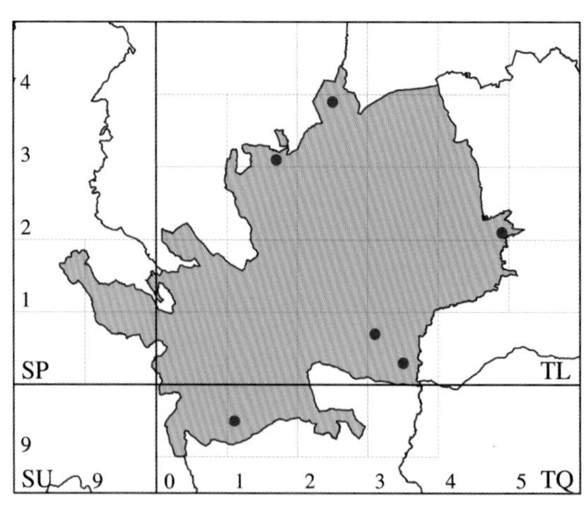

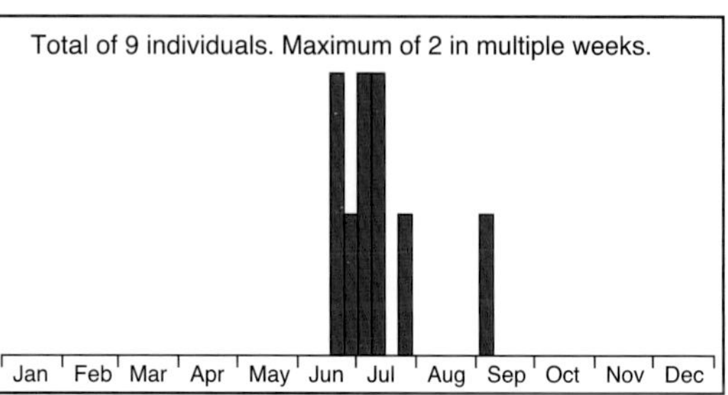

This least frequently encountered of the *Trachycera* species is perhaps genuinely scarce in Hertfordshire. Given its preferred foodplant, that is a surprise although the moth is rather local across all of its range in England and Wales.

1441 *Oncocera semirubella* (Scop.)

Recorded:	1834 only
Distribution / Status:	Absent / Possible former resident
Conservation status:	Herts Extinct
Caterpillar food plants:	Not recorded. Elsewhere, Bird's-foot Trefoil and White clover
Flight period:	Elsewhere, June/July
Records in database:	1

The only claim that this pretty moth has to Hertfordshire status is its illustration by J. F. Stephens from a 'Hertford' specimen in *Illustrations of British Entomology* **4**: 314 (published in 1834). The record given by Parsons (1993) for the pre-1970 period relates to the same source.

1445 *Pempelia formosa* (Haw.)

Recorded:	1897 – 1999
Distribution / Status:	Very local / Rare resident
Conservation status:	Herts Rare
Caterpillar food plants:	Not recorded. Elsewhere, elm, especially in hedges
Flight period:	June. Elsewhere, June to August
Records in database:	8

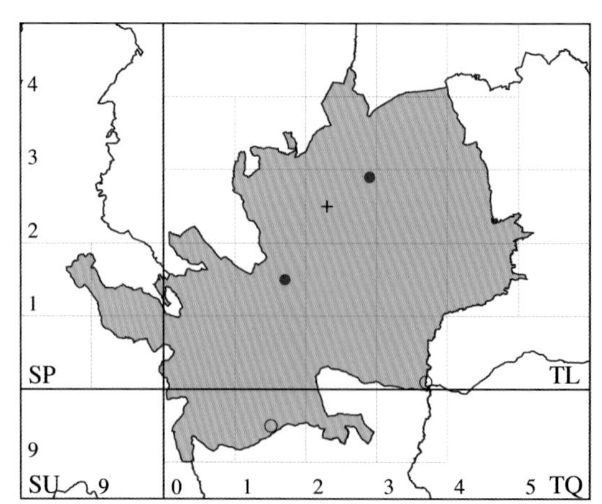

It is tempting to suggest that the 1970s epidemic outbreak of Dutch Elm Disease caused the decline of this species in Hertfordshire, where it is now rather rare. Regrettably, we have insufficient historical records to know – the need for continuous recording of moths, and other wildlife, year on year is clear from this!

1449 *Elegia similella* (Zinck.) = *Microthrix similella* (Zinck.)

Recorded:	1977 – 2006
Distribution / Status:	Local / Common resident
Conservation status:	No perceived threats
Caterpillar food plants:	Not recorded. Elsewhere, oaks – usually high up
Flight period:	June/July
Records in database:	24

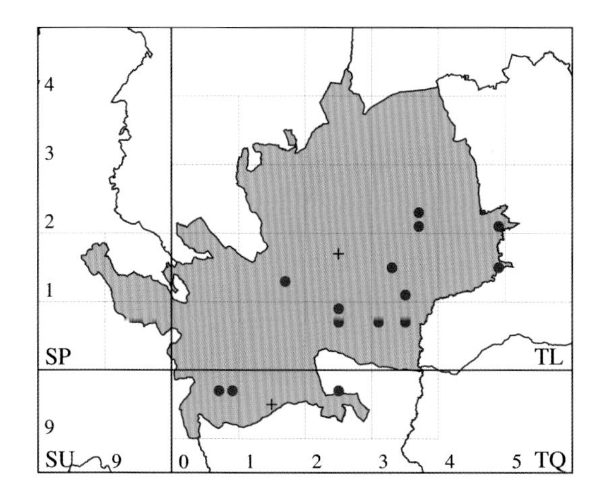

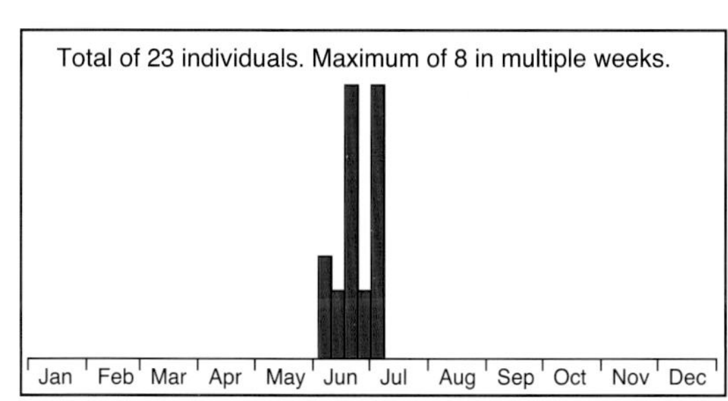

The trick of finding this moth is to get high up in an oak tree; moth traps on the observation/deer-shooting platforms built in oak trees in woodlands should be tried, but the moth can also be beaten from branches that are accessible from these raised vantage points. It is likely to be found in number wherever there are semi-mature or mature oak trees in a woodland setting.

1450 *Ortholepis betulae* (Goeze) = *Metriostola betulae* (Goeze)

Recorded:	1890 – 1937
Distribution / Status:	Absent / Possible former resident
Conservation status:	Herts Extinct
Caterpillar food plants:	Not recorded. Elsewhere, birch
Flight period:	Not recorded. Elsewhere, July
Records in database:	3

Griffith (1890) records this species for the Sandridge area, but we cannot tell exactly where it was found. Later it is recorded from Bushey Heath during 1902 by P. J. Barraud. There do not appear to be any other Hertfordshire records of this species, which frequents birches growing on sandy heaths.

1451 *Pyla fusca* (Haw.)

Recorded:	1902 – 2005
Distribution / Status:	Local / Uncommon resident
Conservation status:	No perceived threats
Caterpillar food plants:	Not recorded. Elsewhere, on species of *Erica* and *Vaccinium*
Flight period:	July to September. Elsewhere, June to August
Records in database:	9

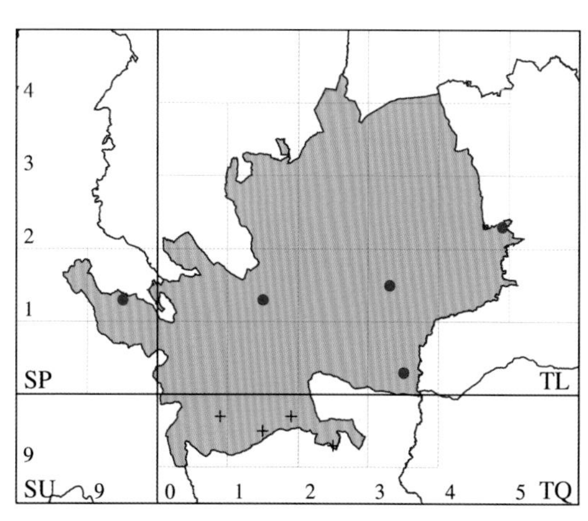

Goater (1986) gives the flight period as June and July, but the species was added to the Hertfordshire fauna by A. E. Gibbs from Bricket Wood, in September 1902 (Barraud, 1903) and we have two September records in more recent years, at Hertford on 28th September 2004 (Andrew Wood) and at Harpenden on 1st September 2005 (Phil Gould). Thus, the moth appears to be double-brooded here. It is worth emphasising that confusion is possible with adults of 1450: *Ortholepis betulae*, though that does not fly in September either.

1452 *Phycita roborella* ([D.& S.])

Recorded:	1885 – 2006
Distribution / Status:	Widespread / Common resident
Conservation status:	No perceived threats
Caterpillar food plants:	Not recorded. Elsewhere, oak
Flight period:	July/August
Records in database:	168

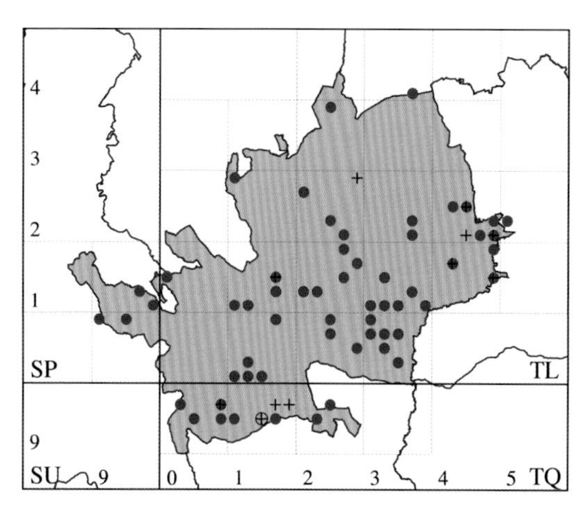

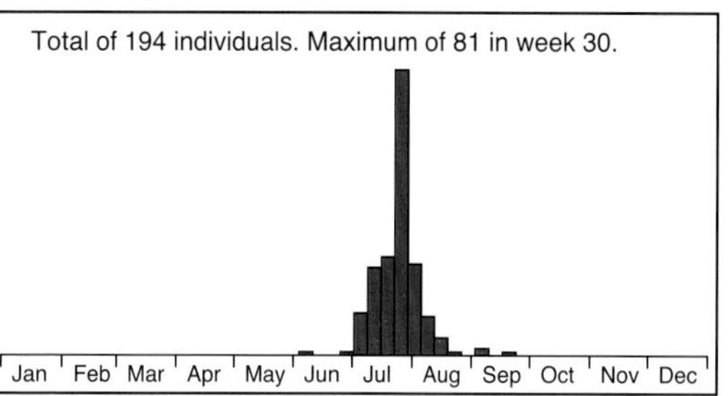

Although likely to be confined absolutely to oak as a larva, the adult moth is nevertheless widespread and is expected more or less everywhere in Hertfordshire a light trap is put out.

1454 *Dioryctria abietella* ([D.& S.])

Recorded: 1979 – 2006
Distribution / Status: Random / Immigrant
Conservation status: -
Caterpillar food plants: Not recorded. Elsewhere, Pine, Spruce and Fir cones and shoots
Flight period: June to August
Records in database: 23

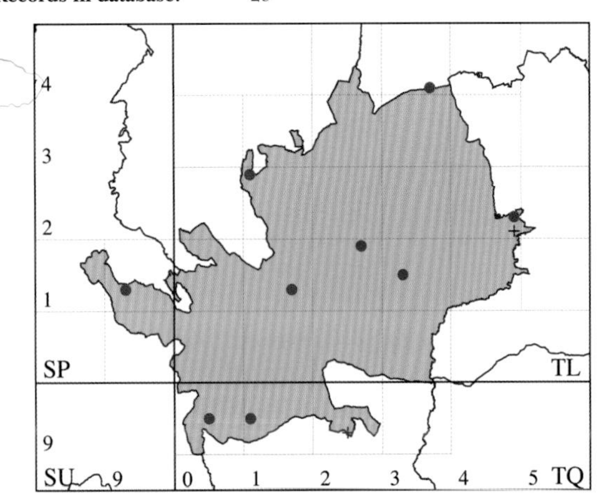

There is no evidence of residency in Hertfordshire. All available records are given: Totteridge, 1979 (Ian Lorimer); Bishops Stortford, 1987 (Colin Plant); Bishops Stortford, 1989 (Colin Plant); Bishops Stortford, 1991 (Colin Plant); Bishops Stortford, 1994 (Tony King); Royston, 1999 (John Chainey); Hertford, 2001 (Andrew Wood); Rickmansworth, 2001 (Paul Clack); Oxhey, 2001 (Joan Thompson); Rickmansworth, 2001 (Paul Clack); Hertford, 2003 (Andrew Wood); Bishops Stortford, 10th August 1987 (Colin Plant); Datchworth, 29th July 1997 (Steve Palmer); Wheathampstead, 12th July 2001 (Trevor Chapman); Hexton Chalk Pit, 21st July 2001 (Colin Plant); Hertford, 14th August 2001 (Andrew Wood); Oxhey, 6th July 2002 (Joan Thompson); Hertford, a female, 12th July 2005 (Andrew Wood); Royston, 13th July 2005 (John Chainey); Hertford, a female, 13th July 2005 (Andrew Wood); Bishops Stortford, 13th July 2005 (James Fish & Julian Reeves); Bishops Stortford, a male, 19th August 2005 (James Fish & Julian Reeves); Bishops Stortford, a male, 26th August 2006 (James Fish & Julian Reeves) and Tring Sewage Farm, a male, 9th June 2007 (Colin Plant).

1454a *Dioryctria schuetzeella* Fuchs

Recorded: 1996 – 2003
Distribution / Status: Local / Uncommon resident
Conservation status: Herts Scarce
Caterpillar food plants: Not recorded. Elsewhere, Norway Spruce
Flight period: Late June to late August
Records in database: 6

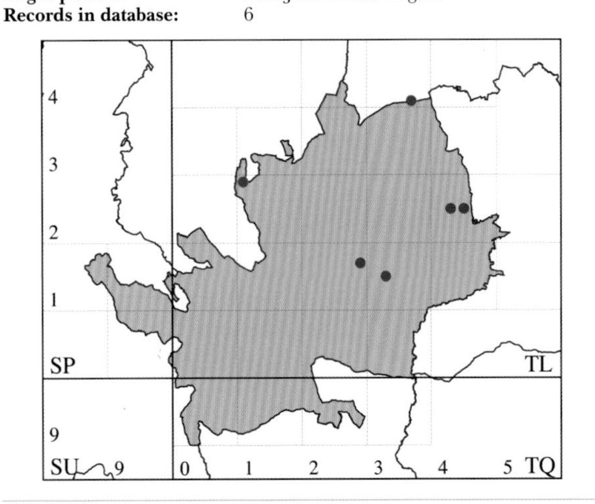

Our six records are from Royston, 2001 (John Chainey), Patmore Heath, 22nd August 1996 (Colin Plant); Bramfield Woods, 29th July 2000 (Colin Plant); Hexton Chalk Pit, 21st July 2001 (Colin Plant), Hertford, 26th June 2003 (Andrew Wood) and Albury, 10th July 2003 (Colin Plant). Unlike 1454: *Dioryctria abietella* it apparently does not migrate and the dates of the Hertfordshire records do not seem to contradict this. Thus, the records in Hertfordshire evidently represent a small and rather localised resident population.

1455 *Dioryctria simpliciella* Hein. = *mutatella* Fuchs

Recorded: 2000 – 2004
Distribution / Status: Local / Uncommon resident
Conservation status: Herts Scarce
Caterpillar food plants: Not recorded. Elsewhere, Scot's Pine and Corsican Pine
Flight period: June to September
Records in database: 7

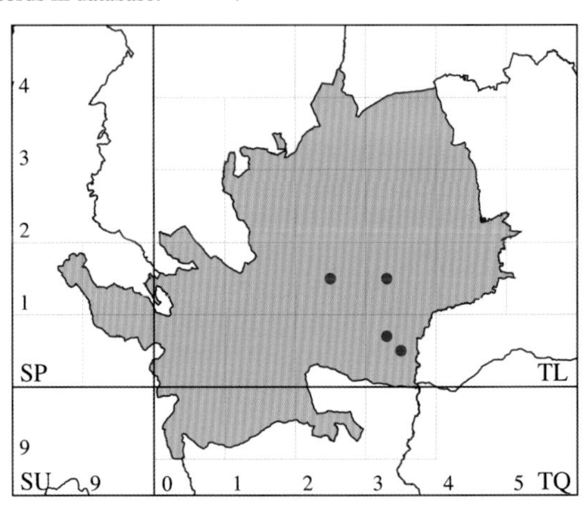

We have seven records from just four localities, as follows: Digswell, 23rd September 2000 (Tom Gladwin); Hertford, 30th August 2002, 6th June, 26th June and 31st August 2003, Thunderfield Grove, 28th July 2003 (Mark Cooper) and Broxbourne Woods, 15th July 2004 (Colin Plant). Interestingly, apart from at Andrew's Hertford garden there is no overlap of localities with 1454a: *Dioryctria schuetzeella* – in spite of both species being associated with Scots Pine. Separation of the two usually requires examination of the genitalia.

1457 *Hypochalcia ahenella* ([D.& S.])

Recorded: 1890 – 2001
Distribution / Status: Very local / Uncommon resident
Conservation status: Herts Rare
Caterpillar food plants: Unknown, probably Common Rock Rose
Flight period: June to August
Records in database: 10

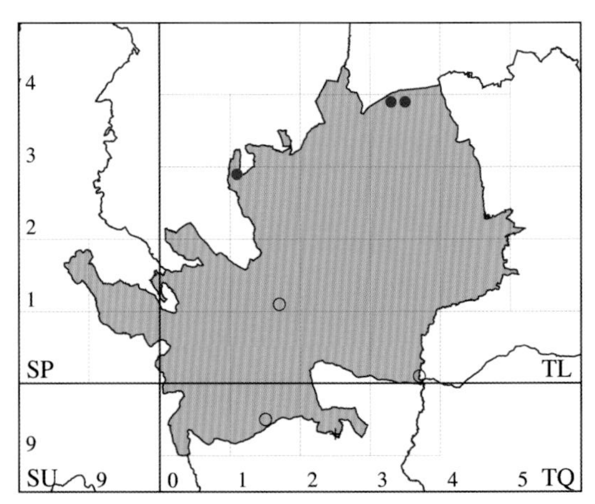

Our modern records show a species that is confined to chalk grassland. It is a rather less than striking beast in the adult stage and may have been overlooked as a 'grass moth' by non-specialists at several sites (though few sites with good quality chalk grassland remain). The historical records are from Sandridge village (Griffith, 1890), the Cheshunt area (Boyd, 1901), Bushey Heath (Barraud, 1902), Harpenden in 1937 (C. B. Williams) and Totteridge in 1979 (Ian Lorimer).

1458 *Myelois circumvoluta* (Fourc.) = *cribrella* (Hb.)

Recorded: 1834 – 2006
Distribution / Status: Widespread / Common resident
Conservation status: No perceived threats
Caterpillar food plants: Creeping Thistle; Spear Thistle
Flight period: June to August
Records in database: 96

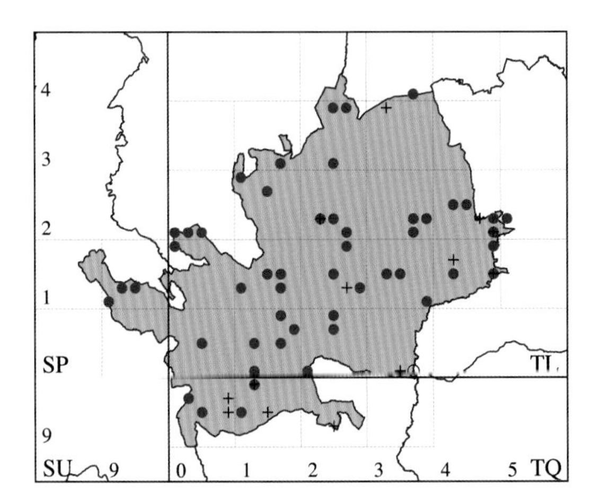

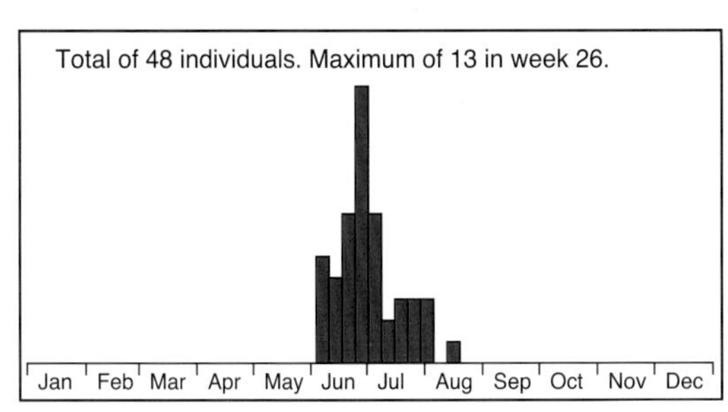

This is a widespread and common moth in Hertfordshire and is easily reared by collecting dead thistle stems in winter; adults will emerge in late May if kept indoors. Although recorded in Hertfordshire since at least 1834 there is anecdotal evidence that this was a scarce species during the 1970s and early 1980s and that it has increased in number since then, though we have no firm supporting evidence for this.

1461 *Assara terebrella* (Zinck.)

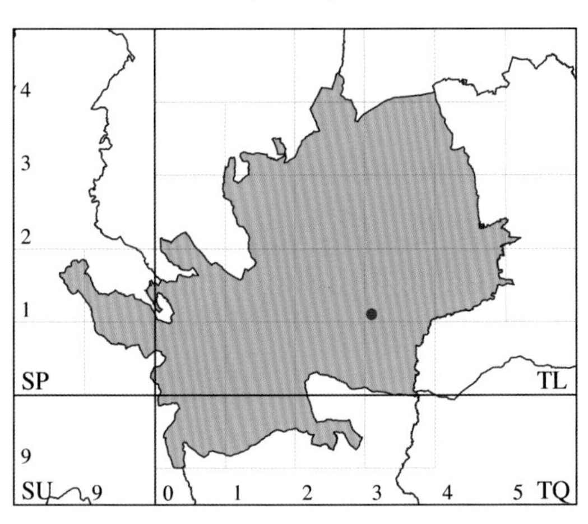

Recorded: 2005 only
Distribution / Status: Extremely local / Rare resident
Conservation status: Herts Rare
Caterpillar food plants: Not recorded. Elsewhere, in Spruce cones
Flight period: June. Elsewhere, June to August
Records in database: 1

One adult caught in my light trap at Bayfordbury Pinetum on 18th June 2005 is the only Hertfordshire example. Given the nature of the site it is likely to be resident here, but it is not expected elsewhere in the county.

1462 *Pempeliella dilutella* ([D.& S.]) = *Pempelia diluta* (Haw.)

Recorded: 2004 – 2006
Distribution / Status: Extremely local / Uncommon resident
Conservation status: Herts Vulnerable
Caterpillar food plants: Not recorded. Elsewhere, Wild Thyme and Creeping Thyme, perhaps associated with ants
Flight period: June/July
Records in database: 2

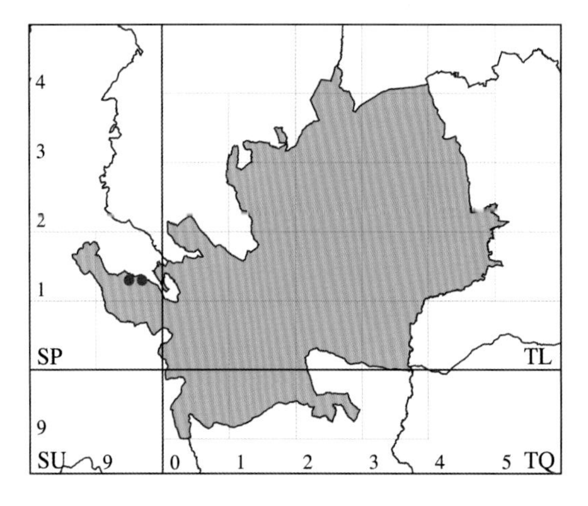

We have just two records of this chalk downland species – in the two tetrads affected by Aldbury Nowers near Tring, on 17th July 2004 (Colin Plant) and 23rd June 2007 (Mark Cooper). The habitat is much degraded and this species must be treated as Vulnerable to further habitat loss. It may benefit from the large scale habitat restoration being undertaken during 2007. The moth needs to be looked for at the other chalk grassland sites in the county – notably Hexton Chalk Pit, Ashwell Quarry and Therfield Heath.

1463 *Pempeliella ornatella* ([D.& S.])

Recorded: 1945 only
Distribution / Status: Absent / Former resident
Conservation status: Herts Extinct
Caterpillar food plants: Not recorded. Elsewhere, Wild Thyme and Creeping Thyme
Flight period: July
Records in database: 2

Our only records are from Tring, on 11th and 16th July 1945 (A. L. Goodson).

1465 *Nephopterix angustella* (Hb.)

Recorded: 1900 – 2006
Distribution / Status: Local / Rare resident, perhaps also immigrant or vagrant
Conservation status: Herts Rare
Caterpillar food plants: Not recorded. Elsewhere, Spindle berries
Flight period: June/July
Records in database: 17

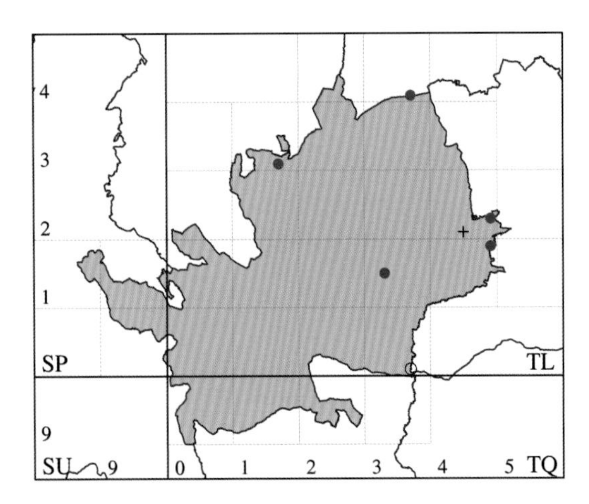

Goater (1986) records this species from Cambridgeshire and Essex to Herefordshire and Devon, stating that it prefers calcareous soils, inhabiting hedges and scrub wherever the foodplant grows. Our two most northerly dots confirm the association with calcareous soils, but the remaining five might relate to immigrants or vagrants.

1467 *Ancylosis oblitella* (Zell. 1848)

Recorded:	1976 – 2005
Distribution / Status:	Random / Immigrant
Conservation status:	-
Caterpillar food plants:	Not recorded. Elsewhere, goosefoots
Flight period:	Late July to September
Records in database:	6

This is a moth of the Thames Estuary in Essex and Kent, where the larvae feed on goosefoots and have been established originally from immigrant parents) since 1956; adults can be disturbed from vegetation and are attracted to light. During 1976 there was either a population explosion or a large-scale immigration and moths were reported inland as far as Hertfordshire (Goater, 1986). That year in fact produced our first records, from Barry Goater's own garden at Bushey, on 12th August, 7th & 20th September. Subsequent records are from Totteridge in 1977 (Ian Lorimer), Much Hadham on 29th July 1991 (Colin Plant) and Bishops Stortford, 28th July 2005 (James Fish and Julian Reeves). The records referred to by Parsons (1993) are those from Bushey and Totteridge.

1469 *Euzophera cinerosella* (Zell.)

Recorded:	2002 only
Distribution / Status:	Random / Vagrant
Conservation status:	-
Caterpillar food plants:	Not recorded. Elsewhere, Wormwood, in the root then the stem
Flight period:	July. Elsewhere, June to August
Records in database:	2

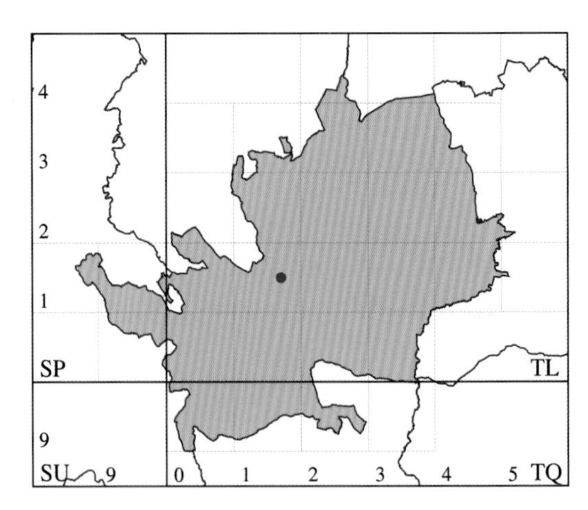

One on each of 7th and 16th July 2002 at Marshall's Heath (John Murray) are our only county records. These correctly named moths were probably vagrants from some distance away.

1470 *Euzophera pinguis* (Haw.)

Recorded:	1900 – 2006
Distribution / Status:	Widespread / Common resident
Conservation status:	No perceived threats
Caterpillar food plants:	Not recorded. Elsewhere, under Ash bark (especially pollards)
Flight period:	June to early September
Records in database:	204

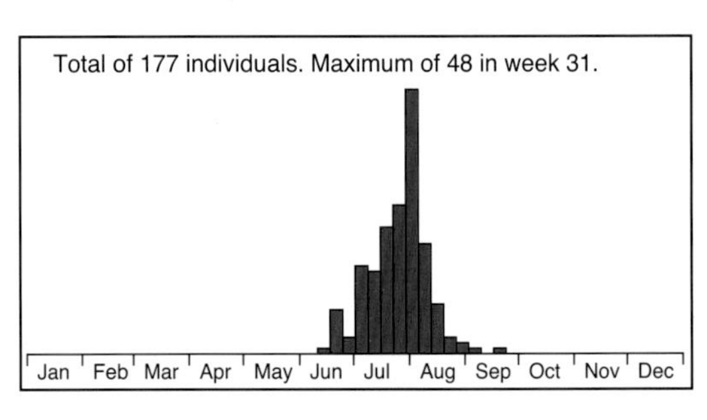

Most site lists will include this species which is as often beaten from vegetation as it is found in light traps. The apparent lack of records in the north-east is perhaps a result of under-recording.

1473 *Ephestia elutella* (Hb.) Cacao Moth

Recorded: 1885 – 1969
Distribution / Status: Absent / Former temporary resident
Conservation status: Pest species
Caterpillar food plants: Stored food and other products
Flight period: June to October
Records in database: 6

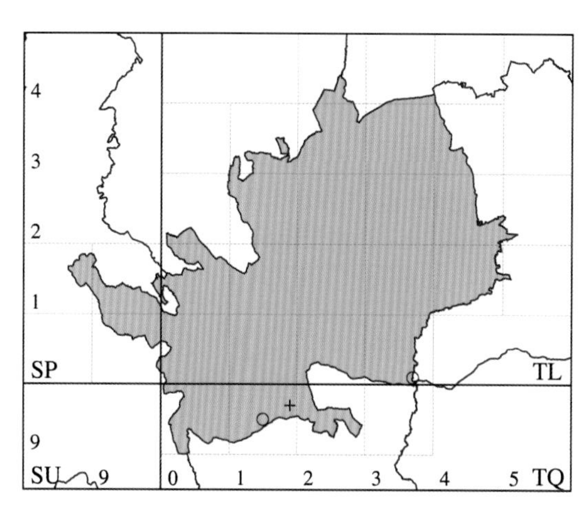

Nineteenth-century reports are from the Sandridge area (Griffith, 1880), Hitchin in 1885 (A. H. Foster), the Cheshunt area (Griffith, 1901) and Bushey Heath (Barraud, 1902). Since then it has been recorded at Harpenden in 1933 by C. B. Williams and at Borehamwood on 1st June 1969 by Eric Bradford. Only the last of these was dissected and so it is possible that the others are misidentified. There are no records since, in spite of dissecting large numbers of *Ephestia* species.

1474 *Ephestia parasitella* Stdgr. ssp. *unicolorella* Stdgr.

Recorded: 1974 – 2006
Distribution / Status: Widespread / Common resident
Conservation status: No perceived threats
Caterpillar food plants: Dead ivy leaves in a dry rot hole in an elm tree; birds' nests incorporating dead leaves
Flight period: May to July
Records in database: 189

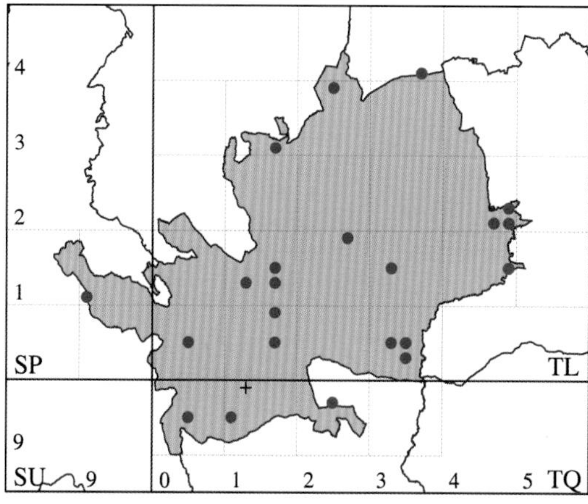

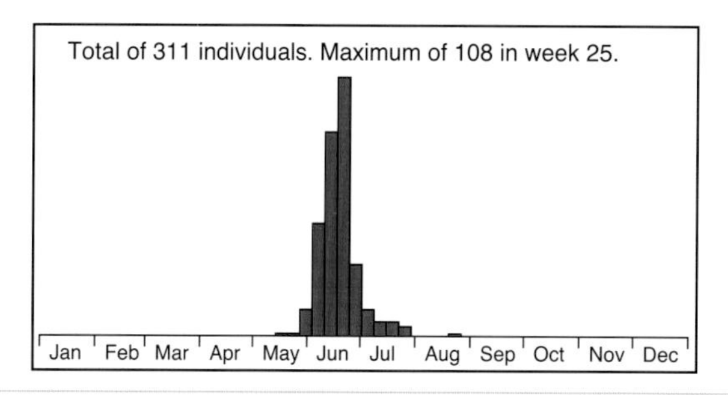

This is probably the only *Ephestia* species that can survive out-of-doors in Hertfordshire. Nevertheless, correct separation from both 1473: *Ephestia elutella* and 1478b: *Vitula biviella* requires genitalia dissection; this has been done for all the moths included in the distribution map.

1475 *Ephestia kuehniella* Zell. 1879 Mediterranean Flour Moth

Recorded: 1971 – 2000
Distribution / Status: Extremely local / Temporary resident
Conservation status: Pest species
Caterpillar food plants: Flour and bran. Elsewhere, Stored food and other products
Flight period: March and October. Elsewhere, April to October
Records in database: 3

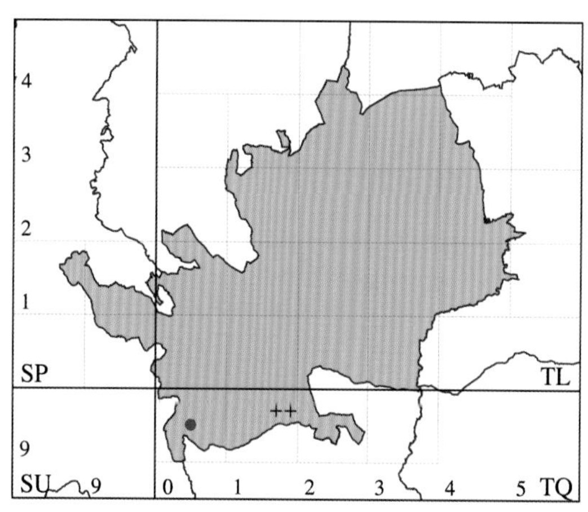

The Hertfordshire records are from Drayton Road, Borehamwood, one on wall in the house, 9th October 1978 (Eric Bradford); Haberdashers' Aske's School, 11th March 1971, infesting bran for locust cages (Barry Goater) and Rickmansworth, 1999 (John Chainey). A record from Watford in a published list is rejected as the author carried out no dissections. Specimens from 'Enfield, Herts' in the collection of the late Eric Bradford relate to a flour mill at Ponders End, Middlesex and are not Hertfordshire records.

1476 *Ephestia cautella* (Walker) Dried Currant Moth

Recorded: 1901 – 1969
Distribution / Status: Absent / Former temporary resident
Conservation status: Pest species
Caterpillar food plants: Almond (nut). Elsewhere, Stored products, especially fruits and nuts
Flight period: March. Elsewhere, May/June.
Records in database: 2

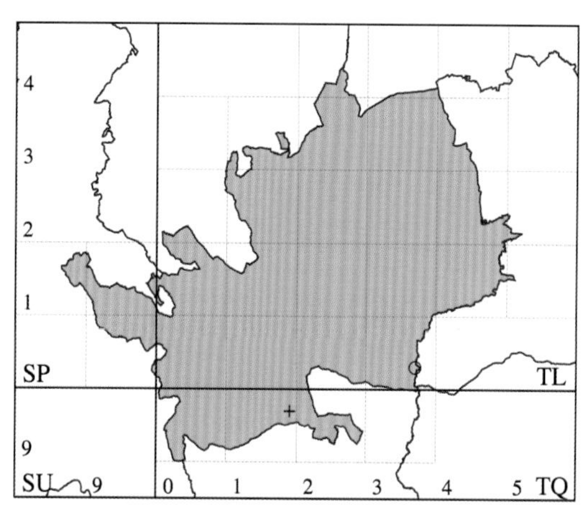

This species is listed for the Cheshunt area (Boyd, 1901) and one was bred from an Almond nut purchased in Borehamwood, 28th March 1969 (Eric Bradford). There are no other Hertfordshire records.

1478 *Ephestia calidella* (Guen.) Dried Fruit Moth

Recorded: 1901 only
Distribution / Status: Absent / Former temporary resident
Conservation status: Pest species
Caterpillar food plants: Not recorded. Elsewhere, dried fruit and nuts
Flight period: Elsewhere, August/September
Records in database: 1

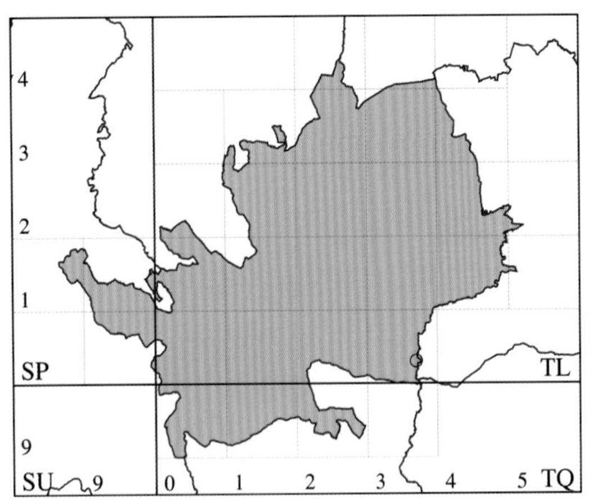

Our only record is for 'Cheshunt – in shops' (Boyd, 1901). No specimen has been traced and examined.

1478b *Vitula biviella* (Zell.)

Recorded: 2004-2005
Distribution / Status: Random / ?Immigrant
Conservation status: Insufficiently known
Caterpillar food plants: Not recorded.
Flight period: July
Records in database: 2

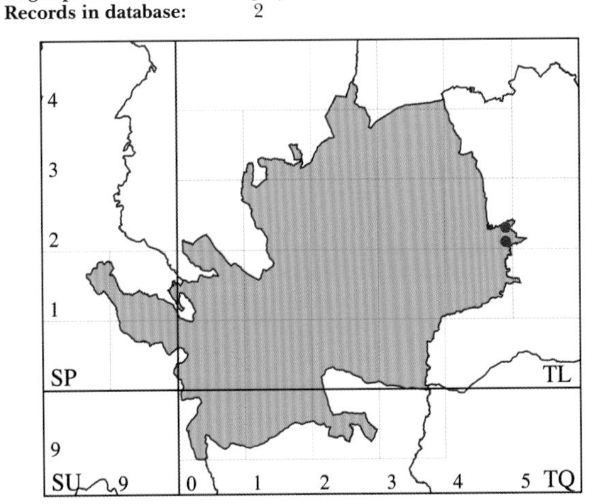

One extremely worn male, taken in a garden light trap in Bishops Stortford by James Fish and Julian Reeves on the night of 28th July 2005, was dissected by Rachel Terry during 2007; the genitalia slide was photographed and the image circulated by e-mail to colleagues, whereupon Jeff Higgott recognised it as this species. Later, during April 2008, Brian Goodey found two examples amongst the backlog of material grom my own garden elsewhere in the town, caught on 31st July 2004. It was added to the British list from Kent as recently as 1997 (Clancy and Parsons, 1999) and has recently also turned up in Middlesex and Suffolk. It cannot usually be separated from 1473: *Ephestia elutella* or 1474: *Ephestia parasitella* without examination of the genitalia (though candidates may be selected by eye if fresh); accordingly, it is possibly more widespread in Hertfordshire than is currently realised.

1479 *Plodia interpunctella* (Hb.) Indian Meal Moth

Recorded: 1921 – 2006
Distribution / Status: Widespread / Common resident
Conservation status: Pest species
Caterpillar food plants: Dried semolina powder, wild bird seed, 'cornflakes'. Elsewhere, on other stored products
Flight period: All year (indoors)
Records in database: 12

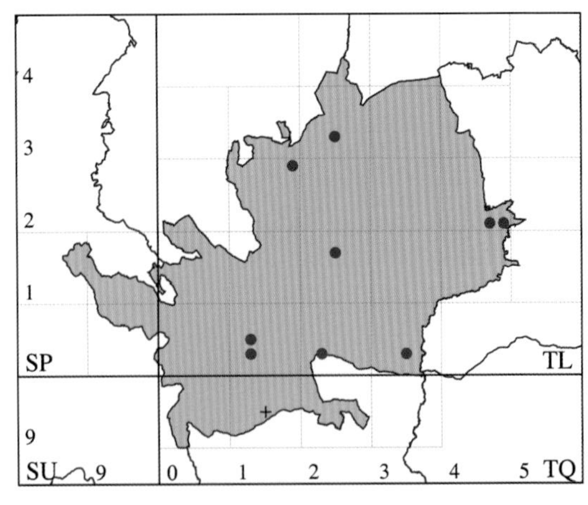

The Indian Meal Moth is probably unable to thrive outside heated human habitations and is unlikely to become established here. Indoors, it is a common and probably largely unreported pest of farinaceous materials.

1480 *Homoeosoma nebulella* ([D.& S.])

Recorded: 1901 – 1902
Distribution / Status: Absent / Extinct
Conservation status: Herts Extinct
Caterpillar food plants: Not recorded. Elsewhere, flowers and seeds of Ragwort, Tansy, Ox-eye Daisy and Spear Thistle
Flight period: Elsewhere, July and September
Records in database: 2

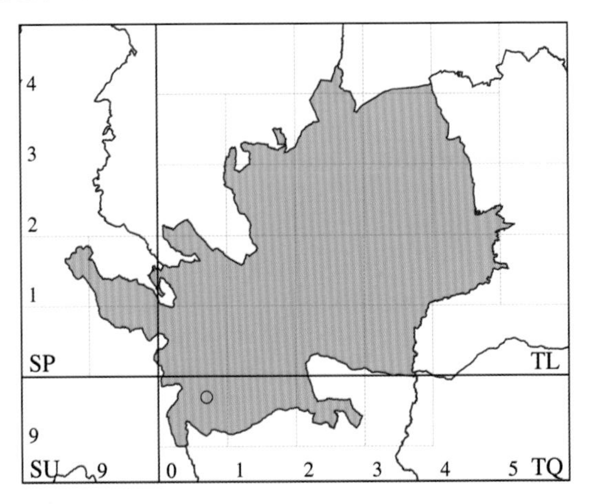

Our two records are from Whippendell Wood in 1901 (Cottam) and the St Albans area (Gibbs, 1902). Elsewhere in Britain it resides in coastal areas and on both chalky and sandy sites inland. As with other species of *Homoeosoma*, identification almost always requires genitalia examination and so might perhaps be overlooked on the chalk downland sites of the county, though all candidates so far seen from there have proved not to be this species.

1481 *Homoeosoma sinuella* (Fabr.)

Recorded: 1901 – 2005
Distribution / Status: Local / Common resident
Conservation status: No perceived threats
Caterpillar food plants: Not recorded. Elsewhere, in the rootstock of Ribwort Plantain and other plantains
Flight period: June to August
Records in database: 36

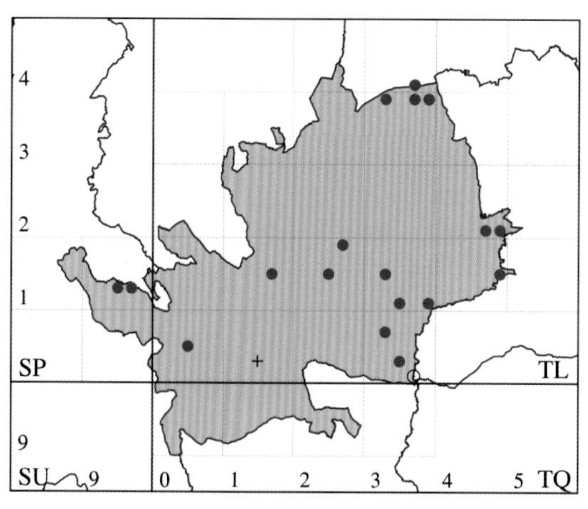

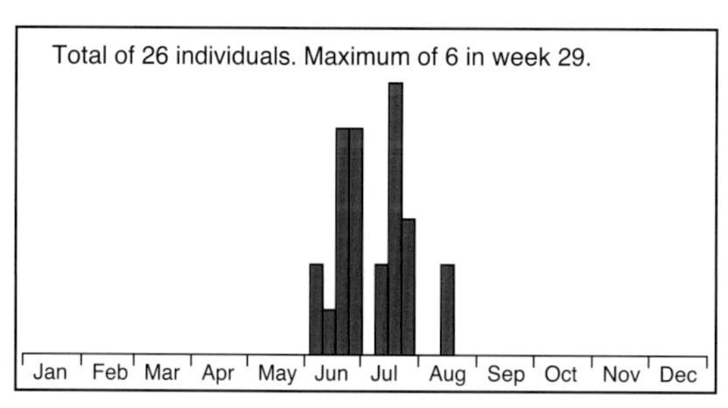

Many examples can be recognised on sight, though some are impossible to separate from other members of the genus without critical examination and that technique is recommended in all cases. It seems likely to be a widespread and common moth in Hertfordshire.

[1482 *Homoeosoma nimbella* (Duponchel)

Our only record of an occurrence in Hertfordshire is that of an unconfirmed identification listed by Parsons (1993) for the pre-1970 period. No data are available to support this record and the species cannot be separated without either examination of wing veins or genitalia – implying that a voucher specimen must be retained. There are only a handful of British records and Hertfordshire is not amongst those listed by Goater (1986). This record cannot be accepted as proven and is rejected.]

1483 *Phycitodes binaevella* (Hb.)

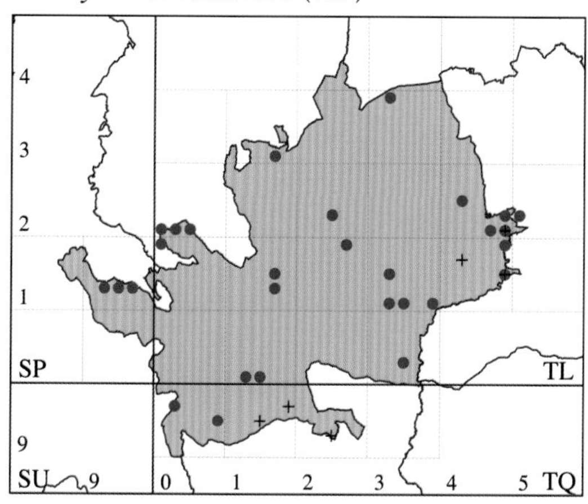

Recorded: 1933 – 2006
Distribution / Status: Widespread / Common resident
Conservation status: No perceived threats
Caterpillar food plants: Not recorded. Elsewhere, in the flower head of Spear Thistle
Flight period: June to early August
Records in database: 56

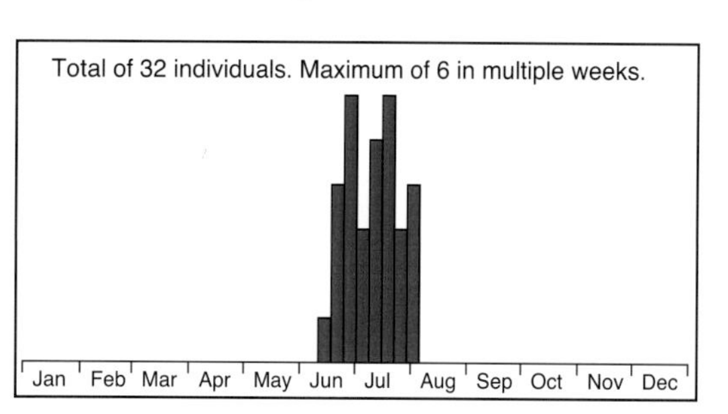

Though some specimens can be named on overall appearance, confirmation by dissection is regarded as highly desirable. This process seems to confirm that the moth is widespread and common in the county.

[1484 *Phycitodes saxicola* Vaughan

One recorded from Waltham Cross in 1901 cannot be accepted unless a voucher specimen is located and the genitalia examined.]

1485 *Phycitodes maritima* (Tengst.)

Recorded: 2001 – 2004
Distribution / Status: Local / Uncommon resident
Conservation status: Herts Scarce
Caterpillar food plants: Not recorded. Elsewhere, in the flower heads of Yarrow and Ragwort
Flight period: August
Records in database: 5

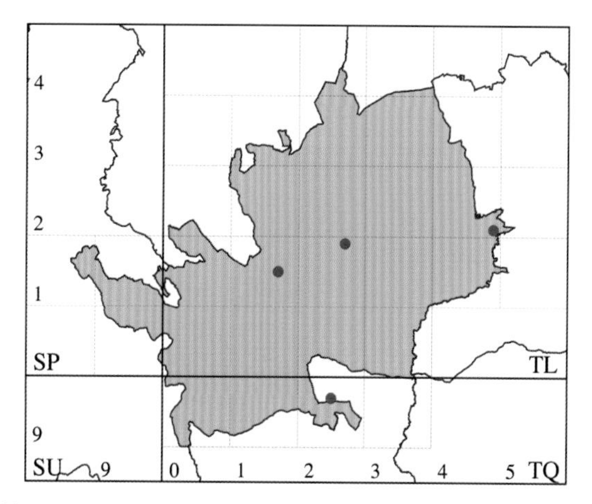

This species cannot be recognised without dissection and all records included in the distribution map have been so obtained. The pattern suggests that this species may be overlooked in some parts; the foodplants are more or less ubiquitous.

1486 *Apomyelois bistriatella* (Hulst) spp. *subcognata* (Ragonot) = *neophanes* (Durrant)

Recorded: 1942 only
Distribution / Status: Absent or overlooked / Extinct or Rare resident
Conservation status: Herts Extinct
Caterpillar food plants: Under fungus *Daldinia concentrica* on burnt gorse
Flight period: Elsewhere, June/July
Records in database: 1

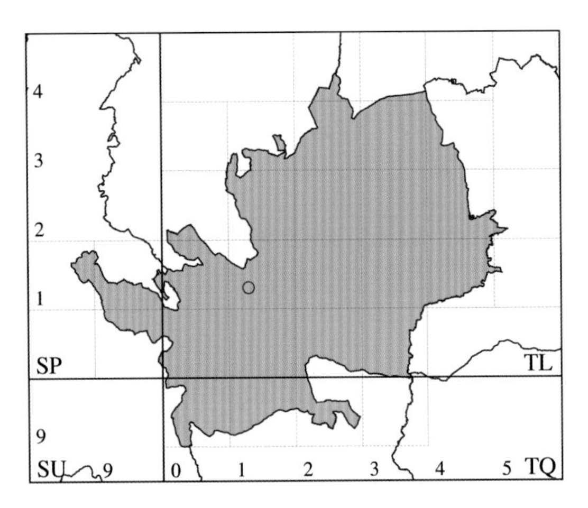

Adults were bred by Messrs. Edelsten and Fryer, from larvae collected under the fungus *Daldinia concentrica* growing on burnt Gorse on Harpenden Common during 1942. Foster (1944) notes that this was the first Hertfordshire record for the species; we have no reports since then. It should be noted that the species which breeds under *Daldinia* fungus on birch trunks may not be this one. The adults may be confused with other species.

PTEROPHORIDAE

The Pterophoridae are the plume moths – a most distinctive and easily recognised group amongst the moths. The forewing is split at the tip, to varying degrees, so that the forewing has two lobes and the hind wing is similarly divided twice, to create three lobes. Each lobe, especially of the hind wing, is fringed with cilia so that the lobes resemble feathers – or plumes. There are currently 41 British species, of which Hertfordshire has records for 24, though of these 5 are regarded as extinct in the county and two others have not been seen for several years. Many species are most easily found in their early stages.

1488 *Agdistis bennetii* (Curtis)

Recorded: 1994 – 2003
Distribution / Status: Random / Vagrant
Conservation status: -
Caterpillar food plants: Not recorded. Elsewhere, Sea Lavender
Flight period: August
Records in database: 2

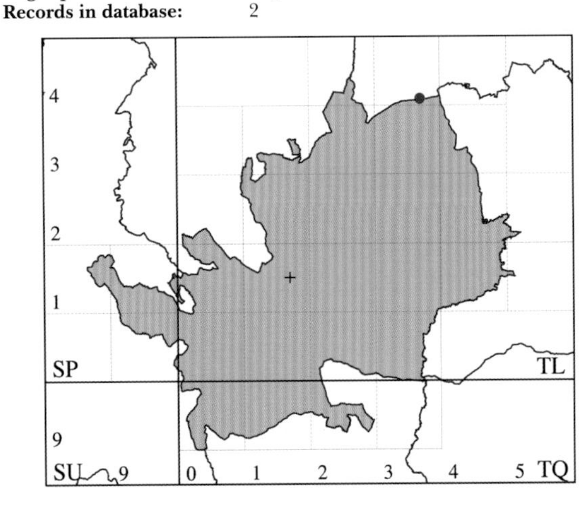

Our two records are from Marshall's Heath on 19th August 1994 (John Murray) and Royston on 6th August 2003 (John Chainey & Jenny Spence). Both are likely to be wanderers from the Essex coast where the species breeds.

1489 *Oxyptilus pilosellae* (Zell.)

Recorded: 1905 only
Distribution / Status: Absent / Former resident
Conservation status: Herts Extinct
Caterpillar food plants: Not recorded. Elsewhere, Mouse-ear Hawkweed
Flight period: August
Records in database: 1

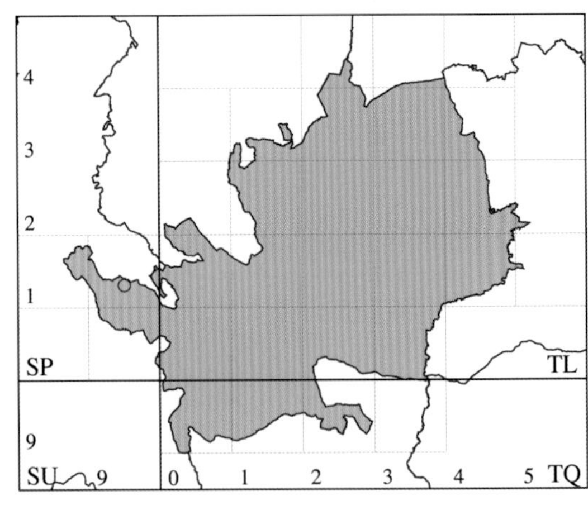

Five examples were taken by T. F. Furnival on the canal bank near Tring Station, on 13th August 1905, but remained unidentified. On going abroad, Furnival presented his Lepidoptera collection to P. J. Barraud, whose identification of the moths was subsequently confirmed by T. A. Chapman. Apparently, Furnival was accompanied on site by Mr T. A. Court, who also collected several specimens (Gibbs, 1907). The report is repeated by Foster (1937); there are no additional records available. Martin Honey very kindly examined the Natural History Museum collection during May 2007 and confirms that there are six examples of *pilosellae* there, collected at Tring on 13th August 1905, though they bear Court's name, not Furnival's, and had been erroneously placed under *britanniodactyla*.

1490 *Oxyptilus parvidactylus* (Haw.)

Recorded: 1990 only
Distribution / Status: Extremely local or absent / Former resident
Conservation status: Herts Endangered
Caterpillar food plants: Not recorded. Elsewhere, Mouse-ear Hawkweed
Flight period: Not recorded. Elsewhere, June/July
Records in database: 1

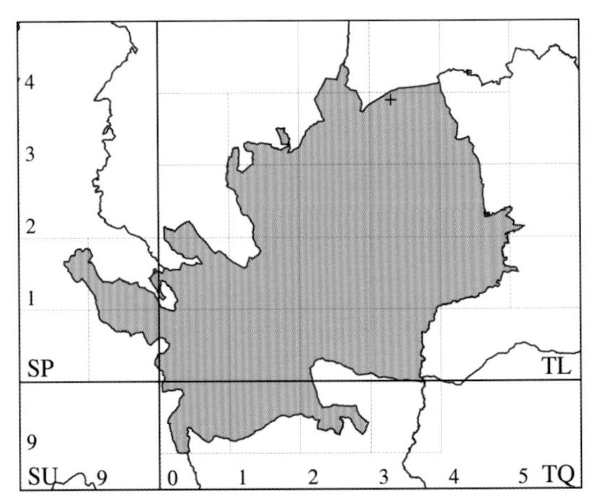

Church Hill at Therfield Heath provides our only record of this chalkland species, where it was noted by Raymond Uffen during 1990. It may still be present, but in adjacent Bedfordshire it has not been seen since the single county record in 1987 and in the South Essex chalk pits it was last noted in 1980. It may be overlooked in Hertfordshire. Whilst at a national level is certainly not under any special threat, in our county appropriate habitat is at a premium and if the moth is still present it is best treated as Endangered for this reason.

1494 *Capperia britanniodactyla* (Gregson)

Recorded:	1905 – 2004
Distribution / Status:	Extremely local or absent / Rare resident, probably overlooked
Conservation status:	Herts Rare
Caterpillar food plants:	Wood Sage
Flight period:	July
Records in database:	2

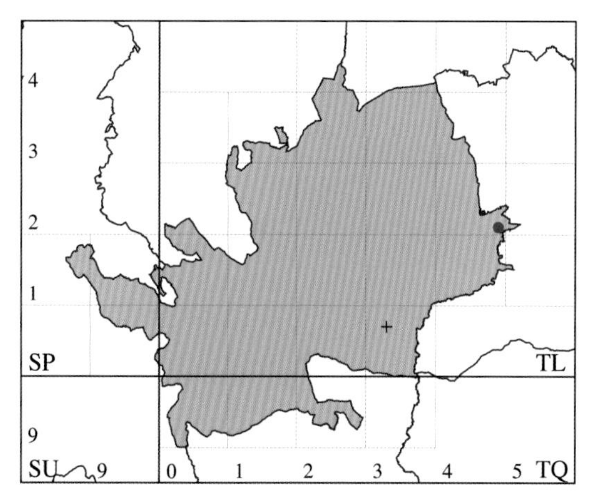

This moth was found as larvae at Broxbourne Wood, where it was last noted by David Agassiz in 1976 and adults reared. A male at mv light on 15 July 2004 in my garden in Bishops Stortford must surely have been a wanderer from some other breeding site since, according to Colin Hart, it is not known to be migratory. Wilted and 'felled' plants of Wood Sage could usefully be searched for the green caterpillar. There is a literature reference to a specimen in the Natural History Museum labelled "Tring, 13th August 1905", but Martin Honey has checked this and reports that it is an incorrectly identified example of 1489: *Oxyptilus pilosellae*.

1495 *Marasmarcha lunaedactyla* (Haw.)

Recorded:	1884 – 2006
Distribution / Status:	Widespread / Common resident
Conservation status:	No perceived threats
Caterpillar food plants:	Spiny Restharrow
Flight period:	Late June to early August
Records in database:	27

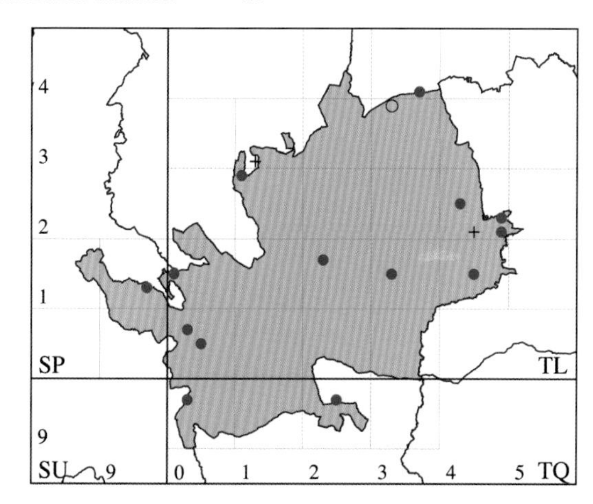

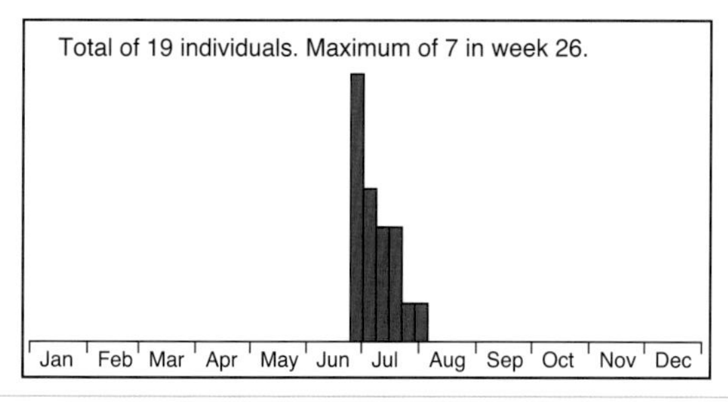

Our only breeding record is from the 'Tring district' on 25th July 1903, where A. E. Gibbs and T. F. Furnival, described it as locally common amongst small patches of *Ononis spinosa* (Gibbs, 1904a). During 2003 larger than usual numbers were noted and it was recorded in that year, and since, in places where it had not previously been reported in spite of moderate to good coverage in the past. This may suggest an influx of moths from outside the county which boosted a small existing resident population. At the end of 2006 it appears to be a moderately widespread resident in the county.

1496 *Cnaemidophorus rhododactyla* ([D. & S.])

Recorded:	1834 – 1987
Distribution / Status:	Extremely local or absent / Former resident or extinct
Conservation status:	Herts Endangered
Caterpillar food plants:	Dog Rose
Flight period:	Elsewhere, July/August
Records in database:	9

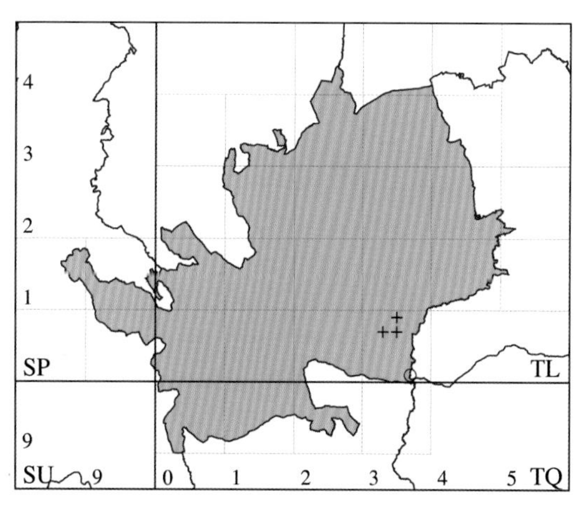

Stephens (1834) records "Hertford" and this almost certainly relates to the Broxbourne Woods National Nature Reserve complex where the moth was a resident for many years, particularly in Danemead Wood. The last confirmed record of larvae there was on 8th June 1977 (Barry Goater) though it may have persisted a few years beyond that date until ill-advised management activities cut down and burned the few rose bushes that supported the moth at Danemead in order to create clearings. Our only record outside this woodland area is that given by Boyd (1901) for Cheshunt Marsh.

1497 *Amblyptilia acanthadactyla* (Hb.)

Recorded:	1900 – 2006
Distribution / Status:	Widespread / Common resident
Conservation status:	No perceived threats
Caterpillar food plants:	Not recorded. Elsewhere, flowers and seeds of Hedge Woundwort and other plants
Flight period:	June to April, hibernating as an adult
Records in database:	293

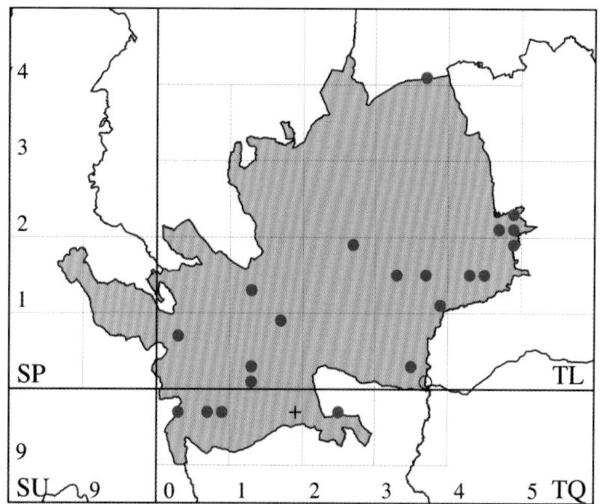

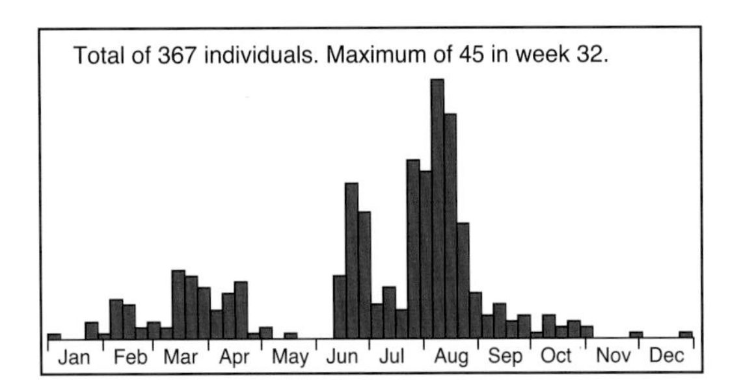

It is possible to state with reasonable certainty that this moth was a very local and rare resident from at least the 1980s to 2002; the lack of historic records suggests that it has been uncommon for rather longer. It started to increase during 2002 becoming widespread and very common from 2003 onwards. Of the 293 Hertfordshire records, six were made in all years up to 2002, eight were made during 2002 and all the rest were made from 2003 to 2006.

1498 *Amblyptilia punctidactyla* (Haw.)

Recorded: 1999 – 2003
Distribution / Status: Extremely local / Rare resident
Conservation status: Herts Rare
Caterpillar food plants: Not recorded. Elsewhere, flowers and seeds of Hedge Woundwort and other plants
Flight period: Elsewhere, June to April, hibernating as an adult
Records in database: 3

One was noted at Digswell in 1999 (Tom Gladwin) and I caught another at Astonbury Wood, near Stevenage, on 6th July 2002. A third was caught by Elizabeth Goodyear in her garden at Ware on 26th February 2003 and named by me. The last two were identified by genitalia dissection; the first might best be treated as requiring conformation. There are no further valid Hertfordshire records.

1501 *Platyptilia gonodactyla* ([D.& S.])

Recorded: 1900 – 2005
Distribution / Status: Local / Common resident
Conservation status: Insufficiently known
Caterpillar food plants: Coltsfoot
Flight period: May to late June then late July to mid-September
Records in database: 18

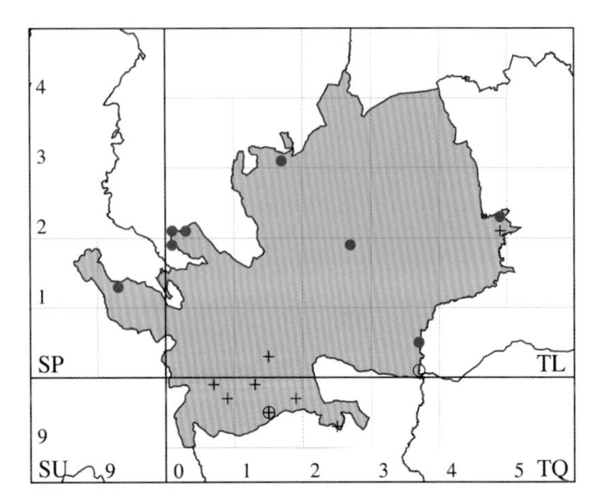

Unlike 1503: *G. ochrodactyla* and 1504: *G. pallidactyla*, this species has two adult generations in each year; an unusually late example was recorded on 11th October 1963 at the ATV Studios in Borehamwood. It seems odd that all the older records lie in the south whilst all the modern captures relate to the north of the county. The lack of historical records in the north may be under-recording; the lack of current records in the south is probably not and may suggest a decline.

1503 *Gillmeria ochrodactyla* ([D.& S.])
= *Platyptilia ochrodactyla* ([D.& S.])
= *Gillmeria tetradactyla* (L.)

Recorded: 1901 – 2005
Distribution / Status: Local, probably under-recorded / Resident
Conservation status: Insufficiently known
Caterpillar food plants: Not recorded. Elsewhere, in the stem, roots and shoots of Tansy
Flight period: Late June/July. Elsewhere, July/August
Records in database: 6

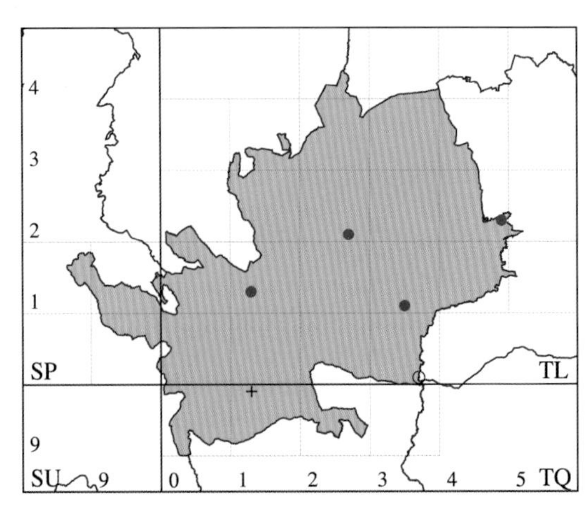

The foodplant is not uncommon in the county and so the moth may be under-recorded. There is no reason to suppose that it is not widely distributed, though it may be locally so.

1504 *Gillmeria pallidactyla* (Haw.) = *Platyptilia pallidactyla* (Haw.)

Recorded:	1890 – 2006
Distribution / Status:	Widespread / Common resident
Conservation status:	No perceived threats
Caterpillar food plants:	Sneezewort. Elsewhere also in stems and roots of Yarrow
Flight period:	Late June to early August
Records in database:	39

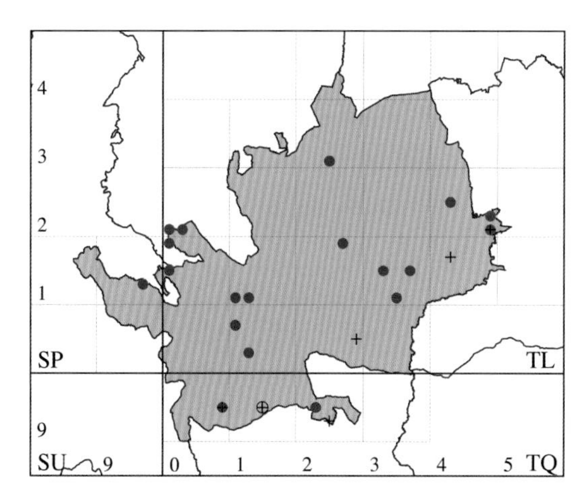

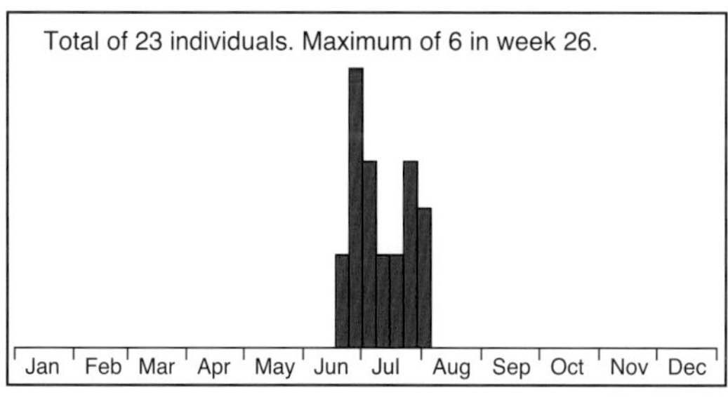

Our only breeding record is from a site in Harcourt Road, Bushey, where a meadow with much Sneezewort supported larvae in 1966 (Barry Goater), but the meadow is long gone along with many other suitable sites. Nevertheless, the moth appears to persist and is evidently widespread in Hertfordshire.

1507 *Stenoptilia zophodactylus* (Dup.)

Recorded:	1884 – 1886
Distribution / Status:	Absent or overlooked / Local and rare resident or absent
Conservation status:	Insufficiently known
Caterpillar food plants:	Not recorded. Elsewhere, Common Centaury, Red Centaury, Gentian and Yellow-wort
Flight period:	Not recorded. Elsewhere July to September
Records in database:	2

This plume moth is listed for the Sandridge area by Griffith (1884) without a date or locality and is also noted for Hitchin in Leech (1886). Foster (1937) repeats both records, but gives no others. There are scattered records in adjacent Bedfordshire, though none particularly recent; it is possible that this moth still persists on the chalk in Hertfordshire where one or more of the known foodplants grow. Confusion is possible with 1509: *S. pterodactyla*.

1508 *Stenoptilia bipunctidactyla* (Scop.)

Recorded:	1884 – 2006
Distribution / Status:	Very local / Uncommon resident
Conservation status:	Herts Endangered
Caterpillar food plants:	Not recorded. Elsewhere, Field Scabious
Flight period:	Elsewhere, May/June then August to October
Records in database:	10

The need to dissect most adult examples of this species to obtain an accurate identification has probably resulted in some under-recording. Too few people actively engage in the searching for early stages of plume moths in Hertfordshire. However, the moth seems genuinely rare and comparison of current records with past observations are strongly indicative of a decline.

1509 *Stenoptilia pterodactyla* (L.)

Recorded:	1890 – 2005
Distribution / Status:	Widespread / Common resident
Conservation status:	No perceived threats
Caterpillar food plants:	Not recorded. Elsewhere, Germander Speedwell
Flight period:	Late May to early August
Records in database:	32

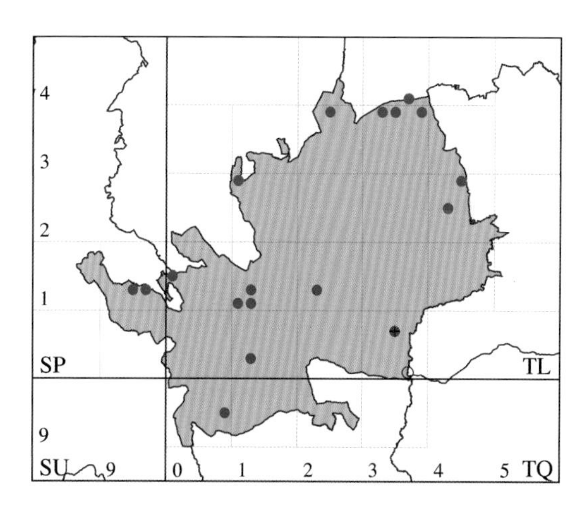

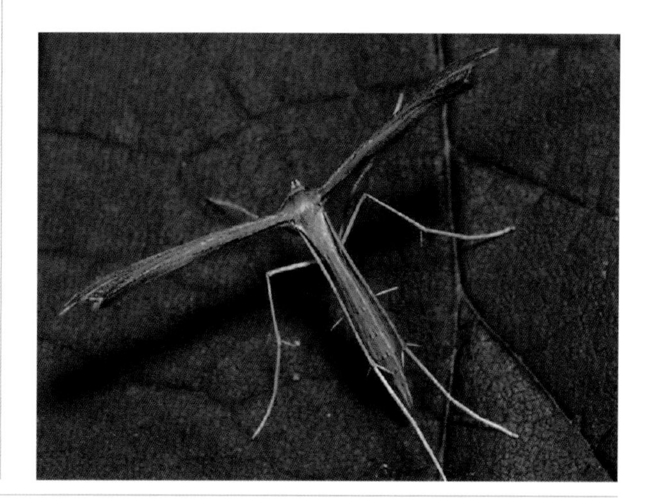

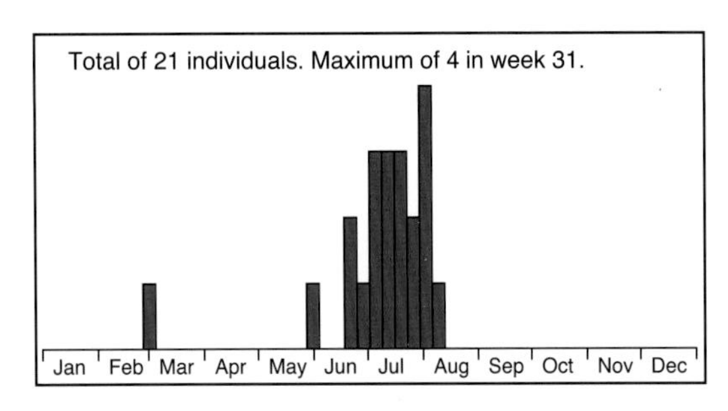

In the field, candidates for this species amongst otherwise 'brown' plume moths are selected by the shining white hind legs, visible when viewed from above and behind – a character shared with 1507: *S. zophodactylus*, which flies later, from July to September, and which is generally smaller and grey in appearance. Separation of the two may, however, sometimes require dissection; most of the records in the map have been so verified, including all late July and August examples.

1510 *Merrifieldia leucodactyla* ([D.& S.])

Recorded:	1930 only
Distribution / Status:	Absent / Former resident
Conservation status:	Herts Extinct
Caterpillar food plants:	Not recorded. Elsewhere on Wild Thyme
Flight period:	Not recorded. Elsewhere, June to August
Records in database:	1

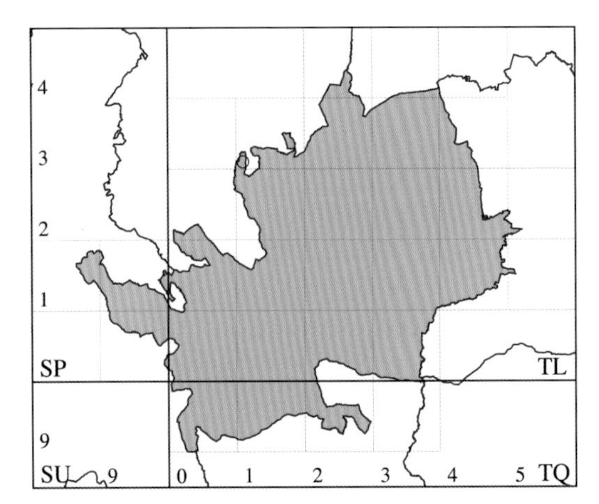

Foster (1941) adds this species to the county list (as *Alucita tetradatyla*) from 'near Hexton (Fryer)'. It is unclear exactly where this record was made. The nearby Pegsdon Hills are largely in Bedfordshire and so indeed is most of the suitable habitat in this area today – though seventy or so years ago that was probably not the case. Given that Fryer reported the moth to Foster as a Hertfordshire record we must assume that it was indeed taken inside the county boundary. There are no other Hertfordshire records. The Bedfordshire moth book (Arnold et al, 1997) notes that the moth is confined in that county to the Pegsdon Hills where it is uncommon. In older literature, this species may be listed under the name *tridactyla*.

1512 *Merrifieldia baliodactylus* (Zell.)

Recorded:	1937 – 1997
Distribution / Status:	Extremely local / Rare resident
Conservation status:	Herts Vulnerable
Caterpillar food plants:	Not recorded. Elsewhere, on Marjoram
Flight period:	July
Records in database:	3

Foster (1937) lists Hexton, without dates, but the names of the observers suggest the records are from the twentieth rather than from the nineteenth century. More recently, Raymond Uffen found this species at Tingley Wood, near Pirton, on 16th July 1994 and David Manning records it from Ravensdell Wood on 23rd July 1997. There are no other records.

1513 *Pterophorus pentadactyla* (L.) White Plume

Recorded:	1885 – 2006
Distribution / Status:	Widespread / Common resident
Conservation status:	No perceived threats
Caterpillar food plants:	Bindweed
Flight period:	June to early August
Records in database:	152

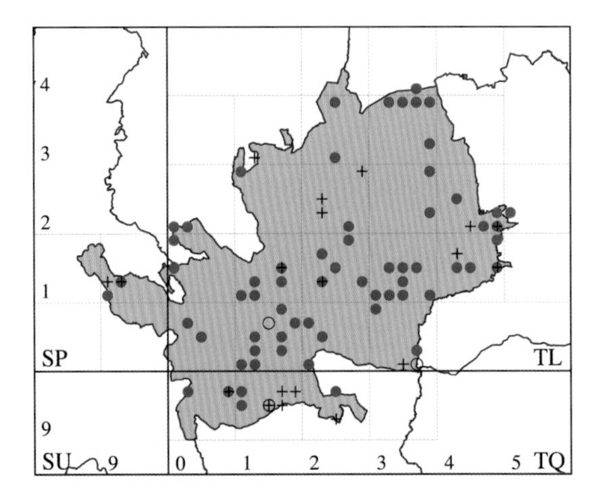

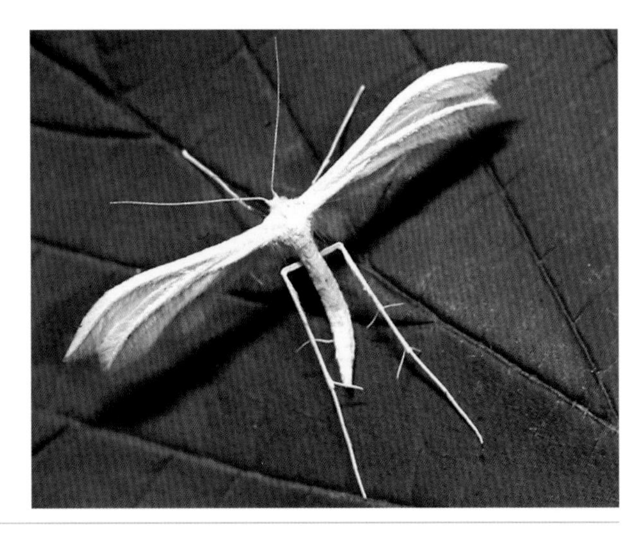

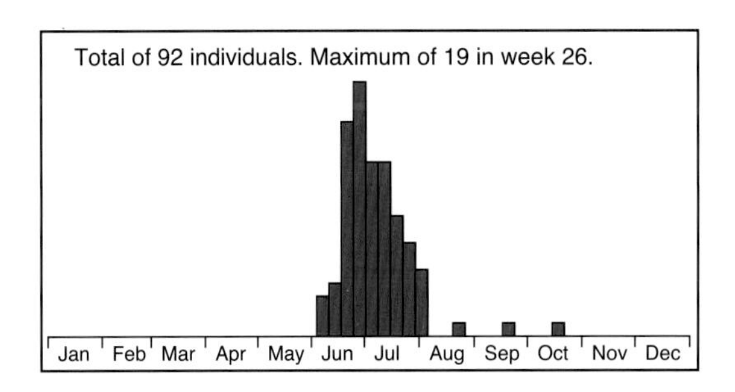

The White Plume moth is likely to be found wherever the large, white-flowering bindweeds grow and is probably under-recorded. During 2003, several later than usual adults were noted and an especially late example was captured at light in Bishops Stortford on 21st October 2006 (James Fish & Julian Reeves).

1514 *Pterophorus galactodactyla* ([D.& S.])

Recorded: 1904 only
Distribution / Status: Absent / Former resident
Conservation status: Herts Extinct
Caterpillar food plants: Not recorded. Elsewhere, Great Burdock
Flight period: Elsewhere, June/July
Records in database: 1

Gibbs (*Trans. Herts.* **12**: 159 – 164) lists the only county record from St Albans in 1904. He identified the moth amongst specimens of micros sent to him by Miss Alice Dickinson.

1515 *Pterophorus spilodactylus* (Curtis)

Recorded: 1884 – 1918
Distribution / Status: Absent / Former resident
Conservation status: Herts Extinct
Caterpillar food plants: Not recorded. Elsewhere, White Horehound
Flight period: Elsewhere, July/August
Records in database: 2

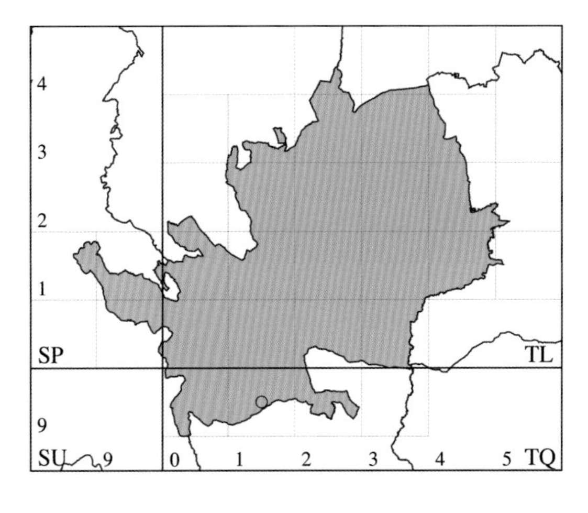

Griffith (1884) listed this species for the Sandridge area (not mapped). Foster (1937) adds 'Bushey Heath (Barraud)'. Barraud was certainly collecting around the turn of the twentieth century and was a contemporary of Gibbs. He was apparently still active in 1918, but I have no trace of him after that year; the record was most likely made prior to the First World War.

1517 *Adaina microdactyla* (Hb.)

Recorded: 1885 – 2006
Distribution / Status: Local / Common resident
Conservation status: Herts Scarce
Caterpillar food plants: Hemp Agrimony – galling the stem
Flight period: June and August
Records in database: 12

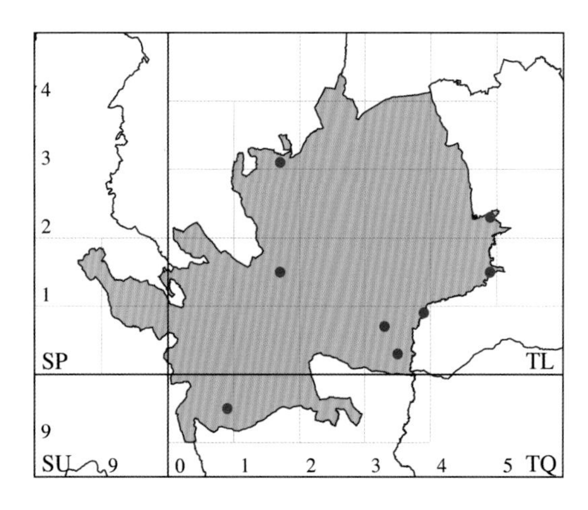

Though adults attend light traps, few people actually record this species, which is rather easily recorded by looking for the galls (swellings) on the stems of the foodplant. It is likely to be found wherever stands of the foodplant persist unmanaged.

1518 *Ovendenia lienigianus* (Zell.)

Recorded: 1982 only
Distribution / Status: Absent or under-recorded / Rare resident, perhaps extinct
Conservation status: Insufficiently known
Caterpillar food plants: Mugwort
Flight period: Elsewhere, July
Records in database: 1

Larvae were found to be common on Mugwort plants on a verge of the B1000 road west of Hertford, on 31st May 1982 (Raymond Uffen); the species has not been seen in Hertfordshire since, though I have found larvae in the Stort Valley on the Essex side of the border near Bishops Stortford. The foodplant grows widely throughout the county, but the ruderal habitats that support larger patches of it are increasingly rare and it may be that the general tidying of Hertfordshire is putting this species at risk.

1519 *Ovendenia carphodactyla* (Hb.)

Recorded: 1990 – 2003
Distribution / Status: Very local / Resident and ?Immigrant/ Vagrant
Conservation status: Insufficiently known
Caterpillar food plants: Not recorded. Elsewhere, Carline Thistle and Ploughman's Spikenard
Flight period: Elsewhere, June and August/September
Records in database: 2

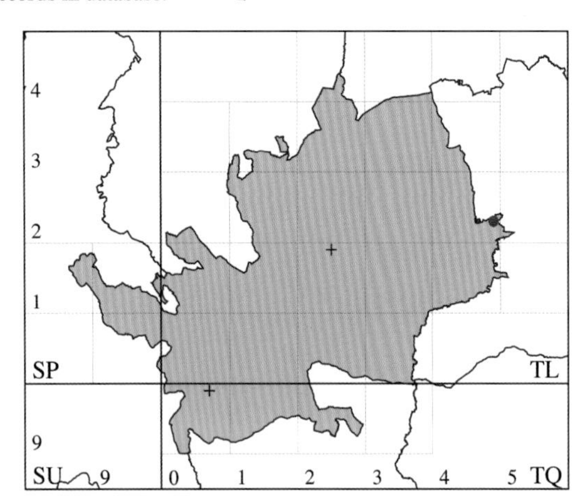

At Mardley Heath, several adults were seen flying at dusk around Ploughman's Spikenard on an area of chalky spoil during June 1982 (Raymond Uffen). Larvae were also found in flower heads on the bank of Heath Road, abutting the A1(M) road at least up to the year 2000, but the plant is now much diminished. Larvae were found in shoots of clump of Ploughman's Spikenard on 4th April 1993 above the north bank of the motorway spur on the edge of Great Westwood gravel pit. A record from Bishops Stortford on 14th August 2003 (James Fish & Julian Reeves) perhaps relates to an immigrant or vagrant example, though local breeding is not impossible.

1523 *Oidaematophorus lithodactyla* (Tr.)

Recorded: 1890 – 2003
Distribution / Status: Extremely local / Rare resident
Conservation status: Insufficiently known
Caterpillar food plants: Not recorded. Elsewhere, Ploughman's Spikenard and Fleabane
Flight period: July/August
Records in database: 5

This moth is listed for the Sandridge area (Griffith, 1884) and from Waltham Cross in 1905 (Gibbs, 1906). In reporting the latter, Gibbs noted that these were the only two Hertfordshire records to that date. The Sandridge record is not mapped. Since then, Raymond Uffen has noted it at Mardley Heath during 1990, with adults emerging from larvae on a garden variety of *Inula* and also taken in his garden light trap on 26th June. He has made finds since then on the bank in Heath Road, but these are undated. Raymond also found larvae along Ermine Street at Box Wood on 17th August 2001 and I caught an adult at light on Oughtonhead Common on 12th July 2003. These all probably represent resident populations.

1524 *Emmelina monodactyla* (L.) Common Brown Plume

Recorded: 1885 – 2006
Distribution / Status: Widespread / Common resident
Conservation status: No perceived threats
Caterpillar food plants: Bindweed and Field Bindweed
Flight period: All year
Records in database: [1225]

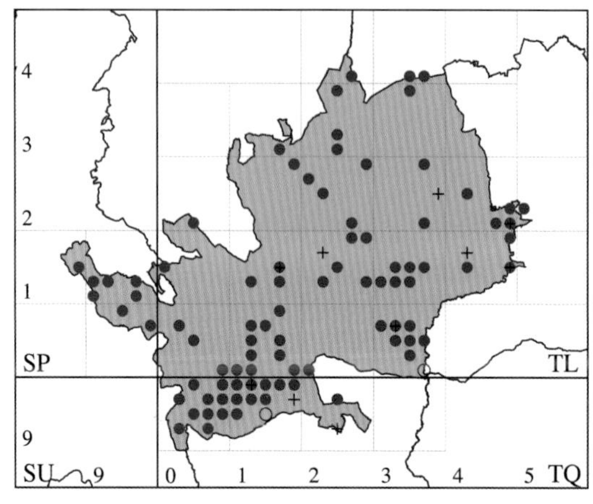

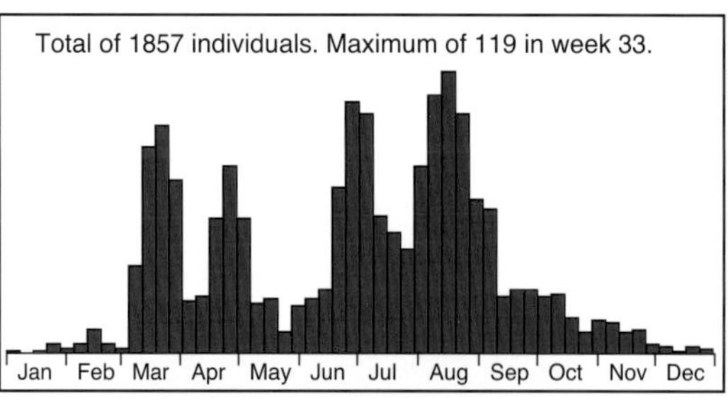

Recently, an additional plume moth, *Emmelina argoteles* (Meyrick) was discovered in Britain at Wicken Fen (Higgott, 2006). Unfortunately, it is impossible to separate this from our Common Brown Plume moth by any means other than dissection of the genital apparatus. The European literature suggests, however, that *Emmelina argoteles* might be restricted to marshy habitats; certainly the several dissections I have performed religiously throughout 2007 prove all of my garden examples to be *monodactyla*. The Common Brown Plume moth is apparently an abundant species in Hertfordshire. It hibernates as an adult and can be found in every week of the year (though there appear to be no records in the chart for week 2). The distribution map and flight period chart show all records and may include examples of *argoteles*; the number of records in the database is given above in square brackets for this same reason. This latter species could occur in the few remaining Hertfordshire wetland sites and ought to be specifically looked for.

BOMBYCOIDEA
LASIOCAMPIDAE

A group of large-bodied, furry moths that are mostly brown in colour. The hind wing has an expanded lobe at the base and there is no frenulum. Both sexes have bipectinate antennae which are exaggerated in the males to resemble feathers. The males of some species are day-flying, usually in bright sunshine, very fast and difficult to net for examination. The females of all are nocturnal. An effective means of recording lasiocampids is to put an unmated female in a cage and wait for the males to arrive, usually quite rapidly, attracted to her pheromones. Of the 12 British species we have records for eight in Hertfordshire, though two are rare and two appear to be extinct.

1631 *Poecilocampa populi* (L.) December Moth

Recorded:	1828 to 2006
Distribution / Status:	Widespread / Common resident
Conservation status:	Herts Stable
Caterpillar food plants:	Common Hawthorn
Flight period:	Late October to December
Records in database:	308

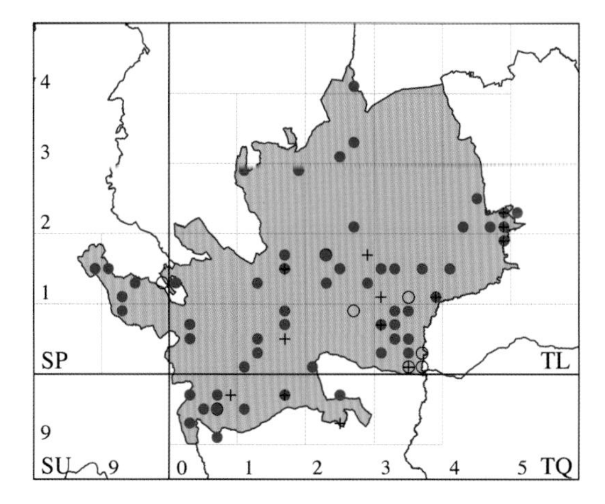

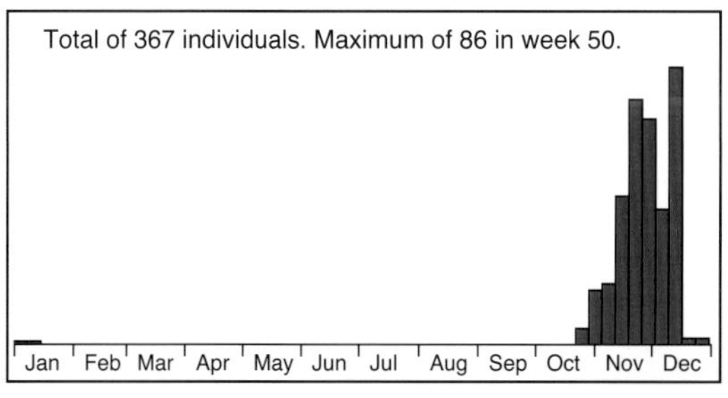

A widespread and common species, but overlooked in many areas perhaps because some people do not run traps late enough in the year. Adults of both sexes come to light traps in large number and adults are rarely recorded by any other method. They fly early in the evening from around 5 or 6 pm and appear to stop after two or three hours since, on several occasions, traps that were not turned on until about 10 pm failed to attract any examples of this species in areas where the moth is present.

1632 *Trichiura crataegi* (L.) Pale Eggar

Recorded:	1884 to 2005
Distribution / Status:	Very local / Rare resident
Conservation status:	UK BAP Watch List Herts Endangered
Caterpillar food plants:	Not recorded. Elsewhere on various trees and bushes
Flight period:	Late August to mid-September
Records in database:	36

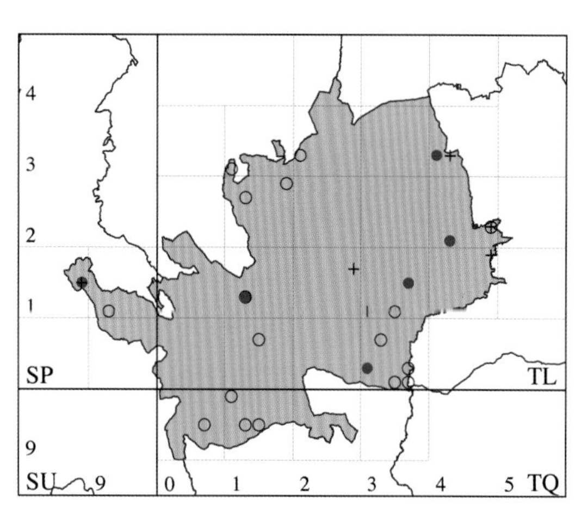

According to volume 7, part 2, of *The Moths and Butterflies of Great Britain and Ireland*, published in 1991, the Pale Eggar is widespread and locally common in the south-east of England. This is not our experience. Nationally the moth has suffered a population decline of 75 per cent during the past 25 years and now qualifies as 'Vulnerable' under the IUCN criteria. For Essex, to our east, Goodey (2004) gives this species as 'resident, scarce'. His map shows 32 ten-kilometre squares with records in the period 1960 to 1989 and a further 12 with records prior to 1960, but of these 44 squares, only 12 have also recorded the moth since 1989. The moth has apparently been lost from 32 ten-kilometre squares (although it has also been recorded post-1989 in two previously blank squares). In Bedfordshire, to our north-west, Arnold et al (1997) note that Pale Eggar is 'well distributed, but never recorded in large numbers'. Their maps reflect ten-kilometre squares only so it is not possible to interpret that statement; nevertheless, it begins to look as if this is in fact a moth that has vanished from many of the places where it was found fifty or more years ago. Our earliest record of this moth in Hertfordshire is from the Sandridge area (Griffith, 1884) and it was evidently widely distributed in both the late nineteenth and early twentieth centuries as the open circles on the distribution map indicate. In the period since Foster's 1937 list it was noted in a garden light trap in Tring in 1945 (A. L. Goodson) and in 1947 at Bishops Stortford (Craufurd). There were 8 in the Harpenden light trap during 1952 (Bell, 1954), but there are no more records until Jim Reid recorded it at Bramfield Wood on 4th September 1970, Bayfordbury on 9th September 1971 and Meesdenhall Wood on 14th September 1974. It was common in Geoff Senior's garden in Much Hadham in the 1970s, but vanished from the list after 1979. Charles Watson recorded one at light in his garden in Bishops Stortford on 11th September 1979 and again on 18th September 1985, Jim Fish and Julian Reeves trapped one at the light trap in their adjacent gardens in another part of Bishops Stortford on 6th September 1993,

Elizabeth Goodyear had one in Ware on 28th August 2002 and Jim Reid took one at light in Scales Park on 29th September 2002. There is circumstantial evidence of a resident population at Cuffley, where Alan Bolitho recorded adults in his garden on 30th August 1999, 25th and 27th August 2002 and then 30th August 2005 – our most recent records.

1633 *Eriogaster lanestris* (L.) Small Eggar

Recorded:	1828 to 1971
Distribution / Status:	Former resident
Conservation status:	Herts Extinct
Caterpillar food plants:	Blackthorn. Elsewhere also on hawthorn and reputedly other plants
Flight period:	Not recorded – elsewhere February and March
Records in database:	22

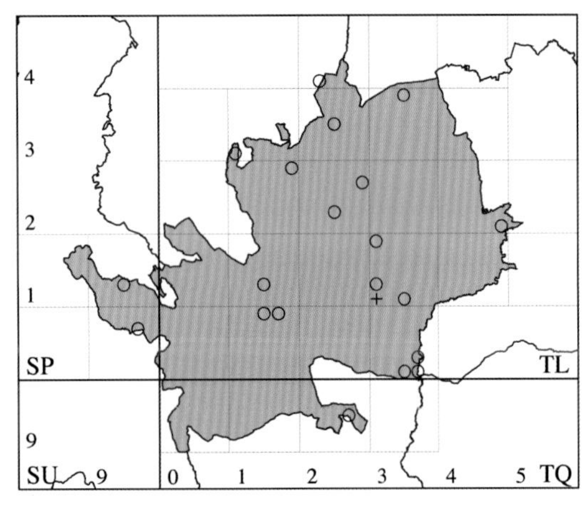

This appears to have been a widespread and common species across the county at the end of the nineteenth century. For example, Gibbs (1894) records larvae at East Barnet, reported by Mr Pilbrow and notes 'the hedges in many places nearly ruined by them'. There are many other records, though the only other positive references to larvae are from Harpenden Common, where Mr A. Lewis found a larval web on Sloe during June 1892 (Gibbs, 1893) and 'One brood, Cheshunt Wash' (Boyd, 1901). Foster (1937) lists it from Bishops Stortford (Taylor, Mellows), Stevenage (Matthews), St Albans (Jackson), Hitchin, Hexton, Baldock, Royston and Ashwell (Foster) Berkhamsted (Benson), Watton (Bull) and Tring (Ellison, Goodson). The lack of dates is a great pity, because since that 1937 publication there have been only two records – one of a single adult at Walkern in 1940 (J. Birdsall) and another in 1971 at Bayfordbury. The latter is unusual, though correct since it is supported by voucher specimens. Jim Reid found two males attracted to the greenhouse lighting on the rather early dates of 11th and 29th January 1971. His log-book comment for the week before the 29th also says 'very warm and sunny – Brimstone seen near Welwyn'. The Small Eggar clearly started a serious decline in Hertfordshire somewhere between the early 1900s and the 1940s. There were several active lepidopterists in parts of the county during the 1940 to 1970 period, including P. B. M. Allan and others in the Bishops Stortford area, and there can be no doubt that if this species was present it would have been found and reported. It does not appear, however, in Allan's 1950 list of the Lepidoptera of Bishops Stortford, nor does it feature in any other unpublished lists I have seen. On the other hand, rather few people are running light traps in February and March and so it is just possible that this moth still persists in a very few places where mature, un-pruned blackthorn thickets remain.

1634 *Malacosoma neustria* (L.) Lackey

Recorded:	1883 to 2006
Distribution / Status:	Widespread, but very local resident
Conservation status:	UK BAP Watch List Herts Threatened
Caterpillar food plants:	Common Hawthorn; Domestic Apple
Flight period:	Mid-June to mid-August
Records in database:	218

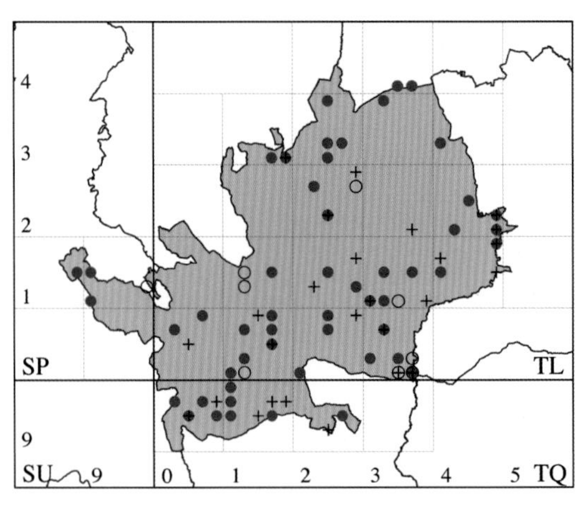

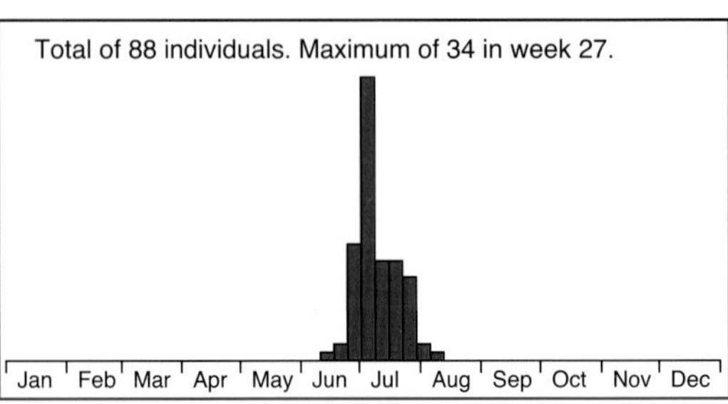

Foster (1937) listed the Lackey as being 'common in all districts'. Today, however, the distribution is somewhat patchy and there are apparently areas where the moth seems to be lacking. The larvae live gregariously in silk webs on the foodplant and can give a false illusion of abundance, causing severe defoliation in a small area whilst being quite absent for some considerable distance in the surrounding area. In spite of this, however, it seems that there has been a real decline in numbers, though this is something that cannot be quantified on available data. Given that the national population of this species has declined by 90 per cent since the year 1970 perhaps it is one that should give us cause for concern in the county.

[1635 *Malacosoma castrensis* (L.) Ground Lackey

Gibbs (1894) reports (on page 76) that during 1893 he visited Col. Gillum at his home in Church Hill House, East Barnet and had been able to make a list of the Colonel's captures in East Barnet. These included '*Bombyx castrensis*' taken in one of the hedges on Church Farm. Gibbs was meticulously careful over the position of the county boundary and there can be no doubt that the record was in Hertfordshire and not Middlesex. The identity seems most unlikely. Foster (1937) lists 'East Barnet (Gillum)', clearly the same record and also 'Bishops Stortford (Mellows)'. This latter record does not appear in the P. B. M. Allan's (1950) list of Lepidoptera of the Bishops Stortford area in spite of the fact that Mellows collaborated with Allan over this work. My own copy of the list was originally owned by Clifford Craufurd, who knew Mellows well and who annotated the list with additional information; no annotation concerning Ground Lackey appears. On the basis of available information I cannot admit this species to the Hertfordshire list.]

1637 *Lasiocampa quercus* (L.) Oak Eggar

Recorded:	1829 to 2006
Distribution / Status:	Local / Uncommon resident
Conservation status:	Herts Stable
Caterpillar food plants:	Not recorded. Elsewhere deciduous trees and shrubs
Flight period:	Late June to early August
Records in database:	67

Foster (1937) has the Oak Eggar 'Reported from all districts' and this is a pretty fair assessment of the present day status in the county of this large insect. The moth is nevertheless local and we have no records of breeding in the county. Records fall into two categories – occasional females taken in light traps and, more frequently, day-flying males. Unlike the northern subspecies of this moth, which feeds on heather, our southern subspecies is supposed to feed on a variety of deciduous trees and shrubs; in the London Area these include Common Hawthorn, Bramble and Hazel. Consequently, there appears to be a behavioural difference, with the diurnal males avoiding open situations and instead apparently associating with edge habitats such as hedges and woodland margins.

1638 *Macrothylacia rubi* (L.) Fox moth

Recorded: 1829 to [1937]
Distribution / Status: Former resident
Conservation status: Herts Extinct
Caterpillar food plants: Not recorded. Elsewhere, heathers, bilberry, creeping willow and others
Flight period: Not recorded. Elsewhere, May/June
Records in database: 11

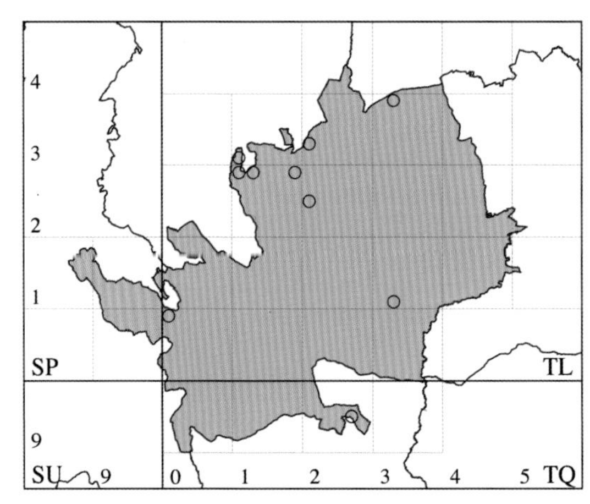

First listed for the county from Hertford by Stephens (1829), all but two records relate to the calcareous soils along the north-west edge of the county. Foster recorded it on the Hertfordshire side of the Pegsdon Hills in 1906 (Gibbs, 1907) and at Therfield Heath in 1916. Foster also lists Berkhamsted Common (Rothschild), East Barnet (Gillum), Stevenage (Matthews), Hexton, Willbury Hill and Hitchin (Foster; Palmer) in his 1937 county list; though none of the records are dated most were made several years earlier than the year of publication. There are no other records known to me and the species appears to have become extinct in Hertfordshire during the first three decades of the twentieth century. J. F. Stephens' Hertford record and Colonel Gillum's record from East Barnet do not sit well with the overall distribution, perhaps indicating that the moth was formerly more widespread than the few records suggest.

1640 *Euthrix potatoria* (L.) Drinker

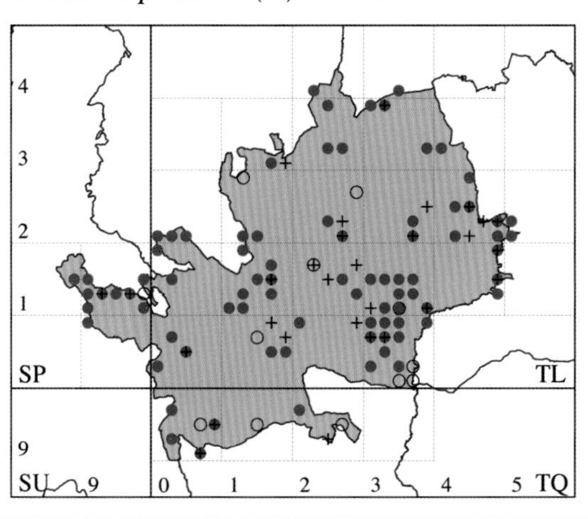

Recorded: 1829 to 2006
Distribution / Status: Widespread / Common resident
Conservation status: Herts Stable
Caterpillar food plants: Reed
Flight period: Late June to early August, extremes June and mid-August
Records in database: 226

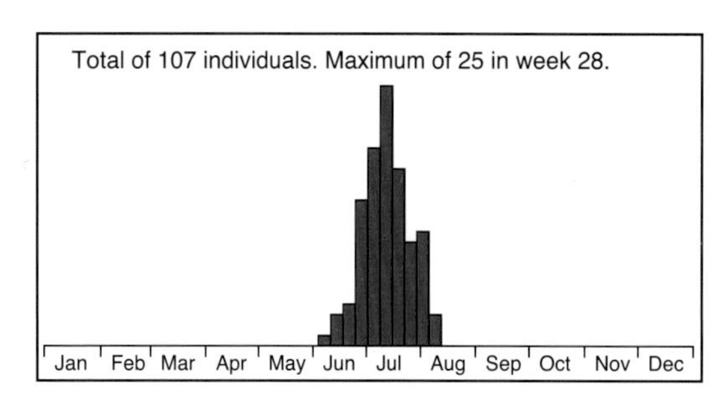

Foster (1937) lists the Drinker as common in all districts and our map indicates that this situation is unchanged with reports from the entire county – including the arable north-east.

1642 *Gastropacha quercifolia* (L.) Lappet

Recorded: 1829 to 1995
Distribution / Status: Extremely local / Rare resident
Conservation status: Herts Endangered
Caterpillar food plants: Blackthorn
Flight period: Late May to early August (pre-1995 data)
Records in database: 47

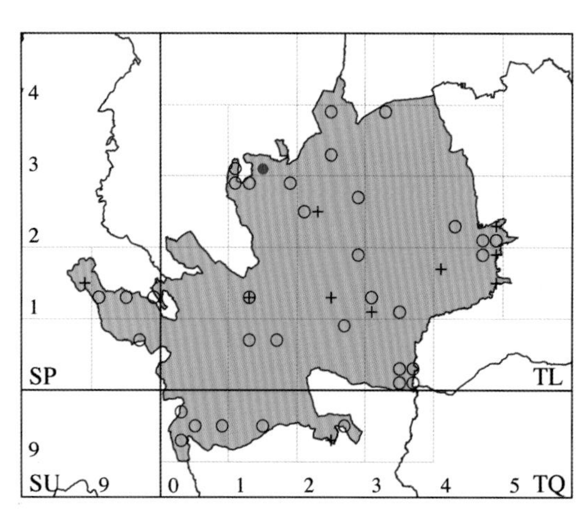

Gibbs (1901) notes the Lappet as 'unusually plentiful' during 1900, noting that several were taken on the street lamps of St Albans that year and almost every local list for the next thirty or forty years also contains this species. Allan (1950) commented, for the Bishops Stortford area, that the Lappet was 'Plentiful in the larval stage on Sloe in the autumn. In 1934 it was abundant as far north as Cambridge, the larvae being so common as to be a nuisance when beating'. Comments such as these are fairly typical of the 1930s and 1940s and the moth was probably present in every Blackthorn hedge in the county. Today it is either resident at excessively low density or else it is extinct with us. The principal decline in Hertfordshire (and also the London Area) appears to have taken place during the 1950s and coincides perfectly with two major changes in agricultural practice – the advent of agropesticides such as DDT and the large-scale removal of hedges to increase the size of fields in order to satisfy the post-war need for increased food supplies. In more recent times, occasional attempts at re-establishing itself have met with stiff resistance in the form of the flail-mower. The winter flailing of hedges ranks alongside DDT as one of the most environmentally damaging innovations of the twentieth century. By 1985, when the Bishops Stortford Natural History Society came to revise the local list that Allan had published in 1950, the Lappet was listed as 'widely distributed but not common'. Conversation with the late

Charles Watson and others who had a hand in its production suggests strongly that it was based more on a perception of a few years earlier than the true situation at 1985. I moved to live in Bishops Stortford in October 1986 and in spite of considerable trapping effort have recorded the species there only once – a male at Sawbridgeworth Marsh on 17th July 1990; in my opinion it had more or less vanished by the mid-1980s. The only post-1960 records available are from Stevenage in 1967 (Jack Newton), Totteridge, 5th July 1973 (Ian Lorimer), Bishops Stortford, 5th August 1979 (Charles Watson), Harpenden, 17th July 1990 (Adrian Riley), Sawbridgeworth Marsh, 17th July 1990 (Colin Plant), Bishops Stortford, 8th July 1993 (James Fish and Julian Reeves), Long Marston, 9th July 1994 (Alan Bernard) and Pirton, 1995 (Dug Heath).

SATURNIIDAE

Worldwide there are around 1,300 species of saturniid moths, but most are tropical and Europe can muster just six, of which only one is present in Britain.

1643 *Saturnia pavonia* (L.) Emperor Moth

Recorded:	1829 – 2006
Distribution / Status:	Uncommon resident / Local
Conservation status:	Herts Stable
Caterpillar food plants:	Bramble. Elsewhere on heathers, sallow and Meadowsweet.
Flight period:	Late April to mid May
Records in database:	52

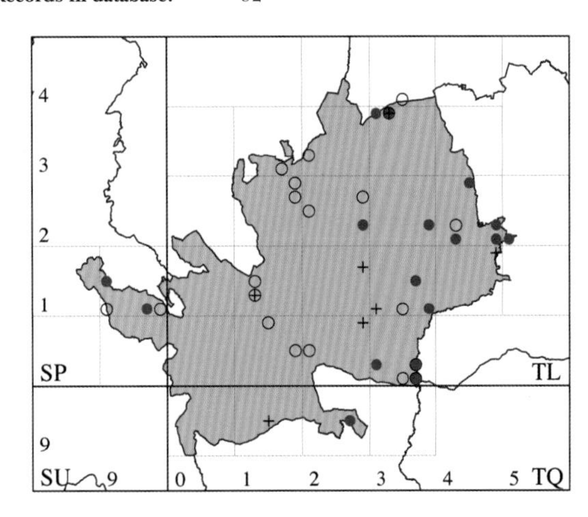

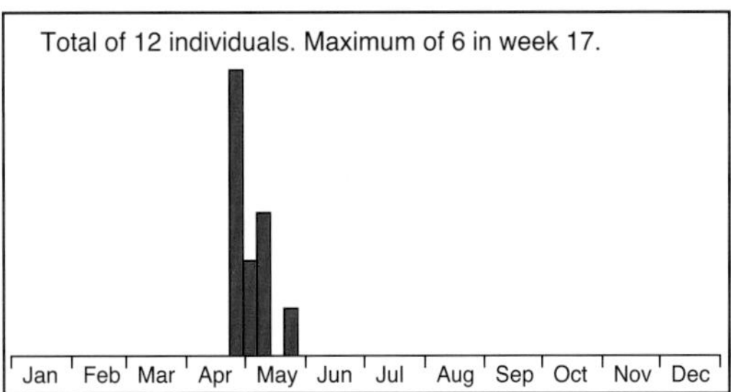

Although female Emperors sometimes come to light traps, this is a rare event, whilst the large and striking caterpillars are surprisingly well camouflaged and are extremely difficult to find, especially when feeding in difficult to search bramble patches. Thus, the easiest means of recording is to 'assemble' males. Pupae are easily purchased at most of the autumn entomological fairs or by post; these should be kept separately so that when the adults emerge they are not mated. Virgin females emit pheromones and these attract the males. Placing such a female in a small cage constructed of an old wire coat hanger and a bit of net curtain it can then be driven around the county and periodically hung out of the car window. Males will arrive within a few minutes if they are present and can be recorded. If they take longer than three of four minute then they may have travelled from some distance and should not be recorded for that precise location. Many of the dots on the map result from me walking a single unmated female about in April 2002; if I had been able to spend more time then I suspect that there would be more dots on the map. However, whilst the map perhaps reflects a degree of under-recording the number of crosses and open circles does suggest that there may be a fairly urgent need to visit these areas and attempt to assemble males. If the moth really has vanished from such a large number of sites that would be a matter of some concern and would call for a revision of its current conservation status.

[— *Actias selene* (Hübner, 1810) Indian Moon Moth

A male in a light trap at Totteridge on 6th June 1971 was clearly an escaped or a released specimen and is excluded from the species total for the county.]

ENDROMIDAE

This family of moths is unusual in that it is represented in the entire of the Palaearctic Region by a single species only. Males are day-flying.

[1644 *Endromis versicolora* (L.) Kentish Glory

Foster (1941) adds this striking species to the county list from 'Ware. One female in 1933 (Gerard)'. This is a most unlikely record. Mark Young, writing in *Moths and Butterflies of Great Britain & Ireland* volume 7, notes that 'Records are hopelessly confused by specimens labelled from place of emergence rather than capture and this may explain doubtful past records from .... Hertfordshire ...'. Gerard has been responsible for a number of records that may be interpreted in this way. These include the only county records of 2103: Plain Clay (*Eugnorisma depuncta*), 2217: Star-wort (*Cucullia asteris*) and an unacceptable record of 2219: Striped Lychnis (*Shargacucullia lychnitis*). Whilst taken in the context of other records for each individual species, some are possibly correct, the fact that Gerard has so many 'unusual' records is perhaps suspicious? On the basis of available evidence I cannot accept the Ware record and accordingly the Kentish Glory is not admitted as a Hertfordshire moth.]

DREPANOIDEA
DREPANIDAE

Traditionally, the Drepanidae and the Thyatiridae have been treated as families within the Geometroidea. However, recent thinking creates a new superfamily, the Drepanoidea and relegates the Thyatiridae to subfamily status within the Drepanidae. I have followed this thinking here, though it has no effect on our understanding of moths in Hertfordshire and need concern nobody apart from taxonomists. The Drepaninae are the Chinese Character, a bird-dropping mimic, along with the familiar 'hook-tips', which resemble dead leaves when at rest. Adults lack functional mouth-parts and do not feed. The sub-family is represented by just seven species in Britain, of which we can muster five in Hertfordshire.

DREPANINAE

1645 *Falcaria lacertinaria* (L.) Scalloped Hook-tip

Recorded:	1887 – 2006
Distribution / Status:	Local / Common resident
Conservation status:	Herts Stable
Caterpillar food plants:	birch
Flight period:	April – June and July/August, in two generations
Records in database:	74

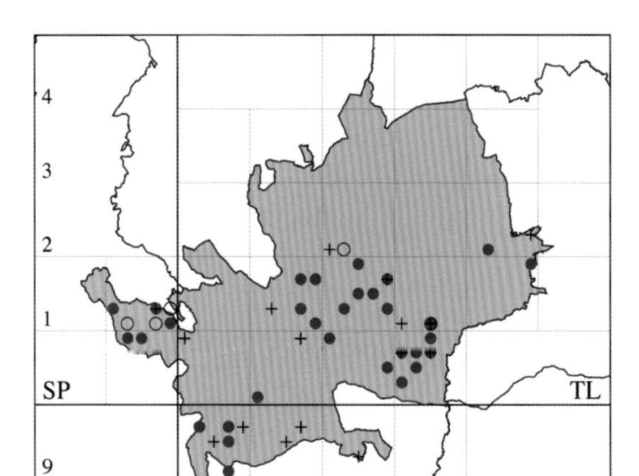

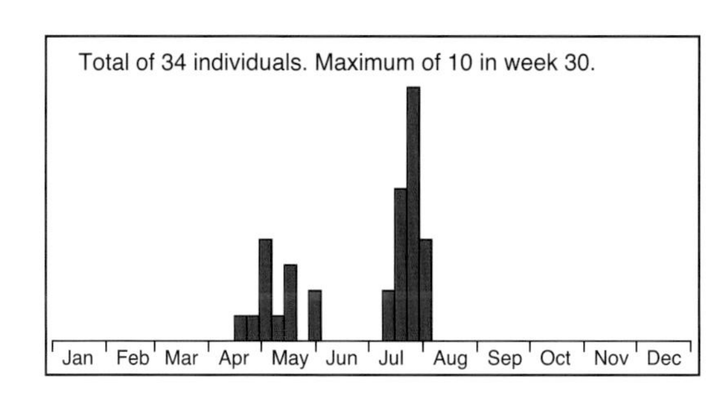

The absence of this species from the north of the county appears to be genuine and perhaps reflects the calcareous soils that render the area generally unsuitable for birch trees. Interestingly, however, this theory is less well-supported by the distribution of 1648: Pebble Hook-tip, also a birch feeder and whose alternative foodplant of alder is rare in the north-west. The 1997 Bedfordshire moth book shows records in that county along our north-west border; perhaps we have more work to do here! In the southern two-thirds of the county, on the other hand, the moth is likely to turn up in light traps wherever birch trees can be found, both in woodlands and in more suburban settings such as parks and gardens. Adults and larvae can be shaken from birch trees in the appropriate season.

1646 *Watsonalla binaria* (Hufn.) Oak Hook-tip

Recorded:	1887 – 2006
Distribution / Status:	Widespread / Common resident
Conservation status:	UK BAP Watch List Herts Stable
Caterpillar food plants:	English oak; Sessile oak
Flight period:	May/June and mid July – September in two broods
Records in database:	302

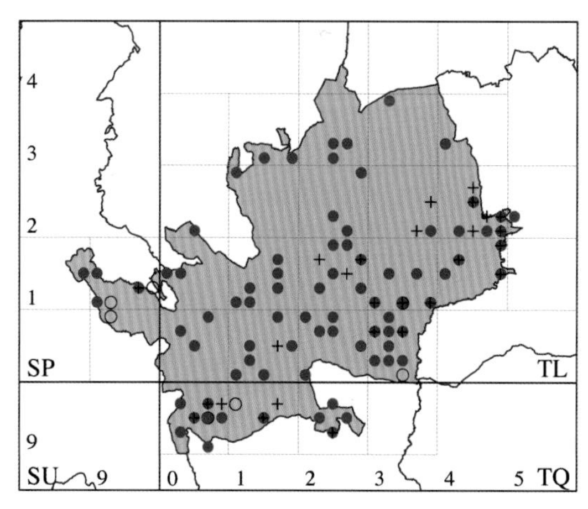

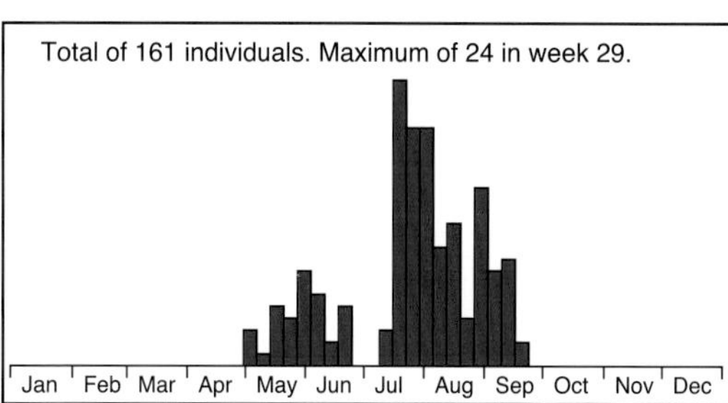

Although restricted as a caterpillar to oak trees, adult males of this moth frequently turn up in garden light traps in areas where the nearest oak tree appears to be some distance away, suggesting either that the males may wander considerably (unlike the closely related 1647: Barred Hook-tip), or that they are able to thrive on small, isolated oaks in gardens and other habitats. Females are less often seen, though they do come to light occasionally.

1647 *Watsonalla cultraria* (Fabr.) Barred Hook-tip

Recorded:	1895 – 2006
Distribution / Status:	Local / Common resident
Conservation status:	Herts Stable
Caterpillar food plants:	Beech
Flight period:	May/June and July-September
Records in database:	85

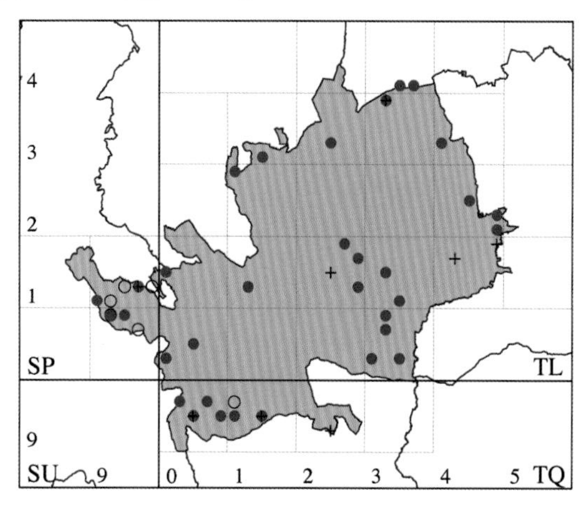

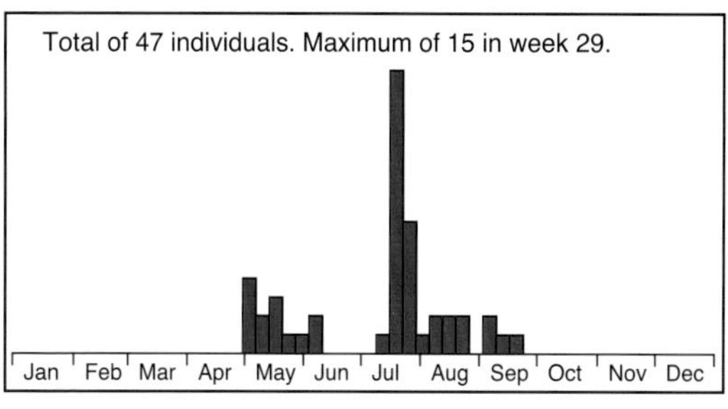

This moth is probably under-recorded, because it rarely travels far and so is poorly represented in light trap catches in gardens; a light trap placed thirty or so feet from a Beech tree will usually not attract any Barred Hook-tips yet a light placed closely against the trunk of the same tree may catch several. Although adults do come to mercury vapour lights, actinic traps may work better and I have, for example, recorded large numbers of the moth in Bishops Stortford Cemetery by placing an actinic trap at the base of one of the trees that line the road behind a brick wall – just a few inches from the passing public on their way home from the pub! A record from 'Tring, woods near Ashridge House', on 11th June 1887 by A. E. Gibbs in *Transactions of the Hertfordshire Natural History Society and Field Club* **4:** 1 [= Roman 50]) appears likely to fall on the Buckinghamshire side of the border and so our earliest Hertfordshire record is that from Watford made by S. H. Spencer in 1895.

1648 *Drepana falcataria* (L.) Pebble Hook-tip

Recorded:	1834 – 2006
Distribution / Status:	Widespread / Common resident
Conservation status:	Herts Stable
Caterpillar food plants:	Birch. Elsewhere also on Alder
Flight period:	Mid-April to September, in two generations
Records in database:	286

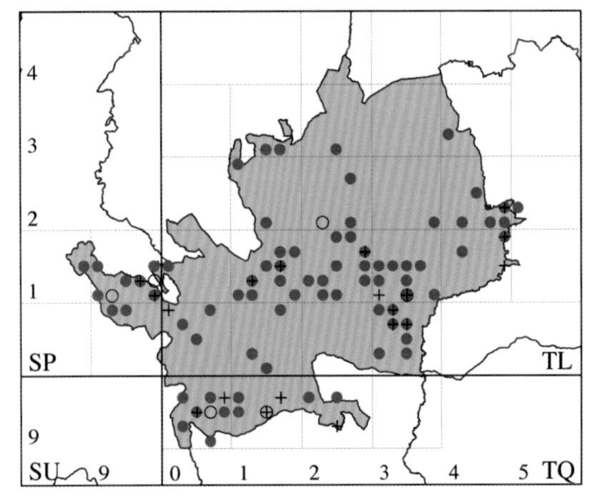

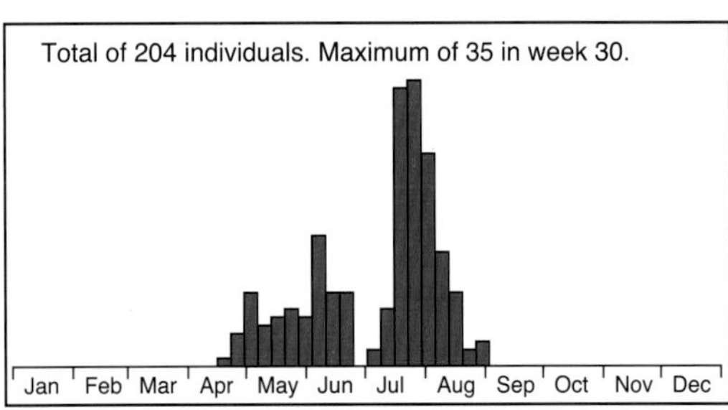

Although there are clearly two generations of adults in a given year, these appear to overlap and it is possible to find adults continuously from mid April to the start of September. Our earliest record is the illustration of a specimen from Hertford in J. F. Stephens *Illustrations of British Entomology* **4:** 6 (published in 1834). In his 1937 county list, Foster lists it from several localities without comment and the implication is that it was widespread and common at that time. Ian Lorimer noted it as decreasing from 1970 to 1979 at his garden light in Totteridge, but any such decline clearly did not continue and the moth is a familiar sight in most areas of the county and probably under-recorded in at least some of the blank patches in the map.

[1650 *Sabra harpagula* (Esper) Scarce Hook-tip

Listed for Hertfordshire by Gibbs (1902) in the *Victoria County History*, but the record was subsequently withdrawn by the same author (see Foster, 1937: 159).]

1651 *Cilix glaucata* (Scop.) Chinese Character

Recorded:	1887 – 2006
Distribution / Status:	Widespread / Common resident
Conservation status:	Herts Stable
Caterpillar food plants:	No data. Elsewhere on Blackthorn, hawthorn and other rosaceous trees and shrubs
Flight period:	Late April to early June then late June to mid September, apparently in three generations
Records in database:	304

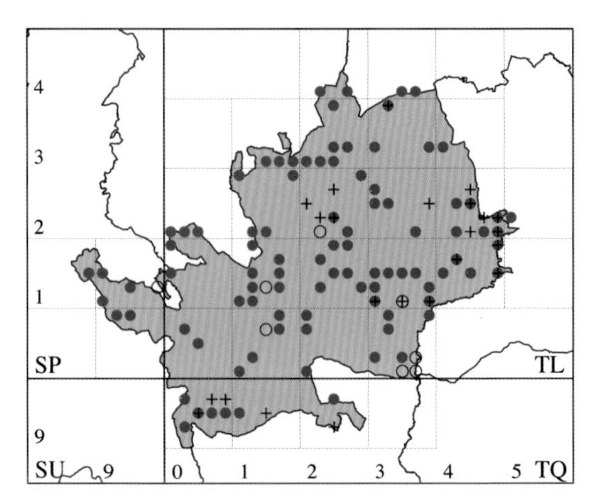

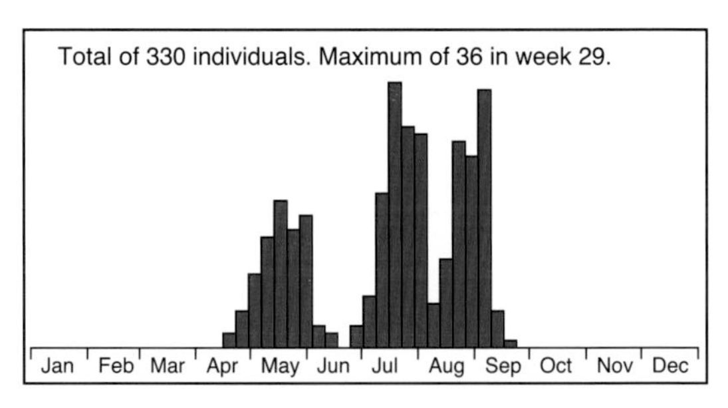

Perceived wisdom is that the Chinese Character has two generations per year, but the data plotted above, though using relatively small numbers, seem to indicate that in Hertfordshire we actually have three. The year 1887 is a 'safe estimate' for the earliest Hertfordshire record, but in reality it has probably been recorded long before then. It was listed by R. W. Bowyer for the Haileybury College area, for the period up to 1888, from the St Albans area, 'within two or three miles of the Town Hall', in the period before 1889 by Gibbs and from the area east of Bamville Wood Farm (near Harpenden Common) in the years before 1889, again by A. E. Gibbs. It appears to have remained common and widespread throughout the period between then and now.

THYATIRINAE

As stated earlier, this group of moths is currently treated as a subfamily of the Drepanidae. The group includes the rather attractive Buff Arches (*Habrosyne pyritoides*) and even more pretty Peach Blossom (*Thyatira batis*) both of which feed on brambles. Remaining species feed on tree leaves. Most of this group resemble members of the Noctuidae in general form, though their genitalia structure is somewhat different. The Common Lutestring more closely resembles a geometrid, and is sometimes misidentified by beginners as 1764: Common Marbled Carpet, although it differs in several significant respects. There are ten European species of which nine are found in Britain. Of these, Hertfordshire supports eight, but there is an unconfirmed record of the ninth.

1652 *Thyatira batis* (Linnaeus, 1758) Peach Blossom

Recorded: 1887 – 2006
Distribution / Status: Widespread / Common resident
Conservation status: Herts Stable
Caterpillar food plants: Bramble
Flight period: Mid-May to early August
Records in database: 169

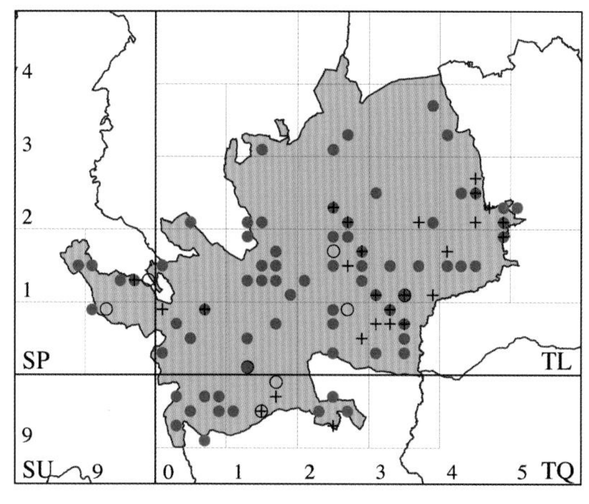

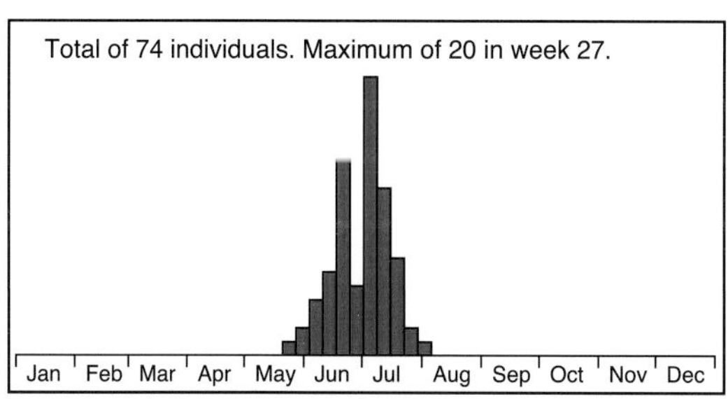

It is of interest to compare the distribution of this species with that of the next; whilst the Peach Blossom is apparently restricted to bramble, the Buff Arches can also feed on raspberry, hazel and hawthorn. Given the desolate nature of much of northern Hertfordshire it appears possible that the thinner distribution of the Peach Blossom in that part of Hertfordshire may be genuine. Elsewhere in the county, this distinctive moth is almost invariably expected in light traps, whether in the garden or 'out and about'. Larvae were located on bramble at Northaw Great Wood on 17th July 1969 (Barry Goater); all other reports are of adults.

1653 *Habrosyne pyritoides* (Hufn.) Buff Arches

Recorded: 1828 – 2006
Distribution / Status: Ubiquitous / Resident
Conservation status: Herts Stable
Caterpillar food plants: Bramble. Elsewhere on Raspberry, Hazel and hawthorn
Flight period: June to August
Records in database: 666

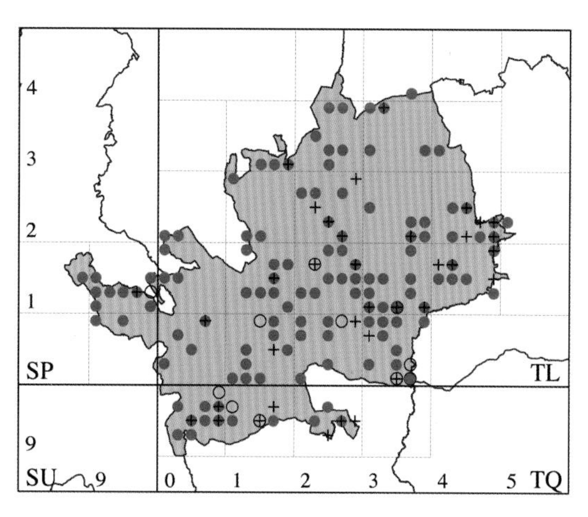

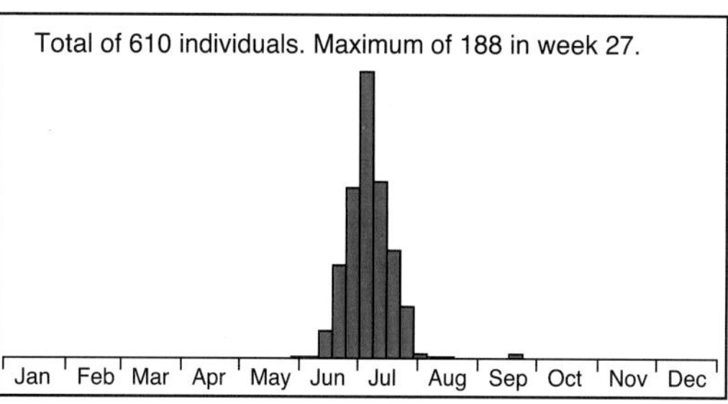

From its first report in the county, as a woodcut of a Hertford specimen in J. F. Stephens *Illustrations of British Entomology* **3**: 48 (published in 1829), to the present day this has apparently always been a common moth here. As intimated under the previous species, a foodplant other than bramble is perhaps used in the north of the county. The adult moth is not prone to variation and there is rather little more that can be said about it. It is single-brooded; a verified late report of a single adult in Bishops Stortford on 19th September 2004 (Jim Fish and Julian Reeves) is exceptional.

1654 *Tethea ocularis* (Linnaeus) ssp. *octogesimea* (Hb.) Figure of Eighty

Recorded: 1902 – 2006
Distribution / Status: Widespread / Common resident
Conservation status: Herts Stable
Caterpillar food plants: Not recorded. Elsewhere on Aspen and poplars
Flight period: Mid-May to July
Records in database: 303

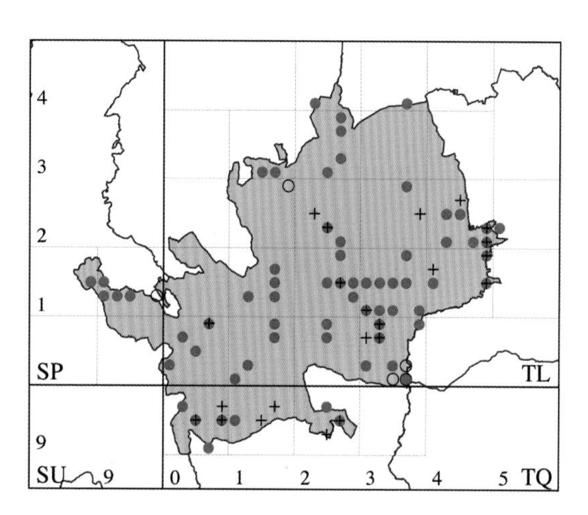

British examples of this species relate to subspecies *octogesimea* (Hübner); the nominotypical subspecies is prevalent in mainland Europe, but absent from Britain. The melanic form, presumably ab. *fusca* Cockayne, represented about 75 per cent of the Hertfordshire population during 1995 to 2006, although

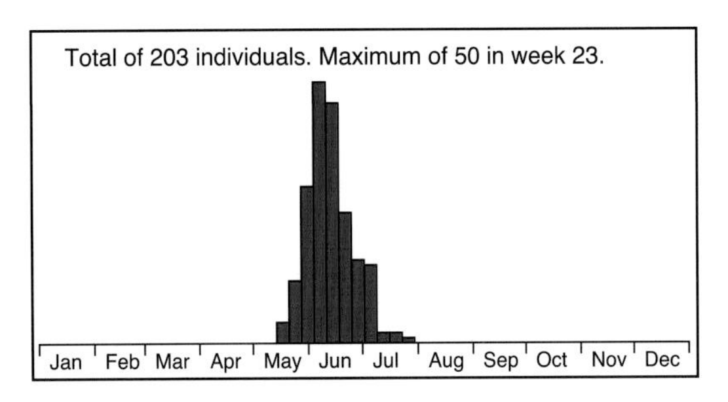

this is an estimate based largely on my own field survey and examination of other collections rather than a figure based on solid data, as the forms are rarely reported. It is interesting to note that in 1979 Ian Lorimer noted that the proportion of melanics at Totteridge was 'consistently increasing', suggesting that prior to that date the typical form may have been more common. Our earliest record is that from Wilstone Reservoir on 17th July 1902 (Barraud, 1903). (Foster, 1937) lists it from Bricket Wood, Hitchin, Watford, Hoddesdon, Aldenham and Berkhamsted, though the latter is incorrect and refers to four taken at sugar and light at Ashridge in 1934 (Hodgson, 1939). It appears to have been a common and widespread species throughout the last hundred years at least.

1655 *Tethea or* ([D.& S.]) Poplar Lutestring

Recorded: 1887 – 2006
Distribution / Status: Local / Uncommon resident
Conservation status: Herts Stable
Caterpillar food plants: Aspen
Flight period: May to August
Records in database: 79

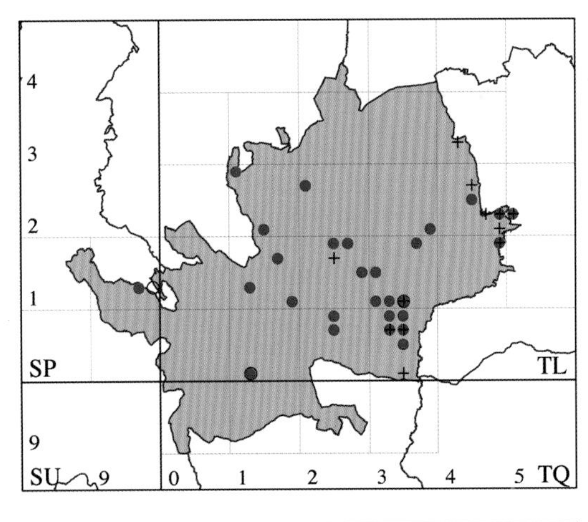

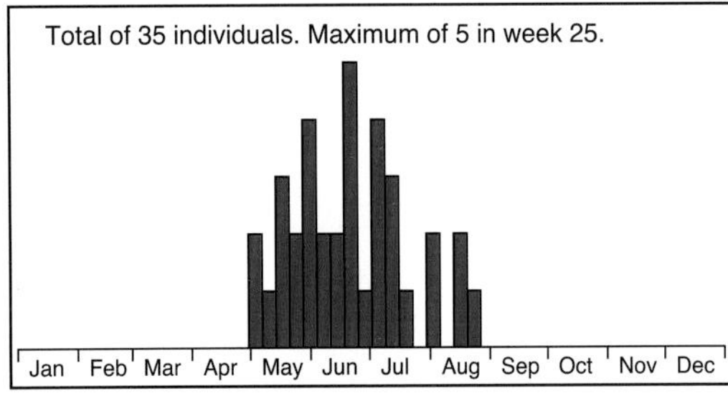

There is a long and drawn-out adult flight period from early May to the end of August in Hertfordshire, but in keeping with the situation elsewhere there are no peaks. This and the appearance of apparently freshly emerged moths throughout the flight period suggests that adults continuously emerge throughout the summer rather than the first out being particularly long-lived. Confusion is possible with the last species, 1654: Figure of Eighty, especially amongst the darker forms. Various degrees of melanism are exhibited by the present species in Hertfordshire though neither very bright non-melanics nor really dark examples have been seen and most are rather intermediate examples that defy naming. Young larvae found on aspen at Hoddesdon were exhibited at the South London Entomological and Natural History Society meeting on 28th June 1950 by T. R. Eagles (*Proceedings of the South London Entomological and Natural History Society 1950 – 51*: 11).

[1656 Tetheella fluctuosa (Hb.) Satin Lutestring

Volume 7, part 2, of *Moths and Butterflies of Great Britain and Ireland* (Harley Books) shows a post-1960 'dot' in ten-kilometre grid square TL21 – which is entirely within Hertfordshire. The text of the Thyatiridae chapter of *MBGBI* was written by Barry Goater, who informs me that the maps were prepared by Maitland Emmet. Extensive searches have failed to reveal where the data went after Maitland's death. Goater used to live in Hertfordshire and both he and I agree that a record of Satin Lutestring is rather improbable; on this basis, and in the absence of evidence to the contrary, I am inclined not to admit this species to the Hertfordshire list.]

1657 *Ochropacha duplaris* (L.) Common Lutestring

Recorded: 1900 – 2006
Distribution / Status: Local / Uncommon resident
Conservation status: Herts Stable
Caterpillar food plants: Not recorded. Elsewhere on birch, occasionally Hazel, oak and Alder
Flight period: June and July
Records in database: 24

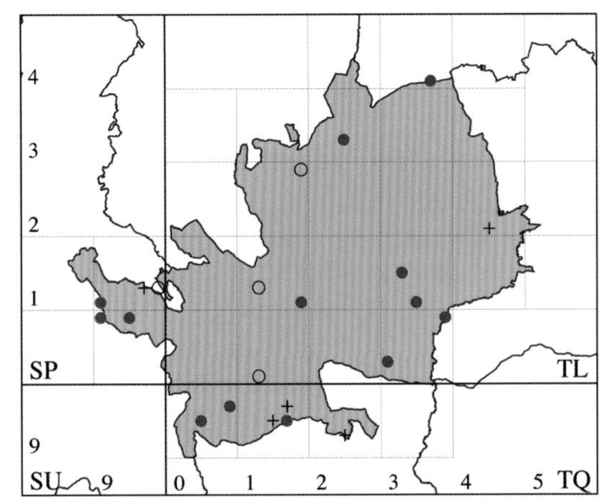

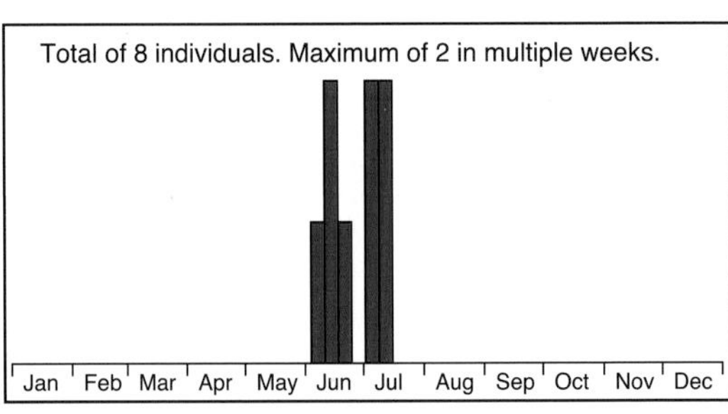

It seems that there is great scope for confusion on the part of the inexperienced of this species with 1764: *Chloroclysta truncata*, the Common Marbled Carpet. Much of the problem undoubtedly lies in the fact that a more or less plain, sooty-brown industrial melanic form accounts for 100 per cent of the population here; typical specimens are probably not likely to be confused, but are apparently not reported in Hertfordshire. Unfortunately, older records in Foster's 1937 list do not record the form of the moths encountered and it is not possible to know when the melanic form emerged here. The melanic form that we encounter is perhaps ab. *obscura* Tutt, but several standard identification guides also refer to an additional 'sooty brown form prevalent in the London area' unhelpfully failing to either define or name it. There is scope for interesting genetic research here if anyone is looking for a subject for their PhD thesis! Whilst it is highly likely that some individuals are being overlooked as Common Marbled Carpets, the moth is nevertheless not a regular attendee at the traps on recording trips and so whilst there is bound to be a level of under-recording, that level may not be necessarily high and the moth is perhaps genuinely local in distribution. It may, however, be better attracted to sugar than to light?

1658 *Cymatophorima diluta* ([D.& S.]) ssp. *hartwiegi* (Reisser) Oak Lutestring

Recorded:	1887 – 2005
Distribution / Status:	Local / Uncommon resident
Conservation status:	UK BAP Watch List Herts Scarce
Caterpillar food plants:	English Oak; Sessile Oak
Flight period:	September/October
Records in database:	14

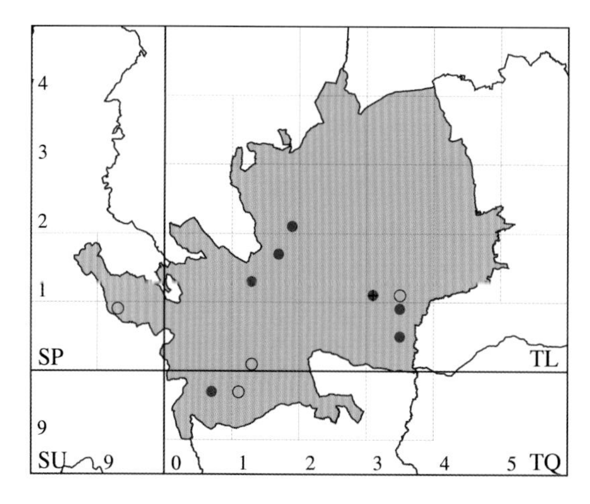

British examples of this species relate to subspecies *hartwiegi* (Reisser); the nominotypical subspecies is absent from Britain. Adults are rather uncommon at light, preferring the sugar patch, though when they do decide to come they often appear in large number. Our earliest record is from Bricket Wood in 1887 (A. E. Gibbs) and all records relate to oak woodlands except for one in the light trap on the Rothamsted Estate at Harpenden during 1999. More sugaring and less light trapping would likely produce an increase in the records of this species.

1659 *Achlya flavicornis* (L.) ssp. *galbanus* (Tutt) Yellow Horned

Recorded:	1896 – 2006
Distribution / Status:	Widespread / Common resident
Conservation status:	Herts Stable
Caterpillar food plants:	Silver Birch
Flight period:	February to April, occasional later dates
Records in database:	67

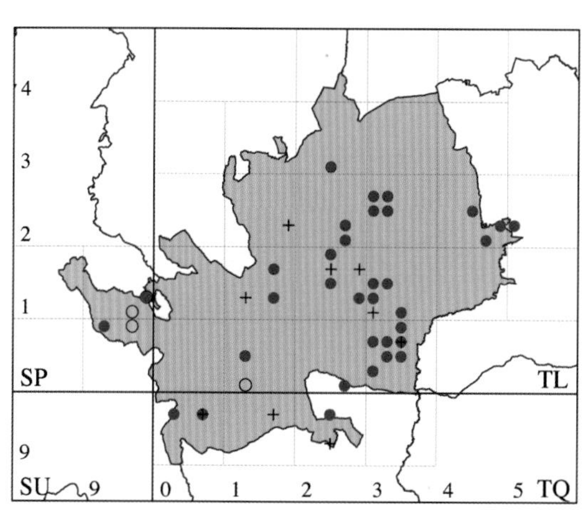

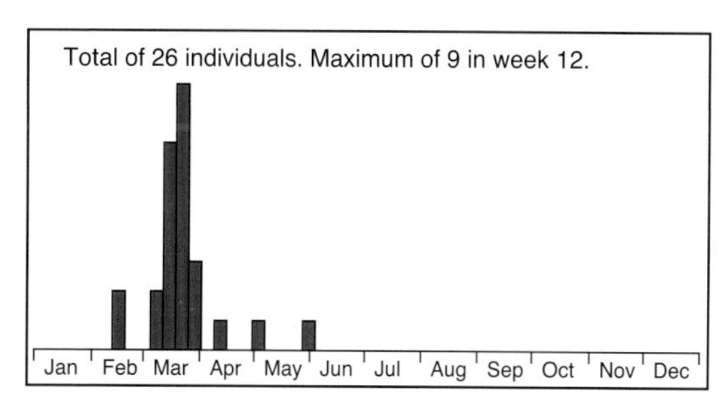

British examples of this species relate to subspecies *galbanus* (Tutt); the nominotypical subspecies is absent from Britain. Grey forms approaching the appearance of the typical subspecies found in Europe occur at relatively low density, perhaps 15 to 20 per cent of the Hertfordshire population during 1995 to 2006, but these are melanic *galbanus* and not true *flavicornis*. It is of interest that Ian Lorimer, recorded it as 'Fairly common. All melanic' at Totteridge during 1979. The adult is attracted easily to light if the trap is placed directly under birch trees. At Hares Garden Wood near Tring on 13th February 2004 a trap placed against the trunk of an isolated mature birch caught this species as predicted to an incredulous audience whilst none of the other nearby traps caught any, in spite of there being a smattering of birch trees throughout the woodland. Three unusually late dates recorded in the county are 4th May 2003 at Whippendell Wood (Dave Murray), 16th May 1896 at Bricket Wood (S. H. Spencer) and on 3rd June 2004 at Thunderfield Grove (Mark Cooper). The flight chart excludes historical data.

1660 *Polyploca ridens* (Fabr.) Frosted Green

Recorded:	1887 – 2006
Distribution / Status:	Widespread / Common resident
Conservation status:	Herts Stable
Caterpillar food plants:	English Oak
Flight period:	April/May
Records in database:	72

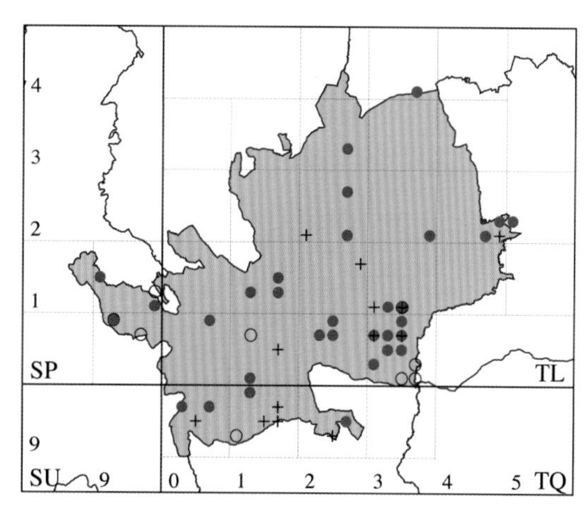

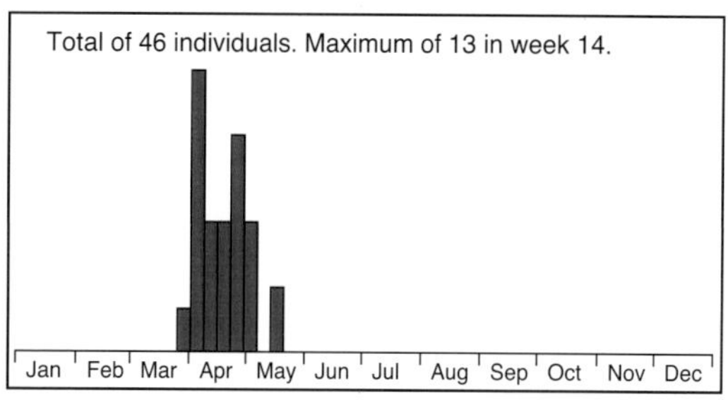

This dark moth is often mistaken for a cuculliine noctuid, though the early date would rule out members of that subfamily. It is likely to be found wherever mature oaks grow, typically in woodland. A larva was beaten from English Oak at

Oxhey Woods in 1938 (Eric Classey); young saplings apparently do not support the caterpillar. The adult moth is very variable. At Bushey, Barry Goater recorded that 100 per cent of the population was referable to the melanic ab. *unicolor* Cockayne, in which the whole wing surface is dark blackish green with darker veins and no other markings. This form is currently very common in the woods around Bishops Stortford, though it forms perhaps only 50 per cent of the catch with the lighter ab. *fumosa* Warnecke, in which the pattern shows through, also present. I have not personally seen any typical, non-melanic examples in Hertfordshire, though some may be unreported.

GEOMETROIDEA
GEOMETRIDAE

With around 900 species in Europe, of which about one third can be seen in Britain, the geometers are one of the largest groups of moths. The all-time Hertfordshire total is 233 species, although 36 of these have not been seen for many years and may be extinct in the county. The majority of geometers rest with their wings flat against the surface (planiform), making full use of their wing markings as camouflage. Presumably it is wing markings that dictate whether the forewings cover the hindwings or whether all four wings surfaces are visible. Our two Orange Underwing species (and some others in Europe) roll their wings around the twig on which they are resting to further enhance their cryptic presentation. Other geometers rest with their wings closed vertically above the body (veliform) in the manner of a butterfly whilst another group positions the resting wings in a 'tent' over the body (tectiform). The family is divided into several subspecies of which six affect Hertfordshire, from the relatively small Archiearinae (2 species), Alsophilinae (1 species), Geometrinae (7 species) and Sterrhinae (25 species) to the much larger Larentiinae (which includes the pugs) and Ennominae.

ARCHIEARINAE

1661 *Archiearis parthenias* (L.) Orange Underwing

Recorded: 1828 – 2005
Distribution / Status: Local / Uncommon resident
Conservation status: Herts Stable
Caterpillar food plants: Not recorded. Elsewhere, on birches
Flight period: Mid-March/April
Records in database: 37

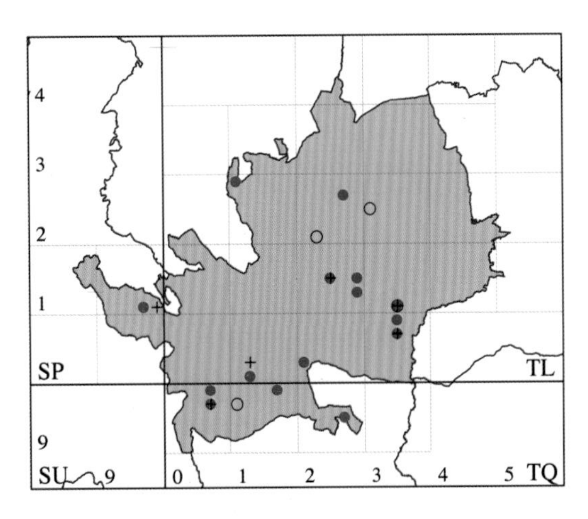

This day-flying moth flits about the tops of birch trees on sunny afternoons in March and early April. Sometimes it will descend to ground level where it may settle on a sunlit patch, but more

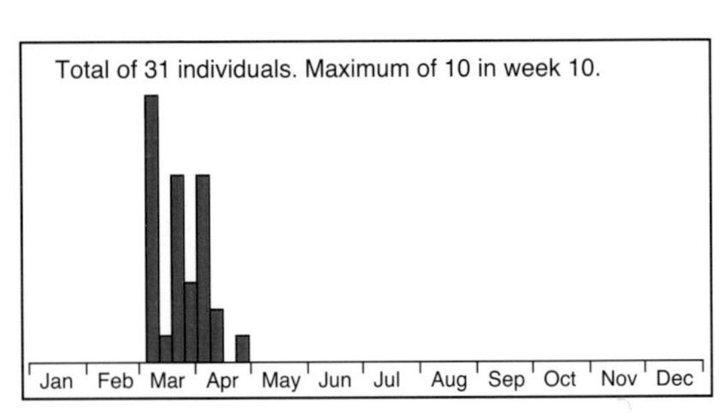

often than not it keeps a healthy few centimetres beyond the reach of the net, which is unfortunate since separation from 1662: Light Orange Underwing requires careful examination. The different foodplants are of help, but in many places it is hard to be certain that the odd aspen tree is not hidden away amongst the birches. One or other species is present along the Bishops Stortford Ring Road where it passes through Birchanger Woods; I have seen it there almost annually since 1987, but both trees are present and the moth has *never* come within reach so neither species shows a map dot in that area of the county. Orange Underwing is probably more widespread than the map suggests, but the apparent notion that the removal of tall birches from woodlands is beneficial in some way to the long-term woodland structure is ill-conceived and does little to allow this insect to thrive.

1662 *Archiearis notha* (Hb.) Light Orange Underwing

Recorded: 1932 – 2004
Distribution / Status: Local / Very local resident
Conservation status: Herts Scarce
Caterpillar food plants: Not recorded. Elsewhere, on Aspen
Flight period: April
Records in database: 14

The problems of identification have been mentioned under the last species. Particular care has been exercised to ensure that records of either species have not been accepted where the observer may have based the identification solely on foodplant association. With this in mind the Light Orange Underwing appears to be far less frequently encountered than the Orange Underwing, although that is not to say there is no under-recording. Foster's 1937 list reported only Broxbourne Common, Broxbourne Woods and Bricket Wood, the latter in 1932. Only four records made since 1994 have dates; these put the flight period from 31st March to 30th April, but the number of moths is clearly too low to be significant. Two historical records also fall within April.

ALSOPHILINAE

1663 *Alsophila aescularia* ([D.& S.]) March Moth

Recorded: 1887 – 2006
Distribution / Status: Ubiquitous / Abundant resident
Conservation status: Herts Stable
Caterpillar food plants: Hornbeam. Elsewhere on various trees
Flight period: January - April
Records in database: 379

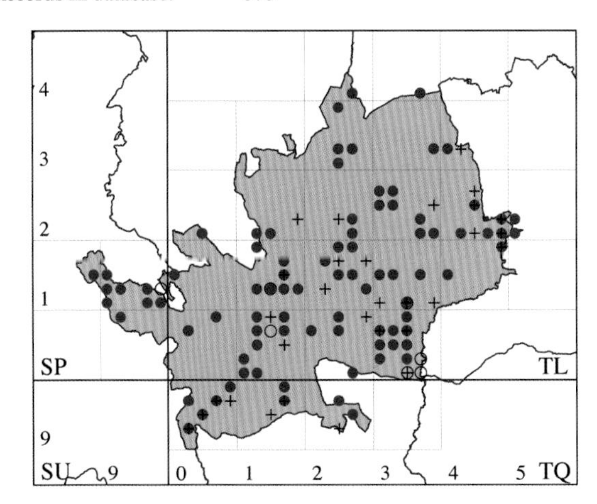

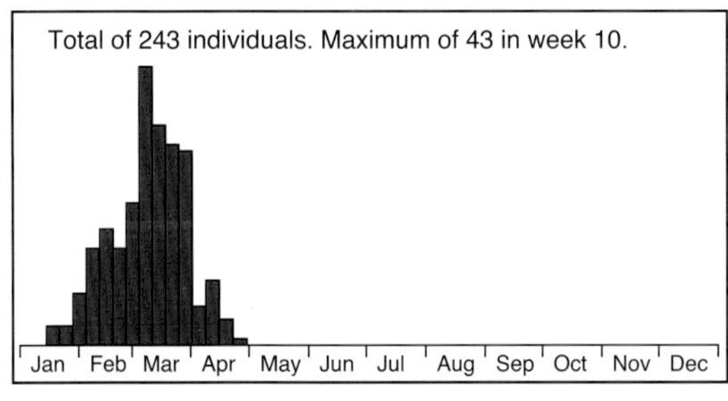

Early records are available from Haileybury College, St Albans and Harpenden Common, all prior to 1888. The moth was 'Common in all districts' according to Foster (1937) and this is the situation today. The date of the first emergence of adults may have crept forward over the years, though we have little useable historical data to compare with the current data set. The colloquial name itself suggests a species that flies in March, but whilst this is certainly its peak period, it is often seen much earlier. The extremes are at the Haberdasher's Aske's School on 12th December 1964 (Barry Goater), Royston on 15th May 1999 (John Chainey & Jenny Spence) and Danemead Wood on 20th May 2000.

GEOMETRINAE

1665 *Pseudoterpna pruinata* (Hufn.) ssp. *atropunctaria* Walker Grass Emerald

Recorded: 1884 – 1999
Distribution / Status: Local – perhaps absent / Very rare resident – perhaps extinct
Conservation status: Herts Endangered
Caterpillar food plants: Elsewhere Gorse, Broom and Petty Whin
Flight period: July
Records in database: 9

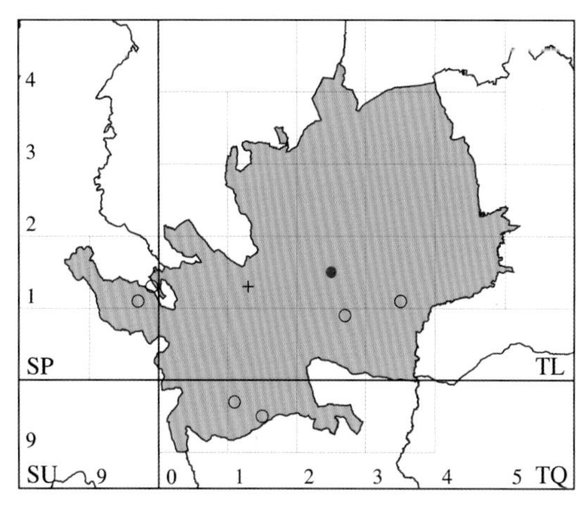

British examples of this are all referable to subspecies *atropunctaria* Walker; the nominate subspecies is found on mainland Europe. All Hertfordshire records are given: Sandridge area, prior to 1884, not mapped (Griffith, 1884); Haileybury College area, for the period up to 1888 (R. W. Bowyer); Gladstone Road Watford, 1893 (S. H. Spencer); Bushey Heath, 1902 (P. J. Barraud); Northchurch Common, 1938 (S. B. Hodgson); Essendon, 1938 (L. S. Hodson); Ashridge, 1938 (S. B. Hodgson); Rothamsted Estate, Harpenden – frequent in the Barnfield trap up to 1949 when that trap ceased to operate, 'a few' in traps 26 (operating 1965 to 1999), 27 (operated 1966 to 1999) and 33 (operated 1972 – 1999) from 1967 to 1983, but none since (Riley, 1999) and Warren Way, Digswell, 17th July 1999 (Tom Gladwin). Apart from the Digswell record, which was from atypical habitat, the last record of this species in the county was 24 years ago and it is feared that it is now no longer present. If refound, it should be treated as Endangered.

1666 *Geometra papilionaria* (L.) Large Emerald

Recorded: 1884 – 2006
Distribution / Status: Local / Common resident
Conservation status: Herts Stable
Caterpillar food plants: No records. Elsewhere on Birch, occasionally Alder, Hazel and Beech.
Flight period: Mid-June to mid August
Records in database: 110

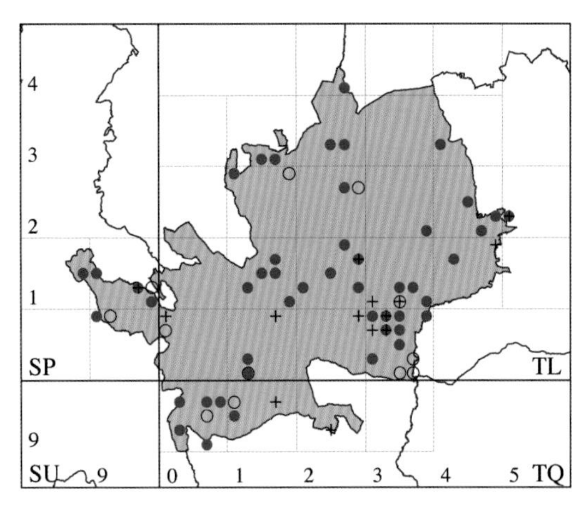

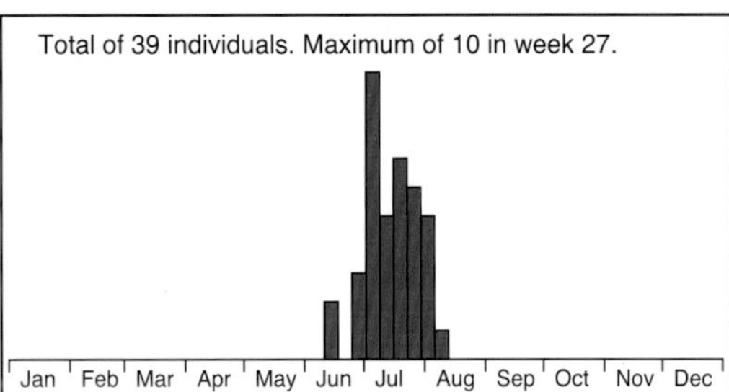

The Large Emerald is mostly found in woodlands, and then usually in association with mature Birch trees. It usually attends light traps in very low numbers from midnight onwards and in spite of a perception that it is rare the map shows that it is actually quite widespread. Fresh examples are striking, but after they have been on the wing for a few days they fade to near white and may not be immediately recognised by the inexperienced.

1667 *Comibaena bajularia* ([D.& S.]) Blotched Emerald

Recorded: 1884 – 2006
Distribution / Status: Local / Common resident
Conservation status: Herts Stable
Caterpillar food plants: English Oak
Flight period: Mid-June to August
Records in database: 136

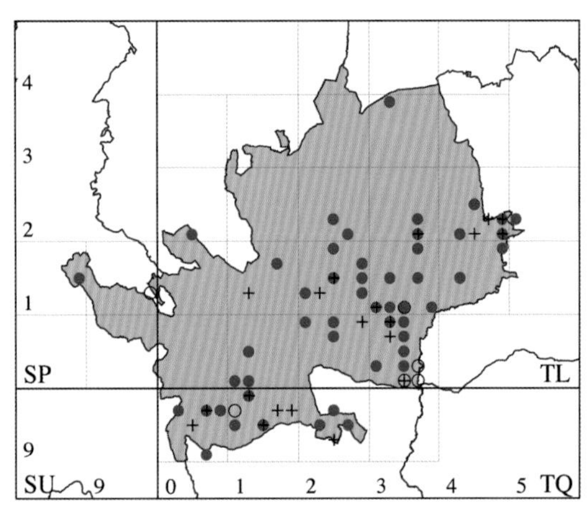

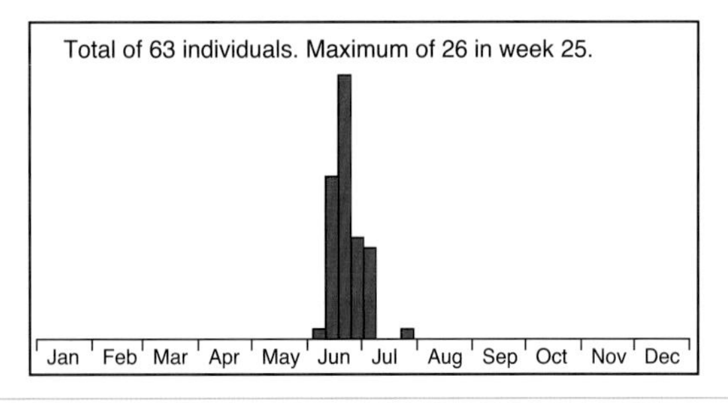

The larval requirement of this species for oak is reflected in the lack of records from the northern part of the county where examples of that tree are few and far between. In the mid and south of Hertfordshire the moth is likely to be present in most places, though only rarely does it attend the trap in more than single figures. The record for Berkhamsted in Foster (1937) is in error for Ashridge, where it was 'not uncommon at light in one oak wood' (Hodgson (1939).

1669 *Hemithea aestivaria* (Hb.) Common Emerald

Recorded: 1887 – 2006
Distribution / Status: Widespread / Common resident
Conservation status: Herts Stable
Caterpillar food plants: Common Hawthorn, Silver Birch, and probably other trees
Flight period: June to mid August
Records in database: 512

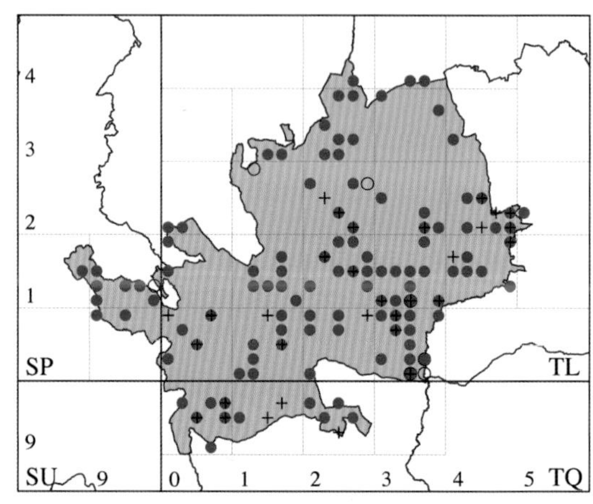

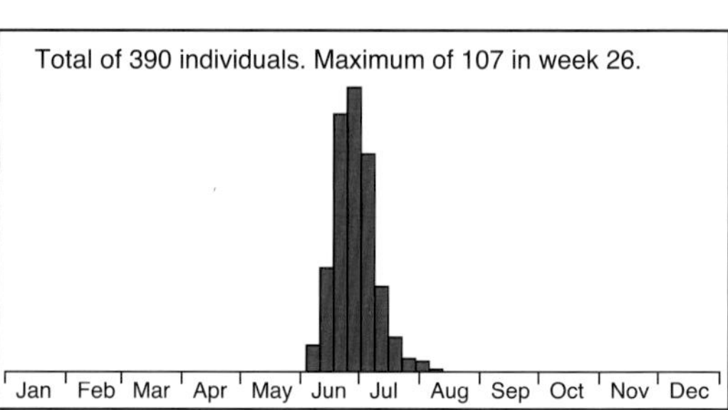

Past records indicate that this has always been, as now, a common moth in Hertfordshire. Penultimate instar larvae were found on Common Hawthorn at Kensworth Quarry in May 2003 and on Silver Birch at Birchanger Wood, Bishops Stortford in May 2006 – adults being reared in both cases to confirm the identification.

1670 *Chlorissa viridata* (L.) Small Grass emerald

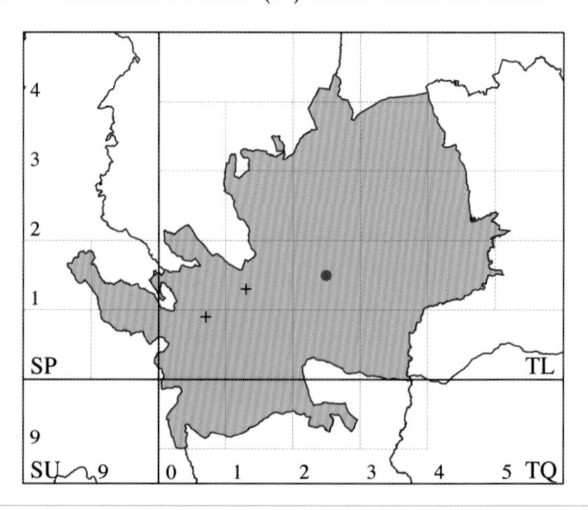

Recorded:	1976 – 1999
Distribution / Status:	Absent / Vagrant
Conservation status:	-
Caterpillar food plants:	No data. Elsewhere, on heather, birch and sallow
Flight period:	Elsewhere in June and July
Records in database:	4

We have just four records of this moth in Hertfordshire, from the Rothamsted Estate, Harpenden on 14th July 1948 and 13th August 1976 (Riley, *Entomologist's Record* **111:** 79), from a garden in Hemel Hempstead in 1994 (Malcolm Newland) and from a garden in Digswell on 17th July 1999 (Tom Gladwin). The 1976 record was on an exceptionally late date at the end of the long hot summer of that year during which many unusual sightings of moths across Britain were attributed to wandering stimulated by the weather conditions. The two more recent records defy explanation, but are most unlikely to represent nearby breeding populations. Plant (1993) records the last record in the Greater London area as being made in 1886. The moth is typically associated with heathland in lowland Britain.

1673 *Hemiostola chrysoprasaria* (Esp.) Small Emerald

Recorded:	1884 – 2006
Distribution / Status:	Widespread / Common resident
Conservation status:	UK BAP Watch List Herts Stable
Caterpillar food plants:	Traveller's Joy
Flight period:	June to August then September
Records in database:	403

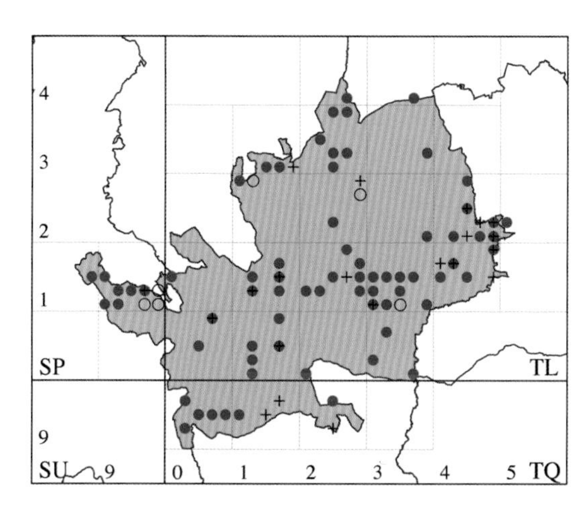

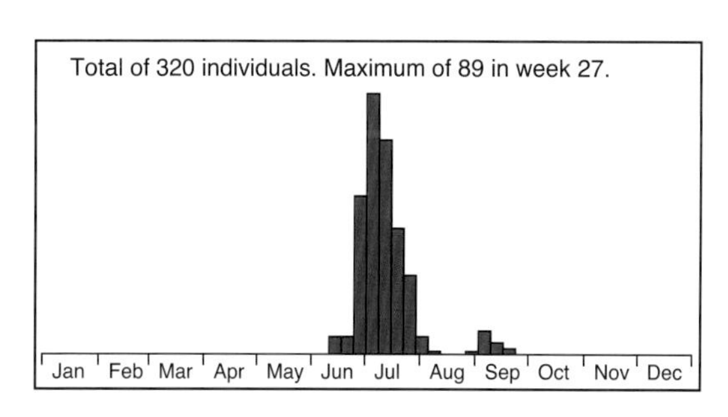

This is normally a single-brooded species. The small second peak of September adults is comprised of one individual at Bishops Stortford in 2003 and then eleven reports in 2006 from Ware (Elizabeth Goodyear), two separate sites in Bishops Stortford (Jim Fish, Julian Reeves and Colin Plant) and Chorleywood (Richard Ellis). It will be interesting to see if this heralds a change or if it is merely an aberration in a single year. The adult moth is present at most sites though rarely is it found in any significant number.

1674 *Jodis lactearia* (L.) Little Emerald

Recorded:	1884 – 2006
Distribution / Status:	Local / Uncommon resident
Conservation status:	Herts Threatened
Caterpillar food plants:	Not recorded. Elsewhere on various trees
Flight period:	June/July
Records in database:	53

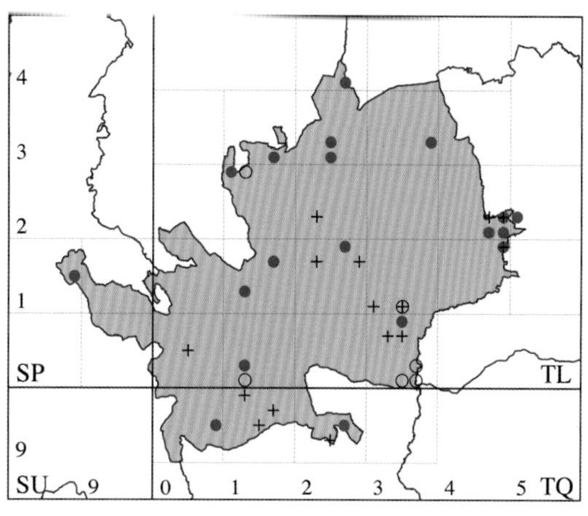

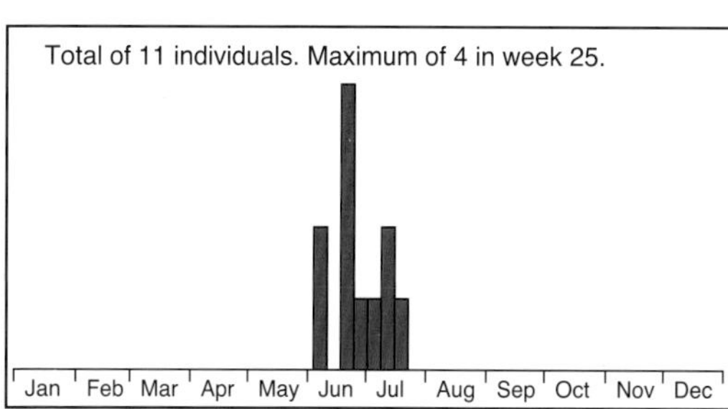

Woodland features at almost all the sites where we have reports of this moth, which is absent from many garden lists. My suggestion (Plant, 1993) that the moth was in general decline across the entire London Area, which includes the southern third of Hertfordshire, is not contradicted by the present results and the map shows clearly a number of sites from which it has not been recorded for some time. Future studies would be wise to record numbers and dates of captures of this species.

STERRHINAE

The 'waves', which is what the Sterrhinae are, perhaps derive that English name from the original Latin *Phalaenae Geometrae Arcuatostriatae*, which was used by Denis & Schiffermüller to define the group. They are a largish group, some of which may present problems of identification. Of the 42 British species, Hertfordshire has records of 26, although one of these may not be valid.

1676 *Cyclophora annularia* (Fabr.) Mocha

Recorded:	1884 - 1916
Distribution / Status:	Absent / ?Former immigrant
Conservation status:	-
Caterpillar food plants:	No records. Elsewhere, on Field Maple
Flight period:	August (one record).
Records in database:	4

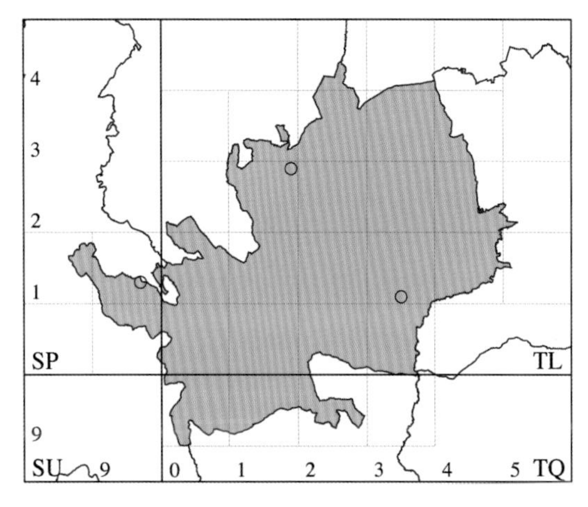

The Mocha is very local in its distribution in southern Britain and is a woodland inhabitant. Our four records are from the Sandridge area (Griffith, 1884), Haileybury College (Bowyer, 1888); Tring, undated (Goodson, in Foster, 1937) and Hitchin, 1916 (Foster). The Sandridge area record cannot be accurately mapped and the precise position of the other three may not be correct, though the map is representative. There are no other records, although Richard Ellis caught one in his garden light trap at Chorleywood, a few tens of metres into Buckinghamshire, on 22nd August 2006; interestingly, another example, a male, was caught on the same date at Hampstead, Middlesex (London) by Ray Softly and it appears that these two examples at least were either immigrant or vagrants. The foodplant grows in all four areas from which we have historical records, but there is nothing to suggest that the moths represent breeding populations.

1677 *Cyclophora albipunctata* (Hufn.) Birch Mocha

Recorded:	1884 – 2006
Distribution / Status:	Local / Uncommon resident
Conservation status:	Stable
Caterpillar food plants:	Silver Birch
Flight period:	May to early June then late July/August
Records in database:	28

Foster (1937) records '*Leucophthalmia orbicularia*, Hübn.' from Bricket Wood by Cottam. Later (Foster, 1942), for the same species he adds 'Berkhamsted district – regular but rare (Bell)', 'Broxbourne Woods, 1936' and 'Oxhey Woods, common in

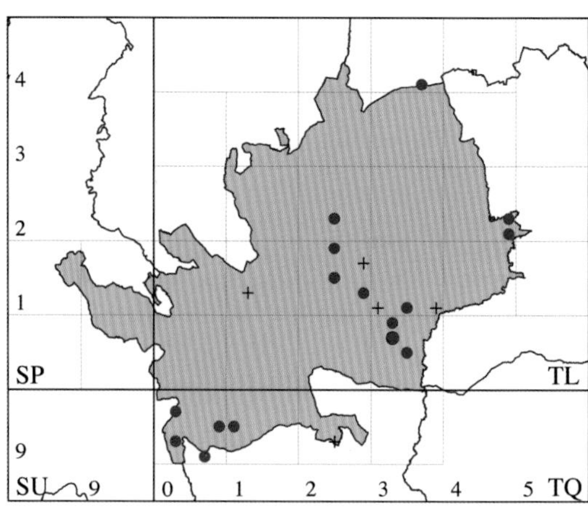

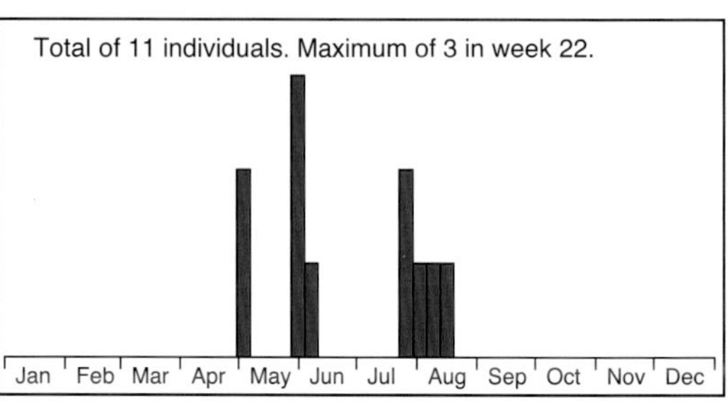

1936–7–8 (Classey)'. These records call for clarification. The name of 1675: Dingy Mocha, *orbicularia* Hb., is synonymous with *pendularia* Clerck, and Foster's next entry in his 1937 list refers to '*Leucophthalmia pendularia*, Clerck' from Sandridge by Griffith. There is no entry for the relatively more common *albipunctata* (Hufn.), a name which is synonymous with *pendularia* auctt., but not with *pendularia* Clerck. It is thus quite unclear what species Foster implied in either entry. Eric Classey has kindly clarified the situation to me by noting that his own record from Oxhey Wood relates to 1677: Birch Mocha; by implication the other records are also referable to this species. This still leaves room for confusion concerning Foster's entry for '*Leucophthalmia pendularia*, Clerck' from Sandridge by Griffith, but the presence of the Dingy Mocha in Hertfordshire seems quite improbable and I am not at all convinced that this was the species intended. Today, the Birch Mocha is locally distributed in woodlands with young birches, apparently preferring trees in the sapling stage.

1678 *Cyclophora puppillaria* (Hb.) Blair's Mocha

Recorded:	1965 - 1969
Distribution / Status:	Random / Rare immigrant
Conservation status:	-
Caterpillar food plants:	-
Flight period:	In Britain, August to October
Records in database:	2

A single misidentified specimen taken at Tring on 14th October 1965 by A. L. Goodson was discovered in the series of

1679: False Mocha in the British collection at the Natural History Museum by John Chainey during May 2007. Our only other record is from Totteridge, where Ian Lorimer caught one in his garden light trap on 22nd October 1969.

1679 *Cyclophora porata* (L.) False Mocha

Recorded: 1884 – 1996
Distribution / Status: Extremely local / ?Former resident ?Immigrant
Conservation status: UK BAP Priority Species. Herts Extinct
Caterpillar food plants: Not recorded. Elsewhere, on oak
Flight period: Elsewhere, May/June and August
Records in database: 6

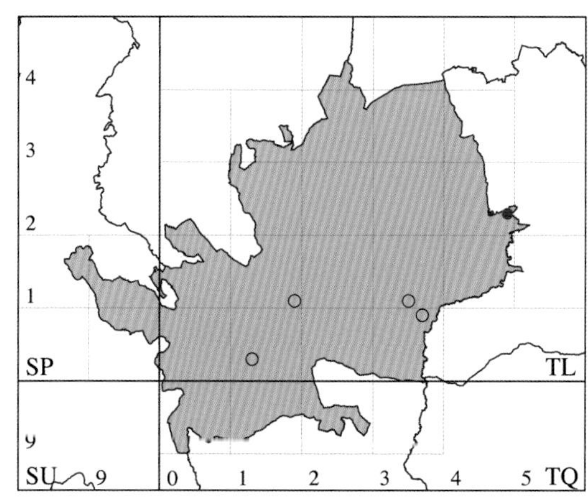

Our only records are for the Sandridge area (Griffith, 1884) – not mapped, the Haileybury College area (Bowyer, 1888), Bricket Wood, Symond's Hyde and Hoddesdon (Foster, 1937) then Bishops Stortford, 14th August 1996 (James Fish and Julian Reeves). Interestingly, Bernard Skinner caught one the same year as the Bishops Stortford record (9th June) in South Croydon, Surrey, representing first London Area record since 1951.

1680 *Cyclophora punctaria* (L.) Maiden's Blush

Recorded: 1884 – 2006
Distribution / Status: Widespread / Common resident
Conservation status: Stable
Caterpillar food plants: English oak
Flight period: April to October in two generations
Records in database: 336

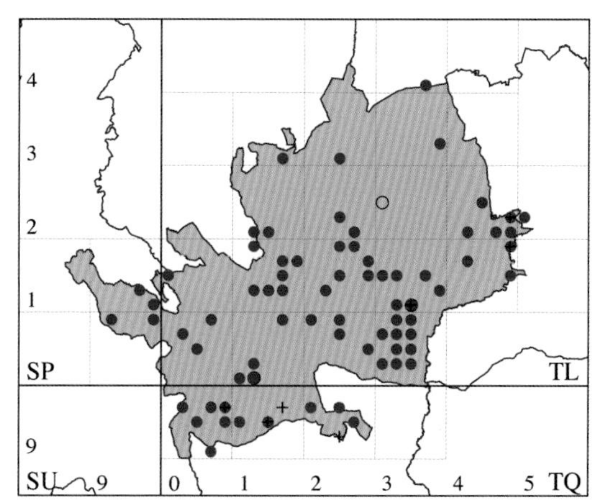

The small number of records (St Albans, Bricket Wood, Sandridge, Haileybury, Hitchin, Letchworth, Hoddesdon, Watford, Broxbourne Woods and Berkhamsted) given by Foster (1937), suggest that the species was widely, but rather locally distributed at the start of the twentieth century. The record from Berkhamsted in Foster (1937) is an error (Hodgson, 1939). Two generations of adults are evident in Hertfordshire; each is separated by a gap of two or three weeks in a given year, although the separation is not apparent in the chart because data from all years from 2000 to 2006 are combined.

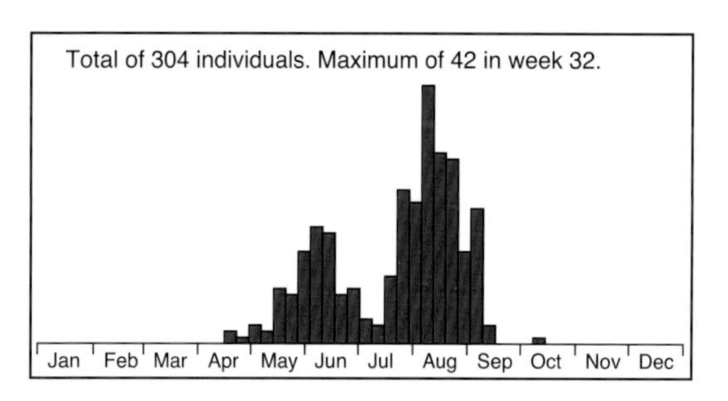

1681 *Cyclophora linearia* (Hb.) Clay Triple-lines

Recorded: 1888 – 2006
Distribution / Status: Local / Uncommon resident
Conservation status: Stable
Caterpillar food plants: Beech
Flight period: May to August
Records in database: 69

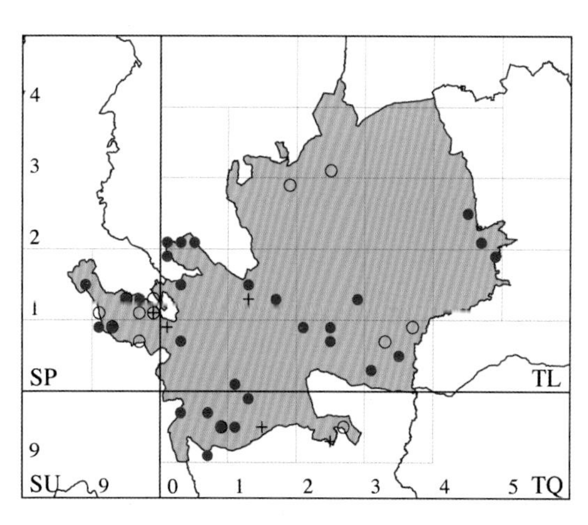

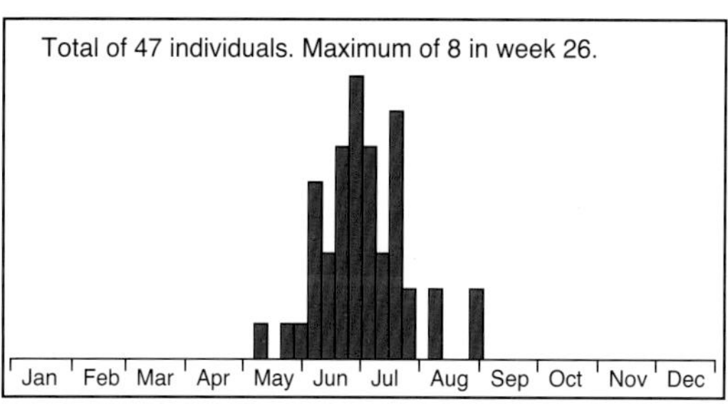

Records given by Foster (1937) suggest that it was local, but not uncommon and this remains the case today; the moth can be expected in association with beech trees throughout the county. The lack of records in the north of the county, perhaps reflects a degree of under-recording.

1682 *Timandra comae* (Schmidt) Blood-vein

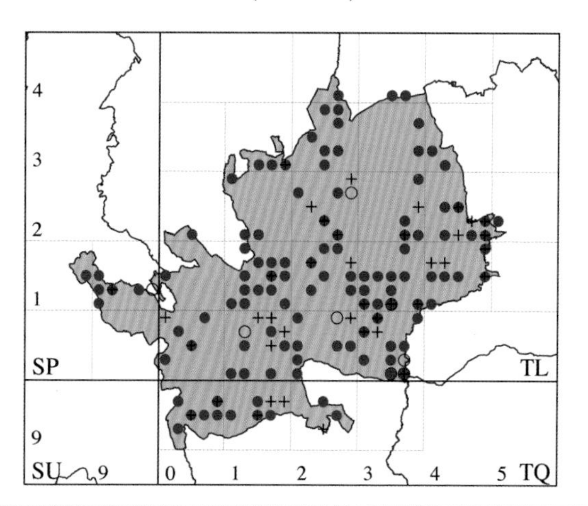

Recorded:	1828 – 2006
Distribution / Status:	Widespread / Common resident
Conservation status:	UK BAP Watch List. Herts Stable
Caterpillar food plants:	Not recorded. Elsewhere, on various Polygonaceae
Flight period:	May to October
Records in database:	642

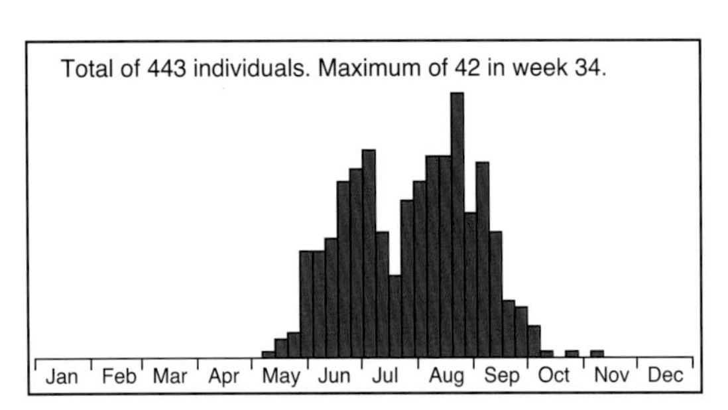

The Blood-vein is illustrated by J. F. Stephens (as *Timandra amataria* L.) from Hertford in *Illustrations of British Entomology* **3**: 202 (published in 1829) and this provides our first record. The moth was, and is, a widespread and common species in Hertfordshire. In southern Britain as a whole the moth is double-brooded, flying from May to July and then in September/October. Hertfordshire flight data is plotted for 2000 to 2006 and no gap is discernible between generations in any single year, with adults on the wing continuously from the second week of May to mid October in all seven years. A late example was noted at Ware on 10th November 2005 (Elizabeth Goodyear). Blood-veins are little given to variation. However, an extreme form with the outer area of all four wings beyond the usual red line entirely purple-red was taken at Bishops Stortford on 24th August 2001 by James Fish and Julian Reeves (now in my own collection); this was illustrated in *British Journal of Entomology & Natural History* **15** (3/4): Plate 2.

1687 *Scopula ornata* (Scop.) Lace Border

Recorded:	1889 – 1922
Distribution / Status:	Absent / Former Resident
Conservation status:	Herts Extinct
Caterpillar food plants:	Not recorded. Elsewhere, on Thyme and Marjoram
Flight period:	Elsewhere, May to August
Records in database:	2

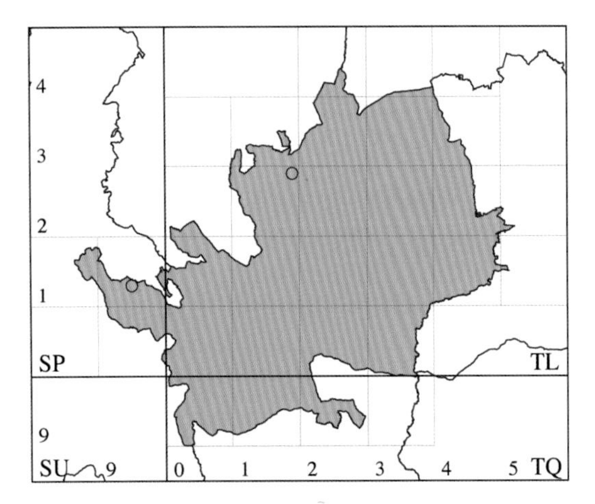

This attractive moth is now extinct in Hertfordshire, almost certainly as a direct consequence of the loss and degradation of its chalk downland habitat. Foster (1937) lists records for the canal bank at Tring Station in 1899 and 1900 (Goodson), for Hitchin – one in 1922 (Easton) and Waltham Common 'on chalk' (Sevastopaulo). Whilst the first two are likely to be correct the last is not acceptable. The only Waltham Common in Hertfordshire is at Waltham Cross where both geology and habitat are not even remotely suitable. Sevastopaulo was a boy at Haileybury School (not all that far from Waltham Cross) and was responsible for other known misidentifications in the lists generated from time to time by the boys at the school. Perhaps Waltham Common in Hampshire was the true location?

[1688 *Scopula rubiginata* (Hufn.) Tawny Wave

The record from Watford in 1890 by Cottam, given in Foster (1937) cannot be substantiated and seems unlikely to be correct. It is not accepted onto the Hertfordshire list.]

1689 *Scopula marginepunctata* (Goeze) Mullein Wave

Recorded:	1889 – 2006
Distribution / Status:	Local – perhaps spreading / Uncommon resident
Conservation status:	UK BAP Watch List. Herts Scarce
Caterpillar food plants:	Not recorded. Elsewhere, polyphagous on herbaceous plants
Flight period:	May to August
Records in database:	32

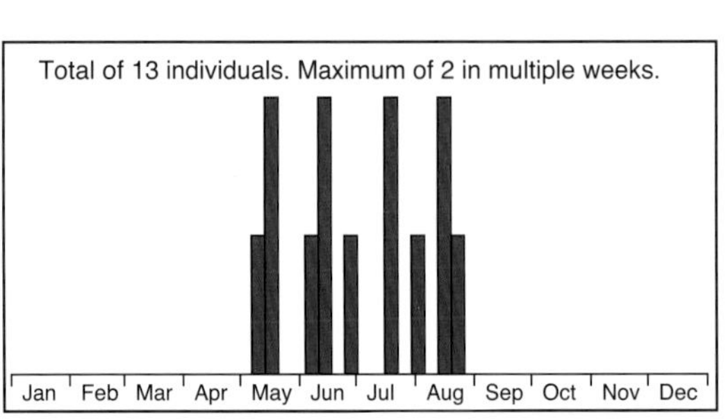

The Mullein Wave is probably a recent colonist of our county. It was recorded in the St Albans area by Gibbs (1889) and from Bushey Heath by Barraud (late nineteenth century), but these are the only historical records of what was evidently then a rare moth. The St Albans area record cannot be accurately mapped. Ray Penrose reported one at Mildred Avenue, Watford in June 1955 and it was of sufficient interest for Bell (1969) to report a capture at Ashridge on 2nd September 1967 (Bell, 1969). There was one at Apsley in 1976 (N. E. Gammon), but that was during the very hot summer when many moths were moving around and appearing in unusual locations. There are no more records until 29th July 1991 when I recorded it in good number on ruderal land adjacent to a pig farm at Much Hadham, where it must surely have been resident, then in 1996 John Murray attracted one to his light trap at Marshall's Heath. It reached the Watford area in 1997 (Colin Everett) and in 1998 appeared again at Marshall's Heath. During 1999, Long Marston in the extreme west (Alan Bernard) and my garden in Bishops Stortford, in the extreme east, added to the records. From 2000 onwards, it appears to have become established across a large area of the county, as the map indicates, although there are still many areas where we have failed to find it.

1690 *Scopula imitaria* (Hb.) Small Blood-vein

Recorded:	1884 – 2006
Distribution / Status:	Widespread / Common resident
Conservation status:	Herts Stable
Caterpillar food plants:	Not recorded. Elsewhere, polyphagous on herbaceous plants and also on privet
Flight period:	June to September in two generations
Records in database:	692

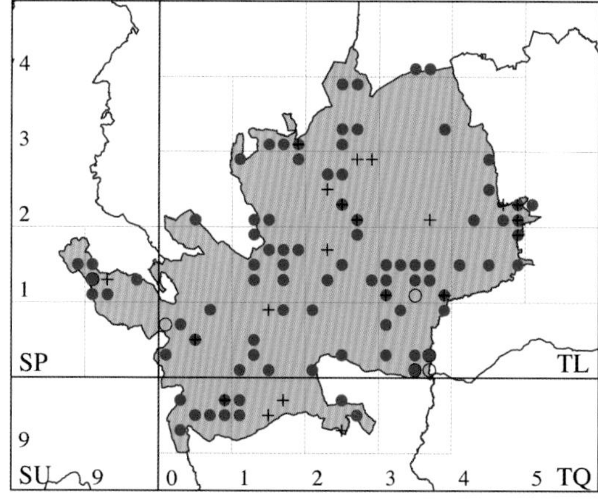

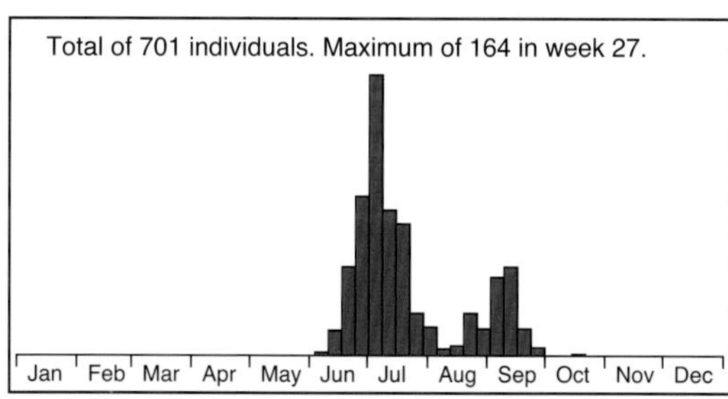

The text books tell us that this species is normally single brooded, with a small second generation of adults appearing only in warm years. In Hertfordshire, there has been a second generation in every year from 2000 to 2006, though this was very small from 2000 to 2002 and then much larger from 2003 to 2006. It is unfortunate that the bulk of data prior to 2000 takes the form of annual lists only, with no details of dates or numbers, so that we are not able to determine if this is a new phenomenon or a continuation of an established norm.

1691 *Scopula emutaria* (Hb.) Rosy Wave

Recorded:	1917 – 1945
Distribution / Status:	Absent / ?
Conservation status:	Herts Extinct
Caterpillar food plants:	Not recorded.
Flight period:	Elsewhere, July
Records in database:	2

Foster (1937) states 'St. Albans, Bricket Wood (Gibbs)'. The species is not included in Gibbs (1889) list of the Lepidoptera of the St Alban district and so must, if correct have been made between 1889 and his death in 1917. Thus 1917 is the arbitrarily assigned year of our earliest county record, though it was undoubtedly before then. The only other record is that made by Goodson at Hemel Hempstead in 1945 (Foster, 1945a). The moth inhabits the edges of permanent bogs at inland sites and is, therefore, unexpected in Hertfordshire. I have not mapped these records and keep an open mind as to their validity.

1692 *Scopula immutata* (L.) Lesser Cream Wave

Recorded:	1970 – 2006
Distribution / Status:	Extremely local / Rare resident
Conservation status:	Herts Endangered
Caterpillar food plants:	Not recorded. Elsewhere, on Meadowsweet and Common Valerian
Flight period:	July/August
Records in database:	5

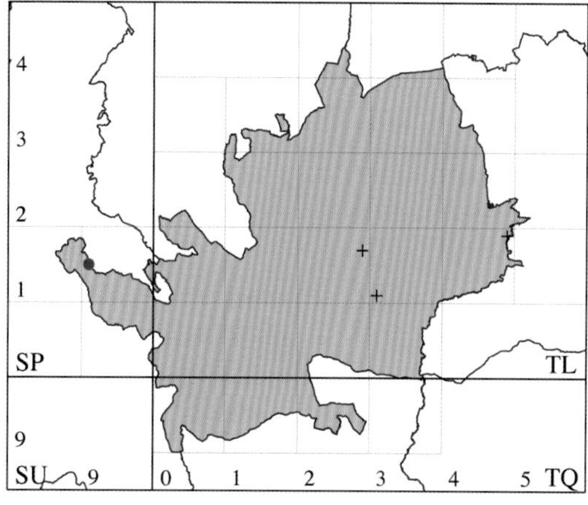

The Lesser Cream Wave was not included in the 1937 Hertfordshire list by Foster and we have only five records since then, affecting just four sites. Jim Reid caught an adult in Bramfield Wood on 27th July 1970 and another at Bayfordbury on 13th July 1973. Charles Watson took one at his garden light in Bishops Stortford on 11th August 1979 and Peter Bygate took singles at Gubblecote on 2nd July 2005 and 22nd August 2006.

1693 *Scopula floslactata* (Haw.) Cream Wave

Recorded:	1884 – 2006
Distribution / Status:	Local / Uncommon resident
Conservation status:	Herts Stable
Caterpillar food plants:	Not recorded. Elsewhere, probably polyphagous on herbaceous plants
Flight period:	Late May to end of July
Records in database:	34

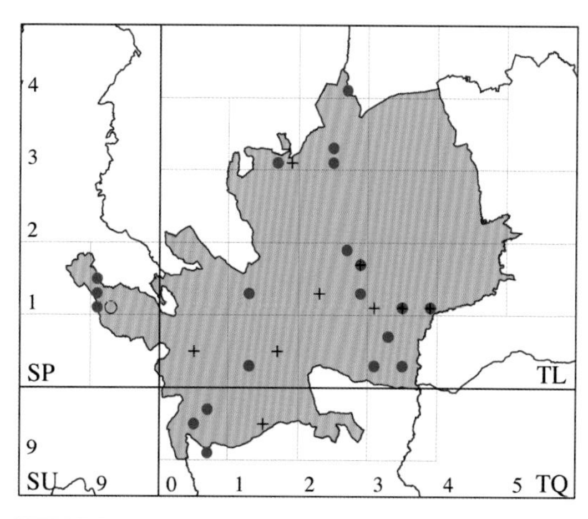

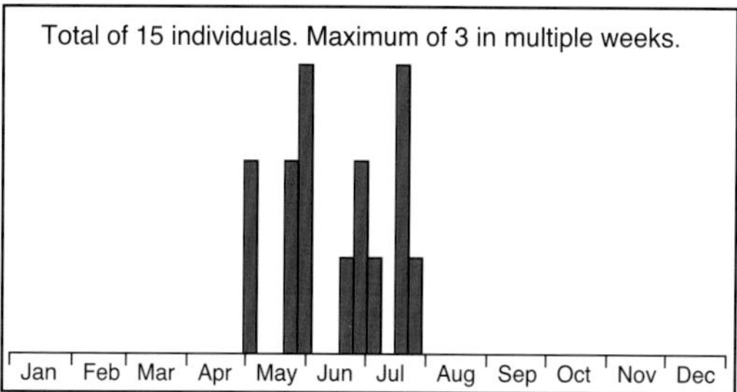

Foster (1937) listed a small number of localities suggesting that this species was tolerably widespread in the county. That seems to be the case today, but the moth is evidently rather localised with several well-trapped sites failing to record it. This may be in part a result of inexperienced observers overlooking it, because whilst the adults do come to light they are not particularly strongly attracted and may settle in the vegetation some distance from the trap. A better way of recording it is to beat hedges and similar edge-habitat vegetation with a stick then net the adults as they fly out.

[1694 *Scopula ternata* (Schrank, 1802) Smoky Wave

The record of two examples of this species (as '*Pylarge fumata* Steph.') to a light run by J. Bell at Northchurch Common in 1937 given in Foster (1942) cannot be substantiated. The species is associated with Heather and Bilberry and is northern and western in its British distribution. Although there are southern records, this one from Hertfordshire is not likely to be correct.]

1696 *Scopula ochrata* (Scop.) ssp. *cantiata* (Prout) Bright Wave

Recorded:	1983 – 1983
Distribution / Status:	Absent / Vagrant or immigrant
Conservation status:	UK Biodiversity Action Plan Priority Species
Caterpillar food plants:	Unknown
Flight period:	Elsewhere, July
Records in database:	1

There is a single Hertfordshire record, from the Rothamsted Estate at Harpenden on 19th July 1983 (Adrian Riley). This is a coastal species. The last record from adjacent Essex was in 1995, in spite of searching and Brian Goodey tells me that he regards it as probably extinct in that county. It is suspected to be an occasional immigrant to Britain, and this may be source of our Hertfordshire record.

[1698 *Idaea muricata* (Hufn.) Purple-bordered Gold

According to Foster (1937), a number were seen flying round a haystack at Bishops Stortford in 1898 by Mellows who would have been 12 years old at that time. Sadly, there are no more haystacks in Bishops Stortford for me to examine! Interestingly, this record does not feature in the 1950 list edited by P. B. M. Allan for the Bishops Stortford Natural History Society, even though it is known (Geoffrey Sell, personal communication) that Charles Mellows collaborated with Allen over the production of that list. It appears that Allen may have rejected the record without commenting that he had done so, perhaps to avoid embarrassment? I do not accept this record here.]

1699 *Idaea rusticata* (H.-S.) ssp. *atrosignaria* Lempke Least Carpet

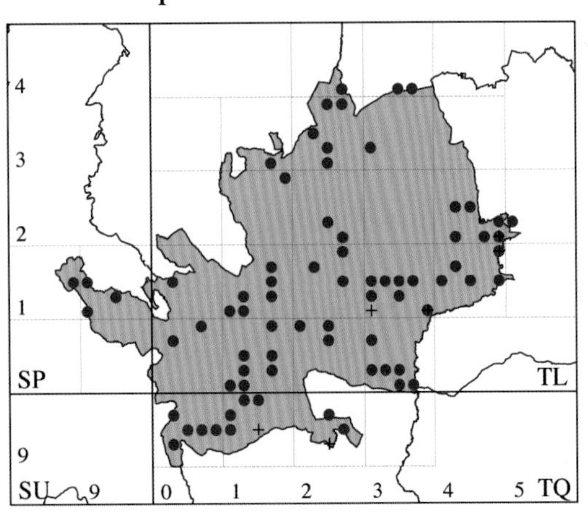

Recorded:	1945 – 2006
Distribution / Status:	Widespread / Common resident
Conservation status:	Increasing
Caterpillar food plants:	Withered leaves of Ivy and Greater Bindweed, probably on many other plants
Flight period:	June to August and then September/October
Records in database:	714

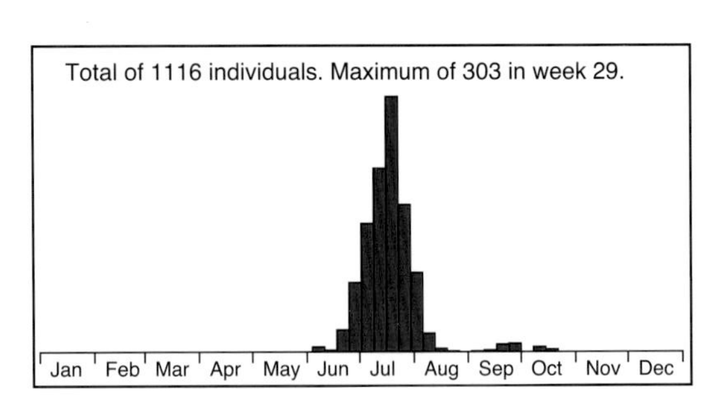

Formerly known as *Idaea vulpinaria*, British examples of this species are all referable to subspecies *atrosignaria* Lempke. Our first report seems to be that from Berkhamsted, where one was found in 1945 by J. H. Bell. This was recorded in Fryer (1948) who noted that it was '...a very local resident in the southern counties and not usually regarded as a migrant'. Ian Lorimer caught a single example at Totteridge on 21st July 1964, noting that it was the first that he had encountered there. One was taken in the Rothamsted Insect Survey trap at Rye Meads on 22nd July 1971 and then Jim Reid caught another at Bayfordbury in 1974. One was taken at light by Peter Waterton in 1976 (Bell, 1977), but the locality is not given [it was probably Welwyn]. Bell comments that this was the second county record, and was clearly unaware of the other records. During the hot summer of 1976, Barry Goater caught one in his garden at Bushey on 2nd July and Ian Lorimer caught another at Totteridge on 8th July. However, if the 1976 drought caused dispersal, the displaced moths do not appear to have established themselves and there are no further known Hertfordshire records until 1987 when I caught one in my garden at Bishops Stortford. It is worth noting that I did not start trapping here until October 1986, so the moth may already have established a presence here, but I did not catch any more until 1998. In 1991 it was caught about half a mile away from my garden on 1st August by Charles Watson and on 17th July 1992 Tony King added it to his garden list on the east side of the town. In the north of Bishops Stortford, James Fish and Julian Reeves did not find it in the trap in their adjoining gardens until 1995. Whilst establishment in Bishops Stortford may have been slow and patchy, the moth nevertheless reached Baldock soon after, where one was captured on 27th July 1997 by Kerry Robinson and the next year Wendy Hatton found it in St Albans on 31st July. Harpenden (Adrian Riley), Datchworth (Steve Palmer), Little Hadham (Geoff Senior), Watford (Ray Penrose) and Blackmore End (Vincent & Betty Judd) were new sites added in 1999 and in 2000 it was noted afresh at Waterford Heath (Vincent Judd), Baldock (Dug Heath) and Aldenham (Colin Everett). Up to the end of 1999, it appears that all reports relate to single adult moths; throughout the seven years from 2000 to 2006, however, many traps began recording between 2 and 5 individuals per night, with occasional higher numbers. The Least Carpet is now a firmly established resident throughout the county. The small peak of adults in September/October on the flight chart is almost entirely the result of sightings made during 2006.

[1701 *Idaea sylvestraria* (Hb.) Dotted Border Wave

The Dotted Border Wave is a UK Biodiversity Action Plan species that is distributed in the western half of Britain, though there are a few old records from the east. Foster (1937) claims that this species (which he lists as '*P. straminata* Tr. (*marginepunctata* Stph. Stnt.) (*circellata*, Guen.)' is recorded in the 'Haileybury (School List)'. This is not the case – at least it does not feature in the list published in the original list by Bowyer (1888). It is unclear what Foster is referring to in any event, since whilst Guenée's *circellata* is certainly the same as Hübner's *sylvestraria*, Treitschke's *straminata* is listed separately in Doubleday's 1862 checklist (which Foster largely followed) and seems to refer to our present day Mullein Wave (*Scopula marginepunctata* Goeze). There is a further published Hertfordshire record in Bell (1957) who notes one allegedly taken in 1955 at Bishops Stortford by C. Craufurd. Craufurd's identification skills cannot be doubted, but there seems to be no record of this species at the Bishops Stortford Natural History Society and the record cannot be substantiated. Craufurd's collection has been lost. This moth is not at all expected in Hertfordshire and on the basis of available evidence is not accepted on the formal county list.]

1702 *Idaea biselata* (Hufn.) Small Fan-footed Wave

Recorded:	1884 – 2006
Distribution / Status:	Ubiquitous / Common resident
Conservation status:	Herts Stable
Caterpillar food plants:	Not recorded. Elsewhere, on plantain, Dandelion and other herbaceous plants
Flight period:	June to August
Records in database:	617

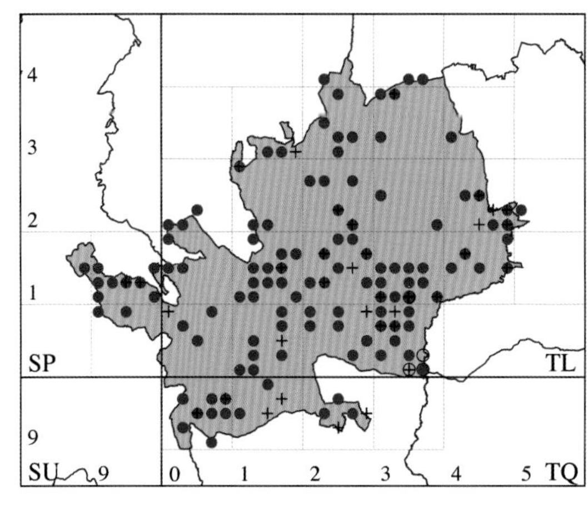

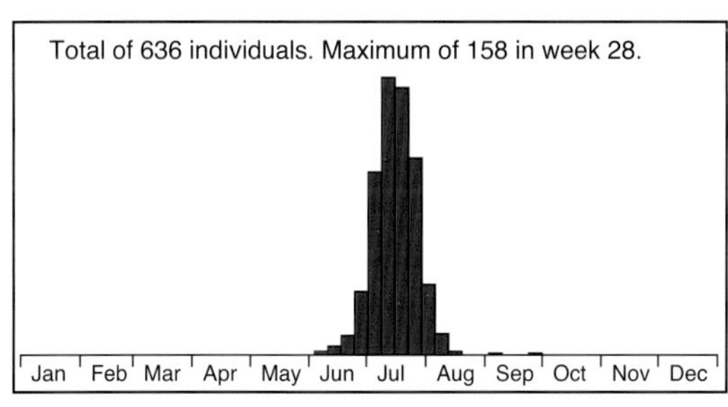

The Small Fan-footed Wave has apparently always been common in Hertfordshire and today is expected to be present on all site lists for the county. A very small second generation of adults was noted during September and October of 2005 and 2006.

1703 *Idaea inquinata* (Scop.) Rusty Wave

Recorded:	1900 – 1900
Distribution / Status:	Absent / Accidental introduction
Conservation status:	Herts Stable
Caterpillar food plants:	Not recorded in Britain
Flight period:	Not recorded in Britain
Records in database:	1

A single adult was found in the packing room at the Tring Museum 'probably introduced', according to Foster (1937) who, with infallible predictability, failed to suggest when this event may have taken place. The species is an adventive to Britain and was found in a number of London shops in the last half of the nineteenth century; most records probably originated from larvae imported with vegetable packing material.

1705 *Idaea fuscovenosa* (Goeze) Dwarf Cream Wave

Recorded:	1884 – 2006
Distribution / Status:	Widespread, perhaps ubiquitous / Common resident
Conservation status:	Herts Stable
Caterpillar food plants:	Not recorded. Elsewhere, on various low herbs
Flight period:	June to August
Records in database:	429

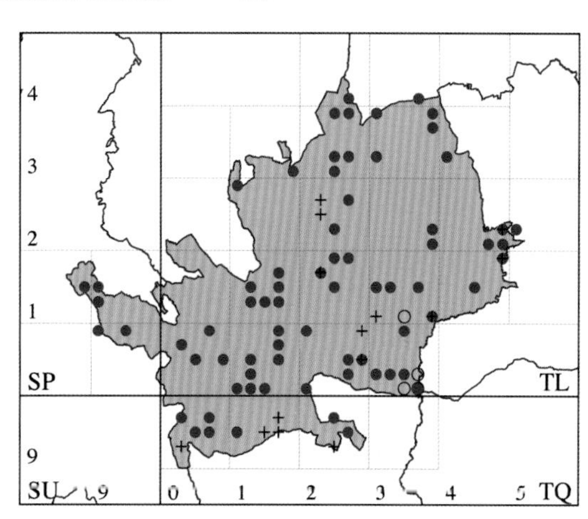

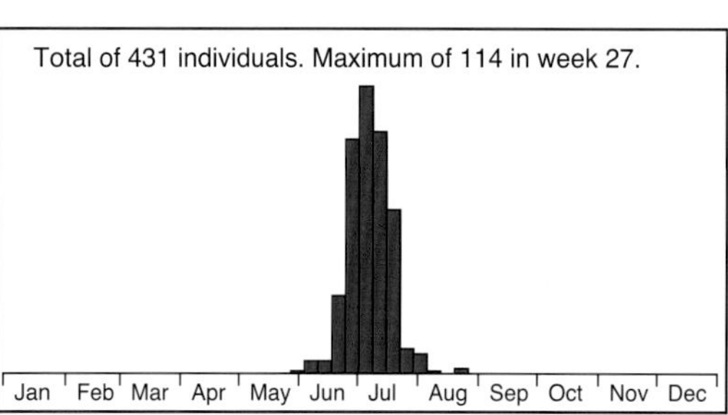

This is another widespread species that is likely to turn up in all places where surveys are undertaken, although it rarely attends light traps in large number and is more easily found by beating edge habitats such as hedges at dusk.

1707 *Idaea seriata* (Schrank) Small Dusty Wave

Recorded:	1884 – 2006
Distribution / Status:	Widespread / Common resident
Conservation status:	Herts Stable
Caterpillar food plants:	Hawthorn. Elsewhere, on many herbaceous plants
Flight period:	May to September in two generations
Records in database:	518

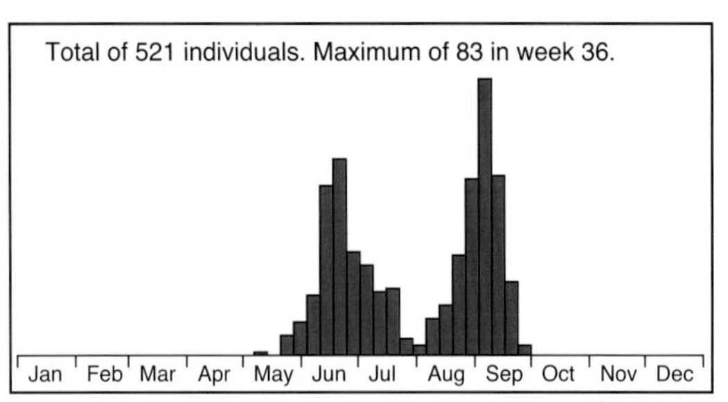

A larva was found feeding on Common Hawthorn at Maple Cross during 2004, and the adult was reared in May 2005 (Ann Piper). This may be a new foodplant record – although the larvae are polyphagous, few people seem to bother to report the foodplant species involved. The adult is frequently mistaken for a pug (*Eupithecia* sp.) and rests in boxes of unidentified pugs until spotted by the duly appointed 'pug expert'! This is especially the case with darker forms, of which at least the darkest are perhaps referable to ab. *bischoffaria* Le Harpe. These really dark examples are apparently rare and most prevalent in the south, towards London. However, the pale 'typical' form is also rare and most Hertfordshire examples of the moth adopt varying degrees of darkness between the two extremes.

1708 *Idaea dimidiata* (Hufn.) Single-dotted Wave

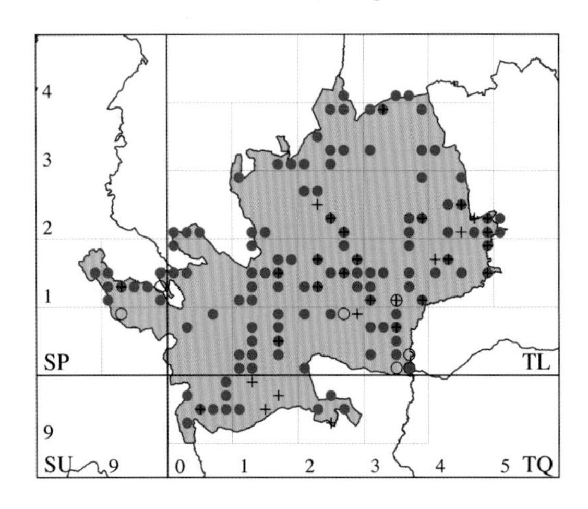

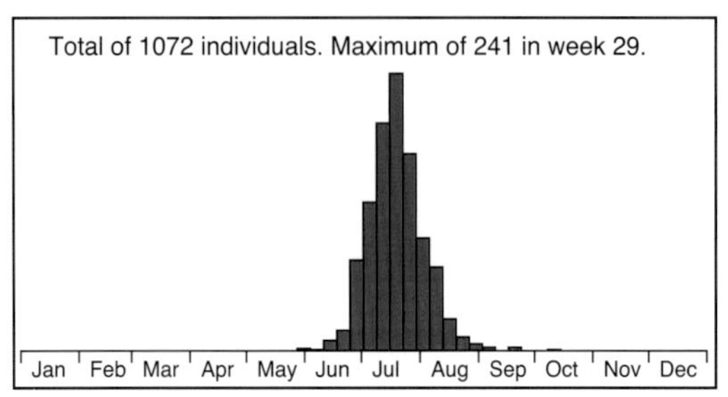

Recorded:	1884 – 2006
Distribution / Status:	Widespread / Common resident
Conservation status:	Herts Stable
Caterpillar food plants:	Not recorded. Elsewhere, on Cow Parsley and Burnet Saxifrage
Flight period:	June to August
Records in database:	884

The text books tell us that this moth likes wet or damp places, but this is not particularly well-reflected in the Hertfordshire data and the moth is pretty much everywhere apart from the driest parts of the arable desert that is the north-east of the county.

1709 *Idaea subsericeata* (Haw.) Satin Wave

Recorded:	1887 – 2006
Distribution / Status:	Local / Rare resident
Conservation status:	Herts Scarce
Caterpillar food plants:	Not recorded. Elsewhere, polyphagous on low herbaceous plants
Flight period:	June (one record in August)
Records in database:	29

Bowyer (1888) records this moth from Haileybury School and this record is repeated by Foster (1937) who adds East Barnet. Thus, it seems the moth has always been rather a scarcity in the county. Almost all the remaining records are of single examples in garden light traps and we have no useful habitat data for this species, which surely must be regarded as uncommon. Dated records all fall within June apart from one exceptionally late (but correct) record from Bishops Stortford on 5th August 2006 (James Fish and Julian Reeves).

1711 *Idaea trigeminata* (Haw.) Treble Brown Spot

Recorded:	1887 – 2006
Distribution / Status:	Widespread / Common resident
Conservation status:	Herts Stable
Caterpillar food plants:	Not recorded. Elsewhere, on many low herbaceous plants
Flight period:	Late May to July
Records in database:	633

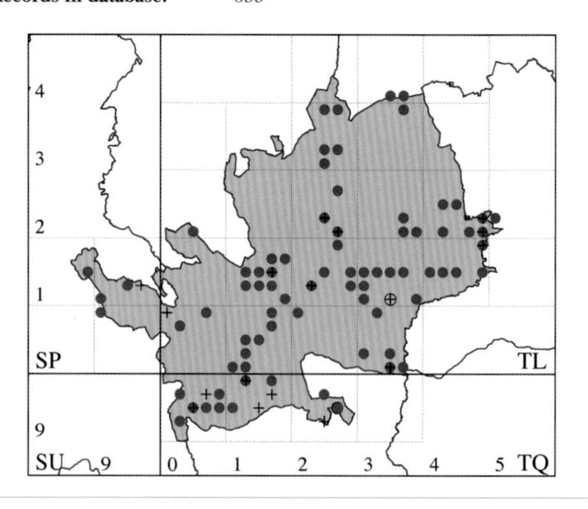

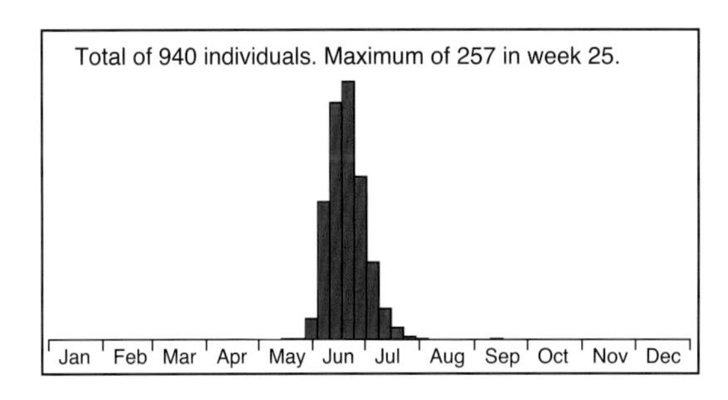

Foster (1937) lists only Haileybury School, East Barnet, Hoddesdon and Berkhamsted, but this may reflect under-recording rather than scarcity. Today, this moth forms a regular part of the catch in almost all moth traps across the county.

1712 *Idaea emarginata* (L.) Small Scallop

Recorded: 1887 – 2006
Distribution / Status: Widespread / Common resident
Conservation status: Herts Stable
Caterpillar food plants: Not recorded. Elsewhere, probably polyphagous on low herbaceous plants
Flight period: May to August
Records in database: 134

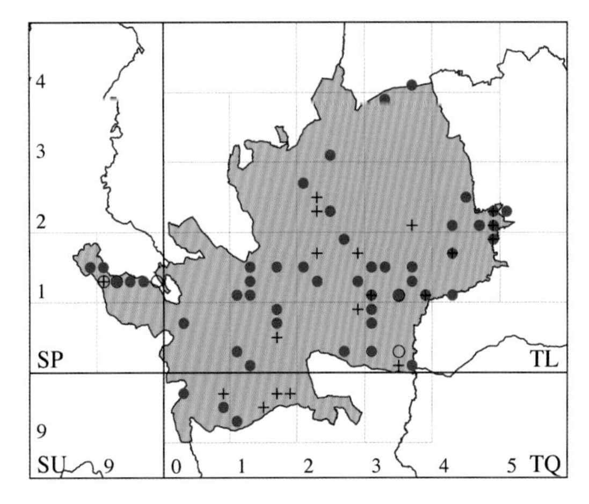

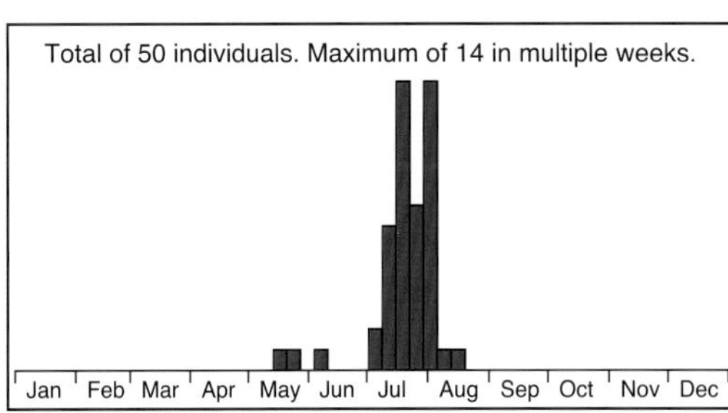

Whilst most of the moths of this species fly in July and August, the chart shows a few earlier records in late May and June suggesting that the full flight period may start earlier than we have been able to detect. It is a species of marshes and other damp places; though not present on everyone's garden moth list, it does not take a lot of damp habitat for the moth to be present.

1713 *Idaea aversata* (L.) Riband Wave

Recorded: 1884 – 2006
Distribution / Status: Ubiquitous / Abundant resident
Conservation status: Herts Stable
Caterpillar food plants: hawthorn. Elsewhere, probably polyphagous
Flight period: June to September
Records in database: 2173

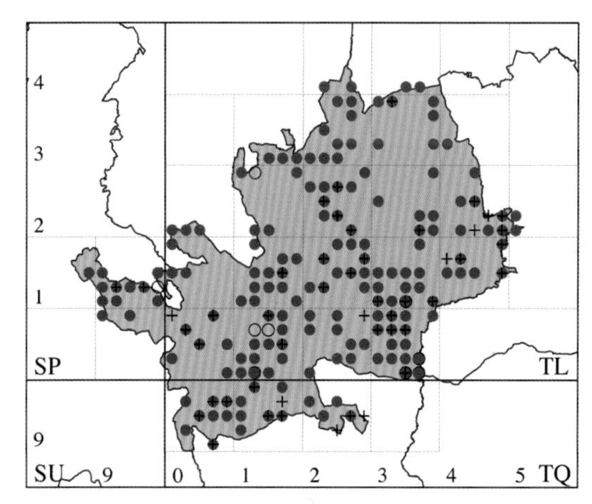

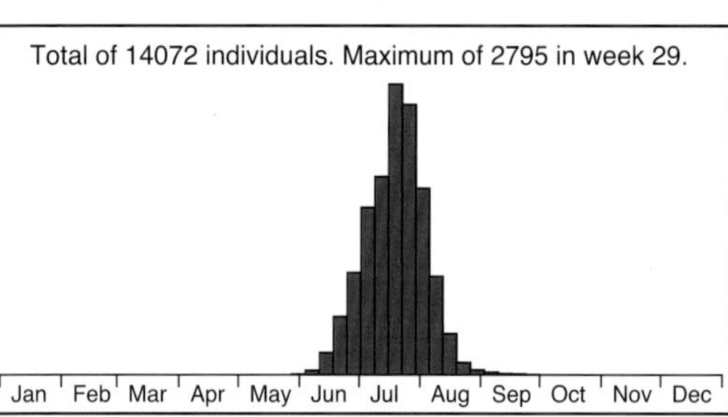

In terms of the number of records in the database, this is the eighth most frequently reported moth species in Hertfordshire. It comes in a banded and an unbanded form and both exhibit a range of colour, from very pale through reddish to very dark. The original description of the moth by Linnaeus was made from the banded form, and so that is the 'typical' Riband Wave; forms that lack the dark band are referable to ab. *remutata* Linnaeus. Various attempts have been made at assessing the percentages of typical and banded forms in Hertfordshire, but the gathering of results is problematic. The moth presents in large numbers, mostly not actually entering the trap and necessitating searching of adjacent vegetation, which is an inconvenience for amateur moth enthusiasts who need to examine the trap quickly before they set off for work. I managed to count my garden catch in Bishops Stortford on most mornings over a three year period from 2000 to 2002 before it got the better of me and the proportion of plain to banded forms stayed more or less constant at 3:1 as the following table shows. The steady rise in numbers of individuals over the three years is also interesting:

Year	percent plain *remutata*	percent banded *typica*	n =
2000	75	25	37
2001	74	26	180
2002	77	23	393

The number of trap nights is identical for each year and the trap position/type did not alter. A somatic mosaic, in which the two left wings are distinctly melanic whilst the right side is the normal ochreous colour was caught at Whetstone on 7th August 1963 (P. Ward, reported in de Worms, 1964). A larva was found feeding on hawthorn at Maple Cross in 2004, and the adult reared in May 2005 (Ann Piper). This may be a new foodplant record. In 2003, several reports of adults in October from across the county perhaps suggest a small second generation of adults?

1715 Idaea straminata (Borkh.) Plain Wave

Recorded: 1890 – 2006
Distribution / Status: Local / Rare resident
Conservation status: Herts Scarce
Caterpillar food plants: Not recorded. Elsewhere, probably polyphagous
Flight period: Late June to early August
Records in database: 26

Many reports of the Plain Wave prove to relate to Riband Waves on closer inspection and separation of the two may be difficult in some cases. In general, it is best not to look too closely – Plain Wave has quite a different 'jizz' about it (to borrow a term from the world of birding). Our earliest record is from Langley Wood, Sandridge (Griffith, 1890) and Foster (1937) also adds Berkhamsted (Tomlinson) and Aldenham Wood, 1933 (H. King). Modern records are rather few and are widely spaced, suggesting that the moth may be present in very low density across much of the county.

1716 *Rhodometra sacraria* (L.) Vestal

Recorded: 1947 – 2006
Distribution / Status: Random / Immigrant
Conservation status: -
Caterpillar food plants: Not recorded. Elsewhere, polyphagous on low herbaceous plants
Flight period: April to November
Records in database: 48

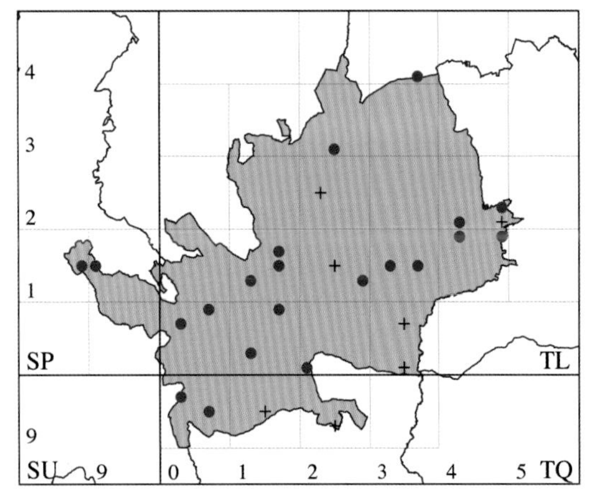

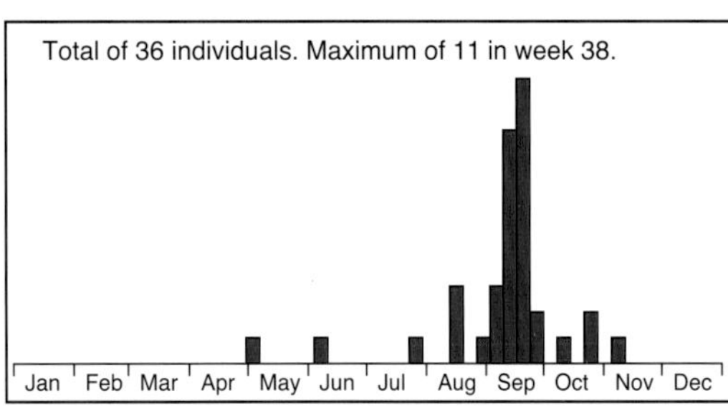

The Vestal is not listed by Foster (1937) and was first noted in the county during 1947 at Radlett, two (C. Wildridge), Harpenden, two (C. B. Williams) and Berkhamsted, four (J. H. Bell) (Fryer, 1950). During 1961, this moth 'came in quantity and stayed to breed' (Bell, 1964), but the only specifics mentioned by Bell are an ab. *labda* at Arkley, taken by T. G. Howarth on 31st August, a fertile male 'normal form' on 23rd September at the same place and 'during August' at the Rothamsted Estate in Harpenden. Remaining records are as follows: Stevenage, at mv light on 12th August 1966 'in coll D. Ruston' (J. Newton); Rothamsted, one taken by R. A. French, on 24th September 1967 (Bell, 1969); Totteridge, 10 October 1978 (R. I. Lorimer); Reddings Avenue, Bushey, 28th September 1983 (B. Goater); Danemead N. R., 28th September 1983 (D. Wilson); Warren Way, Digswell, 18th September 1987 (T. W. Gladwin); West Road Bishops Stortford, 21st September 1987 (C. W. Plant); Capel Manor Environmental Centre, 1987 (Anna Hughes); Warren Way, Digswell, 10th August 1994 (T. W. Gladwin); Bishops Stortford, 18th August 1995 (J. Fish/J. Reeves); Bishops Stortford, 19th September 1995 (J. Fish/J. Reeves); Panshanger Park, 25th September 1995 (T. W. Gladwin); Marshalls Heath, 1998 (J. B. Murray); Belsize Close St Albans, 16th September 1998 (W. Hatton); Rothamsted Estate, 1999 (A. Riley); Little Hadham, 1999 (G. Senior); Royston, 1st September 1999 (J. Chainey); Rothamsted Estate, 4th September 1999 (A. Riley); Hemel Hempstead, 11th September 1999 (M. Newland); Marshalls Heath, 13th September 1999 (J. B. Murray); Hemel Hempstead, 25th September 1999 (M. Newland); Weston, 5th June 2000 (A. Cockburn); Rothamsted Estate, 9th September 2000 (A. Riley); Bishops Stortford, 19th September 2000 (C. Watson); Bengeo, Hertford, 23rd September 2000 (A. Wood); Rickmansworth, 2001 (Anna. Marett); Bishops Stortford, 09 October 2001 (Charles Watson); Bengeo, Hertford, 22nd October 2001 (A. Wood); Bengeo, Hertford, 19th August 2002 (A. Wood); Long Marston, 14th September 2002 (C. W. Plant); Ware, 20th September 2003 (Elizabeth Goodyear); Bengeo, Hertford, 21st September 2003 (A. Wood); Bishops Stortford, 21st September 2003 (J. Fish/J. Reeves); Ware, 1st May 2005 (Elizabeth Goodyear); Long Marston, 12th September 2005 (A. Bernard); Blackmore End, 8th November 2005 (V. Judd); Ashridge Drive, Bricketwood, 25th July 2006 (H. Ellis); Gubblecote, 12th September 2006 (P. Bygate); Chorleywood, 14th September 2006 (R. Ellis); Hemel Hempstead, 14th September 2006 (R. Prue); Much Hadham, 14th September 2006 (Elizabeth Goodyear) and Shenley, 18th September 2006 (W. & P. Page).

LARENTIINAE

1718 *Phibalapteryx virgata* (Hufn.) Oblique Striped

Recorded: 1884 – 1970
Distribution / Status: Absent / Extinct resident
Conservation status: Herts Extinct
Caterpillar food plants: Not recorded. Elsewhere, on bedstraws
Flight period: Not recorded. Elsewhere, May/June and August
Records in database: 3

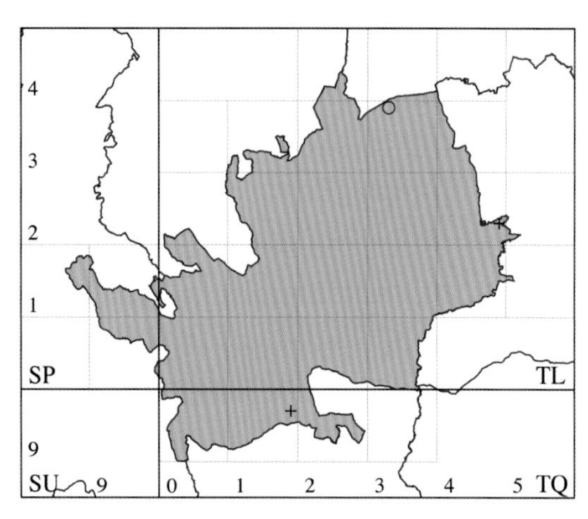

Foster (1916) noted that 'This species occurs commonly on Royston Heath'. Royston Heath, also known today as Therfield Heath, is in fact a chalk downland site, not a heathland at all. Phil Jenner has in his collection several specimens collected there in 1926 by B. Swift and rumours abound that the moth persisted here as late as the 1970s, though there are no firm records. Griffith (1884) had earlier reported it from the Sandridge area; within his definition of that very large area there is no chalkland habitat although areas of acid grassland might then have reflected the habitat of the moth in the Breckland district of Norfolk and Suffolk. Bell (1961) records an example taken by Clifford Craufurd during 1959 at Bishops Stortford. Bishops Stortford seems an extremely improbable locality, but Craufurd was a first rate lepidopterist and there was at that time a small chalk exposure in a quarry along the Farnham Road (still referred to today as the Bishops Stortford Lime Pit) and this is only about a mile across then open fields from where Craufurd lived. The only other Hertfordshire record is from borehamwood, where one was caught by Gaston Prior in 1970.

1719 *Orthonama vittata* (Borkh.) Oblique Carpet

Recorded: 1885 – 1948
Distribution / Status: Absent / Extinct resident
Conservation status: UK BAP Watch List. Herts Extinct
Caterpillar food plants: Not recorded. Elsewhere, on bedstraws
Flight period: Elsewhere, May/June and August/September
Records in database: 9

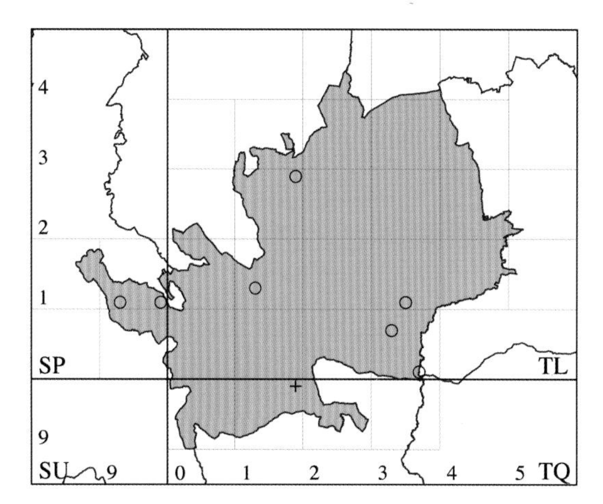

Nineteenth century records are for Hitchin (Durrant, 1885); Haileybury (Bowyer, 1888), Cheshunt Marsh (Boyd, 1901) and Tring (Barraud, 1903). For the twentieth century, Foster (1937) lists Tring (undated), Watford (undated) and Berkhamsted (1921). Since then there are only two confirmed records: 'a few' found by Eric Classey at Broxbourne Woods in 1935 and one at Borehamwood in 1971 (Gaston Prior). Tantalisingly, Alan Cockburn reports two at Weston on 12th June 2006; regrettably no specimen was collected nor photograph taken. By agreement with Alan the record cannot be accepted without further evidence, but it is worth noting that potentially suitable habitat exists in the local area. The moth inhabits 'fenland and marshy places and is widespread throughout much of the British Isles' (Skinner, 1984).

1720 *Orthonama obstipata* (Fabr.) Gem

Recorded: 1898 – 2006
Distribution / Status: Random / Immigrant
Conservation status: -
Caterpillar food plants: Not recorded in Britain
Flight period: June to November
Records in database: 33

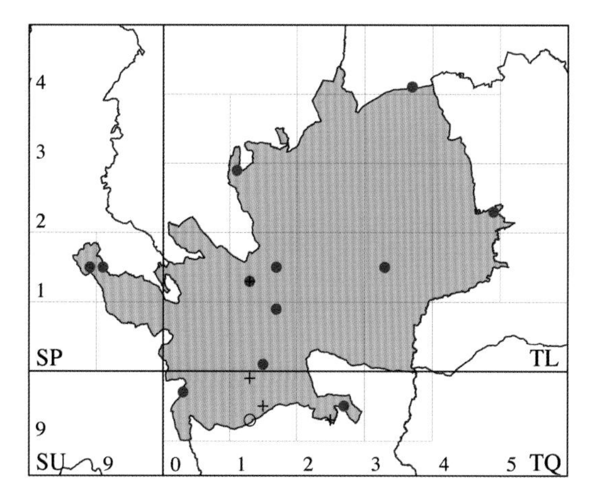

Tring Reservoirs, 21st September 1898, collected by 'Mr. Goodson' identified by N. C. Rothschild, was the first Hertfordshire record (Barraud, 1903). Other records are: Waltham Cross, 1904 (Boyd); Tring, 1908 (Goodson); Harpenden, 12th September 1936 (Roche) and 3 September

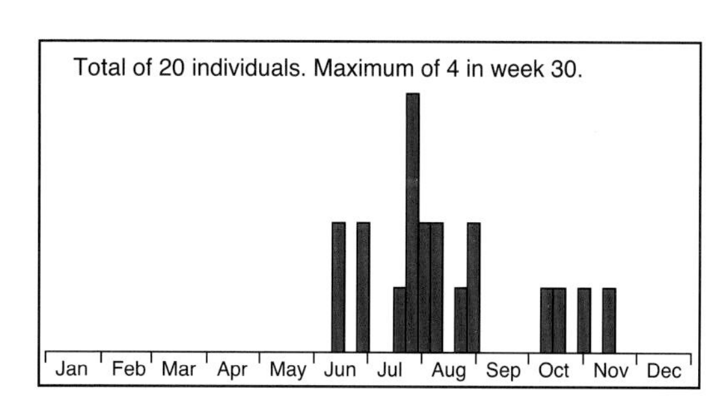

1936 (Williams). Harpenden, one in 1947 (C. B. Williams) and Berkhamsted, five also in 1947 (J. H. Bell) are noted in Fryer (1950). Harpenden, one in [?August] 1952 (C. B. Williams); Totteridge, 1966 (R. I. Lorimer); Totteridge, 1969 (R. I. Lorimer); Rothamsted Estate, Harpenden, 1969 (A. Riley); Colney Street, 1998 (P. Wheeler); Marshalls Heath, 2002 (J. B. Murray); Carpenders Park, October 1934 (E. W. Classey); Aldenham, 28th September 1964 (B. Goater); Totteridge, 16th October 1966 (R. I. Lorimer); Bushey, 17th July 1967 (B. Goater); Bushey, 24th August 1967 (B. Goater); Totteridge, 30th Sepember 1969 (R. I. Lorimer); Bushey, 21st October 1969 (B. Goater); Bushey, 22nd October 1969 (B. Goater); Bishops Stortford, 26th July 1996 (J. Fish & J. Reeves); Bishops Stortford, 28th July 1996 (J. Fish & J. Reeves); Bishops Stortford, 20th July 1998 (J. Fish & J. Reeves); Long Marston, 22nd August 1998 (A. Bernard); St Albans, 13th Oct 1998 (W. Hatton); East Barnet, 25th July 2000 (P. Alton); Royston, 3 August 2000 (J. Chainey); Hexton Chalk Pit, 20th October 2001 (C. W. Plant); Rothamsted Estate, 1st August 2002 (P. Gould); Bishops Stortford, 7th Aug 2002 (J. Fish & J. Reeves); Bishops Stortford, 7th Aug 2002 (J. Fish & J. Reeves); Hertford, 30th Aug 2002 (A. Wood); Royston 30th October 2002 (J. Chainey); Bishops Stortford, 15th June 2003 (J. Fish & J. Reeves); Long Marston, 26th June 2003 (P. Bygate); Rothamsted Estate, Harpenden, 18t November 2003 (P. Gould) and Chorleywood, 26th July 2006 (Richard Ellis).

1721 *Xanthorhoe biriviata* (Borkh.) Balsam Carpet

Recorded: 1964 – 2006
Distribution / Status: Extremely local / Rare resident
Conservation status: UK Red Data Book
Herts Vulnerable
Caterpillar food plants: Not recorded. Elsewhere, on Orange Balsam and Small Balsam
Flight period: Insufficient data. Elsewhere, May/June then mid July to September
Records in database: 5

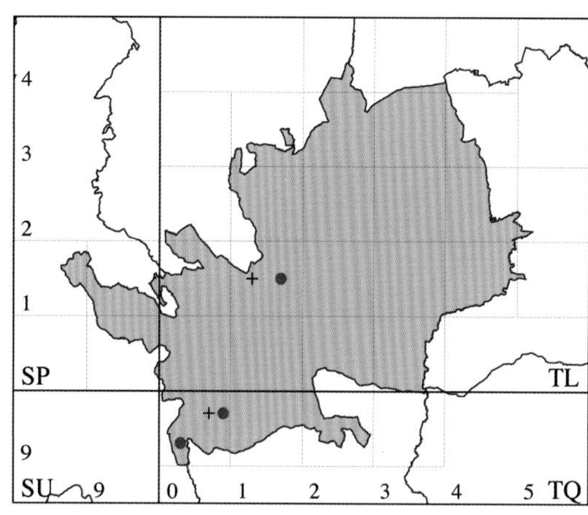

The Balsam Carpet was first discovered as British as recently as 1955 in the Colne Valley between Middlesex and Buckinghamshire, immediately south of our county. Thus, it is no surprise to discover a report, albeit lacking the recorder's name, from Maple Cross area in 1996. More recently, two adults attended the sheet during a Herts Moth Group recording trip on 1st July 2006 at Casiobury Park, Watford, a site also crossed by the River Colne. A voucher specimen for the last mentioned record is in my own collection. The earliest Hertfordshire record, however, is away from the Colne Valley at Whippendell Wood, Watford, where an example was taken at light in on 26th July 1964 by Roy McCormick. Another report is in a letter dated 18th March 1971 from Mrs Joan Nicklen, of the Rothamsted Experimental Station at Harpenden, to the then Hertfordshire moth recorder, Peter Bell, in which it is stated that 'Our latest find is a specimen of *Xanthorhoe biriviata* [at the Rothamsted Estate] on the night of 22nd June 1970 ...'. This record is published in Bell (1971) as new to the Hertfordshire fauna, but oddly is omitted by Riley (1999) in his summary of moths at the Rothamsted Estate; nor is it commented upon by this latter author and it is unclear if this record was missed by Riley or simply deemed unreliable. Both these two records and another by John Murray at Marshal's Heath in 1995 are surprising in that the sites are not near to any appropriate breeding habitat; it is assumed that these single adults were wanderers

1722 *Xanthorhoe designata* (Hufn.) Flame Carpet

Recorded:	1828 – 2006
Distribution / Status:	Local / Uncommon resident
Conservation status:	Herts Stable
Caterpillar food plants:	Not recorded in Britain
Flight period:	April to September in two generations
Records in database:	125

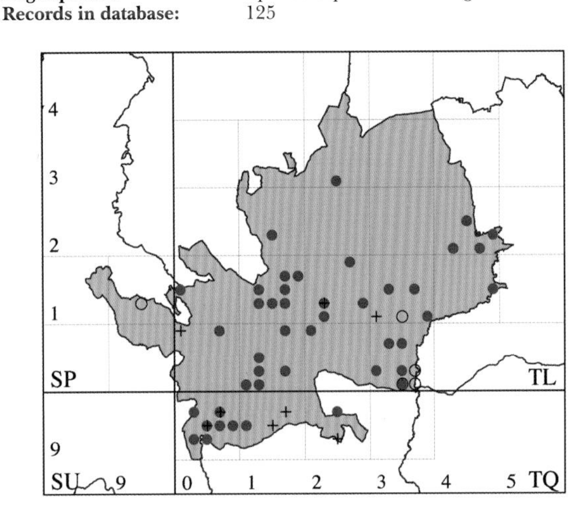

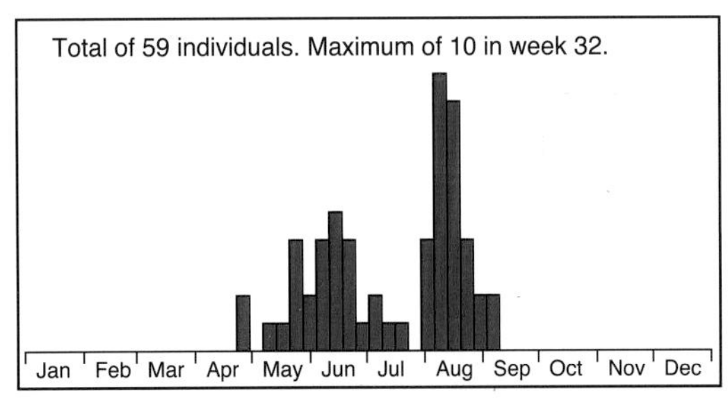

This moth has an affinity with damp woodland, damp hedgerow ditches, scrub-invaded field ponds and similar habitats and so the apparent absence from the north-east of Hertfordshire was predictable. The two generations of adults almost merge, though there is a small but clear gap without records in mid-July. Captive larvae can be fed on various cruciferous plants, but the natural foodplant is apparently unknown in Britain.

1724 *Xanthorhoe spadicearia* ([D.& S.]) Red Twin-spot Carpet

Recorded:	1887 – 2006
Distribution / Status:	Widespread / Common resident
Conservation status:	Herts Stable
Caterpillar food plants:	Not recorded. Elsewhere, polyphagous on herbaceous plants
Flight period:	April – June then July/August
Records in database:	363

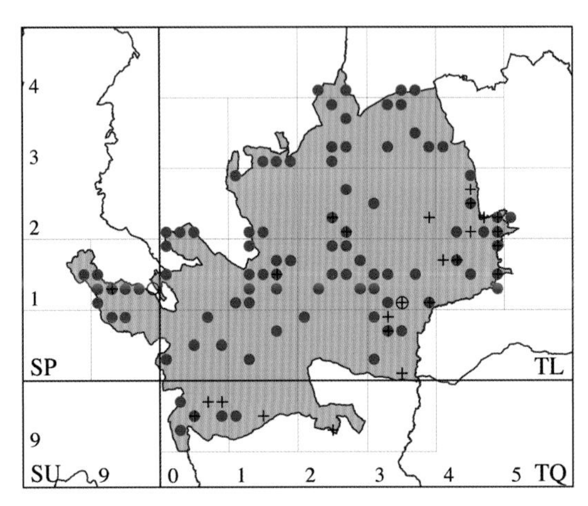

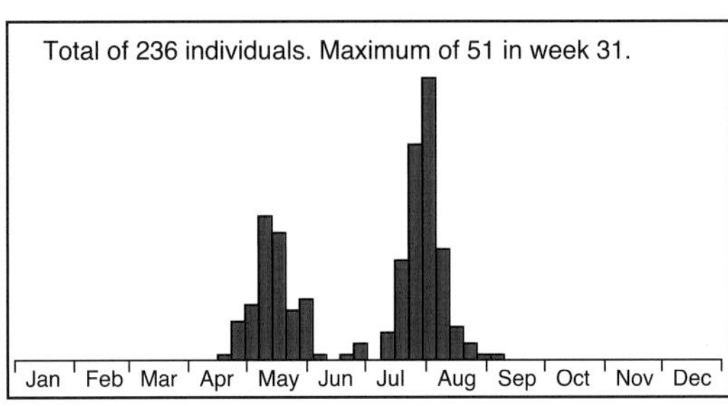

Separation of this species from 1725: Dark-barred Twin-spot Carpet can be extremely difficult and has been discussed by Plant (2005). The Red-twin-spot usually has a red median band on the forewing, but in some forms this band can be very dark or almost black. The Dark-barred Twin-spot, as the common name implies, has the median band of the forewing dark – often black. However, there is a form that has a reddish band (actually the typical form – those with black bands being referable to ab. *unidentaria*). A very widely used character for the separation of the two has been the presence (in Dark-barred) or absence (in the Red) of a notch on the inner edge of the median fascia of the forewing at the costa. However, this character has now been proven to be unreliable and should not be used. In many cases it will be necessary to rub away the scales from the tip of the abdomen of male specimens in order to look at the genitalia with a hand lens. The two species are immediately and easily separated by the length and shape of the costal process that arises from the inner face of each valva. In *X. spadicearia* each process is long and narrow, produced from the tip of the valva and then turning inwards at 90 degrees so that the two often touch or even overlap. In *X. ferrugata* the costal process is short and stout, produced to a short point that scarcely extends beyond the tip of the valva. Both species have an exceptionally long, narrow and curved uncus which should not be confused with the costal processes of the valvae.

1725 *Xanthorhoe ferrugata* (Cl.)
Dark-barred Twin-spot Carpet

Recorded:	1828 – 2006
Distribution / Status:	Local / Common resident, declining in the south
Conservation status:	UK BAP Watch List. Herts Threatened
Caterpillar food plants:	Not recorded. Elsewhere, polyphagous on herbaceous plants
Flight period:	April – June then July/August
Records in database:	161

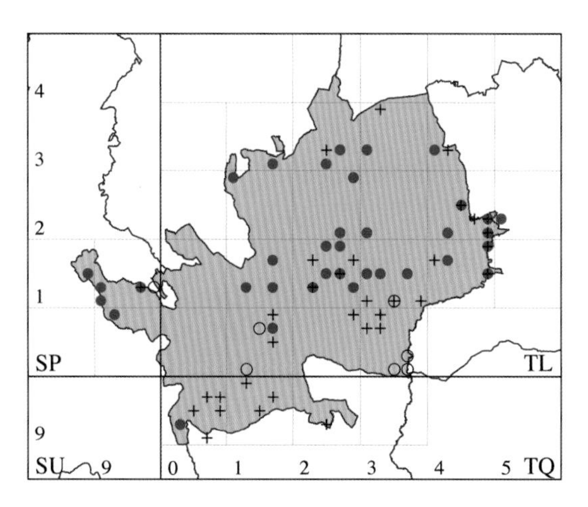

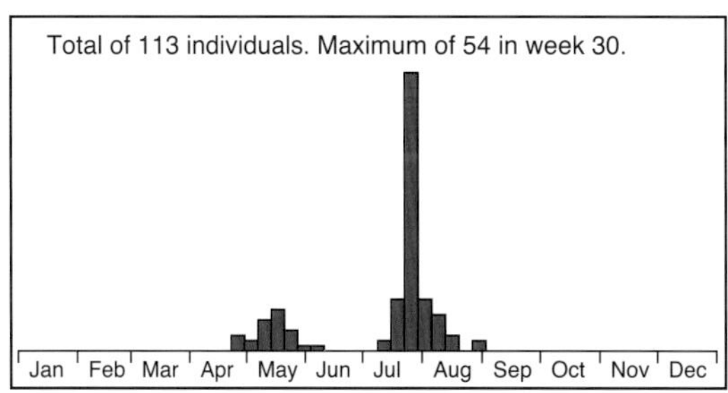

Separation of this species from 1724: Red Twin-spot Carpet (*Xanthorhoe spadicearia*) is difficult and is discussed under that species. This is a nationally declining species and our map suggests that the decline is also evident in our area; this is also reflected in the numbers of records of each species in the database – 363 for Red Twin-spot and 161 for Dark-barred Twin-spot. The map certainly shows a loss of the moth from sites in southern Hertfordshire. In *Larger Moths of the London Area* (1993), which covered the period up to 1991 and included the southern one-third of Hertfordshire, I described it as being 'a widespread and common resident in rural and suburban areas, encroaching upon the more urban parts only slightly more frequently than the preceding species [Red Twin-spot Carpet]'. As a result, it appears that any decline which has taken place has manifested itself in the past 15 or so years only. However, it should be noted that at that period the forewing 'notch' character was in common use as a sole means of identification of adult moths and so the possibility exists that some Red Twin-spots were misidentified as Dark-barred Twin-spots – perhaps making the latter appear more frequent than it really was?

1726 *Xanthorhoe quadrifasiata* (Cl.)
Large Twin-spot Carpet

Recorded:	1828 – 2006
Distribution / Status:	Widespread / Common resident
Conservation status:	Herts Stable
Caterpillar food plants:	Not recorded. Elsewhere, polyphagous on herbaceous plants
Flight period:	June to August
Records in database:	193

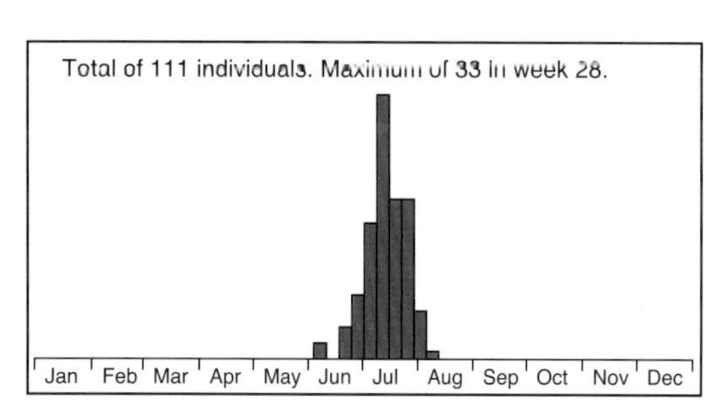

Whilst the whole of Hertfordshire is affected by this common moth it is interesting to consider this in the context of the wider area. The moth is present throughout Essex (Goodey, 2004) and Bedfordshire (Arnold et al., 1997), but practically absent from all of Middlesex and the Surrey sector of south London (Plant, 1993). Collins (1997) confirms it as absent from the entire eastern part of Surrey. This seems to suggest that Hertfordshire lies at the extreme south-west of its distributional range – except that Graham Collins (1997) also shows that it is present in the west of Surrey. There are clearly things that we do not yet know and understand about the ecology of this species.

1727 *Xanthorhoe montanata* ([D.& S.])
Silver-ground Carpet

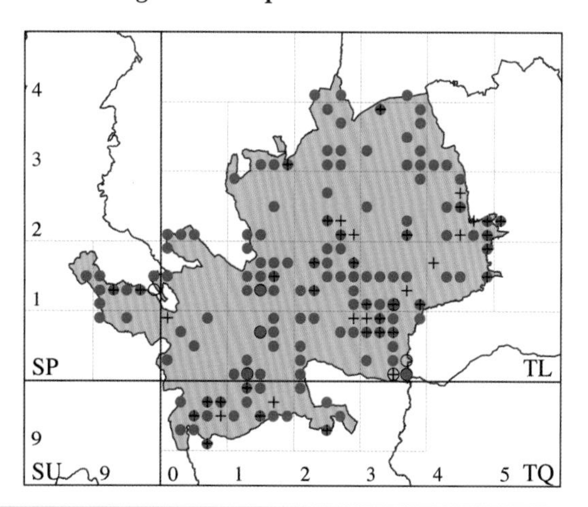

Recorded: 1884 – 2006
Distribution / Status: Ubiquitous / Abundant resident
Conservation status: Herts Stable
Caterpillar food plants: Bedstraw. Probably polyphagous
Flight period: May to July
Records in database: 484

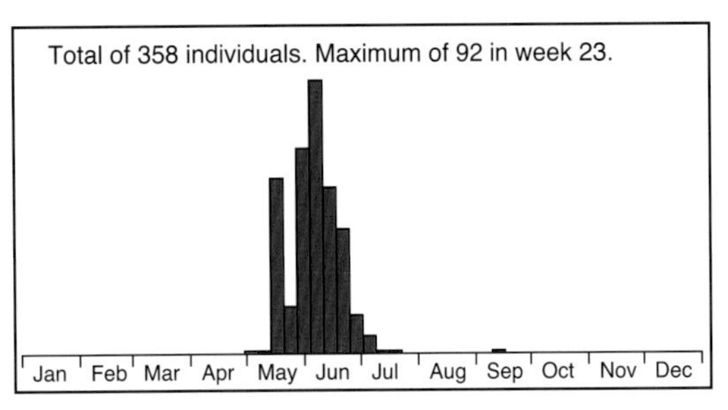

Foster (1937) had this familiar moth as 'Common everywhere, often abundant'. Nothing has changed. On mild evenings in early June it is possible to encounter hundreds of individuals flying at dusk.

1728 *Xanthorhoe fluctuata* (L.) Garden Carpet

Recorded: 1884 – 2006
Distribution / Status: Ubiquitous / Common resident
Conservation status: Herts Stable
Caterpillar food plants: Unidentified Cruciferae
Flight period: April to November in two generations
Records in database: 1599

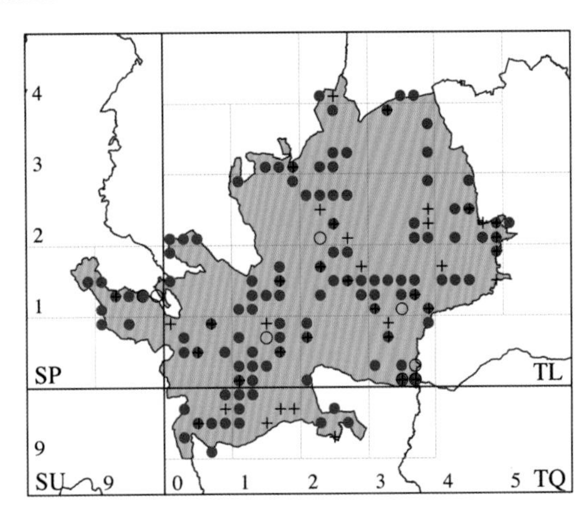

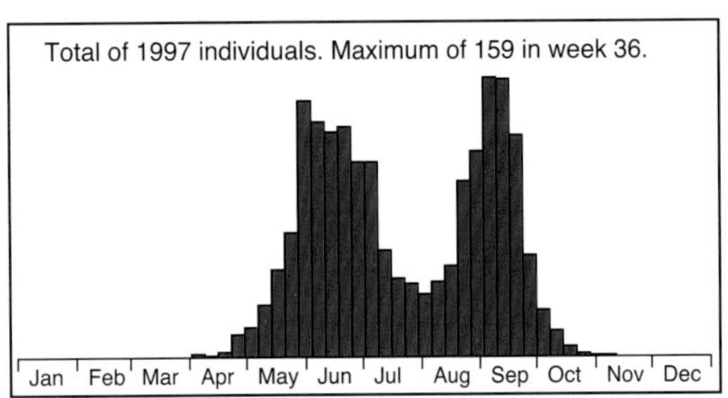

Foster's (1937) statement that the Garden Carpet was 'Abundant everywhere' applies equally today. The chart above shows two clear peaks of adults though the moths can be found continuously from late April to mid October in all years. An exceptionally early example was caught in my garden in Bishops Stortford on 5th February 2002 and an unusually late one elsewhere in the same town on 6th November 2001 (James Fish and Julian Reeves). There is much variation in the dark central band across the forewing; in some examples it is complete whilst in others it is reduced to a square spot on the leading edge. There is also small variation in terms of the degree of whiteness of the wings, but whilst many slightly greyish examples can be found in Hertfordshire the true melanic f. *thules* Prout appears to be rare. In some books, *thules* is erroneously treated as a Shetland Islands subspecies, but the same form is quite common in the London Area (Plant, 1993) and apparently also in other urban areas of England.

1731 *Scotopteryx bipunctaria* ([D.& S.]) ssp. *cretata* (Prout) Chalk Carpet

Recorded: 1828 – 2001
Distribution / Status: Extremely local / Rare resident.
Conservation status: UK BAP Priority Species. Herts Endangered
Caterpillar food plants: Not recorded. Elsewhere, on trefoils and clovers
Flight period: Elsewhere July and August
Records in database: 14

British Chalk Carpets are all referable to subspecies *cretata* (Prout); the nominate subspecies *bipunctaria* is found on mainland Europe. It is recorded from the Hertford area Stephens (1829), but the exact locality is not known. It is also recorded from the same general area in the Haileybury School list (Bowyer, 1888) and it is entirely possible that the latter is in fact Stephens record, though no details were given. Neither record can be accurately mapped and this seems an unlikely part of the county to find this species. It is also listed for the Sandridge area by Griffith (1884) – also not mapped because the precise location is unknown – and from Mackerye End (Griffith, 1890). It was plentiful at Aldbury Down [Aldbury Nowers?] in 1902 (P. J. Barraud) and in the 'Tring district' on 25th July 1903 (A. E. Gibbs and T. F. Furnival). Foster (1937) added Royston, Hexton, Berkhamsted and Apsley End. Hodgson (1939) has it as common on the downs at the Ashridge Estate and at Aldbury Nowers. Later, in a communication to P. J. Bell around 1965, Hodgson states '... about 10 years ago one could hardly move a step on Pitstone Hill in August without flushing this moth. I last saw it in 1956 although I have visited the locality every August'. Pitstone Hill is a boundary site on our border in Buckinghamshire, in the region that is now better known as the Aldbury Nowers Nature Reserve. There are a few other scattered records, all along the north-western side of the county where the Chalk is to be found, but the only recent record is from Hexton Chalk Pit, where it was found by Jim Reid on 6th July 2001. It is entirely likely that this moth persists at a small number of chalky localities along our border with Cambridgeshire, Bedfordshire and Buckinghamshire, but it has certainly been lost from a great many of its former localities. This loss seems to be focused on the 1950s, coinciding neatly with the outbreak of myxomatosis amongst the rabbit population, which allowed scrub to invade the chalk grasslands. Add into the equation the post-war cultivation of many unimproved grasslands and the indiscriminate use of pesticides in the 1950s and sixties and it is not hard to understand what has happened to the Chalk Carpet moth. During early 2007, drastic measures to reinstate the chalk grassland at Aldbury Nowers were instigated; let us hope that this welcome move has not come too late to save the Chalk Carpet from extinction in Hertfordshire.

1732 *Scotopteryx chenopodiata* (L.) Shaded Broad-bar

Recorded:	1887 – 2006
Distribution / Status:	Widespread / Common resident
Conservation status:	UK BAP Watch List Herts Threatened
Caterpillar food plants:	Not recorded. Elsewhere, on vetches and clovers
Flight period:	June to August
Records in database:	340

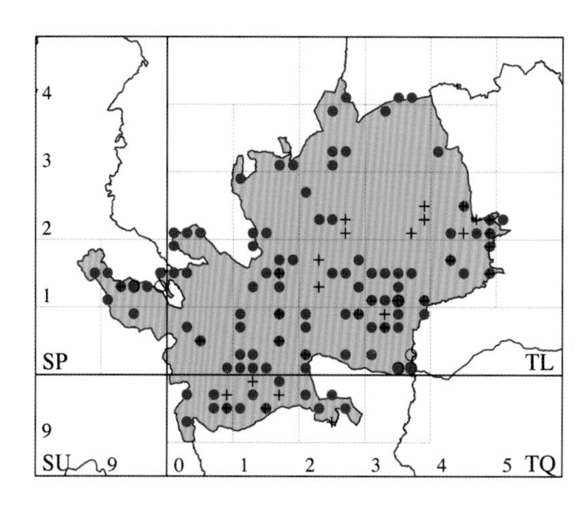

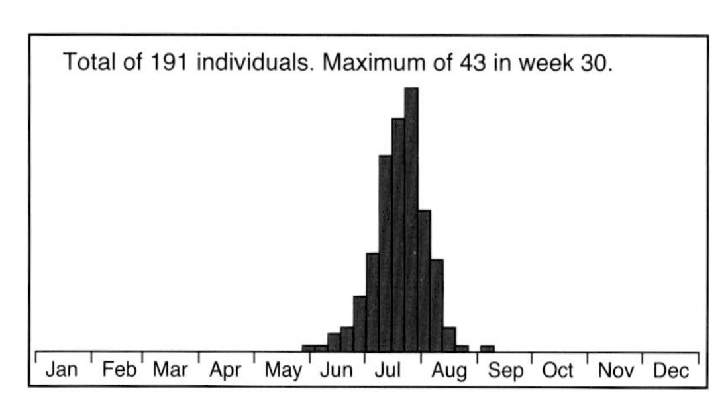

In the eighteenth century the colloquial name for *chenopodiata* was not Shaded Broad-bar, but 'The Aurelian's Curse'. The Aurelian Society was Britain's first entomological organisation and the moth was so named because it was apparently so abundant that it kept getting caught when other quarry was being chased! Today, the Shaded Broad-bar is not uncommon and in some years can be quite numerous, but the absence of large areas of unimproved grassland and other semi-natural habitat means that we are unlikely to be able to justify re-applying that original name.

1733 *Scotopteryx mucronata* (Scop.) ssp. *umbrifera* (Heyd.) Lead Belle

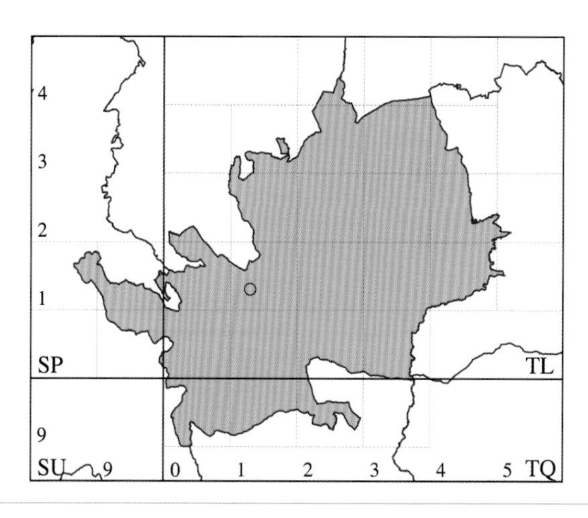

Recorded:	1947 – 1947
Distribution / Status:	Absent / Former vagrant
Conservation status:	-
Caterpillar food plants:	Not recorded.
Flight period:	Not recorded
Records in database:	1

Subspecies *umbrifera* (Heydemann) is the English subspecies of the Lead Belle. In Scotland it is replaced by ssp. *scotica* (Cockayne); the nominate ssp. *mucronata* (Scopoli) is found only on mainland Europe. The separation of Lead Belle from 1734: July Belle is almost always a matter that calls for dissection of the genital apparatus. Hodgson (1939) has this species as 'Frequent at light on commons, Ashridge', but these records are probably in error for the next species and are so treated by me. The only validated record is that made at Harpenden by C. B. Williams in 1947 and reported by Fryer (1948) and Riley (1999). There are no records for the adjacent county of Bedfordshire (Arnold et al, 1997) or for the London Area to the south (Plant, 1993), whilst to the east, in Essex, the Lead Belle was last recorded in 1911 (Goodey, 2004).

1734 *Scotopteryx luridata* (Hufn.) ssp. *plumbaria* (Fabr.) July Belle

Recorded:	1828 – 2001
Distribution / Status:	Absent or extremely local / Extinct or very rare resident
Conservation status:	Herts Endangered
Caterpillar food plants:	Not recorded. Elsewhere, on Gorse and Petty Whin
Flight period:	Elsewhere, June to August
Records in database:	24

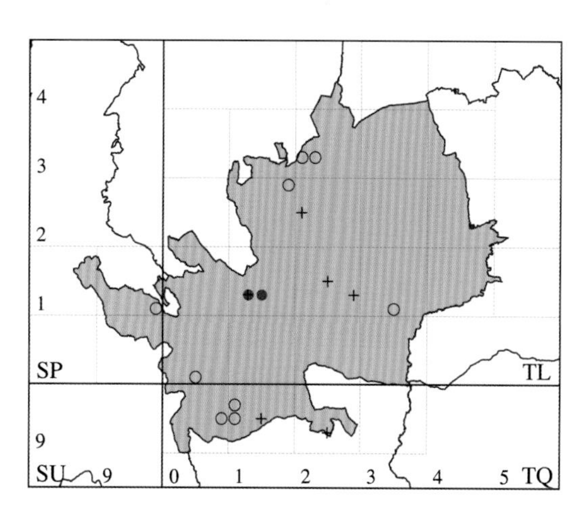

Subspecies *plumbaria* (Fabricius) is the English subspecies of the July Belle. Apart from those from the Sandridge area (before 1884) and the Hertford area (before 1829), which cannot be located adequately, all known records are mapped, including those mentioned under 1733: Lead Belle for the reasons stated under that species. There are only three records for the last twenty years; these are Symonds Green fields, 6th August 1991 (Gavin Boyd), East Common, Harpenden, 1995 (C. C. Doncaster) and Rothamsted Estate, Harpenden, 2001 (Phil Gould). These are all rather surprising, but perhaps there remains a small isolated population on Harpenden Common? This site requires careful survey in the next few years and if the moth is found immediate conservation measures should be introduced. Otherwise, this species is perhaps now extinct in Hertfordshire?

1735 *Catarhoe rubidata* ([D. & S.]) Ruddy Carpet

Recorded:	1884 – 2006
Distribution / Status:	Local / Uncommon resident
Conservation status:	Herts Scarce
Caterpillar food plants:	Not recorded. Elsewhere, on bedstraws
Flight period:	Mid-June to early August
Records in database:	20

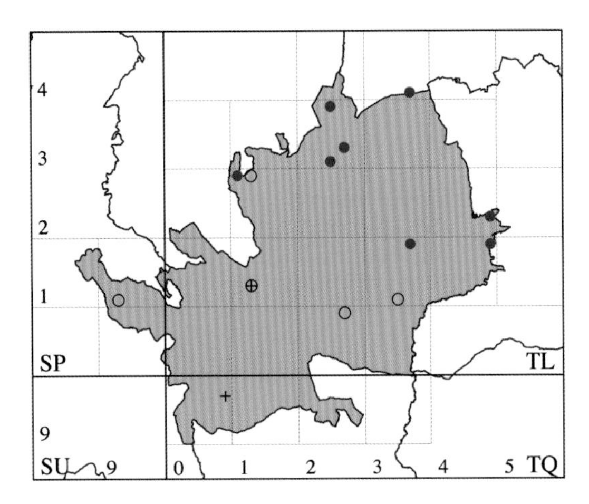

Records of adults span the period from the second week of June to the first week of August, but there are too few to warrant the plotting of a flight chart. The low number of reports may well reflect the dependency of modern-day lepidopterists on light trapping; far more adults will usually be found by gently tapping hedges at dusk. The Ruddy Carpet is certainly local with us, but is probably unrecorded in at least some places. Most records relate to chalky soils, but the moth is probably not confined to calcareous habitats.

1736 *Catarhoe cuculata* (Hufn.) Royal Mantle

Recorded:	1876 – 2006
Distribution / Status:	Local / Uncommon resident
Conservation status:	Herts Scarce
Caterpillar food plants:	Not recorded. Elsewhere, on bedstraws
Flight period:	Elsewhere, June/July
Records in database:	16

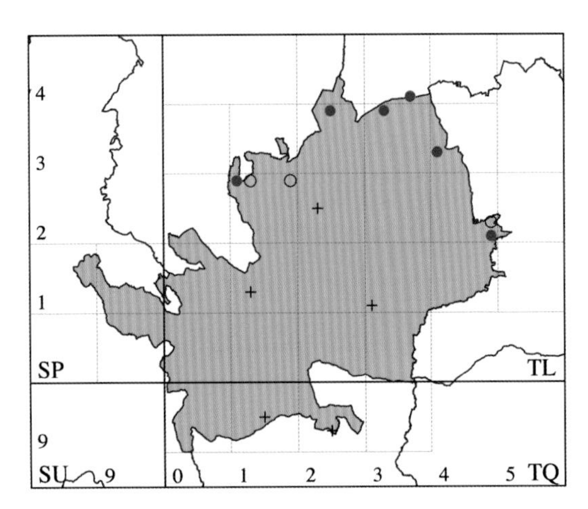

Apart from one vagrant example, modern records are confined to the chalk along the north-west boundary, where it may rest undetected in a few more sites than the map indicates. Away from this area the records seem initially puzzling as the moth prefers chalky soils, but at least some can be explained. For example, our earliest record reads: 'On 27th July 1876 I took a very good specimen of *Anticlea sinuata* in a chalky lane near the village of Farnham, about two miles from Bishops Stortford' (A. J. Spiller, *Entomologist* **10**: 48). Farnham is on the Boulder Clay, but there is a chalk quarry along the lane and it is almost certain that this is where the moth was found. The record was repeated by P. B. M. Allan in his 1950 Bishops Stortford list, who comments 'Not recorded since'. All the more surprising, then, was the single example that attended my garden moth trap in Bishops Stortford on 2nd July 2006. This was surely a wanderer from some distance, as quite probably were the moths that form the other records away from the chalk at Totteridge, 21st July 1961 (Ian Lorimer), Rothamsted Estate, 1964 (per Adrian Riley), Stevenage, 3rd August 1966 (Jack Newton), Bushey, 12th July 1968 (Barry Goater) and Bayfordbury, 1974 (Jim Reid).

1738 *Epirrhoe alternata* (Mull.) Common Carpet

Recorded:	1884 – 2006
Distribution / Status:	Ubiquitous / Abundant resident
Conservation status:	Herts Stable
Caterpillar food plants:	Cleavers; unknown bedstraw species
Flight period:	May to September
Records in database:	909

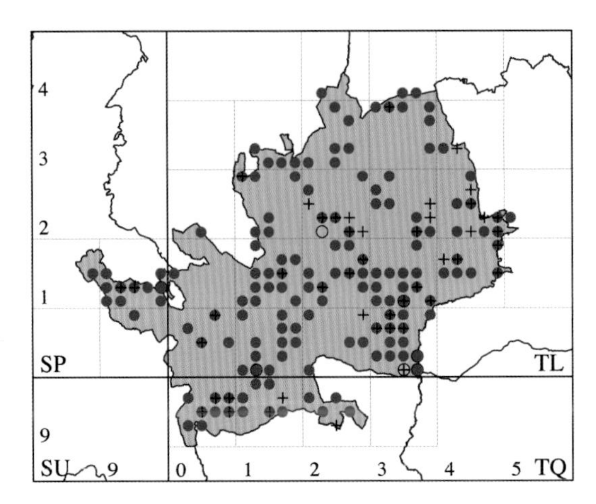

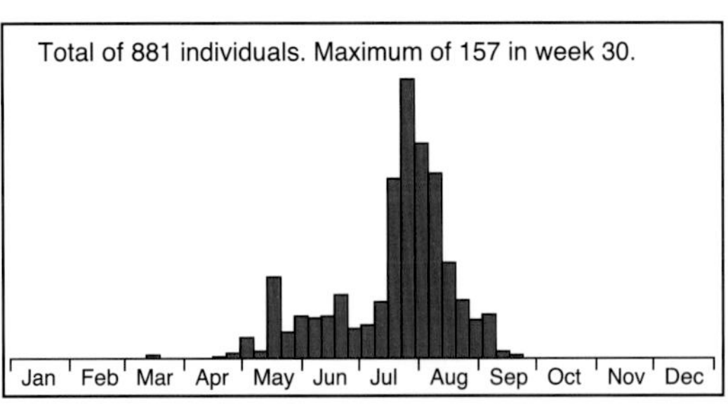

Foster (1937) lists this species as abundant in all districts and the same applies today. The flight chart shows a somewhat protracted emergence from the end of April to mid September, but whilst there is a clear peak of adults in July /August there is no statistically significant spring peak. There is no doubt from field observations that freshly emerged adults can be found throughout the flight period and it appears likely, therefore, that this species may be continuously brooded. This would go some way to explain the exceptional record on 15th March 2005 along the Icknield Way at Deacon Hill (S. Penn).

1739 *Epirrhoe rivata* (Hb.) Wood Carpet

Recorded: 1884 – 2005
Distribution / Status: Local / Rare resident
Conservation status: Herts Rare
Caterpillar food plants: Not recorded. Elsewhere, on bedstraws
Flight period: Insufficient data. Elsewhere, mid June to early August
Records in database: 28

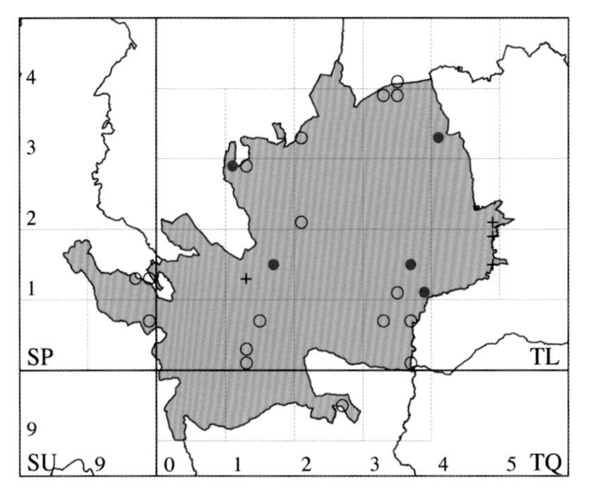

All known records are mapped; the number of former sites combined with the intensity of the recording effort from 2000 to 2006 gives cause for some concern that this is a species in serious decline in Hertfordshire. The record from 'Tring, woods near Ashridge House', on 11th June 1887 (field meeting report by A. E. Gibbs in *Transactions of the Hertfordshire Natural History Society and Field Club* **4**) appears likely to fall on the Buckinghamshire side of the border, though this scarcely matters as there are other reports from that area included in the map.

1740 *Epirrhoe galiata* ([D. & S.]) Galium Carpet

Recorded: 1904 – 1970
Distribution / Status: Absent / Extinct resident
Conservation status: UK BAP Watch List. Herts Extinct
Caterpillar food plants: Not recorded. Elsewhere, on bedstraws
Flight period: Elsewhere, May to July
Records in database: 2

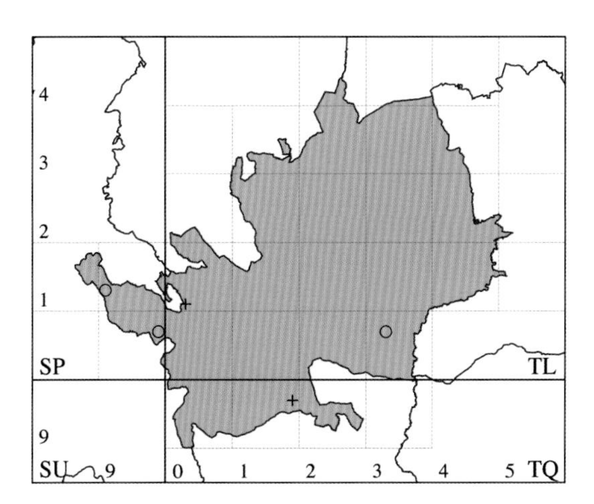

Gibbs (1905) lists the first county record from 'near Sparrowswick Wood', where an example was taken by Alice Dickinson in 1904. Gibbs notes that it is primarily coastal, but found inland 'not uncommonly on cretaceous formations' [chalk] and adds that it is recorded for Middlesex. The latter statement is true: it is noted from Harrow in 1876 (de Worms, 1957) and from Enfield Chase in 1891 (Cockerell, 1892) – both rather surprising records in unsuitable habitat. It is not recorded from Essex at all (Goodey, 2004) and in adjacent Bedfordshire there are just two unconfirmed records from 1951 and 1956. Back in Hertfordshire, Foster (1937) mentions the Sparrowswick record and adds St Albans, Wormley, Tring and 'near Berkhamsted'. Bell (1954) gives a record at Water End in 1952 by J. Donahaye. That observer also records 1881: *Trichopteryx carpinata* on the same date - a record that is clearly incorrect and which therefore casts severe doubts upon his *galiata* record as well; I have not mapped this record. Finally, there is a single report from Borehamwood in 1970 (Gaston Prior) which I am treating as a reliable record of a wandering individual.

1742 *Camptogramma bilineata* (L.) Yellow Shell

Recorded: 1884 – 2006
Distribution / Status: Widespread or ubiquitous / Abundant resident
Conservation status: Herts Stable
Caterpillar food plants: Stinging nettle. Probably polyphagous on low herbaceous plants
Flight period: May to September
Records in database: 775

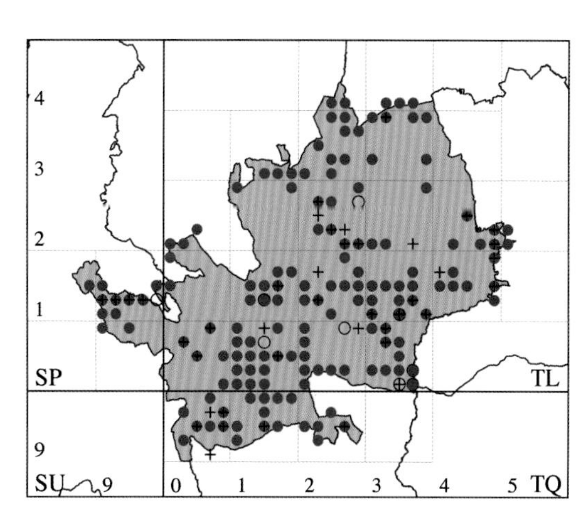

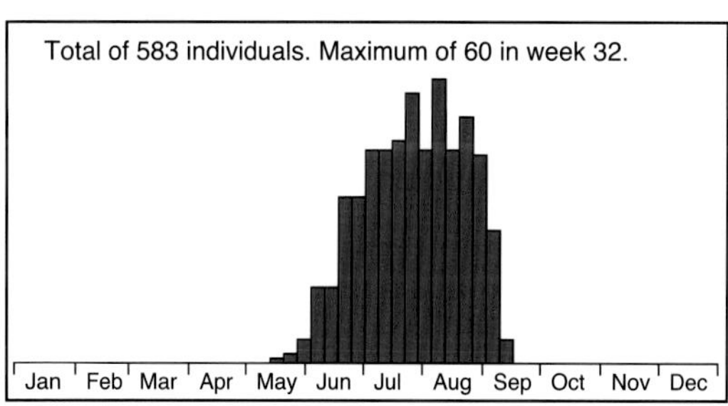

'Abundant in all districts', said Foster in his 1937 list; the same applies in 2007. Adults appear freshly emerged over continuous period from mid-May to mid-August, beyond which most individuals are worn, suggesting that the species is more or less continuously brooded with an adult lifetime of about four weeks, though this theory requires proper testing.

[1744 *Entephria caesiata* (([D.& S.]) Grey Mountain Carpet

Bell (1964) recorded that an example of this species was taken in the Rothamsted light trap [Rothamsted Estate, Harpenden] in August 1961. The record is not even mentioned in Riley's summary of moths caught at the Rothamsted Estate (Riley, 1999) and current staff in the Entomology Department there are unable to trace the original record. In spite of the surprise expressed by Bell, the record is clearly ridiculous and cannot be accepted. The moth is found in mountain and moorland habitats in the north and west of Britain, is not known to migrate and is quite absent from the south-east.]

1745 *Larentia clavaria* (Haw.) Mallow

Recorded: 1828 – 2006
Distribution / Status: Local / Common resident
Conservation status: Herts Stable
Caterpillar food plants: Not recorded. Elsewhere, on Mallow and Garden Hollyhocks
Flight period: September to November
Records in database: 163

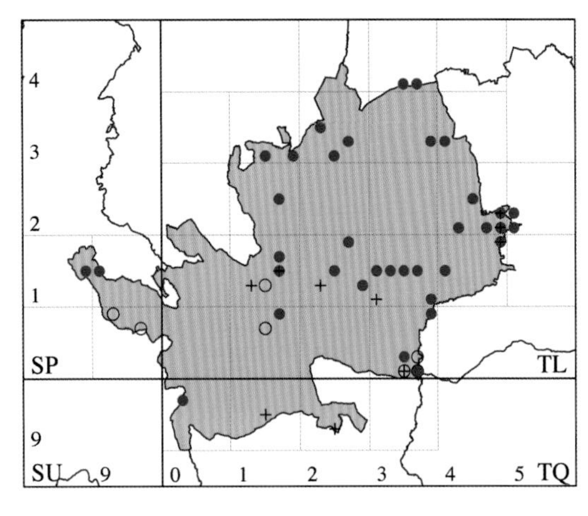

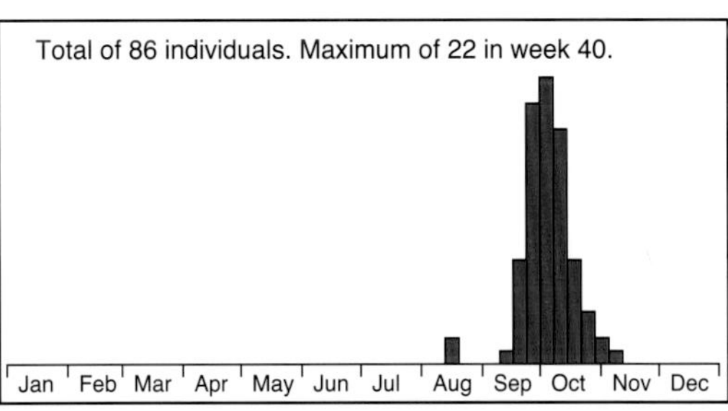

The map is probably more faithful to the location of light traps than to the spread of the moth across Hertfordshire. The flight period coincides with a period of inactivity on the part of some lepidopterists so that the number of records from sites that are not gardens is diminished: examination of the database shows that of the 36 post-1994 solid dots on the map 28 are from gardens. The extreme early record in the flight chart is of an adult in Hertford on 19th August 2006 (Andrew Wood).

1746 *Anticlea badiata* ([D.& S.]) Shoulder Stripe

Recorded: 1884 – 2006
Distribution / Status: Widespread / Common resident
Conservation status: Herts Stable
Caterpillar food plants: 'wild rose'
Flight period: March/April
Records in database: 204

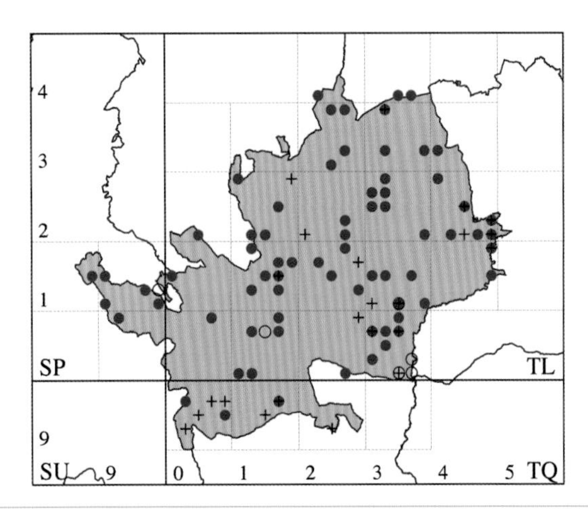

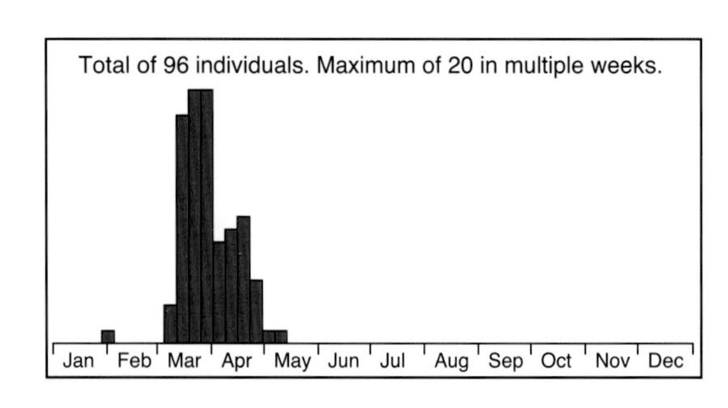

This is a familiar spring species in Hertfordshire, appearing about a fortnight earlier than 1747: Streamer in most years. An exceptionally early adult was noted at Ware on 4th February 2002 by Liz Goodyear.

1747 *Anticlea derivata* ([D.& S.]) Streamer

Recorded: 1884 – 2006
Distribution / Status: Widespread / Common resident
Conservation status: Herts Stable
Caterpillar food plants: Dog Rose
Flight period: April/May
Records in database: 230

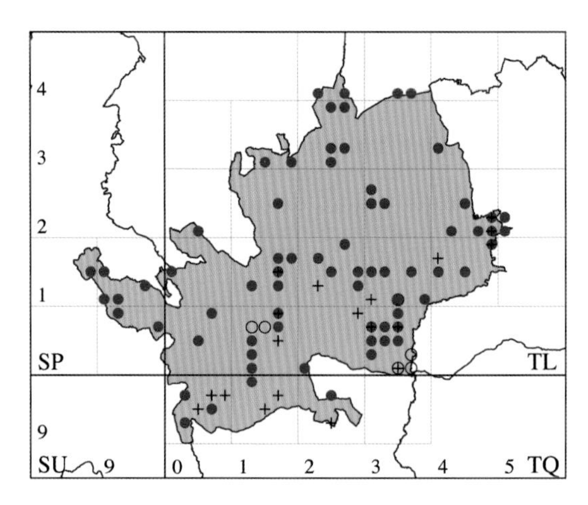

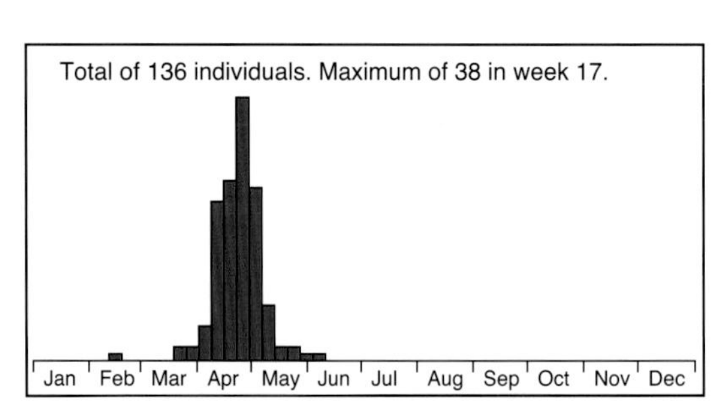

This is another common species of spring, flying slightly later than the Shoulder-stripe in any given year. An early adult was noted at Weston, on 18th February 2003 (Alan Cockburn). An extreme aberrant form, captured at Ashwell Chalk Quarry in April 2005 by Emil de Maria and Vincent & Betty Judd and now in my collection is illustrated in *British Journal of Entomology & Natural History* **19**: Plate 4, Figure 3.

1748 *Mesoleuca albicillata* (L.) Beautiful Carpet

Recorded: 1884 – 2006
Distribution / Status: Local / Uncommon resident
Conservation status: Herts Scarce
Caterpillar food plants: Not recorded. Elsewhere, on bramble, raspberry and strawberry
Flight period: Elsewhere, June/July
Records in database: 20

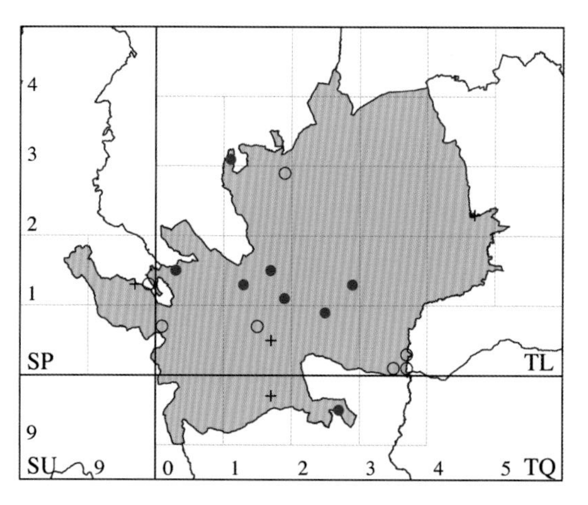

The Beautiful Carpet is a woodland moth that appears scarce in Hertfordshire, as in adjacent counties, but since it is very reluctant to come to light traps it may simply be under-recorded. Hertfordshire adult records, where a date is provided, are from 4th June to 17th July, but there are not enough reports to allow a flight chart to be drawn.

1749 *Pelurga comitata* (L.) Dark Spinach

Recorded:	1828 – 2006
Distribution / Status:	Widespread, but very local / Rare resident
Conservation status:	UK BAP Watch List Herts Vulnerable
Caterpillar food plants:	Chenopodiaceae (several unidentified species)
Flight period:	Late July to mid-August
Records in database:	56

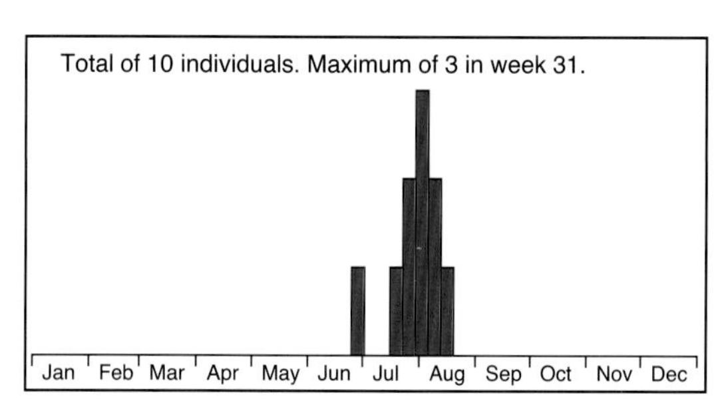

At the national level, the population level of Dark Spinach moths has apparently declined by 95 per cent since 1970 and the insect now formally qualifies as an Endangered species under the formal IUCN criteria. Numerical data for Hertfordshire is lacking, but 53 per cent of the recorded tetrad records do not record this species in the post-1994 period, in spite of searching in most of them. All known records are plotted on the map, though the placing of some of the older records is approximate. A decline in this species in the London Area was predicted by me (Plant, 1993). I commented that as pressure increases in London to build on derelict plots where the foodplant grows the moth would inevitably become scarcer. Goosefoot (*Chenopodium*) and Orache (*Atriplex*) are both common plants, but their distribution in Hertfordshire is very patchy and the moth's distribution probably follows this closely. Modern desires for tidiness in the urban and suburban environments will also contribute to the demise of the foodplants and to the overall loss of habitat for Dark Spinach moths.

1750 *Lampropteryx suffumata* ([D.& S.]) Water Carpet

Recorded:	1828 – 2006
Distribution / Status:	Local / Common resident
Conservation status:	Herts Stable
Caterpillar food plants:	Not recorded. Elsewhere, on bedstraws
Flight period:	Late March to early May
Records in database:	48

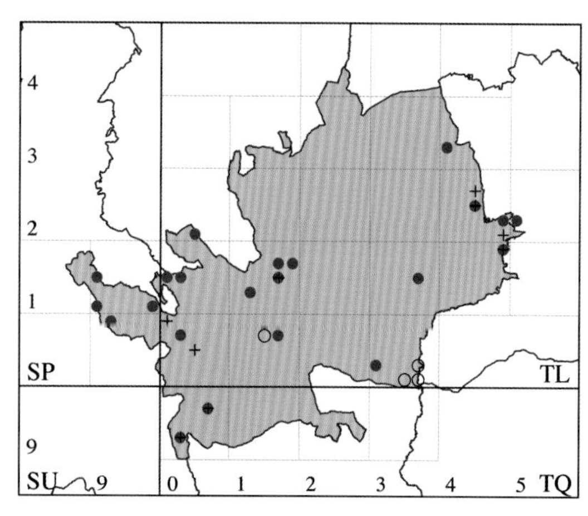

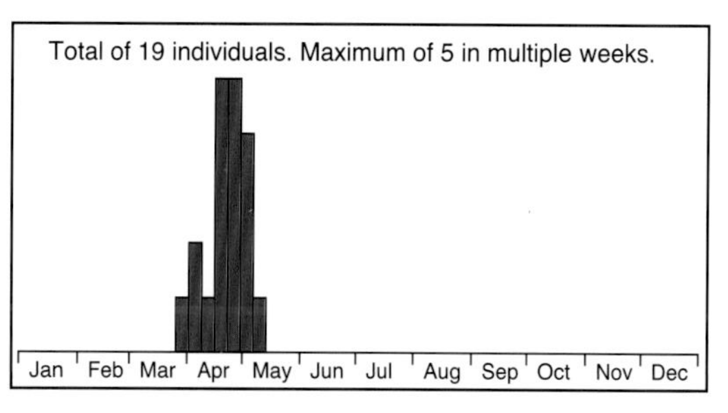

This moth has an affinity with dense Blackthorn thickets, for reasons that are not at all clear. If an actinic trap (ideally), or an mv lamp if no actinic is available, is placed under the dense cover it will likely fill with Water Carpets by the morning. If however, after setting the trap you are not scratched and bleeding from the blackthorn, then you have not put the trap far enough in and you may not catch any. The moths do wander, but not very far and this is illustrated by the fact that of the symbols on the distribution map only five relate to garden light traps. The moth is probably under-recorded.

1752 *Cosmorhoe ocellata* (L.) Purple Bar

Recorded:	1828 – 2006
Distribution / Status:	Widespread / Common resident
Conservation status:	Herts Stable
Caterpillar food plants:	Not recorded. Elsewhere, on bedstraws
Flight period:	May to August in two generations
Records in database:	172

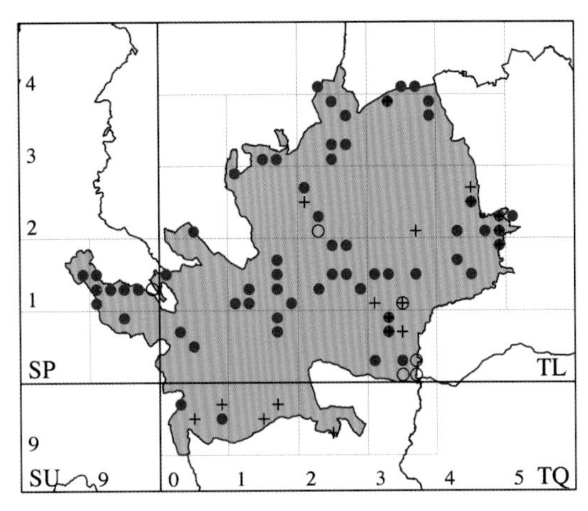

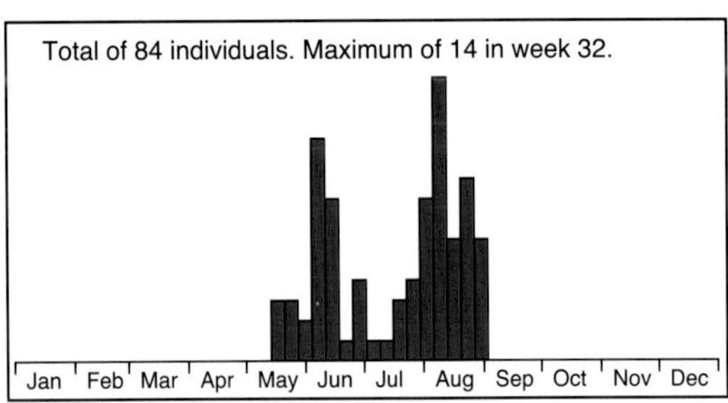

Though the flight chart shows continuous records from mid-May to early September, this combines all data for the years 2000 to 2006; in any single year there is a gap of two or three weeks between generations of adults.

1754 *Eulithis prunata* (L.) Phoenix

Recorded:	1828 – 2006
Distribution / Status:	Widespread / Common resident
Conservation status:	Herts Stable
Caterpillar food plants:	Blackcurrant
Flight period:	June to mid August
Records in database:	300

Although not usually present in particularly large numbers, this is nevertheless a common moth, as any visitor to my garden fruit cage will soon discover! The gap in records in the north-east is probably genuine as there are probably no currants grown in this entirely arable region of the county.

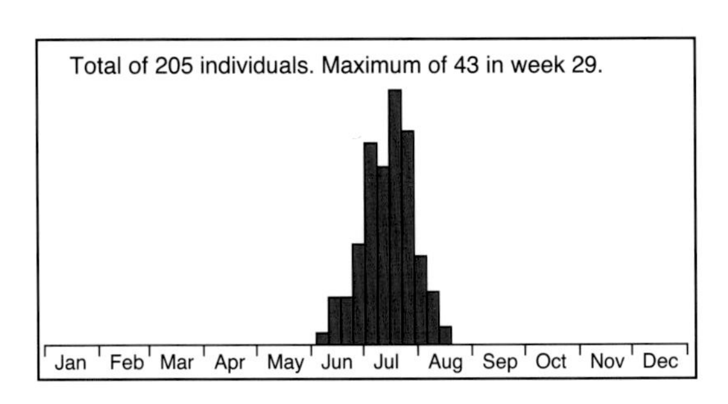

1755 *Eulithis testata* (L.) Chevron

Recorded:	1884 – 2003
Distribution / Status:	Local / Rare resident
Conservation status:	Herts Vulnerable
Caterpillar food plants:	Not recorded. Elsewhere, on sallow, Aspen and birch
Flight period:	July/August
Records in database:	25

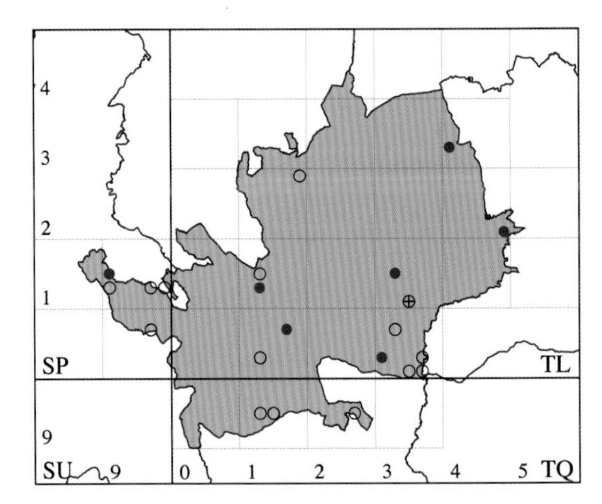

The Chevron seems to be a declining species in Hertfordshire, although the reasons for this are completely unknown. It is apparently absent from many former sites and has not been recorded since 2003 anywhere in the county. Foster (1937) merely listed localities for the moths without comment, but he did note quite a few for this species suggesting that it was quite widespread in the late nineteenth and early twentieth century.

1757 *Eulithis mellinata* (Fabr.) Spinach

Recorded:	1828 – 2005
Distribution / Status:	Local / Resident
Conservation status:	UK BAP Watch List Herts Vulnerable
Caterpillar food plants:	Elsewhere on Redcurrant and Blackcurrant
Flight period:	June/July
Records in database:	92

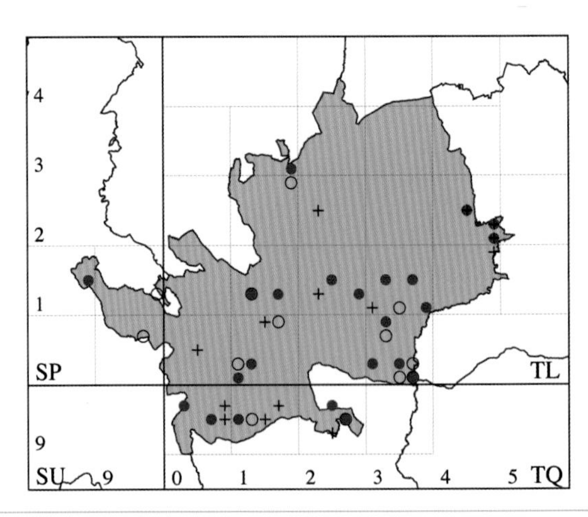

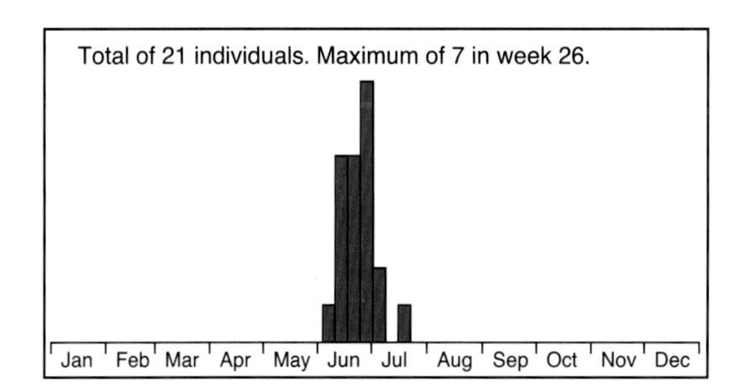

The Spinach has declined drastically over the whole of Britain, showing a 95 per cent population decrease since 1970. Some 48 per cent of Hertfordshire map squares from which there have been records no longer seem to support the moth, though not all have been thoroughly searched. Foster (1937), lists a number of records indicating that this moth was evidently quite widespread in the early part of the twentieth century, but plotting these and all other records on the map seems to show that there are large areas where the moth has apparently never been seen. In fact, the map symbols all more or less correspond to areas of human habitation, presumably where the foodplants are grown in gardens and allotments and the moth is in fact rather a rarity in the non-urban countryside. The losses of this moth are quite likely to reflect the declining popularity of allotments in particular and of domestic fruit growing in general. It will be interesting to see if any increase in 'green gardening' techniques is followed a few years later by a resurgence of the Moth.

1758 *Eulithis pyraliata* ([D.& S.]) Barred Straw

Recorded:	1884 – 2006
Distribution / Status:	Widespread / Common resident
Conservation status:	Herts Stable
Caterpillar food plants:	Not recorded. Elsewhere, on bedstraws
Flight period:	June/July
Records in database:	335

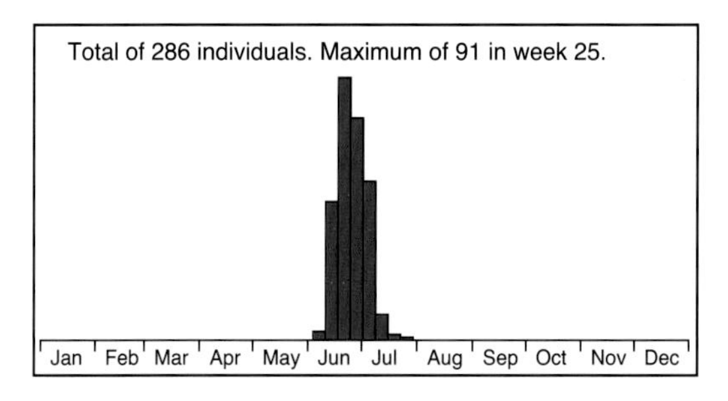

The Barred Straw is a familiar site at moth traps across the county. It has a very precise flight period, in June and July with no records at all outside that period. Care should be taken by newcomers to the study of moths not to confuse it with 1757: Spinach.

1759 *Ecliptopera silaceata* ([D.& S.]) Small Phoenix

Recorded:	1884 – 2006
Distribution / Status:	Widespread / Common resident
Conservation status:	UK BAP Watch List. Herts Stable
Caterpillar food plants:	Not recorded. Elsewhere, on willow herbs and Enchanter's Nightshade
Flight period:	Late April to June then July/August
Records in database:	284

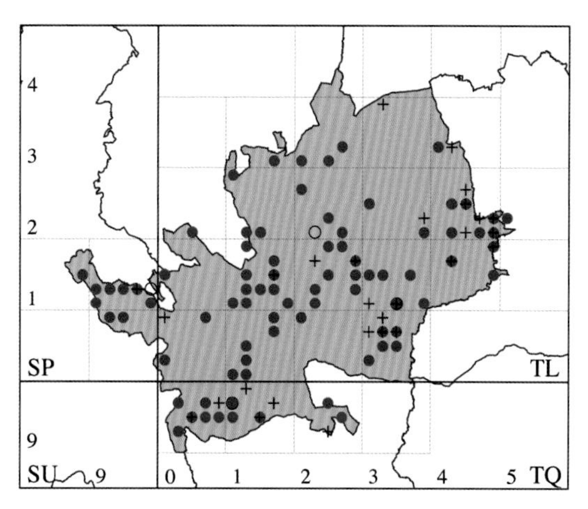

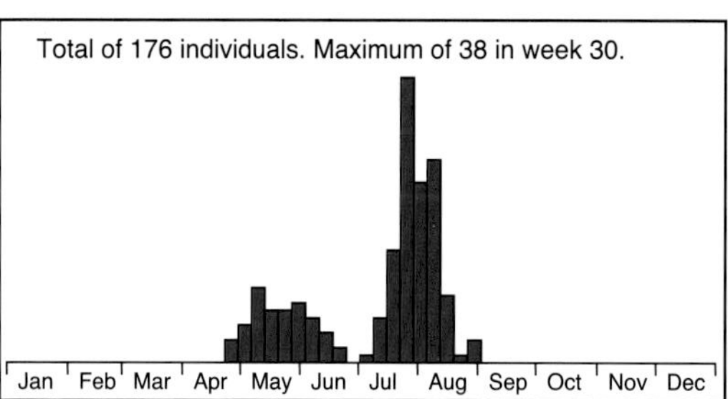

Typical Small Phoenix, the form that was originally described as this species, has a solid central band across the fore wing and appears scarce in Hertfordshire, perhaps forming as little as 15 – 20 per cent of the population. Far more common is f. *insulata* Haworth, in which two white lines cross the band and isolate a small dark oval area. This familiar form could perhaps be confused by inexperienced observers with some of the forms of 1773: Broken-barred Carpet in May and June, though that species does not fly later in the year.

1760 *Chloroclysta siterata* (Hufn.) Red-green Carpet

Recorded:	1904 – 2006
Distribution / Status:	Widespread / Common resident
Conservation status:	Increasing
Caterpillar food plants:	English Oak. Probably on other trees
Flight period:	September to May
Records in database:	386

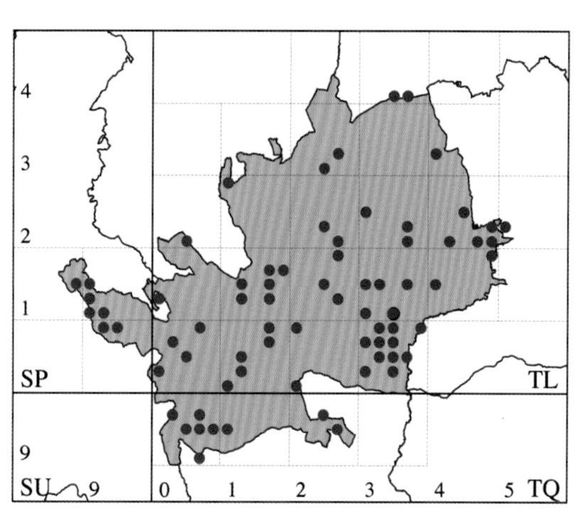

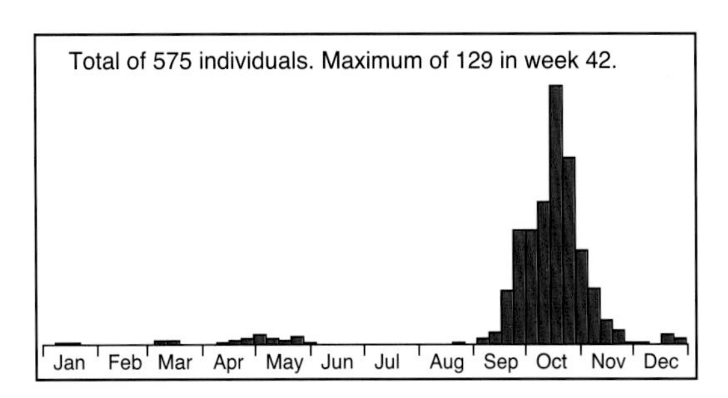

The Red-green Carpet must be considered alongside 1961: Autumn Green Carpet, which is now apparently extinct in Hertfordshire, but which was evidently quite widespread here at the end of the nineteenth century. The 1939 edition of Richard South's *The Moths of the British Isles* suggests that the two species had similar ranges in Britain in the early part of the twentieth century, but I can find no evidence to support this in Hertfordshire. Gibbs (1905) lists the first county record from Tring, where a larva was taken in 1904 by A. T. Goodson and the adult reared. Gibbs continues by saying that 'Mr. Barrett in *British Lepidoptera* says that it occurs in Cambs, Beds, and Essex. It is often abundant in its favourite haunts, chiefly in the southern counties, and in such localities comes freely to ivy-bloom'. Barrett's volumes were published from 1893 to 1907. Foster (1937) lists only this same record. Both authors ignore the apparent mention of this species on the Haileybury School list (Bowyer, 1888) as well as the 1880s record from the Sandridge area by Griffith; both are thought more likely to refer to 1761: Autumn Green Carpet, but even if I am incorrect the overall situation is not altered. There are no further reports until 1996, when Vincent and Betty Judd caught an example at Claggsbottom Wood near Ayot St Lawrence. The next year, 1997, Maurice Pledger caught the moth at the car park light on an oak tree outside the Huntsman pub in Hoddesdon and then also at Monks Green, Broxbourne, whilst Vincent and Betty Judd caught another, this time in their garden at Blackmore End. In 1998, it turned up in Andrew Wood's garden in the Bengeo area of Hertford, at Marshall's Heath (John Murray) and at Cuffley (Alan Bolitho). By 1999 it was clear that this moth was here to stay, with repeat appearances at most sites and new locations at Harpenden, Danemead Wood, East Barnet, Waterford Heath and three separate sites in Bishops Stortford. The colonisation of the county from 1996 onwards is real – apart from the 1904 record there were no Red-green Carpets resident here before that year; in this context the quote from Barrett, given above by Gibbs, is surprising.

1761 *Chloroclysta miata* (L.) Autumn Green Carpet

Recorded:	1888 – 1967
Distribution / Status:	Absent / Former resident
Conservation status:	Herts Extinct
Caterpillar food plants:	Not recorded. Elsewhere, on deciduous trees
Flight period:	Elsewhere, September to April
Records in database:	17

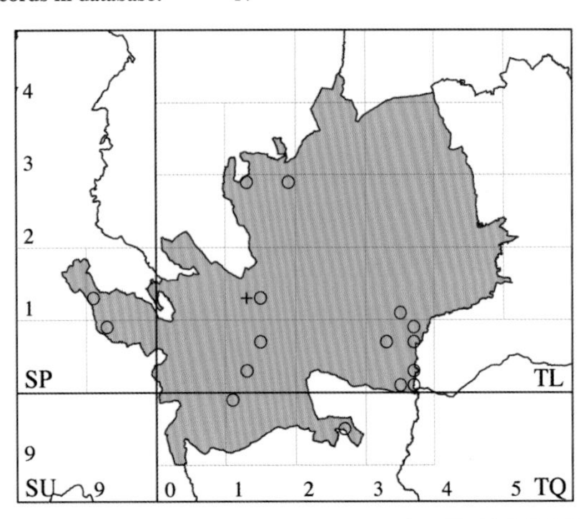

Reference has already been made under the previous species to early misidentified records of Autumn Green Carpet from the Sandridge area (Griffith, 1888) and from Haileybury School (Bowyer, 1888). Others from the era include within two or three miles of St Albans Town Hall and the area east of Bamville Wood Farm, near Harpenden Common (Gibbs, 1889). Foster (1916) had it as 'Not uncommon at light' [in north Hertfordshire] and in his 1937 list he adds Tring, Hitchin, East Barnet, Bricket Wood, Wilstone, Watford, Cheshunt, Berkhamsted, Broxbourne, Hoddesdon and Harpenden. For the latter locality, Riley (1999) states that there were three in the traps during the 1930s, one in 1949 and one in 1967, with none since that last date. Hodgson (1939) notes it as 'scarce at light at High Scrubs (near Berkhamsted)'. This wood lies south of Tring. The mapped old records show a strong association with some of the county's older woodland complexes, especially the Broxbourne Woods complex. However, although it may just possibly persist in some of the woodlands over towards our border with Buckinghamshire, where recording effort has been less. the Autumn Green Carpet has now not been seen in our county for 40 years and is certainly almost extinct here.

1762 *Chloroclysta citrata* (L.) Dark Marbled Carpet

Recorded:	1884 – 2005
Distribution / Status:	Local / Rare resident
Conservation status:	Herts Scarce
Caterpillar food plants:	Not recorded. Elsewhere, on various trees and bushes
Flight period:	July and August
Records in database:	52

The very few records that have dates associated with them confirm the national situation in which this moth flies in July and August. Records from May and October have all, on checking carefully, been found to refer to misidentified **1764:** Common Marbled Carpet. Although the two can usually be separated fairly easily, both are very variable species and so the extra information that outside the July/August window they are more likely to be Common Marbled Carpet may help some people. Foster (1937) reported that it was 'Common everywhere', but that may have been an oversimplification of a distribution not too different from that which we see today.

1764 *Chloroclysta truncata* (Hufn.) Common Marbled Carpet

Recorded:	1884 – 2006
Distribution / Status:	Ubiquitous / Abundant resident
Conservation status:	Herts Stable
Caterpillar food plants:	Hazel, Hornbeam, oak. Probably on other trees as well
Flight period:	May to July then August to October
Records in database:	1,526

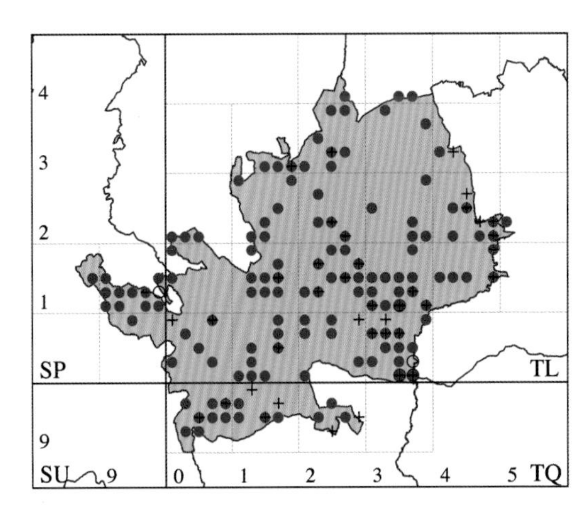

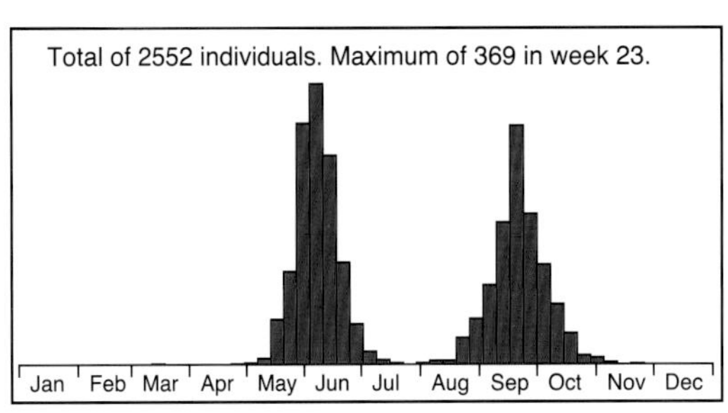

As with the last species, Foster (1937) listed this species as common everywhere and on this occasion there is no disagreement; the same situation persists today. Two very distinct generations of adults are evident and there is a single record outside these peaks on 17th March 2000 in my own garden trap at Bishops Stortford. Marbled Carpets appear in a huge range of colour forms and many are casually recorded in Hertfordshire, although melanic varieties dominate. The specimen illustrated by Skinner (1984 and 1998), at Plate 8, Figure 35, is ab. *perfuscata* Haworth; this dominates many catches and may form 80 per cent of the specimens in the Hertfordshire spring brood. Skinner's specimen illustrated at Plate 8, Figure 34, with the large brown patches on the fore wings, is the most frequent form in the autumn brood and in my own garden 95 per cent of the autumn 2006 generation are of this form. Non-melanic forms are present, but apparently rare.

1765 *Cidaria fulvata* (Forster) Barred Yellow

Recorded: 1887 – 2006
Distribution / Status: Widespread / Common resident
Conservation status: Herts Stable
Caterpillar food plants: Dog Rose
Flight period: June to late July
Records in database: 406

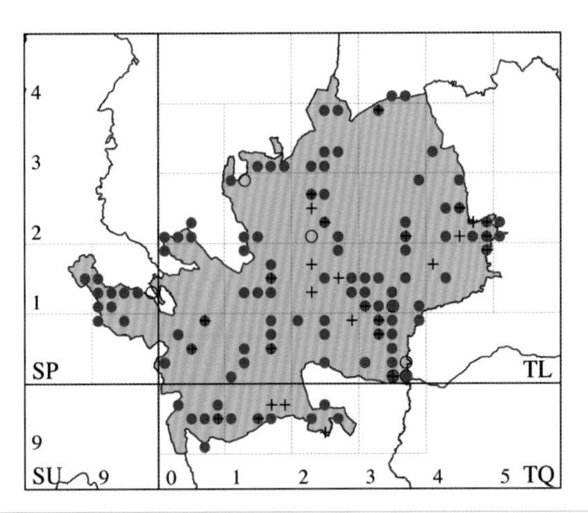

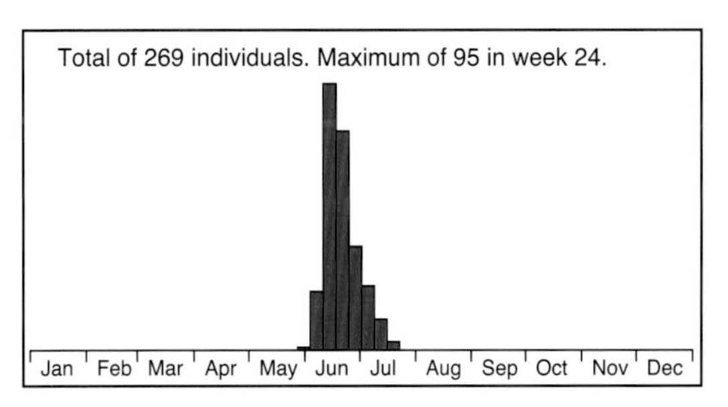

This widespread Hertfordshire moth is on the wing for a relatively short period of about six or seven weeks in the summer and is expected wherever Dog Rose grows in hedges and elsewhere.

.

1766 *Plemyria rubiginata* ([D.& S.]) Blue-bordered Carpet

Recorded: 1887 – 2006
Distribution / Status: Widespread / Common resident
Conservation status: Herts Stable
Caterpillar food plants: Not recorded. Elsewhere, on various trees
Flight period: June/July
Records in database: 195

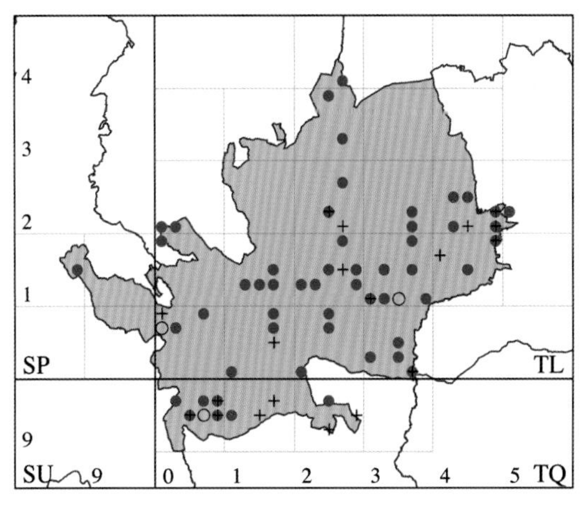

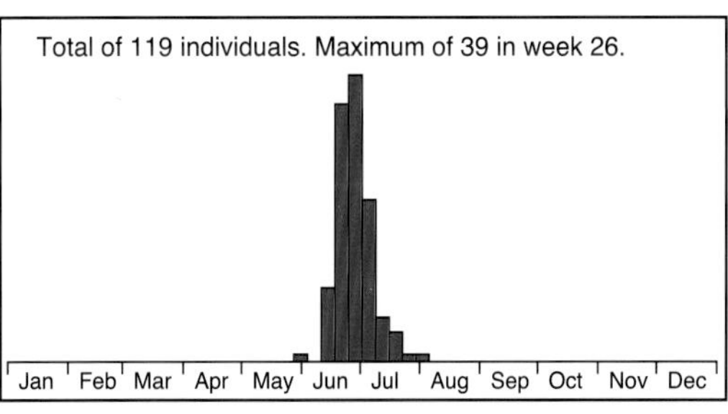

Foster (1937) lists a number of records indicating that this delicate little moth was evidently quite widespread in the early part of the twentieth century. This remains the case in the early part of the twenty-first, though adults usually sit on the outside of moth traps and so have either flown away or been eaten by birds when the trap operator arrives to examine the catch.

1767 *Thera firmata* (Hb.) Pine Carpet

Recorded: 1890 – 2005
Distribution / Status: Local / Rare resident
Conservation status: Herts Scarce
Caterpillar food plants: Scots Pine
Flight period: Elsewhere, August to October
Records in database: 28

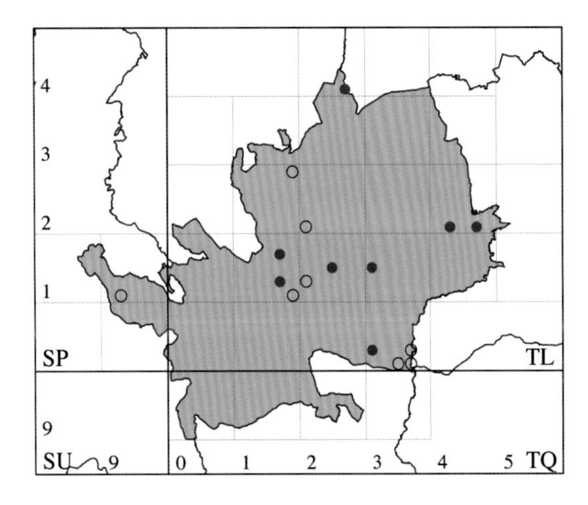

Dated Hertfordshire records are all in September, but the moth is rarely encountered here and so data are sparse. It is likely to be found wherever there are Scots Pine trees, but these tend to be tall and isolated and so unless a trap can be run near them in the appropriate season the moth is likely to remain at least partly under-recorded.

1768 *Thera obeliscata* (Hb.) Grey Pine Carpet

Recorded: 1938 – 2006
Distribution / Status: Widespread / Abundant resident
Conservation status: Stable
Caterpillar food plants: Scots Pine. Elsewhere also on spruce
Flight period: May to July then September to November in two generations
Records in database: 392

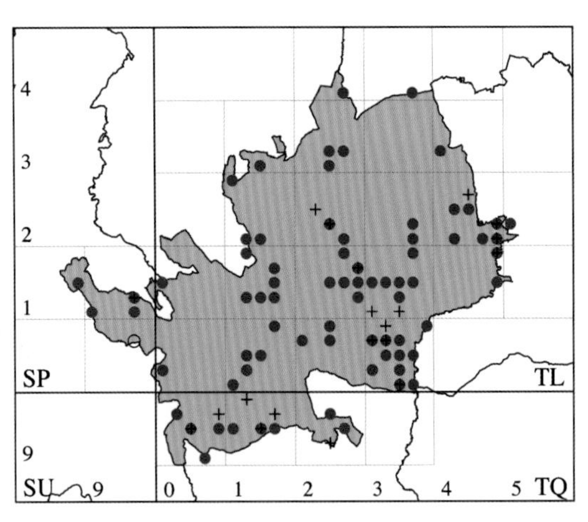

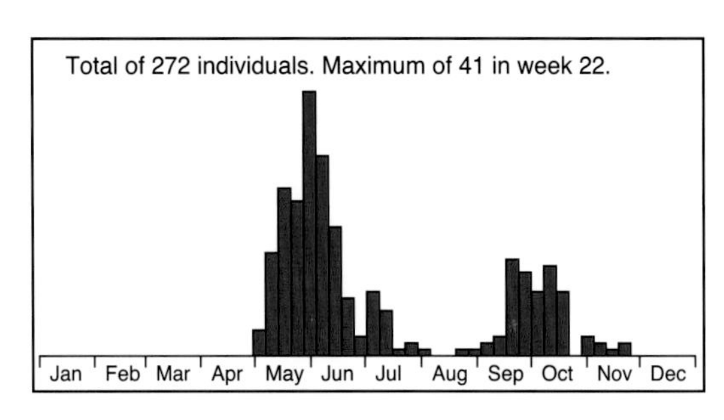

J. F. Stephens illustrates *Thera britannica* (as *variata*) from Hertford in his *Illustrations of British Entomology* (**3:** 272) published in 1829, and Foster (1937) gives several localities, also as *variata*. However, Fryer (1948) suggests that these are open to question and may relate to *T. obeliscata*. Under the entry for *obeliscata*, Foster (1937) lists only Hitchin. As there is room for doubt I have excluded these from the maps of both species, and the earliest confirmed report of *obeliscata* in the county is that from Hockeridge Wood in 1938. The separation of *obeliscata* (Grey Pine Carpet) from *britannica* (Spruce Carpet) is often quite difficult. The best guide is perhaps the segments of the male antennae, as the following illustration from Skou (1986) shows:

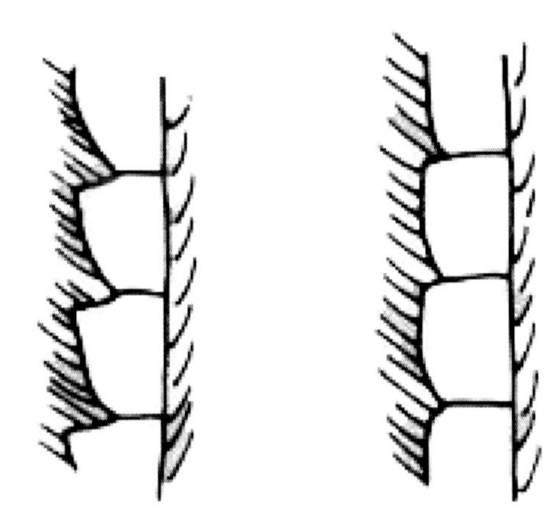

Antennae of male *Thera* species: Left: Spruce Carpet (*Thera britannica*). Right: Grey Pine Carpet (*Thera obeliscata*).

Some females may not be separable without dissection. The moth is very often found where neither Scots Pine nor Spruce grows and there must surely be an undiscovered alternative foodplant.

1769 *Thera britannica* (Turner) Spruce Carpet

Recorded: 1945 – 2006
Distribution / Status: Widespread / Common resident
Conservation status: Herts Stable
Caterpillar food plants: Not recorded. Elsewhere, on spruce
Flight period: May to July then September to November in two generations
Records in database: 377

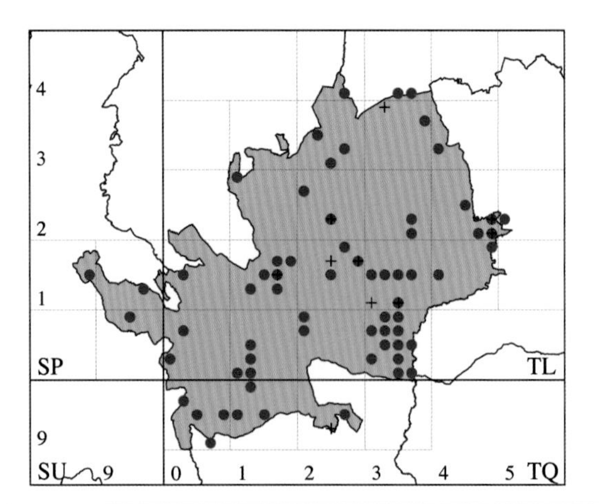

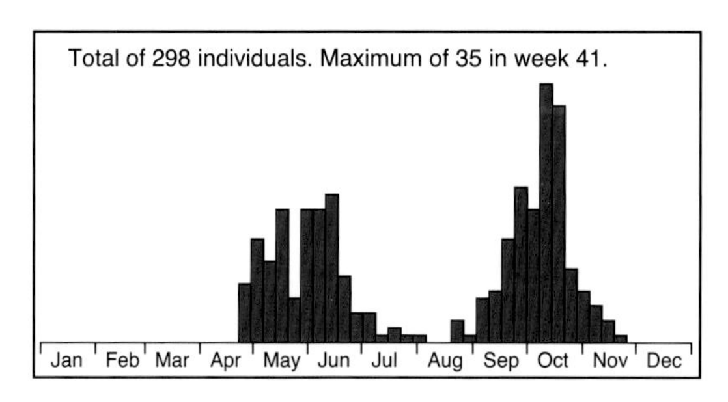

As discussed under the last species, Fryer (1948) suggests that the records in Foster (1937) are open to question. In so commenting, he formally reintroduces *T. britannica* to the county list on the strength of a valid specimen taken at Berkhamsted in 1945 by J. H. Bell. Since then, it has proved to be a widespread and common species.

[1770 *Thera cognata* (Thunb.) Chestnut-coloured Carpet

Bowyer (1880) lists this northern and western moorland and sea-cliff species from Haileybury School; Boyd (1901) has it as 'common' at Cheshunt. Another report, from Watford in May 1953, is listed in Penrose (1980). None of these is likely to be correct and none is accepted here.]

1771 *Thera juniperata* Juniper Carpet

Recorded:	1902 – 2006
Distribution / Status:	Local / Common resident
Conservation status:	Increasing
Caterpillar food plants:	Not recorded. Elsewhere, on Juniper and Cupressaceous trees
Flight period:	Early October to mid-November
Records in database:	220

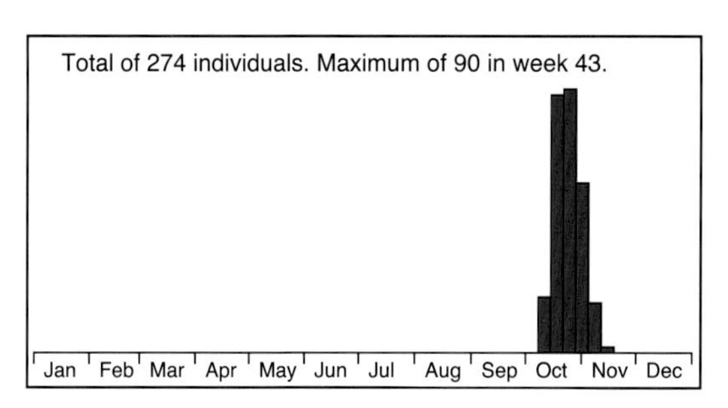

Our earliest record is from 'Tring' in October 1902 (Barraud, 1903) and probably relates to native Juniper on the chalk downland. However, there are no more records of the moth until one was taken at Totteridge on 19th October 1963 by Ian Lorimer (Bell, 1964; de Worms, 1964). It was recorded again at Totteridge on 15 October 1973, and Lorimer (manuscript list) reports these two as the only examples captured from 1954 to 1980, suggesting that they may have originated with introduced shrubs. One was taken at Hadley Wood Station in 1970 (Peter Alton), but there were no more until one in association with Lawson's Cypress trees in my garden at Bishops Stortford in 1987. The next was at Welwyn, 17th October 1990 (Raymond Uffen) then it was found in a different location in Bishops Stortford in 1993 and annually thereafter (James Fish and Julian Reeves). Wendy Hatton caught one in St Albans on 15th October 1997 and at Cuffley, Alan Bolitho caught it on 16th October 1997. In 1999 it suddenly appeared across the county in a number of sites and has remained here ever since. There can be no doubt that native Juniper is *not* the larval foodplant other than in the extreme west of the county and everywhere else the caterpillar is using either garden varieties of Juniper or, more likely, Lawson's Cypress and similar trees.

1771a *Thera cupressata* (Geyer) Cypress Carpet

Recorded:	2006 only
Distribution / Status:	Local / Recent colonist – probably establishing
Conservation status:	No perceived threats
Caterpillar food plants:	Not recorded. Elsewhere, on *Cupressus macrocarpa*
Flight period:	Elsewhere, May/June then September to November
Records in database:	1

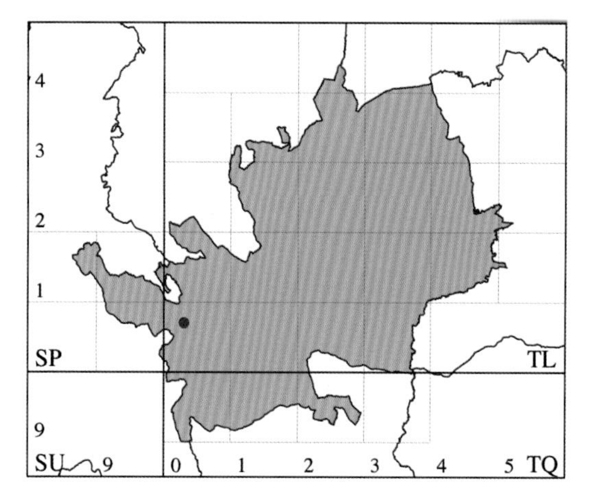

The only county record of this recent arrival in Britain is from Hemel Hempstead, where Roger Prue caught one in his garden light trap on 14th October 2006. It is a species that is likely to become established as a resident and extend its range to include Hertfordshire.

1773 *Electrophaes corylata* (Thunb.) Broken-barred Carpet

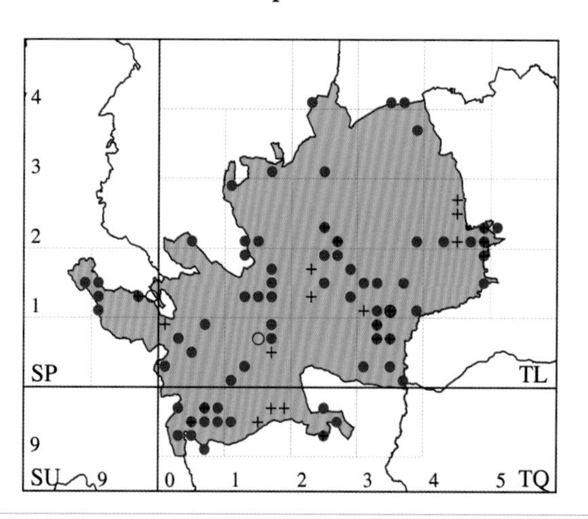

Recorded:	1887 - 2006
Distribution / Status:	Widespread / Common resident
Conservation status:	Herts Stable
Caterpillar food plants:	Not recorded. Elsewhere, on deciduous trees
Flight period:	May/June
Records in database:	315

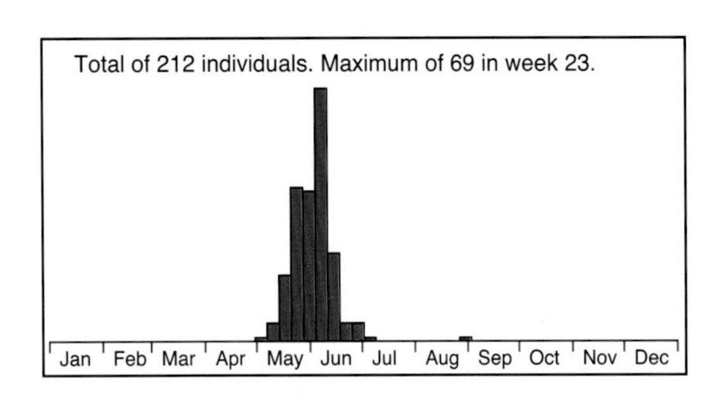

Some examples of the Broken-barred Carpet might be confused with 1759: Small Phoenix by beginners; both are common species in the county. Not all Broken-barred Carpets have the central bar of the forewing broken. In the London Area it is about half and half (Plant, 1993) but we have no numerical data for the frequency of either form in Hertfordshire.

1774 *Colostygia olivata* ([D.& S.]) Beech-green Carpet

Recorded:	1890 - 1936
Distribution / Status:	Absent / Former resident
Conservation status:	Herts Extinct
Caterpillar food plants:	Not recorded. Elsewhere, on bedstraws
Flight period:	Elsewhere, July/August
Records in database:	4

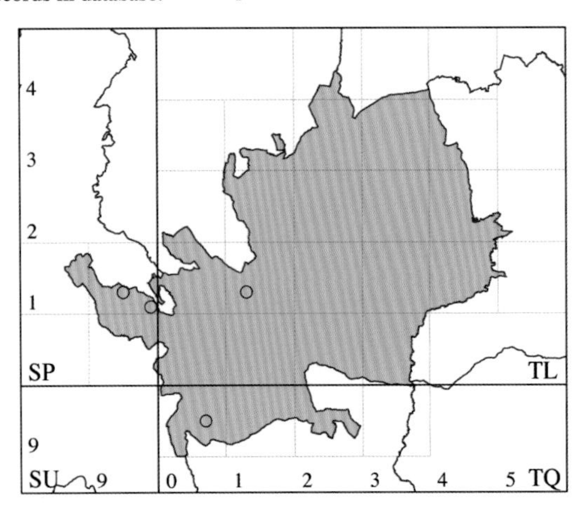

Richard South disturbed a single moth from herbage growing on a bank by the road-side at Rickmansworth on 31st July 1890 (*Entomologist* **23**: 291). Foster (1937) lists 'Tring (Elliman)' and 'Nr. Berkhamsted 'in Herts' (Searle *teste* Benson)'. Neither locality should be taken literally and the map dots are allocated according to the following logic to create a general impression of the former distribution. Tring was generally a euphemism for anywhere within walking distance of Tring Station and typically involved an excursion across Aldbury Nowers to Aldbury and Ashridge via Berkhamsted Common. The fact that it was necessary to specify that the Berkhamsted record was in Hertfordshire, rather than Buckinghamshire, suggests that it was actually Berkhamsted Common; the two reports at least refer to the same general area if not the same site. This is probably the same locality as that for the record given in Hodgson (1939), who reports 'Three in Berkhamsted—Ashridge area, 1932 – 6 (J. H. Bell)' and the record is repeated by Foster (1942) who states that 'J. Bell noted it *sparingly* in the Ashridge district' (Foster, 1942). The map also shows one that was caught in the light trap on the Rothamsted Estate at Harpenden during 1935, but these are the only reliable records. The moth is generally confined to chalk or limestone and reaches the eastern limit of its southern England range in the Buckinghamshire Chilterns. It was evidently once a resident in the chalk woodlands in the west of Hertfordshire but is now extinct here, as indeed it is also in Essex. Bell (1957), lists one moth caught by Clifford Craufurd at Bishops Stortford in 1955, but this is now generally accepted to be an error and is excluded from the map.

1775 *Colostygia multistrigaria* (Haw.) Mottled Grey

Recorded:	1888 - 2002
Distribution / Status:	Local / Rare resident
Conservation status:	Herts Endangered
Caterpillar food plants:	Not recorded. Elsewhere, on bedstraws
Flight period:	March/April
Records in database:	10

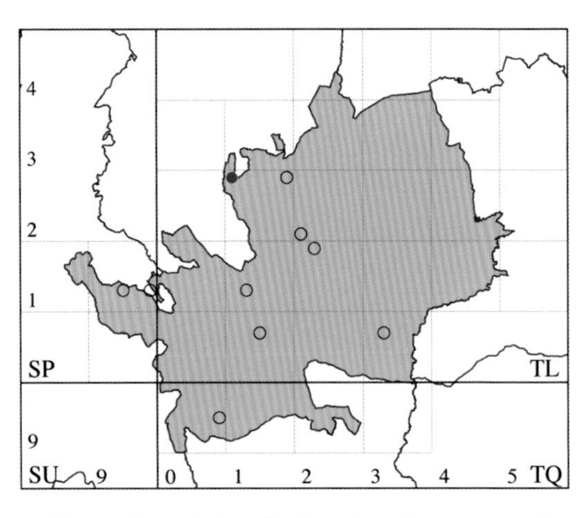

We had long feared that the Mottled Grey was extinct in Hertfordshire; although formerly widespread, as the map shows, it had not been seen since 1939, when it was 'well distributed and fairly common at light' at Ashridge Hodgson (1939). The last records in the adjacent county of Essex were in 1974 and although not searched for there it is considered extinct in the county (Goodey, 2004). The last Bedfordshire report was in 1947 (Arnold, 1997) and the last Middlesex records were during the 1880s (Plant, 1993). However, my capture of a single male during a search specifically targetted at this species in Hexton Chalk Pit on 30th March 2002 gives hope that it is merely under-recorded because of its very early flight period. Nevertheless, with a reasonably large number of light traps now operating all year across much of the county the absence of reports is worrying indeed.

1776 *Colostygia pectinataria* (Knoch) Green Carpet

Recorded: 1884 – 2006
Distribution / Status: Ubiquitous / Abundant resident
Conservation status: Herts Stable
Caterpillar food plants: Not recorded. Elsewhere, on bedstraws
Flight period: April to September, peaking in May/June then August September
Records in database: 792

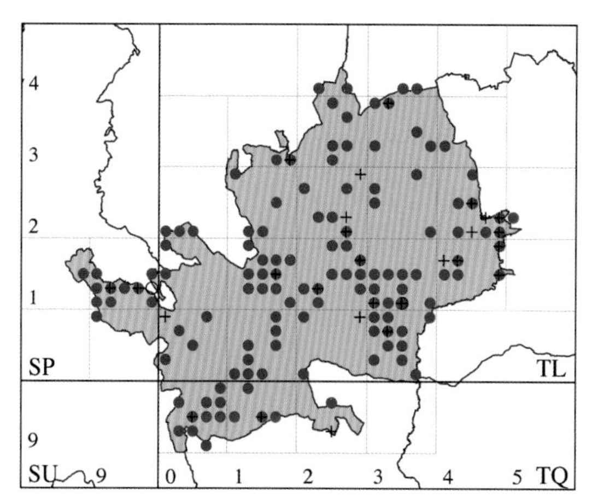

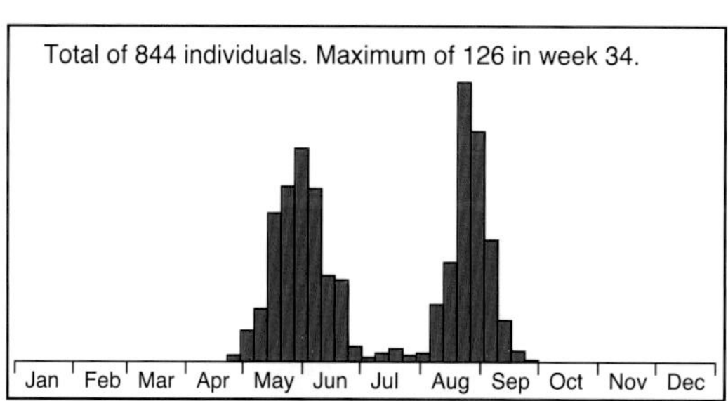

Although there are two very clear peaks of adult flight shown in the chart there is also a very much smaller peak in July. The records indicate that this is not an artefact created by combining several years' worth of data, but that in fact July adults have been recorded in all years for which we have records since as long ago as 1976. The result is that the moth can be seen more or less any time between late April and the end of September.

1777 *Hydriomena furcata* (Thunb.) July Highflier

Recorded: 1884 – 2006
Distribution / Status: Ubiquitous / Abundant resident
Conservation status: Herts Stable
Caterpillar food plants: Common Sallow (catkins). Elsewhere also on other trees
Flight period: Late May to August, peaking in July
Records in database: 364

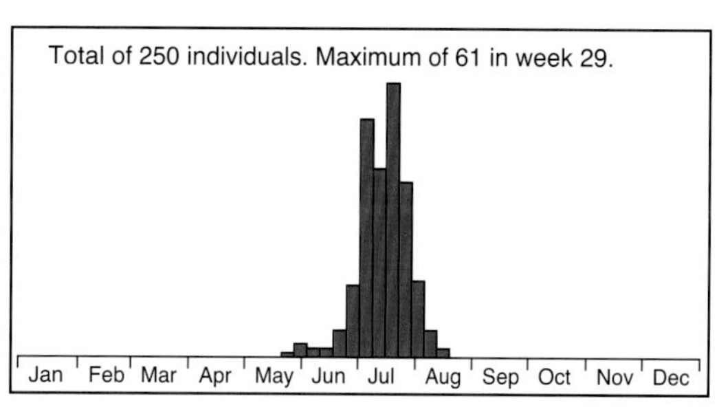

The July Highflier appears in a huge variety of colour forms, some of which cause great confusion amongst the inexperienced. Hazel is cited as a foodplant in adjacent Essex; the ubiquitous nature of this moth suggests that it may utilise several foodplants, but at the same time anyone wishing to attract large numbers is best advised to put out a trap in a sallow carr.

1778 *Hydriomena impluviata* ([D.& S.]) May Highflier

Recorded: 1887 – 2006
Distribution / Status: Local / Rare resident
Conservation status: Herts Vulnerable
Caterpillar food plants: Not recorded. Elsewhere, on Alder
Flight period: May/June
Records in database: 47

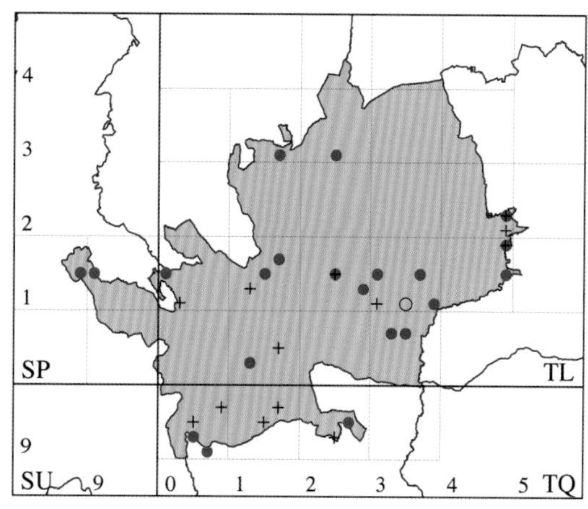

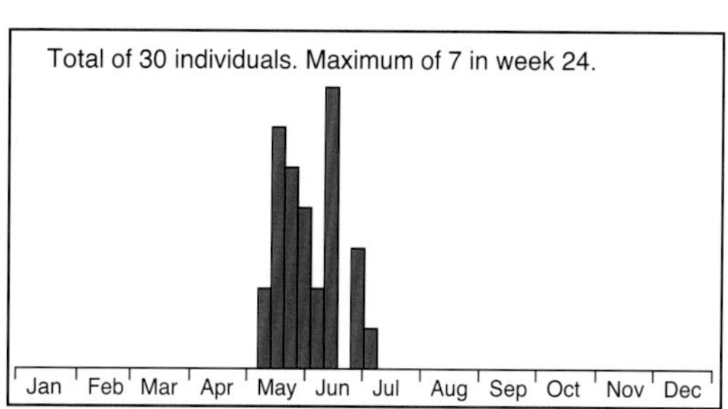

The slightly earlier date of this species helps to distinguish it from 1777: July Highflier, although there is a considerable overlap of the two. The May Highflier appears to be genuinely local in Hertfordshire, doubtless constrained by the lack of alder trees. Though it rarely appears in large number it has certainly vanished from several site lists in the last ten or so years and appears to be declining in our county.

[1779 *Hydriomena ruberata* (Freyer) Ruddy Highflier

The record for May 1953 in Penrose (1980) is an identification error as indeed is, almost certainly, that from Bishops Stortford made by Clifford Craufurd in 1937 and listed Allan (1959).]

1781 *Horisme vitalbata* ([D.& S.]) Small Waved Umber

Recorded: 1884 – 2006
Distribution / Status: Local / Common resident
Conservation status: Herts Stable
Caterpillar food plants: Traveller's Joy
Flight period: April to August in two generations
Records in database: 367

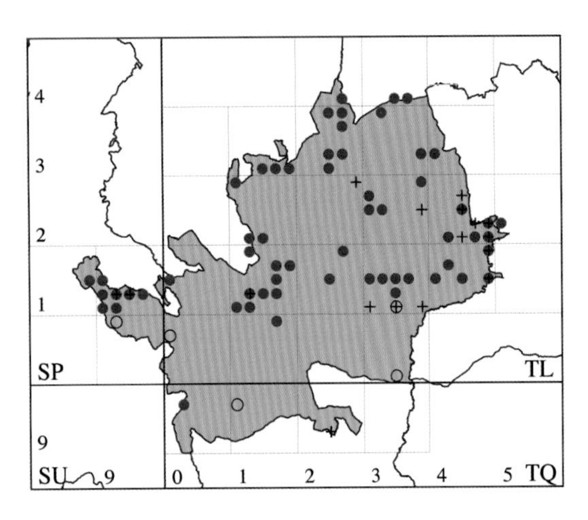

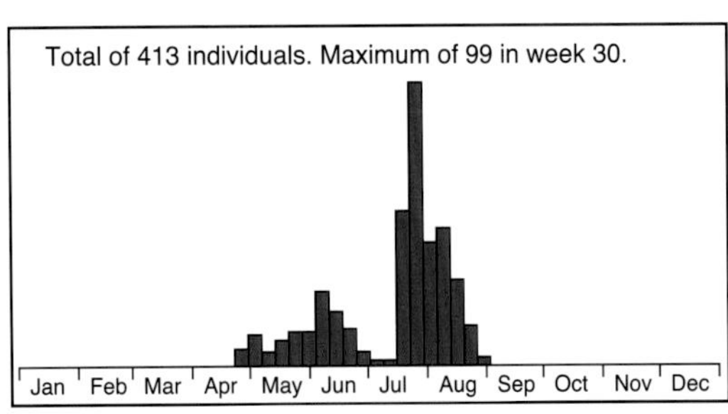

Although wandering individuals might theoretically turn up almost anywhere, the Small Waved Umber is restricted to the chalk and to the slightly calcareous soils of the north of Hertfordshire, positively avoiding the London Clay Basin and the various associated base-poor glacial gravels deposited upon it. Discussion on the distribution of the next two species is relevant to the Small Waved Umber. Beginners should take care not to confuse this species with 1936: Waved Umber.

1782 *Horisme tersata* ([D.& S.]) Fern

Recorded: 1828 – 2006
Distribution / Status: Local / Common resident
Conservation status: Herts Stable
Caterpillar food plants: Traveller's Joy
Flight period: June to mid-August
Records in database: 212

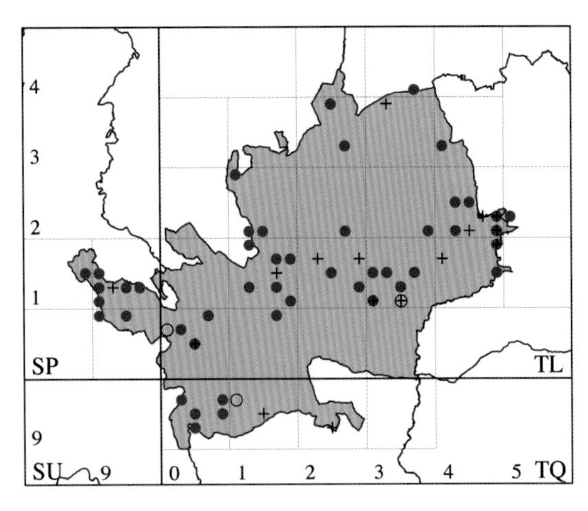

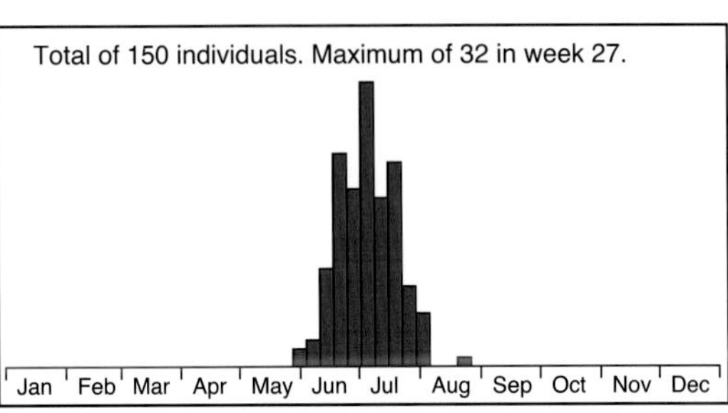

The distribution of the Fern in Hertfordshire is more or less the same as that of 1781: Small waved Umber, in that both species are absent from the London Clay in the south-east sector, but there are two marked differences – the greater number of records in the south-west corner and the lesser number in the northern central area. It seems strange that Small waved Umber is under-recorded in the south-west, where the Fern *is* recorded and equally unexpected that the Fern is absent from the north in areas where the Small Waved Umber is present. Both species share the same foodplant. However, the 'band' of records of The Fern across the county is also evident in the next map, for 1784: Pretty Chalk Carpet and so these distributions may be genuine. Perhaps the Small Waved Umber is more able to thrive on the foodplant regardless of its habitat setting whilst The Fern and the Pretty Chalk Carpet have additional requirements. Clearly there is scope for a more detailed investigation.

1784 *Melanthia procellata* ([D.& S.]) Pretty Chalk Carpet

Recorded: 1828 to 2006
Distribution / Status: Local / Uncommon resident
Conservation status: UK BAP Watch List
Herts Vulnerable
Caterpillar food plants: Traveller's Joy
Flight period: June to August
Records in database: 57

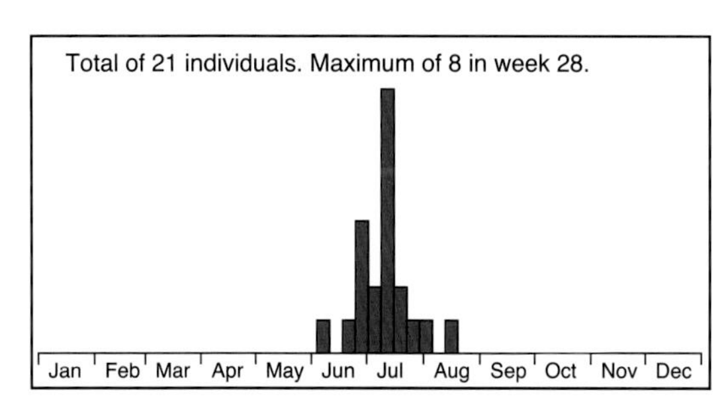

Discussion under 1781: Small Waved Umber and 1782: The Fern are relevant to the present species. All of the records that form the band of dots which extends south-westwards from the extreme eastern tip of the county at Bishops Stortford are on the Chalky Boulder Clay; those on the north-west boundary of the county are on the Chalk or associated calcareous drifts. Within these two areas the Pretty Chalk Carpet is widely, but locally distributed, though rarely encountered above single figures. The stray record in TL 30 was at Cuffley in 1998 (Alan Bolitho). The other two apparent anomalies, in TQ 19 and TQ 29 are for Borehamwood and Totteridge in the mid 1960s. The Pretty Chalk Carpet has apparently undergone a national population decline of 87 per cent since 1970. We have no numerical data to permit any comparison with the national trend, but we do record 17 map tetrads where there are older records but none since 1995; this represents 40 per cent of all recorded tetrads.

1786 *Spargania luctuata* ([D.& S.]) White-banded Carpet

Recorded:	1992 – 1992
Distribution / Status:	Absent / Former immigrant
Conservation status:	-
Caterpillar food plants:	Not recorded
Flight period:	Not recorded
Records in database:	1

Our only valid record is of a presumed immigrant example in Martin Townsend's former garden in Harpenden on 31st May 1992 (Townsend, 1994). It turned up along with several other immigrant species after a warm south-easterly wind. Waterton (1979) in his first report on Hertfordshire Lepidoptera after taking over as Recorder from Peter Bell, lists a single example of *S. luctuata* as having been recorded at Brocket Park. He gives neither date nor recorder – something that was to become a characteristic of his few reviews. That record cannot be substantiated and must be treated as an identification error.

1787 *Rheumaptera hastata* (L.) Argent and Sable

Recorded:	1920 – 1972
Distribution / Status:	Absent / Former Resident
Conservation status:	UK BAP Priority Species. Herts Extinct
Caterpillar food plants:	Not recorded. Elsewhere, on birch
Flight period:	Elsewhere, May and June
Records in database:	8

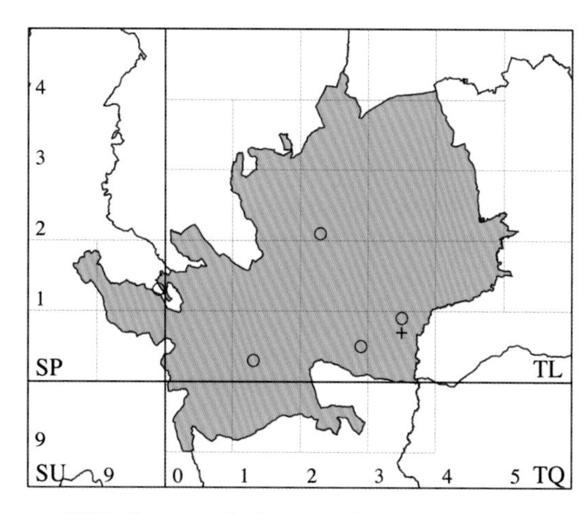

Foster (1937) lists records from Northaw Great Wood in 1920, 1921 and 1922, from 'Bricket' in 1929, and from Ashridge. (Hodgson, 1939), elaborates on the latter record, stating that Rev. A. K. Hervey found a single moth at Ashridge on 25th May 1934. Two examples in the R. S. Ferry collection at Mill Green Museum, examined by me, are labelled as having been taken by Ferry at Knebworth in June 1947. Within the Broxbourne Woods complex, Baron Charles de Worms recorded one at 'Hoddesdon' in 1948 (almost certainly in Hoddesdonpark Wood) and more recently Jim Reid notes it in the scout camp area of Danemead Wood on 8 June 1972 'It was a lovely day and a beautiful fresh specimen, flying across a ride between birches. I returned many times that year and for a few years after in the hope of seeing another, but never a sign'. The mature birch trees remain in the latter locality, and it would be desirable to carry out a proper survey for this species, which flies by day in warm, sunny weather during May and June. This species has been extinct in Essex since 1925 (Goodey, 2004) and the last confirmed Bedfordshire record was in 1956 (Arnold et al, 1989).

1788 *Rheumaptera cervinalis* (Scop.) Scarce Tissue

Recorded:	1884 – 2006
Distribution / Status:	Local / Rare resident
Conservation status:	Herts Threatened
Caterpillar food plants:	Garden Barberry
Flight period:	Mid-April to early June
Records in database:	78

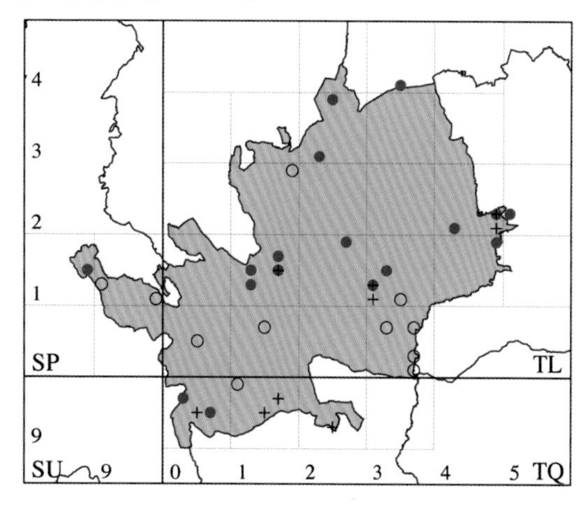

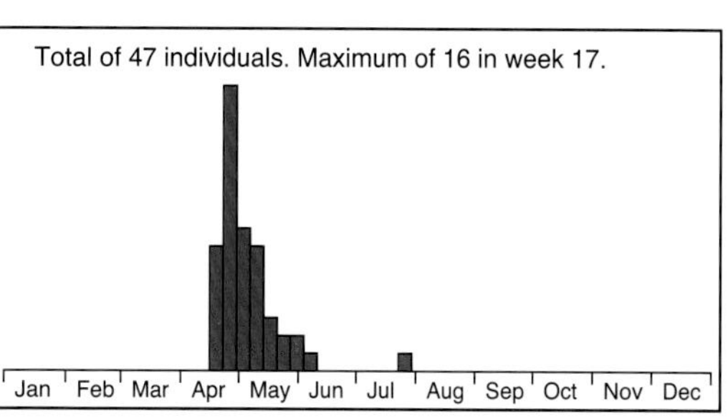

Older records suggest that this moth was quite widespread in the county in the early part of the twentieth century. However, this is not the case today and the decline is quite likely to be a direct consequence of the deliberate removal of barberry from hedges between then and now – barberry is a host of a fungal disease of cereal crops. The species would have been categorised as 'Herts Vulnerable' were it not for the fact that cultivated Barberry plants in larger gardens evidently support it just as well as the native plant (for example, an adult was reared from a pupa under a garden barberry plant in Bishops Stortford during 1989). Gardens might even prove to be more productive for this moth than hedges in Hertfordshire. Adult moths are often very difficult to separate from those of 1790: Tissue.

1789 *Rheumaptera undulata* (L.) Scallop Shell

Recorded: 1884 – 2003
Distribution / Status: Extremely local / Rare resident
Conservation status: Herts Vulnerable
Caterpillar food plants: Not recorded. Elsewhere, on sallow, Aspen and Bilberry
Flight period: Elsewhere in June and July
Records in database: 10

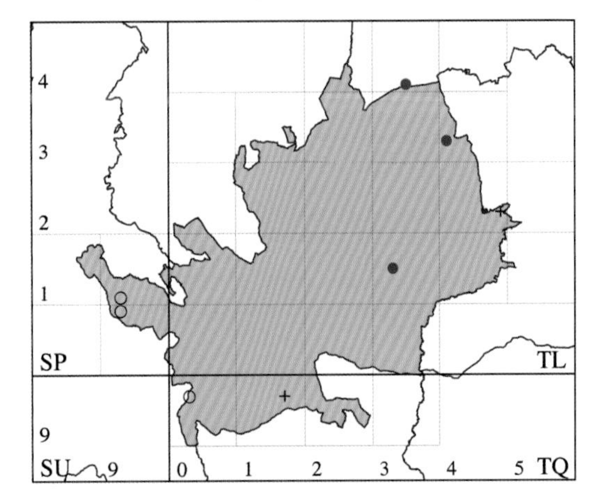

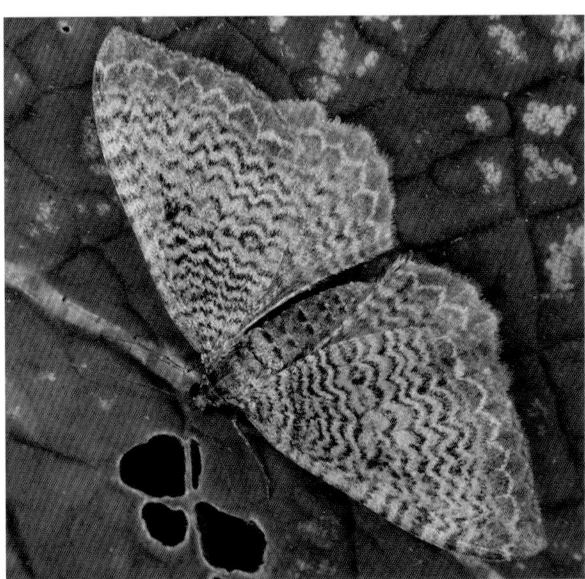

The Scallop Shell is a very rare moth in Hertfordshire and one about which we know very little. We have not been able to find it at historic sites in Wick Wood, Tring and at Chorleywood, though on the positive side, three new sites are mapped, at Royston in 2001 (Tim Wilson), Scales Park in 2002 (Jim Reid) and Hertford, on 10th July 2003 (Andrew Wood). The crosses on the map represent records at the Haberdasher's Aske's School, 20th July 1964 (Barry Goater) and at Bishops Stortford, 16th July 1993 (James Fish and Julian Reeves).

1790 *Triphosa dubitata* (Linnaeus, 1758) Tissue

Recorded: 1884 – 2001
Distribution / Status: Extremely local / Rare resident
Conservation status: Herts Vulnerable
Caterpillar food plants: Buckthorn
Flight period: Elsewhere, August to May
Records in database: 15

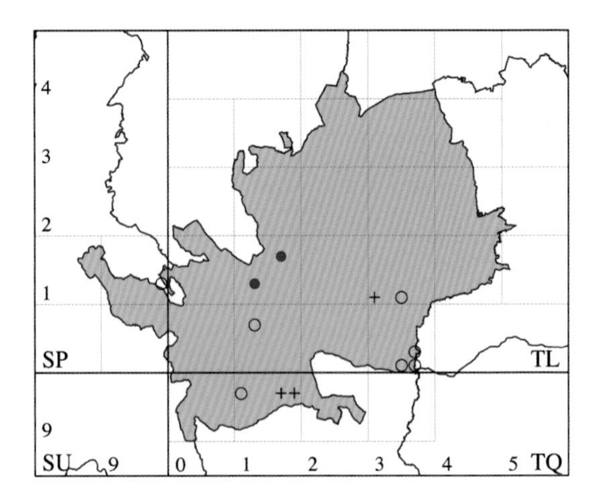

This is typically a species of woodland edge habitats on chalk downland and so the complete absence of records from the chalk in Hertfordshire is both surprising and unexplained. On the other hand, the moth comes but sparingly to light and is more easily found by searching for larvae, and so there must be some measure of under-recording. It was first listed for Hertfordshire from the Sandridge area (Griffith, 1884), but evidently has never been a common moth with us. Single examples in light traps on the Rothamsted Estate, Harpenden and at Hall Wood at Kimpton, 2001 (Vincent and Betty Judd) are the most recent findings. Larvae were found to be common on Buckthorn plants at the Haberdashers' Aske's School from 1979 onwards and adults moths were reared (Barry Goater).

1791 *Philereme vetulata* ([D.&S.] Brown Scallop

Recorded: 1884 – 2006
Distribution / Status: Local / Uncommon resident
Conservation status: Herts Scarce
Caterpillar food plants: Buckthorn
Flight period: Late June and July
Records in database: 31

This is a very local species on the chalk of the north-west boundary area of the county – probably overlooked in the Hitchin/Hexton/Pirton area where there are several historical records in an area we have not visited enough at the appropriate season. Records from the central area are more

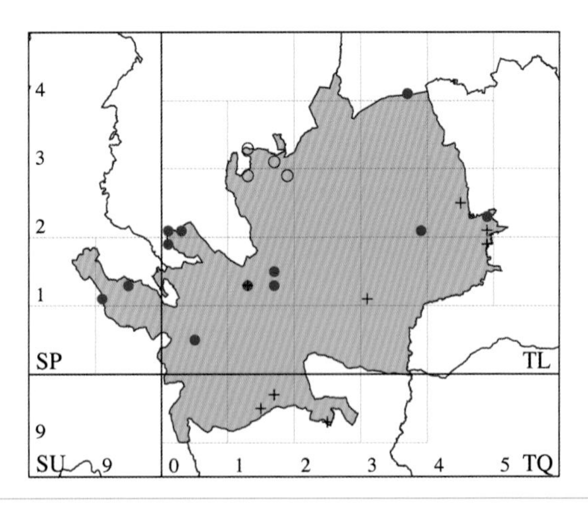

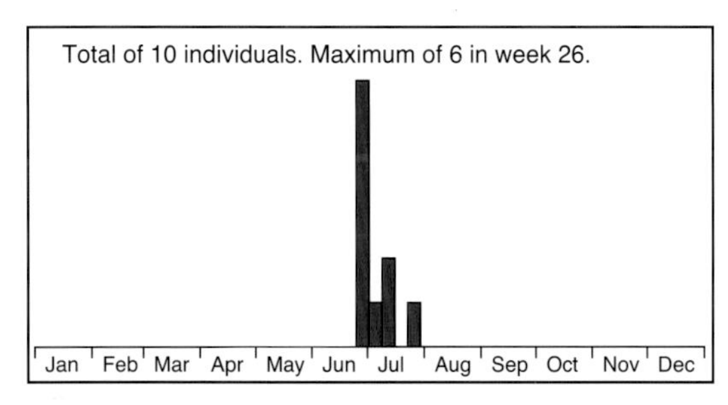

surprising and it seems that garden buckthorns may be a suitable foodplant for the larvae. In the extreme south Richard Lorimer found 'the first ever here' at Totteridge in 1964 whilst at the Haberdashers' Aske's School near Bushey, Barry Goater caught one on 20th July in the same year and found five larvae on *Rhamnus*, 14th May 1965 and for several years subsequently. An adult was trapped at light in Bushey on 6th July 1976 but there are no records from the south of the county since then.

1792 *Philereme transversata* (Hufn.) ssp. *britannica* Hufn. Dark Umber

Recorded:	1828 – 2006
Distribution / Status:	Local / Common resident
Conservation status:	Herts Stable
Caterpillar food plants:	Buckthorn
Flight period:	Late June to mid-August
Records in database:	105

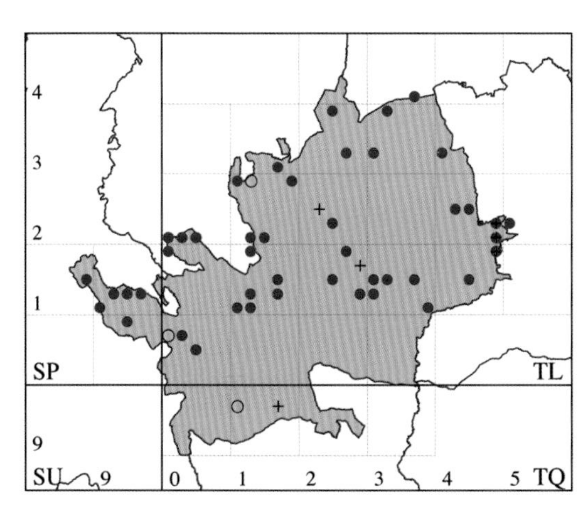

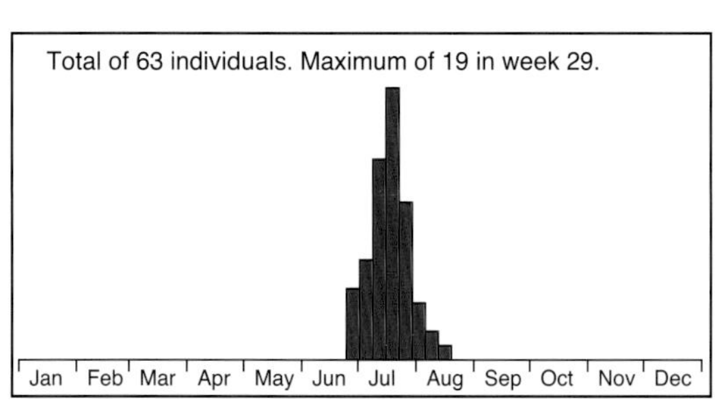

British examples of this species are referable to subspecies *britannica*, with the nominotypical form confined to mainland Europe. The adults come freely to light traps and are likely to be present on most sites where the ground is slightly calcareous. The absence of records from the London Clay area is obvious and seemingly real. Larvae were found on Buckthorn at the Haberdashers' Aske's School in 1965 and several years subsequently (Barry Goater).

1793 *Euphyia biangulata* (Haw.) Cloaked Carpet

Recorded:	1884 – 1998
Distribution / Status:	Extremely local / Rare resident
Conservation status:	Herts Endangered
Caterpillar food plants:	Not recorded. Elsewhere, on chickweed and stitchwort
Flight period:	July
Records in database:	9

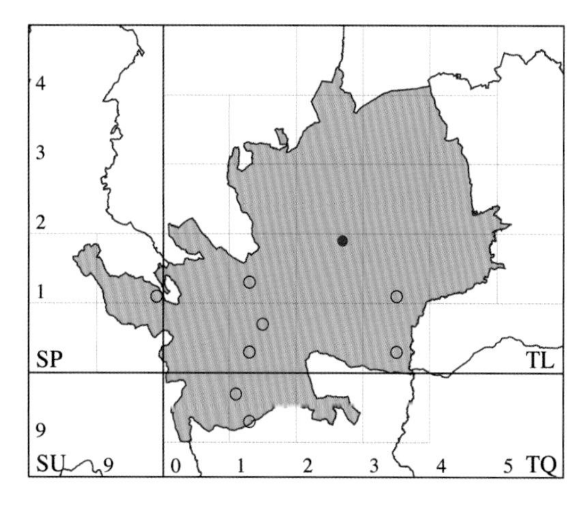

One at Raffin Park, Datchworth on 15th August 1998 (Steve Palmer) was something of a surprise. The moth is not given to migratory movements so this one must be a wanderer from a colony somewhere in the county. Foster (1937) records a surprising number of localities (under its former name of *picata* Hb.), but in view of the very high recording effort from 2000 to 2006 in appropriate habitat at the appropriate time of year we can be quite certain that if present as a breeding species it is now very rare indeed. A record from Scratch Wood, 1937 (Foster, 1942) is actually in the Middlesex vice-county.

1794 *Euphyia unangulata* (Haw.) Sharp-angled Carpet

Recorded:	1884 – 2006
Distribution / Status:	Very Local / Uncommon resident
Conservation status:	Herts Rare
Caterpillar food plants:	Not recorded. Elsewhere, on chickweed and stitchwort
Flight period:	June to early August
Records in database:	16

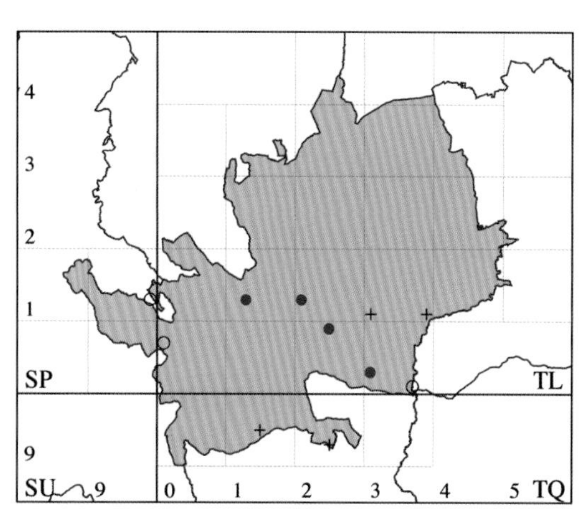

Older woodlands that retain some semblance of a proper woodland structure, with herb-rich rides that support the foodplant are likely to produce Sharp-angled Carpet moths if sufficient recording is undertaken. The moths rarely attend light traps in numbers greater than one; the absence of moths from the entire north of the county, both now and historically, is probably the true situation.

The November Moth group – *Epirrita* species

Three species of the November Moth group occur in Hertfordshire, namely 1795: *Epirrita dilutata* (November Moth), 1796: *Epirrita christyi* (Pale November Moth) and 1797: *Epirrita autumnata* (Autumnal Moth). All three demonstrate a variety of pattern forms, from well-marked to completely unmarked and plain. All range from light grey to black. Although many text books put forward allegedly helpful pointers for separation of the species, these are usually heavily caveated with words such as 'often' and 'usually'. The reality is that it is not possible to separate these three species reliably without looking at the terminalia of the males. This can be done easily without any dissection, by brushing away the scales at the tip of the abdomen, below, and looking at the spacing of the two 'pegs' on the hind edge of the last segment in combination with the presence or absence of a 'tooth' on the genital clasper. Females cannot be separated in the adult stage. The Hertfordshire records which follow for these three species are those based either on such an examination or on breeding records. Specimens named by wing pattern alone are not included; this includes almost all historical records. A fourth member of this group, 1798: *Epirrita filigrammaria* (Small Autumnal Moth), has not so far been recorded in the county.

1795 *Epirrita dilutata* ([D.& S.])

Recorded: 1964 – 2006
Distribution / Status: Widespread / Abundant resident
Conservation status: Herts Stable
Caterpillar food plants: English Elm; English Oak; Sessile Oak; Silver Birch; Common Hawthorn; Hazel
Flight period: October/November
Records in database: 157

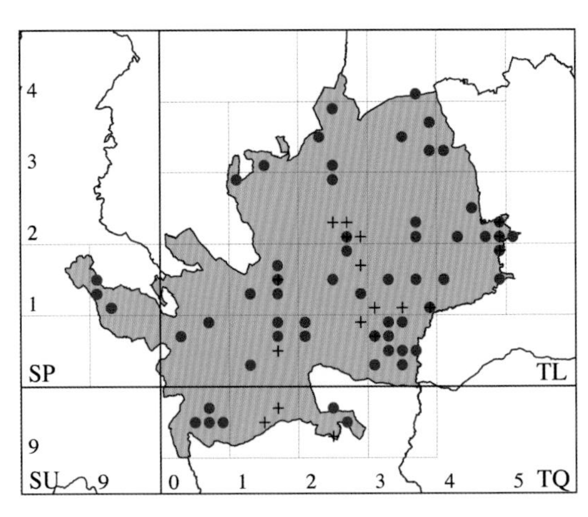

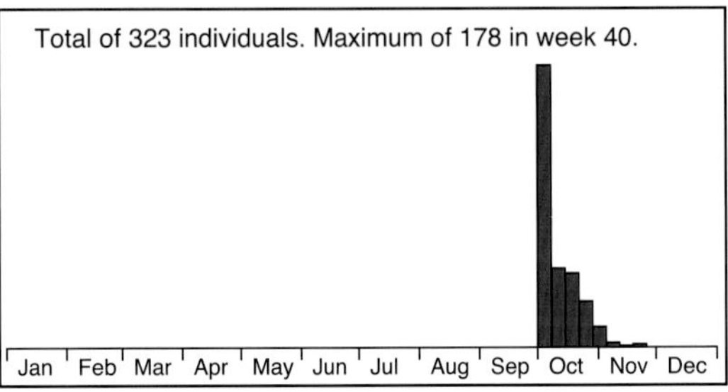

This is apparently the most widespread and most abundant of the triad of November moths, at least in our county. More or less plain, melanic forms (ab. *obscurata* Staudinger and ab. *melana* Prout) dominate the population in some areas, but not in others, though there is not really enough available data to discern any geographical trends.

1796 *Epirrita Christyi* (Allen) Pale November Moth

Recorded: 1945 – 2006
Distribution / Status: Local / Common resident
Conservation status: No perceived threats
Caterpillar food plants: English Oak; Silver Birch; Hawthorn; Hazel
Flight period: October/November
Records in database: 19

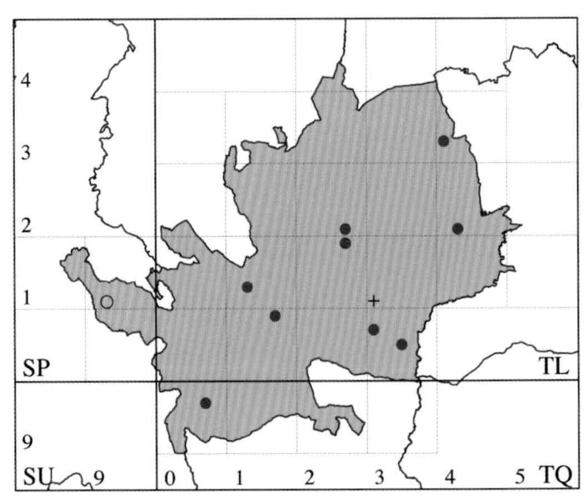

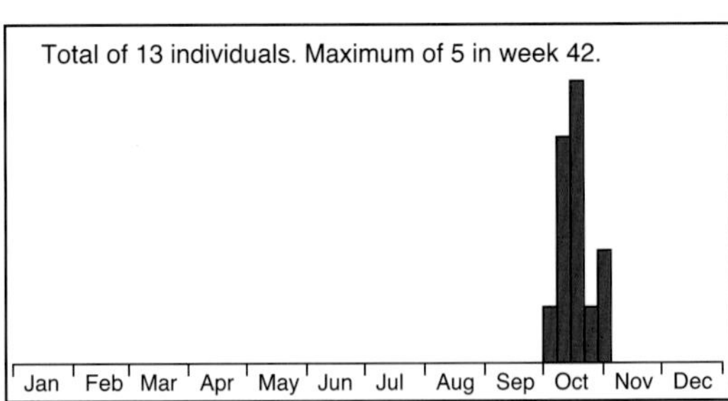

Although evidently local in distribution, this moth can be as numerically abundant as the November Moth, with several hundreds in moth traps or flying in country lanes at dusk.

1797 *Epirrita autumnata* (Borkh.) Autumnal Moth

Recorded: 1945 – 2006
Distribution / Status: Very local / Rare resident
Conservation status: Herts Scarce
Caterpillar food plants: Not recorded. Elsewhere, on birch and Alder
Flight period: October/November
Records in database: 18

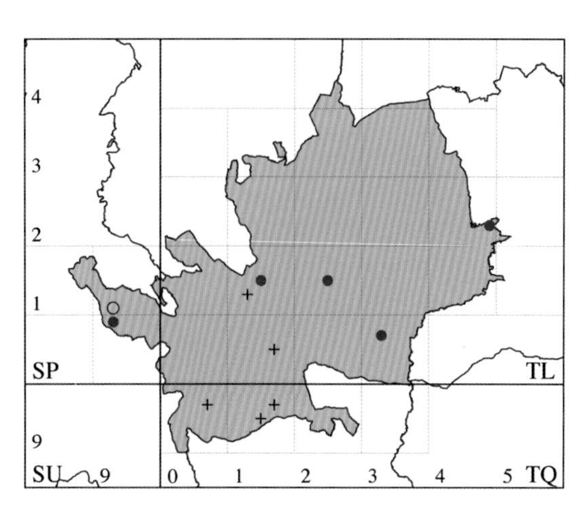

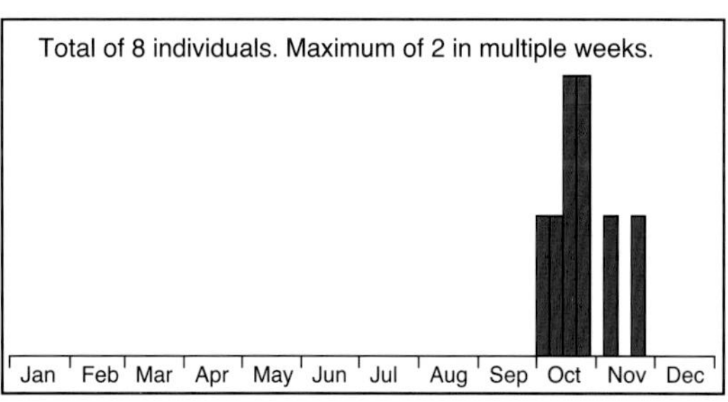

This is the least frequently encountered member of the group and it appears to be genuinely very local and rare in Hertfordshire. We have no Hertfordshire-based foodplant data, but birch is prevalent in the area around all sites where we have a modern record. The apparent loss from the south-west will be worrying if it is true.

1799 *Operophtera brumata* (L.) Winter Moth

Recorded: 1884 – 2006
Distribution / Status: Ubiquitous / Abundant resident
Conservation status: Herts Stable
Caterpillar food plants: English Oak; Sessile Oak; Hornbeam; Hawthorn; Blackthorn; elm species; Lime (street trees); Field Maple; Crab Apple; domestic Apple; Beech; Lombardy Poplar, White Willow; Common Sallow.
Flight period: November to January
Records in database: 447

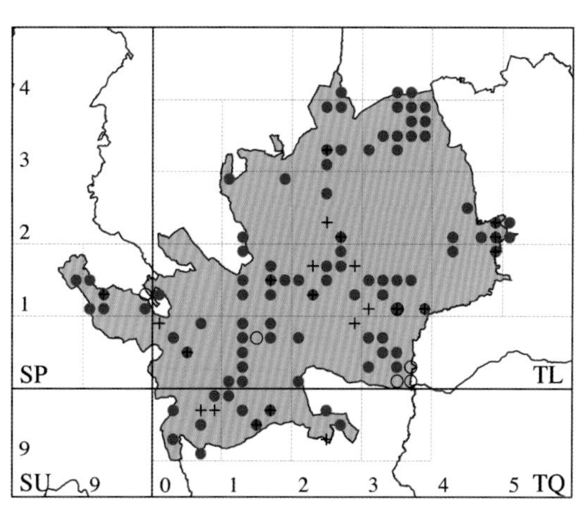

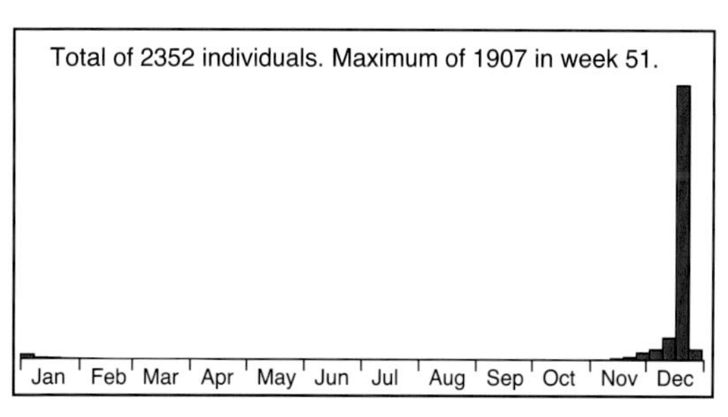

Abundant everywhere. Males start to come to light at around 7 pm in November and the wingless females may be found between about 6.30 and 7.30 pm on trunks, but are mated rapidly and thereafter walk up to the canopy and can no longer be found without considerable physical effort. Males continue to fly throughout the night and sometimes attend the trap 'carrying' a female.

1800 *Operophtera fagata* (Scharf.) Northern Winter moth

Recorded: 1893 – 2005
Distribution / Status: Local / Common resident
Conservation status: Herts Stable
Caterpillar food plants: Silver Birch; Hornbeam; Lombardy Poplar
Flight period: December
Records in database: 33

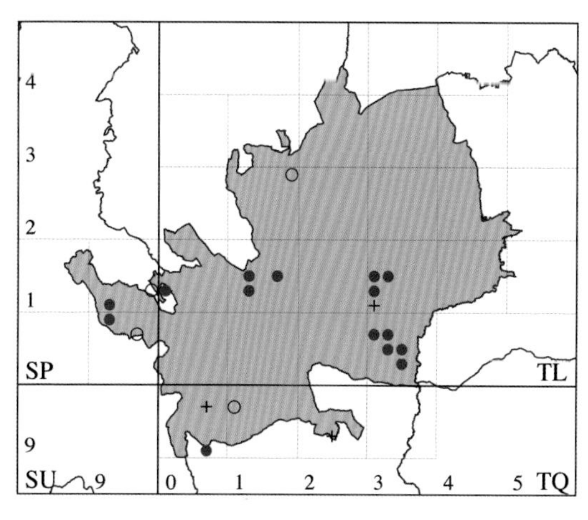

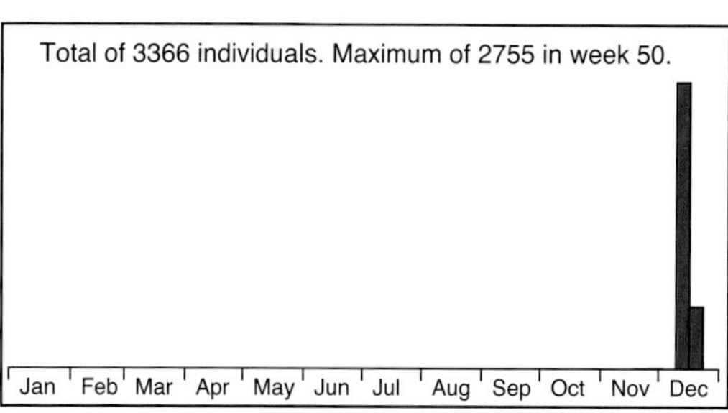

A record from his garden in Gladstone Road, Watford, by S. H. Spencer in 1893, was apparently the first Hertfordshire record. Other older records are from Bushey Heath, Hitchin, Watford, St Albans and Berkhamsted (1937). Unfortunately, a prevailing view amongst some people that the Northern Winter Moth is not 'allowed' this far south has meant that some candidate specimens were released before they could be examined more carefully and so the map may well reflect a degree of under-recording.

1802 *Perizoma affinitata* (Steph.) Rivulet

Recorded: 1828 – 2006
Distribution / Status: Widespread but local / Common resident
Conservation status: Herts Stable
Caterpillar food plants: Inside seed capsule of Red Campion
Flight period: May to July
Records in database: 64

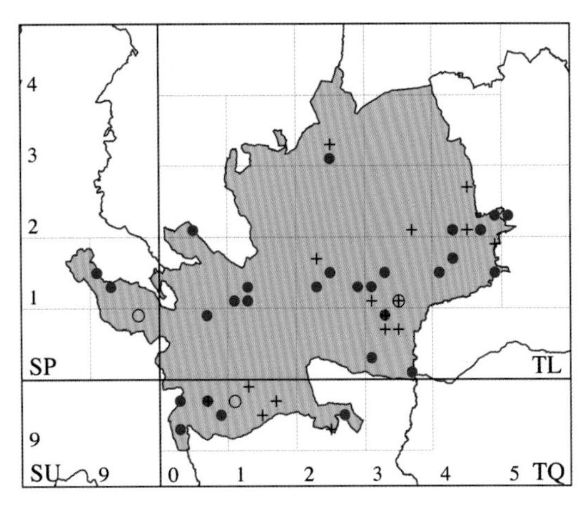

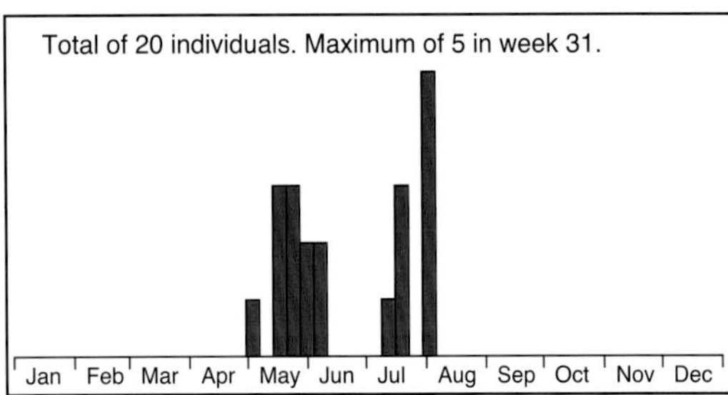

Separation of this species from 1803: Small Rivulet must not be performed on the basis of size, since both species vary in size considerably. The character given in Skinner (1984; 1998) works on all Hertfordshire material examined. The number of dated records is small, but confirms that Rivulet starts to appear a couple of weeks before the Small Rivulet. The absence of woodlands or hedgerows with Red Campion in the north of the county is reflected in the distribution map.

1803 *Perizoma alchemillata* (L.) Small Rivulet

Recorded: 1828 – 2006
Distribution / Status: Widespread / Very common resident
Conservation status: Herts Stable
Caterpillar food plants: Not recorded. Elsewhere, on Hemp Nettle seeds and flowers
Flight period: June to August
Records in database: 278

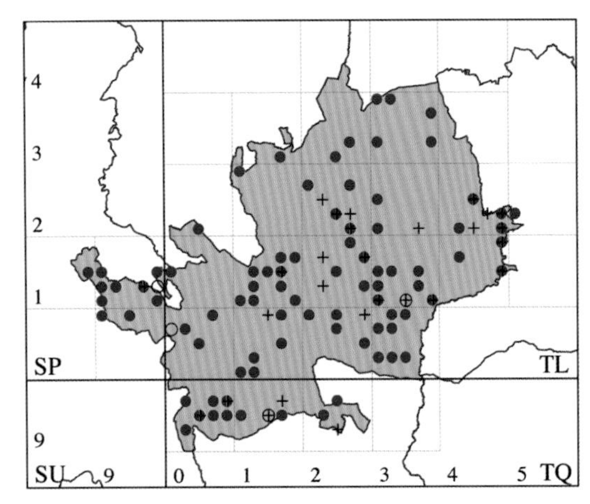

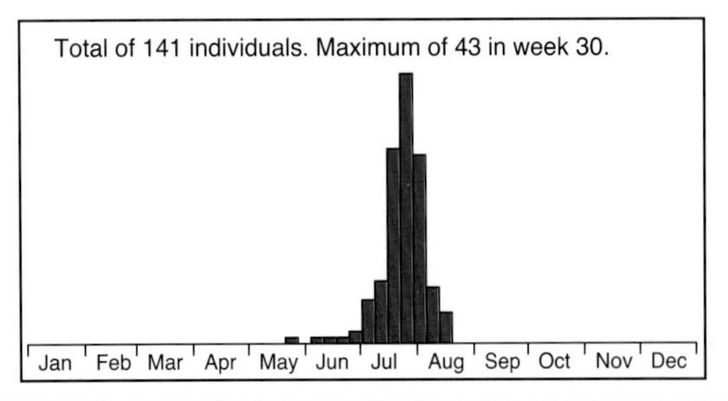

This species seems far more frequent than 1802: Rivulet and in common with views expressed in some other texts the foodplant appears to be absent from many sites where the moth is present, suggesting there must be an unknown alternative awaiting discovery. Larvae have, however, been found on Hemp Nettle, for example at a marsh by the river at Jacott's Hill, Casiobury, 14th September 1966 (Barry Goater).

1804 *Perizoma bifaciata* (Haw.) Barred Rivulet

Recorded: 1926 – 2006
Distribution / Status: Local / Rare resident
Conservation status: Herts Scarce
Caterpillar food plants: Red Bartsia (on the developing seeds)
Flight period: Mid-July and August
Records in database: 30

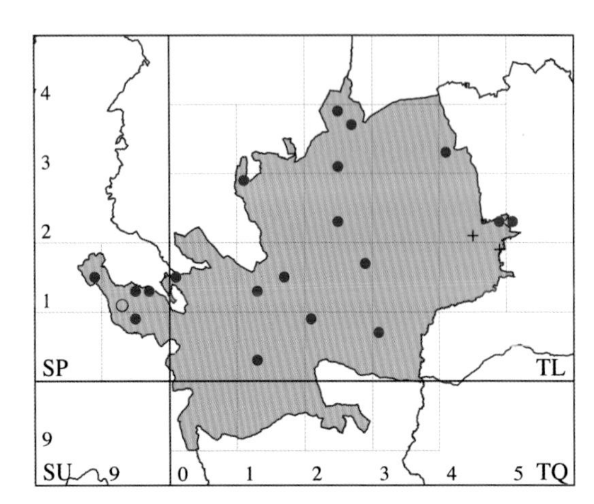

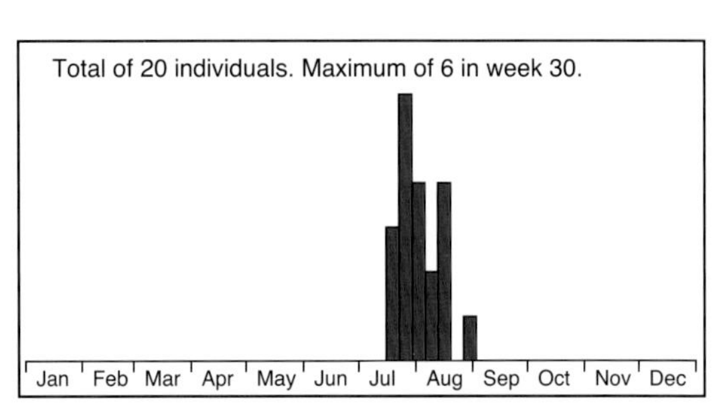

The foodplant is frequent in ruderal habitats, such as field edges, in many parts of Hertfordshire although it does not appear to be everywhere one looks: the distribution pattern of the moth reflects this and the moth seems to be quite uncommon with us.

1807 *Perizoma albulata* ([D.& S.]) Grass Rivulet

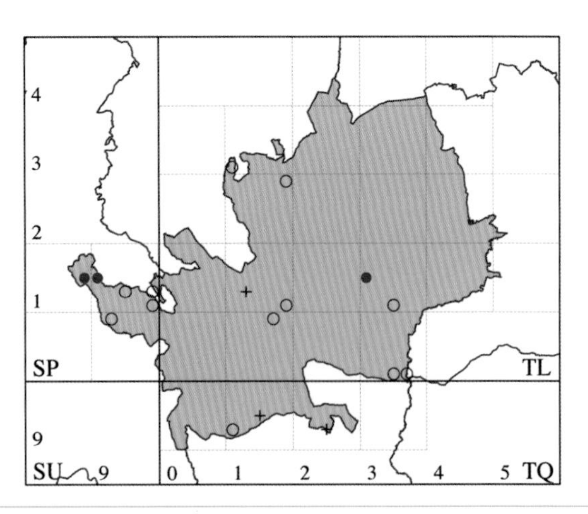

Recorded: 1887 – 2005
Distribution / Status: Extremely local / Rare Resident
Conservation status: UK BAP Watch List. Herts Endangered.
Caterpillar food plants: Yellow-rattle
Flight period: Late May to June, elsewhere to end of July

Records in database: 20

Nationally, we are informed, there has been a 96 per cent decline in population since 1970; in Hertfordshire we cannot provide numerical data, but it appears to have been lost from 83 per cent of formerly occupied sites. These two facts combined warrant the designation of the Grass Rivulet as Endangered in a county context. Foster (1937) recorded it as fairly common, but the record from Berkhamsted is incorrect and, according to Hodgson (1939) relates to Aldbury Nowers and the Ashridge Estate. Today there remain just three localities for this moth in Hertfordshire. It is still resident in the far west in the Long Marston area and it was noted in addition at Waterford Heath on 5th June 2000 (Vincent and Betty Judd), though whether or not it is resident in the latter place is unclear. The reasons for the decline are unknown, though doubtless the distribution of Yellow Rattle plants will be a factor and the very poor floral diversity of most road verges in the county is perhaps a clue? Certainly the mania for monocultural verges, usually of Perennial Rye-grass, neatly mown right up to the bases of the hedgerow bushes (not to mention the cutting of the bushes) will not help.

1808 *Perizoma flavofasciata* (Thunb.) Sandy Carpet

Recorded: 1828 – 2006
Distribution / Status: Widespread / Common resident
Conservation status: No perceived threats
Caterpillar food plants: Not recorded. Elsewhere, in Red, White and Bladder Campion seed pods
Flight period: May to July
Records in database: 112

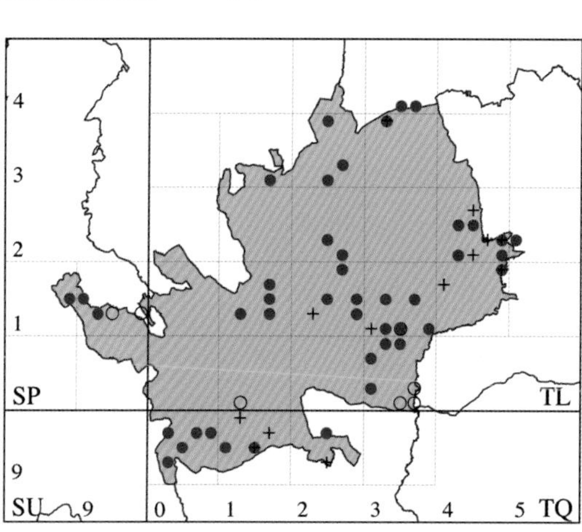

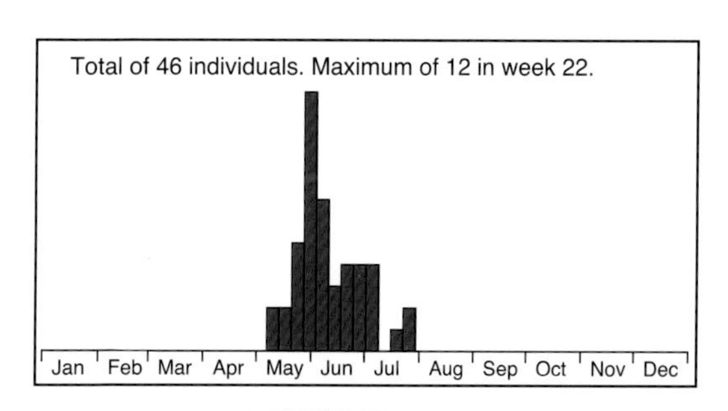

This is a widely distributed species, but it seldom enters moth traps and the best way of recording it is by wandering along hedgerows at dusk with a torch when they will fly around freely and often in great number.

1809 *Perizoma didymata* (L.) Twin-spot Carpet

Recorded: 1884 – 2006
Distribution / Status: Local / Common resident
Conservation status: Herts Stable
Caterpillar food plants: Cow Parsley. Elsewhere, on various low plants
Flight period: Late May to the end of July
Records in database: 56

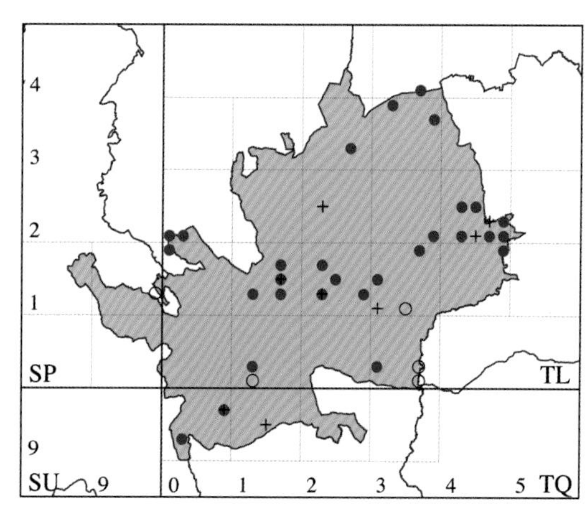

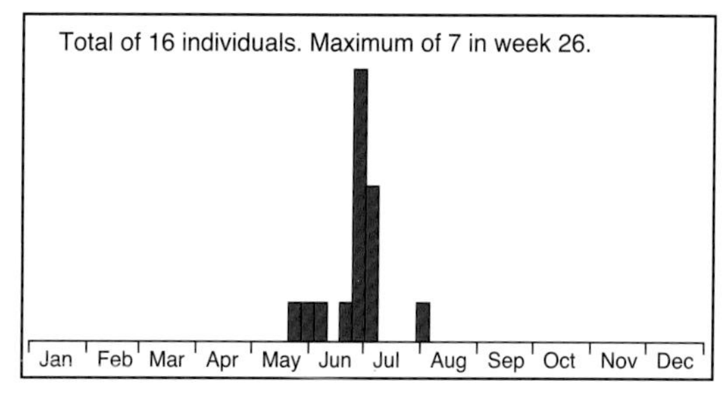

Foster (1937) lists this species as 'Common in all districts'. The same situation applies today but numerically this moth is poorly represented. It rarely comes to light traps, but is found by 'dusking' and is sometimes disturbed from vegetation by beating. I found larvae on Cow Parsley along a lane to the north of Bishops Stortford during 1993, but this is unlikely to be the only food plant used.

THE PUGS

With the exception of a few that are recognisable on sight, most of the many British species are some shade of brown or grey, with wing patterns that seem to be remarkably similar from species to species – they all look the same! They are the 'LBJs' (Little Brown Jobs) of the mothing world. Sadly, I am not able to disagree with these sentiments and whilst, with experience, some at least of them can be named by eye most will require some form of critical examination. With most males, this will only involve brushing the scales away from underneath the tip of the abdomen to reveal the chitinised 'plate' which varies in shape between species. For a few, in which the plates are rather similar, as well as for females, dissection of the genitalia is necessary for correct identification. I have been rigorous, draconian even, in the acceptance of records of pugs. Where the observer is still alive, I have insisted in most cases on seeing specimens and dissecting these, rejecting records that do not satisfy my demands. This has won me few friends, but hopefully assures the accuracy of the information that is now expounded. Where the observer has long since passed on to the great collecting ground in the sky it has not always been possible to trace voucher specimens; this affects most records made prior to 1937 and included in Foster's list of that year. In such cases a judgement has been made concerning the likely reliability of the records, particularly in the light of similar species that have been discovered in Britain since the original records were made.

1811 *Eupithecia tenuiata* (Hb.) Slender Pug

Recorded: 1887 – 2006
Distribution / Status: Widespread / Common resident
Conservation status: Herts Stable
Caterpillar food plants: Common sallow (catkins)
Flight period: May, then late June to mid-August
Records in database: 62

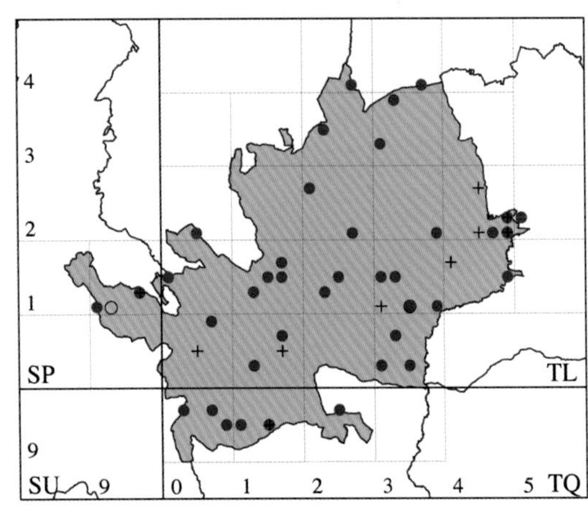

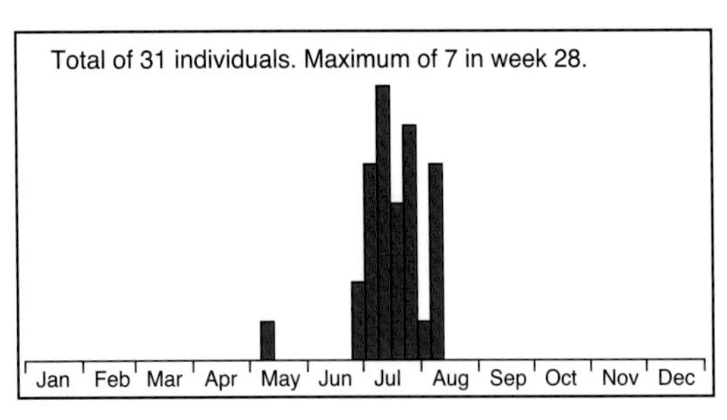

The flight period data is slightly at odds with the national situation, where we are told that adults fly in June and July. In Hertfordshire they persist well into August, but don't start until the end of June. Before this date we have only two records, both of males taken by me at Patmore Hall Wood near Bishops Stortford on 24th May 1989 and Hillfield Park Reservoir on 11th May 2002.

1812 *Eupithecia inturbata* (Hb.) Maple Pug

Recorded: 1937 – 2006
Distribution / Status: Widespread / Common resident
Conservation status: Herts Stable
Caterpillar food plants: Field Maple (flowers)
Flight period: July/August
Records in database: 56

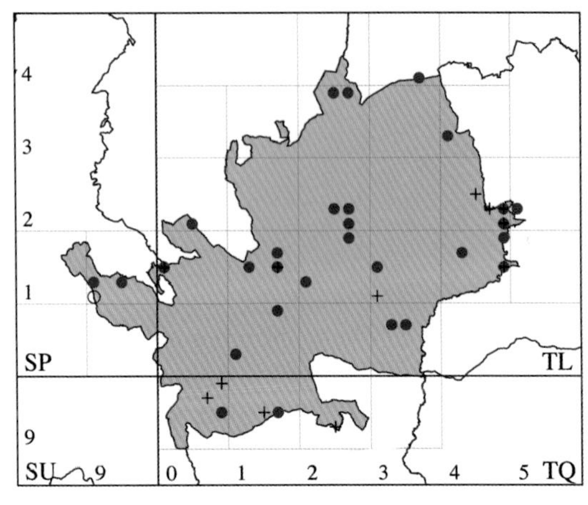

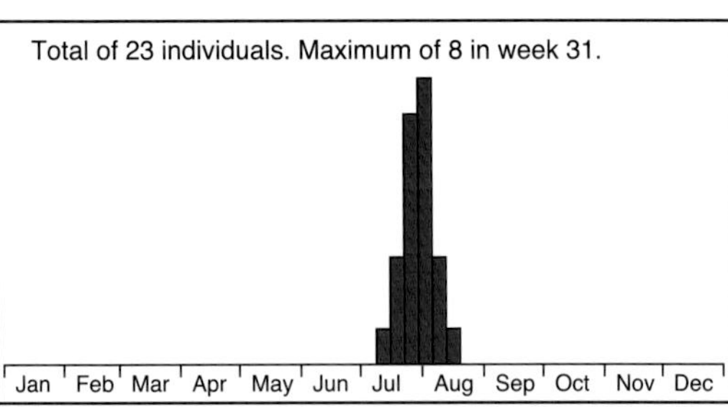

Foster (1937) lists 'Tring', without a date and this remains our earliest Hertfordshire record. At Whippendell Wood, many were bred in 1960 from larvae beaten from flowers of a large Field Maple tree by Barry Goater.

1813 *Eupithecia haworthiata* Doubl. Haworth's Pug

Recorded: 1884 – 2006
Distribution / Status: Widespread / Common resident
Conservation status: Herts Stable
Caterpillar food plants: Traveller's Joy (flowers)
Flight period: June to August
Records in database: 59

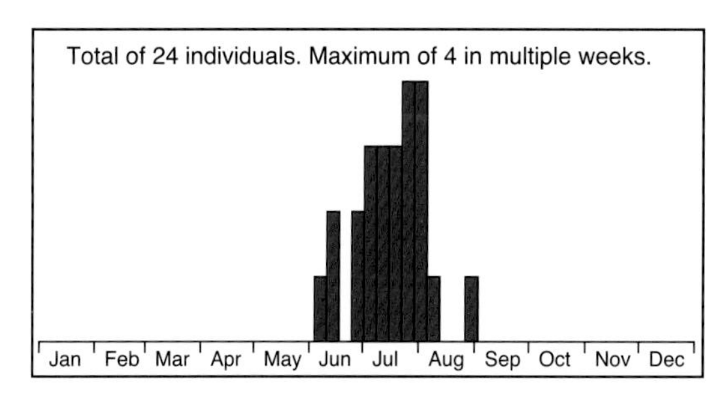

Most moths are finished by the end of August, but I caught a late male on 1st September 2000 at Much Hadham, in woodland next to the Henry Moore Foundation.

1814 *Eupithecia plumbeolata* (Haw.) Lead-coloured Pug

Recorded: 1884 – 1979
Distribution / Status: Absent or Extremely local / Former, or very rare resident
Conservation status: Herts Endangered
Caterpillar food plants: Common Cow Wheat. Elsewhere, also on Yellow-rattle
Flight period: Not recorded. Elsewhere, May/June
Records in database: 3

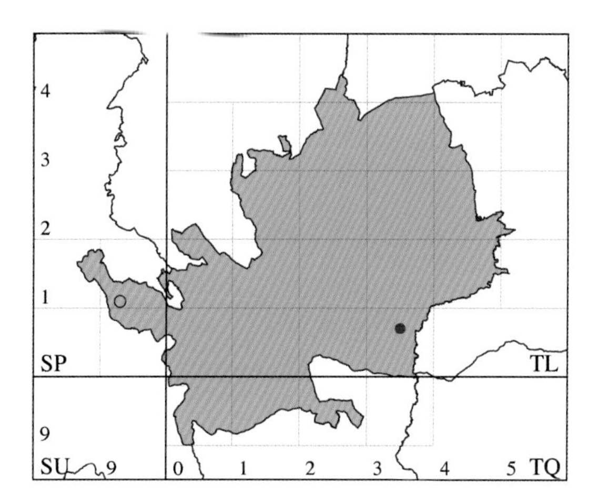

This species is listed for the Sandridge area (Griffith, 1884). The Sandridge area was a large one, extending several miles in each direction from the village and it is not possible to have any idea where the moth was found, although in those far off days it is rather easy to imagine that suitable habitat was likely to abound. However, Foster (1937) lists only this Sandridge record, suggesting that even if the habitat and foodplants were in place the moth was perhaps not finding them. There are only two further reports – from Hemel Hempstead, where A. L. Goodson recorded it in 1945 (Foster, 1945a), and from the Danemead Wood area of the Broxbourne Woods complex in 1979 where larvae were found on Common Cow Wheat by Rob Dyke. In Essex, to our east, it was last recorded in 1974 and is now considered extinct there (Goodey, 2004).

1815 *Eupithecia abietaria* (Goeze) Cloaked Pug

Recorded: 1938 – 2001
Distribution / Status: Random / Rare immigrant
Conservation status: -
Caterpillar food plants: Not recorded. Elsewhere, on spruces and firs
Flight period: July
Records in database: 3

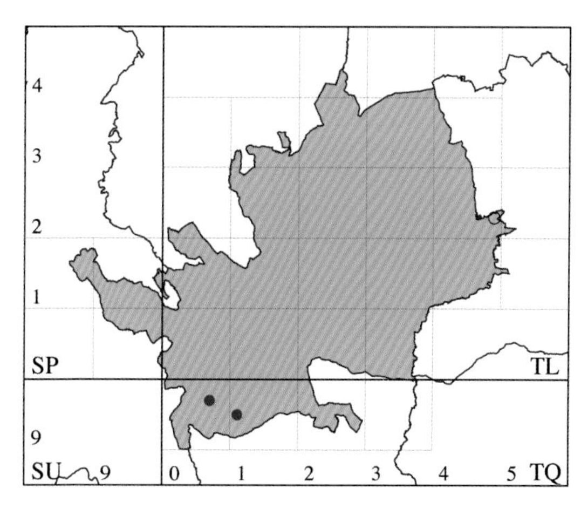

There are three Hertfordshire records: Bishops Stortford, 'two specimens at light and others reported 1938 (C. S. Colman)' (Foster, 1945); my own from Whippendell Wood, Watford, one at light on 7th July 2001 and Raglan Gardens, Oxhey, one at light on 7th July 2001 (Joan Thompson). The last two mentioned, from the same date in 2001, are in my collection and form a part of an unprecedented immigration to Britain of this species during the first week of July 2001, with ten examples, in addition to the Hertfordshire two, recorded elsewhere in southern Britain.

1816 *Eupithecia linariata* ([D.& S.]) Toadflax Pug

Recorded: 1884 – 2006
Distribution / Status: Widespread / Common resident
Conservation status: Herts Stable
Caterpillar food plants: Common Toadflax
Flight period: Late May to mid-September
Records in database: 166

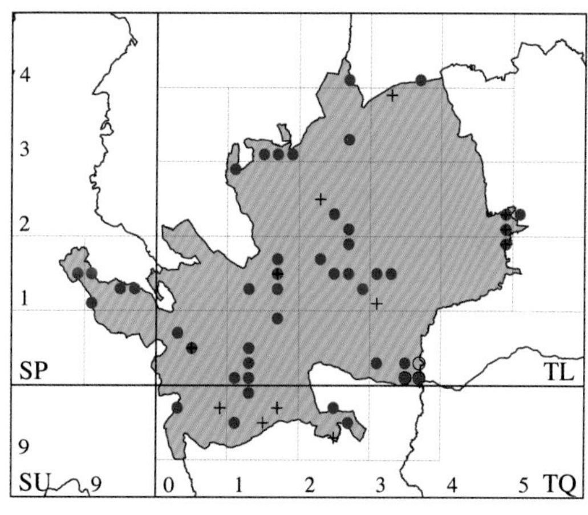

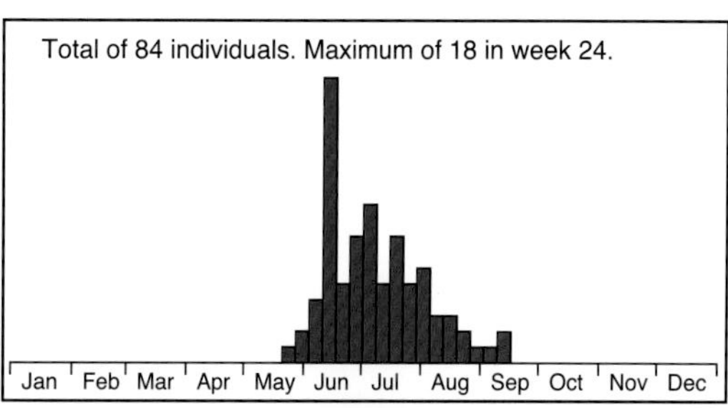

Adults of this species in Hertfordshire regularly fly from June until the start of September. This is at odds with Skinner (1984; 1998) who gives 'single-brooded flying in July and August' and Emmet (1991a) who gives the same months. However, our data agree with the statement in Riley (2003) that 'The moth is on the wing from late May to mid-September'. Riley also notes that 'There appear to be peaks of emergence during late June and mid-August, suggesting two protracted and overlapping broods'. The possibility that May/June examples are misidentified Foxglove Pugs has been eliminated and does not apply.

1817 *Eupithecia pulchellata* Stephens Foxglove Pug

Recorded: 1937 – 2006
Distribution / Status: Widespread / Common resident
Conservation status: Herts Stable
Caterpillar food plants: Foxglove (flowers)
Flight period: Mid-April to late August
Records in database: 236

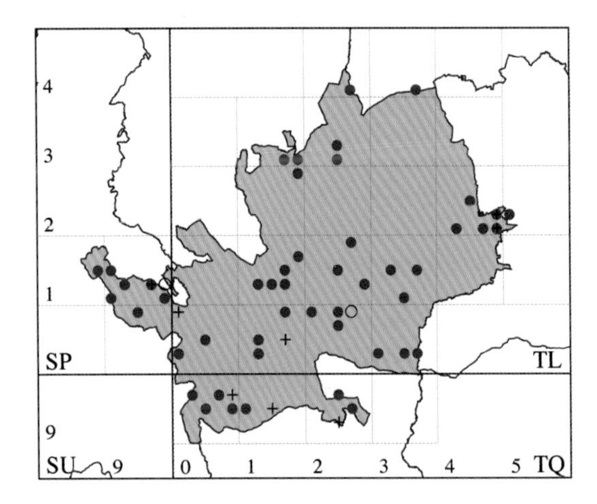

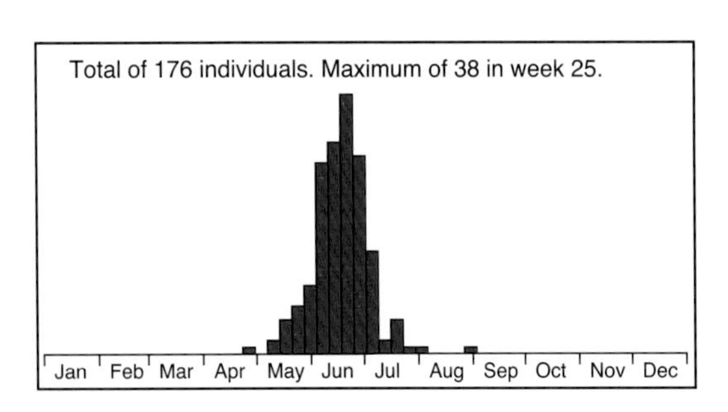

Our observed flight period of adults is precisely that recorded by Riley (2003), but unlike the last species there is only a single generation of adults in each year. The moth is likely to be found wherever foxgloves grow in the county.

1819 *Eupithecia exiguata* (Hb.) Mottled Pug

Recorded: 1884 – 2006
Distribution / Status: Widespread / Abundant resident
Conservation status: Herts Stable
Caterpillar food plants: Blackthorn (flowers). Elsewhere, also on hawthorn and Sycamore.
Flight period: Mid-April to mid-July
Records in database: 643

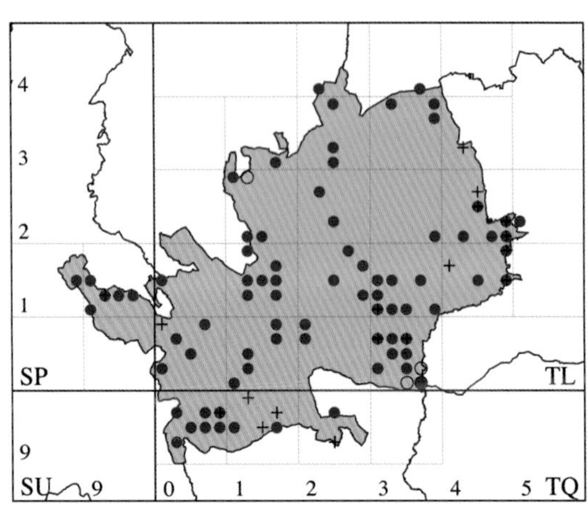

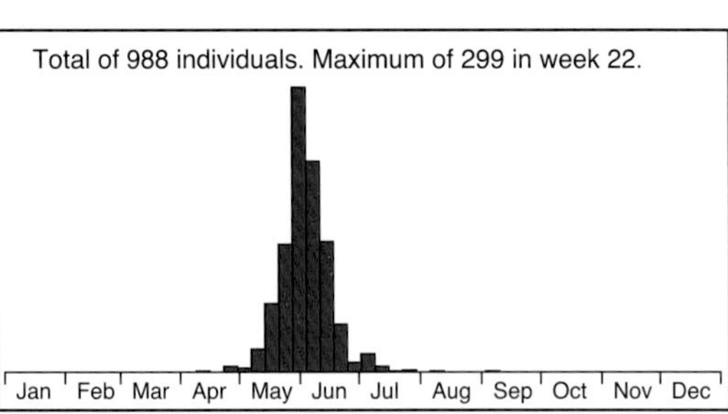

This is a relatively distinctive species, at least at the start of its flight period when few other pugs are on the wing to cause confusion. It is very common in garden light traps.

1820 *Eupithecia insigniata* (Hb.) Pinion-spotted Pug

Recorded: 1919 – 1920
Distribution / Status: Absent / Former resident
Conservation status: Herts Extinct
Caterpillar food plants: Not recorded. Elsewhere, on hawthorn and apple (leaves)
Flight period: Elsewhere, May
Records in database: 2

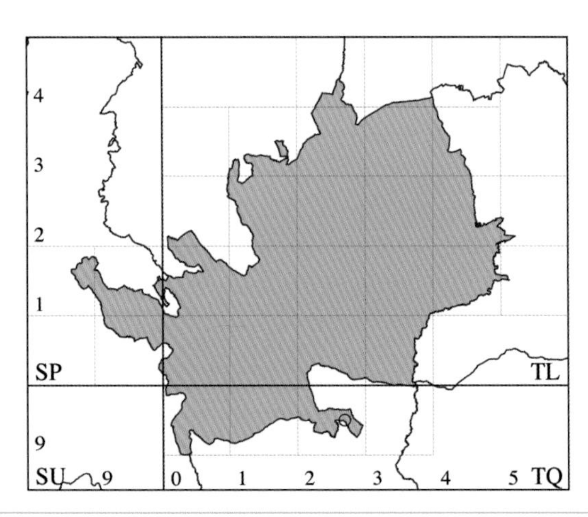

This rather distinctive pug, one of the few that can be instantly recognised, is apparently absent from Hertfordshire, the only records being from New Barnet in 1919 and 1920, recorded by H. E. Bull. It is apparently very rare in Bedfordshire and in Essex it is a rare vagrant, last seen in 1985 on the coast at Bradwell. The distribution map in Riley (2003) appears likely to paint an over-optimistic picture of this moth in the south-east of England.

1821 *Eupithecia valerianata* (Hb.) Valerian Pug

Recorded:	1937 – 1991
Distribution / Status:	Extremely local or absent / Rare resident or Extinct
Conservation status:	Herts Endangered
Caterpillar food plants:	Not recorded. Elsewhere, on Common Valerian and Marsh Valerian
Flight period:	June/July
Records in database:	7

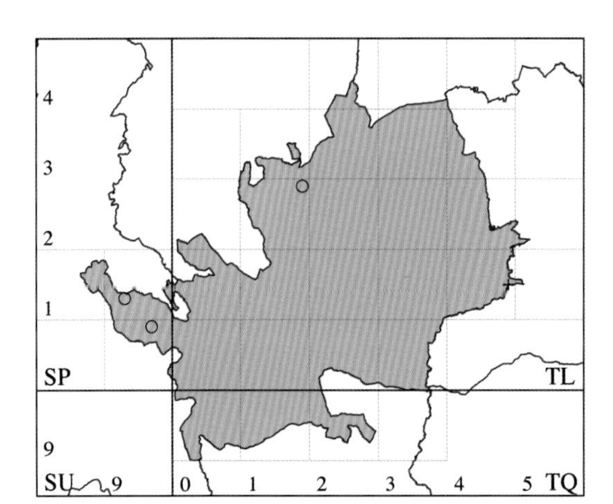

Foster (1937) lists only Tring and Hitchin. Later (Foster, 1942) he adds Northchurch, collected by J. Bell. The only other records for the county are my own from Sawbridgeworth Marsh, where I caught adults at light on 14th June 1989, 17th and 27th July 1990, 20th and 24th June 1991. The moth may still be at Sawbridgeworth, but given the scarcity of wetland habitat in the county and the vulnerability of the foodplant the moth should be treated as Endangered.

1822 *Eupithecia pygmaeata* (Hb.) Marsh Pug

Recorded:	1945 – 2003
Distribution / Status:	Very local / Rare resident
Conservation status:	Herts Threatened
Caterpillar food plants:	Not recorded. Elsewhere, on Field Mouse-ear
Flight period:	June/July
Records in database:	12

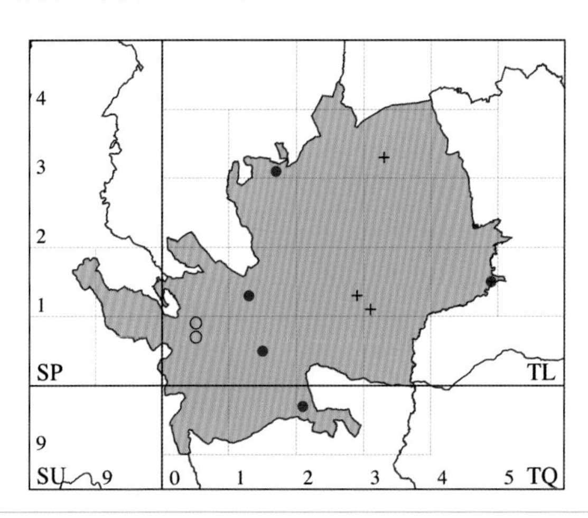

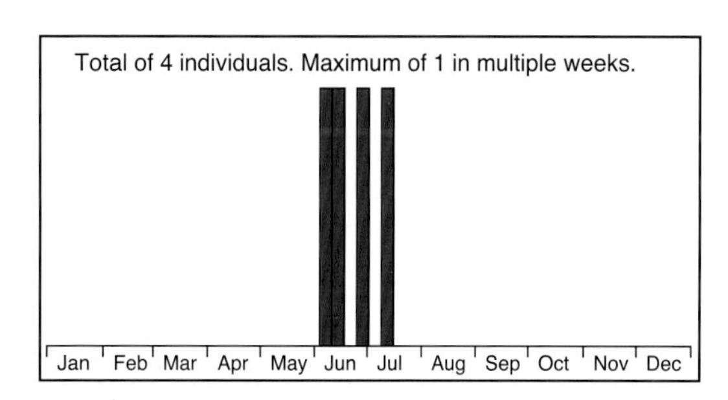

First recorded at Hemel Hempstead in 1945 by A. L. Goodson (Foster, 1945a), there is a wide spread of records across the county, but although the moth is probably to some degree under-recorded it is by no means common and should be regarded as 'Threatened' in Hertfordshire.

1823 *Eupithecia venosata* (Fabr.) Netted Pug

Recorded:	1884 – 2006
Distribution / Status:	Local / Uncommon resident
Conservation status:	Herts Scarce
Caterpillar food plants:	Not recorded. Elsewhere, on Bladder Campion (flowers)
Flight period:	May/June
Records in database:	43

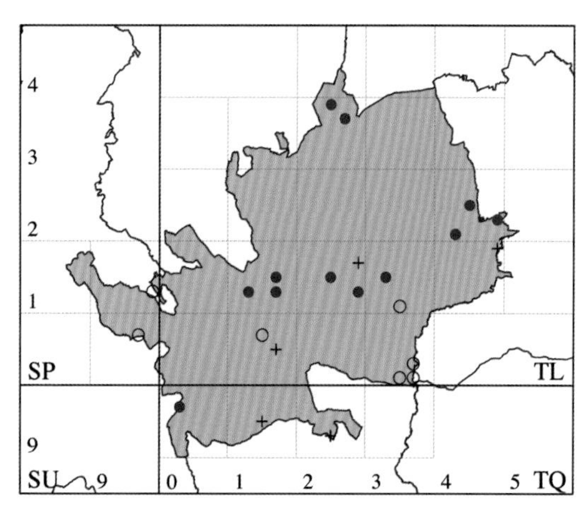

There is a wide scattering of records, but there is also some evidence of a decline of this extremely variable species. For example, the late Charles Watson recorded it regularly in his garden in Bishops Stortford from 1978 to 1987, but not thereafter until his death in 2005. I moved to my house, about half a mile away from Charles in October 1986 and

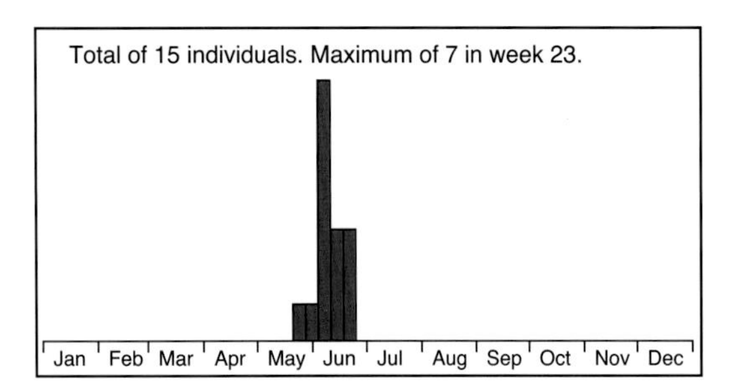

have never found the moth here. At Totteridge, Ian Lorimer recorded two only in the years from 1954 to 1980, one in 1962 and one on 8th June 1970.

1825 *Eupithecia centaureata* ([D.& S.]) Lime-speck Pug

Recorded:	1884 – 2006
Distribution / Status:	Widespread / Common resident
Conservation status:	Herts Stable
Caterpillar food plants:	Knapweed, Ragwort; Tansy (flower). Probably polyphagous on flowers
Flight period:	May to September
Records in database:	423

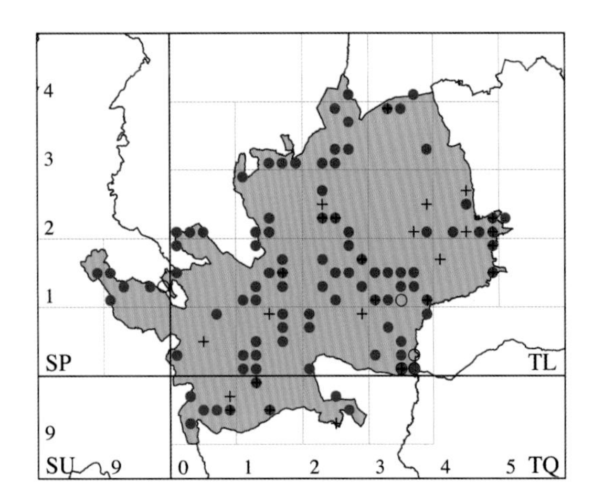

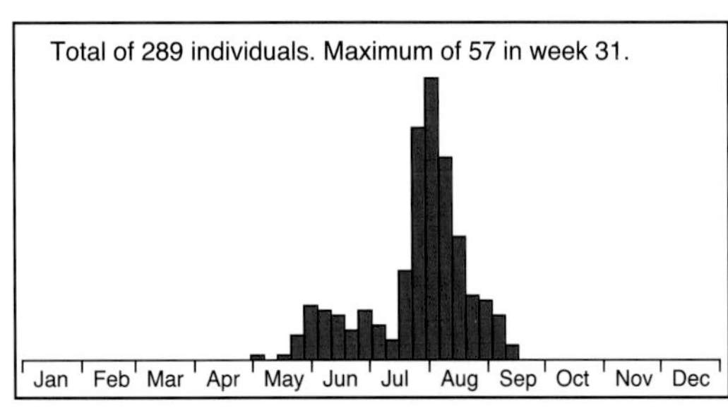

One of the few distinctive pug species, the Lime-speck has always been a very common species in the county. The flight period data suggests two protracted and overlapping generations of adults each year.

1826 *Eupithecia trisignaria* H.- S. Triple-spotted Pug

Recorded:	1890 – 1890
Distribution / Status:	Absent / Former resident
Conservation status:	Herts Extinct
Caterpillar food plants:	Angelica
Flight period:	Elsewhere, June/July
Records in database:	1

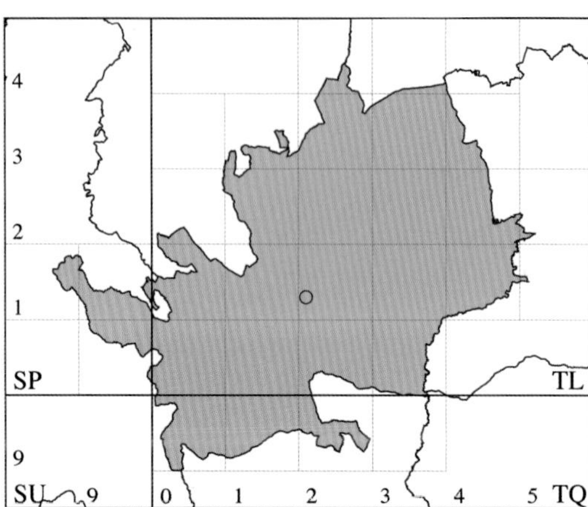

Our only verified record is from Brocket Hall where Griffith (1890) records a few larvae on *Angelica* at Brocket Hall Park 'and elsewhere'. A more recent record from a garden light trap in the Bricket Wood area on 7th July 2005 may be correct, but cannot be substantiated as there is no voucher specimen.

1827 *Eupithecia intricata* (Zett.) ssp. *arceuthata* (Frey.) Freyer's Pug

Recorded:	1960 – 2006
Distribution / Status:	Widespread / Common resident
Conservation status:	Stable
Caterpillar food plants:	Lawson's Cypress, Leyland Cypress. Elsewhere also on Juniper and Chinese *Thuja*.
Flight period:	May to September in two generations
Records in database:	298

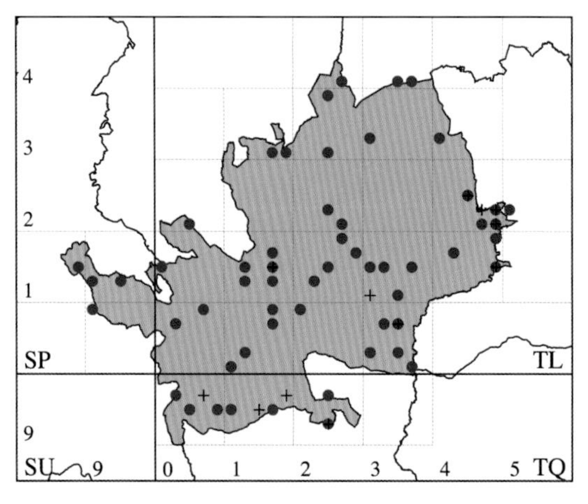

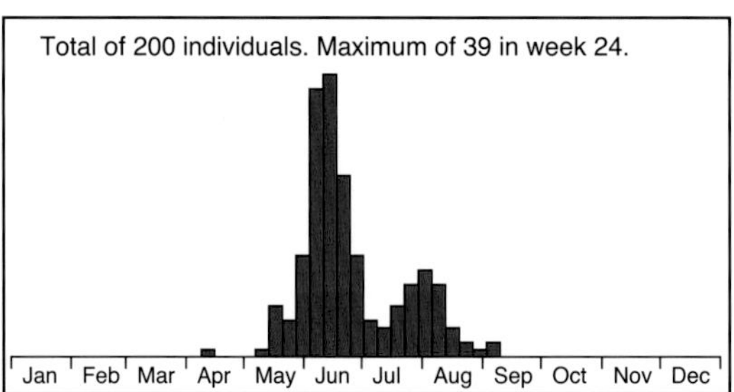

The nominotypical subspecies *intricata* Zett. is not found in the British Isles, where the species is represented by subspecies *hibernica* Mere (Mere's Pug) in the west of Ireland, subspecies *millieraria* Wnukowsky (Edinburgh Pug) in northern England and Scotland and subspecies *arceuthata* Freyer (Freyer's Pug) in the south of England and the Midlands. Hertfordshire examples are exclusively the latter subspecies, which in the past was regarded as a full species. Juniper is confined to the extreme west of the county where the moth may or may not have been established for a long time – it was originally added to the British list in 1860 from larvae collected in Buckinghamshire. However, the rest of us had to wait for the garden trade in ornamental conifers to get going and the moth has either followed, or been introduced with, these trees. The first county record on file is from Whippendell Wood, Watford in 1960 (Barry Goater). Ian Lorimer records the species as new to Totteridge around the same time (I have a note of one in 1964 which he reports as the second ever there). There are no more records until the 1970s, but this may have been due to a lack of recorders; colonisation of Hertfordshire has certainly taken place between 1960 and the mid 1980s. Today it is expected more or less everywhere. Our records show that there is a second peak of adults in August/September, at odds with the univoltine nature of this species throughout Europe. We have 25 such 'late' records – one in each of the years 1965, 1975, 1978, 1988, 1997 and 1999 and then 19 in the years from 2000 to 2006.

1828 *Eupithecia satyrata* (Hb.) Satyr Pug

Recorded: 1900 – 2006
Distribution / Status: Extremely local / Rare resident
Conservation status: Herts Scarce
Caterpillar food plants: Not recorded. Elsewhere, on the flowers of various herbaceous plants
Flight period: Late May to late July
Records in database: 13

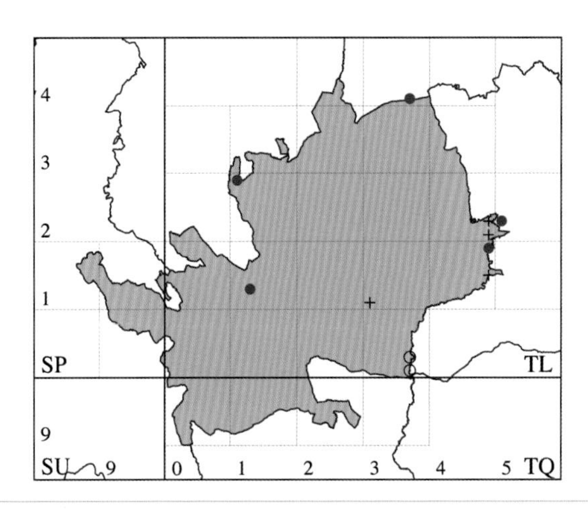

In our eastern neighbour of Essex, larvae have never been found and the occasional adults (e.g., 1967, 1972, 1973 and 1985 – last record) are considered vagrants (Goodey, 2004). In Bedfordshire, on the other hand, larvae are recorded (on Mugwort), although the species appears to be rare with the last record in 1987 (Arnold et al 1997). I suspect that Satyr Pug is an overlooked, but very localised and probably rare resident in Hertfordshire, though I can offer nothing in the way of supporting evidence as all our records are of adults. Foster (1937) notes it as 'near Drayton, ?Herts.'; this is thought to relate to Drayton Beauchamp, Buckinghamshire and so is not relevant to the present work.

1830 *Eupithecia absinthiata* (Cl.) Wormwood Pug

Recorded: 1884 – 2006
Distribution / Status: Widespread / Common resident
Conservation status: Stable
Caterpillar food plants: Mugwort (flowers). Elsewhere, on ragwort and Yarrow and other flowers
Flight period: Late May to early September
Records in database: 176

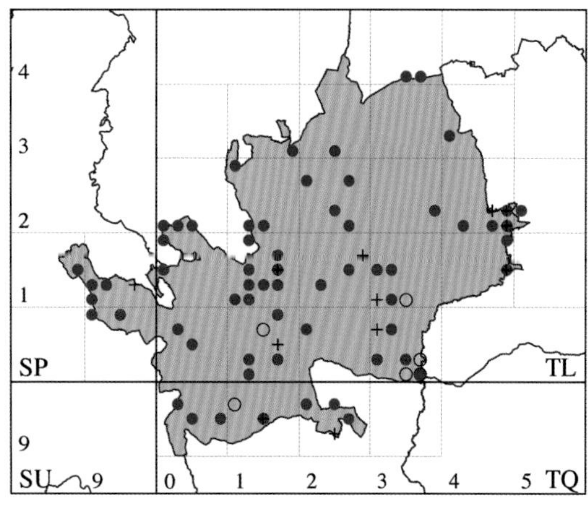

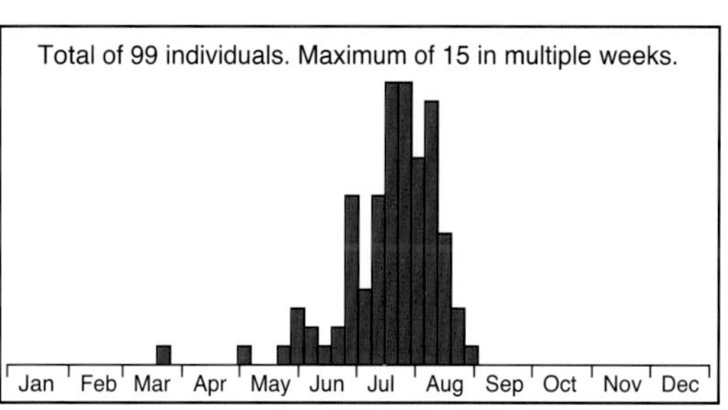

There is a very long flight period with fresh adults appearing throughout though only a single peak is evident, in July/August. A single male taken by me at light in Astonbury Wood on 22nd March 2002 is exceptionally early as is one in Bishops Stortford on 4th May 2006 (James Fish and Julian Reeves), but both are correct. The nearly identical Ling Pug (*Eupithecia goossensiata*) is considered to be a heathland ecotype of the Wormwood Pug and seems to be produced by larvae that have fed on Heather. Unvalidated records of this ecotype are from Bushey Heath and Watford (Foster, 1937) and Tring (Foster, 1942); there are none in the years since then.

[1831 *Eupithecia goossensiata* Mabille Ling Pug

This taxon is considered to be a heathland ecotype of the Wormwood Pug: records are given under that species.]

1832 *Eupithecia assimilata* Doubl. Currant Pug

Recorded: 1884 – 2006
Distribution / Status: Widespread / Common resident
Conservation status: Herts Stable
Caterpillar food plants: Hop; Blackcurrant; Redcurrant
Flight period: April to October in three generations
Records in database: 160

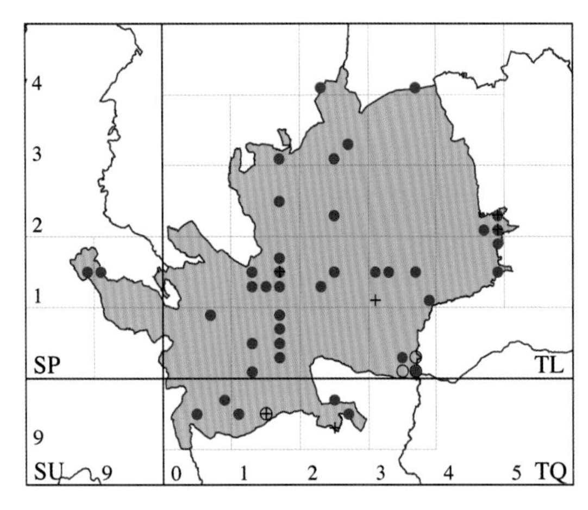

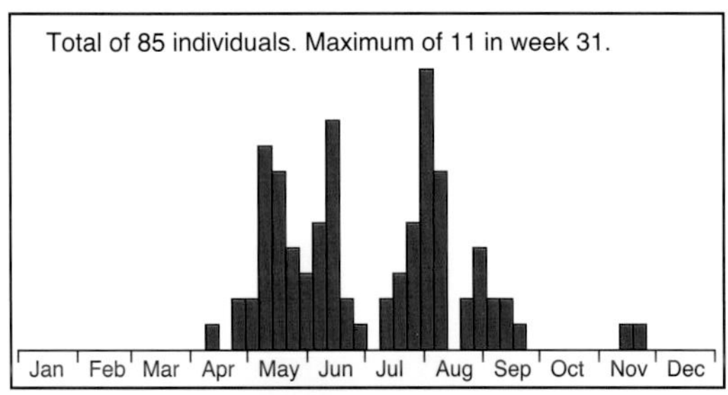

There is clear evidence in the flight chart above that the Currant Pug has switched from two generations per year to three. One on 15th November 2001 at ware (Elizabeth Goodyear) and a male at Hertford on 24 November 2001 (Andrew Wood) are exceptionally late examples.

[1833 *Eupithecia expallidata* Doubl. Bleached Pug

Published records are from Hitchin, 23rd July 1928 (Foster, 1937); Bishops Stortford, 1938 by C. S. Colman (Foster, 1945) and Berkhamsted, 1938 by J, Bell (Foster, 1942). None of the specimens has been traced and dissected and it is generally accepted that Hertfordshire records of this species are misidentifications of *E. absinthiata*.]

1834 *Eupithecia vulgata* (Haw.) Common Pug

Recorded:	1884 – 2006
Distribution / Status:	Widespread / Common resident
Conservation status:	Herts Stable
Caterpillar food plants:	Common Hawthorn (flowers)
Flight period:	April to September including a partial second generation
Records in database:	815

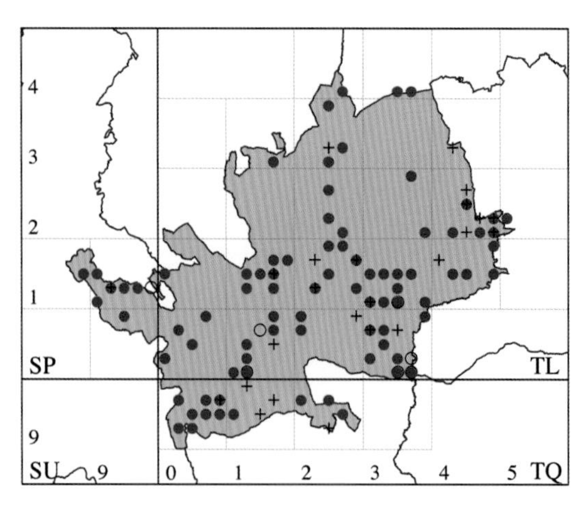

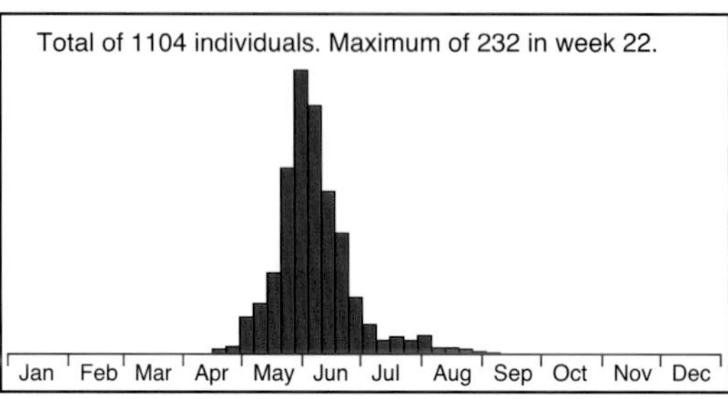

Foster (1937) lists it as common in all districts and nothing has changed. The May/June peak of adults is obvious. However, August records more or less exclusively involve freshly emerged moths and follow a period in July when only worn examples are captured. This is clear indication that the August moths represent a second generation of adults.

1835 *Eupithecia tripunctaria* H.- S. White-spotted Pug

Recorded:	1890 – 2006
Distribution / Status:	Widespread / Common resident
Conservation status:	Herts Stable
Caterpillar food plants:	Angelica. Elsewhere, also on Elder and Hogweed (flowers)
Flight period:	April to August in two generations
Records in database:	216

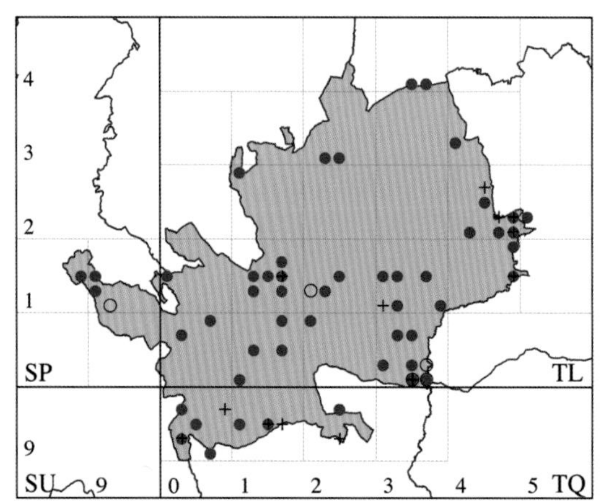

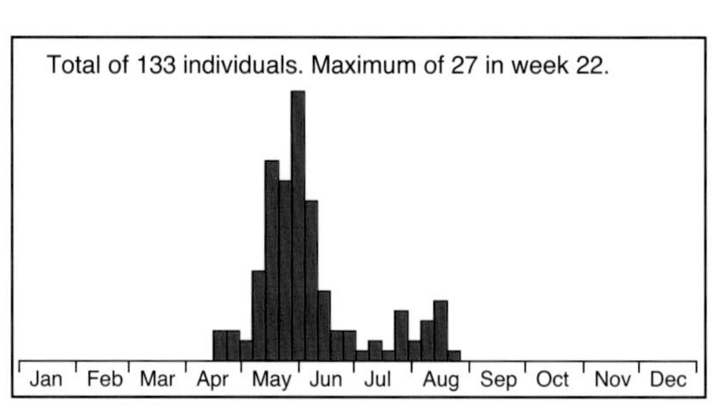

A goodly proportion of presumed melanic Common Pugs prove on dissection to be this species, but not all examples have been dissected so it is not possible to give percentages with absolute certainty. Larvae have been found on Angelica on several occasions in Hertfordshire.

1836 *Eupithecia denotata* (Hb.) ssp. *denotata* Hb. Campanula Pug

Recorded:	1865 – 2005
Distribution / Status:	Extremely Local / Rare resident
Conservation status:	Herts Rare
Caterpillar food plants:	Elsewhere, on Nettle-leaved, Giant and Clustered Bellflowers
Flight period:	May/June
Records in database:	13

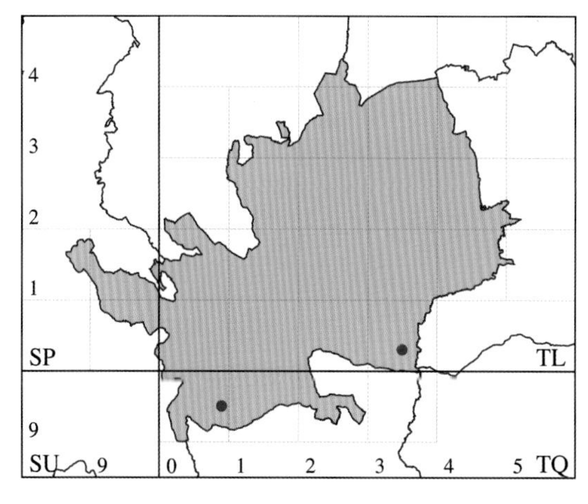

Foster (1937) lists records for '*castigata* Hb., = *jasioneata* (Crewe)' from St Albans (Gibbs, Jackson), Bricket Wood (Gibbs), Sandridge (Griffith), Hitchin (Durrant, Foster), Haileybury (Bowyer), Hoddesdon (G. V. Bull), Tring (Eliman), Cheshunt (Boyd), Bushey Heath (Barraud), Berkhamsted (Tomlinson) and Ashridge (Hervey). Under the heading of '*campanulata* H.- S.' he cites 'Wood near Tring by Rev. H. Harpur Crewe (1865. *Entomologist's Monthly Magazine* **2**: 93 and *Entomologist's Annual* **1866**: 157).' Durrant (1888) queries whether or not the latter location was actually in Hertfordshire. Modern thinking suggests that subspecies *jasioneata* Crewe, the Jasione Pug, is restricted to the south-west Wales, the Isle of Man and Ireland, so that all of our records from Hertfordshire are in fact Campanula Pugs. However, I have not traced any of these specimens and so for the moment I have excluded all these old records from the map. The two records mapped are my own from Croxley Common Moor on 17th May 2003 and Mark Cooper's from Cheshunt on 24th June 2005.

1837 *Eupithecia subfuscata* (Haw.) Grey Pug

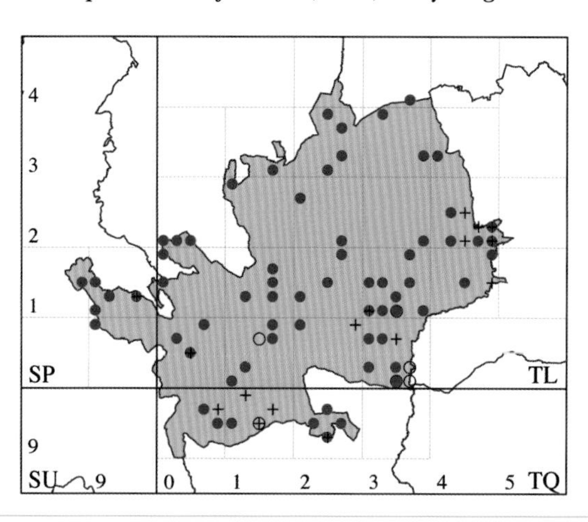

Recorded:	1887 – 2006
Distribution / Status:	Widespread / Common resident
Conservation status:	Herts Stable
Caterpillar food plants:	Not recorded. Elsewhere, polyphagous on flowers and leaves
Flight period:	May to August
Records in database:	217

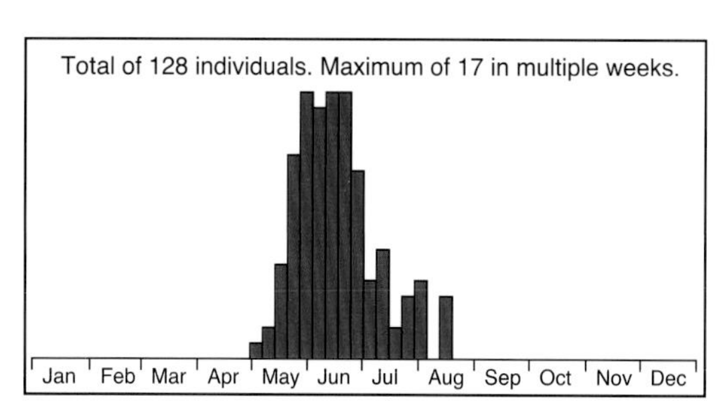

With practice, Grey Pugs can often be recognised without critical examination, though the latter is always desirable for confirmation. The unmarked melanic form *obscurissima* Prout accounts for in the order of 80 per cent of Hertfordshire examples seen. There is a small second generation of adults in Europe.

1838 *Eupithecia icterata* (Vill.) ssp. *subfulvata* (Haw.) Tawny-speckled Pug

Recorded:	1884 – 2006
Distribution / Status:	Widespread / Common resident
Conservation status:	Herts Stable
Caterpillar food plants:	Yarrow (flowers). Elsewhere, also on Sneezewort
Flight period:	July to early September
Records in database:	219

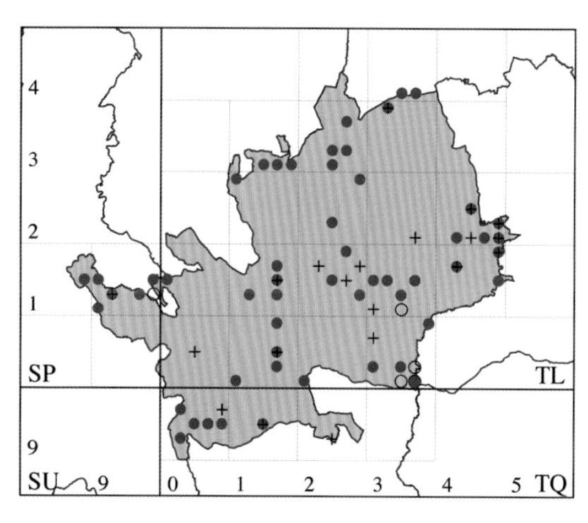

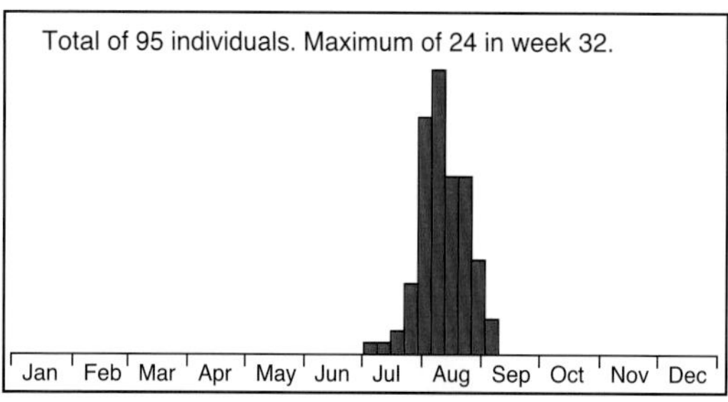

Although there is some variation in overall design, all Hertfordshire examples of this species can be assigned to subspecies *subfulvata* (Haworth). It is a widespread species that appears to have remained single-brooded in spite of possible climatic influences.

1839 *Eupithecia succenturiata* (L.) Bordered Pug

Recorded:	1884 – 2006
Distribution / Status:	Widespread / Common resident
Conservation status:	Herts Stable
Caterpillar food plants:	Not recorded. Elsewhere, on
Flight period:	June to August
Records in database:	159

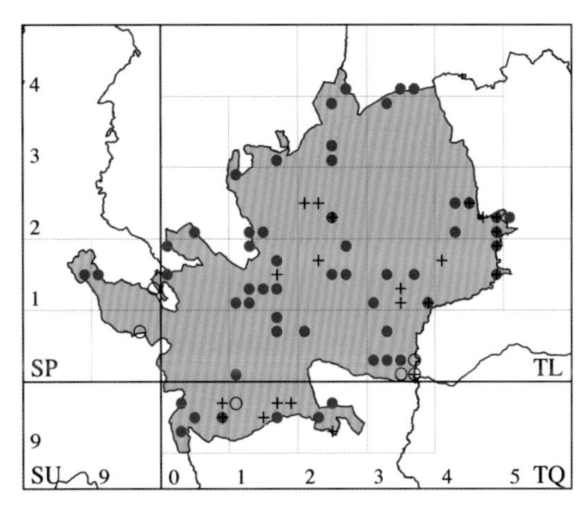

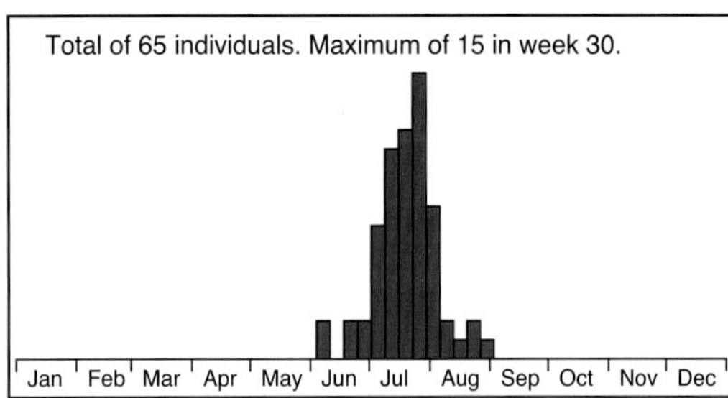

This is a common species throughout the county, but is more frequent along hedges in the countryside than it is in gardens.

1840 *Eupithecia subumbrata* ([D.& S.]) Shaded Pug

Recorded:	1906 – 2006
Distribution / Status:	Local / Common resident
Conservation status:	Herts Stable
Caterpillar food plants:	Not recorded. Elsewhere, on flowers of Field Scabious, hawk-beards, Ragworts and other plants
Flight period:	May to August
Records in database:	50

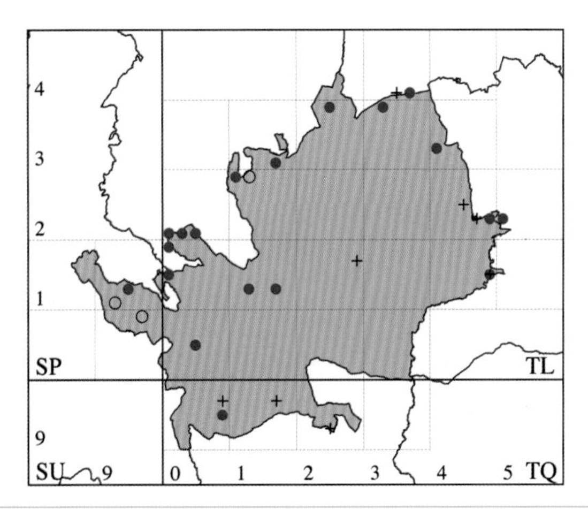

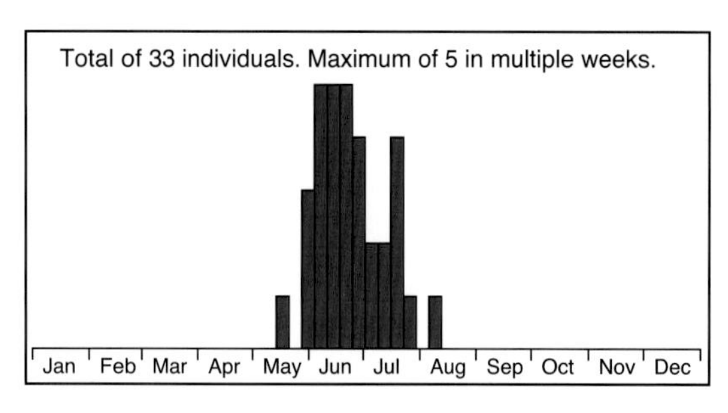

The spread of records around the perimeter of the county suggests that chalk-based habitats are preferred – either the chalk itself or the Chalky Boulder Clay elsewhere. However, a few do not relate to such base-rich areas.

1841 *Eupithecia millefoliata* (Rossl.) Yarrow Pug

Recorded:	1987 – 2006
Distribution / Status:	Local / Uncommon resident
Conservation status:	Herts Scarce
Caterpillar food plants:	Yarrow
Flight period:	May to August
Records in database:	28

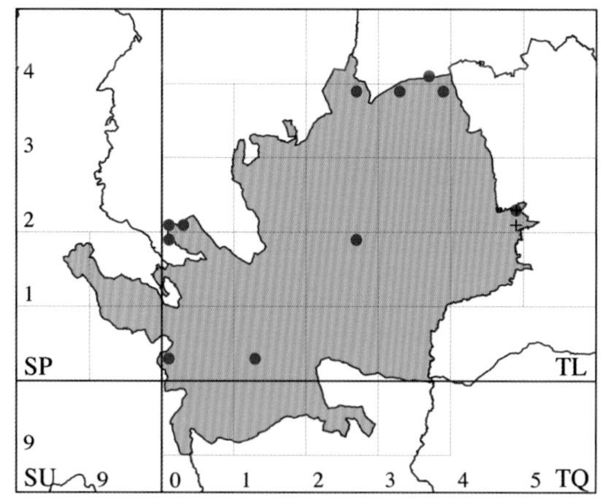

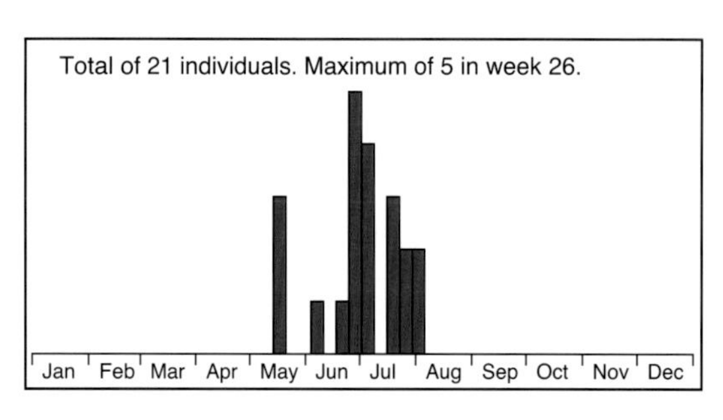

This species is not listed by Foster (1937). Waterton (1983) reports an example in a garden at Royston during 1981, but this record is now known to have been made on the Cambridgeshire side of the border. The first Hertfordshire record was that made by me when a single example entered my Bishops Stortford light trap on 28th July 1987. Six years elapsed before the next Hertfordshire record, on 6th June 1993 in a different part of the same town (James Fish and Julian Reeves), but it is difficult to imagine that the moth was not becoming established in the town in the intervening period. It was noted in Bishops Stortford over most of the following years, but the first record away from here was that of larvae at Therfield (= Royston) Heath on 9th October 1999 (John Chainey and Jenny Spence). The next year they caught an adult in their Royston garden – on our side of the border. Today it is probably widely, but locally established with us though the bulk of records reflect the distribution of the more keen moth enthusiasts who can be bothered to collect and name pugs.

1842 *Eupithecia simpliciata* (Haw.) Plain Pug

Recorded: 1887 – 2006
Distribution / Status: Local / Uncommon resident
Conservation status: Herts Scarce
Caterpillar food plants: Not recorded. Elsewhere, on goosefoot and orache seed heads
Flight period: Mid-June to mid-August
Records in database: 34

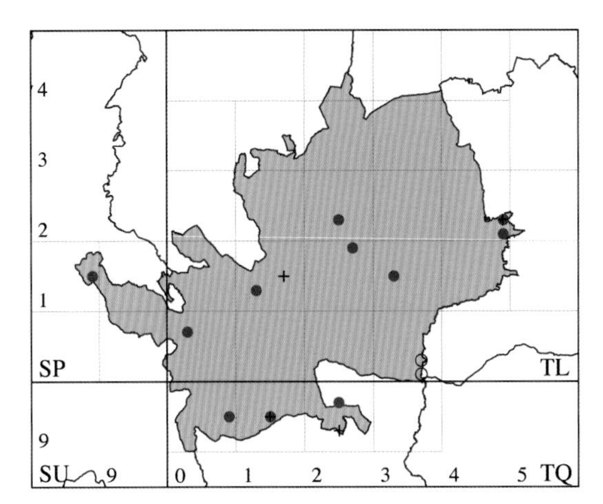

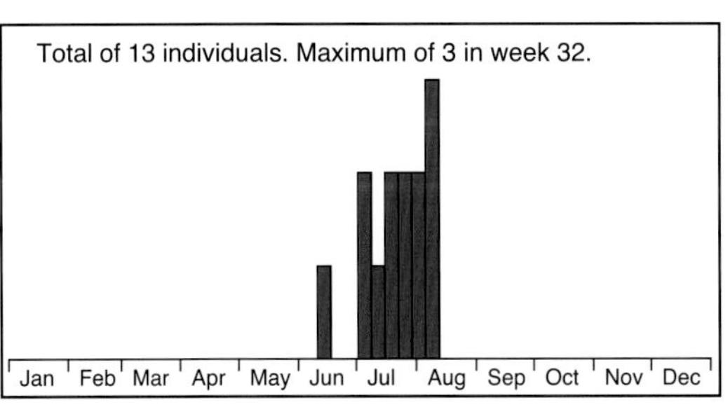

The Plain Pug is rarely recorded other than sparingly, and many sites appear not to support it, though sites that are capable of providing adequate foodplant for a long enough time period are rather few and far between in Hertfordshire.

1842a *Eupithecia sinuosaria* (Evers.) Goosefoot Pug

Recorded: 1992 – 1992
Distribution / Status: Random / Extremely rare immigrant
Conservation status: -
Caterpillar food plants: Not recorded. Overseas, on flowers of goosefoots and oraches
Flight period: June
Records in database: 1

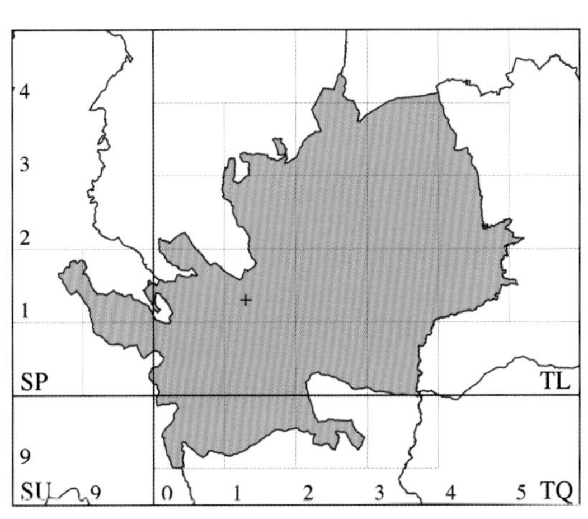

The second of only three British examples of this moth was caught in the Rothamsted trap at Harpenden during the weekend from 19th to 21st June 1992 (Townsend & Riley, 1992). In the recent guide to British Pugs, Riley (in Riley & Prior, 2003) incorrectly cites his own co-authored reference as Townsend & Riley, 1991; happily this *faux pas* in which the moth was evidently reported before it was captured preceded my time as Editor of the journal! A previous British record was made in Somerset a week earlier and a later one was made in East Kent in 2005 (*Atropos* **27**: 65).

1843 *Eupithecia distinctaria* H.- S. ssp. *constrictata* Guen. Thyme Pug

Recorded: 1905 – 1905
Distribution / Status: Absent / Probable former resident
Conservation status: Herts Extinct
Caterpillar food plants: Not recorded. Elsewhere, on Thyme flowers
Flight period: Elsewhere, June/July
Records in database: 1

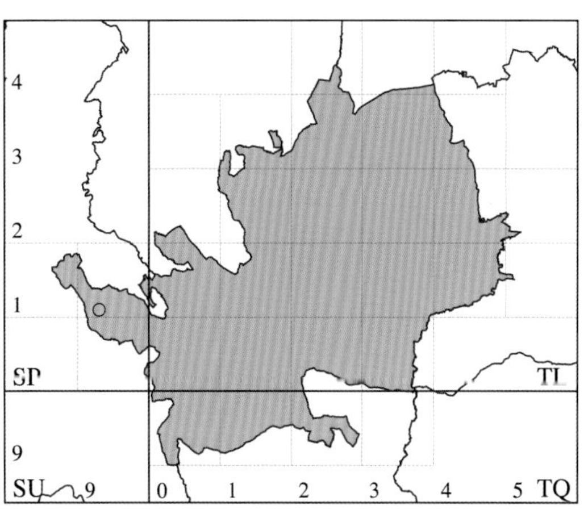

Foster (1941) adds this species to the county list from 'Tring, I, vii, 1905 (A. Goodson *teste* L. B. Prout)'. The specimen is in the Natural History Museum's main collection under the name *constrictata*, although it has '*E. tenuiata*' written by hand on one of its labels. It is a female with the abdomen partly chewed, probably by Museum Beetle. The identification has been checked and confirmed by John Chainey. There are no other Hertfordshire records.

1844 *Eupithecia indigata* (Hb.) Ochreous Pug

Recorded: 1900 – 2006
Distribution / Status: Local / Common resident
Conservation status: Herts Stable
Caterpillar food plants: Not recorded. Elsewhere, on Scots Pine (buds and shoots)
Flight period: May to July
Records in database: 45

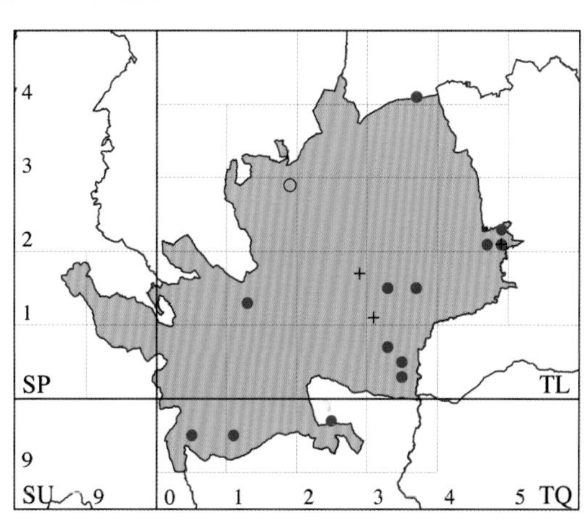

Though we have not recorded the foodplant in Hertfordshire, Scots Pine trees are situated near to my garden and in a direct sight-line with the trap position; the moth is common here and I regularly catch other Scots Pine associates. In his 1937 list,

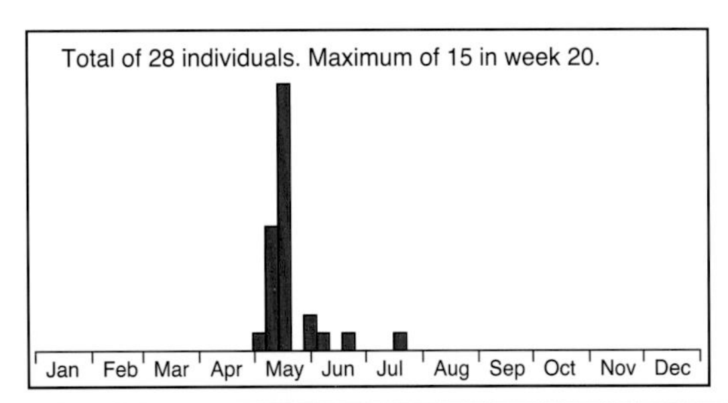

Foster listed just one record – that made of a single moth by himself at Hitchin in 1900. In the 1970s it was recorded near the Pinetum at Bayfordbury and since then it has shown itself to be widespread, but very local and never far from mature Scots Pine trees.

1845 *Eupithecia pimpinellata* (Hb.) Pimpinel Pug

Recorded: 1884 – 2006
Distribution / Status: Very Local / Uncommon resident
Conservation status: Herts Scarce
Caterpillar food plants: Not recorded. Elsewhere, on Burnet-saxifrage (seed capsules)
Flight period: June/July
Records in database: 7

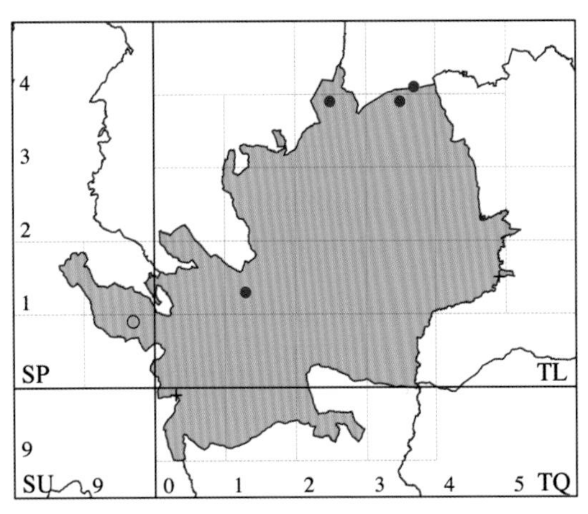

First listed for the Sandridge area (Griffith, 1884), Foster (1937) adds Tring and later (Foster, 1942), he records Northchurch, undated by J. Bell. Other records are from Sarrat Bottom, 1974 (John Chainey), Rothamsted Estate, 1999 (Adrian Riley), Sawbridgeworth Marsh, 14th June 1989 (Colin Plant), Therfield Heath, 26th September 1999 (John Chainey), Royston, 27th July 2000 (John Chainey) and Ashwell Quarry, 27th July 2002 (Colin Plant).

1846 *Eupithecia nanata angusta* Prout Narrow-winged Pug

Recorded: 1828 – 2006
Distribution / Status: Extremely local / Vagrant and rare resident
Conservation status: Herts Rare
Insufficiently known (as a resident)
Caterpillar food plants: Not recorded. Elsewhere, on Heather
Flight period: July
Records in database: 20

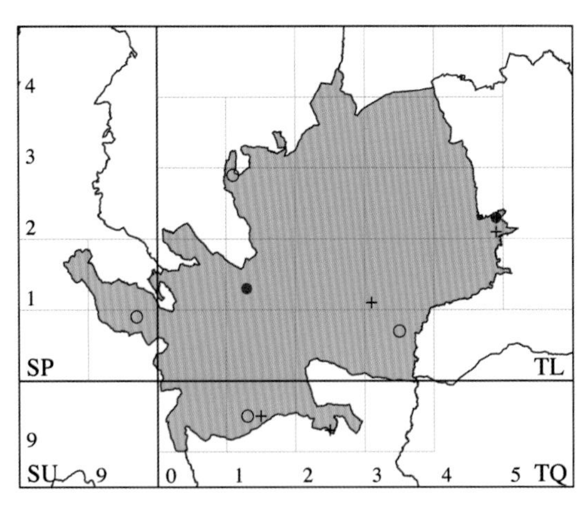

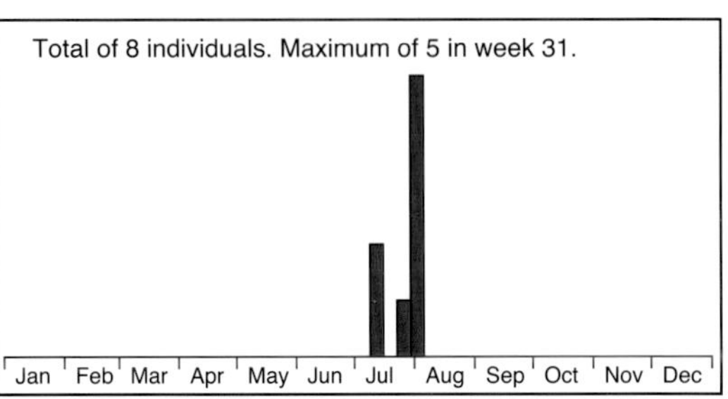

The moth is illustrated by J. F. Stephens from Hertford in *Illustrations of British Entomology* **3**: 289 (published in 1829) and it is listed for the Sandridge area by Griffith (1884). Foster (1937) adds Hexton in 1908, Bushey Heath and Hoddesdon. Barry Goater records it from Bushey in 1965, Jim Reid at Bayfordbury in 1974 and Ian Lorimer at Totteridge in 1977. What these have in common is that they are all single records that are not repeated in subsequent years, as are those from my garden in 1991 and Harpenden in 1999. However, the adjoining gardens of James Fish and Julian Reeves in Bishops Stortford record adults in 1993, 1997, 1998, 1999, 2001 2002 and 2004, suggesting likely residency in the area, perhaps on garden plantings of Heather.

1848/9 *Eupithecia innotata* (Hufn.) f. *fraxinata* Crewe Ash Pug

Recorded: 1884 – 2006
Distribution / Status: Very local / Rare resident
Conservation status: Herts Scarce
Caterpillar food plants: Not recorded. Elsewhere, on Ash
Flight period: May to July
Records in database: 43

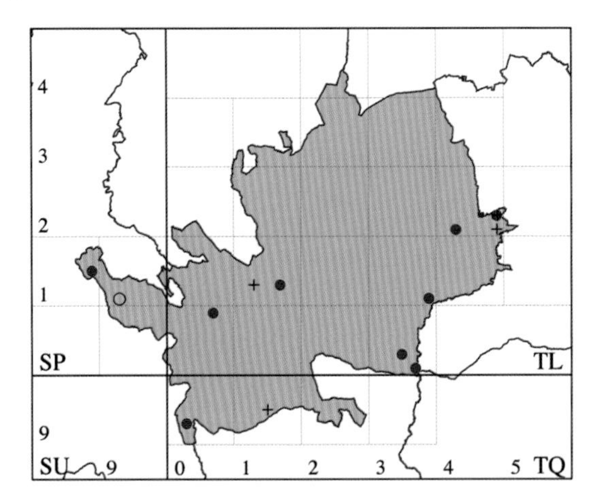

Bradley (2000) considered that Ash-feeding British '*fraxinata* Crewe', the Ash Pug, are a form of *innotata* (Hufn.), the Angle-barred Pug, whose nominotypical form is confined to the south and south-east coast and feeds on Sea Buckthorn. Riley & Prior

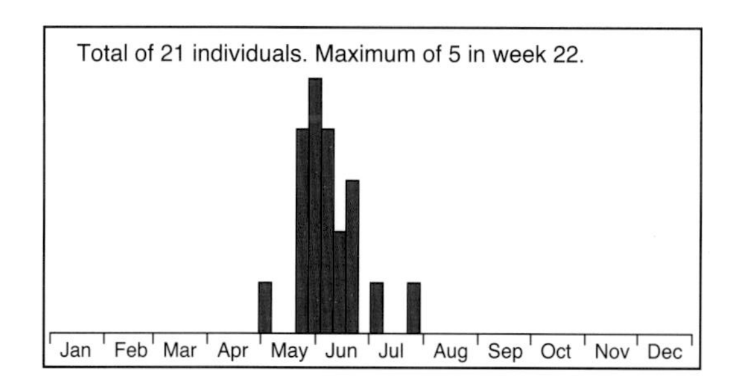

(2003) treat *fraxinata* Crewe as a full species and in its synonymy lists '*innotata* sensu Stephens, *not* Hufnagel'. Neither of these two works is a taxonomic view and both merely express the opinion of the authors without any justification being presented. However, Mironov (2003) in reviewing the European pugs, states that the Continental *innotata* and the British *fraxinata* are conspecific and that the correct name is *innotata*. This view is accepted here. The moth is rare and very local in Hertfordshire.

1851 *Eupithecia virgaureata* Doubl. Golden-rod Pug

Recorded:	1884 – 2006
Distribution / Status:	Extremely local / Rare resident
Conservation status:	Herts Rare
Caterpillar food plants:	Elsewhere, hawthorn (first brood) and Golden-rod and other plants (second brood)
Flight period:	Elsewhere, May/June and August
Records in database:	5

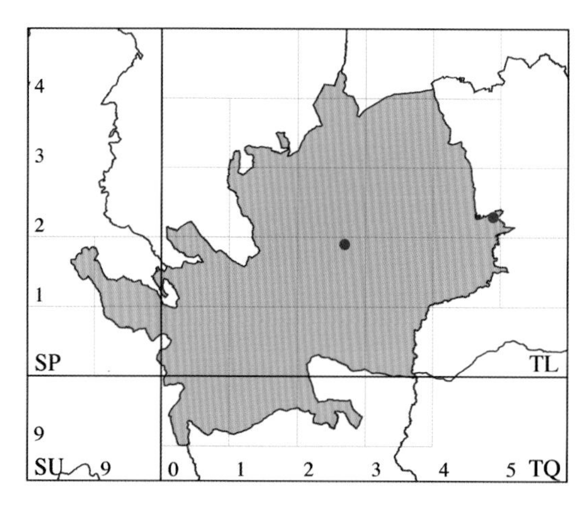

Modern records are from Bishops Stortford on 20th June 1995 and again in 1999 (James Fish and Julian Reeves), and Datchworth, on 31st July 2000 (Steve Palmer).

1852 *Eupithecia abbreviata* Steph. Brindled Pug

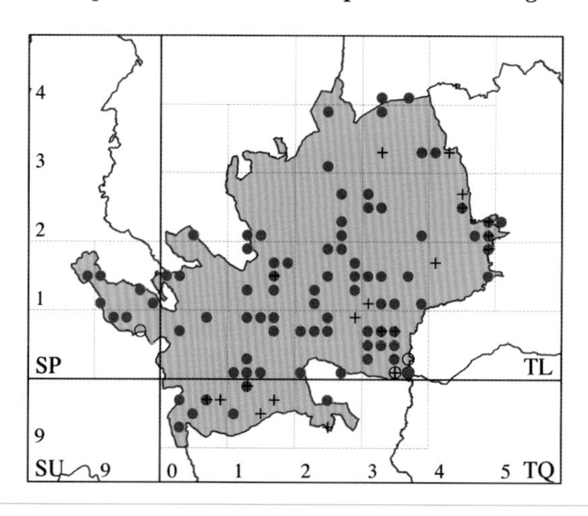

Recorded:	1884 – 2006
Distribution / Status:	Widespread / Abundant resident
Conservation status:	Herts Stable
Caterpillar food plants:	English Oak. Elsewhere, also on hawthorn
Flight period:	March to May, rarely into June
Records in database:	483

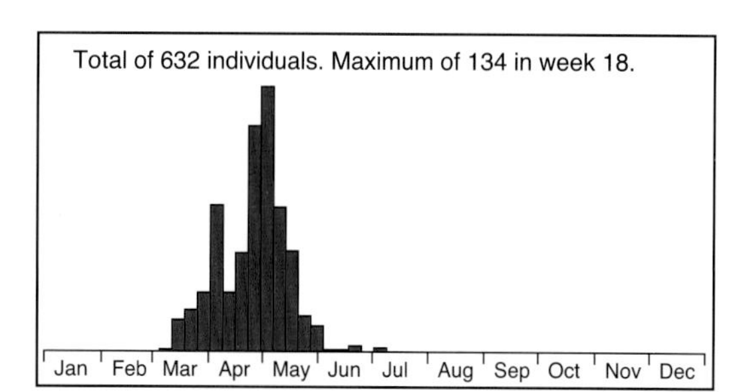

The more or less unmarked melanic ab. *hirschkei* Bastelberger forms in the order of 40 per cent of the Hertfordshire population, but few people report captured forms so the figure is an estimate. The handful of June records was made in 2000 and 2003 with a single very late report at Wheathampstead on 6th July 2002 (Trevor Chapman).

1853 *Eupithecia dodoneata* Guen. Oak-tree Pug

Recorded:	1933 – 2006
Distribution / Status:	Widespread / Common resident
Conservation status:	Herts Stable
Caterpillar food plants:	hawthorn (on the sepals and hips)
Flight period:	Mid-April to July
Records in database:	155

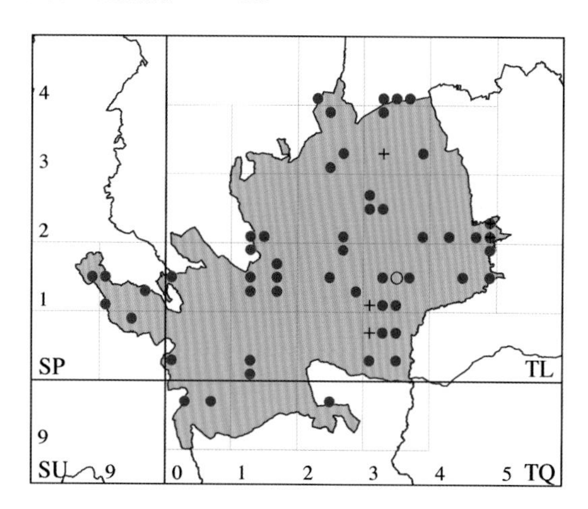

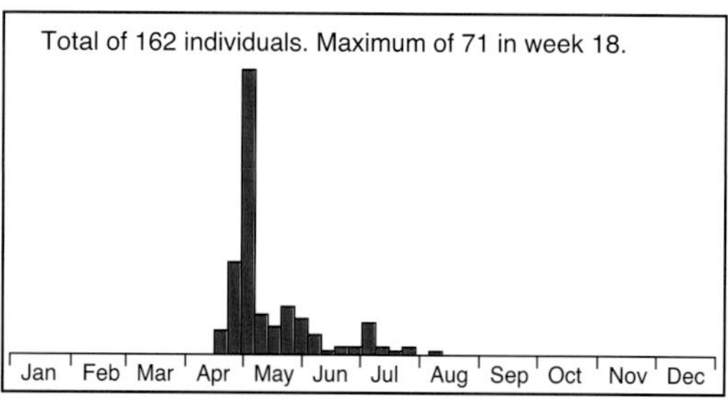

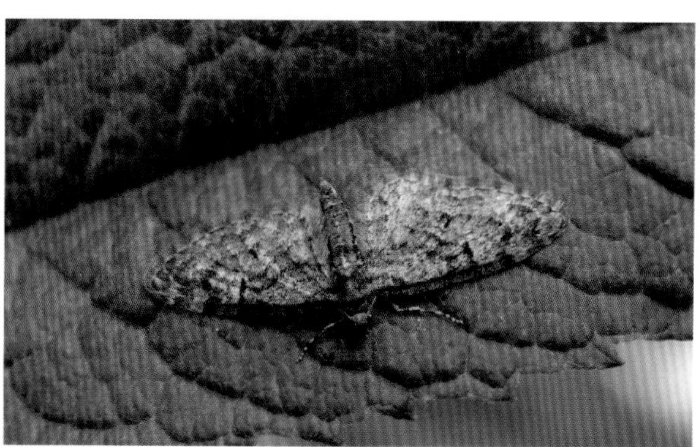

Foster (1941) adds this species to the county list from Ware in 1933; the reason for the lack of earlier records is unclear. Today the moth is very common, though often hard to separate from 1852: Brindled Pug. It should be noted that despite its colloquial name the larvae do not, apparently, feed on oak.

1854 *Eupithecia pusillata* ([D.& S.]) Juniper Pug

Recorded:	1884 – 2006
Distribution / Status:	Local / Uncommon resident
Conservation status:	Herts Stable
Caterpillar food plants:	Not recorded. Elsewhere, on Juniper, *Thuja* and *Chamaecyparis*
Flight period:	Late June to October
Records in database:	38

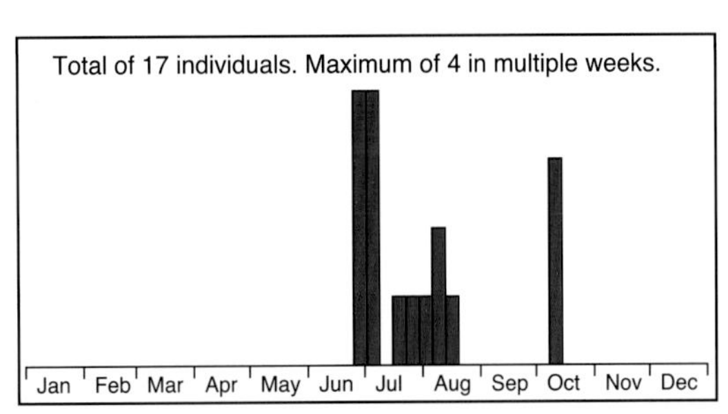

Juniper is confined to a very few places in the west of the county, so garden plantings of ornamental conifers probably support the bulk of the Hertfordshire population, which is widespread but distinctly local across the southern two-thirds of the county.

1855a *Eupithecia ultimaria* Boisd. Channel Islands Pug

Recorded:	1988 – 1988
Distribution / Status:	Random / Rare immigrant
Conservation status:	-
Caterpillar food plants:	Not recorded. Elsewhere, on Tamarisk
Flight period:	June
Records in database:	1

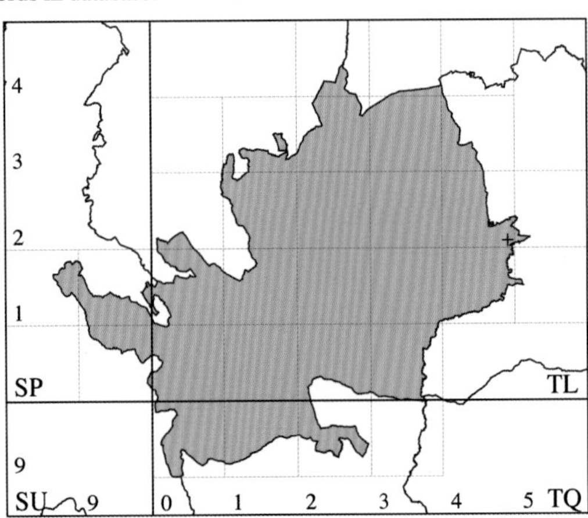

The first mainland British example of the Channel Islands Pug was caught at light by Tony Davis at Bishops Stortford in June 1989 and identified by Adrian Riley (Riley, 1991).

1856 *Eupithecia lariciata* (Frey.) Larch Pug

Recorded:	1884 – 2006
Distribution / Status:	Local / Uncommon resident
Conservation status:	Herts Stable
Caterpillar food plants:	Not recorded. Elsewhere, on Larch
Flight period:	May to August
Records in database:	38

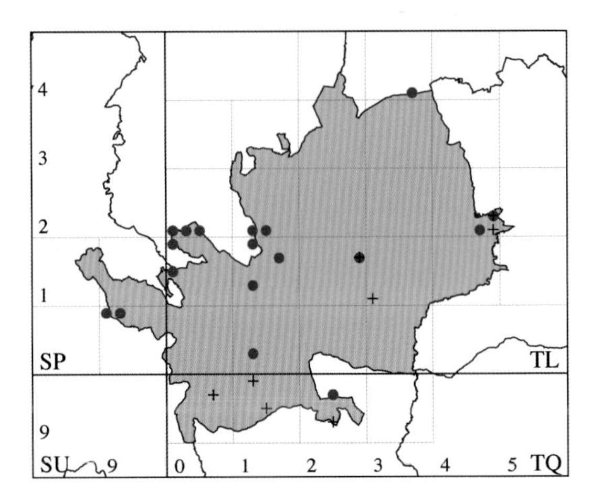

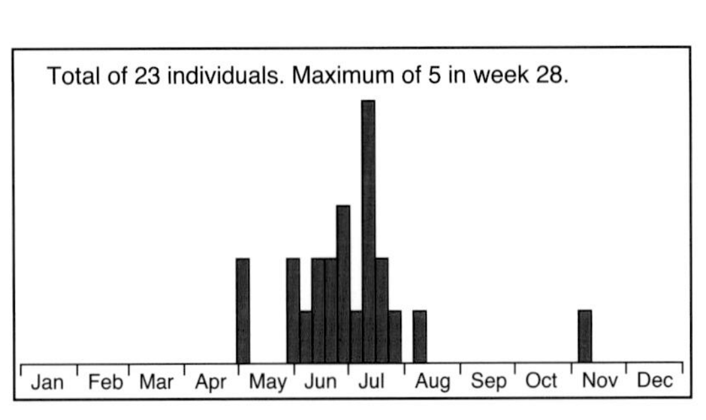

The available data suggest that this is a rather scarce pug in Hertfordshire. An extremely late example was taken by me at Hares Garden Wood, near Tring, on 10th November 2004.

1857 *Eupithecia tantillaria* (Boisd.) Dwarf Pug

Recorded:	1894 – 2006
Distribution / Status:	Local / Common resident
Conservation status:	Stable
Caterpillar food plants:	Not recorded. Elsewhere, on spruces, larches, firs and pines
Flight period:	May/June
Records in database:	24

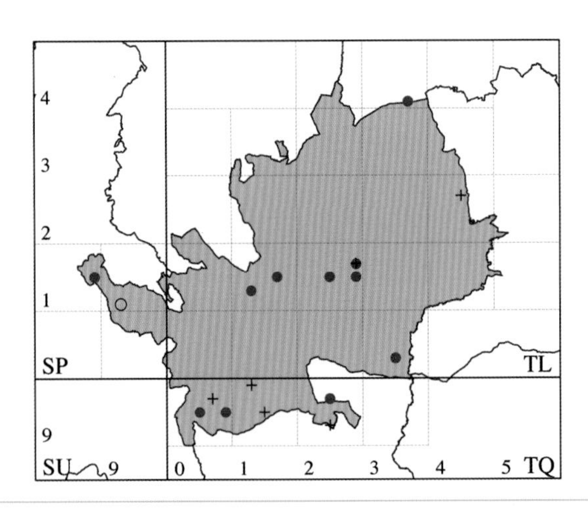

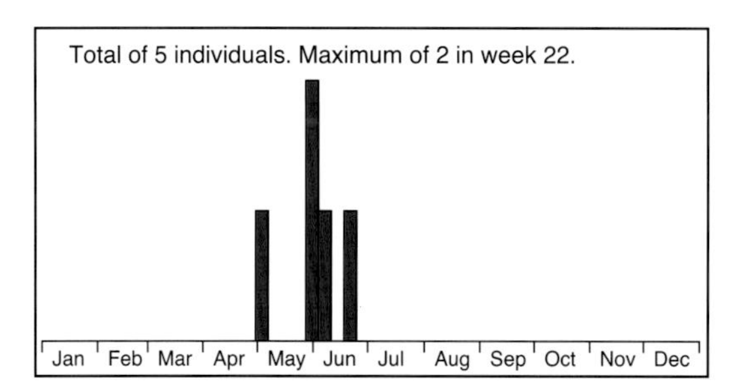

This is one of the more easily recognised pugs, and it also flies quite early in the year when fewer than usual confusion species are on the wing. Although only locally distributed, the moth can appear in large numbers in a single moth-trap.

1858 *Chloroclystis v-ata* (Haw.) V-Pug

Recorded:	1906 – 2006
Distribution / Status:	Widespread / Common resident
Conservation status:	Herts Stable
Caterpillar food plants:	Not recorded. Elsewhere, on flowers of a range of plants
Flight period:	May to August
Records in database:	136

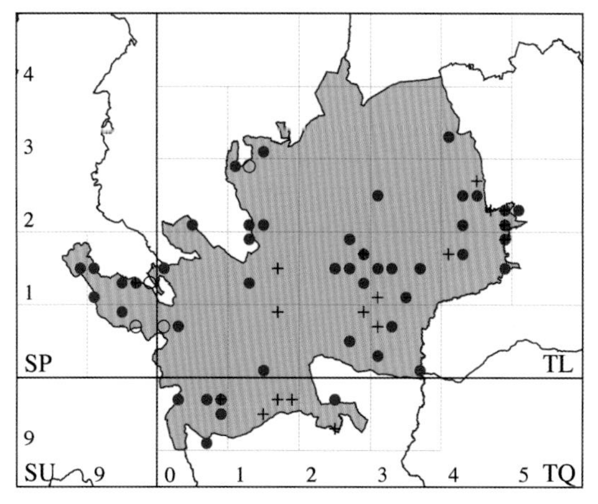

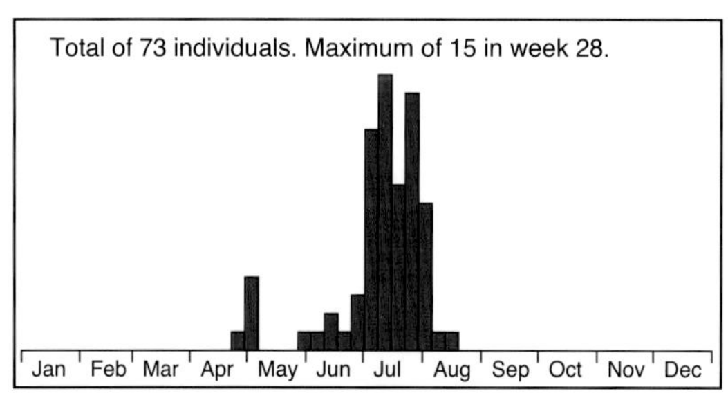

Fresh examples are bright green and render the moth easily recognisable, but these soon become worn. The characteristic 'V' shape on the fore wing usually remains visible, however. It is a common species throughout our county.

1859 *Pasiphila chloerata* Mab. Sloe Pug

Recorded:	1974 – 2006
Distribution / Status:	Local / Uncommon resident
Conservation status:	Herts Stable
Caterpillar food plants:	Blackthorn (flowers)
Flight period:	June to mid-July
Records in database:	102

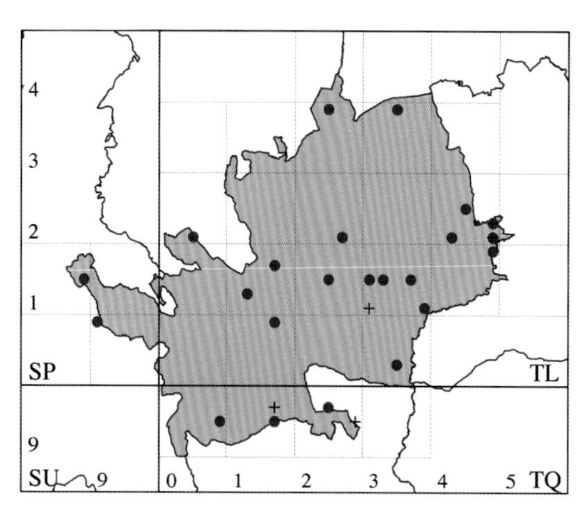

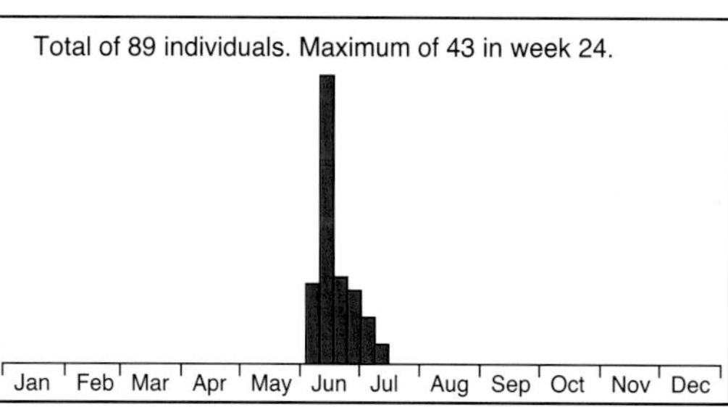

The Sloe Pug was not found in Britain until 1971, although subsequent earlier specimens have been located in collections; consequently, some old records of 1860: Green Pug may possibly relate to this species. Our first certain record was made at Bayfordbury in 1974, by Jim Reid. Although freshly emerged adults are relatively easy recognised on forewing pattern, these are rarely encountered in light traps and separation from Green Pug is problematic. The females show clear differences in the genitalia; the most accurate drawings are to be found in Mironov (2003). Males are more of a problem. The abdominal plates are shown as differing in Riley (2003) and other works, but these drawings are misleading and a careful reading of the author's own text confirms this. The shape of the genital valvae is perhaps the most helpful character, but the aedeagus of either species can be made to look like that of the other by altering pressure on the cover slip.

1860 *Pasiphila rectangulata* (L.) Green Pug

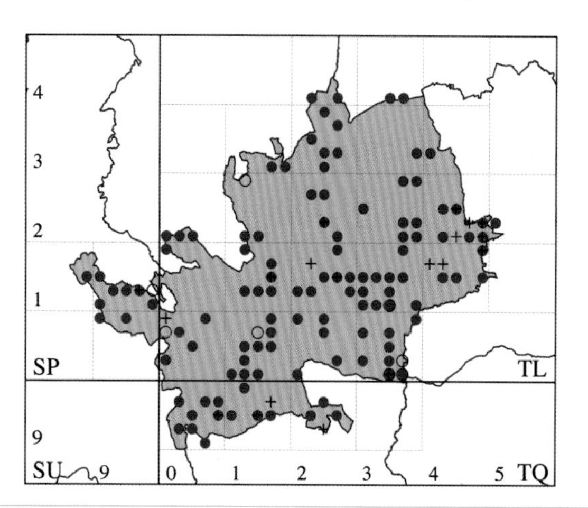

Recorded:	1974 – 2006
Distribution / Status:	Ubiquitous / Abundant resident
Conservation status:	Herts Stable
Caterpillar food plants:	Common Hawthorn and Blackthorn (flowers)
Flight period:	May to August
Records in database:	811

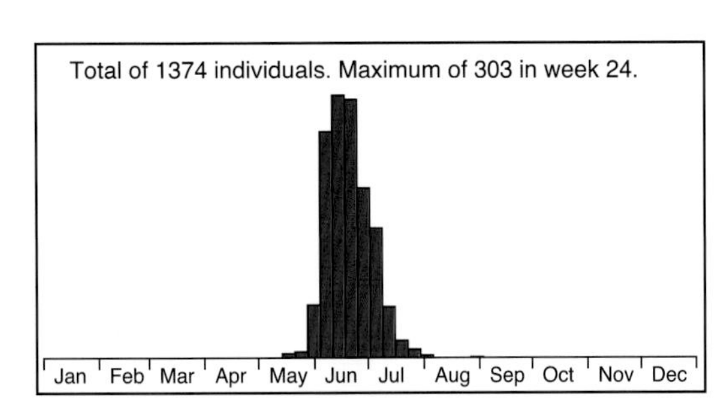

All our historic records for the county predate the recognition of 1859: Sloe Pug in Britain and so cannot be regarded as reliable; comments on the separation of the two species are given under the Sloe Pug heading. Our first confirmed record of Green Pug is from 1974. Exceptionally early and late individuals were noted in my garden Bishops Stortford on 5th February 2002 and in Andrew Wood's garden in Hertford on 2nd September 2002.

1862 *Gymnoscelis rufifasciata* (Haw.) Double-striped Pug

Recorded:	1900 – 2006
Distribution / Status:	Ubiquitous / Common resident
Conservation status:	Herts Stable
Caterpillar food plants:	Not recorded. Elsewhere, polyphagous
Flight period:	March to September in two broods
Records in database:	1281

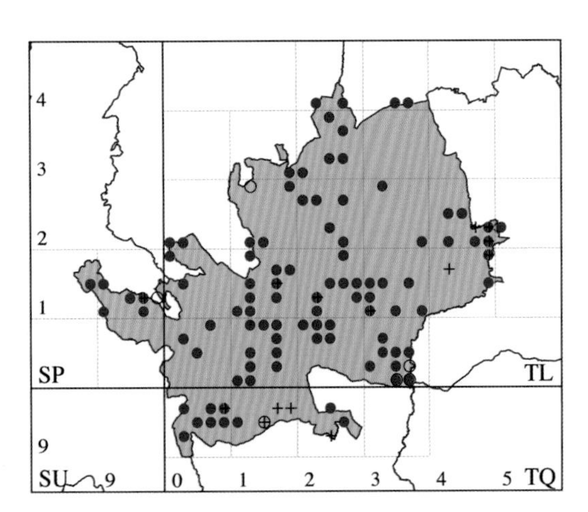

The two generations of adults are distinct from the flight chart, but occasional moths appear at any time and the only month or which we have no records at all is January. The presence of *red* scales on the forewing and/or thorax of this species betrays its identity and allows separation of even the most worn examples from other pug species.

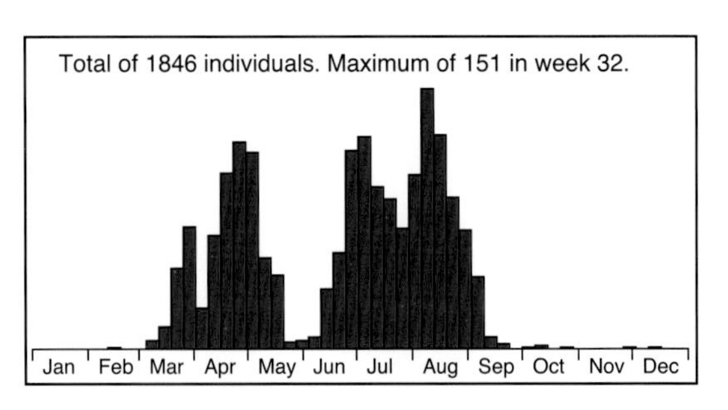

1864 *Chesias legatella* ([D.& S.]) Streak

Recorded:	1887 – 2006
Distribution / Status:	Local / Uncommon resident
Conservation status:	UK BAP Watch List Herts Vulnerable
Caterpillar food plants:	Broom
Flight period:	Mid-October to early November
Records in database:	22

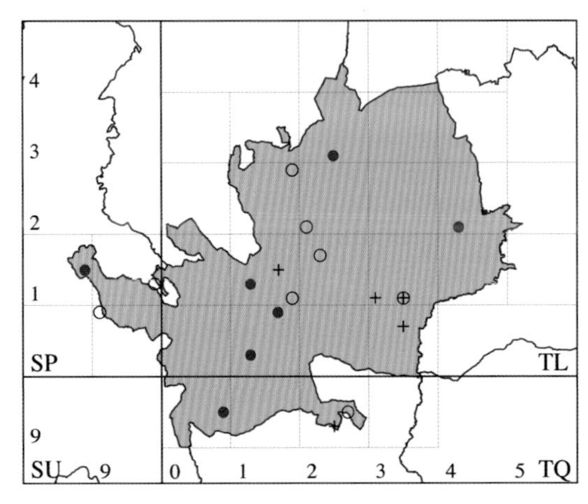

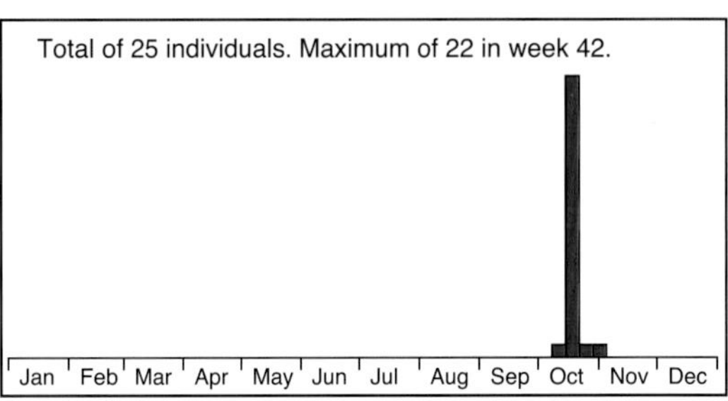

There is a wide spread of records and the moth is probably under-recorded because of its late flight period. Places with long-established plants of Broom are likely to support it, but the value of recently planted areas, such as roadside embankments, is currently unknown.

1865 *Chesias rufata* (Fabr.) Broom-tip

Recorded:	1900 – 2005
Distribution / Status:	Extremely local / Rare resident
Conservation status:	UK BAP Watch List Herts Rare
Caterpillar food plants:	Not recorded. Elsewhere, on Broom
Flight period:	Elsewhere, April to June
Records in database:	4

The two older records are from Carneles Green in 1900 (W. C. Boyd) and Hertford Heath in 1991 (anonymous record at BRC Monks Wood – taken on trust as being correct). The only modern record is of one extremely worn male at mv light in Bishops Stortford, on 28th April 2005 (James Fish and Julian Reeves). This moth was so worn it could only be named by examination of its genitalia. The early flight period may contribute to under-recording (almost all April/May trapping in recent years seems to have been undertaken in domestic

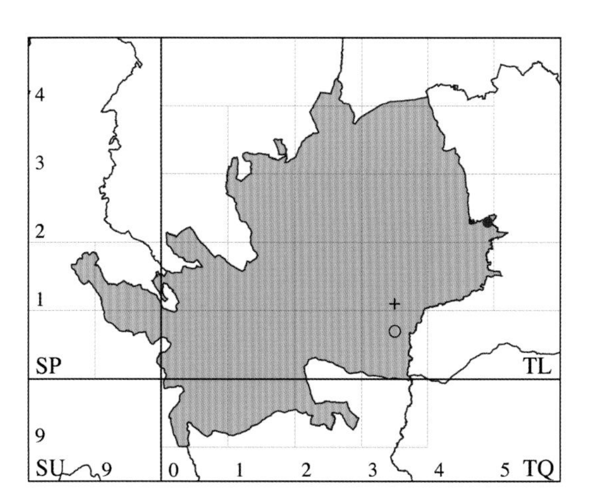

gardens and few people venture out to sites where the moth might occur). Nevertheless, 1864: The Streak, another broom-feeder, which is on the wing at a different time when under-recording is likely to apply, is evidently rather more widespread, and so the Broom-tip is probably genuinely scarce in comparison. The pupa of the Broom-tip overwinters twice and this may be a factor affecting the abundance of the species.

1867 *Aplocera plagiata* (L.) Treble-bar

Recorded:	1887 – 2006
Distribution / Status:	Widespread / Common resident
Conservation status:	Herts Stable
Caterpillar food plants:	Perforate St John's-wort. Probably also on other St John's-worts
Flight period:	May/June and August/September in two generations
Records in database:	264

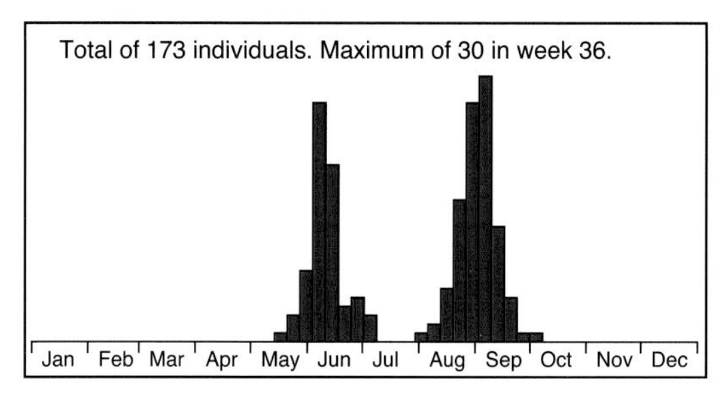

Foster (1937) lists a number of records but then, under *A. efformata*, suggests that the latter species may be confused with the former. In view of this, all records of these two species presented by Foster, other than the record of *efformata* from Tring, have been ignored and old records in the map are based on confirmed identifications only. It is evidently quite widespread.

1868 *Aplocera efformata* (Guen.) Lesser Treble-bar

Recorded:	1937 – 2006
Distribution / Status:	Local / Uncommon resident
Conservation status:	Herts Scarce
Caterpillar food plants:	St John's-wort (unknown species).
Flight period:	May/June and August/September in two generations
Records in database:	24

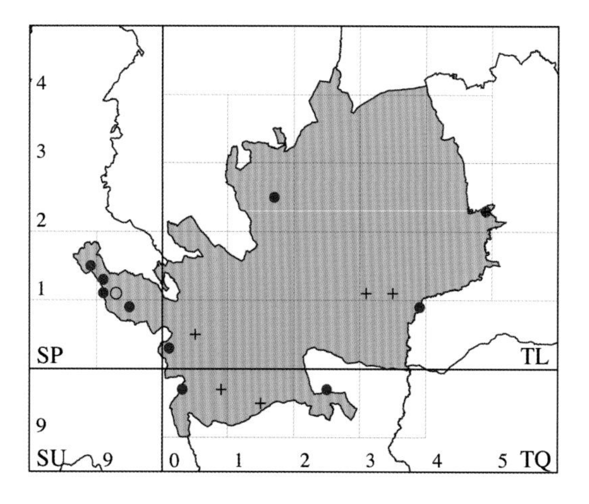

Foster (1937) lists only Tring, though he adds that it is probably elsewhere and un-separated from *A. plagiata*. Given that all accepted records of the two treble-bar species have been verified, it is evident that the present species is currently rare in comparison with 1867: Treble-bar. However, as discussed under that last species, old records have been excluded and so do not feature on the map, so that it is not possible to determine if there has been any decline of Lesser Treble-bar in Hertfordshire.

1870 *Odezia atrata* (L.) Chimney Sweeper

Recorded:	1887 – 2006
Distribution / Status:	Very local / Rare resident
Conservation status:	Herts Vulnerable
Caterpillar food plants:	Not recorded. Elsewhere, on Pignut flowers
Flight period:	Elsewhere, June/July
Records in database:	16

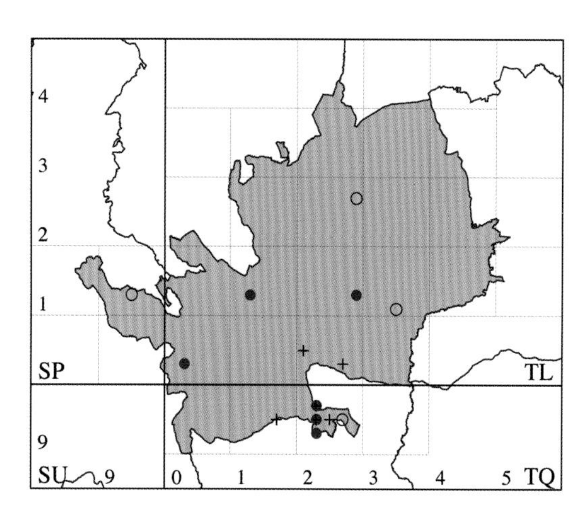

This day-flying moth is a characteristic species of undisturbed meadows, as is its foodplant and is likely to be found wherever the latter is established. Regrettably, however, such sites are now rather scarce in the county and were it not for the fact that the few which remain are mostly nature reserves the moth would be classed as Endangered rather than Vulnerable in Hertfordshire.

1872 *Discoloxia blomeri* (Curtis) Blomer's Rivulet

Recorded: 1901 – 1962
Distribution / Status: Absent / Extinct
Conservation status: -
Caterpillar food plants: Not recorded. Elsewhere, on Wych Elm
Flight period: Elsewhere, May to July
Records in database: 3

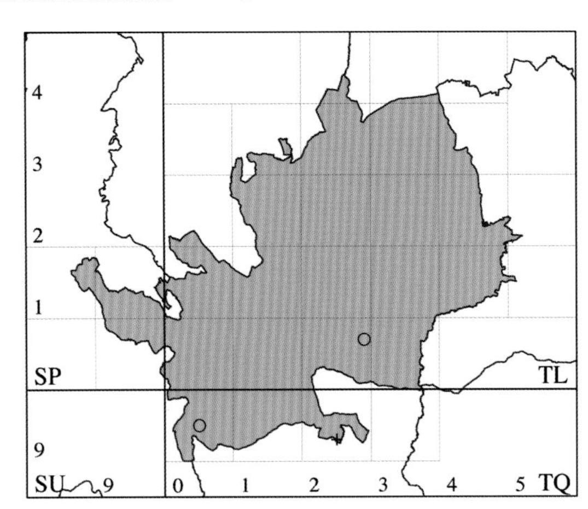

Blomer's Rivulet is resident in the south-west, Wales and the north-west of England and is unexpected in Hertfordshire, where we have three old records. Gibbs (1901) cites Rickmansworth; the dot on the map is arbitrarily placed in the centre of the ten-kilometre square. H. M. Edelsten recorded one at light near Little Berkhamsted (Foster, 1937); unfortunately, Foster failed to report the year. The third was taken at Totteridge by Ian Lorimer on 5th August 1962.

1874 *Euchoeca nebulata* (Scop.) Dingy Shell

Recorded: 1884 – 2006
Distribution / Status: Local / Uncommon resident
Conservation status: Herts Threatened
Caterpillar food plants: Not recorded. Elsewhere, on Alder
Flight period: June/July
Records in database: 17

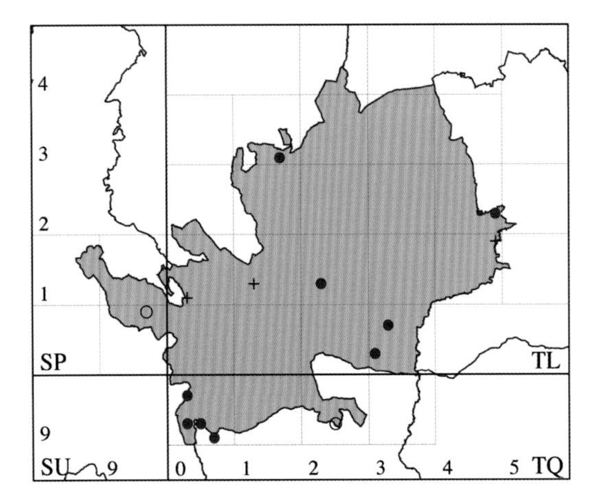

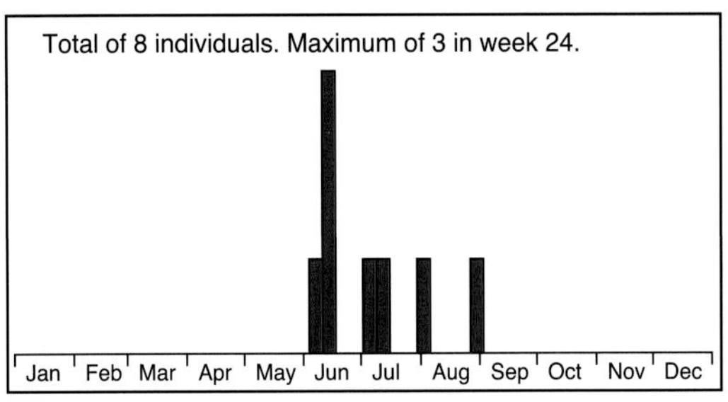

The Dingy Shell is not noted for moving great distances and so unless a trap is positioned within alder carr the moth is unlikely to be recorded. Nevertheless, it is likely to be extremely local in our county and because damp alder woodland is a scarce commodity it is regarded as Threatened.

1875 *Asthena albulata* (Hufn.) Small White Wave

Recorded: 1884 – 2006
Distribution / Status: Widespread / Common resident
Conservation status: Herts Stable
Caterpillar food plants: Not recorded. Elsewhere, on Hazel, birch and Hornbeam
Flight period: Late May to August
Records in database: 86

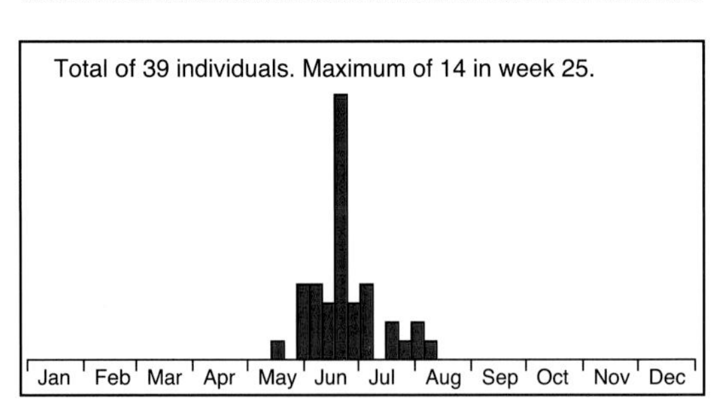

The Small White Wave is a woodland moth and only seen outside that habitat on exceptional occasions. Thus, it is missing from many garden moth trap lists and the absence of records in the north-east of the county is probably genuine; gaps in the south are more likely to reflect under-recording.

1876 *Hydrelia flammeolaria* (Hufn.) Small Yellow Wave

Recorded: 1828 – 2006
Distribution / Status: Widespread / Common resident
Conservation status: Herts Stable
Caterpillar food plants: Not recorded. Elsewhere, on Field Maple
Flight period: June/July
Records in database: 181

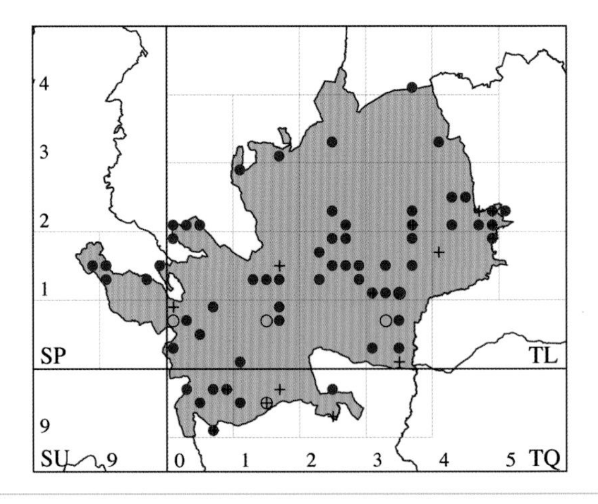

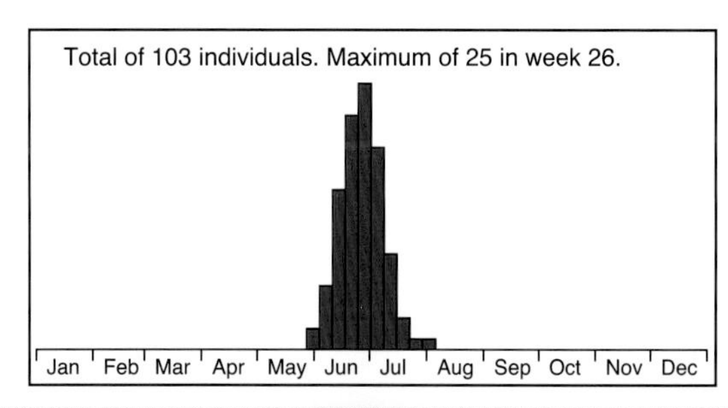

The foodplant is widespread in Hertfordshire and the moth is probably in attendance at most places where the tree is found, though only ever caught in small number.

1877 *Hydrelia sylvata* ([D.& S.]) Waved Carpet

Recorded: 1902 – 1935
Distribution / Status: Absent / Extinct
Conservation status: -
Caterpillar food plants: Not recorded. Elsewhere, on Alder
Flight period: Elsewhere, June/July
Records in database: 2

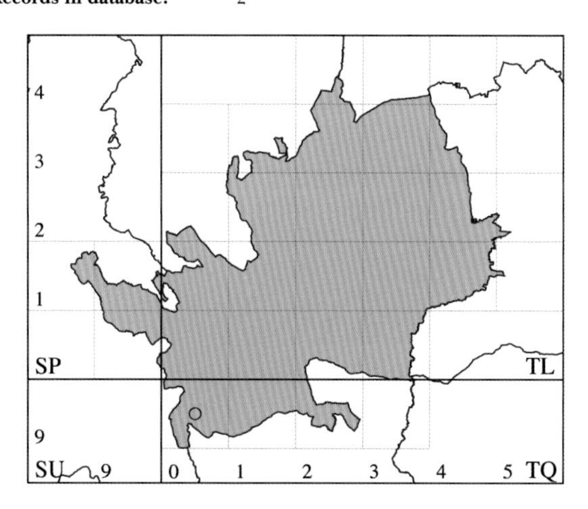

Gibbs (1902) records *sylvata* (Hb.) at Hitchin, one at light in 1902. Foster (1937) interprets this as '*Euchoeca testaceata* Don. (*Sylvata* Hb.)' – so even though the true author of *sylvata* is not Hübner it is clear which species is intended. The species is unexpected and it would be easy to dismiss this as an error, but there is one further record from a most reliable observer in the form of Eric Classey, at Rickmansworth in 1935 (in the archive of the Ruislip and District Natural History Society, per A. M. George).

1878 *Minoa murinata* (Scop.) Drab Looper

Recorded: 1902 – 1902
Distribution / Status: Absent / Posible former resident
Conservation status: UK BAP Priority Species. Herts Extinct
Caterpillar food plants: Not recorded. Elsewhere, on Wood Spurge
Flight period: Elsewhere, May/June
Records in database: 1

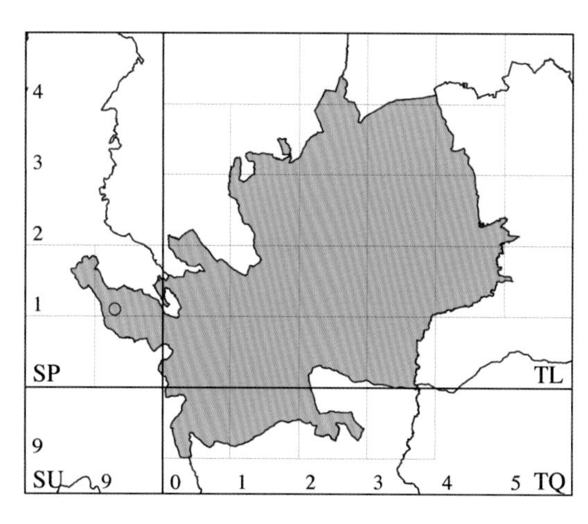

Foster (1937) lists 'Tring (Foulkes)'. The date is unknown, but Foulkes' name is absent from the list of '... contributors to this list whose records have been added since the 1902 list of Gibbs.' and so the record is presumed to relate to a nineteenth century report. The moth is currently found in the Gloucestershire/Herefordshire/Welsh Borders area and in a band running, approximately, from Dorset north-eastwards to Berkshire, with just two satellite sites in Kent (Parsons, et al, 2005).

1879 *Lobophora halterata* (Hufn.) Seraphim

Recorded: 1884 – 2006
Distribution / Status: Widespread / Common resident
Conservation status: Herts Stable
Caterpillar food plants: Aspen
Flight period: Late April to early June
Records in database: 77

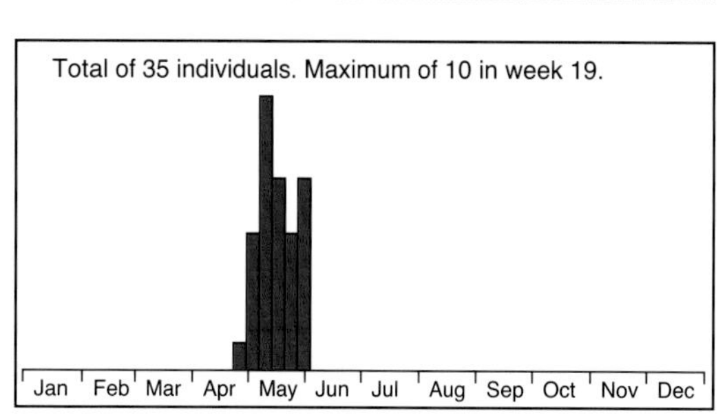

There is a striking absence of records from the north of the county; elsewhere, the moth is common and expected wherever there are Aspen trees. Examples are frequently, sent to me as an unidentified species, but the clue to the identity, at least of the males, lies in the scientific name. A 'haltere' is the vestigial hind wing appearing as a clubbed projection on the side of a fly (Diptera). An examination of the upper surface of the hind wings of a male Seraphim reveals the presence of what appears to be a very small third pair of wings.

1880 *Trichopteryx polycommata* ([D.& S.]) Barred Tooth-striped

Recorded: 1937 – 1937
Distribution / Status: Absent / Former resident
Conservation status: UK BAP Priority Species. Herts Extinct
Caterpillar food plants: Not recorded. Elsewhere, on Wild Privet and Ash
Flight period: March/April
Records in database: 1

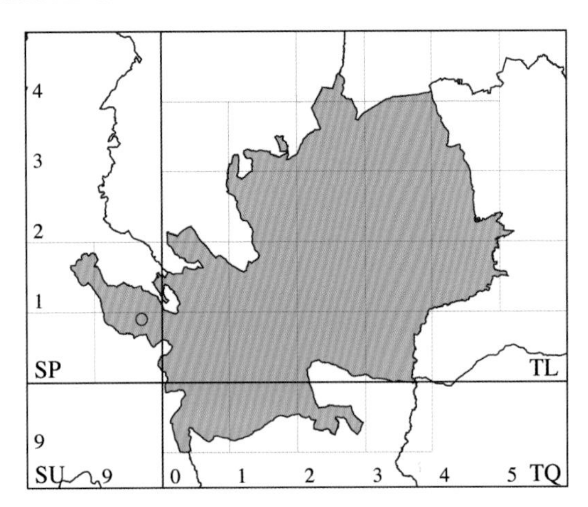

An example was taken at Northchurch Common by J. Bell in 1937 (Foster, 1942). Intensive searching for this moth undertaken by me and others during 2005, 2006 and 2007 has failed to reveal its presence and it must, regrettably, be presumed extinct with us.

1881 *Trichopteryx carpinata* (Borkh.) Early Tooth-striped

Recorded: 1936 – 1983
Distribution / Status: Absent / Former resident
Conservation status: Herts Extinct
Caterpillar food plants: Not recorded. Elsewhere, on Honeysuckle, sallow, birch and Alder
Flight period: April/May
Records in database: 11

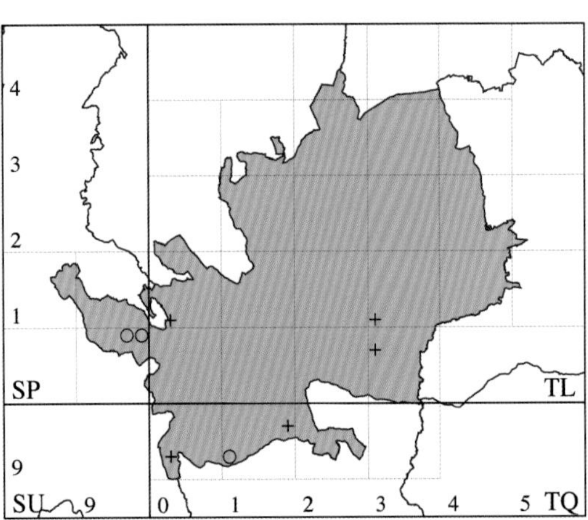

The lack of records for nearly a quarter of a century seems to suggest that this moth is no longer with us. It had a stronghold in Oxhey Wood, where Eric Classey caught several in 1936, 1937 and 1938 and it is also reported from Northchurch Common in 1939. Bell (1954) gives a record at Water End, 1952 (J. Donahaye), but the reliability of this record is called into question by some clear misidentifications elsewhere on the original list. It was caught at Borehamwood in 1968 by Gaston Prior, then at Bayfordbury in 1974 and Wormley Wood in 1977, both by Jim Reid. Ched George recorded it at Bottom Wood, Maple Cross on 15th April 1983 and this is the Hertfordshire dot on the map in my London moth book (Plant, 1993). We have no other records for Hertfordshire.

1882 *Pterapherapteryx sexalata* (Retz.) Small Seraphim

Recorded: 1884 – 2006
Distribution / Status: Widespread / Common resident
Conservation status: Herts Scarce
Caterpillar food plants: Not recorded. Elsewhere, on Sallow
Flight period: July/August
Records in database: 14

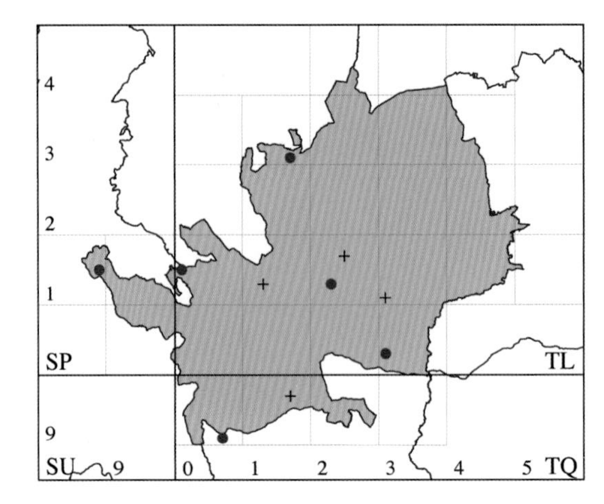

This small moth is possibly overlooked amongst the catch in damp sallow carr, though it comes readily to mv light traps. It is also sometimes found in damp woodlands that are not sallow-dominated, though the presence of at least one such bush is required.

1883 *Acasis viretata* (Hb.) Yellow-barred Brindle

Recorded: 1887 – 2006
Distribution / Status: Widespread / Common resident
Conservation status: Herts Stable
Caterpillar food plants: Not recorded. Elsewhere, on Holly, Ivy, Wild Privet, Dogwood and Guelder Rose (flowers and leaves)
Flight period: April to June then late July to early September, in two generations
Records in database: 2

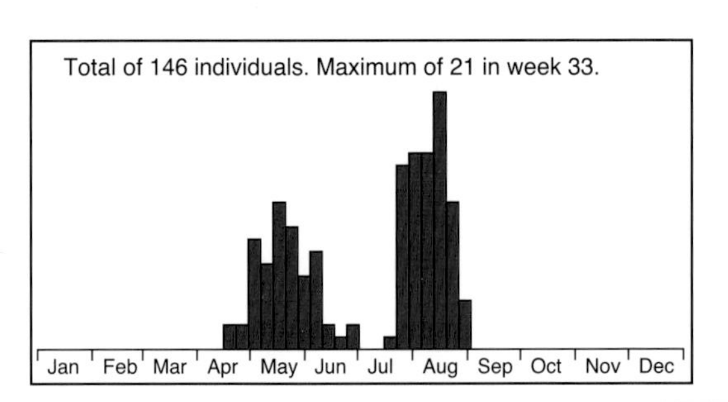

For reasons that are not at all clear to me, this is *the* moth most frequently brought to me for identification after the captor has failed to allocate a name (as distinct from species that have been allocated an incorrect name). Moths vary from green to yellow in hue; in worn examples the median fascia becomes more prominent. It is found widely across the county in several different habitat types.

ENNOMINAE

1884 *Abraxas grossulariata* (L.) Magpie

Recorded: 1887 – 2006
Distribution / Status: Widespread / Common resident
Conservation status: Herts Stable
Caterpillar food plants: Blackthorn; Gooseberry
Flight period: July/August
Records in database: 262

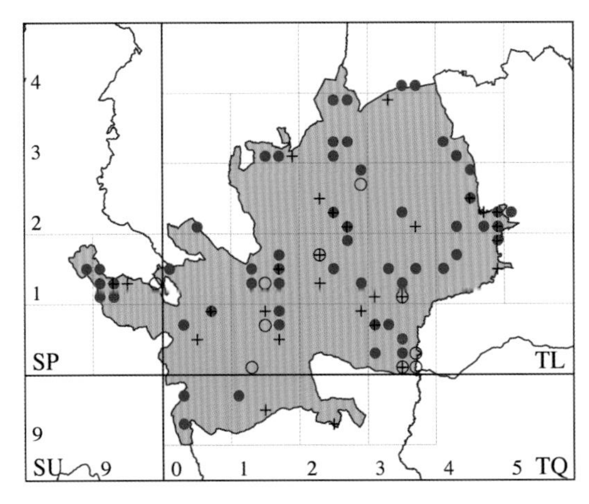

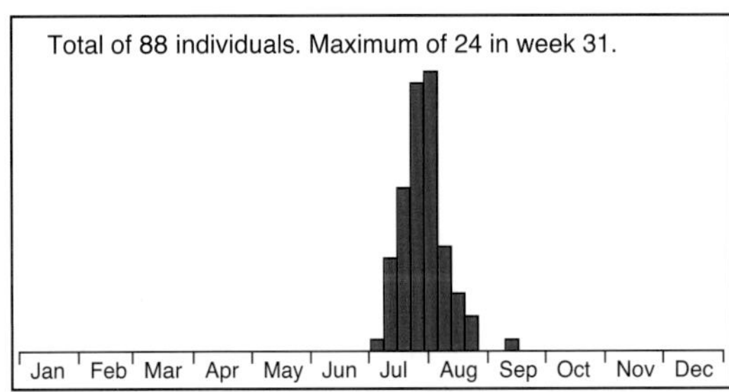

Foster (1937) remarks that the Magpie Moth was 'Common everywhere'. It was especially abundant in 1959 and Bell (1961) describes it as being '..... in amazing mid-summer profusion in the lanes of north-west Hertfordshire in that gloriously sunny summer'. Almost every garden and allotment was plagued with the larvae of this attractive moth in the early 1950s and it was regarded as a considerable pest. By the late 1980s, however, it had become scarce; by the early 1990s it was regarded as a 'nice' moth to catch. The reason for the drastic decline is probably the decline in the practice of fruit growing in domestic gardens – coinciding with the rise of a 'supermarket culture' from the 1960s onwards. However, in the early 2000s it appears to be on the increase again; gooseberries and blackcurrants planted in my garden in October 2005 were affected by several batches of larvae in 2006 for the first time in many years.

1885 *Abraxas sylvata* (Scop.) Clouded Magpie

Recorded: 1884 – 2006
Distribution / Status: Extremely local / Rare resident
Conservation status: Herts Vulnerable
Caterpillar food plants: Not recorded. Elsewhere, on Wych Elm and English Elm
Flight period: July
Records in database: 20

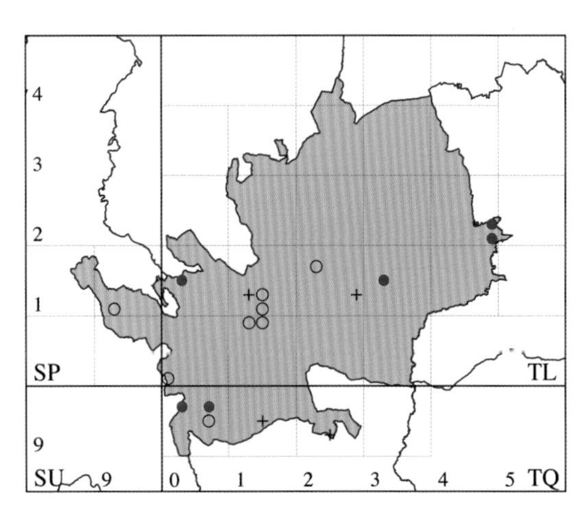

Past records indicate this to have been a common species up to at least the 1950s whilst present records indicate that it is now rare, though perhaps increasing again. However, we do not have adequate records to confirm the popularly held notion that the decline of this species coincided with the Dutch Elm disease epidemic of the 1970s – though this seems at least likely to have been a contributing factor. Though English Elm is eaten by the larvae, present populations appear to be associated with Wych Elm – a species that generally survived the disease. The undisputed decline may have been governed by other factors.

1887 *Lomaspilis marginata* (L.) Clouded Border

Recorded: 1884 – 2006
Distribution / Status: Widespread / Common resident
Conservation status: Herts Stable
Caterpillar food plants: Sallow
Flight period: May to August
Records in database: 565

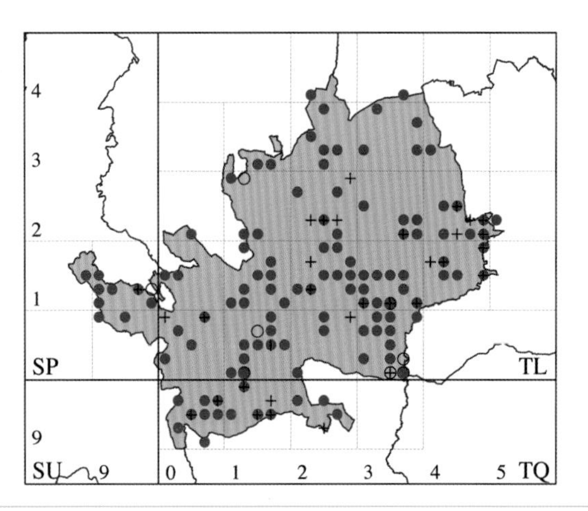

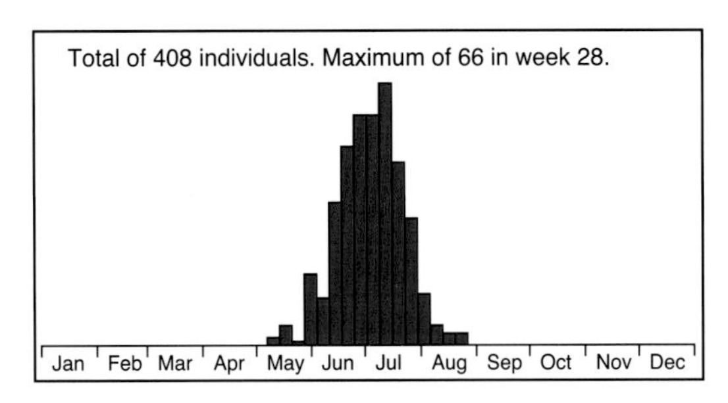

The Clouded Border is expected on most trapping sessions in Hertfordshire between mid-May and mid-August. There is considerable variation in the extent of black markings between individual moths, but no particular geographical or seasonal trend towards more or fewer markings is discernible.

1888 *Ligdia adustata* ([D.& S.]) Scorched Carpet

Recorded: 1829 – 2006
Distribution / Status: Widespread / Common resident
Conservation status: Herts Stable
Caterpillar food plants: Not recorded. Elsewhere, on Spindle
Flight period: April to August in two generations
Records in database: 369

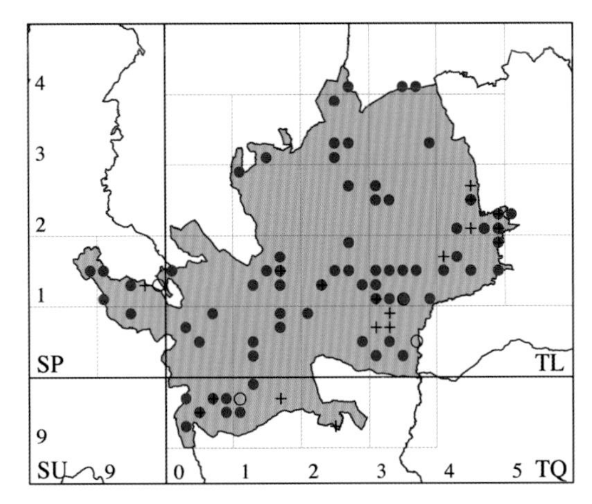

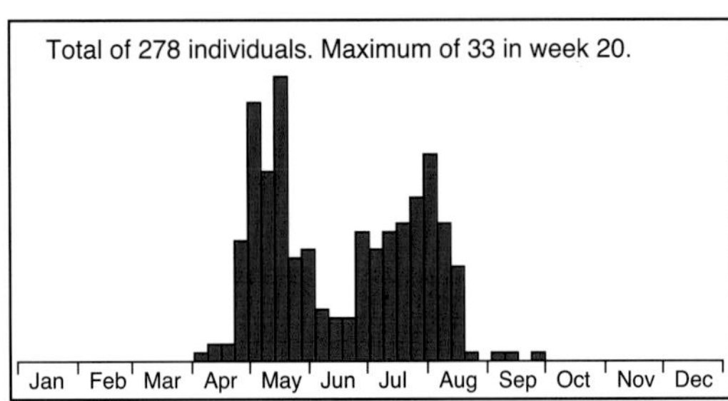

Adults appear in two peaks, as indicated in the chart, but these are separated in any given year so that the impression given by the chart that moths can be found all summer long is a false one. All of the September records shown were made in 2006, suggesting a partial third generation in that year only.

1889 *Macaria notata* (L.) Peacock Moth

Recorded: 1867 – 2006
Distribution / Status: Local / Uncommon resident; ?Immigrant
Conservation status: Stable
Caterpillar food plants: Not recorded. Elsewhere, on birch
Flight period: May to August, probably in two generations
Records in database: 50

The seasonal spread of records is in keeping with the appearance of two adult generations elsewhere in the south of England, although the numbers in the chart are too low for the

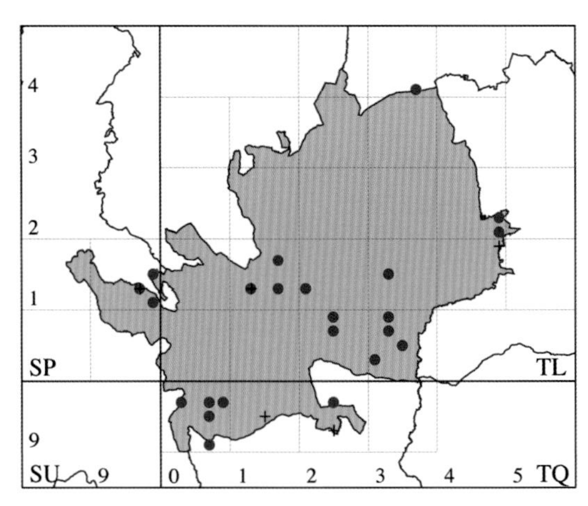

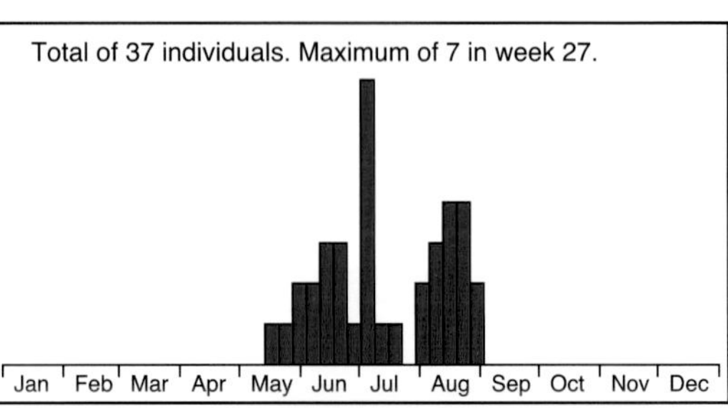

apparent peaks to be significant. Although certainly resident, there may also be evidence of immigration or vagrancy: On 5th August 2006 I caught one in my garden for the first time here after continuous trapping since October 1986; The following night, 6th August 2006 James Fish and Julian Reeves also took it for the first time in eleven years of trapping in their adjoining gardens elsewhere in Bishops Stortford – a remarkable co-incidence. There was considerable immigrant activity at the time.

1891 *Macaria signaria* (Hb.) Dusky Peacock

Recorded: 1992 – 1992
Distribution / Status: Random / Rare immigrant
Conservation status: -
Caterpillar food plants: Elsewhere, on various conifers
Flight period: July
Records in database: 1

Our only record is of one in the light trap on the Rothamsted Estate, Harpenden on 2nd July 1992 (Adrian Riley).

1893 *Macaria liturata* (Cl.) Tawny-barred Angle

Recorded: 1884 – 2006
Distribution / Status: Widespread / Common resident
Conservation status: Herts Stable
Caterpillar food plants: Scots Pine. Elsewhere also on Spruce
Flight period: May to August
Records in database: 227

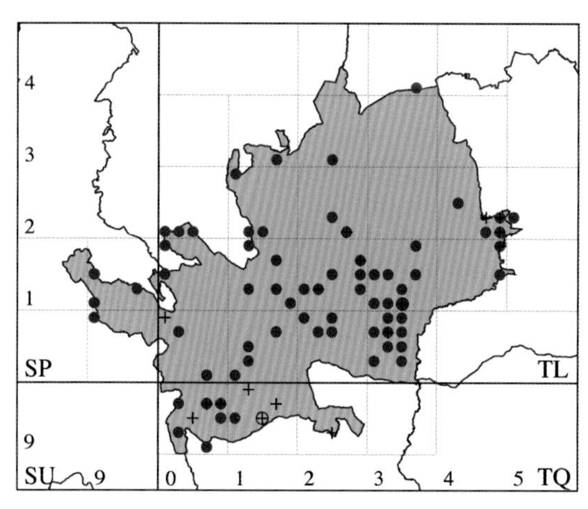

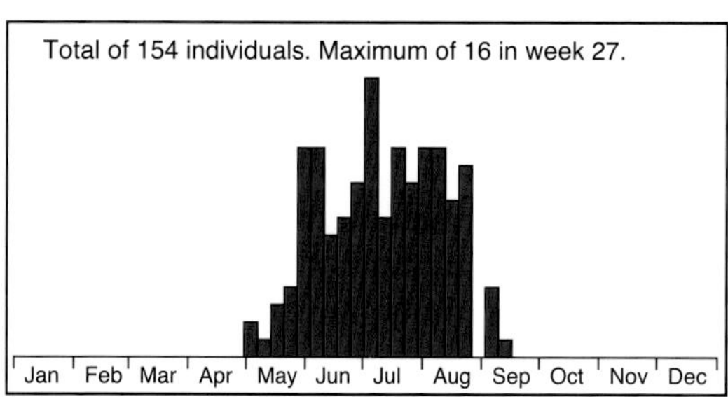

The melanic form *nigrofulvata* Collins is currently common in Hertfordshire – perhaps affecting 40 per cent of examples caught. Ian Lorimer noted that at Totteridge these melanic forms started to appear in 1969, but were still uncommon by 1979 (his trap was operated from 1954 to 1980). Unfortunately Ian retired to Orkney and so there is no later data from that site. There is no comparative data from any other Hertfordshire sites.

1894 *Chiasmia clathrata* (L.) Latticed Heath

Recorded:	1828 – 2006
Distribution / Status:	Local / Uncommon resident
Conservation status:	UK BAP Watch List. Herts Threatened
Caterpillar food plants:	Not recorded. Elsewhere, on clovers and trefoils
Flight period:	May to September
Records in database:	159

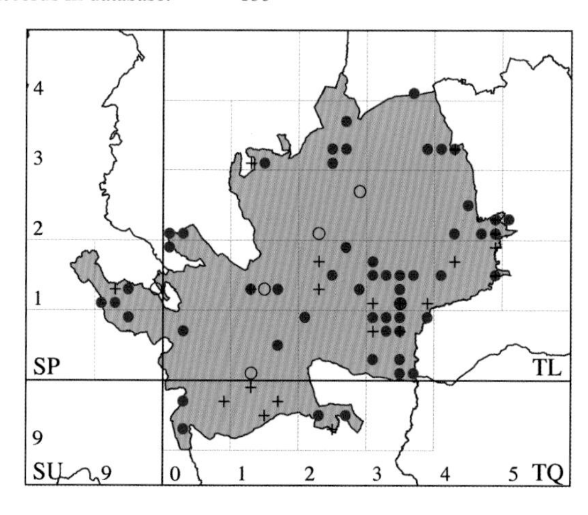

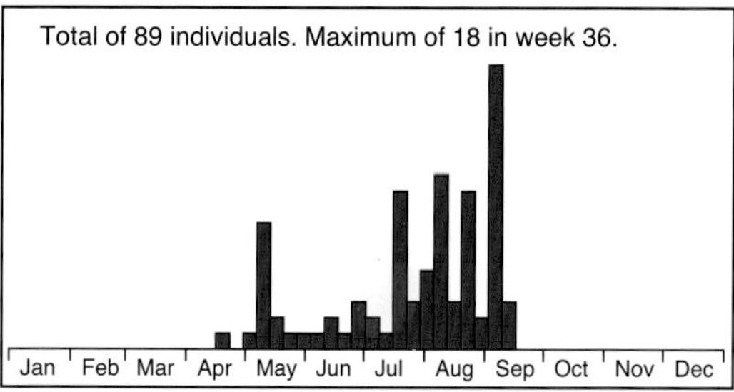

At the national level, the population of the Latticed Heath has apparently declined by 87 per cent since 1970. The Hertfordshire data indicates a failure to record the moth in the post-1994 period from 19 of the total of 52 tetrads in which there is any record – theoretically suggesting a loss from 37 per cent of sites. This should be weighed against a measure of under-recording. It was widely reported in the nineteenth century and listed as 'Usually abundant in all districts' in Foster's 1937 county list. Where it is found today it is common. There are probably two generations of adults per year, as elsewhere in the south of England, but the separate peaks are hard to discern in the chart because of the low overall numbers plotted.

1896 *Itame brunneata* (Thunb.) Rannoch Looper

Recorded:	1920 – 1960
Distribution / Status:	Random / Rare immigrant
Conservation status:	-
Caterpillar food plants:	Elsewhere, on Bilberry
Flight period:	Elsewhere, June/July
Records in database:	2

There is a reference to this species for Hertfordshire in Meyrick's *Revised handbook* (1928: 280). Since there are no other literature records for the county prior to 1928 this presumably certainly relates to the example caught in Bishops Stortford by C. Mellows on 25th June 1920 and reported in *Entomologist* **53**: 236. Another was taken in a light trap at Ashridge by A. L. Goodson on 2nd July 1960, reported by Bretherton in the *Proceedings of the British Entomological and Natural History Society* **1972**: 118. The date of 2nd August given in the 1960 Migration Report by French (*Entomologist* **95**: 211) is wrong; Bernard Skinner has kindly examined the specimen in the Natural History Museum and confirms that the data label reads 2nd July. According to Bell (1962) this particular moth was 'somewhat larger and paler than the Scottish ones'. It was one of eight immigrant examples recorded in southern Britain during 1960, other good years being 1920, with 10 reported, and 1956, with 8 reported (Skinner, 1984; 1998).

1897 *Macaria wauaria* (L.) V-Moth

Recorded:	1884 – 2004
Distribution / Status:	Extremely local or absent / Former or very rare resident
Conservation status:	UK BAP Watch List. Herts Endangered
Caterpillar food plants:	Blackcurrant. Elsewhere also on Redcurrant and Gooseberry
Flight period:	July to mid-August
Records in database:	56

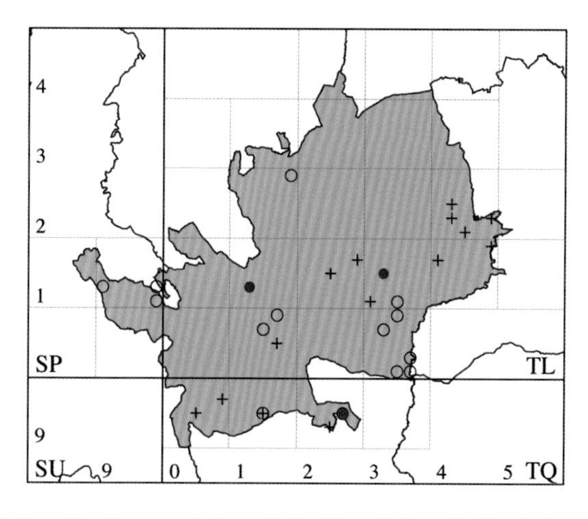

Nationally, the population of the V-moth has declined 97 per cent since the year 1970. In Hertfordshire, our only post-1994 records (the solid dots on the map) are for 1996 and 1998 Hertford (Andrew Wood), 1999 Harpenden (Adrian Riley) and

2004 East Barnet (Peter Alton). On the basis of recorded map tetrads, therefore, this moth has declined here by 90 per cent — a value that closely reflects the national picture. The decline in Hertfordshire appears to be genuine as the moth has been specifically searched for in several of its former haunts. The demise of the allotment garden may, of course, be responsible for some of the losses, which appear to have taken place, principally, during the 1960s and 1970s, since the literature suggests that it was still widespread and common in 1959 and personal experience demonstrates that it was rare by 1986. An additional cause might be over-zealous winter pruning and burning (the eggs overwinter on the plants); it is not hard to imagine that 'in the old days' composting might have been favoured over burning in many fruit gardens.

[1901 *Cepphis advenaria* (Hb.) Little Thorn

Recorded only from Haileybury by Stockley (listed in Foster, 1937). This record cannot be substantiated. However, Foster (1942) later has J. Bell recording 'several at light' at Northchurch – without date or comment, but probably during the 1930s. This record, also, cannot be accepted on present evidence].

1902 *Petrophora chlorosata* (Scop.) Brown Silver-line

Recorded: 1828 – 2006
Distribution / Status: Widespread / Abundant resident
Conservation status: Herts Stable
Caterpillar food plants: Bracken
Flight period: Mid-April to early July
Records in database: 146

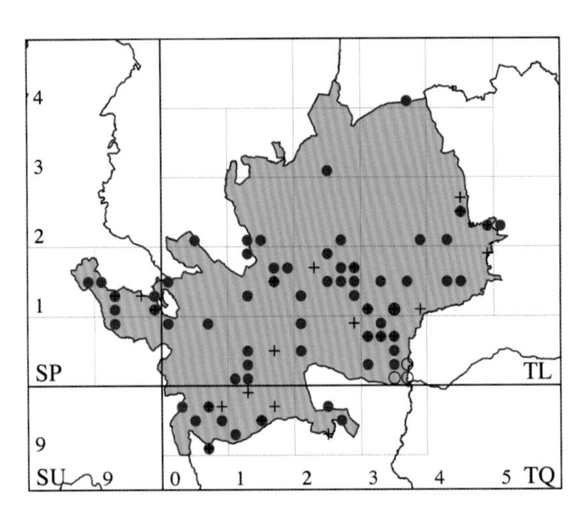

Large tracts of bracken are not a prominent feature of Hertfordshire, but it appears that even small patches of the plant in lanes and small woodlands can support the Brown Silver-line – which may sometimes attend light traps in colossal numbers on balmy evenings.

1903 *Plagodis pulveraria* (L.) Barred Umber

Recorded: 1888 – 2006
Distribution / Status: Extremely local / Rare resident
Conservation status: Herts Rare
Caterpillar food plants: Not recorded. Elsewhere, on sallow, Hazel, hawthorn and birch
Flight period: May/June
Records in database: 8

Gibbs (1889; 1892) records this species in Bricket Wood and Bowyer (1888) includes it in the list for Haileybury. Foster (1937) adds Broxbourne Woods and Berkhamsted. Hodgson (1939) notes that the moth was scarce and irregular at light at Ashridge, High Scrubs Wood and Long Green Berkhamsted and so it was with some interest that I caught one at Hares

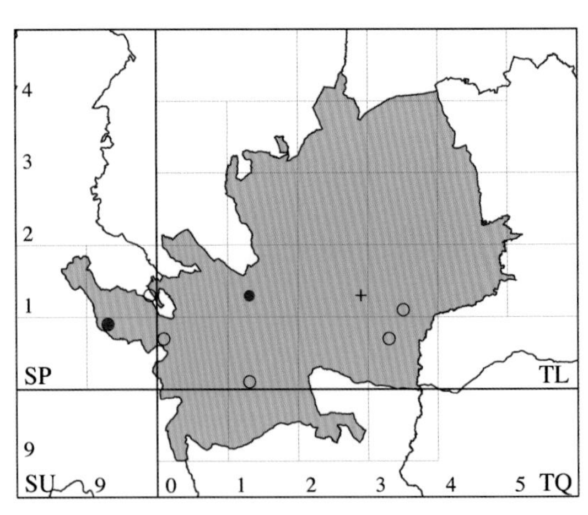

Garden Wood – a continuation of High Scrubs Wood – on 10th May 2004 after a gap of 65 years. The only other records are from Panshanger Park on 6th June 1971 (Tom Gladwin) and on the Rothamsted Estate and Harpenden during 1999 (Adrian Riley), these latter two most likely to have been vagrant examples.

1904 *Plagodis dolabraria* (L.) Scorched Wing

Recorded: 1887 – 2006
Distribution / Status: Widespread / Common resident
Conservation status: Herts Stable
Caterpillar food plants: Not recorded. Elsewhere, on oak, birch, sallow and other trees
Flight period: Late May to early June
Records in database: 323

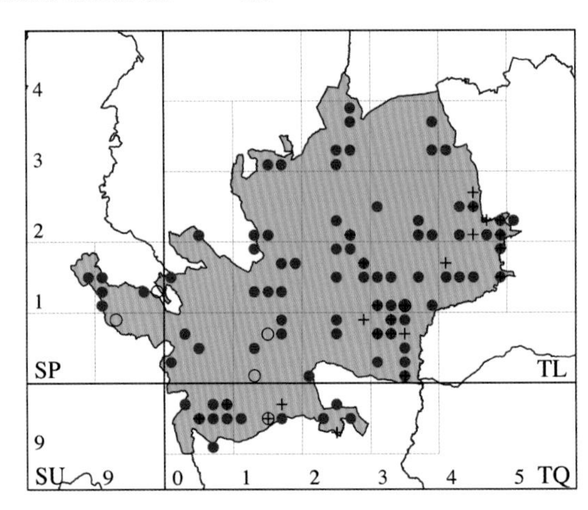

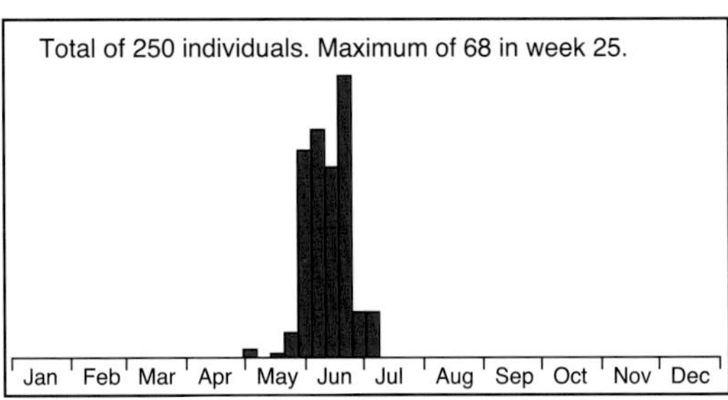

Skinner (1998) notes that males dominate light trap samples; this is certainly the case in Hertfordshire, where the number of reported females is minuscule.

1905 *Pachycnemia hippocastanaria* (Hb.) Horse Chestnut

Recorded: 1966 – 1966
Distribution / Status: Absent / Former vagrant
Conservation status: -
Caterpillar food plants: Not recorded. Elsewhere, on Heather
Flight period: Elsewhere, May and August
Records in database: 1

A male at Totteridge on 17th September 1966 by Ian Lorimer is the only valid Hertfordshire record. The record for August 1958 in Penrose (1980) is almost certainly an identification error and is excluded from the database.

1906 *Opisthograptis luteolata* (L.) Brimstone Moth

Recorded: 1884 – 2006
Distribution / Status: Ubiquitous / Abundant resident
Conservation status: Herts Stable
Caterpillar food plants: Blackthorn and Common Hawthorn. Elsewhere, also on other rosaceous trees and shrubs
Flight period: April to October
Records in database: 2,339

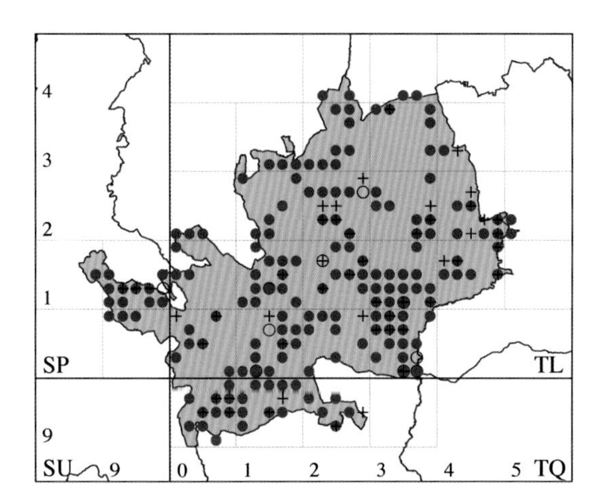

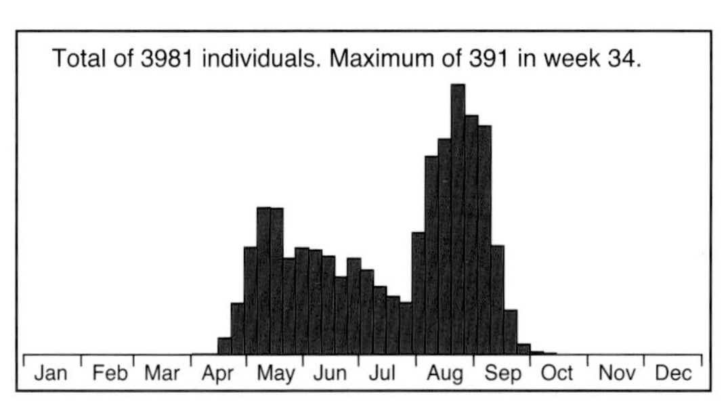

The Brimstone is the fifth most reported moth in Hertfordshire. Adults are on the wing from April to October and our data support the statement by Skinner (1998) that there are three broods spread over two years. A specimen of ab. *nebulosa* West was taken at Totteridge in 1963 (Ian Lorimer) and illustrated in the report of the Annual Exhibition of the South London Entomological and Natural History Society for that year, also mentioned in West (2004).

1907 *Epione repandaria* (Hufn.) Bordered Beauty

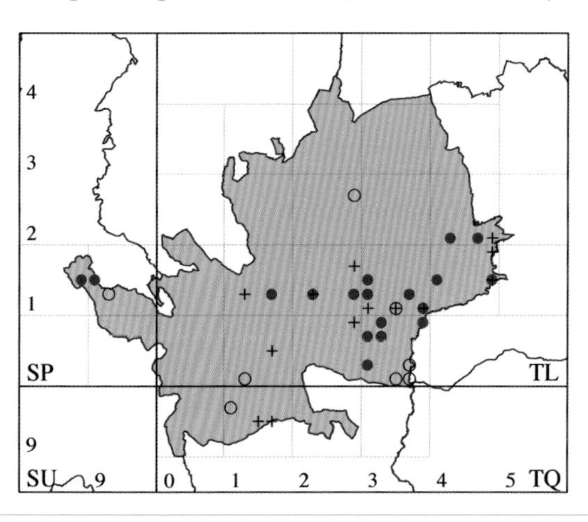

Recorded: 1887 – 2006
Distribution / Status: Local – declining / Uncommon resident
Conservation status: Herts Vulnerable
Caterpillar food plants: Sallow
Flight period: Late June to September
Records in database: 49

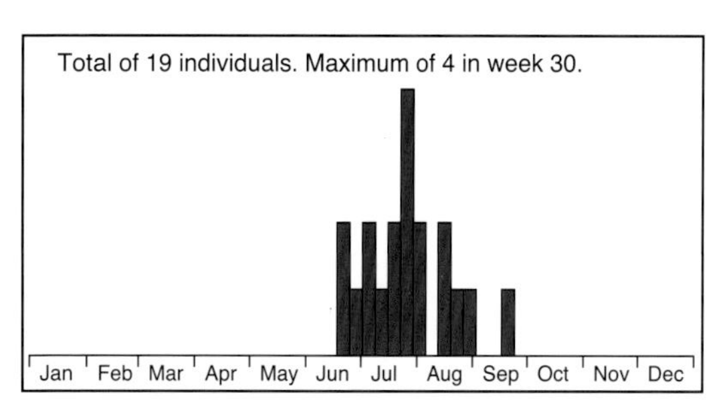

Damp woodland, with a high proportion of sallow and areas of rank vegetation is the ideal site for the Bordered Beauty, which appears to have vanished from 49 per cent of its recorded sites in the county. The causes of the decline are not clear, but are almost certainly linked to habitat loss, both through development and as a result of the drastically reduced 'water table'.

1909 *Pseudopanthera macularia* (L.) Speckled Yellow

Recorded: 1884 – 2006
Distribution / Status: Local / Common resident
Conservation status: Herts Scarce
Caterpillar food plants: Wood Sage
Flight period: May/June
Records in database: 46

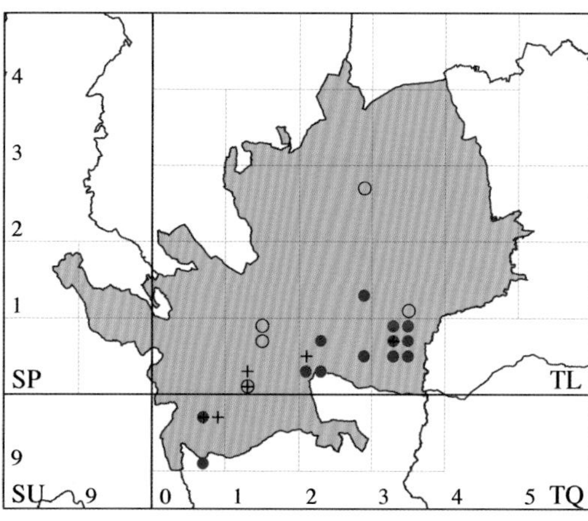

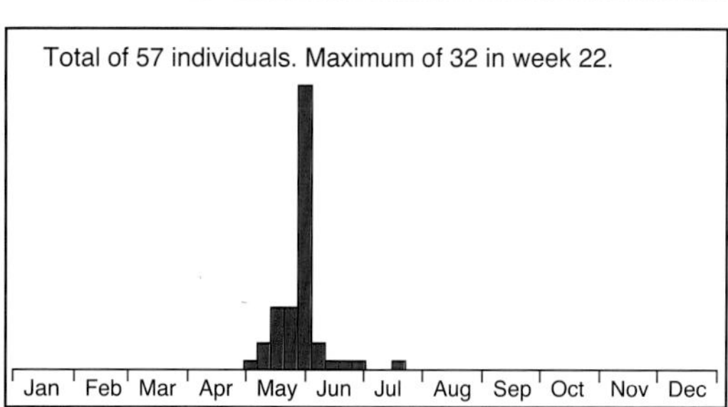

Broad-leaved woodland in the south of the county with wide rides that contain the foodplant support the Speckled Yellow, which flies in the afternoon sunshine, often in large numbers. It is not expected to be found in many other places where it is not already recorded.

1910 *Apeira syringaria* (L.) Lilac Beauty

Recorded: 1884 – 2006
Distribution / Status: Widespread / Common resident
Conservation status: Herts Stable

Caterpillar food plants:	Wild Honeysuckle. Elsewhere, also on Wild Privet and Ash
Flight period:	June/July and a small second generation in August/September
Records in database:	162

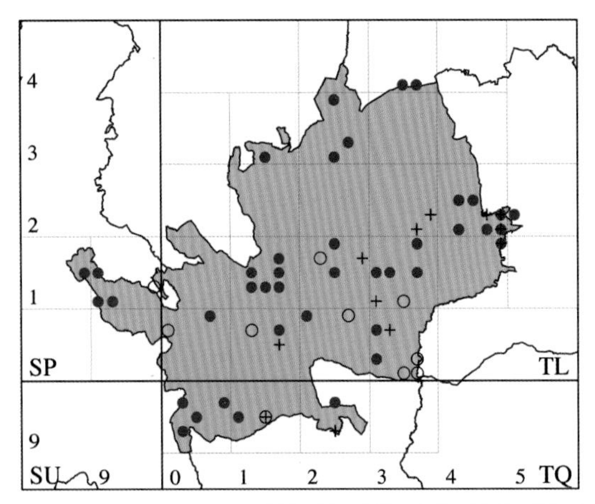

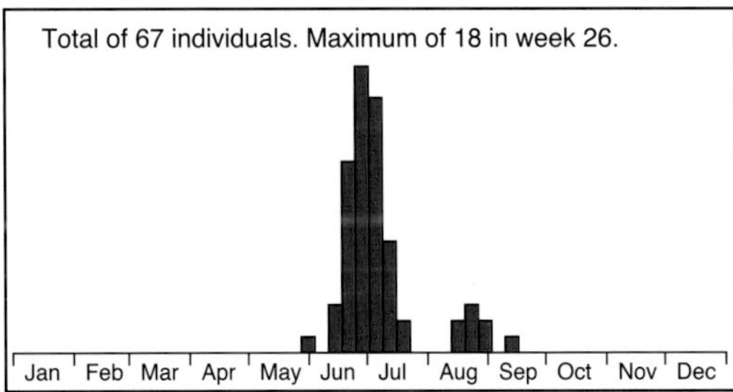

The moth is expected at most sites in Hertfordshire. The small second generation of adults indicated in the flight chart has been observed from 2002 to 2006 and is apparently a new phenomenon.

1911 *Ennomos autumnaria* (Wern.) Large Thorn

Recorded:	1954 – 2006
Distribution / Status:	Local / Uncommon resident
Conservation status:	Herts Scarce
Caterpillar food plants:	Not recorded. Elsewhere, on various trees
Flight period:	September
Records in database:	33

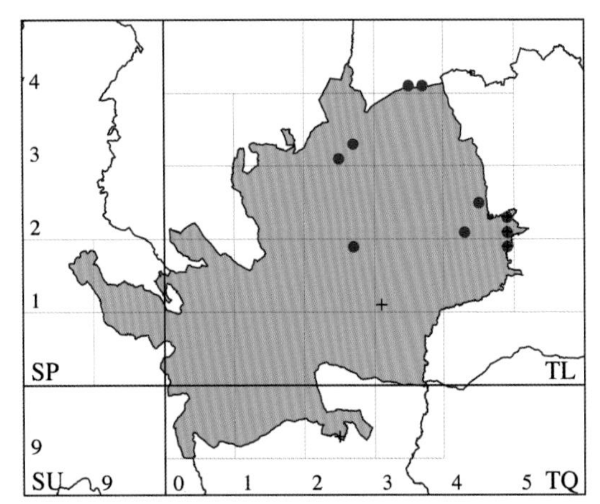

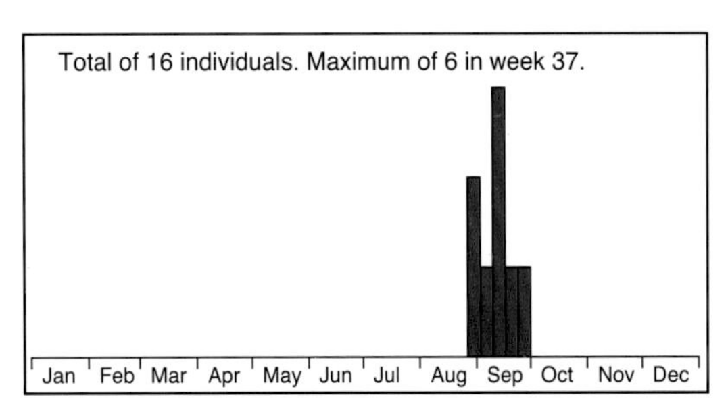

Two at Sawbridgeworth Marsh in 1954 (D. Oldacre), three at light in Bishops Stortford in 'autumn' 1954 at Geoffrey Sell's garden and four in Clifford Craufurd's trap [Galloway Road, Bishops Stortford] between 26 and 30 September 1955 (Bell, 1957) are evidently the first county records. All known Hertfordshire records are mapped. The moth is confined to the north-east half of the county and provides a mirror image of the distribution of 1912: August Thorn, which is rare in the north-east, but frequent in the south-west. Why these two species appear to be almost mutually exclusive is quite unknown. In the London Area the distribution is similarly confined to the extreme east (Plant, 1993). There are signs that the Large Thorn has declined in numbers over the past ten years; it is, for example, now a rare capture in my garden trap in Bishops Stortford having been a regular visitor in the late 1980s and early 1990s.

1912 *Ennomos quercinaria* (Hufn.) August Thorn

Recorded:	1884 – 2006
Distribution / Status:	Local / Common resident
Conservation status:	UK BAP Watch List. Herts Stable
Caterpillar food plants:	Not recorded. Elsewhere, on various trees
Flight period:	July to September
Records in database:	62

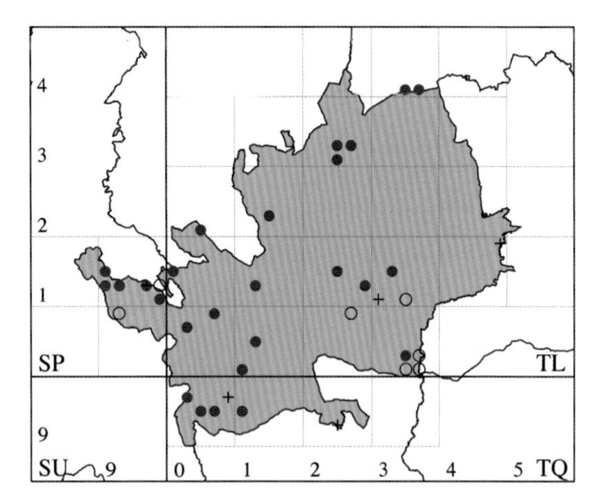

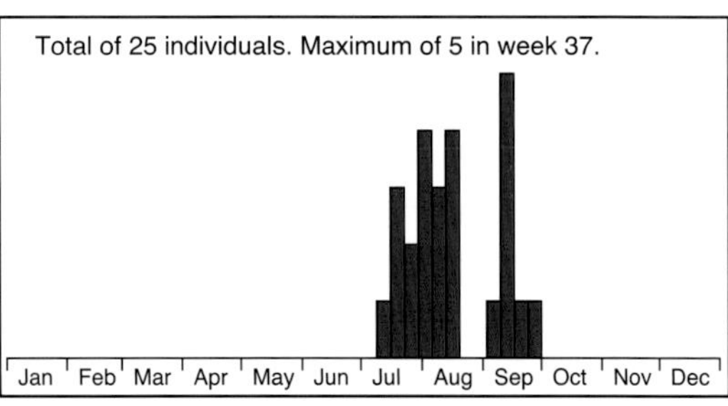

As discussed under the last species, the distribution of the August Thorn is a mirror-image of that for 1911: Large Thorn and the only range overlap seems to be in the north of the county; the lack of records in the north-east sector reflects the real situation. The August Thorn is thought to be declining in numbers at the national level, but there is no evidence of any such reduction in Hertfordshire.

1913 *Ennomos alniaria* (L.) Canary-shouldered Thorn

Recorded:	1884 – 2006
Distribution / Status:	Widespread / Common resident
Conservation status:	Stable
Caterpillar food plants:	Alder and Sallow. Elsewhere, on various trees
Flight period:	Late July to early September
Records in database:	221

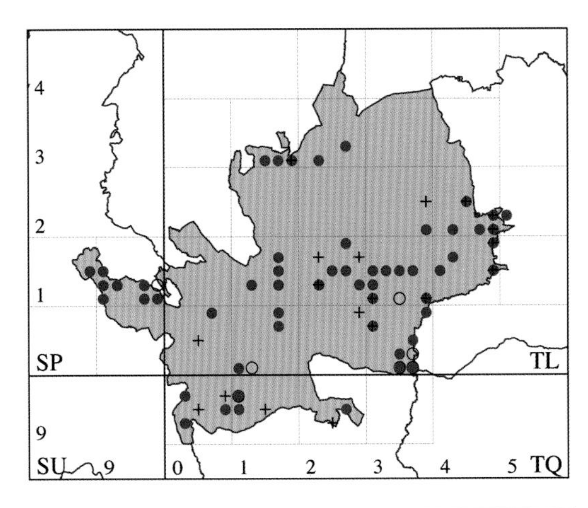

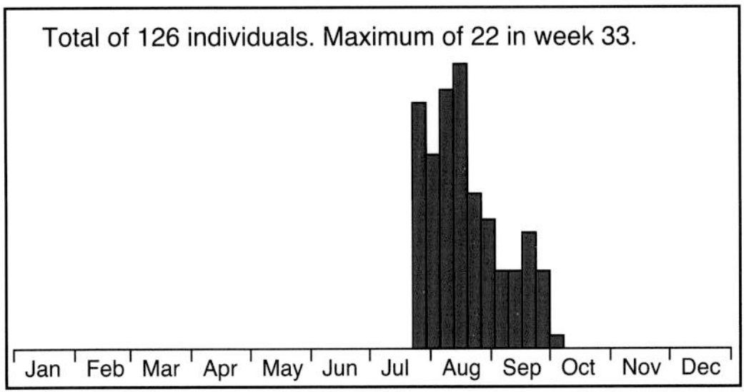

Readily distinguished by the canary yellow thorax, this is a very common species, especially in woodlands but also in gardens and most other habitats.

1914 *Ennomos fuscantaria* (Haw.) Dusky Thorn

Recorded:	1883 – 2006
Distribution / Status:	Widespread / Uncommon resident
Conservation status:	UK BAP Watch List
Caterpillar food plants:	Ash
Flight period:	Late July to September
Records in database:	555

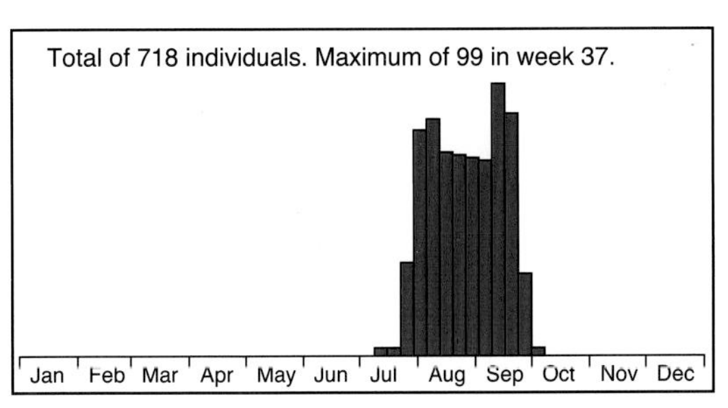

There has been an apparent national population decline of 98 per cent since 1970. Our map shows 21 tetrads from which it has been recorded in the past, but not since the end of 1994, suggesting a possible loss from 24 per cent of Hertfordshire sites. Although the general feeling is that the decline is artificial (a function, to some degree, of under-recording), and that the Dusky Thorn is still numerically common here, our results must be treated as an early warning that, perhaps, all is not rosy in the garden.

1915 *Ennomos erosaria* ([D.& S.]) September Thorn

Recorded:	1828 – 2006
Distribution / Status:	Local / Uncommon resident
Conservation status:	UK BAP Watch List. Herts Threatened
Caterpillar food plants:	Not recorded. Elsewhere, on oak, lime and birch
Flight period:	July and August
Records in database:	66

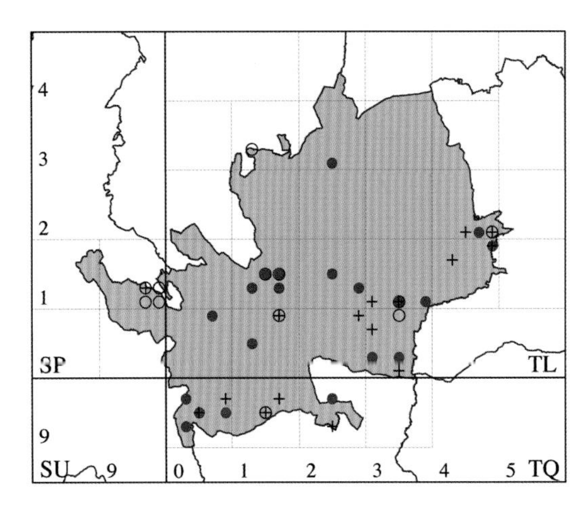

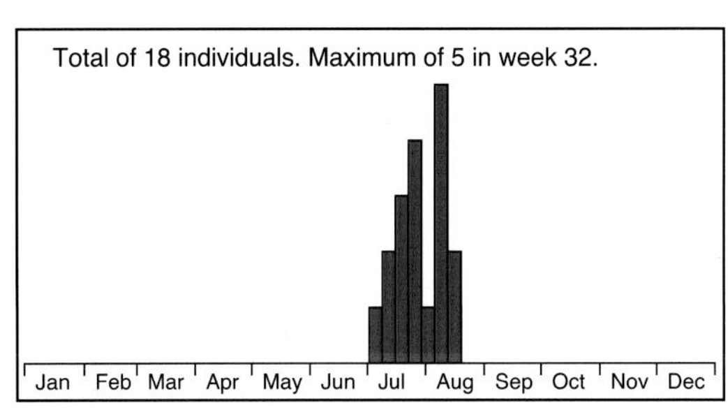

The September Thorn has never been especially numerous in Hertfordshire, though it is present in a reasonable number of sites in the south of the county. The map shows a possible loss from 47 per cent of all recorded sites and this should be interpreted in the light of 91 per cent population decline, nationally, since 1970.

1917 *Selenia dentaria* (Fabr.) Early Thorn

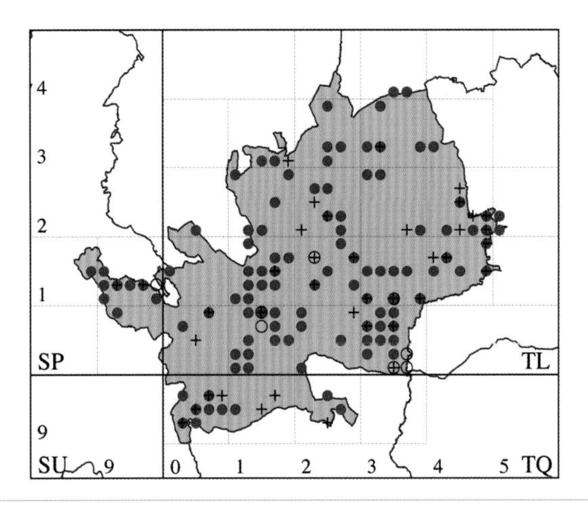

Recorded:	1884 – 2006
Distribution / Status:	Widespread / Common resident
Conservation status:	Herts Stable
Caterpillar food plants:	Not recorded. Elsewhere, on various trees
Flight period:	March/April then July/August in two generations
Records in database:	640

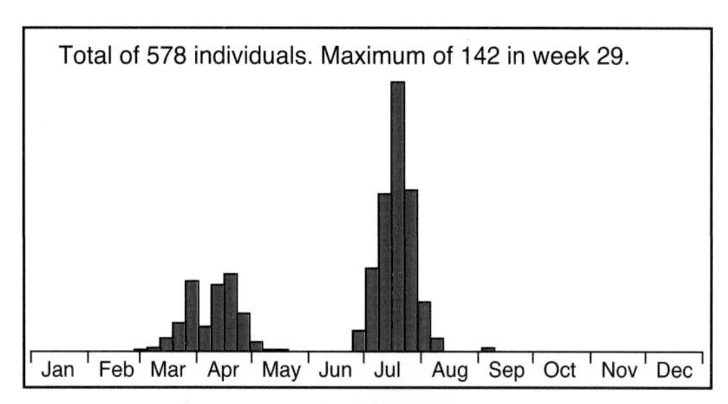

The males and females of Early Thorn are of different appearance and both differ between the spring and summer generation. All rest with wings firmly closed over the back in the manner of a butterfly – a fact that easily separates them from the Purple Thorn which flies at the same time, but rests more like a Skipper with wings partly open (see the two pictures on this page).

1918 *Selenia lunularia* (Hb.) Lunar Thorn

Recorded:	1887 – 2006
Distribution / Status:	Local / Uncommon resident
Conservation status:	Herts Threatened
Caterpillar food plants:	Not recorded. Elsewhere, on oak, ash and birch
Flight period:	May/June
Records in database:	29

The Lunar Thorn flies between the two generations of both 1917: Early Thorn and 1919: Purple Thorn and earlier in the year than other thorns, so that identification is rather easy. This is a far from common moth in Hertfordshire and rather

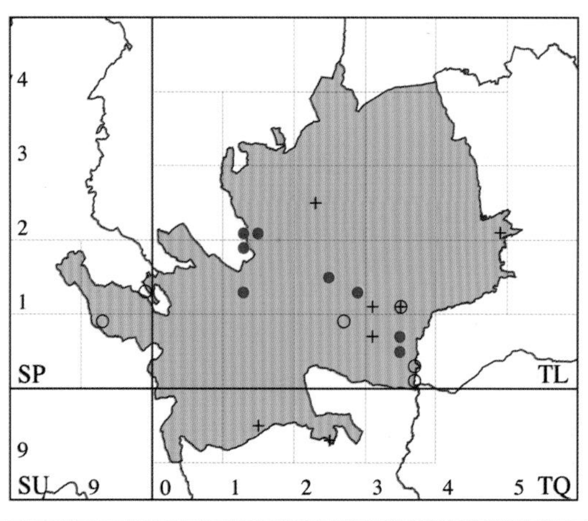

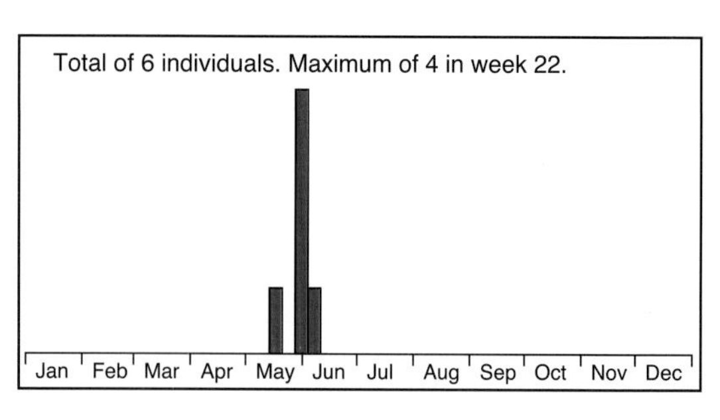

worryingly the map suggests that we have lost it from 60 per cent of recorded map tetrads; it is treated as Threatened in the county. Rather few records are from gardens and the moth is more or less confined to woodlands.

1919 *Selenia tetralunaria* (Hufn.) Purple Thorn

Recorded:	1893 – 2006
Distribution / Status:	Widespread / Common resident
Conservation status:	Herts Stable
Caterpillar food plants:	English Oak and Ash. Elsewhere, on various other trees
Flight period:	April/May then July/August in two generations
Records in database:	285

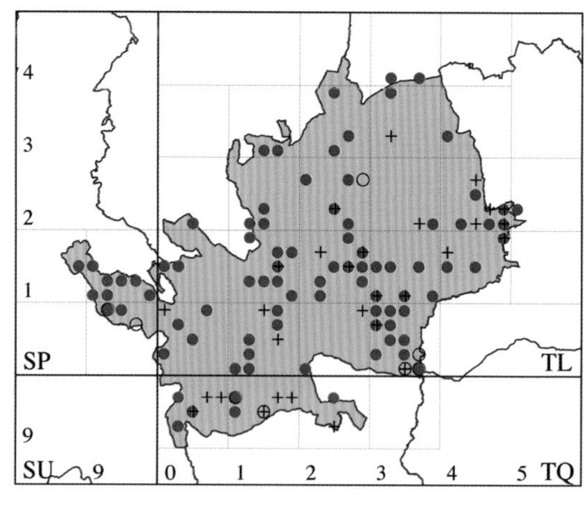

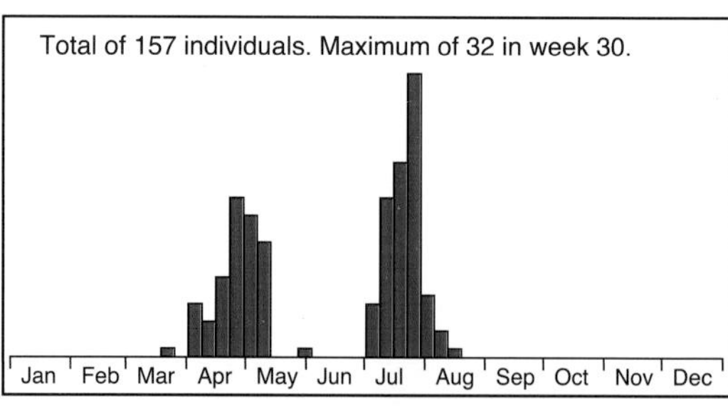

Though more at home in woodland, this moth is also found from time to time in garden moth traps and is expected on most site lists. Nevertheless, the map shows an apparent loss from 17 per cent of recorded sites since the end of 1994.

1920 *Odontopera bidentata* (Cl.) Scalloped Hazel

Recorded:	1884 – 2006
Distribution / Status:	Widespread / Common resident
Conservation status:	Herts Stable
Caterpillar food plants:	Garden Privet. Elsewhere, on a range of deciduous and coniferous trees
Flight period:	Late April to June
Records in database:	328

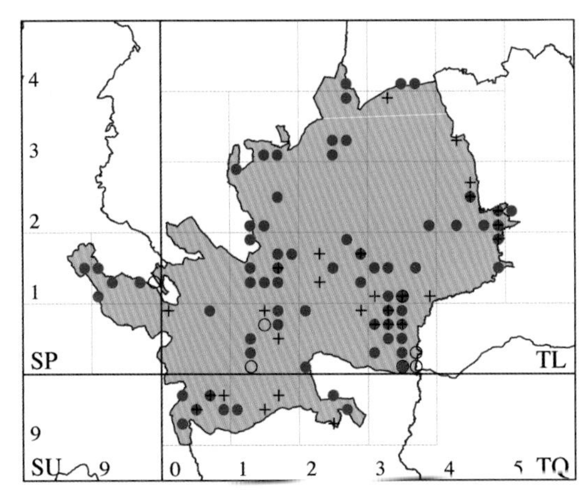

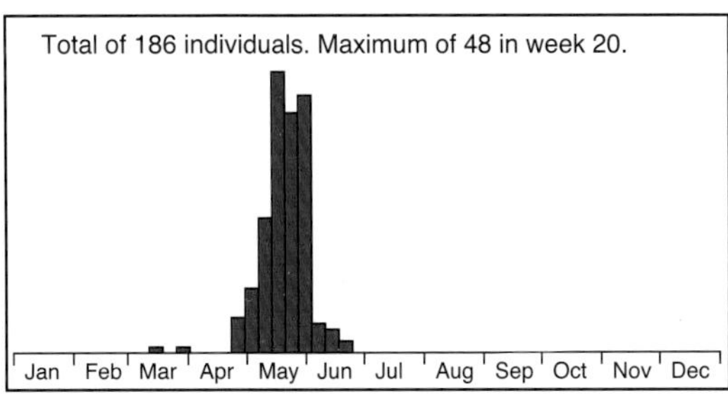

The Scalloped Hazel is amongst the most frequent moths on site lists. The melanic ab. *nigra* Prout, which is more or less unmarked and dark brown is occasionally encountered, but affects only a very few examples and is regarded as a rarity in Hertfordshire.

1921 *Crocallis elinguaria* (L.) Scalloped Oak

Recorded:	1884 – 2006
Distribution / Status:	Ubiquitous / Common resident
Conservation status:	Herts Stable
Caterpillar food plants:	Not recorded. Elsewhere, on various trees
Flight period:	Late June to early September
Records in database:	1065

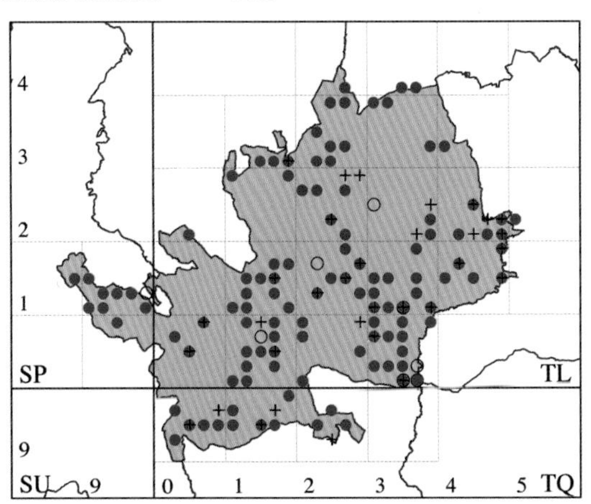

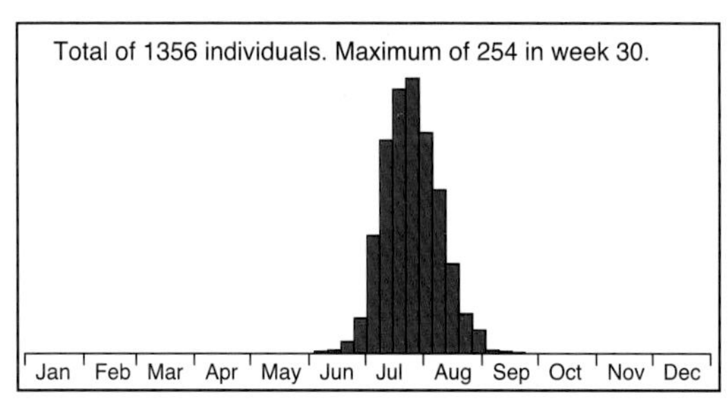

With 1,065 records in the database, the Scalloped Oak ranks 31st in the 'league table' of Hertfordshire moth records. It is expected everywhere, though rarely are more than two or three examples present themselves in a single night's captures.

1922 *Ourapteryx sambucaria* (L.) Swallow-tailed Moth

Recorded:	1884 – 2006
Distribution / Status:	Widespread / Common resident
Conservation status:	Herts Stable
Caterpillar food plants:	Domestic Apple; Blackthorn; Hawthorn.
Flight period:	Mid-June to mid-August
Records in database:	731

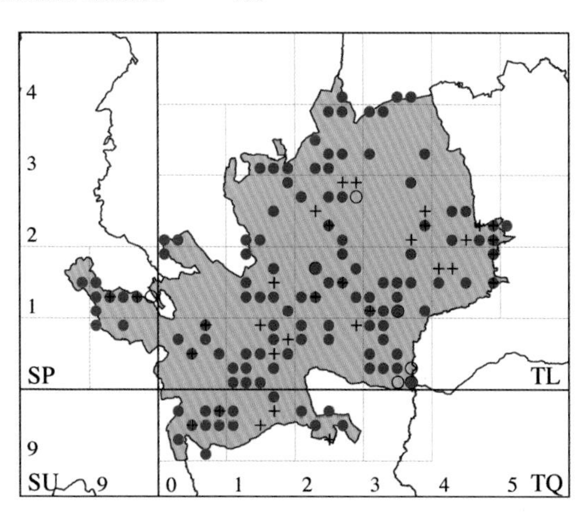

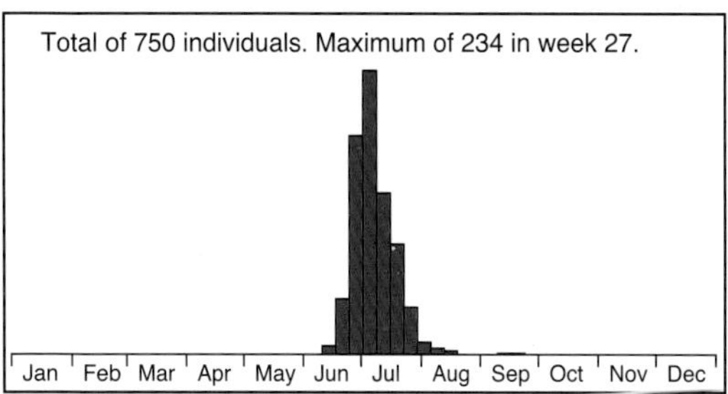

The larvae of the Swallow-tailed Moth are 'stick caterpillars', camouflaged to resemble twigs, and can be very hard to find. If using a beating tray it is a good idea not to be too hasty to shake out the debris – allow it time to start moving!

1923 *Colotois pennaria* (L.) Feathered Thorn

Recorded:	1884 – 2006
Distribution / Status:	Widespread / Common resident
Conservation status:	Herts Stable
Caterpillar food plants:	Hornbeam, Silver Birch, Wild Rose, sallow, Blackthorn
Flight period:	October/November
Records in database:	450

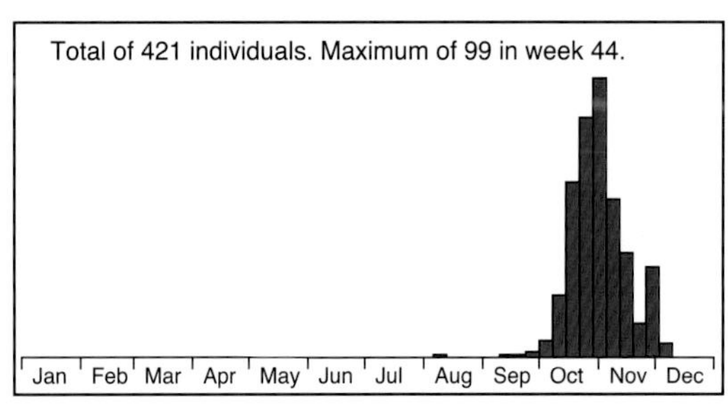

Almost all adult records relate to male moths and it seems that the female is uncommon at mv or actinic light. However, females can be quite easily found by walking through the woods with a lamp and netting them as they fly about.

1924 *Angerona prunaria* (L.) Orange Moth

Recorded:	1884 – 2006
Distribution / Status:	Perhaps absent / Former or very rare resident, perhaps vagrant
Conservation status:	Herts Endangered
Caterpillar food plants:	Not recorded. Elsewhere, on various trees and shrubs including privet.
Flight period:	Elsewhere, June/July
Records in database:	10

Old records are few, but suggest that this moth was resident in at least the south of the county at the end of the nineteenth century, perhaps also in the north (the most northerly record on the map is from Apsley End in 1903). The two more recent records are from Patmore Heath on 1st July 1993 (Charles Watson) and from Bishops Stortford on 6th July 2003 (James Fish and Julian Reeves) and may reflect small, cryptic resident populations or, perhaps, vagrant individuals. If resident, populations should be treated as Endangered.

1925 *Apocheima hispidaria* ([D.& S.]) Small Brindled Beauty

Recorded:	1880 – 2006
Distribution / Status:	Widespread / Common resident
Conservation status:	Herts Stable
Caterpillar food plants:	English Oak
Flight period:	February/March
Records in database:	69

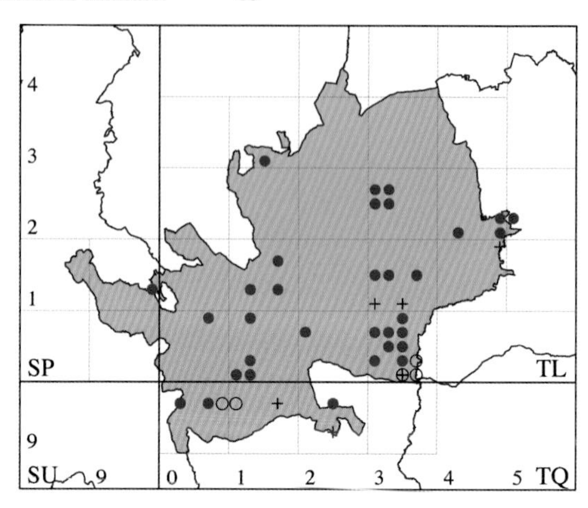

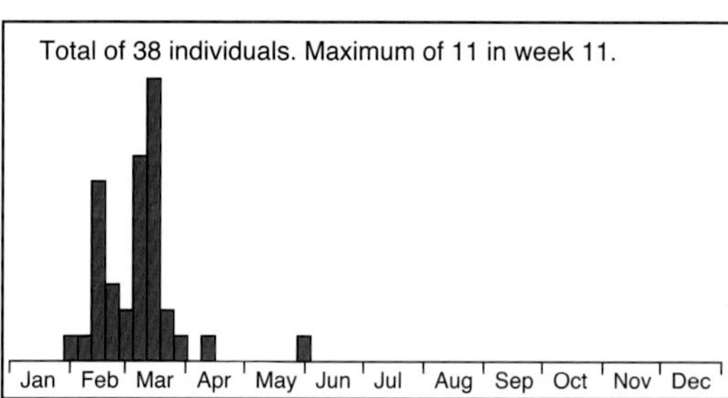

The early date of this moth and the fact that it favours woodlands rather than most gardens implies a degree of under-recording and it is probably widespread across most of the county.

1926 *Apocheima pilosaria* ([D.& S.]) Pale Brindled Beauty

Recorded:	1884 – 2006
Distribution / Status:	Widespread / Common resident
Conservation status:	Herts Stable
Caterpillar food plants:	Not recorded. Elsewhere, on deciduous trees and shrubs
Flight period:	Mid-January to end of March
Records in database:	240

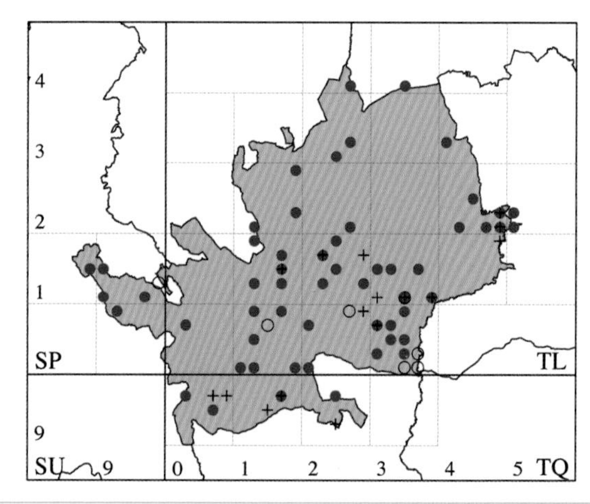

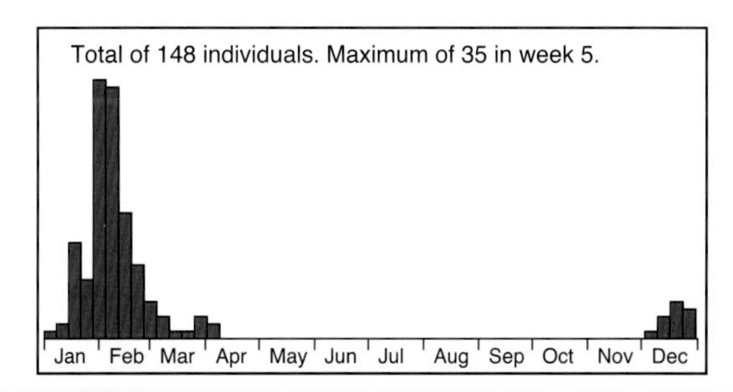

The Pale Brindled Beauty is one of the earliest moths to appear in the year and is very common in most woodlands. December adults were first recorded in 2004 and have occurred in all years since then.

1927 *Lycia hirtaria* (Cl.) Brindled Beauty

Recorded:	1892 – 2006
Distribution / Status:	Widespread / Common resident
Conservation status:	UK BAP Watch List. Herts Threatened
Caterpillar food plants:	Not recorded. Elsewhere, on various deciduous trees
Flight period:	April/May – sometimes earlier
Records in database:	229

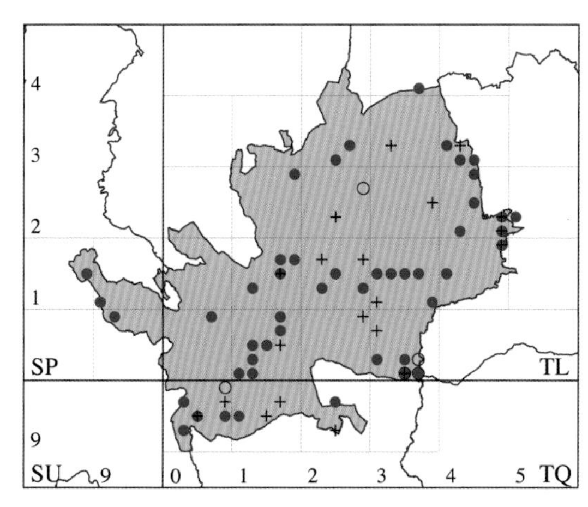

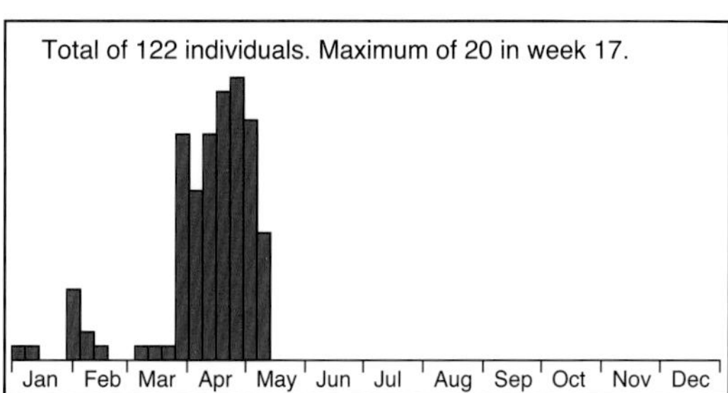

The January to March records of adults are all from the year 2005, apart from a single adult in February 2006. It is not clear if this represents just a 'flash in the pan', the start of a trend or under-recording in earlier years. The moth is common throughout the county and it is a surprise that larvae have, apparently, not been found here.

1930 *Biston strataria* (Hufn.) Oak Beauty

Recorded:	1884 – 2006
Distribution / Status:	Widespread / Common resident
Conservation status:	Herts Stable
Caterpillar food plants:	English Oak, Silver Birch
Flight period:	Mid-February to mid-April
Records in database:	240

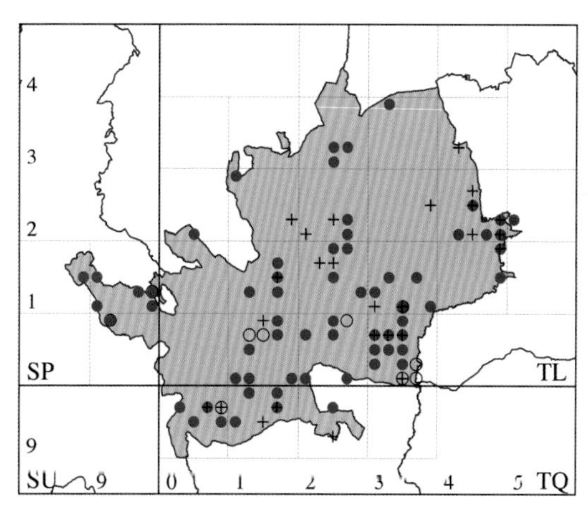

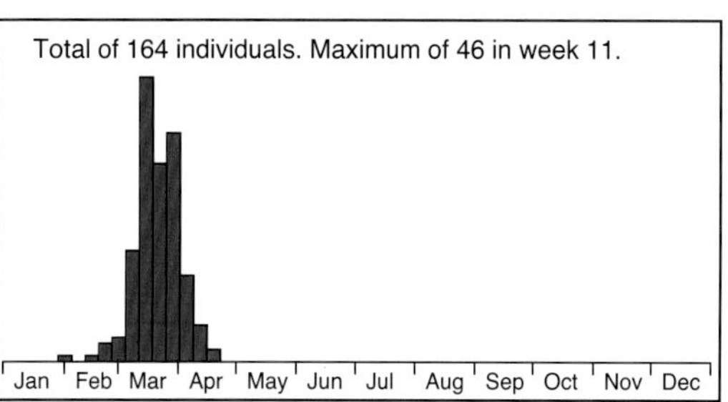

Variation is minimal within this attractive species. Occasionally very dark examples turn up in light traps, but almost all examples attracted to light are males and so rearing the next generation from dark females is seldom possible. Most records are from woodlands, though garden light traps are sometimes visited.

1931 *Biston betularia* (L.) Peppered Moth

Recorded:	1888 – 2006
Distribution / Status:	Widespread / Common resident
Conservation status:	Herts Stable
Caterpillar food plants:	English Oak, Birch, Larch
Flight period:	Mid-May to early August
Records in database:	1045

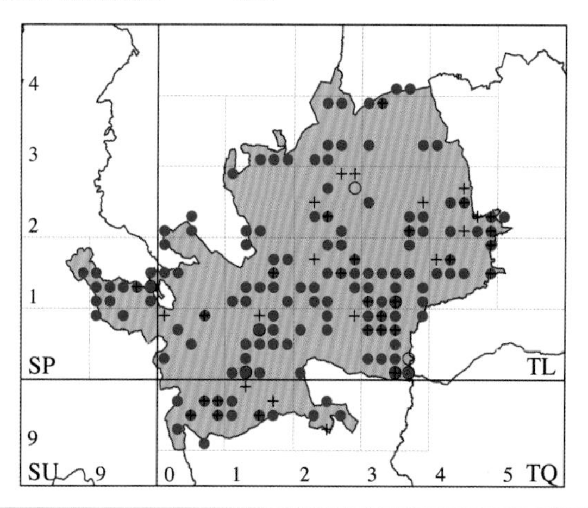

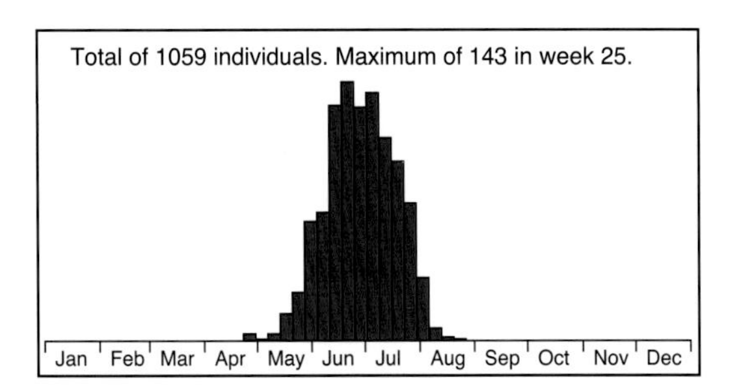

The typical white-with-black-spots form of this moth and the well-known almost entirely black industrial melanic, f. *carbonaria* Jordan, are both a familiar sight in Hertfordshire. Unfortunately, we appear to have no data concerning the proportions of the two until 1937, when Foster's list of that year notes that it was common in all districts, with black forms 'becoming much more common of late years'. The pendulum appears to have swung back, however, and the typical form now dominates the population with *carbonaria* representing as little as around 10 per cent of the total catch from 1995 to 2006. The intermediate f. *insularia* Thierry-Mieg is a genetic form occasionally reported, but for which I have seen no reliable Hertfordshire records. Reports, where checked, relate to intermediates between typical and *carbonaria* forms and appear likely to be hybrids – not true *insularia*. The larval record from Larch was a surprise as broad-leaved trees are usually preferred.

1932 *Agriopis leucophaearia* ([D.& S.]) Spring Usher

Recorded:	1884 – 2006
Distribution / Status:	Widespread / Common resident
Conservation status:	Stable
Caterpillar food plants:	English Oak, Sessile Oak
Flight period:	Mid-January to end of February
Records in database:	161

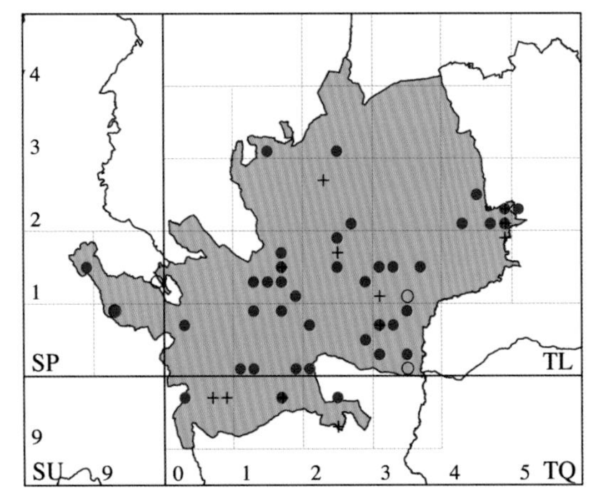

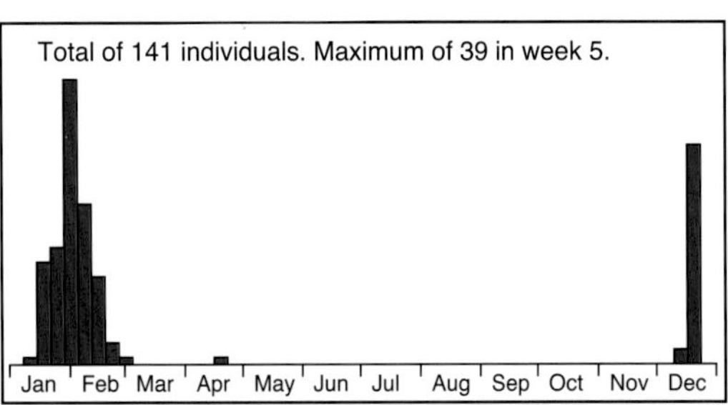

December records all relate to the years 2004 and 2005, but otherwise the moth is on the wing in January and February. The wingless females can be found on the trunks of the host tree after dark and males are generally in attendance and eggs are quite easily obtained from pairs found *in copula*. The males are hugely variable and this variation seems to be more or less random at any given site.

1933 *Agriopis aurantiaria* (Hb.) Scarce Umber

Recorded:	1884 – 2006
Distribution / Status:	Local / Abundant resident
Conservation status:	Herts Stable
Caterpillar food plants:	Silver Birch
Flight period:	November/December
Records in database:	123

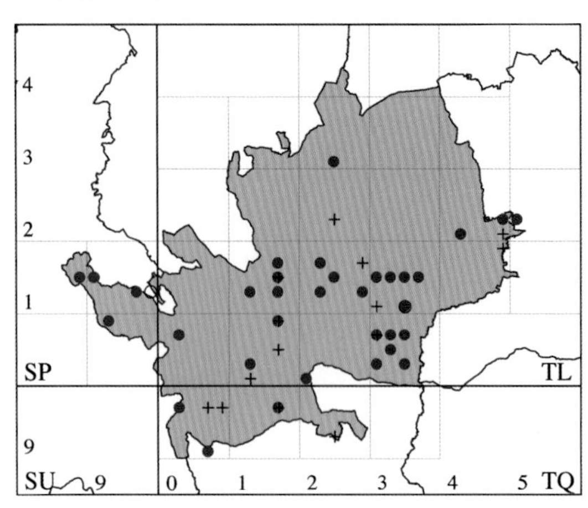

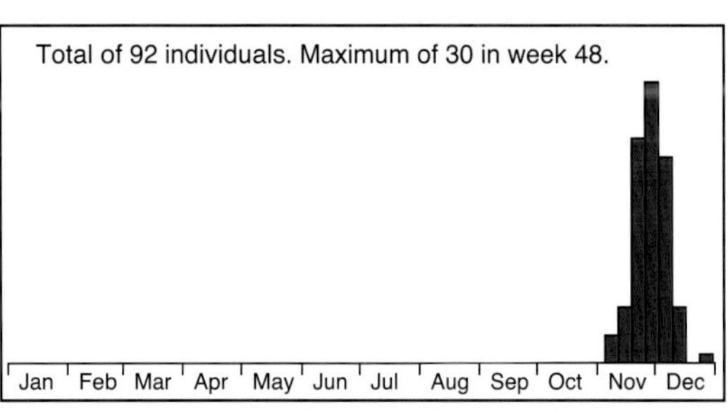

Males appear to start flying at around 9 pm, and are rarely captured in traps before this time. The main flight appears to be from about 10 pm onwards, the evidence for which is as follows: At several mercury vapour light traps operated along the ride leading from the West Car Park at Broxbourne Wood on 19th November 2003, prior to 10 pm, there were almost no Scarce Umbers. However, at approximately 11.30 pm at least one thousand males were attracted to the bank of six 1000 watt spot lights on a vehicle breakdown truck in the car park and there were many more flying in the lane nearby between 11 pm and midnight away from any lights.

1934 *Agriopis marginaria* (Fabr.) Dotted Border

Recorded:	1884 – 2006
Distribution / Status:	Widespread / Common resident
Conservation status:	Herts Stable
Caterpillar food plants:	English Oak, Hornbeam, Hazel, Common Hawthorn
Flight period:	Mid-January to mid-April
Records in database:	355

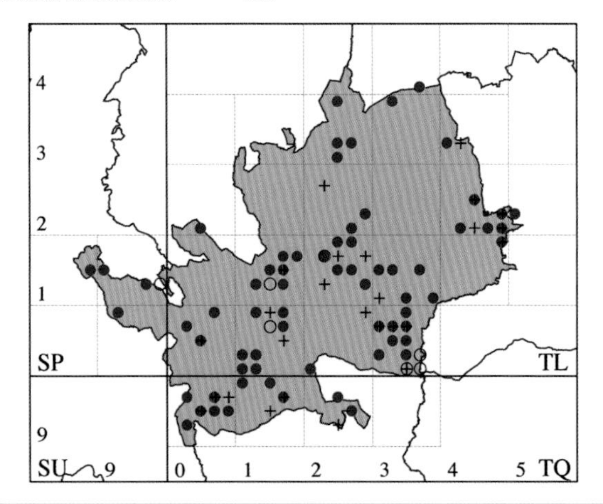

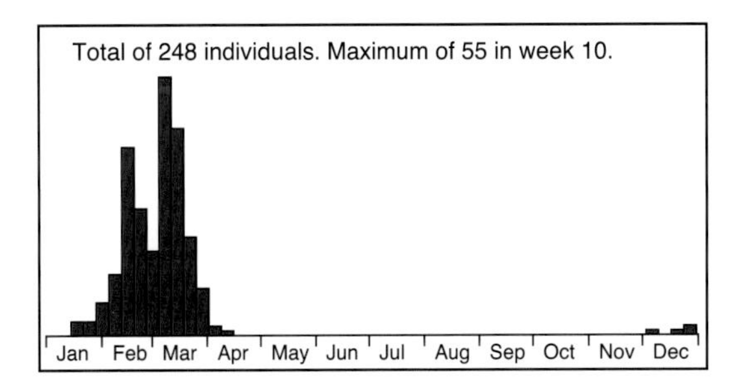

December records in the chart relate to the years 2002 and 2004 only, but the phenomenon is not new as there was a record from Fulling House Mill, Welwyn in 1946 (R. Ferry). In mild winters, early emergence in December is not excessive for a moth that typically flies from mid-January.

1935 *Erannis defoliaria* (Cl.) Mottled Umber

Recorded: 1884 – 2006
Distribution / Status: Widespread / Common resident
Conservation status: Herts Stable
Caterpillar food plants: Hornbeam, Beech, Silver Birch, Wild Rose, Blackthorn, Lombardy Poplar, English Oak, Sessile Oak, Wild Honeysuckle, Sycamore, Common Hawthorn
Flight period: October to January
Records in database: 309

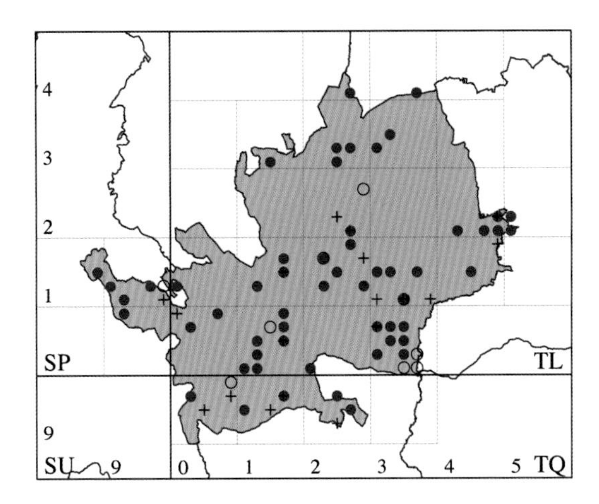

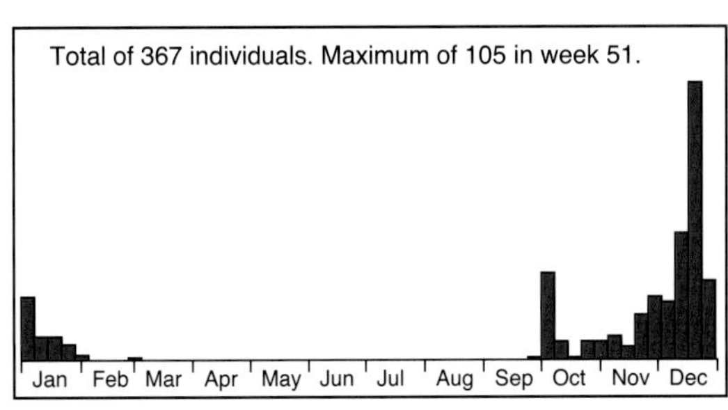

The moth appears in October in most years and is on the wing more or less continuously in mild spells between then and early February. Unusually for a 'macro' moth, a high proportion of the modern records are of the distinctive caterpillar; this is reflected in the several foodplant records.

1936 *Menophra abruptaria* (Thunb.) Waved Umber

Recorded: 1888 – 2006
Distribution / Status: Widespread / Common resident
Conservation status: Stable
Caterpillar food plants: Not recorded. Elsewhere, on Garden Privet and Lilac
Flight period: April/May
Records in database: 268

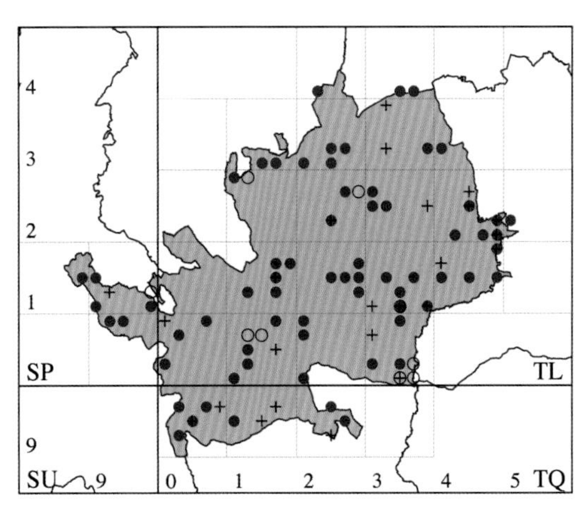

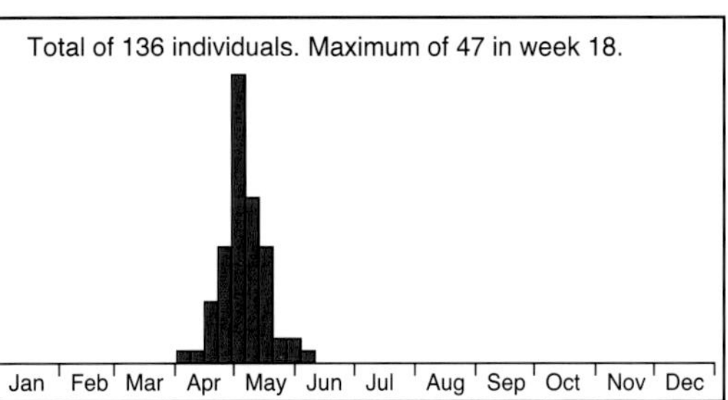

The Waved Umber is superficially similar to 1781: Small Waved Umber and July/August reports of Waved Umber certainly relate to that species. The first generation of Small Waved Umber is on the wing at the same time as the Waved Umber, however, although the former peaks as the latter declines. The Waved Umber is more widespread and likely to be encountered away from the chalk that is favoured by the other species.

1937 *Peribatodes rhomboidaria* ([D.& S.]) Willow Beauty

Recorded: 1884 – 2006
Distribution / Status: Ubiquitous / Abundant resident
Conservation status: Herts Stable
Caterpillar food plants: Not recorded. Elsewhere, polyphagous on trees
Flight period: Late May to mid-October in three generations
Records in database: 2,438

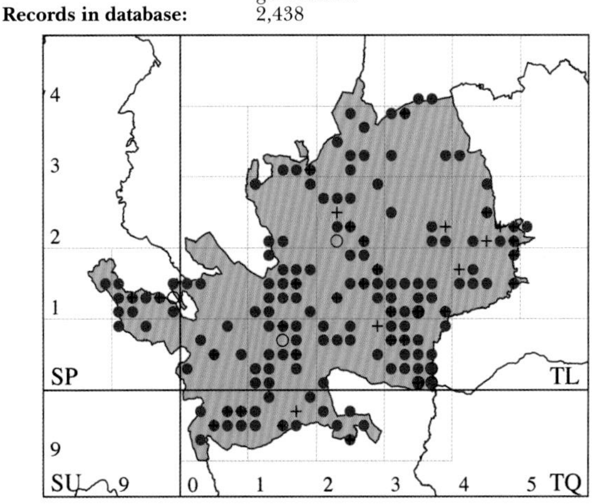

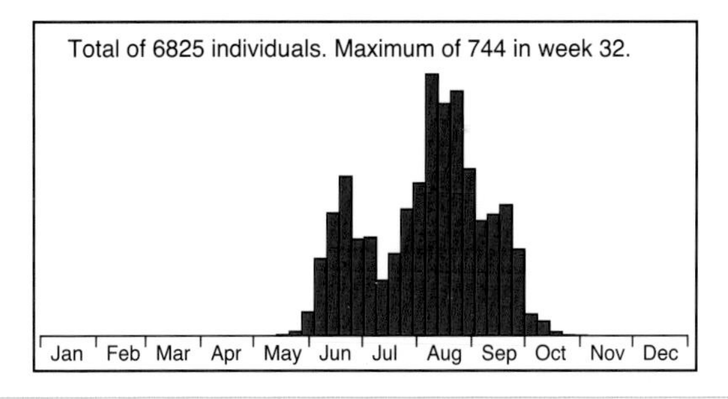

With 2,438 records in the database, the Willow Beauty is the fourth most frequently reported moth in the county and the most frequent geometrid. Foster (1937) noted it as 'Common in all districts'. Formerly double-brooded there is now a third generation of adults every year, but this is small and overlaps with the tail end of the second generation. Third brood adults are smaller than the norm – often excessively so.

1940 *Deileptenia ribeata* (Cl.) Satin Beauty

Recorded: 1976 – 2002
Distribution / Status: Extremely local / Rare vagrant
Conservation status: —
Caterpillar food plants: Not recorded. Elsewhere, on Yew and pine trees
Flight period: June/July
Records in database: 6

The Satin Beauty is a rare moth in Hertfordshire, as it is in the London Area and Essex; it is probably a vagrant to all three areas. There are rather more records in Bedfordshire, though it is very local there. Hertfordshire records are from Aldbury Common, 14th July 1976 (Barry Goater), Digswell, 7th June 1988 (Tom Gladwin), Rothamsted Estate, Harpenden, 1992 (Adrian Riley), Panshanger Park, 1997 (Tom Gladwin), Scales Park, 22nd July 2000 (Jim Reid) and Balls Wood, 13th July 2002 (Colin Plant).

1941 *Alcis repandata* (L.) Mottled Beauty

Recorded: 1884 – 2006
Distribution / Status: Widespread / Common resident
Conservation status: Herts Stable
Caterpillar food plants: Common Hawthorn, Blackthorn, English Oak, Wild Honeysuckle
Flight period: June/July
Records in database: 779

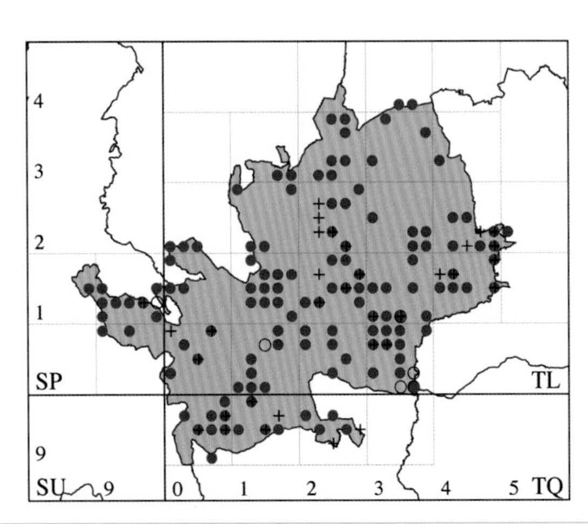

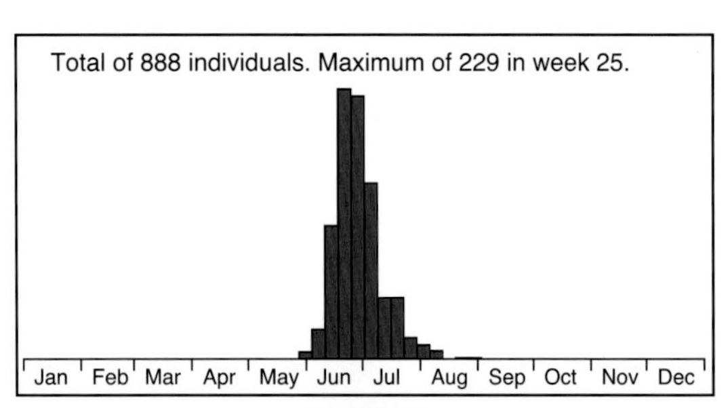

The Mottled Beauty is confused by some inexperienced observers with 1937: Willow Beauty, though fresh adults of Mottled Beauty typically start to appear as the first generation of Willow Beauties are becoming worn. However, this is not a foolproof guide and wing pattern must be looked at properly. Mottled Beauties appear in a variety of forms, though few extreme varieties are recorded for Hertfordshire.

1943 *Hypomecis roboraria* ([D.& S.]) Great Oak Beauty

Recorded: 1888 – 2006
Distribution / Status: Local / Uncommon resident
Conservation status: Herts Scarce
Caterpillar food plants: English Oak
Flight period: June/July
Records in database: 32

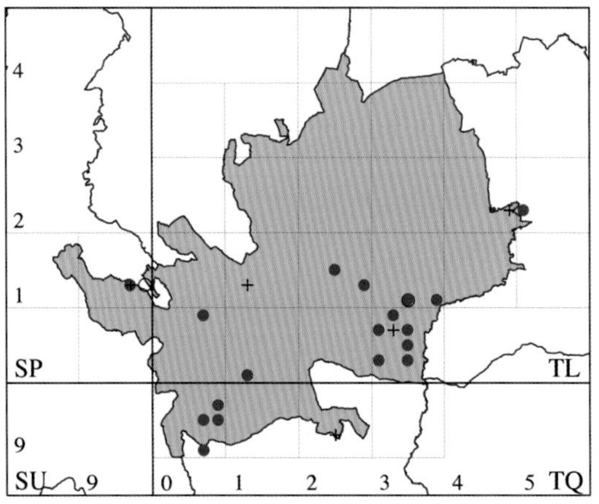

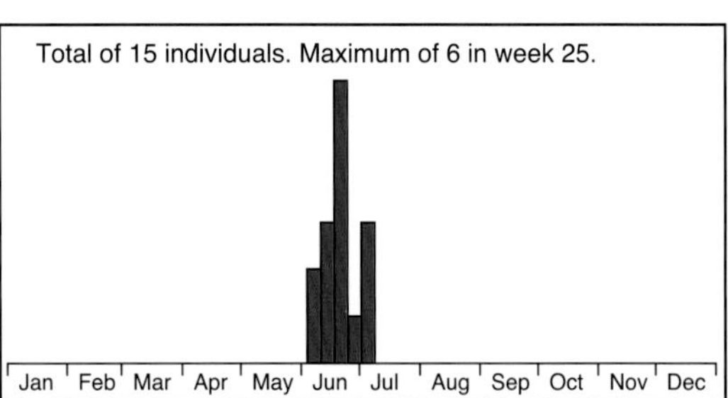

The Great Oak Beauty is confined to the ancient woodlands containing mature oak trees on the clay-based, damper soils in the south of the county. Adults rarely wander; though one was caught in Bishops Stortford in 1993 (James Fish and Julian

Reeves) and probably originated in Birchanger Wood, from where there I recorded it on 8th June 2000.

1944 *Hypomecis punctinalis* (Scop.) Pale Oak Beauty

Recorded: 1892 – 2006
Distribution / Status: Widespread / Common resident
Conservation status: Herts Stable
Caterpillar food plants: Birch. Elsewhere, also on oak
Flight period: May to July
Records in database: 238

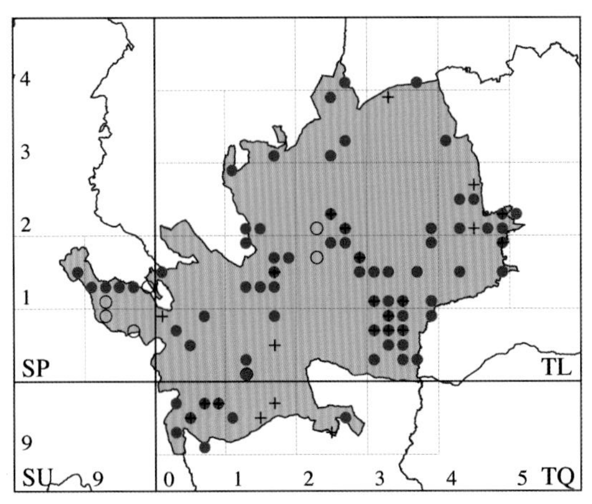

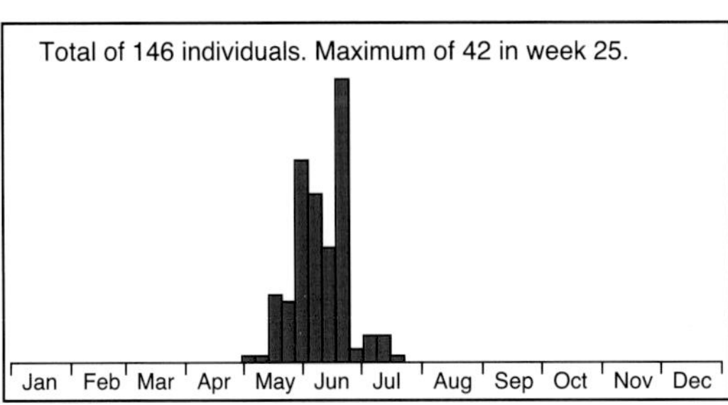

Whilst oak is probably the favoured foodplant, birches will also suffice and so it is no surprise that Pale Oak Beauty is far more widespread than 1943: Great Oak Beauty and evidently thrives away from both ancient woodland and mature oak trees.

1945 *Cleorodes lichenaria* (Hufn.) Brussels Lace

Recorded: 1884 – 1937
Distribution / Status: Absent / Former resident
Conservation status: Herts Extinct
Caterpillar food plants: Not recorded. Elsewhere, on various lichens growing on trees
Flight period: Elsewhere, June to August
Records in database: 7

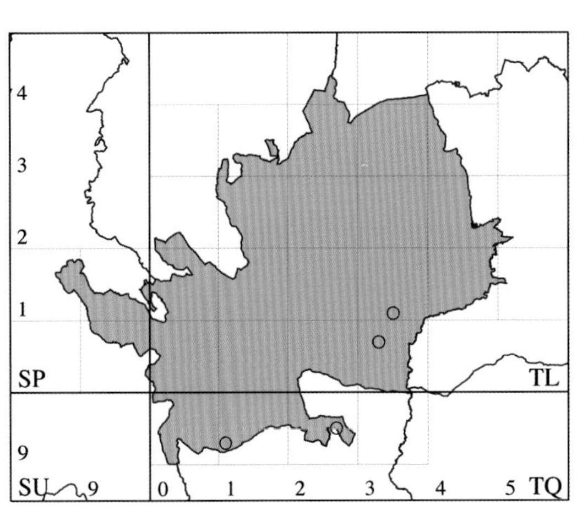

First listed for the county from the Sandridge area (Griffith, 1884), it is also included in the Haileybury School list by Bowyer (1888) and from the Cheshunt area (almost certainly the Broxbourne Woods and now mapped as such) by Boyd (1901). A record from East Barnet (Gillum) and another from Oxhey Wood (Rowland-Brown) relate to the same era. One more recent record, from Broxbourne Wood, by H. M. Edelsten, was included by Foster (1937). Brussels Lace is most frequent in the south-west of Britain and is absent from most of south-east England.

The Engrailed/Small Engrailed species pair

Separating adults of these two species is often impossible – even after genitalia examination. Happily, in Hertfordshire the Small Engrailed flies between broods of Engrailed so that most examples can be named by date. Opinions vary on whether the Small Engrailed is a valid species or just a form of the Engrailed. It is worth pointing out that the double-brooded species that we know as *bistortata* (the Engrailed) also occurs across Europe, but the species that we call *crepuscularia* (Small Engrailed) appears to be endemic to Britain. Agassiz (2003) informs us, however, that the name *crepuscularia* was first assigned to a moth caught in Vienna and so that must, of course, apply to the European species. Thus, our *bistortata* is really *crepuscularia* and our *crepuscularia* is in need of a valid new name! This has no direct relevance to Hertfordshire, but if comparing our data with European information the potential for confusion should be taken into account.

1947 *Ectropis bistortata* (Goeze) Engrailed

Recorded: 1938 – 2006
Distribution / Status: Widespread / Common resident
Conservation status: Herts Stable
Caterpillar food plants: Wild Currant
Flight period: March/April, June/July – increasingly, August/September
Records in database: 365

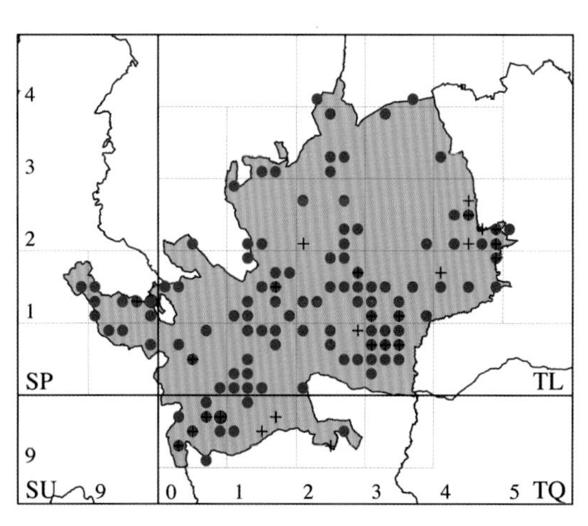

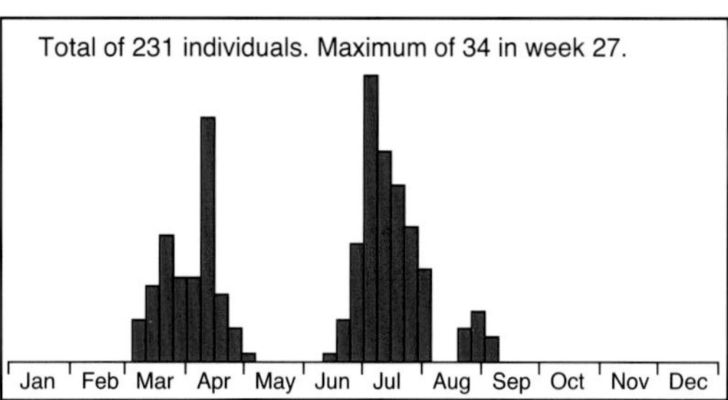

Skinner (1998) says that, nationally, the Engrailed flies in March/April and then from late June to early August. Our data agree with this, but the second period divides into two generations of adults so that the moth is triple-brooded in Hertfordshire. I have omitted from the map all records where there may be uncertainty about the identification; this includes all the records made prior to Foster's 1937 county list.

1948 *Ectropis crepuscularia* ([D.& S.]) Small Engrailed

Recorded: 1962 – 2006
Distribution / Status: Widespread / Common resident
Conservation status: Herts Stable
Caterpillar food plants: Not recorded. Elsewhere, on various trees and shrubs
Flight period: May/June in a single generation
Records in database: 62

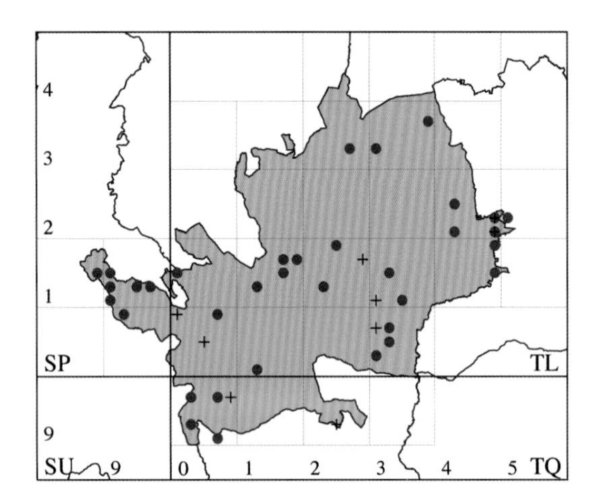

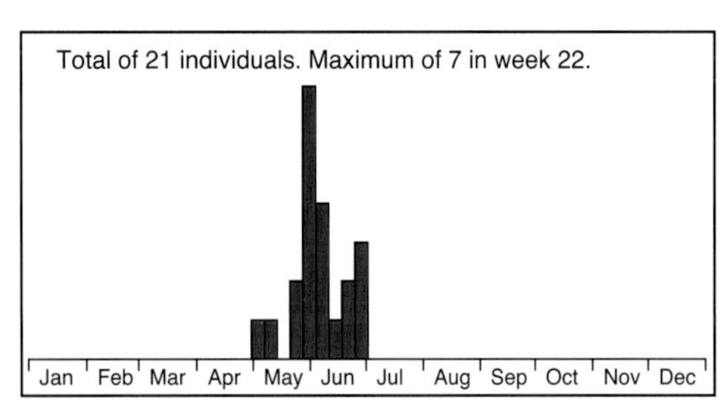

As with the last species, many doubtfully identified moths have been ignored for the purpose of this summary – our earliest confirmed record is from 1962. Nationally, the Small Engrailed flies from mid-May to mid-June, varying with season and this fits with observed Hertfordshire data. Judging from the number of records in the database, the Small Engrailed is far less frequently encountered than the Engrailed.

1949 *Paradarisa consonaria* (Hb.) Square Spot

Recorded: 1900 – 2005
Distribution / Status: Local / Rare resident
Conservation status: Herts Rare
Caterpillar food plants: Not recorded. Elsewhere, polyphagous on trees
Flight period: Elsewhere, April to June
Records in database: 9

Tring in the west and Broxbourne Woods in the east are the only sites listed by Foster (1937) and the record from Tring was almost certainly made at High Scrubs, probably between 1900 and 1937. The moth was found here again in 1938 by S. B. Hodgson, who recorded it at Hockeridge Wood in the same year. I found it at Hares Garden Wood (an extension of High Scrubs) on 10th May 2004 suggesting that it is still resident in these woods adjacent to the Buckinghamshire border. The Broxbourne Woods record was at least as long ago as 1900, perhaps earlier. Hugh Lansdown found the moth at Hertford Heath in 1994 whilst Mark Cooper caught examples in Thunderfield Grove on 5th June 2004, demonstrating a continuing presence in the east. The one remaining record, in the central area, is from Shenley in 2005 (Bill and Pearl Page).

1950 *Parectropis similaria* (Hufn.) Brindled White-spot

Recorded: 1888 – 2006
Distribution / Status: Local / Uncommon resident
Conservation status: Herts Stable
Caterpillar food plants: Not recorded. Elsewhere, on birch, oak and lime
Flight period: Mid-May/June
Records in database: 75

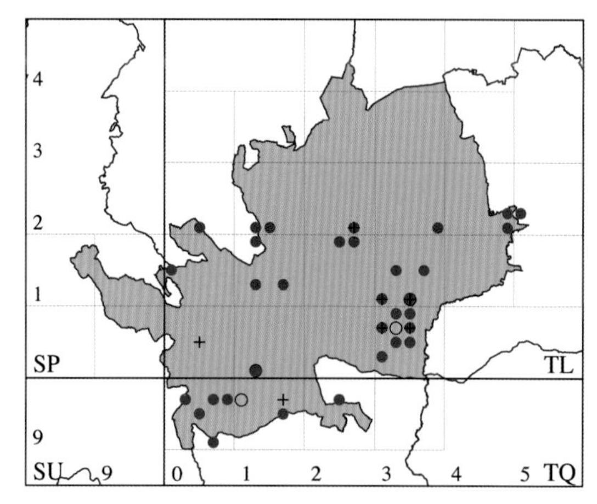

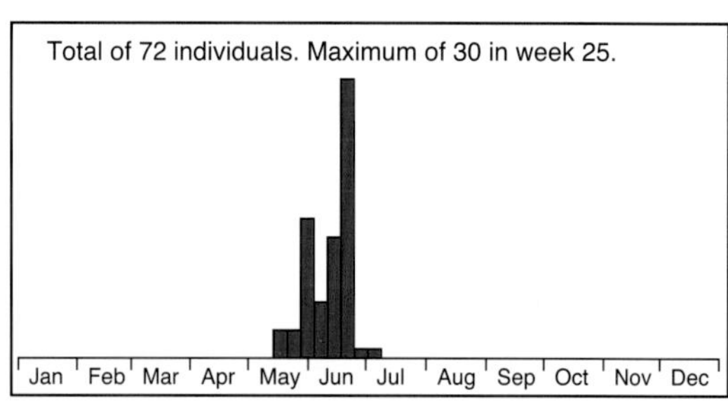

Formerly known as *Paradarisa extersaria*, the Brindled White-spot is essentially a woodland insect and seems to be absent from the northern portion of Hertfordshire, but likely to be resident in most southern woodlands.

1951 *Aethalura punctulata* ([D.& S.]) Grey Birch

Recorded: 1903 – 2006
Distribution / Status: Local / Common resident
Conservation status: Herts Stable
Caterpillar food plants: Not recorded. Elsewhere, on birch
Flight period: Late April to June
Records in database: 54

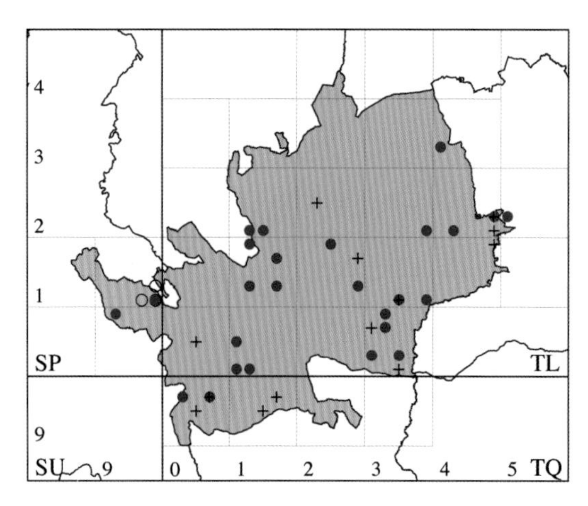

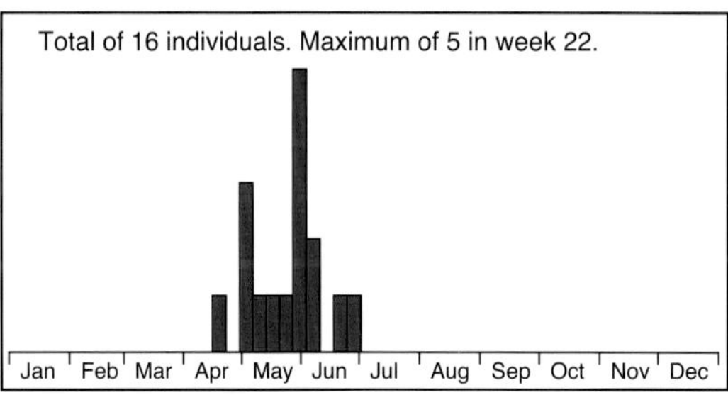

Foster (1937) lists several sites; although these are listed without dates all of the named recorders appear in Foster's list of 'contributors ... whose records have been added since the 1902 list of Gibbs'. Thus, the earliest year for which we can record the species in the county is 1903, though the actual first year is probably later. Most woodlands with mature birch trees appear likely to support this species, though young birch trees so far have not generated records.

1952 *Ematurga atomaria* (L.) Common Heath

Recorded: 1828 – 2006
Distribution / Status: Absent / Former resident
Conservation status: Herts Extinct
Caterpillar food plants: Not recorded. Elsewhere, on Heather, Heath, clovers and trefoils
Flight period: Elsewhere, May/June
Records in database: 13

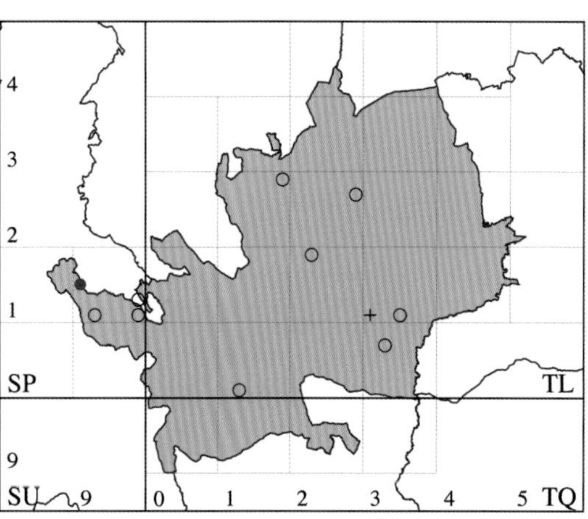

The Common Heath appears to have been lost from the Hertfordshire fauna. The map shows a wide spread of records, almost all pre-dating Foster's 1937 list. It was common on Rabley Heath near Knebworth (Foster, 1916) but twenty or so years later Foster (1937) lists only eight records, all apparently made prior to 1916. Hodgson (1939), states that the species was 'very scarce' (at Ashridge). It was 'v. common' in the area around Walkern between 1940 and 1950' (J. Birdsall) and at the same time Birdsall described the Latticed Heath as merely 'common'. The situation today is somewhat reversed and the moth is probably extinct as a resident. The rather surprising recent record, from Gubblecote, on 11th May 2005 (Peter Bygate) was surely a wanderer?

1954 *Bupalus piniaria* (L.) Bordered White

Recorded: 1895 – 2006
Distribution / Status: Local / Common resident
Conservation status: Herts Stable
Caterpillar food plants: Not recorded. Elsewhere, on pines
Flight period: Mid-May to mid-July
Records in database: 98

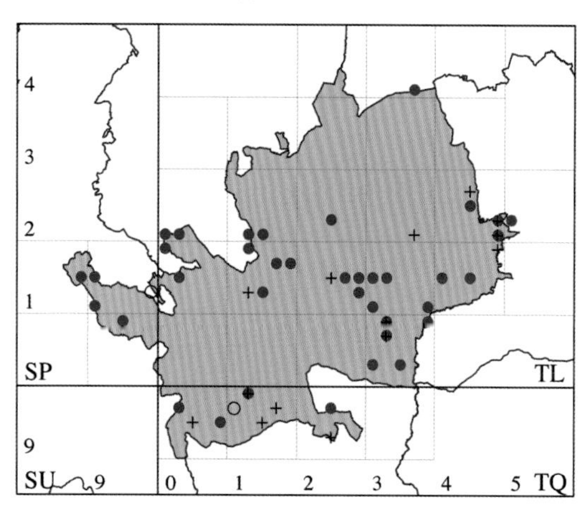

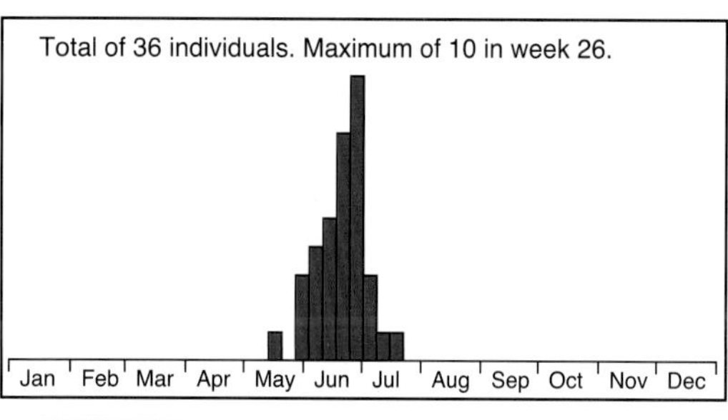

The colour of Bordered White adults differs with sex and latitude. In the south of Britain, most males are yellow and most females are orange whilst in Scotland males tend to be white and the females brown. There is almost no information on Hertfordshire colour forms, but all the records that I have confirmed here are of yellow males. The moth can be super-abundant in some pine plantations further north and there is no reason to suppose good numbers are not present in Hertfordshire – though happily we have relatively few coniferous deserts to support it.

1955 *Cabera pusaria* (L.) Common White Wave

Recorded: 1884 – 2006
Distribution / Status: Widespread / Common resident
Conservation status: Herts Stable
Caterpillar food plants: Not recorded. Elsewhere, on various trees and shrubs
Flight period: Late May to August
Records in database: 619

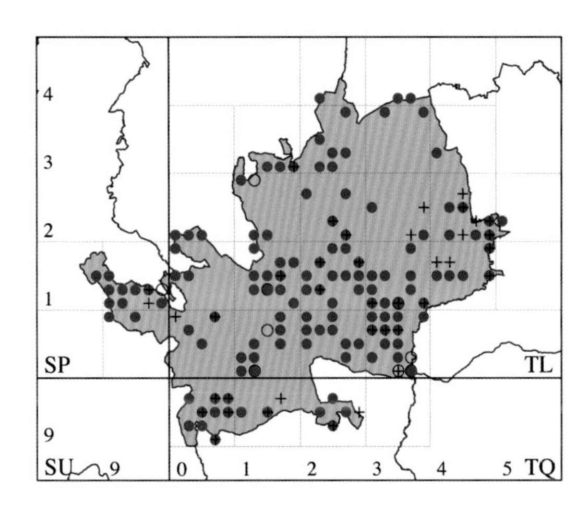

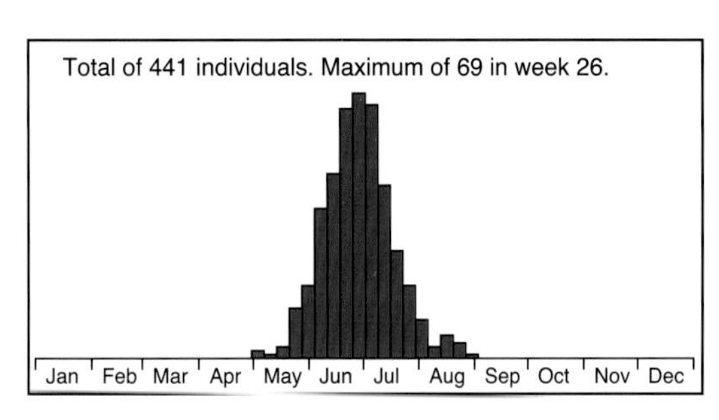

Both this species and 1956: Common Wave are frequent visitors to light traps, but it is interesting to note that the number of records of Common White wave in the database is more or less double the quantity of those for the other species. The flight data does not appear to support the notion of there being two generations of adults in the south of Britain and a single protracted emergence seems more likely to be the case in Hertfordshire.

1956 *Cabera exanthemata* (Scop.) Common Wave

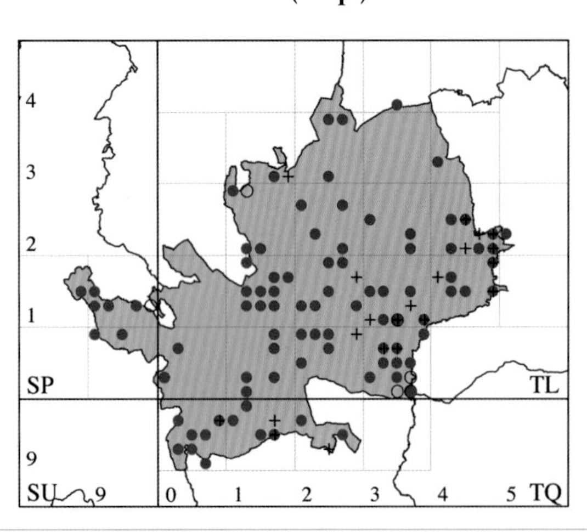

Recorded: 1884 – 2006
Distribution / Status: Widespread / Common resident
Conservation status: Herts Stable
Caterpillar food plants: Not recorded. Elsewhere, on *Salix* species
Flight period: Late May to August
Records in database: 320

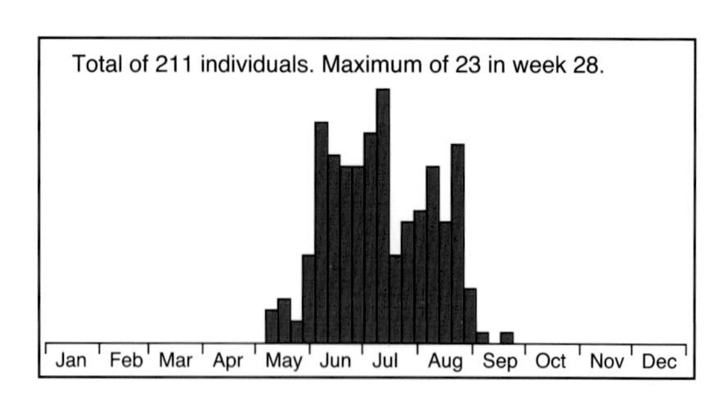

In contrast to 1955: Common White Wave, which is allegedly double-brooded, but appears in reality to be univoltine, this species, whilst allegedly single-brooded in most years is very clearly bivoltine, with peaks of adults in late June and August.

1957 *Lomographa bimaculata* (Fabr.) White-pinion Spotted

Recorded: 1888 – 2006
Distribution / Status: Local / Common resident
Conservation status: Herts Stable
Caterpillar food plants: Blackthorn
Flight period: Late April to June
Records in database: 153

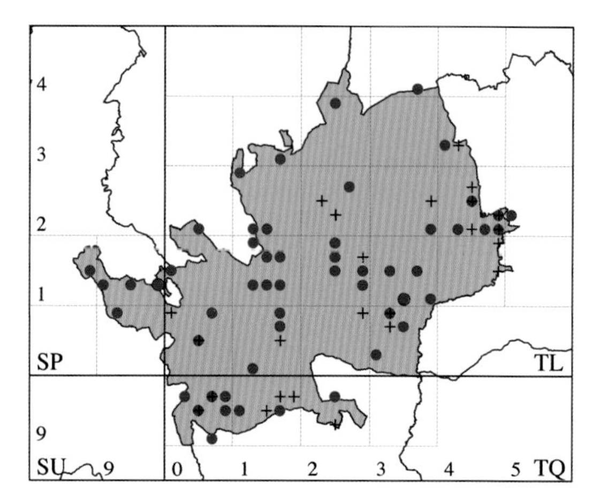

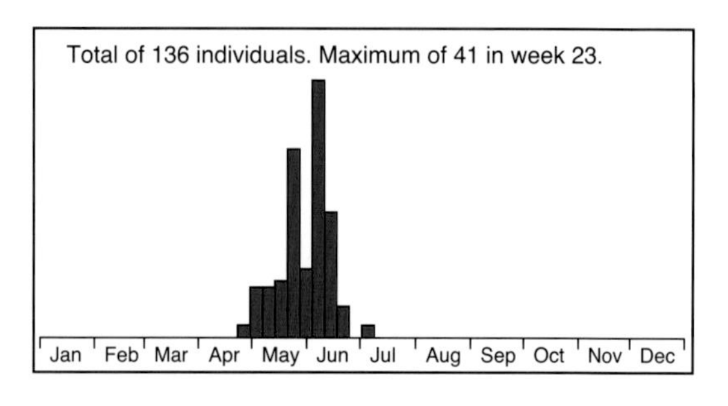

The White-pinion Spotted fluctuates wildly in number with periods of scarcity lasting several years and then periods when it is very common; however, it seems to be truly absent from a number of sites in the county and so is categorised as Local rather than Widespread. Although the caterpillar apparently also feeds on hawthorns, there is a very strong association with Blackthorn in Hertfordshire.

1958 *Lomographa temerata* ([D.& S.]) Clouded Silver

Recorded: 1884 – 2006
Distribution / Status: Widespread / Common resident
Conservation status: Herts Stable
Caterpillar food plants: Common Hawthorn. Elsewhere on several rosaceous trees
Flight period: Late May to end of July
Records in database: 795

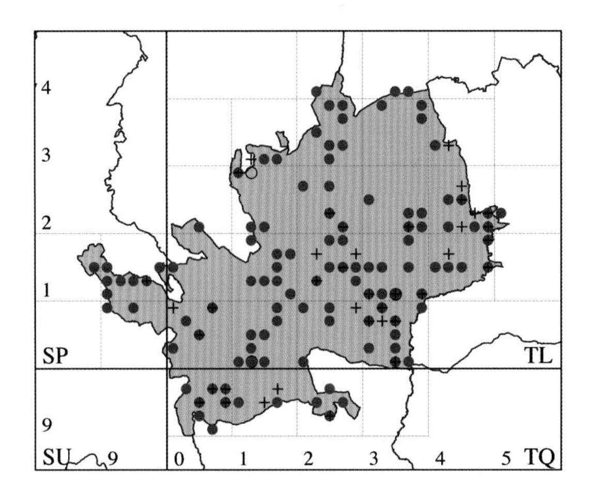

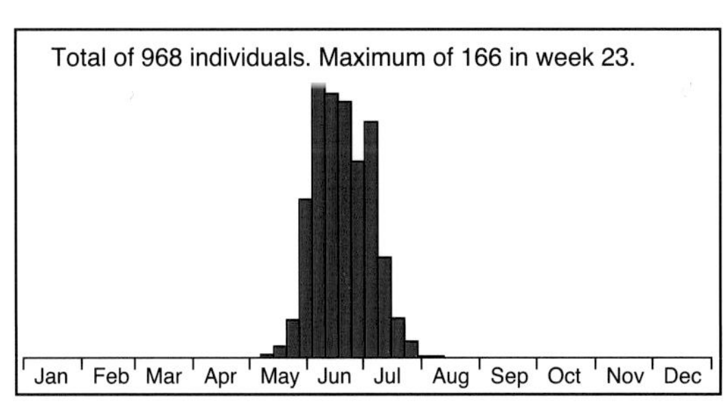

The Clouded Silver is one of the most frequent species seen in car headlights at dusk along country lanes, but once it is really dark the moth appears much harder to find in this way. It is attracted readily to light, but most moths sit around the outside of the trap and fly away as soon as daylight arrives, giving the false impression that they are few in number.

1960 *Thera primaria* (Haw.) Early Moth

Recorded: 1888 – 2006
Distribution / Status: Widespread / Common resident
Conservation status: Herts Stable
Caterpillar food plants: Not recorded. Elsewhere, on hawthorn and Blackthorn
Flight period: January to mid-March
Records in database: 180

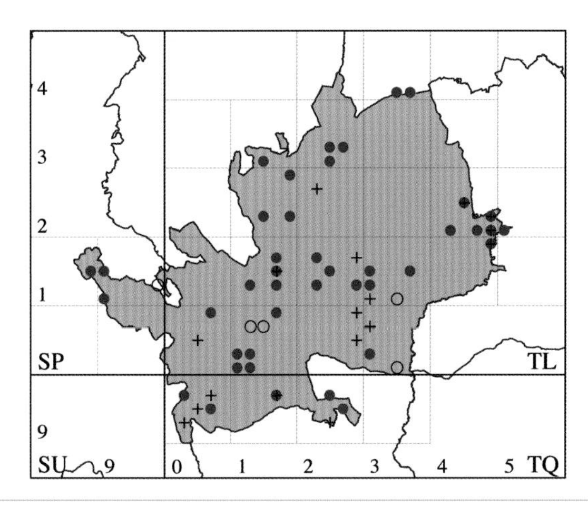

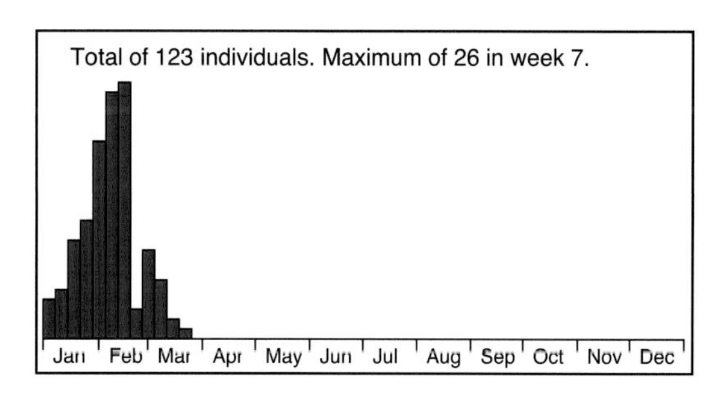

The Early Moth is far more common and widespread than many people realise. It is only weakly attracted to mv light, but is frequent at porch lights, in lit telephone boxes and at other tungsten-filament sources of light. It is easily found by torchlight at dusk along hedges containing Blackthorn and/or hawthorn. The patchy distribution in Hertfordshire reflects a degree of under-recording.

1961 *Campaea margaritata* (L.) Light Emerald

Recorded: 1888 – 2006
Distribution / Status: Ubiquitous / Common resident
Conservation status: Herts Stable
Caterpillar food plants: Common Hawthorn. Elsewhere, on various deciduous trees
Flight period: June/July and August/September, in two generations
Records in database: 962

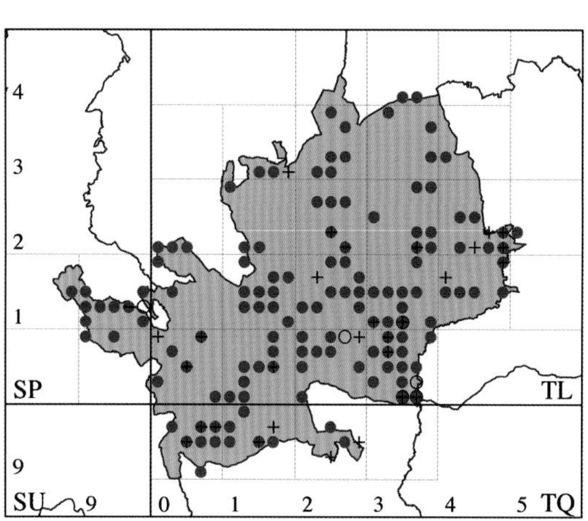

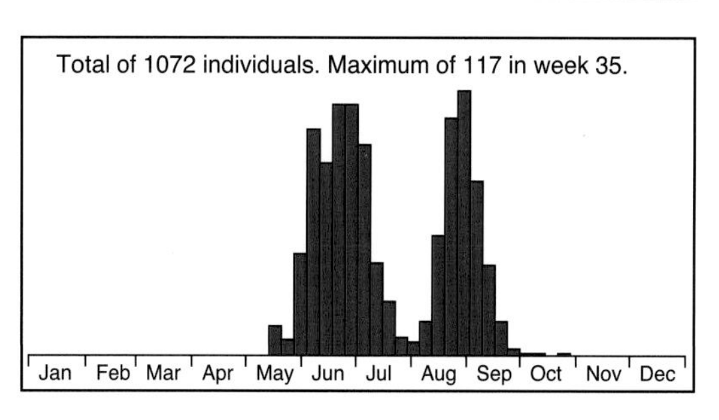

Although green when freshly emerged, adult Light Emerald moths fade very rapidly to an off-white colour so that green examples are rather scarce in light traps. Males are smaller than females, sometimes considerably so in the second generation.

1962 *Hylaea fasciaria* (L.) Barred Red

Recorded: 1893 2006
Distribution / Status: Widespread / Common resident
Conservation status: Herts Stable
Caterpillar food plants: Scots Pine. Elsewhere, on pines and spruces
Flight period: Mid-June to early August
Records in database: 84

It seems likely that pines other than Scots Pine are used by Hertfordshire larvae and the moth is frequent, though almost always as singletons, at light traps across the county. The striking green aberration *prasinaria* [D.& S.], does not appear to have been recorded in the county, but a female example of ab. *grisearia* Fuchs came to my garden light trap in Bishops Stortford on 24th June 1988. An exceptionally late specimen at St Albans on 25th September 2006 (Wendy Hatton) was green with a reddish median fascia.

1964 *Charissa obscuratus* ([D.& S.]) Annulet

Recorded:	1953 – 1971
Distribution / Status:	Absent / Former resident
Conservation status:	Herts Extinct
Caterpillar food plants:	Not recorded. Elsewhere, on various low plants
Flight period:	Elsewhere, July and August
Records in database:	3

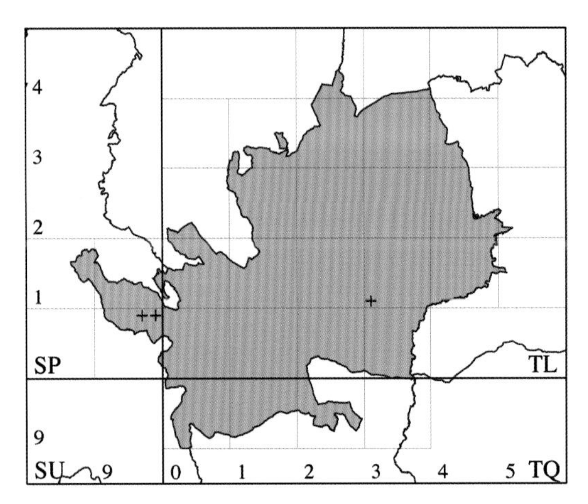

The Annulet is incorrectly listed by Foster (1937) as being recorded at Hoddesdon by G. V. Bull and the record is repeated by P. J. Bell in *Ent. Rec.* **67**: 238. During 1955, in response to the latter publication, G. V. Bull, in a letter to P J. Bell in his role as county moth recorder, states that he had no record of the capture (Bell, 1957). The first genuine Hertfordshire records are from Northchurch, where one came to light in 1953 (Bell, 1955) and one by the same observer on Berkhamsted Station platform on 29 July 1955 (*Ent. Rec.* **67**: 238). A badly worn example was taken at Bayfordbury in 1971 (Jim Reid) and identified from the genitalia slide.

[1966 *Siona lineata* (Scop.) Black-veined Moth

Listed for the county by Gibbs (1902) in the *Victoria County History* but withdrawn by the same author (see Foster, 1937: 159). This almost certainly refers to the report from Berkhamsted in 1869 (as *Scoria dealbata* L.) by C. L. Raynor (*Entomologist* **5**: 264), who writes ' I was ... surprised to come across a single specimen whilst collecting on Berkhamsted Common, in July, 1869. I cannot be mistaken as to its identity, having seen many specimens of this insect, and compared mine with them.' The Black-veined moth was at that time confined to a very small area around Wye in Kent. Today it hangs on to its British status, very precariously, in just two fields in that same area. This extremely unlikely Hertfordshire record is not supported by a voucher specimen that can be traced today.]

1967 *Aspitates gilvaria* ([D.& S.]) Straw Belle

Recorded:	1829 – 2006
Distribution / Status:	Local / Rare vagrant
Conservation status:	UK BAP Priority Species
Caterpillar food plants:	Not recorded. Elsewhere, on various herbaceous plants
Flight period:	Elsewhere, July/August
Records in database:	3

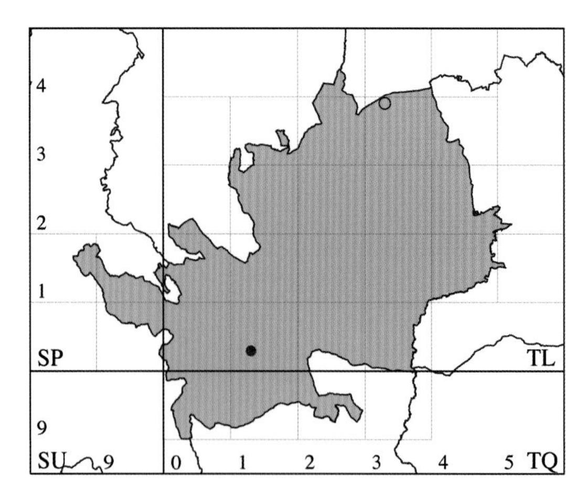

There are three confirmed Hertfordshire records**:** The moth is illustrated from a 'Hertford' specimen in Stephens' *Illustrations of British Entomology* **3**: 208 (published in 1829) and one was collected on Royston Heath [= Therfield Heath] in 1924 (G. V. Bull). The Hertford record cannot be mapped as the precise location of the record is unknown. An exceptionally late example was taken in a garden light trap in Ashridge Drive, Bricketwood on 21st October 2006 (Henry Ellis); the date might suggest that this was an immigrant example.

1968 *Semiaspilates ochrearia* (Rossi) Yellow Belle

Recorded:	1834 – 1961
Distribution / Status:	Local / Rare vagrant
Conservation status:	-
Caterpillar food plants:	Not recorded. Elsewhere, on various herbaceous plants
Flight period:	Elsewhere, May/June and August/September
Records in database:	2

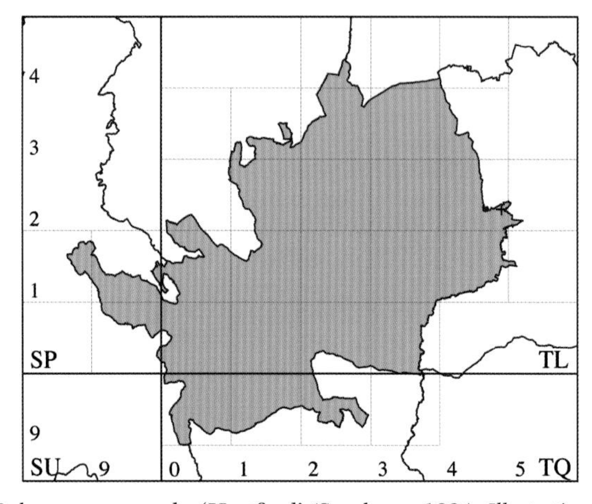

We have two records: 'Hertford' (Stephens, 1834. *Illustrations of British Entomology*' and Bishops Stortford, 20 May 1961 (Clifford Craufurd) – the latter clearly a wanderer from some distance (Bell, 1964). The Hertford record is not mapped.

1969 *Dyscia fagaria* (Thunb.) Grey Scalloped Bar

Recorded:	1909 – 1914
Distribution / Status:	Absent / Former resident
Conservation status:	Herts Extinct
Caterpillar food plants:	Not recorded. Elsewhere, on Heather and Heath
Flight period:	Elsewhere, May to July
Records in database:	2

According to S. B. Hodgson, Mr J. H. Bell informed him in 1939 that '*Crocata belgaria* (= *Dyscia fagaria*) occurred regularly on Berkhamsted Common from 1909 to 1914, the best place being on and around the golf course'. From his return to the

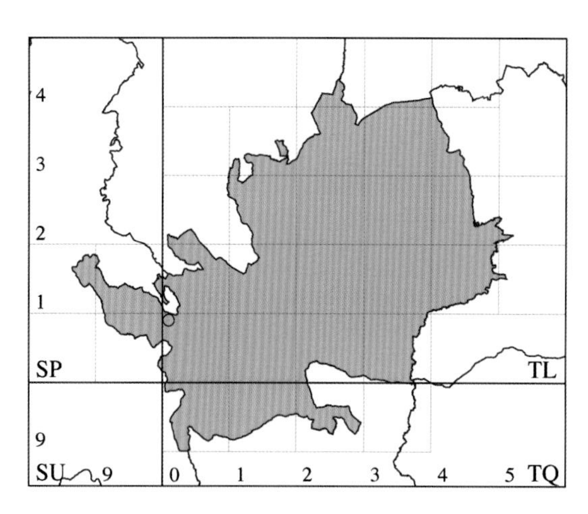

district in 1932 until the time of this communication in 1938, Bell apparently failed to refind this species in this site. Hodgson himself searched the area for both larvae and adults in 1939 and 1940, but was similarly unsuccessful. In concluding that the moth had now vanished from Berkhamsted Common, Hodgson noted that there was, nevertheless, '... still a fair amount of Ling (a food-plant)'. There do not appear to be any other Hertfordshire records of this species.

1970 *Perconia strigillaria* (Hb.) Grass wave

Recorded: 1888 – 1902
Distribution / Status: Absent / Former resident
Conservation status: Herts Extinct
Caterpillar food plants: Not recorded. Elsewhere, on Heather, Heath, Gorse and Broom
Flight period: Elsewhere, June/July
Records in database: 2

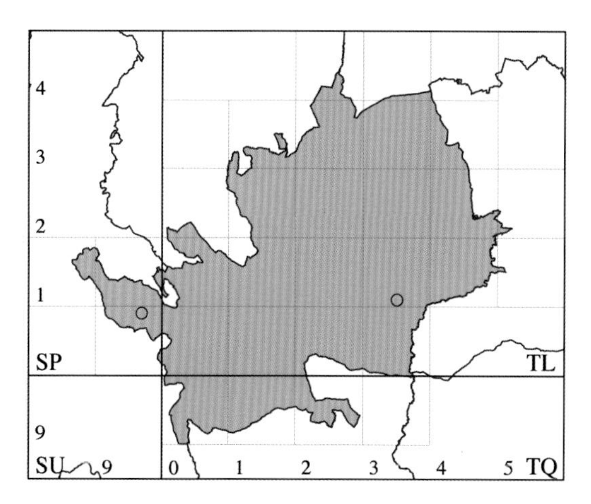

The listing by R. W. Bowyer (1888) for the Haileybury College area perhaps relates to Hertford Heath, where Heather grows in a small area today and probably grew over a larger area then. The only other Hertfordshire record is from Bricket Wood by Spencer, listed in Gibbs (1902). There are no other Hertfordshire records known.

SPHINGIDAE

The hawk-moths include some of the largest of Lepidoptera and are familiar to most people. The larvae bear a characteristic 'horn' on the tail end which renders them easily recognisable. There are around a thousand species world-wide, but in Britain we have just 26, of which some are resident and some reach us only as immigrants from overseas. Hertfordshire can boast 16 species, of which seven are residents, two are probably extinct residents and seven occur as primary immigrants.

1972 *Agrius convolvuli* (L.) Convolvulus Hawk-moth

Recorded: 1859 – 2006
Distribution / Status: Random / Frequent immigrant
Conservation status: -
Caterpillar food plants: No data
Flight period: July to November
Records in database: 42

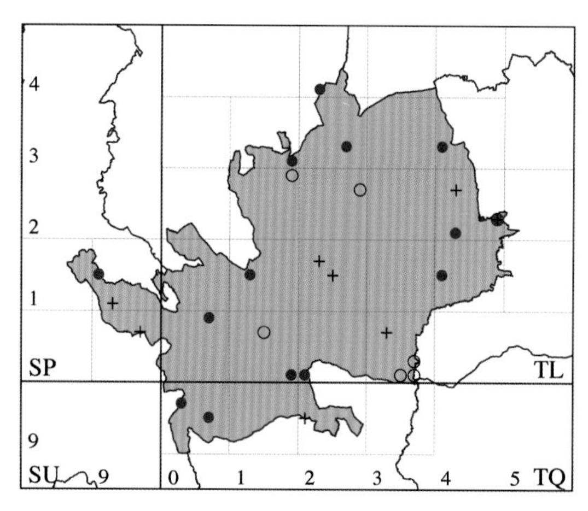

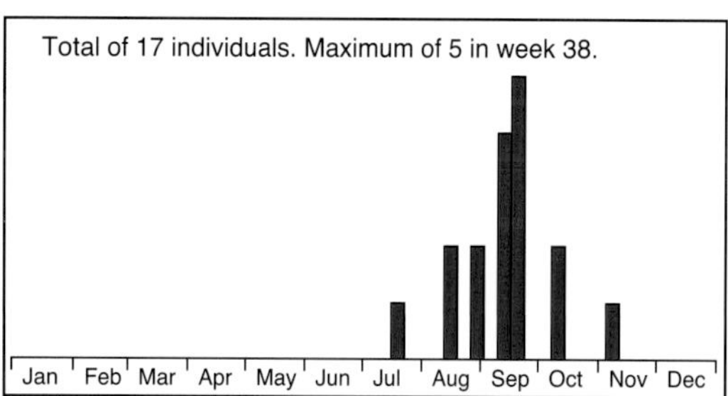

Hertfordshire records to hand are as follows: Cheshunt, September 1859 – 'my nephew W. Boyd of Cheshunt, Herts, caught in his garden, within the first fortnight of this month, ten specimens of *S. convolvuli*' (Gaviller, 1859. *Entomologist's Weekly Intelligencer* **7**: 3; Sandridge area, three in 1874 (Griffith, 1884); Hitchin, three in 1875 (Cottam, *Transactions of the Watford Natural History Society* **1**: 108). It is interesting to note that Cottam was prompted to write the Note because the Meteorological Society had '... requested that occasional appearances in considerable numbers, of insects usually scarce, should be noted with a view to elucidation of *seasonal phenomena* ...'. The ignorance at that date of immigration by moths is evident; Watford, 1875 at least eight (A. Cottam, *Transactions of the Watford Natural History Society* **1**: 108 and *Entomologist's Monthly Magazine* **12**: 139); 'A fine female of this insect was brought to me on 15th September [1883]; it was taken at rest on a door plate. *S. convolvuli* occurs here [Hitchin] and at Baldock nearly every year' (Hartley, *Entomologist* **16**: 235); Cheshunt, by A. Gaviller (W. C. Boyd, *Entomologist's Weekly*

Intelligencer **7**: 3); Cumberland Road, St. Albans, September 1887 (Gibbs. 1893); St Albans, 1888 (Gibbs, 1889); Hitchin, 26th September 1895 (S. H. Spencer); Cheshunt area, 1900, (W. C. Boyd); Walkern, 1940, (J. Birdsall); Bishops Stortford, 1945 – '… though not so commonly as in 1944; four or five moths were recorded in the town and a caterpillar was found in a garden; quite an event!'; Arkley, 12th October 1953 (*SLENHS* ***1953–54:*** 32); Bishops Stortford, one on 26 August 1954 (C. Craufurd); Bishops Stortford, one on 8 October 1959 (C. Craufurd); Berkhamsted, one on a lamp-post taken by Mrs H. H. S. Hayward (Bell, 1961); Tring, two in September 1960 by A. L. Goodson (Bell, 1962); Welwyn, one found dead in 1976 by Peter Waterton (Bell, 1977); Warren Way, Digswell, 14 September 1976, (T. W. Gladwin); Cowheath Wood, August 1977, (D. Webster); Furneux Pelham (village), 22 September 1991, (P. Jenner); Latimer Close, Hemel Hempstead, 10 Oct 1995, (M. Newland); Lyndsey Close, Bishops Stortford, 13 Oct 1995, (J. Fish); The Manse, Little Hadham, 1999, (G. Senior); Quickswood, 31 August 2001, (Dug Heath); Quickswood, 22 September 2001, (Dug Heath); Gubblecote, Long Marston, 14 August 2003, (Peter Bygate); Quickswood, 19 August 2003, (Ellie May); Shenley, 30 August 2003, (Bill & Pearl Page); Quickswood, 16 September 2003, (Dug Heath); Bishops Stortford, 20 September 2003, (John Horrocks); Hitchin, 16 July 2005, (Angus Kindley); Pentley Park, Welwyn Garden City, July 2005, (Tim Hill); Anstey, 07 November 2005, (George Martin); Whitelands Avenue, Chorleywood, 16 September 2006, (Richard Ellis); Yorke Road, Croxley Green, 16 September 2006, (Colin Grant); Shenley, 16 September 2006, (Bill and Pearl Page); Hemel Hempstead, 19 September 2006, (F. Tuck); Harpenden (RIS trap 475), 23 September 2006, (Phil Gould) and High Street, Hunsdon, 23 September 2006, (Sue Staniforth).

1973 *Acherontia atropos* (L.) Death's-head Hawk-moth

Recorded:	1869 – 2006
Distribution / Status:	Random / Immigrant and temporary resident
Conservation status:	Stable
Caterpillar food plants:	Potato
Flight period:	July to October
Records in database:	24

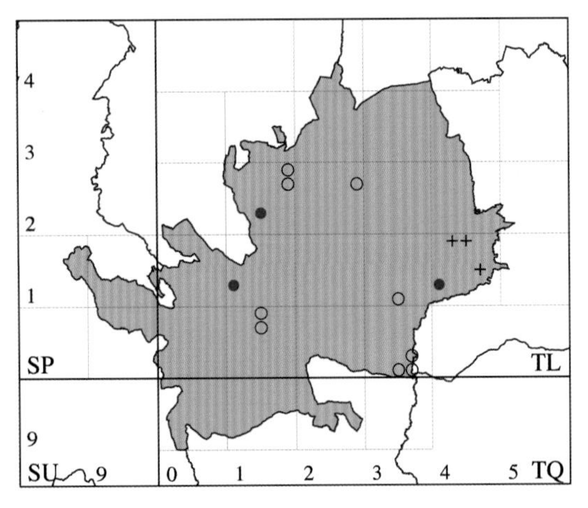

Hertfordshire records known are as follows: Lilley, 1869 (Rev. P. H. Jennings, *Entomologist* **2**: 325); Watford, 1875 – 'The neighbourhood of Watford is singularly prolific of that fine insect the death's head moth (*Acherontia Atropos*), and search in any large potato field towards the end of July will probably be successful' (J. H. James, 1875. *Transactions of the Watford Natural History Society* **1**: 64); Haileybury College area, 1887 (Bowyer, 1889); Grange Street, St Albans, Jul 1892, (A. Lewis); Campbell Street, St Albans, 12th July 1892, (Mrs Ashdown); near Hitchin, 1895, (F. Latchmore); Hitchin, 1895, (H. Gatward); Cheshunt area, 1900, (W. C. Boyd); Cheshunt area, 1900, (W. C. Boyd); Larvae in the potato field around St Albans during 1902 (Miss Dickinson, reported in Barraud P. J., 1903); Leasey Bridge, a pupa on 18th October 1905 in a potato field and given to Miss Alice Dickinson and another at Sandbridgebury Farm, also in 1905 (Gibbs, 1906); An adult in the middle of the North Road near Baldock [presumably the Great North Road = the A1] in 1905 found by A. H. Foster (Gibbs, 1906); Larvae were 'often reported' in the fields around Walkern during the 1940s (J. Birdsall); One at Kimpton School House in September 1945 reported by Mr Patrick (Foster, 1946); One at The Hoo, Whitwell, 14th September 1949 by R. S. Ferry (specimen in Mill Green Museum); One 'taken at a Hemel Hempstead Fire Brigade practice' by R. B. Benson in 1950 (Bell, 1953); One at Bishops Stortford on 17 September 1955 (C. Craufurd) was one of a total of 381 reported British examples that year – the 'best' year for the species since 1933, when 101 were reported; St Albans, one in early September 1976 taken by N. E. Gammon (Bell, 1977); near Stevenage, a larva taken by Peter Waterton and reared by a Mr Cox of Little Wymondley (Bell, 1977); Much Hadham, 15th September 1991 (David Wilson); High Wych, 10th October 1991, (Bob Reed); Breachwood Green, 15th August 2003 (M. Bremner); Rothamsted Estate, 15th September 2004 (R. Harrington) and Hunsdon, 4th July 2006 (Sue Staniforth).

1976 *Sphinx ligustri* L. Privet Hawk-moth

Recorded:	1828 – 2006
Distribution / Status:	Widespread / Common resident
Conservation status:	Herts Stable
Caterpillar food plants:	Privet. Elsewhere, also on Lilac and Ash
Flight period:	June/July
Records in database:	465

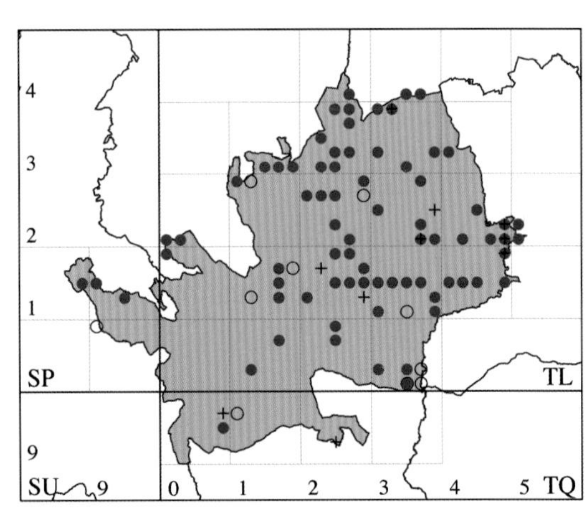

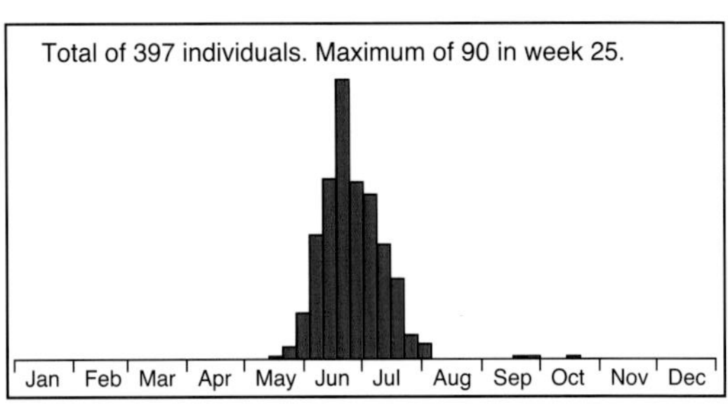

Although a commonly encountered moth today, the Privet Hawk-moth was formerly more local in its distribution. An increase in reports is noted from the late 1990s onwards with many older observers expressing surprise at finding it at various sites; the increase has been greatest in the north and east and there are significantly less reports from the south-west of the county in spite of more or less even survey effort. Although we have insufficient historical data to confirm the supposition, this population fluctuation appears unlikely to be an isolated event. Foster (1946) notes that in 1945 this moth was '... getting commoner and Mr Crawfurd *(sic)* tells me that at least forty-seven specimens were recorded by him [*in Bishops Stortford*] in thirty-five days'.

1978 *Hyloicus pinastri* (L.) Pine Hawk-moth

Recorded:	1844 – 2006
Distribution / Status:	Widespread / Common resident and probable immigrant
Conservation status:	Herts Stable
Caterpillar food plants:	Scots Pine
Flight period:	May to August
Records in database:	247

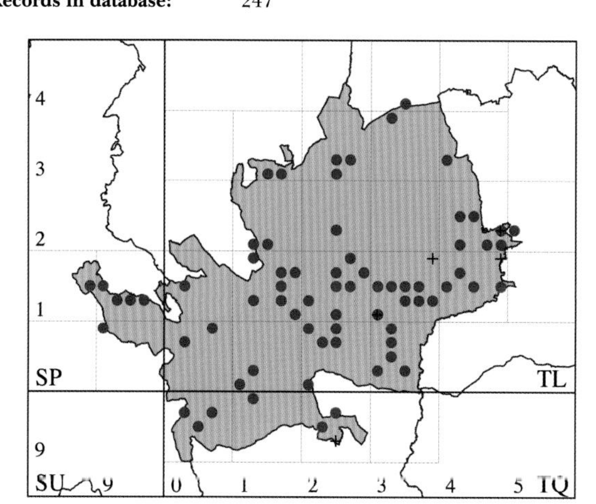

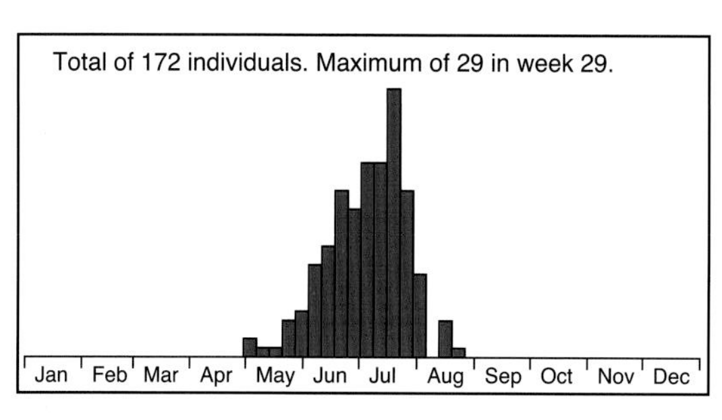

Foster (1937) notes that the diary of H. W. Lucas records Hitchin '*1844.9.Mo/18. Had a curious and rare moth brought yesterday called the pine hawk moth, said to be rarely found in England*'. This appears to be the first Hertfordshire record, although there was one at Colney Hatch Wood, just over the border in Middlesex, in about 1800 (Haworth, 1803). There appear to be no more records until one at Northchurch on 31 July 1948 (Bell, 1952, who regarded the Hitchin record as 'very doubtful' but without any justfication). Curiously, Bell (1953) records the third county example, at Harpenden during June 1951 by C. B. Williams, without any expression of surprise or any other comment. Riley (1999) indicates no further records of this species at Rothamsted until one in 1990 and one in 1996. Lorimer recorded singles at Totteridge on 23rd July 1953, 27th July 1953 and 1st June 1954, but caught no more in the garden trap before leaving the area in 1980. The next report was from the northern outskirts of Bishops Stortford, with one on 9th July 1955 (Clifford Craufurd), but there were no more until Charles Watson caught one on the southern side of the town in 1992. In the same town, there were none in my garden from 1986 to 2001, with my first arriving in 2002, perhaps suggesting that earlier records from Bishops Stortford may relate to immigrants or vagrants from elsewhere; the trap has been in direct view of a line of mature Scots Pine trees throughout the entire period. From the early 1990s onwards, the number of records increased from all over the county and by 2000 it was clear that the moth was common and established as a resident. In southern Europe, our Pine Hawk is replaced by a different species, *Sphinx maurorum* Jordan, the Southern Pine Hawk. The two are identical in appearance and can only be separated by characters of the genitalia, which are striking and easy to see with a hand lens; since Hertfordshire Pine Hawks originate from immigrant stock, it would not go amiss to check occasional specimens.

1979 *Mimas tiliae* (L.) Lime Hawk-moth

Recorded:	1828 – 2006
Distribution / Status:	Widespread / Common resident
Conservation status:	Herts Stable
Caterpillar food plants:	lime, Wych Elm, cherry, birch
Flight period:	April to July
Records in database:	409

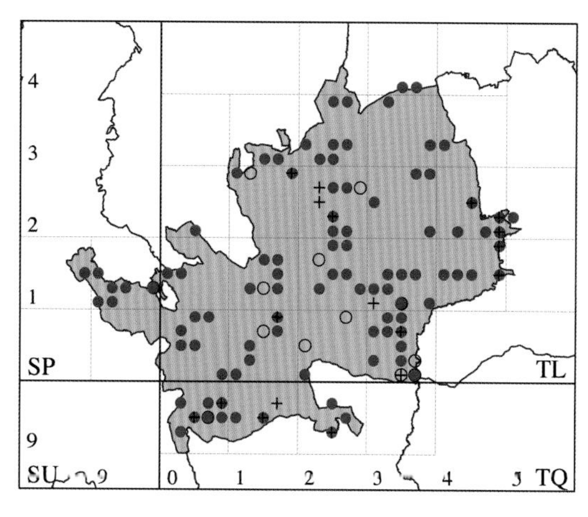

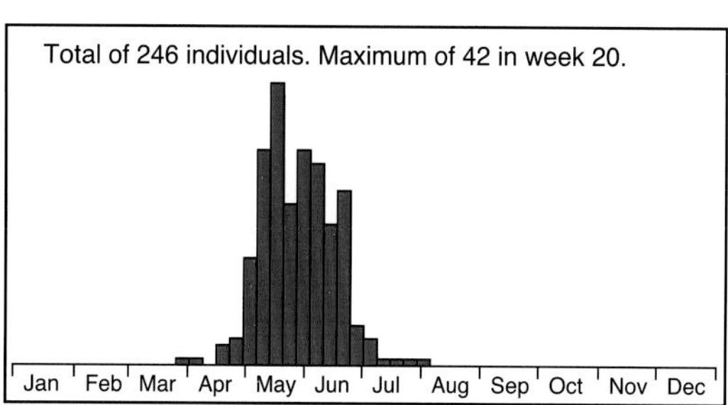

Although still a common species and still present at all its known sites, numbers may have declined over the last ten or so years. Nevertheless it is still expected to be present at almost every site where it is looked for in Hertfordshire.

1980 *Smerinthus ocellata* (L.) Eyed Hawk-moth

Recorded:	1828 – 2006
Distribution / Status:	Widespread / Common resident
Conservation status:	Herts Stable
Caterpillar food plants:	White Willow, Weeping Willow, Common Sallow
Flight period:	Mid-May to mid-July
Records in database:	239

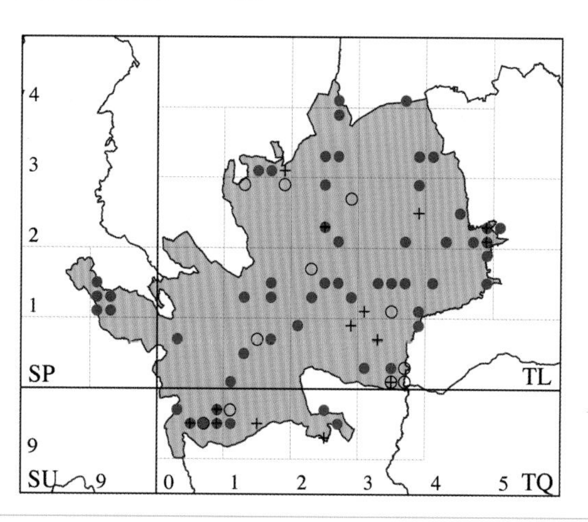

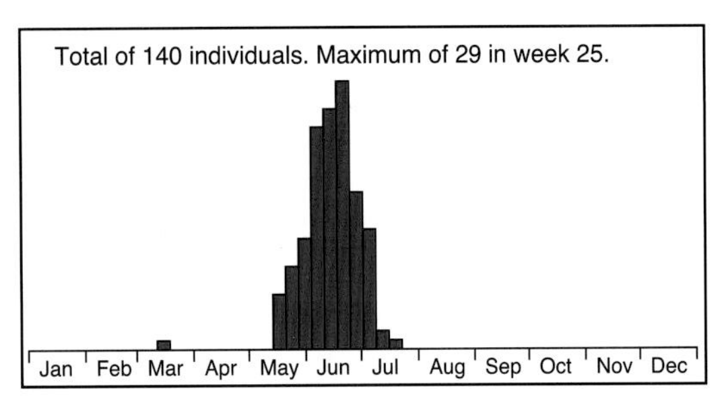

Although widespread, the Eyed Hawk-moth seems to prefer damp areas, perhaps because it favours sallows and willows as larval foodplants. Adults appear to fly late at night and often do not attend light traps until after midnight, so that traps taken in early will often not record this moth. Two extreme dates, one early on 17th March 2000 and one late, on 22nd July 1996 were both made in my garden light trap in Bishops Stortford.

1981 *Laothoe populi* (L.) Poplar Hawk-moth

Recorded:	1873 – 2006
Distribution / Status:	Ubiquitous / Common resident
Conservation status:	Herts Stable
Caterpillar food plants:	Common Sallow, White Willow, birch. Elsewhere also on poplar
Flight period:	May/June and July to September in two generations
Records in database:	927

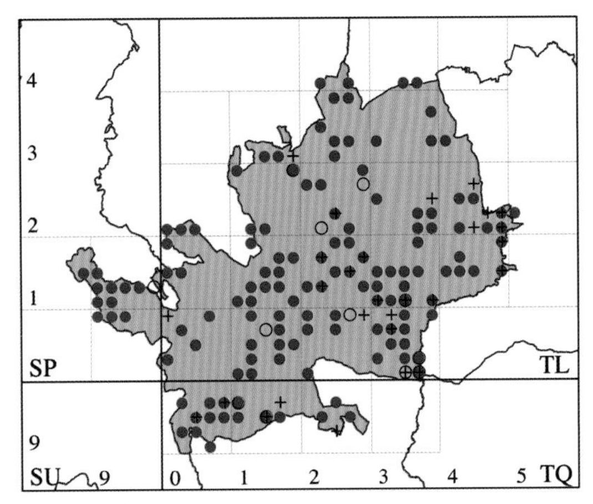

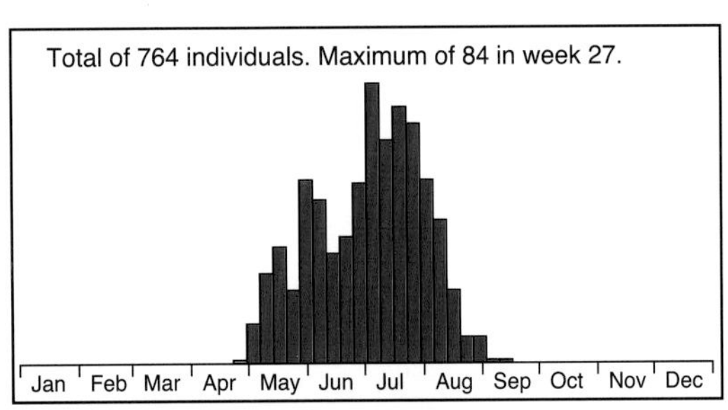

Skinner (1984; 1998) suggests that this species is usually single-brooded with occasional autumn generations; this is not the case in Hertfordshire, where a second generation has been the norm from 2000 to 2006 and is usually larger (in terms of moth numbers). The chart confuses the matter by combining years; if individual year records were to be plotted there would be a gap of about two weeks between the two peaks. A female was watched for about ten minutes, between 14.50 and 15.00 hours, by Andrew Middleton, egg-laying *during daylight* at Broxbourne Wood, on 2 August 2002. The moth was watched fluttering around the tip of a birch tree, approximately 20 feet tall, periodically stopping to lay eggs.

1982 *Hemaris tityus* (L.) Narrow-bordered Bee Hawk-moth

Recorded:	1888 – 1946
Distribution / Status:	Absent / Former resident
Conservation status:	UK BAP Priority Species. Herts Extinct
Caterpillar food plants:	Elsewhere, on Devil's-bit Scabious
Flight period:	May to July
Records in database:	10

Griffith (1884) lists *Macroglossum bombyliformis*, without any authority name, for the Sandridge district. The specific epithet *bombyliformis* has been applied to both the Narrow-bordered Bee Hawk-moth (*bombyliformis* sensu Esper) and the Broad-bordered Bee Hawk-moth (*bombyliformis* sensu Ochsenheimer). Griffith purports to be following names in the checklist by Doubleday (1862) which presents the two species as:

Fuciformis	***Bombyliformis***
Fuciformis, Linn.	*Bombyliformis*, Esp.
Bombyliformis, Och.	*Fuciformis*, Steph.

It was presumably on this basis that Foster (1937) included Griffith's record under the heading of *fuciformis* (Linnaeus) – Doubleday's '*Fuciformis*' and hence the Broad-bordered Bee Hawk-moth. However, all of Foster's other '*bomyliformis* Esp.' records are from woodlands (indicating that Broad-bordered Bee Hawk-moth was intended) and all his records of '*fuciformis* Linn.' are away from woodland in sites where Devil's-bit Scabious is likely to have been present at that time (indicating Narrow-bordered Bee Hawk-moth). Griffith's Sandridge area was '... a district six miles long by 2 miles wide, having the village of Sandridge at about its middle point'; if we assume that 'wide' means east-west, then the area is almost entirely open countryside, though probably included Symondshyde Great Wood. It is not at all clear which species Griffith intended. Thus, our earliest records of Narrow-bordered Bee Hawk-moth in Hertfordshire are from Welwyn, one in 1888 (Buller), near Tring Station, one taken and two others seen, 29th May 1922 (Croft), Royston Heath, one in 1922 (G. V. Bull), Hexton, one seen 28 May 1922 (Palmer), Graveley, one on 3rd June 1923 (Easton), Hitchin, one in the porch of the Victoria Inn, 2½ miles up Bedford Road, 28th July 1924 (Buller) and Hexton, one at *Arabis*, 1934 (Whiteman). These are all listed by Foster (1927). A single specimen '*caught on wing mid day, May 1940, Fulling Mill Welwyn*' by Roger Ferry is in the Mill Green Museum (seen by me). Fryer (1948) recorded an example at Essendon by L. S. Hodson in 1946. Bell (1954) notes two caught in Rothamsted Manor Gardens by J. B. Free in 1952. These were apparently reported to Bell by C. B. Williams, but there is no evidence to suggest that Williams, whose identification abilities were impeccable, ever saw the specimens. This latter record is, therefore, treated as unconfirmed.

1983 *Hemaris fuciformis* (L.) Broad-bordered Bee Hawk-moth

Recorded:	1888 – 1986
Distribution / Status:	Absent / Former resident
Conservation status:	Herts Extinct
Caterpillar food plants:	Wild Honeysuckle
Flight period:	Elsewhere, May/June
Records in database:	11

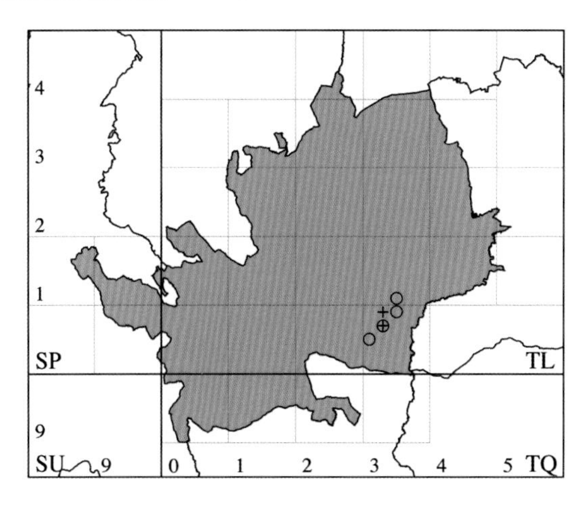

Nomenclatural confusion is discussed under the last species. The Broad-bordered Bee Hawk-moth was formerly resident in the Broxbourne Woods complex, much of which is now a National Nature Reserve. Unfortunately, it no longer appears to be present. Ignoring the confusing Sandridge record by Griffith (1884), the first certain report appears in the Haileybury School list (Bowyer, 1888). Gibbs (1893) reports it from Wormley in 1892 – 'Mr H. Warner, of Wormley, says that the broad-bordered bee clearwing moth (*S. fuciformis*) is to be taken in his neighbourhood. It seems to be very local, and is generally found in one particular swampy spot at the roadside, but it also frequents the woods where the bugle is plentiful'. Foster (1937) also lists Broxbourne Common in 1920 and 1921 (G. V. Bull) 'larvae plentiful' (Edelsten) and Broxbourne Woods (Boyd). In more recent times, the moth has been confined to restricted areas of the Broxbourne Woods complex, where it was a resident of some of the cleared areas before regrowth with conifers. Thus, in 1973 it was fairly common at the Brickendon end of Hoddesdonpark Wood (Jim Reid) and on 27th May 1974 (P. Waterton) and August 1977 (D. Webster) it was also recorded in Cowheath Wood. The last record appears to be a sighting on 15th June 1986, when by Ian Johnson saw one feeding on Ragged Robin during a Ruislip Natural History Society field trip to the Broxbourne Woods complex. The identity was confirmed during a repeat visit the next day with Kathleen and Philip Stead. A record from the Tring area given in Foster (1937) might suggest another focus for the species, but the precise locality and the date are obscure and it is possible that this report relates to misidentified Narrow-bordered Bee Hawk-moth, which was present in that area at the time the record was probably made. This record is omitted from the distribution map for the time being.

1984 *Macroglossum stellatarum* (L.) Humming-bird Hawk-moth

Recorded:	1828 – 2006
Distribution / Status:	Random / Regular immigrant
Conservation status:	-
Caterpillar food plants:	bedstraws; Red Valerian
Flight period:	All year except December and February
Records in database:	448

Records are too numerous to list individually. The first is the illustration of a Hertford area specimen in J. F. Stephens' *Illustrations of British Entomology* **1**: 134 (1828). It was also listed

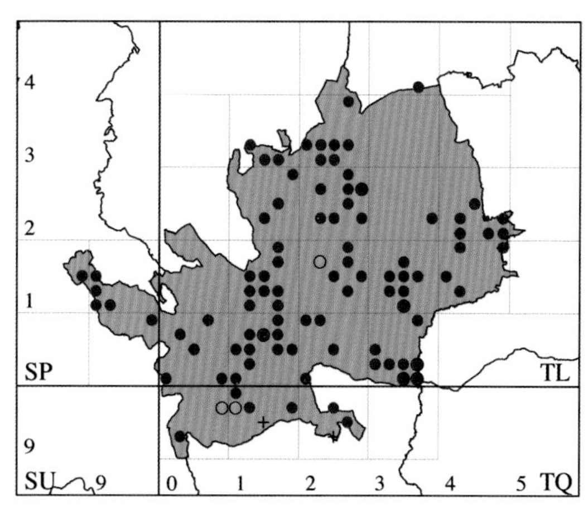

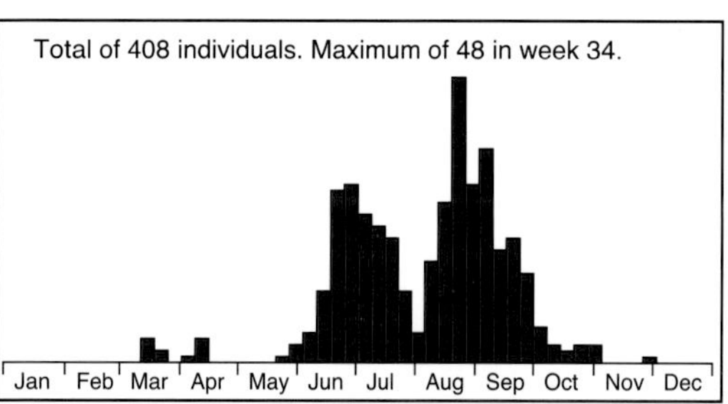

for the Sandridge area (Griffith, 1884) and for the Haileybury College area (Bowyer, 1888). Gibbs (1889), lists it for St Albans and Foster (1937) says that it was 'recorded from all districts, occasionally fairly common'. There are further records from Tring, in June 1943 (J. J. Flower) and Dudswell in the same year ('several' : J. J. Bell). Adults were bred from larvae found feeding on Red Valerian 'a most unusual food-plant' at Bishops Stortford in 1947 (Clifford Craufurd) and my daughter Rosie Plant found a mature larva wandering across the pavement in West Road, Bishops Stortford, evidently looking for a pupation site, in July 2003. Bell (1977) reports numerous Hertfordshire reports in 1976, but lists none of them and has left no archive. 2003 was an unusually good year for this species. There is a late-season record of one in St Albans town centre on 27th November 2003, seen by Vic Arnold. Details of all Hertfordshire records for which data are available are stored on the Herts Moth Database.

1985 *Daphnis nerii* (L.) Oleander Hawk-moth

Recorded:	1876 – 1876
Distribution / Status:	Random / Extremely rare immigrant
Conservation status:	-
Caterpillar food plants:	Overseas, on Oleander and Periwinkle
Flight period:	Elsewhere, August to October
Records in database:	1

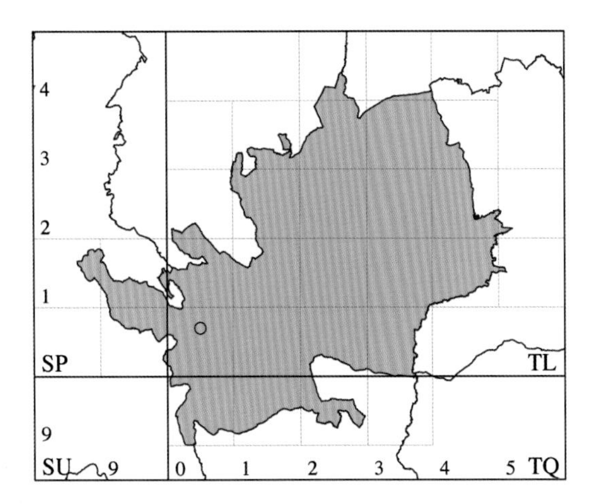

Piffard (1876. *Entomologist's Monthly Magazine* **13**: 138), reports 'I have just seen a specimen of *C. nerii* (the Oleander Hawk), taken by a gardener on the 15th October, in a garden near here, in the Alma Road. It is now in the possession of – Pitts, Esq., House Surgeon at the Infirmary of Hemel Hempstead'. Durrant (1888) repeats the record giving the same (correct) date, but Fry (1876. *Transactions of the Watford Natural History Society* **1**: 174) gives a different date, 13th October 1876, and adds that the specimen is a male. In subsequent reports, the specimen reportedly passed into the collection of G. T. Porritt of either Leeds (according to W. C. Boyd in *Entomologist's Monthly Magazine* **5**: 147) or Huddersfield (according to A H. Foster, 1937). There are no other Hertfordshire records of this large and colourful hawk-moth.

1987 *Hyles gallii* (Rott.) Bedstraw Hawk-moth

Recorded: 1859 – 2003
Distribution / Status: Random / Rare immigrant
Conservation status: -
Caterpillar food plants: Elsewhere on bedstraw, *Fuchsia* and willow-herbs
Flight period: Elsewhere, May to August
Records in database: 6

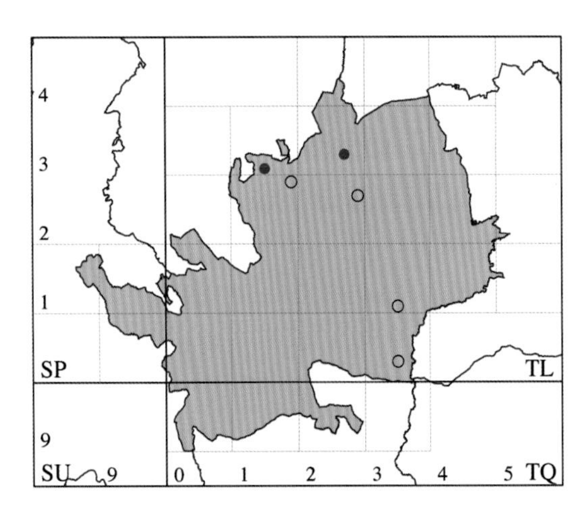

All known Hertfordshire records are listed**:** Cheshunt, 1859 – 'my nephew W. Boyd, within the first fortnight of this month .... and he did get *D. galii* into his net, but in his eagerness to secure it safely, it escaped' (Gaviller *Entomologist's Weekly Intelligencer* **7**: 3); Cheshunt Street, 12th August Boyd (1901) who, curiously, does not list his own earlier record given by Gaviller; Hitchin, one in 1888 (Gatward). In his 1916 paper on the Lepidoptera of North Hertfordshire, foster gives this as 'about the year 1880'; Listed by Bowyer (1888) for the Haileybury College area 'once', for an unspecified date prior to 1888; One was taken at the Walkern searchlight by Brian Waldock, on 28 July 1943, and was 'eagerly swapped by Rev. Greenham for a Convolvulus' (J. Birdsall); Danefield Road, Pirton, 23rd July 1997 (Dug Heath) and Quickswood, 15th July 2003 (Dug Heath).

1990 *Hyles livornica* (Esp.) Striped Hawk-moth

Recorded: 1868 – 2004
Distribution / Status: Random / Rare immigrant
Conservation status: -
Caterpillar food plants: Not recorded
Flight period: May, June and August
Records in database: 13

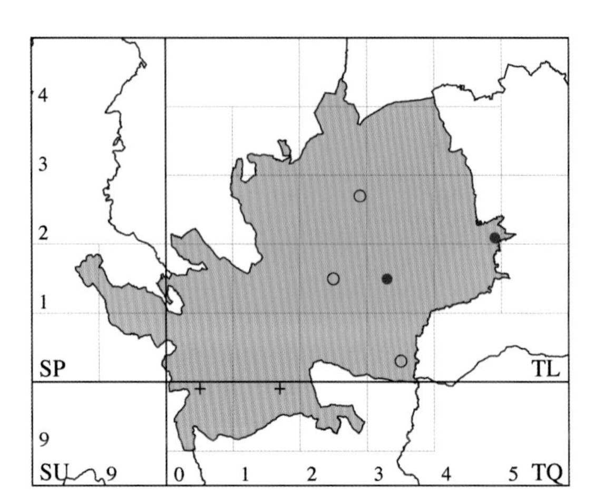

Cheshunt Street, 25th August 1868 (Boyd, 1868 & 1901; Gibbs, 1904a); Battler's Green, Aldenham, one in 1898 and another between 1898 and 1904, by Miss Ada Selby (Gibbs, 1904a); Rabley Heath, Knebworth, June 1931 (Harvey) in Foster (1937); One taken at a searchlight at Walkern on 1 August 1943 (Rev. W. D. W. Greenham); Unknown locality in southern Hertfordshire – at the meeting of the South London Entomological and Natural History Society held on 10th May 1950, 'Mr W. Wildridge reported that *Celerio livornica* Esp. had recently been taken in Herts.' (*SLENHS* ***1950 – 51****:* 9); Arkley, one on 27 March 1957 (Bell, 1959); Sarratt, a female resting among tall grass on 28th June 1962 (J. Mosedale, reported in de Worms, 1964); Radlett, at the end of June 1962 (R. A, French, reported in Bell, 1964); Walkern, 1st August 1943, (W. D. W. Greenham); Bengeo Street, Hertford, 28th June 2003 (Andrew Wood) and West Road, Bishops Stortford, 13th June 2004 (Colin Plant).

1991 *Deilephila elpenor* (L.) Elephant Hawk-moth

Recorded: 1828 – 2006
Distribution / Status: Ubiquitous / Common resident
Conservation status: Herts Stable
Caterpillar food plants: Rosebay Willow-herb; garden *Fuchsia;* Square-stemmed Willow-herb; Water Betony, garden Balsam (*Impatiens fulva*)
Flight period: June/July
Records in database: 1,031

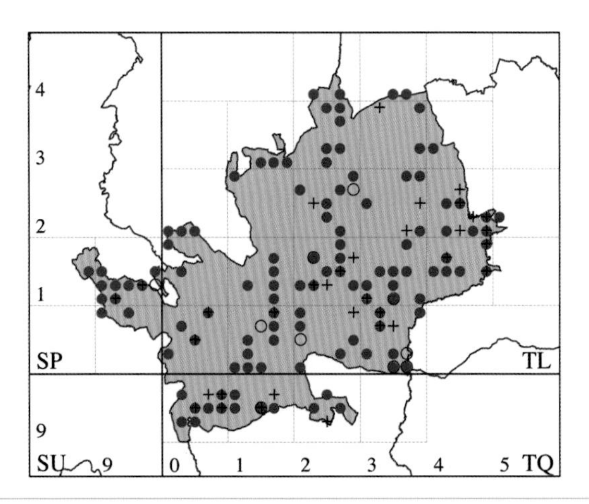

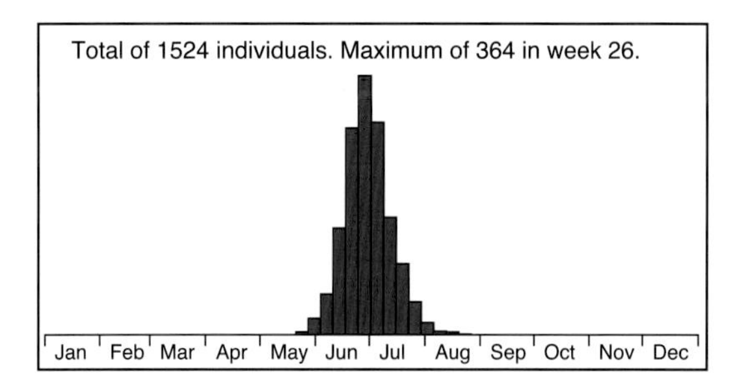

With over one thousand records in the database this striking 'pink elephant' is amongst the most frequently reported species in Hertfordshire. This is very largely due to the many reports of caterpillars received from the general public who find them wandering away from their foodplant in search of a suitable subterranean spot in which to pupate and pass the winter. Hodgson (1939) notes adults feeding from flowers of honeysuckle and rarely at sugar and flowing sap from pine at Ashridge.

1992 *Deilephila porcellus* (L.) Small Elephant Hawk-moth

Recorded: 1884 – 2006
Distribution / Status: Local / Uncommon resident
Conservation status: Herts Stable
Caterpillar food plants: bedstraw
Flight period: Late May to early July
Records in database: 150

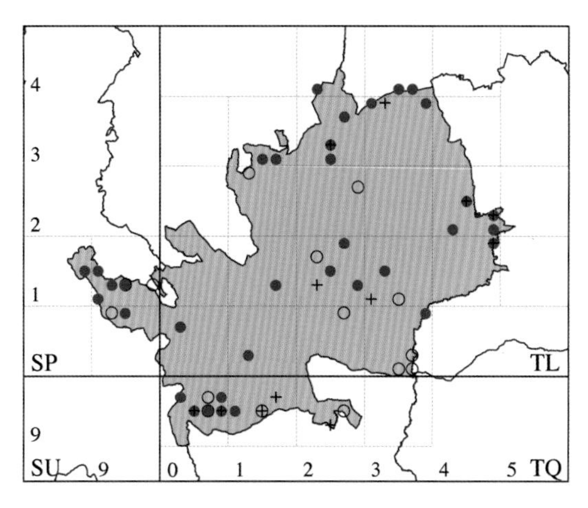

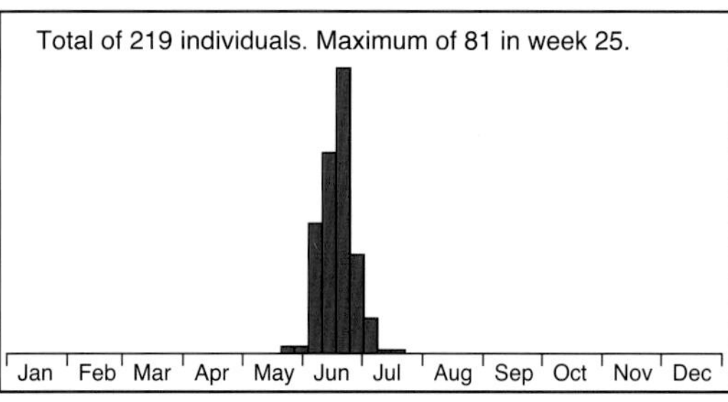

Although rather locally distributed and nowhere especially numerous, the Small Elephant Hawk-moth is nevertheless a familiar site in Hertfordshire for those who bother to look. During 2006 there were more sightings than usual (41 of the 150 records in the database emanate from that year); this might indicate a range expansion or perhaps immigration from overseas.

1993 *Hippotion celerio* (L.) Silver-striped Hawk-moth

Recorded: 1901 – 1958
Distribution / Status: Random / Rare immigrant
Conservation status: -
Caterpillar food plants: Elsewhere apparently polyphagous
Flight period: Elsewhere, April/May and August to October
Records in database: 2

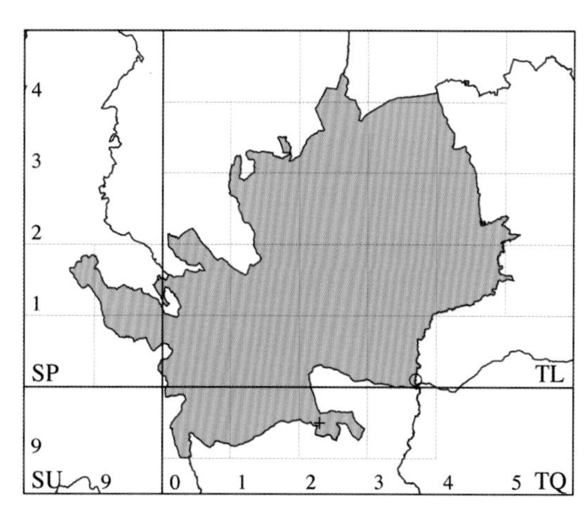

There are two Hertfordshire records. 'One at Waltham Cross' (Boyd, 1901) – Boyd was summarising records for the Cheshunt area and it is not possible to infer the year of the record from this entry; Arkley, one on 3rd October 1958 (T. G. Howarth). The record given by me for Oxhey in 1893 (Plant, 1993) in fact refers to an adult caught by H. Rowland-Brown at Oxhey Grove, near Harrow Weald, Middlesex (see Rowland-Brown, 1893).

NOTODONTIDAE

The 'prominents' and their allies take their group name from the projecting tuft of scales on the hind margin of the forewings. The British species all feed on the leaves of deciduous trees and shrubs and most are widespread and common, though a few are very rare and a few may only occur as immigrants from overseas. The overall total of 27 British species includes 2020: *Diloba caeruleocephala* which many researchers prefer to place within the Noctuidae. I have retained it in the Notodontidae here and, counting this species, we have 19 notodontids in Hertfordshire, though one is probably extinct.

1994 *Phalera bucephala* (L.) Buff-tip

Recorded: 1888 – 2006
Distribution / Status: Widespread / Common resident
Conservation status: Herts Stable
Caterpillar food plants: Common Lime, Common Hawthorn, English Elm, Silver Birch
Flight period: Mid-May to early August
Records in database: 557

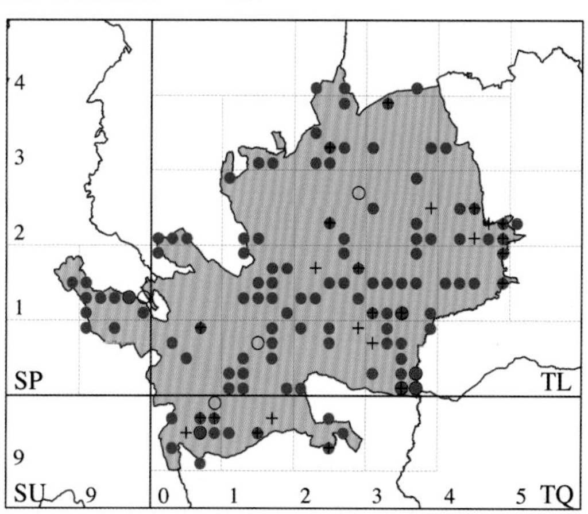

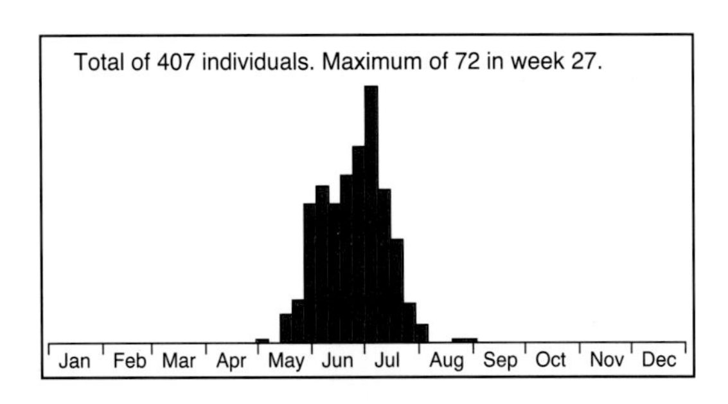

In 1937, Foster reported the Buff-tip as 'Generally abundant in all districts' and nothing much has changed. Lime trees are the most frequently reported pabulum, but this may be because they grow in streets and other places where the general public can see the distinctive caterpillars. In our woodlands and elsewhere, other trees are fed upon and the foodplant list is undoubtedly incomplete. Adults rarely attend light traps before midnight and are often the last species caught when packing up after an evening's trapping.

1995 *Cerura vinula* (L.) Puss Moth

Recorded: 1887 – 2006
Distribution / Status: Local / Rare resident
Conservation status: Herts Vulnerable
Caterpillar food plants: Grey Poplar, Common Sallow,
Flight period: Late April to end of June, elsewhere to late July
Records in database: 73

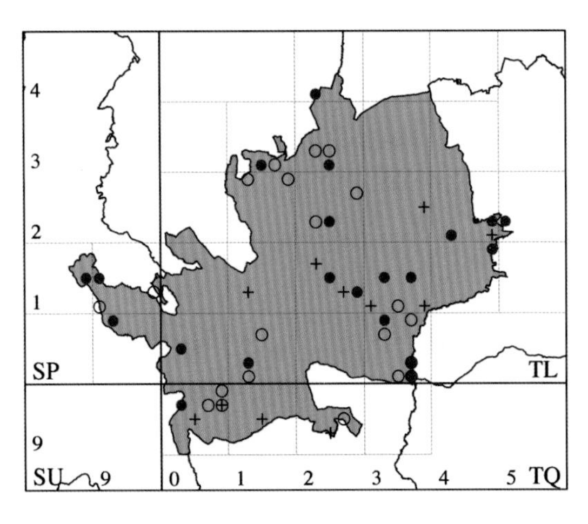

Of the 50 Hertfordshire localities mapped for this moth for all time, only 21 supported it during the 1995 – 2006 period, suggesting a decline of 58 per cent in occupied sites. However, this decline is probably an under-estimate. Most published references to this species imply that it was expected more or less everywhere in the county (the database only records sites mentioned specifically) and because today's recording is comparatively thorough we can be sure that this is not the case

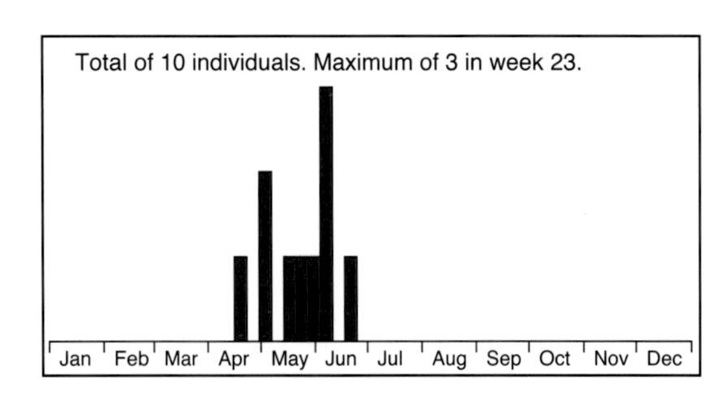

now; the number of sites from which this moth may have vanished is surely much higher. An interesting reference to ectoparasites on a larva, apparently found at Totteridge, is given by Curtis (1878).

1997 *Furcula furcula* (Cl.) Sallow Kitten

Recorded: 1828 – 2006
Distribution / Status: Widespread / Common resident
Conservation status: Herts Stable
Caterpillar food plants: Common Sallow
Flight period: April to August in two generations
Records in database: 194

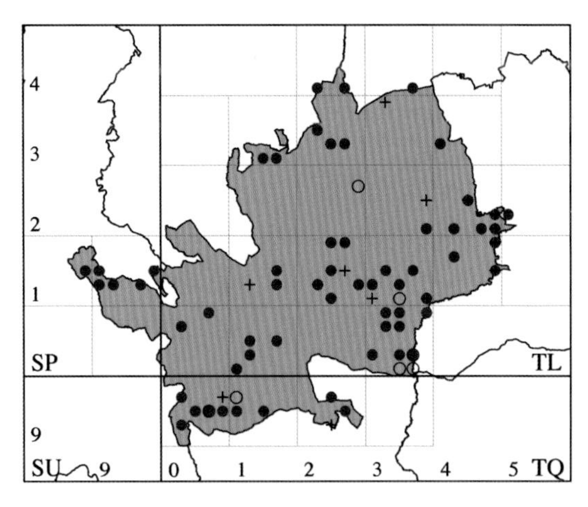

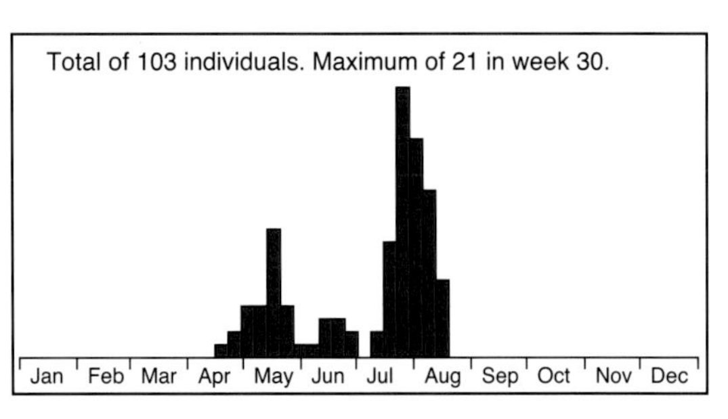

Separation of this species from the next, 1998: Poplar Kitten, causes much confusion, especially as both may fly together at the same site on the same date. The various identification guides should be referred to and only properly identified species should be reported. The Sallow Kitten is widespread and may be expected in all areas where sallows grow, especially in our river valleys and other damp places. Poplar trees are said to also support the larvae in other counties and may do so here, making habitat a wholly unsafe means of identifying moths caught.

1998 *Furcula bifida* (Brahm) Poplar Kitten

Recorded: 1887 – 2006
Distribution / Status: Local / Uncommon resident
Conservation status: Herts Scarce
Caterpillar food plants: poplar
Flight period: May to August in two generations
Records in database: 60

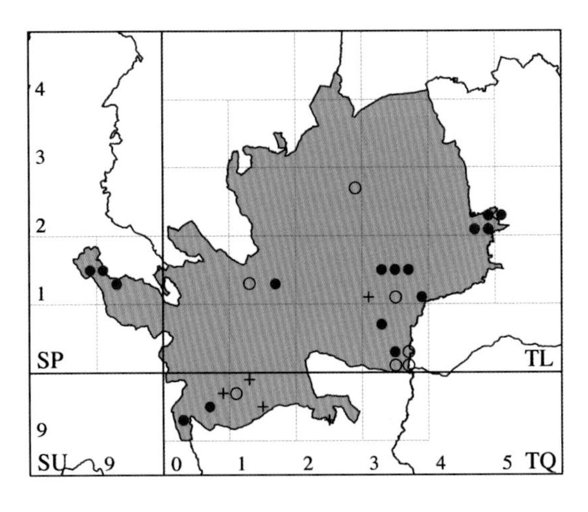

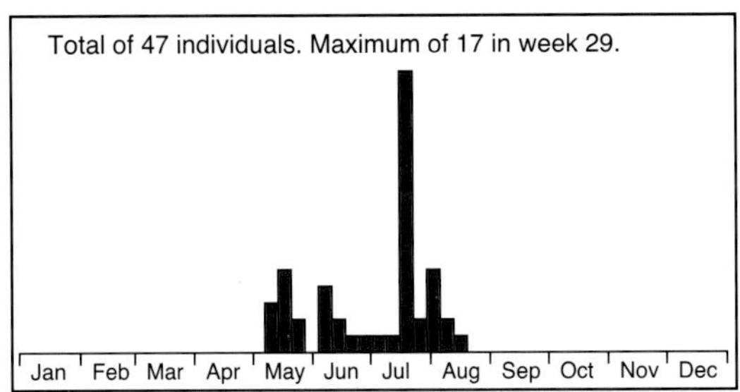

Confusion with 1997: Sallow Kitten has been mentioned under that species. The Poplar Kitten appears to be far less frequent in our county, with only one third the number of records in the database over the same time period and with large areas of the county apparently not supporting it. The reasons for this disparity between the species is not at all clear at the moment.

1999 *Stauropus fagi* (L.) Lobster Moth

Recorded: 1888 – 2006
Distribution / Status: Local / Common resident
Conservation status: Herts Stable
Caterpillar food plants: Beech, English Oak
Flight period: May to mid-July
Records in database: 139

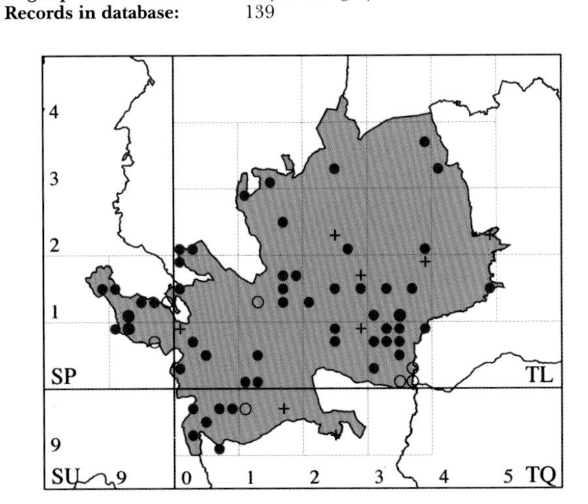

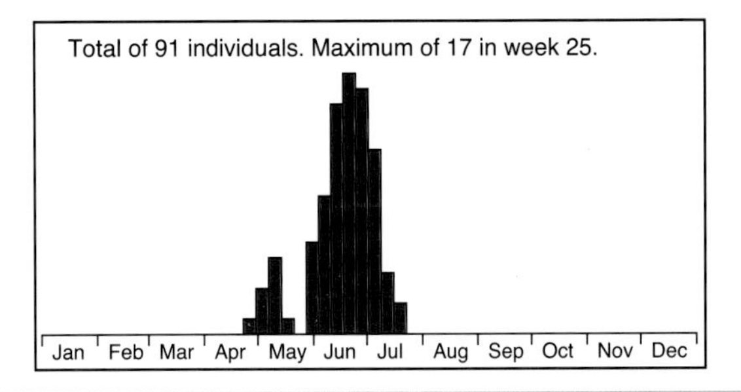

Beech is the main foodplant, and most moths are caught in beech woods or in woods where the trap is placed close to beech trees. Isolated, mature beech trees, such as those in some churchyards and larger gardens are equally capable of supporting the moth, but beech hedges, which are popular in some parts of Hertfordshire, apparently are not. It should be noted that adults may move some distance and arrive in garden traps away from areas where they breed. The distinctive caterpillar is what gives the moth its vernacular name, but they are evidently rather hard to find and perhaps prefer the higher branches of host trees.

2000 *Notodonta dromedarius* (L.) Iron Prominent

Recorded: 1895 – 2006
Distribution / Status: Widespread / Common resident
Conservation status: Herts Stable
Caterpillar food plants: Silver Birch
Flight period: Late April to the end of August
Records in database: 458

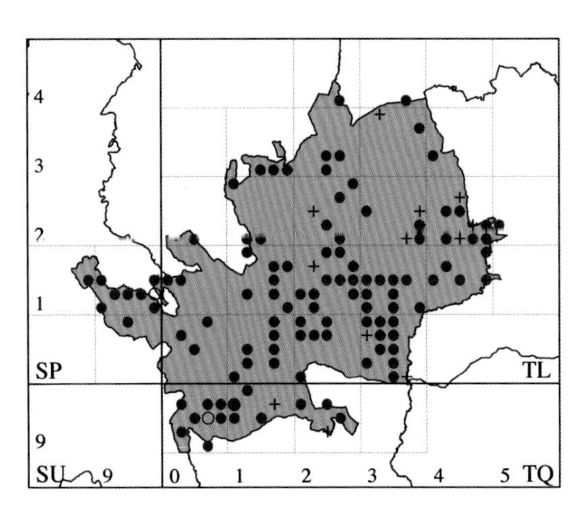

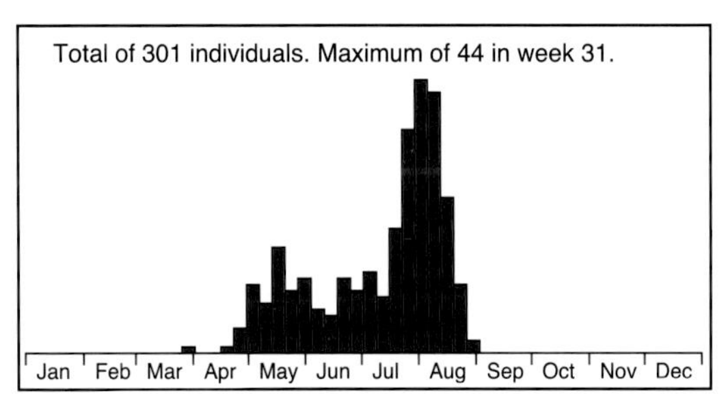

Birch is the main foodplant, though text books tell us that elsewhere it may occasionally feed on Alder and Hazel; these alternative foodplants are likely to be the reason for the presence of the moth in the calcareous northern areas where birches are relatively scarce. There are two generations of adults in each year and though the combination of several years' data in the chart suggests that the moth is found throughout the period from April to August this is not the case and there is usually a gap, albeit rather short, between broods. The early record in the chart was of an adult caught by Dave and Connal Murray at Whippendell Wood, on 31st March 2004.

2003 *Notodonta ziczac* (L.) Pebble Prominent

Recorded: 1887 – 2006
Distribution / Status: Widespread / Common resident
Conservation status: Herts Stable
Caterpillar food plants: Common Sallow
Flight period: Mid-April to mid-August in two generations
Records in database: 370

Unsurprisingly, given the shared foodplant, the distribution map is almost identical to that for 1997: Sallow Kitten, except that the present species has been found in a few additional tetrads. The numbers of individuals in the peaks in the flight chart are also almost identical, showing that both species are present in more or less equal *number* in light trap samples. Interestingly, there are almost twice as many *records* of Pebble Prominent in the database (370, compared with 194 for Sallow Kitten); thus, where a site may produce Sallow Kitten once, it will produce Pebble Prominent on several occasions. This perhaps suggests a greater degree of mobility on the part of the pebble Prominent.

2005 *Peridea anceps* (Goeze) Great Prominent

Recorded:	1888 – 2006
Distribution / Status:	Local / Common resident
Conservation status:	Herts Scarce
Caterpillar food plants:	English Oak, Sessile Oak
Flight period:	Late April to end of May
Records in database:	36

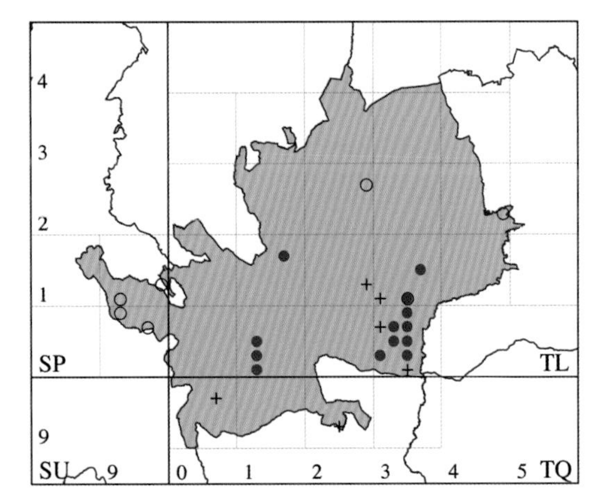

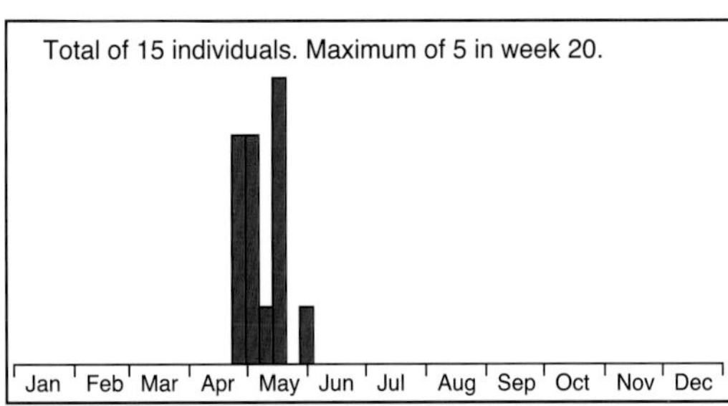

The ancient oak-dominated woodlands on clay soil, flanking the River Lea in the south-east of the county, mostly comprising the various components of the Broxbourne Woods National Nature Reserve, and similar habitat at Bricket Wood are the sites that currently support this large moth. The moth is apparently absent from the ancient woodland that is the Epping Forest National Nature Reserve on the east side of the River Lea in Essex and it is possibly significant that woodland there rests on a deposit of glacial gravel rather than clay (in fact there do not appear to be any records at all of this moth from Essex). There are old records from Whippendell Wood and the moth must surely still be there undetected? The apparently stray record in TL 11 is from Hall Wood, Kimpton (Vincent and Betty Judd) where similar habitat persists. A number of old records are evident in the west, in the woodlands on our border with Buckinghamshire; almost no early season work has been done in this area in recent years and the moth must surely still be there.

2006 *Pheosia gnoma* (Fabr.) Lesser Swallow Prominent

Recorded:	1895 – 2006
Distribution / Status:	Widespread / Common resident
Conservation status:	Herts Stable
Caterpillar food plants:	Silver Birch
Flight period:	April to June then July/August in two generations
Records in database:	313

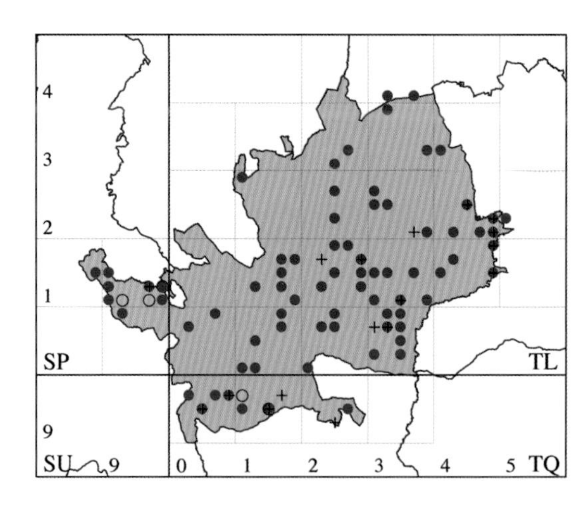

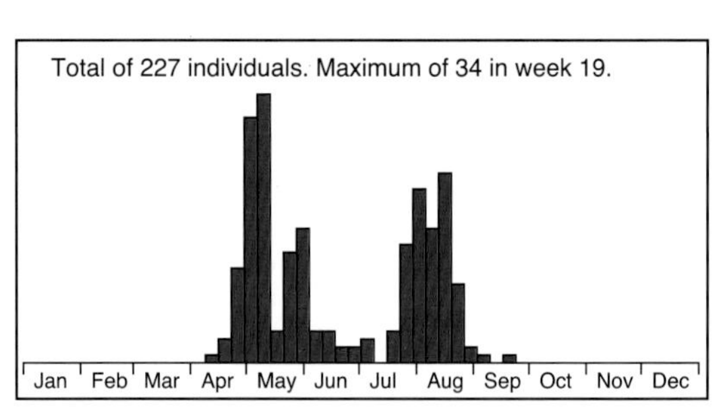

The Lesser Swallow Prominent is a familiar species to everyone who runs a light trap in Hertfordshire, though reports of larvae are less frequent now than in the days before light traps were invented! The white 'wedge' mark on the forewing used to separate this species from 2007: Swallow Prominent can be intermediate and the hind wing character described in Skinner (1998) should be used as the favoured means of separation.

2007 *Pheosia tremula* (Cl.) Swallow Prominent

Recorded:	1893 – 2006
Distribution / Status:	Widespread / Common resident
Conservation status:	Herts Stable
Caterpillar food plants:	Not recorded. Elsewhere, on poplar, willow and sallow
Flight period:	Mid-April to early September
Records in database:	393

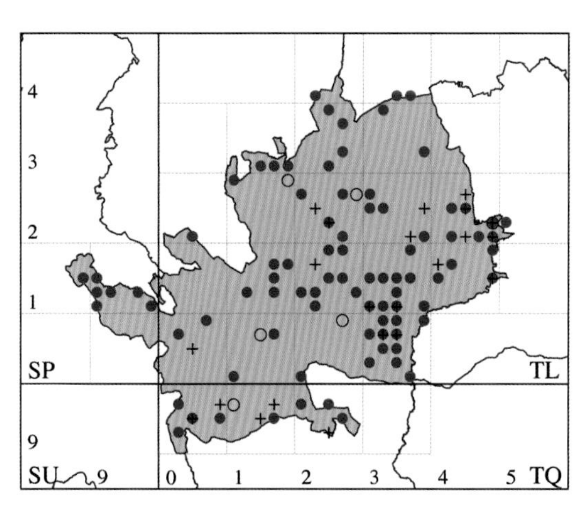

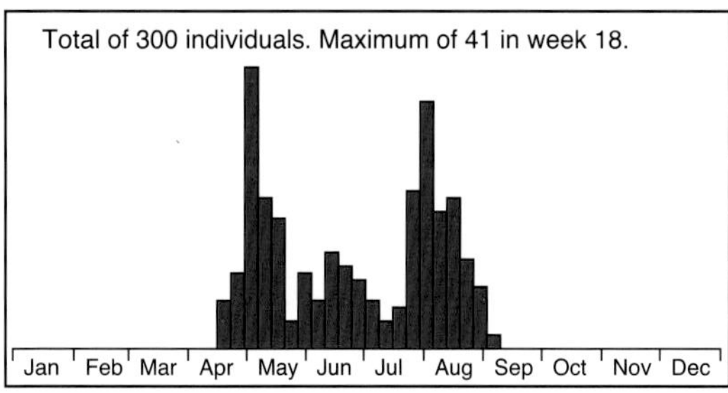

Like the last species, this is also widespread and common across the county. In most of southern Britain there are two adult generations per year, in May/June and then August/September. However, our data from Hertfordshire shows that in this county for 1995 to 2006 the first generation starts in mid-April and the second commences in late July, scarcely extending at all into September. There is also the impression of an extra brood in June and July. This appears likely to be the result of recent trends in weather patterns, with moths emerging early in what we regard as unseasonally warm weather in late April/early May then being knocked back by the return of cold weather in mid-May, with June adults arising from the same generation of over-wintered pupae. However, the reason why not all adults emerge from the same batch of over-wintered pupae in April and early May remains a mystery and perhaps this species has developed overlapping generations in response to changes in weather patterns in recent years?

2008 *Ptilodon capucina* (L.) Coxcomb Prominent

Recorded:	1888 – 2006
Distribution / Status:	Widespread / Common resident
Conservation status:	Herts Stable
Caterpillar food plants:	Common Hawthorn, Silver Birch Elsewhere, on many deciduous trees
Flight period:	Mid-April to August in two generations
Records in database:	309

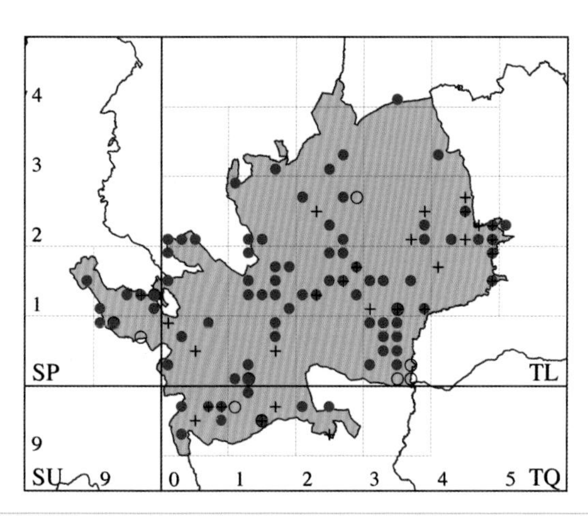

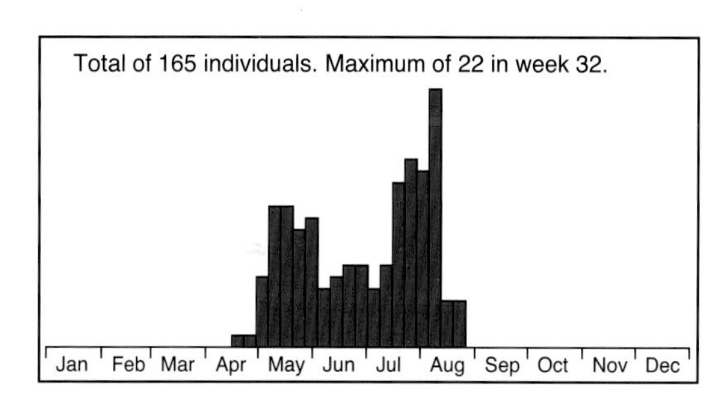

Foster (1937) lists several records across the county, from Tring in the West to Bishops Stortford in the east and from East Barnet in the south to Hitchin in the north; that situation persists today. In the seven years from 2000 to 2006, there was a clear gap between first and second adult generations during June in 2000, 2001, 2002 and 2004, but in 2003, 2005 and 2006 moths were seen more or less throughout the period from May to August. April records are from 2002 and 2006 only.

2009 *Ptilodon cucullina* ([D.& S.]) Maple Prominent

Recorded:	1857 – 2006
Distribution / Status:	Widespread / Common resident
Conservation status:	Herts Stable
Caterpillar food plants:	Field Maple
Flight period:	May to August
Records in database:	233

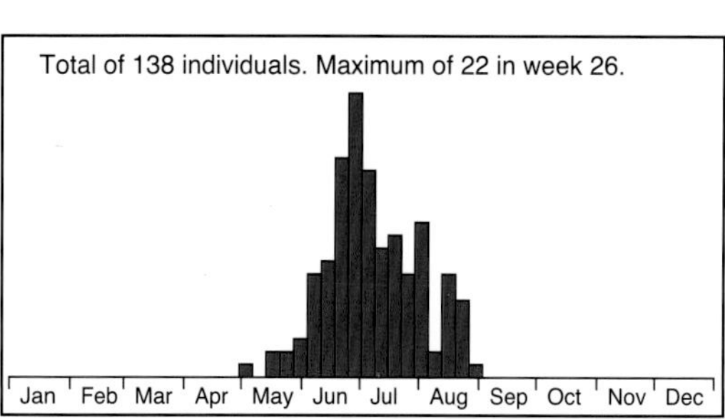

At the time of Foster's 1937 list for the county, there were only two records of this moth: at Tring – 54 larvae (Greene, *Ent. Annual*, **1857**; 114) and '... two larvae once beaten in Herts' (*Quarterly Magazine of the High Wycombe Natural History Society*, 1869: 97 – 104). Further investigation suggests that these two reports might in fact relate to the same record and Durrant (1888) queries whether or not the location was actually in Hertfordshire. S. B. Hodgson (*Transactions of the Hertfordshire Natural History society & Field Club* **20**(5): 353), reports one worn adult at Long Green, Berkhamsted on 13 July 1937, commenting that its apparent absence since the two above records was surprising as the species was common in south Buckinghamshire. There are no further reports until 1955 when one was noted on a fence at Berkhamsted on 2 August (*Entomologist's Record* **67**: 238) and 'two or three' were noted in the same year in Bishops Stortford by Clifford Craufurd (Bell, 1957). In spite of Charles Watson trapping in Bishops Stortford for many years thereafter, he did not get his first until 1990, three years after my first in 1987; the latter year was my first full year of trapping in the town and so there are no data for earlier years. A slow but steady trickle of records, at the rate of four or five per year, came from various parts of the county throughout the early 1990s as the moth apparently established itself over a wide area and by 1998 it was pretty well everywhere – a situation which persists today. The reasons for this recent and rather rapid colonisation of the county are obscure, but since it is apparent that young maple trees can support larvae the possibility exists that the relatively recent mania for planting trees on new road verges may be partly responsible. Elsewhere, it is reported that the larvae can thrive on Sycamore, though there has been no apparent change in the distribution of this tree over the years that the moth has become numerous in our county.

2010 *Odontosia carmelita* (Esp.) Scarce Prominent

Recorded:	1905 – 2006
Distribution / Status:	Very local / Uncommon resident
Conservation status:	Herts Scarce
Caterpillar food plants:	Birch
Flight period:	Mid-April to mid-May
Records in database:	22

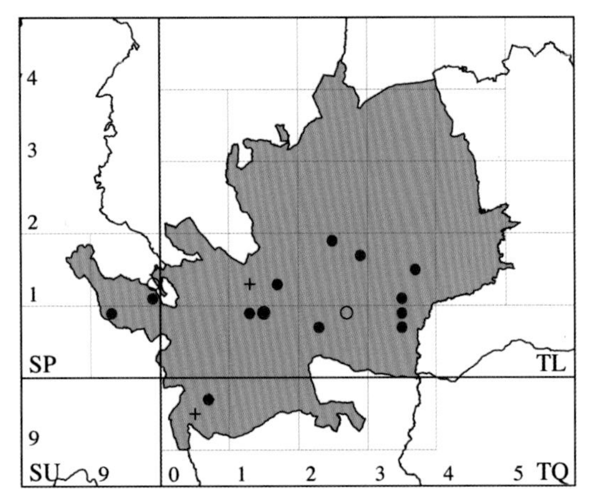

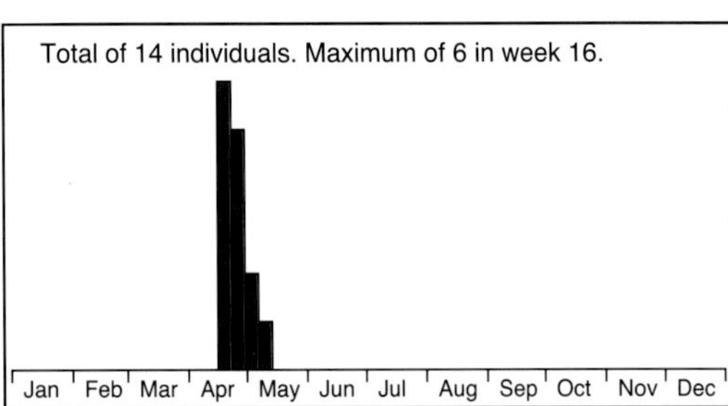

The Scarce Prominent is probably under-recorded because of its early adult flight period, but is nevertheless unlikely to prove a common moth in our county. It is also rather unlikely that its distribution here will extend a great deal further north than the map already indicates, as a woodland habitat containing mature birch trees appears to be necessary for it to thrive; this type of habitat in the south of the county, however, is likely to support it. Our only larval foodplant record is from Ashridge in 1934.

2011 *Pterostoma palpina* (Cl.) Pale Prominent

Recorded:	1828 – 2006
Distribution / Status:	Widespread / Common resident
Conservation status:	Herts Stable
Caterpillar food plants:	Lombardy Poplar. Elsewhere on poplars, aspen and sallow
Flight period:	April to August in two generations
Records in database:	512

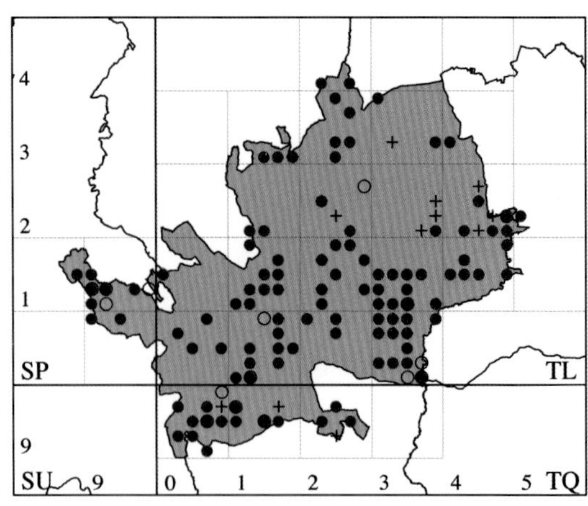

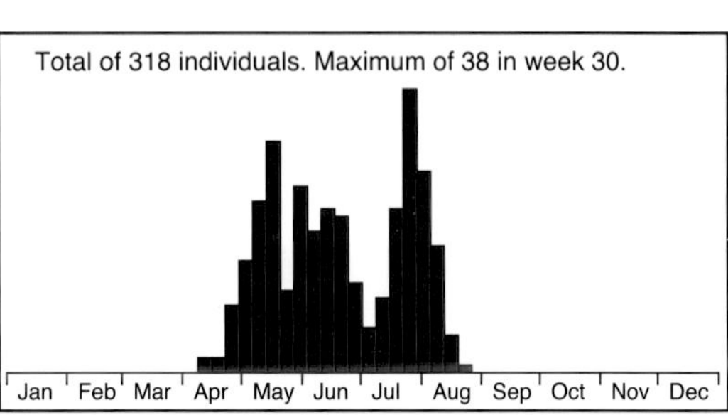

If there is a gap at all when this moth is not flying it is in July, but the records in all years since 1995 show the moth more or less continuously caught throughout the flight period. Thus, although two clear peaks are discernible, the first generation of adults is a lengthy affair. Comments under 2007: Swallow Prominent may be relevant to anyone choosing to research these phenomena.

2014 *Drymonia dodonaea* ([D.& S.]) Marbled Brown

Recorded:	1888 – 2006
Distribution / Status:	Local / Uncommon resident
Conservation status:	Herts Scarce
Caterpillar food plants:	English Oak
Flight period:	May/June
Records in database:	57

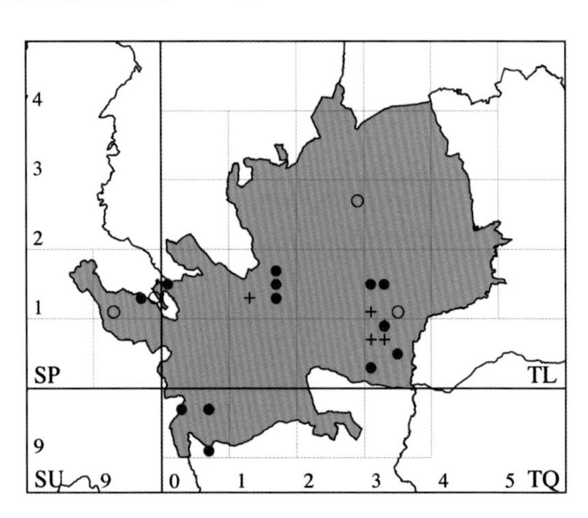

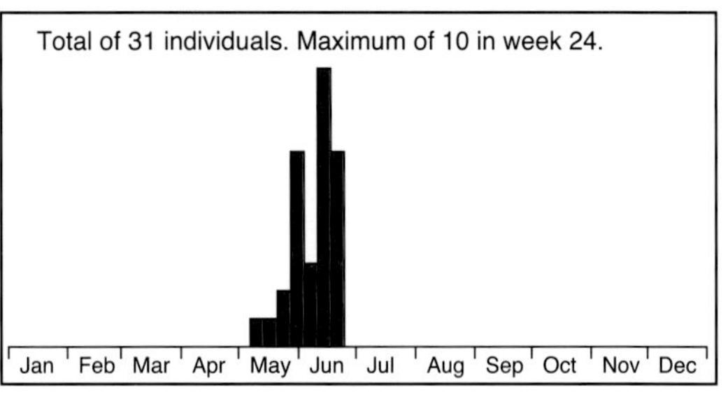

Apart from an early record in Hertford on 18th April 2002 (Andrew Wood) the moth flies consistently in May and June, so aiding in its separation from 2015: Lunar Marbled Brown, which flies throughout April and early May. This species is surprisingly scarce in our county, in stark contrast to the Lunar Marbled Brown with which it shares the same foodplant.

2015 *Drymonia ruficornis* (Hufn.) Lunar Marbled Brown

Recorded: 1888 – 2006
Distribution / Status: Widespread / Common resident
Conservation status: Herts Stable
Caterpillar food plants: English Oak
Flight period: April to mid-May
Records in database: 236

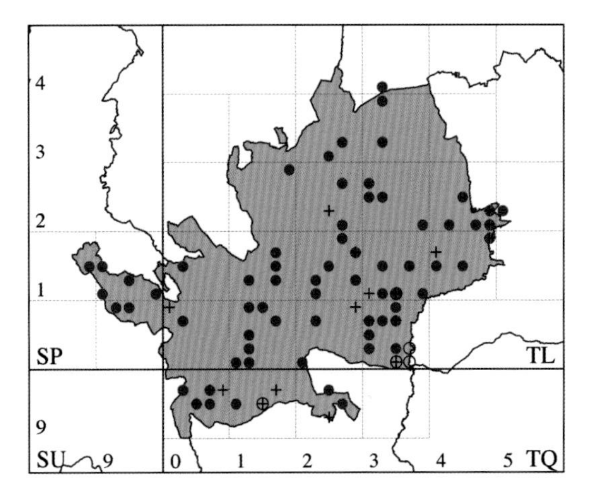

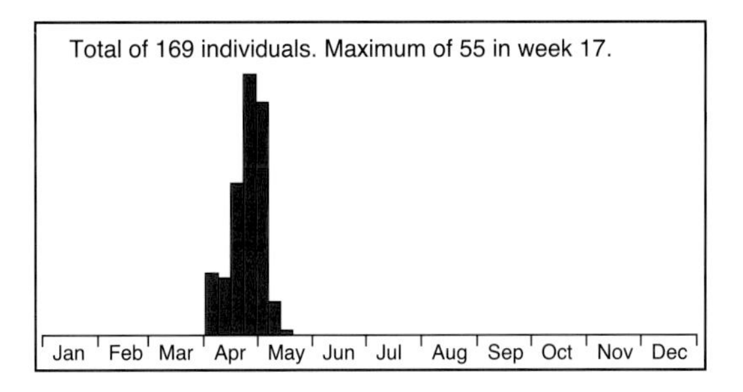

As the number of database records indicate, this species is about five times more frequently encountered than 2014: Marbled Brown, though both share similar habitat and identical foodplants. It is far more widespread and is likely to be found in most parts of the county; the possibility that is has an alternative larval foodplant should not be completely dismissed.

2017 *Clostera pigra* (Hufn.) Small Chocolate-tip

Recorded: 1901 – 1912
Distribution / Status: Absent / Former resident
Conservation status: Herts Extinct
Caterpillar food plants: Not recorded. Elsewhere, on sallows
Flight period: Not recorded. Elsewhere, May and August
Records in database: 5

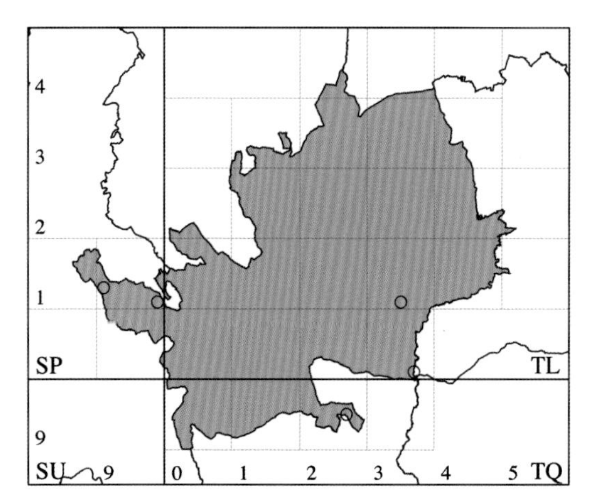

Our elderly records are from Cheshunt Marsh where Boyd (1901) reported it as 'scarce'; from Haileybury School prior to 1900; Brown's Lane, Tring in 1901 and East Barnet towards the end of the nineteenth century, these last all given in Foster (1937). Later, Foster (1942) adds Berkhamsted 'one, 1912' by J. Bell. The species was last seen in Bedfordshire to our north-west in 1803 and apart from one record in 1982 appears to be absent in recent years from Essex to the east. No other records are known.

2019 *Clostera curtula* (L.) Chocolate-tip

Recorded: 1890 – 2006
Distribution / Status: Local / Uncommon resident
Conservation status: No perceived threats
Caterpillar food plants: Not recorded. Elsewhere, on poplars and sallows
Flight period: April/May then late July/August in two generations
Records in database: 161

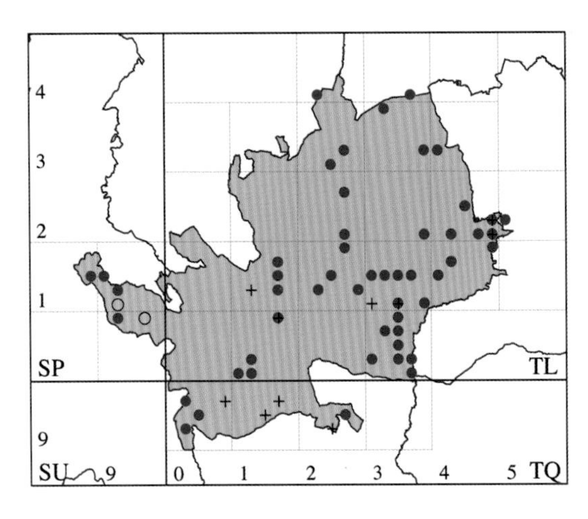

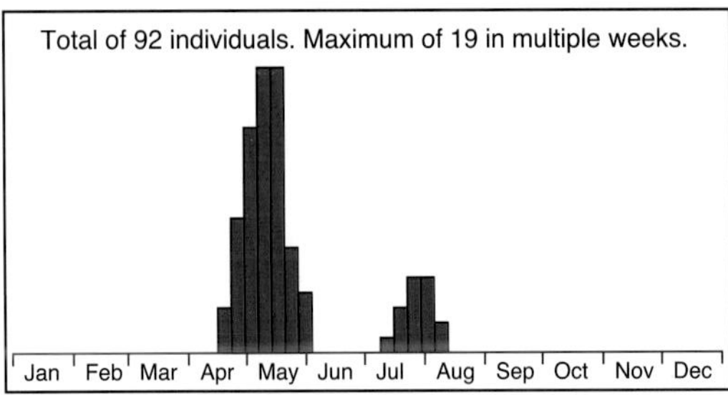

Foster (1937) listed only Sandridge [pre-1890], Bushey Heath (1901) and Broxbourne Common, 1922, suggesting that this may have been an uncommon species at that time. J. Bell recorded just one at Berkhamsted in 1913 (Foster, 1942) and Eric Classey noted it as 'not common' at Broxbourne in the late 1930s. A. L. Goodson took one at Tring in 1953 (now in the Roger S. Ferry Collection at Mill Green Museum). Today, lone individuals typically turn up in traps in suitable habitat over much of the county and occasionally, though not often, wander further afield and arrive in garden light traps.

2020 *Diloba caeruleocephala* (L.) Figure of Eight

Recorded:	1887 – 2006
Distribution / Status:	Widespread / Uncommon resident
Conservation status:	UK BAP Watch List. Herts Vulnerable
Caterpillar food plants:	Common Hawthorn; Blackthorn
Flight period:	October/November
Records in database:	76

I have followed current British practice and retained this species in the Notodontidae, though its affiliations with the Noctuidae may be stronger. National populations have apparently suffered a 95 per cent decline since 1970. Unfortunately, poor reporting means that we have no real idea of its former status in Hertfordshire, with Foster (1937) merely stating 'Recorded from all districts; frequently common'. The low number of circles and crosses on the

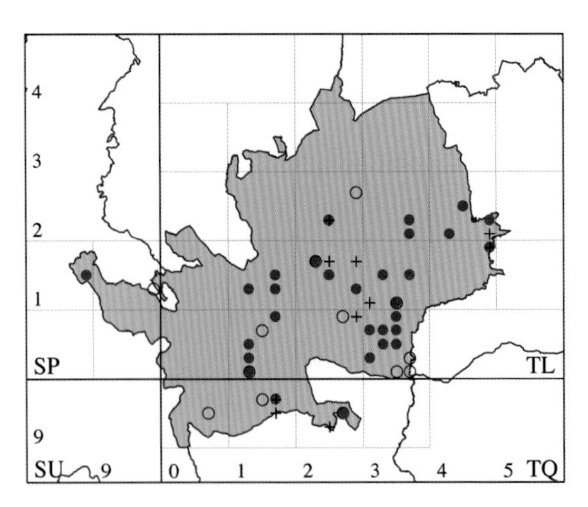

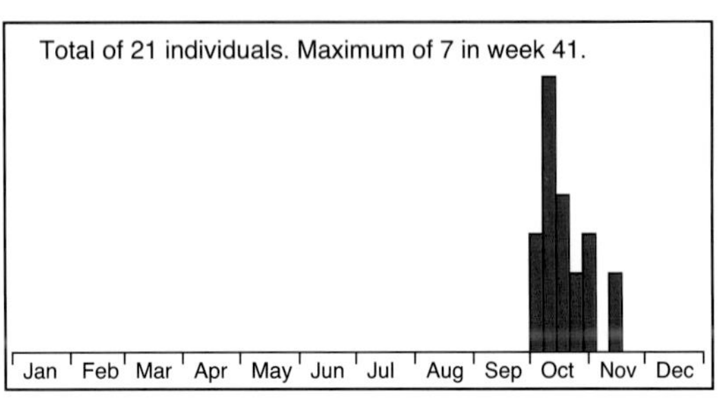

distribution map reflects this and with the exception of a couple that cannot be assigned to a tetrad, all records are included. The present-day distribution shows a remarkable correlation with what Thomasson & Avery (1963) described as 'leached soils'. These would originally have been acid, usually with finer textured subsoil horizons, and include loamy and gravelly drift over chalk, gravely fluvioglacial and river drift, Brickearths, Clay-with-Flints, Pebble Clay, Decalcified Boulder Clay, London Clay and the Reading Beds. The moth is quite absent from Chalk and associated Chalky Drift, Chalk Marl and associated Drift, Gravelly Clay over Gault, Chalky Boulder Clay and the Alluvial deposits and may perhaps always have been so. Foster's statement that it was recorded from all districts is most unlikely to have been true: 'recorded from traditional collecting localities' may have been nearer the truth.

THAUMETOPOEIDAE

2022 *Thaumetopoea processionea* (L.) Oak Processionary

Recorded:	1979 – 1979
Distribution / Status:	Absent / Former immigrant
Conservation status:	Notifiable pest species
Caterpillar food plants:	Not recorded. In Europe on oak – causing extensive defoliation
Flight period:	In Europe, July/August
Records in database:	1

Occasional males occur in Britain, mostly on the south coast, as primary immigrants and this is probably the source of one at Totteridge in 1979 (Ian Lorimer). The frequency of immigrant males is increasing in Britain, but the species, which is a serious pest in parts of Europe, is unable to establish here as long as there are no females. However, during 2006 there was an outbreak of this species in Middlesex as a result of larval nests being introduced on oaks imported from Holland; eradication measures were put into place, but the outbreak was not discovered until the moth had spread from the original point of introduction, so it is possible that some remain and could turn up in southern Hertfordshire. Suspected sightings should be reported immediately, rather than waiting until the end of the year.

LYMANTRIIDAE

The Lymantriidae is a family of about 2,500 species worldwide all of which have 'hairy' caterpillars. In many cases the hairs cause a rash of variable severity in humans and in some cases this may require medical attention. Of the eleven British species we have reports of eight in Hertfordshire, though one is now extinct and one is reported only on two occasions, both as an immigrant.

2025 *Orgyia recens* (Hb.) Scarce Vapourer

Recorded:	1888
Distribution / Status:	Absent / Former resident
Conservation status:	UK BAP Priority Species. Herts Extinct
Caterpillar food plants:	oak. Elsewhere, on various trees
Flight period:	Elsewhere, June/July (female flightless)
Records in database:	3

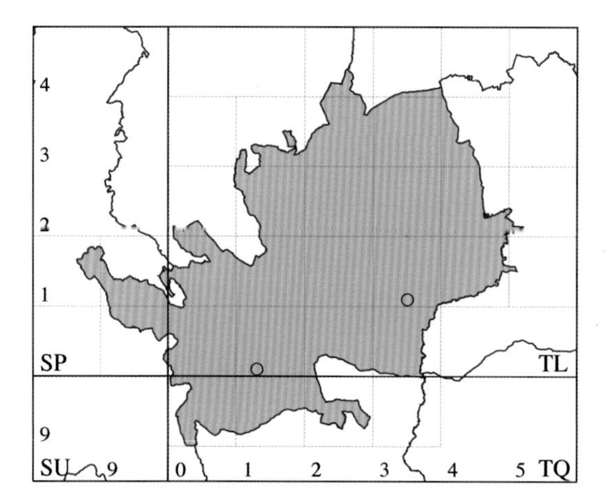

There are three published Hertfordshire records for this nationally rare moth, though two may perhaps relate to the same record. A single larva was found on an oak tree at Bricket Wood in 1884 (Griffith, 1890). It is listed 'once' for the Haileybury School area prior to 1888 (Bowyer, 1888) and Foster (1937) notes both 'Haileybury once (Bowyer)'; and 'Formerly on the Heath (School List)'. The reference to 'The Heath' might relate to Hertford Heath, but there is no data to support that assumption. Volume 9 of *Moths and Butterflies of Great Britain and Ireland* shows a pre-1960 record in ten-kilometre square SP 90: this is assumed to relate to a Buckinghamshire record. Nationally, this species is found mostly in the North Lincolnshire/South Yorkshire area.

2026 *Orgyia antiqua* (L.) Vapourer

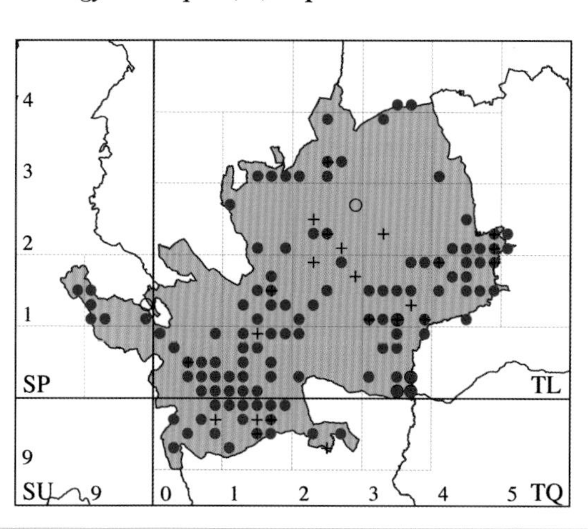

Recorded:	1828 – 2006
Distribution / Status:	Widespread / Common resident
Conservation status:	Herts Stable
Caterpillar food plants:	English Oak, Common Hawthorn, Wild Cherry, *Buddleia* species
Flight period:	June to October in one protracted generation
Records in database:	346

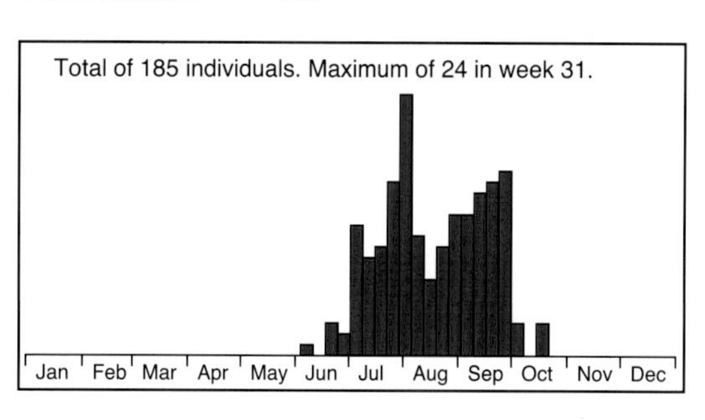

Some records relate to egg masses on oak trunks; these persist long after the larvae have emerged. The females are flightless and are mated almost immediately upon emerging from the pupa. However, if virgin females are reared from larvae these can be used to great effect to 'assemble' the day-flying males, which will usually attend within a few minutes. The moth is on the wing continuously from June to October, but the numbers peak in late July/early August and mid- to late September. This may indicate that there are two broods, a phenomenon suggested by some authors, but a single protracted emergence, perhaps depending on the weather, is more likely; there appear to be no species of moth that overwinter in the egg stage that are also double-brooded in Britain.

[2027 *Dicallomera fascelina* (L.) Dark Tussock

The record of larvae found by G. V. Bull at Hodd Park, Hoddesdon, in 1931, given in Foster (1937), is withdrawn by Foster in his 1940 list of *Corrigenda*. This species is absent from our region of Britain.]

2028 *Calliteara pudibunda* (L.) Pale Tussock

Recorded:	1884 – 2006
Distribution / Status:	Widespread / Common resident
Conservation status:	Herts Stable
Caterpillar food plants:	Rose. Elsewhere on various trees and on Hop.
Flight period:	Late April to June, but see text
Records in database:	413

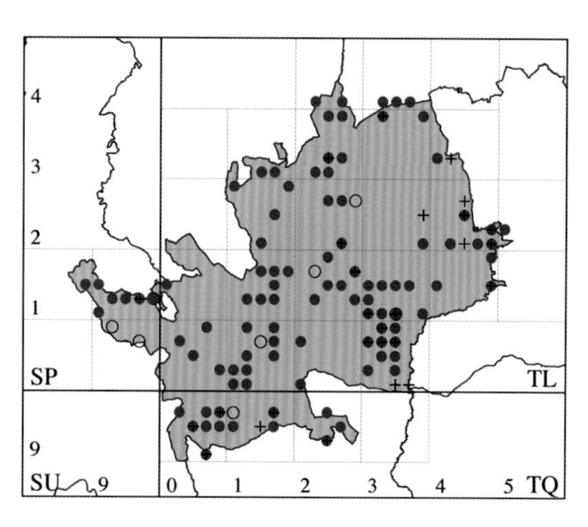

Adults are, typically, on the wing in a single brood from late April to mid-June, but during 2005 there was a small yet clear second generation reported widely across the east of the county in late July and early August, including at Old Grove near Cheshunt (Mark Cooper) and Bishops Stortford (James Fish

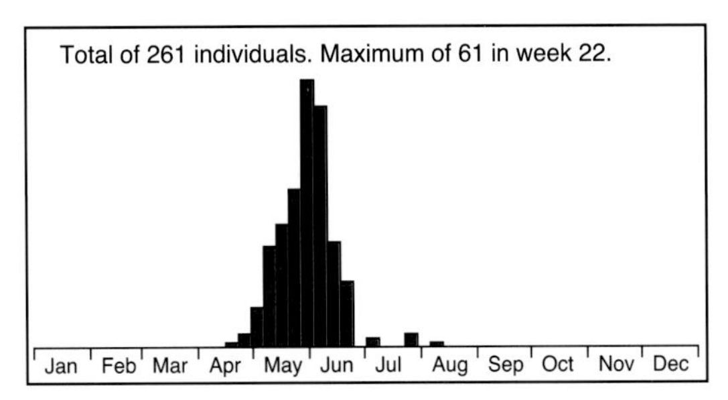

and Julian Reeves). Males account for 95 per cent of adults attracted to light. The more or less uniformly plain, dark form known as *concolor* Staudinger, is apparently scarce, though perhaps not always reported. In the London Area, Plant (1993) reported that the main foodplant was Hop, but this cannot be so in Hertfordshire as the plant is rare in most districts. A single larva was found feeding at night on *Rosa* growing close to ground in the short turf at Church Hill, Therfield Heath, 1 September 2001; feeding in such a low, exposed place is probably unusual.

2029 *Euproctis chrysorrhoea* (L.) Brown-tail

Recorded:	1888 – 2006
Distribution / Status:	Local / Vagrant – temporary resident in the extreme south
Conservation status:	–
Caterpillar food plants:	Whitebeam, Common Hawthorn. Elsewhere on most rosaceous trees and shrubs
Flight period:	July/August
Records in database:	86

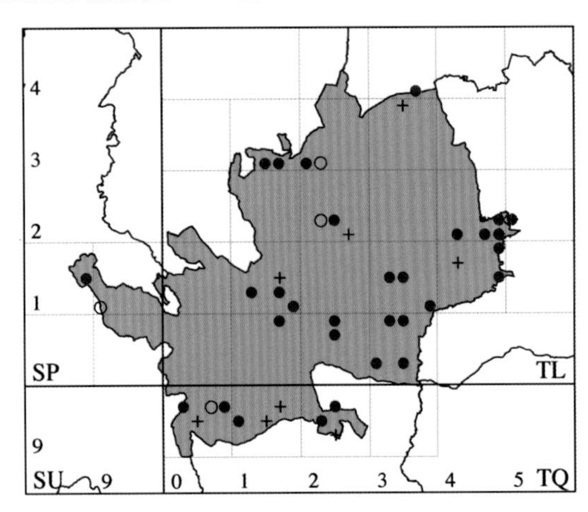

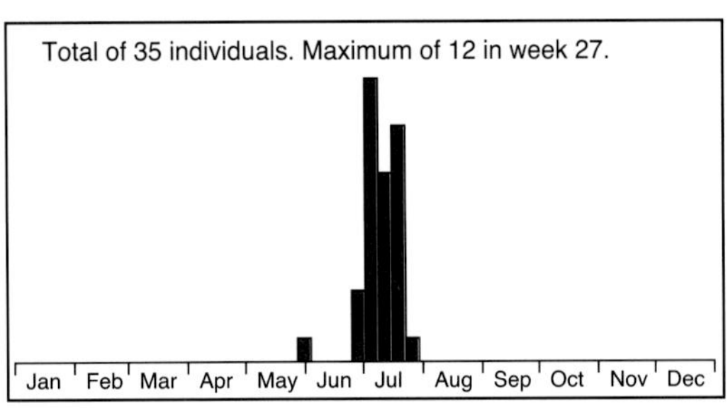

Our earliest dated record is from Haileybury (Bowyer, 1888) and this may or may not pre-date one from East Barnet (Gillum) given by Gibbs (1902) in the *Victoria County History*. Nineteenth and early twentieth-century records are summarised in list form by Foster (1937) and in addition to these two are Stevenage (Matthews), Tring (Rothschild), Bishops Stortford (Mellows), Watford (Heaton), Letchworth, 1910 (Everett) and the Berkhamsted School list, this last almost certainly in Buckinghamshire. The Bishops Stortford record by Chas Mellows must have been made post-1912 when he came to teach at the college there; the Rothschild record would also have been from that same era. Thus it appears that at the tail end of the nineteenth century the Brown-tail was present, but probably rare in the county. There are no further reports until Jim Reid recorded one at Therfield Heath on 2nd July 1973; the year coincides exactly with the start of the sudden colossal and problematic outbreak of larvae in eastern London and the record relates to a wandering male. At Totteridge, where trapping had been continuous since 1954, the first arrival was a male on 3rd July 1976 (the very hot summer) and a second arrived in July 1977, but there were none in 1978 or 1979. These moths were very probably wanderers from the east London area, as was the male in Bishops Stortford on 25th July 1978 (Charles Watson) and another male in Birchanger Wood on 31st July 1980 (Geoffrey Sell). Barry Goater records a male at Bushey on 13th July 1983 and another male at the nearby Haberdasher's Aske's School, Aldenham, on 24th July 1985. Back in Bishops Stortford, where I commenced nightly trapping in October 1986, I caught my first there, a male, on 9th July 1988 with a second male on 23rd July in the same year. Subsequent records are equally few and far between, from Rickmansworth, 12th July 1990 (Ric Sandifer), Much Hadham, 29th July 1991 (Colin Plant), St Albans, 20th July 1995 (Wendy Hatton), Sawbridgeworth Marsh, a male on 29th July 1995 (Colin Plant), Bishops Stortford, 22nd July 1995 and 3rd June 1997 (James Fish and Julian Reeves). Some encounters may have gone unreported, but there are no records in 1998 or 1999, just two in 2000, two in 2001, one in 2002 and one in 2003. A peak of twelve separate reports herald from 2004, but there were only three from 2005. Finally, in 2006 there were ten records. Repeat records in the Bishops Stortford area may suggest a low level of residency, but no larval nests have ever been found here and it is far more likely, given the river valley setting of the town, that the records all relate to wanderers from further south in London. Happily, we do not knowingly have any records of female moths. Larval records for the county as a whole number just two and are restricted to the southern fringes.

The larvae bear hairs that cause an urticating rash in humans and present a considerable medical problem. Local authorities have a duty to destroy larval nests if they are found but, regrettably lack the specialist knowledge to make a correct identification and this sometimes leads to other species being sprayed; this could, potentially, include the extremely rare 1633: Small Egger, which also lives gregariously in silk webs. It might be wise if competent lepidopterists destroy larval nests of Brown-tail in public places to prevent subsequent indiscriminate damage by others.

2030 *Euproctis similis* (Fuessly) Yellow-tail

Recorded:	1888 – 2006
Distribution / Status:	Widespread / Common resident
Conservation status:	Herts Stable
Caterpillar food plants:	English Oak, Common Hawthorn, Dogwood. Probably other trees and bushes.
Flight period:	June to August
Records in database:	584

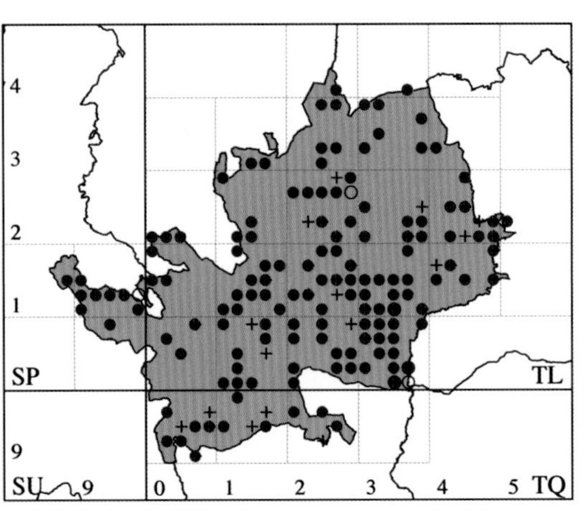

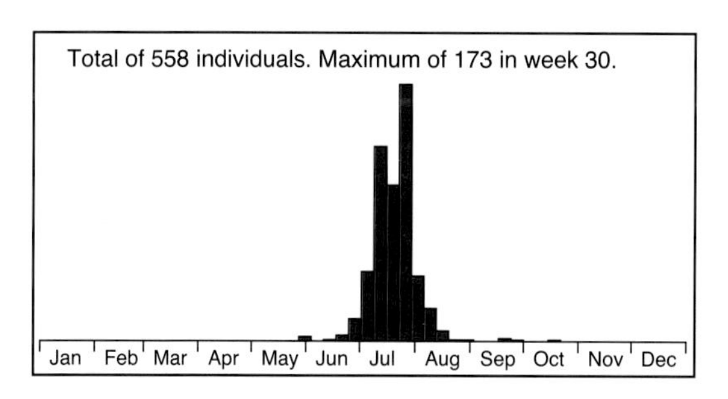

Although very closely related to 2029: Brown-tail, this present species poses no threat to humans whatsoever; nor does it live in communal silk webs. Unusually late adults were noted in light traps in 2003 at Ware on 19th and 21st September (Elizabeth Goodyear) and Oughtonhead Common on 27th September (Colin Plant) then during 2006 with one in Bishops Stortford on 15th October (James Fish and Julian Reeves).

2031 *Leucoma salicis* (L.) White Satin Moth

Recorded: 1884 – 2006
Distribution / Status: Local / Uncommon resident
Conservation status: Herts Threatened
Caterpillar food plants: Common Sallow. Elsewhere also on willows and poplars
Flight period: July/August
Records in database: 84

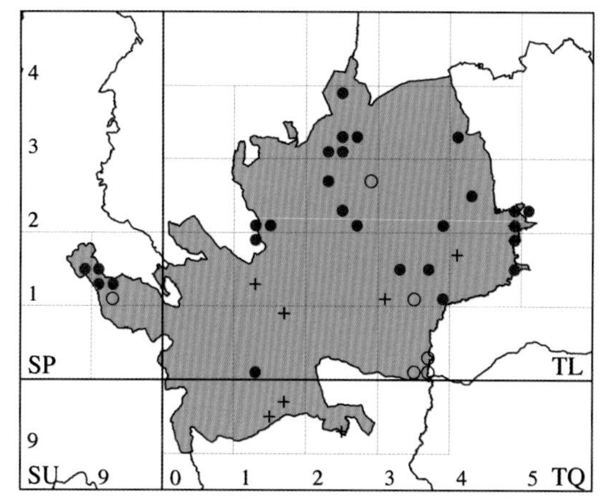

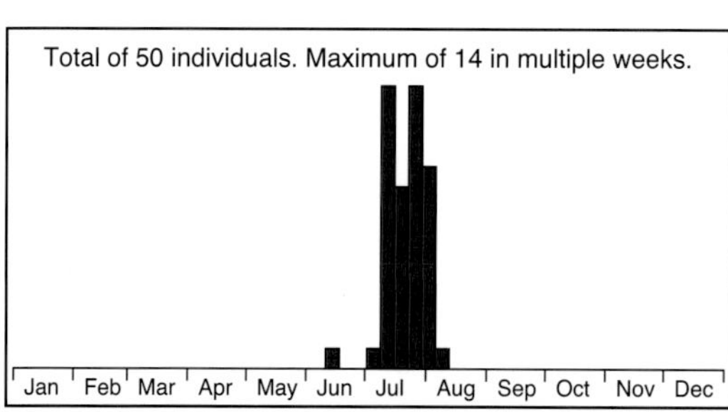

The White Satin has never been a common moth in Hertfordshire, although a small number of late nineteenth century records are listed by Foster (1937). The reason for this apparent scarcity might perhaps lie in the moth not being especially attracted to light; some proper field entomology is called for in order to discover larvae. Nevertheless, there do seem to be large areas of the county from where the moth is absent and in some of these it is possible that former populations are no longer extant. Thus, there is a concern that the species is declining and so it warrants Threatened status on the county list.

2033 *Lymantria monacha* (L.) Black Arches

Recorded: 1884 – 2006
Distribution / Status: Local / Common resident
Conservation status: Increasing
Caterpillar food plants: English Oak, Hornbeam
Flight period: July/August
Records in database: 227

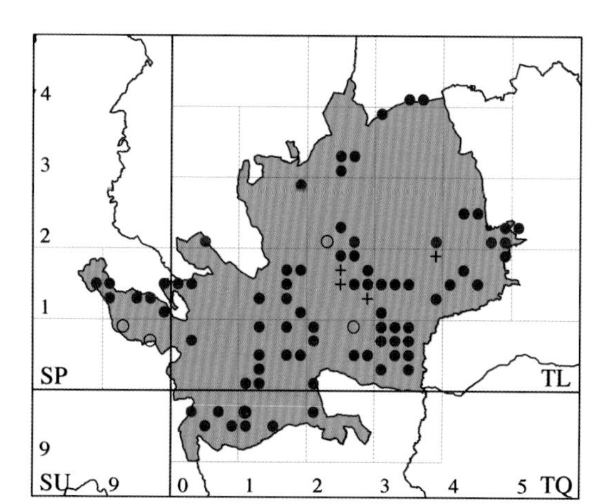

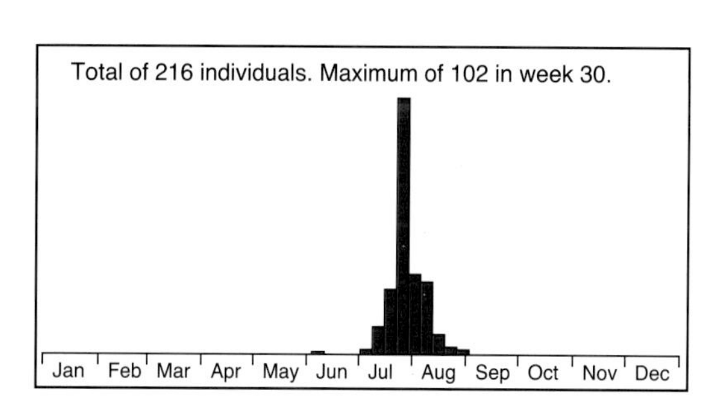

The Black Arches has not always been widespread in Hertfordshire, as the lack of black circles and crosses on the map betrays. It appears to have been permanently established only in the Broxbourne Woods complex in the south-east, where the striking form *eremita* Ochsenheimer, with entirely black forewings, is found in both sexes. This form was reported at nearby Haileybury as long ago as 1890 and persists today; in some years it dominates the population by about 9 to 1. Foster (1937) listed a smattering of records for the species and in Plant (1993) I mapped only a single recent record for the southern third of Hertfordshire. During 1997 and 1998, however, the moth started to expand its range, especially in the south of the county (Plant, 1999). It is now relatively widespread, but more or less confined to mature woodlands, where Hornbeam, rather than the expected oak, seems to be the principal larval foodplant. Other than the fully melanic form, adults vary considerably in the extent of their black markings and these varieties can be found in most places in Hertfordshire.

2034 *Lymantria dispar* (L.) Gypsy Moth

Recorded:	1955 – 1959
Distribution / Status:	Random / Rare immigrant
Conservation status:	Pest species in Europe
Caterpillar food plants:	See text
Flight period:	August
Records in database:	2

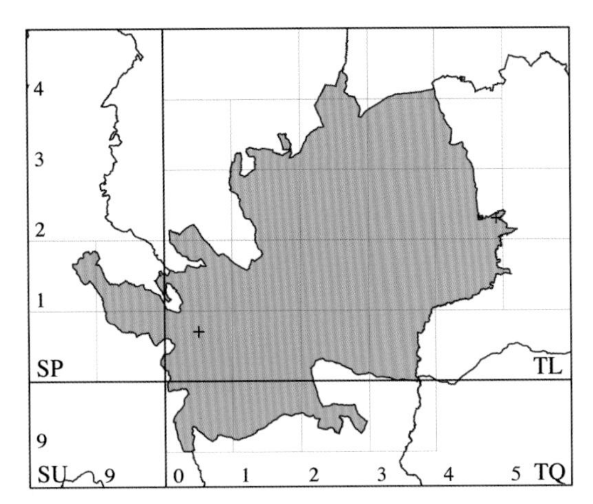

The extinct British form that was established in the Fens was larger and fed on Bog Myrtle and Creeping Willow; the smaller European form feeds on deciduous trees and is a major pest of forests from time to time, often having large 'outbreaks'. Occasional continental males appear in Britain, but as far as is known, only the males are able to move such distances. The larger females are pretty much incapable of fluttering more than a few metres and so it is supposed that Continental Gypsy Moth cannot colonise Britain. Reports of immigrant males are increasingly frequent in Britain. Hertfordshire records are of one at mv light at Bishops Stortford on 22nd August 1955 (Derek Ashwell) and a male at I. D. Woodward's light in Hemel Hempstead in 1959 (Bell, 1961).

ARCTIIDAE

The Arctiidae comprise two subfamilies in Britain, with the footmen and allies in the Lithosiinae and the tiger moths in the Arctiinae. The larvae of the Lithosiinae are slightly hairy and feed on lichens, occasionally on algae, growing on branches, walls and other items; true tiger moth caterpillars feed on a range of herbaceous plants and are profusely hairy. Thirty-five British arctiids divide into 16 Lithosiinae and 19 Arctiinae; the 24 Hertfordshire species comprise 11 in Lithosiinae and 13 in Arctiinae.

LITHOSIINAE

2035 *Thumatha senex* (Hb.) Round-winged Muslin

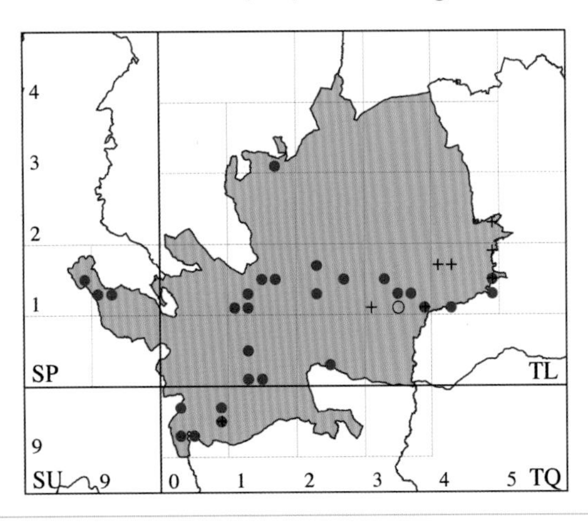

Recorded:	1884 – 2006
Distribution / Status:	Local / Common resident
Conservation status:	Herts Stable
Caterpillar food plants:	Not recorded. Elsewhere, on various lichens
Flight period:	Late June to early August
Records in database:	64

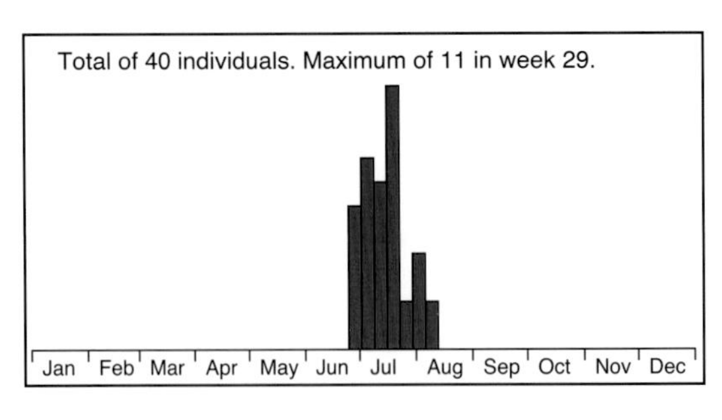

The Round-winged Muslin is a marshland moth that is widespread in the county and it is probably present in most, if not all, wetland sites here. The absence of records from the chalk in the north-west and from the arable desert in the north reflects the lack of suitable habitat and the insect is not at all expected there.

[2036 *Setina irrorella* (Hb.) Dew Moth

Foster (1937) lists 'East Barnet (Bowden)', with no further detail. This is an extremely improbable record and in the apparent absence of a voucher specimen is treated as incorrect.]

2037 *Miltochrista miniata* (Forst.) Rosy Footman

Recorded:	1828 – 2006
Distribution / Status:	Local / Common resident
Conservation status:	Herts Scarce
Caterpillar food plants:	Lichen *Peltigera canina* on oak branch
Flight period:	Late June to early August
Records in database:	25

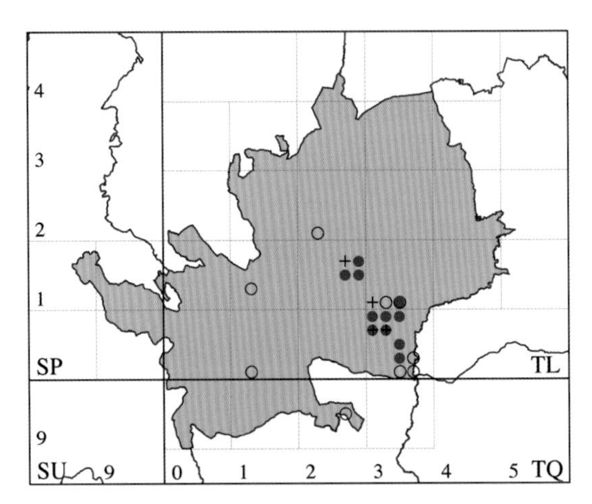

The unusual modern distribution pattern reflects a moth that seems to be confined to larger, continuous tracts of ancient woodland on Chalky Boulder Clay. The old record from Bricket Wood in the south-west is from a small island of decalcified Boulder Clay and it is not hard to believe that in the 1880s when the record was made the woodland was closer to its original semi-natural state than it is now. The records from Harpenden and East Barnet in Foster (1937) probably relate to single examples of vagrants. The larvae feed on *Peltigera canina* lichen on trees and the lichen favours oak and has specific micro-climate requirements. The many fragmented pieces of ancient woodlands and those larger units on different geology do not appear to support this moth.

2038 *Nudaria mundana* (L.) Muslin Footman

Recorded:	1828 – 1937
Distribution / Status:	Absent / Former resident
Conservation status:	Herts Extinct
Caterpillar food plants:	Not recorded. Elsewhere, on various lichens
Flight period:	Elsewhere, late June to early August
Records in database:	10

A glance at the map in *Moths and Butterflies of Great Britain and Ireland* shows that this species has retreated westwards from many sites formerly occupied in the east of Britain, where it is now a rarity. It is regarded as extinct in Hertfordshire and all known records are listed, as follows: Hertford, illustrated by J. F. Stephens (1829. *Illustrations of British Entomology* **2**: 90); Sandridge area (Griffith, 1884); Harpenden, 1880 (Willis); Harpenden, 1885 (J. Hopkinson, *Transactions of the Hertfordshire Natural History Society and Field Club* **1**: 138); 'Local' [in the Cheshunt area] (Boyd, 1901) – note that Boyd's comprehensive list does not include the similar and more common 2035: *Thumatha senex*; Hitchin (Foster, 1934), Tring, Berkhamsted and Chorleywood (Foster, 1937). Few of these can be precisely located and so the presentation of a distribution map would be misleading.

2039 *Atolmis rubricollis* (L.) Red-necked Footman

Recorded:	2001 – 2006
Distribution / Status:	Random / Rare immigrant
Conservation status:	-
Caterpillar food plants:	Not recorded. Elsewhere, on various lichens
Flight period:	July
Records in database:	3

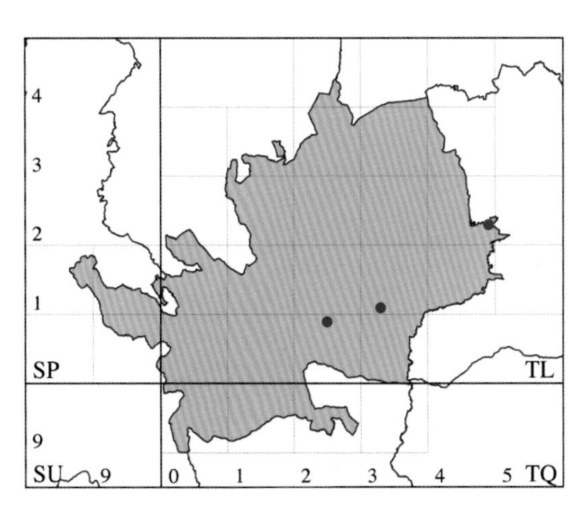

There are three Hertfordshire records, all at times of high immigrant activity when the species was also reported elsewhere in Britain: Balls Park, Hertford, 6th July 2001 and Hatfield House Estate, 3rd July 2006 (both caught by myself) and Bishops Stortford, 4th July 2006 (James Fish and Julian Reeves).

2040 *Cybosia mesomella* (L.) Four-dotted Footman

Recorded:	1828 – 2004
Distribution / Status:	Extremely Local / Rare resident
Conservation status:	Herts Endangered
Caterpillar food plants:	Not recorded. Elsewhere, on various lichens
Flight period:	Elsewhere, mid-June to mid-August.
Records in database:	8

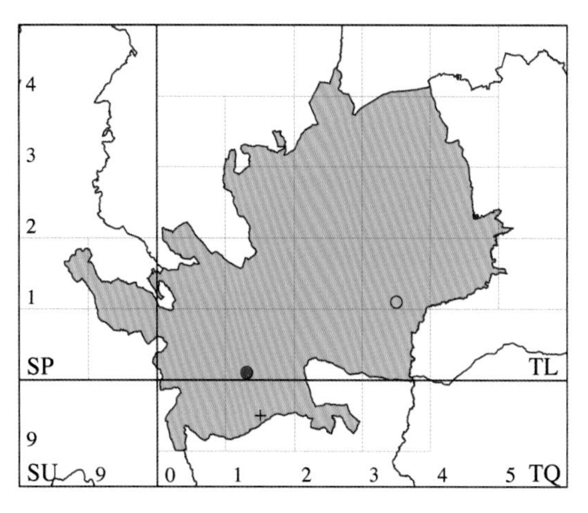

Old records are from Hertford (Stephens, 1829. *Illustrations of British Entomology* **2**: 100), Sandridge area (Griffith, 1884), Haileybury (Bowyer, 1888), Bricket Wood (Gibbs, 1889), Knebworth (Foster, 1937), Broxbourne, Hitchin, 1867 – 80 (Foster, 1937) and Reddings Avenue, Bushey, 30th August 1968 (Barry Goater). It was quite a surprise to rediscover this species at Bricket Wood on 19th June 2004, with several coming to mv light during a Herts Moth Group recording trip. Perhaps small colonies persist elsewhere in the county?

2043 *Eilema sororcula* (Hufn.) Orange Footman

Recorded:	1888 – 2006
Distribution / Status:	Local / Common resident
Conservation status:	Increasing
Caterpillar food plants:	Not recorded. Elsewhere, on various lichens
Flight period:	May/June
Records in database:	83

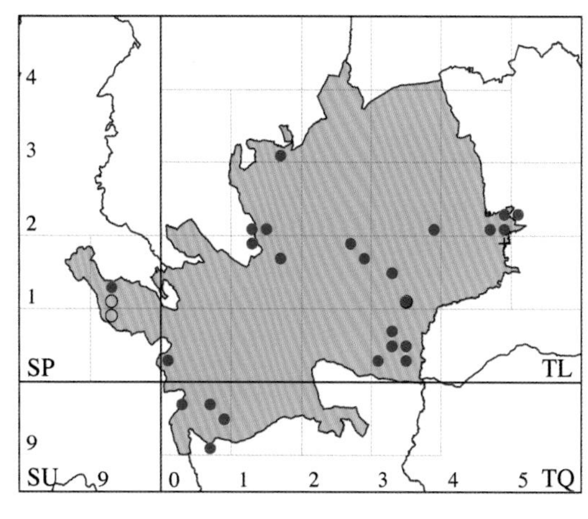

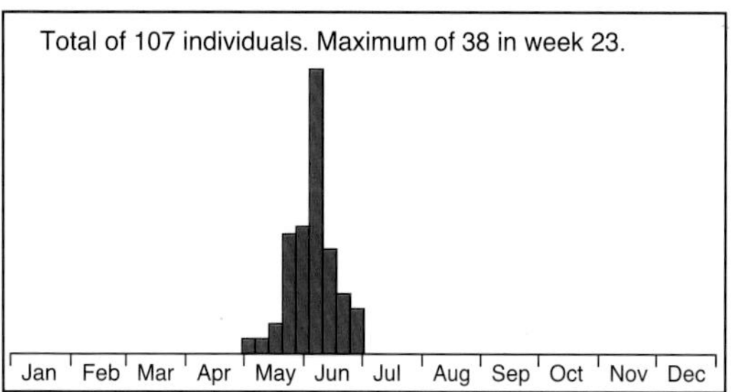

Records in Foster (1937) suggest that the moth was not uncommon in appropriate habitat at the end of the nineteenth century and the early years of the twentieth. This remains the case in 2006, and it is apparently extending its range, but there has almost certainly been a period of scarcity in the interim period. When I prepared the distribution map for this species in the London Area (Plant, 1993), the moth appeared to be rather rare in southern Hertfordshire. 'Appropriate habitat' appears to be larger, continuous tracts of mature, well-structured woodland where the internal microclimate supports the growth of lichens on branches and trunks.

2044 *Eilema griseola* (Hb.) Dingy Footman

Recorded: 1828 – 2006
Distribution / Status: Widespread / Common resident
Conservation status: Increasing
Caterpillar food plants: Not recorded. Elsewhere, on various lichens
Flight period: June to August
Records in database: 113

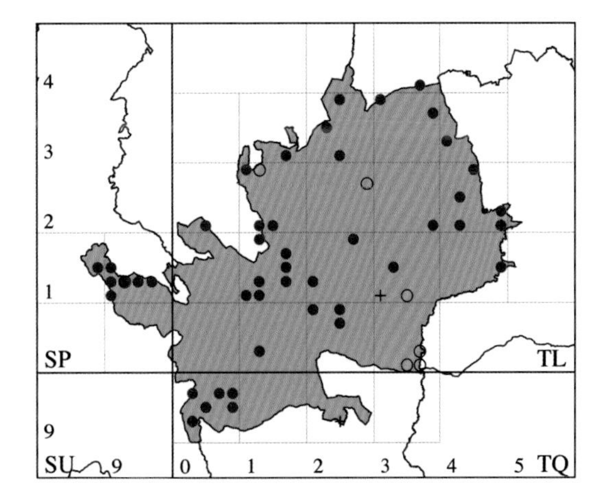

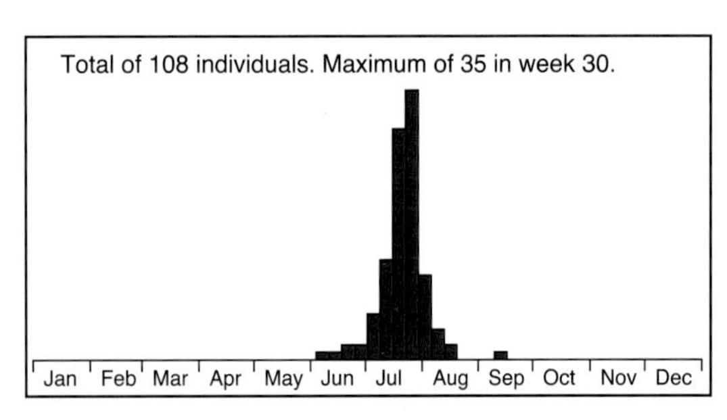

This is supposedly a species of damp woodland; it has evidently extended its range in the past ten years after a preceding period of scarcity and all old records known are plotted. As with 2043: Orange Footman, my London Area map (Plant, 1993) showed a distinct lack of records in southern Hertfordshire; today records are available from most suitable sites and the moth is expected on all woodland site lists. However, it often arrives at the lights rather late in the evening and may be missed if the gear is packed up too early.

[2046 *Eilema pygmaeola* (Doubleday) Pigmy Footman

Foster (1937) lists one at light at Harpenden by C. B. Williams on 21 July 1935. However, Riley (1999) in his definitive list of moths from the Rothamsted Estate at Harpenden, notes that this record is unconfirmed and doubtful. There does not appear to be a voucher specimen and no further information is available to support the record which is, accordingly, now rejected as an error.]

2047 *Eilema complana* (L.) Scarce Footman

Recorded: 1888 – 2006
Distribution / Status: Widespread / Common resident
Conservation status: Herts Stable
Caterpillar food plants: Not recorded. Elsewhere, on lichens
Flight period: Mid-June to mid-August
Records in database: 714

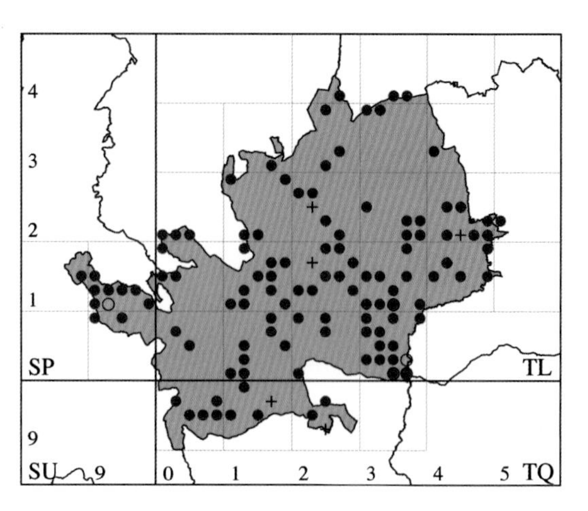

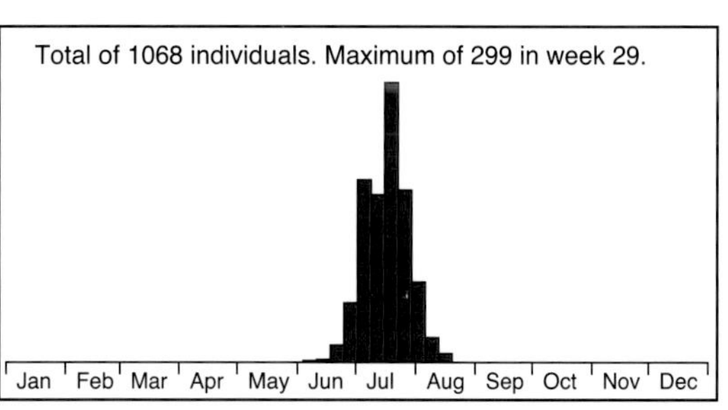

In spite of its colloquial name, the Scarce Footman is by no means scarce, with 714 records in the database compared with 1215 of the Common Footman. It is likely to arrive at light traps across the county regardless of habitat and its larval pabulum here, presumably one or more lichens, is yet to be determined. Separating adults from those of 2050: Common Footman can be difficult in some specimens, though Scarce Footman usually rests with its wings rolled around its body rather than held flat.

2049 *Eilema depressa* (Esp.) Buff Footman

Recorded: 1990 – 2006
Distribution / Status: Widespread / Common resident
Conservation status: Increasing
Caterpillar food plants: Not recorded. Elsewhere, on various lichens
Flight period: Mid-June to mid-August
Records in database: 107

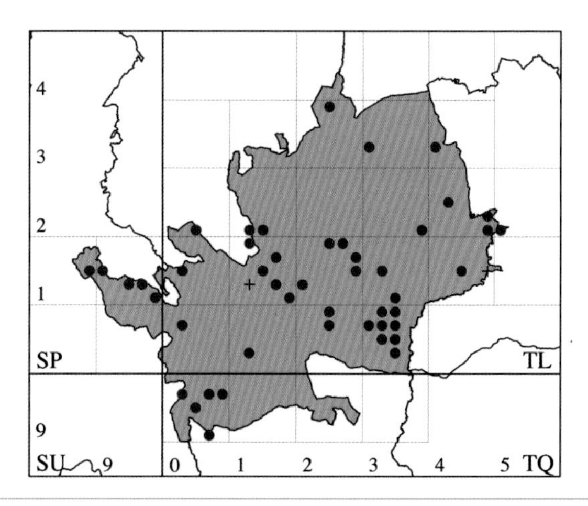

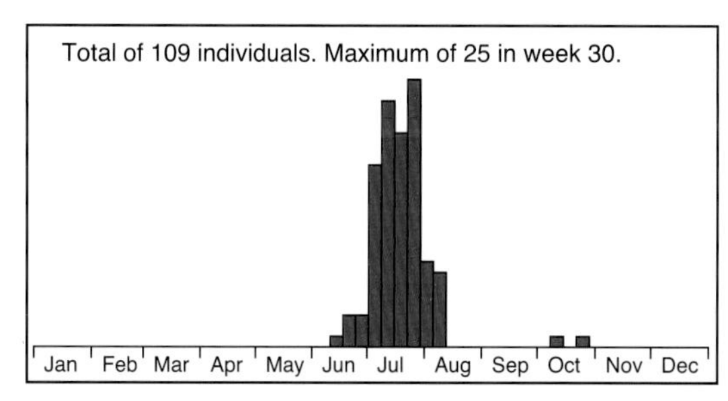

The Buff Footman is absent from Foster's 1937 summary of county records as well as from all previous lists and it is evident that it was not present in the region at that time. Interestingly, it is also absent from the Middlesex list by Buckel & Prout (1889-1901). For the London Area, I showed (Plant, 1993) that a century later there were then still no records in that vice-county whilst in Hertfordshire there was just a single colony at Broxbourne Woods, adding that 'it will be interesting to see if its spread continues and all captures should be recorded and reported'. In Bedfordshire, Arnold et al (1997) state that the moth is a scarce and local species with no records in the area adjacent to Hertfordshire. For Essex, Emmet et al (1985) regarded the Buff Footman as former very rare vagrant now [1985] established as a very local resident. Goodey (2004) notes that it continues to expand its range and is most numerous in the larger woodlands. The present-day map for Hertfordshire shows a spread of records across much of the county and the moth is firmly established here. The colonisation appears to have taken place during the 1990s, with records for that decade from Broxbourne Woods in 1990 and Sawbridgeworth Marsh, 17th July 1990 (both caught by me), Rothamsted Estate, 29th July 1990 (Adrian Riley), Bishops Stortford, 2nd July 1994 (James Fish and Julian Reeves), All Saints, Bishops Stortford, 1995 (R. W. Stroud), Symondshyde Wood, 21st July 1997 (Rob Souter), Monks Green, Broxbourne, 1997 (Maurice Pledger), Mardley Heath, 11th August 1998 and Long Marston, 1999 (Alan Bernard). In the following seven years from 2000 to 2006 the moth was widely reported from across the county. There is no apparent reason for the sudden colonisation/re-colonisation of Hertfordshire by this species or by 2043: Orange Footman and 2044: Dingy Footman, though it is clear that some common factor may be influencing the situation.

2050 *Eilema lurideola* (Zinck.) Common Footman

Recorded: 1884 – 2006
Distribution / Status: Ubiquitous / Common resident
Conservation status: Herts Stable
Caterpillar food plants: Not recorded. Elsewhere, on lichens
Flight period: June to early August
Records in database: 1215

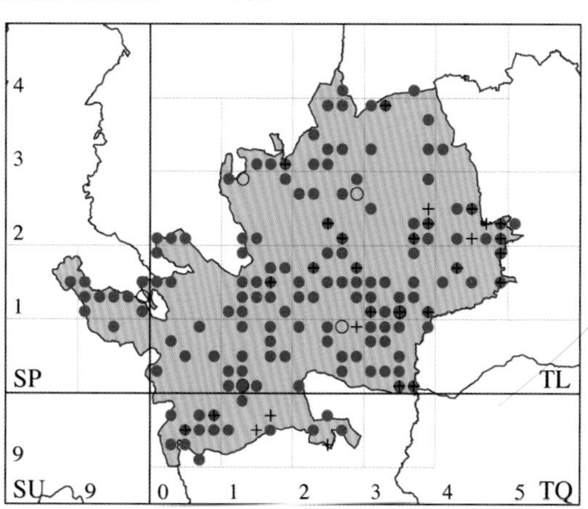

Past records show that the Common Footman has always been in the past as widespread and common as it is today. In 2006 it can be expected at any site in the county and seems to have no particular habitat association.

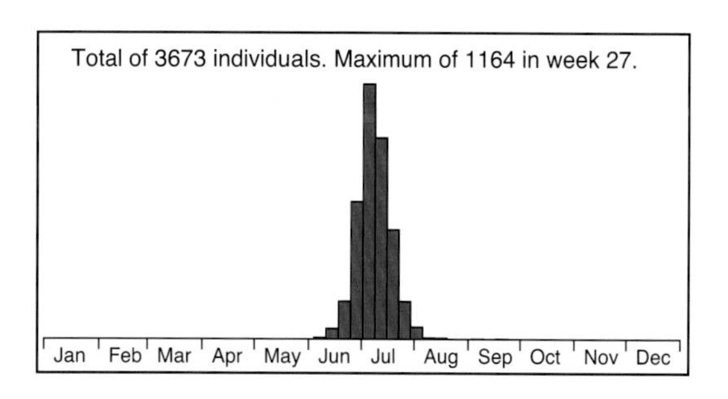

2051 *Lithosia quadra* (L.) Four-spotted Footman

Recorded: 1938 – 2006
Distribution / Status: Random / Rare immigrant
Conservation status: -
Caterpillar food plants: Not recorded. Elsewhere, on lichens
Flight period: July and September
Records in database: 3

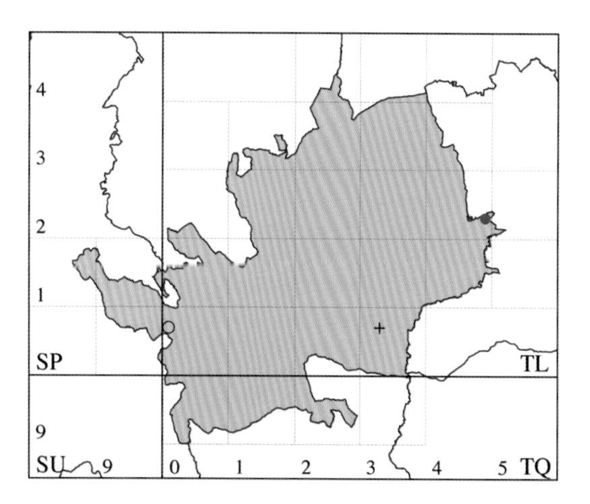

There are three Hertfordshire records of this rare immigrant, from Long Green, Berkhamsted in 1938 (S. B. Hodgson), Broxbourne Wood on 31st July 1985 (Bernard Skinner) and from Bishops Stortford on 21st September 2006 (James Fish and Julian Reeves).

ARCTIINAE

2054 *Utetheisa pulchella* (L.) Crimson Speckled

Recorded: 1874 – 1949
Distribution / Status: Random / Rare immigrant
Conservation status: -
Caterpillar food plants: Not recorded.
Flight period: August
Records in database: 4

Foster (1937) gives two records: 'Hitchin, 1874 (Tuke)' and 'East Barnet, one on Railway Bank near Oakleigh Park Station, 1892 (Rühl)'. The spelling of the station name in Foster's summary report is not as it was in the original, which reads 'captured by Mr Ruhl in May 1892 on G. N. Ry. near Oakley Park Station' (Gibbs, 1894. *Entomologist's Record* **5**: 156). The only recorded 'Oakley' in Hertfordshire is a farm near Albury, nowhere near a railway line and it is assumed that Oakleigh, in what is now the London Borough of Barnet was intended and that Foster corrected the locality without advising the reader of his actions; this is indeed a station formerly owned by the Great North Railway Company. The railway line that passes through Oakleigh Park Station forms the vice-county boundary between Middlesex and Hertfordshire. Whilst it is unclear if the moth was captured on 'our' east side, I feel confident that even if it was not then it must have flown over it at some stage on its way to the west! This Barnet record is the same as that given in *Entomologist* **26**: 223 and mentioned by Plant (1993) in *Larger moths of the London Area*). It is, however, apparently not the same as that mentioned by A. E. Gibbs in his first annual report as Hertfordshire Lepidoptera Recorder (*Transactions of the Hertfordshire Natural History Society and Field Club* **7**: 195) where he records the capture of one at Southgate, by Mr R. Dymond. Southgate (Middlesex) and East Barnet (Hertfordshire) form, in 2005, a single continuous urban sprawl, separated only by the Pymme's Brook; it is assumed that Gibbs assigned the record to its correct county. Allan (1950) lists one taken by F. R. Browning at Hockerill Training College in Bishops Stortford on 10th June 1945 and Bell (1952) lists another taken at Rickmansworth on 15 August 1949 by M. A. Salmon, the latter also noted in the records held by the Ruislip & District Natural History Society (per A. M. George).

2056 *Parasemia plantaginis* (L.) Wood Tiger

Recorded:	1921 – 1940s
Distribution / Status:	Absent / Former resident
Conservation status:	Herts Extinct
Caterpillar food plants:	Not recorded. Elsewhere, on herbaceous plants
Flight period:	Not recorded. Elsewhere, June to August
Records in database:	2

The Wood Tiger was formerly resident in the south-east of Britain, but has retreated westwards and is now absent from the region. One was caught near the Monument on the Ashridge Estate in 1921 and is given in Foster (1937) who also lists 'Berkhamsted School list'. It is thought that these two reports may relate to the same record. Berkhamsted School itself lies outside the vice-county boundary in the 'neck' of the 'Hudnall Hook', but Ashridge Monument is within Hertfordshire. One was taken 'on the outskirts of St John's Wood' (between Wood End and Walkern) in the 1940s (J. Birdsall).

2057 *Arctia caja* (L.) Garden Tiger

Recorded:	1888 – 2006
Distribution / Status:	Extremely local – declining / Rare resident
Conservation status:	UK BAP Watch List. Herts Endangered
Caterpillar food plants:	Creeping thistle
Flight period:	Late June to end of July
Records in database:	88

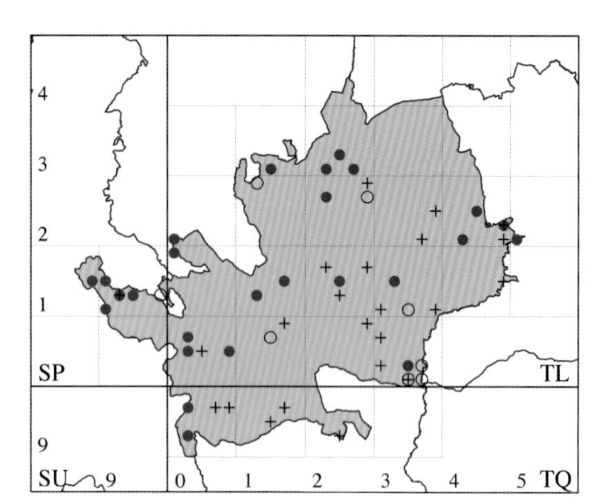

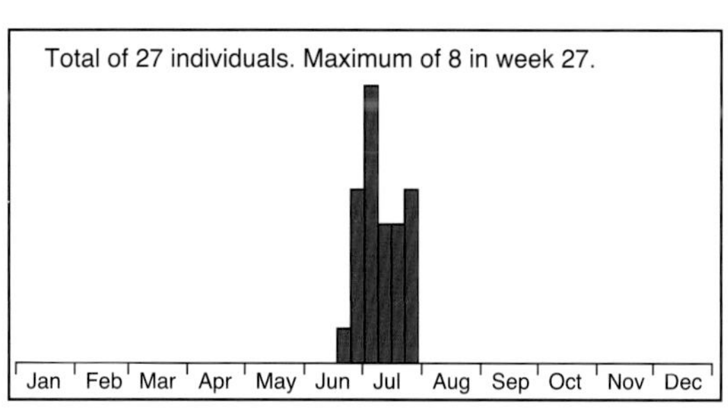

Foster (1937) declared the Garden Tiger Moth as 'reported from all districts and frequently abundant'. Today it is a rare species in the county, though it is occasionally reported from widely scattered localities. The start of the decline cannot be pinpointed with accuracy since detailed record-keeping is a relatively recent phenomenon. As recently as the 1970s it appears still to have been common and Ian Lorimer reported it frequent in his garden trap at Totteridge throughout that decade. There was almost no moth recording in the county throughout the 1980s and in the first half of the 1990s, and this is reflected in the very few records not just of Garden Tigers, but of most other species. From about 1997 recording started in earnest, but it was around this time that we began to realise that the Garden Tiger was in trouble and so people made extra effort to report dates and numbers. There is a consequent rise in records from five for the entire of the 1980s, to 23 for the 1990s and 30 in the 2000s – none of which reflects anything other than recorder bias. It is likely that the decline began in earnest in the mid-1980s and the cause of the decline has been shown to be a consequence of climate change. In simple terms, the Garden Tiger has been lost from areas where January is warmer than February. Thus, it is still found 'up north' and in coastal districts, but has all but vanished from central southern England and south-east inland areas. Occasional arrivals of the moth at light traps are to be expected, as microclimate features will vary, but the overall trend is downwards.

2058 *Arctia villica* (L.) ssp. *britannica* Oberthür Cream-spot Tiger

Recorded:	1828 – 1937
Distribution / Status:	Absent / Former vagrant
Conservation status:	-
Caterpillar food plants:	Not recorded. Elsewhere, on various herbaceous plants
Flight period:	Elsewhere, May/June
Records in database:	8

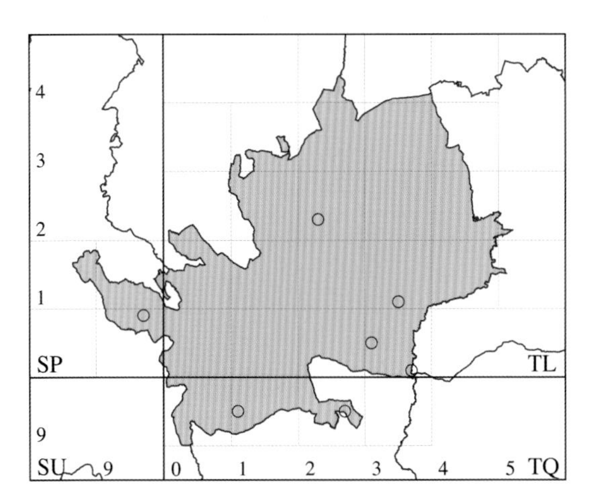

British Cream-spot Tigers are referable to subspecies *britannica* Oberthür; the nominate form is found in Central and Southern Europe. It was included by Stephens (1829) from a Hertford specimen in *Illustrations of British Entomology* **2**: 92 and is listed for Haileybury by Bowyer (1888). Other records included the Cheshunt area (Boyd, 1901), Wormley 'amongst heather 1900', East Barnet, Stevenage and Oxhey railway bank (Foster, 1937). One was noted at rest at Northchurch by J. Bell in 1937 (Foster, 1942). No other Herefordshire records are available.

2059 *Diacrisia sannio* (L.) Clouded Buff

Recorded: 1929 – 1929
Distribution / Status: Absent / Former immigrant
Conservation status: –
Caterpillar food plants: Not recorded. Elsewhere, on various low plants
Flight period: June/July
Records in database: 1

One example was seen in Welwyn, on 14th July 1929 (M. Yeats), originally reported in *Countryside* **8** (new series): 372 and repeated in Foster (1937).

2060 *Spilosoma lubricipeda* (L.) White Ermine

Recorded: 1884 – 2006
Distribution / Status: Ubiquitous / Common resident
Conservation status: UK BAP Watch List
No perceived threats
Caterpillar food plants: Not recorded. Elsewhere, widely polyphagous
Flight period: Late April to early July
Records in database: 647

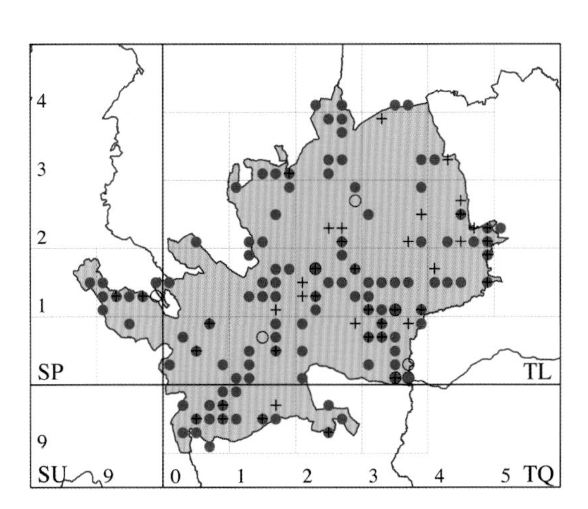

As in the time of Foster's list in 1937, this species is common more or less everywhere in the county. Surprisingly, however, we have no foodplant records for the county.

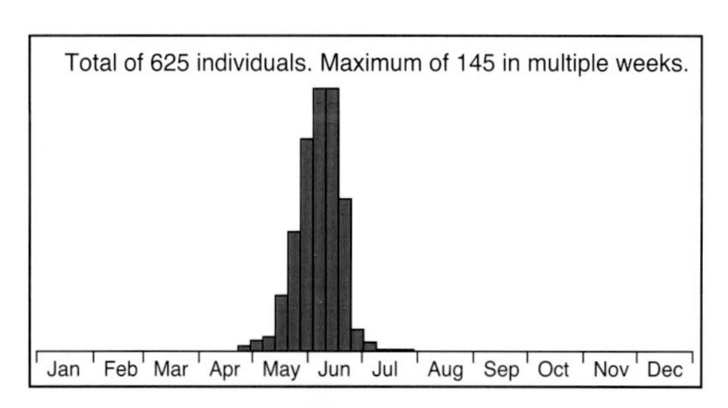

2061 *Spilosoma lutea* (Hufn.) Buff Ermine

Recorded: 1884 – 2006
Distribution / Status: Ubiquitous / Common resident
Conservation status: UK BAP Watch List
No perceived threats
Caterpillar food plants: Groundsel, Garden Blackcurrant. Elsewhere, polyphagous
Flight period: Mid-May to end of July
Records in database: 1006

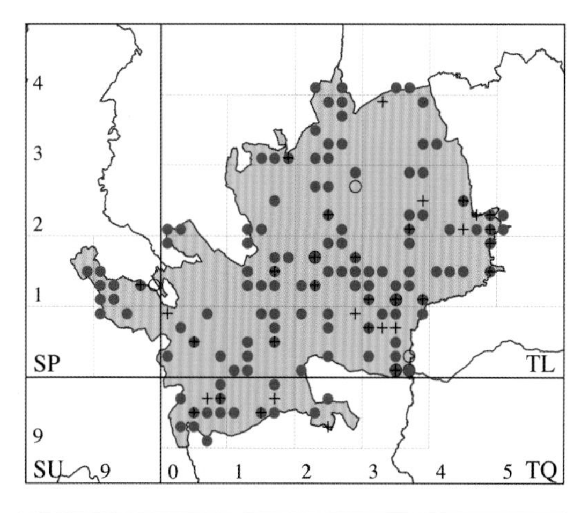

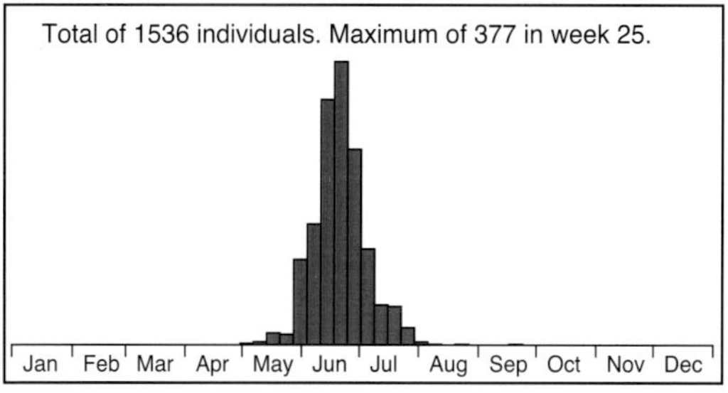

In terms of the number of reports in the database the Buff Ermine is about twice as frequent as 2060: White Ermine and it is found just about everywhere. Although this species is used extensively to study the genetics of in wing pattern in a laboratory setting there is remarkably little variation noted in wild Hertfordshire examples.

2062 *Spilosoma urticae* (Esp.) Water Ermine

Recorded:	1888 – 1940
Distribution / Status:	Absent / Former resident
Conservation status:	Herts Extinct
Caterpillar food plants:	Not recorded. Elsewhere, various low plants in damp situations
Flight period:	Not recorded. Elsewhere, June/July
Records in database:	5

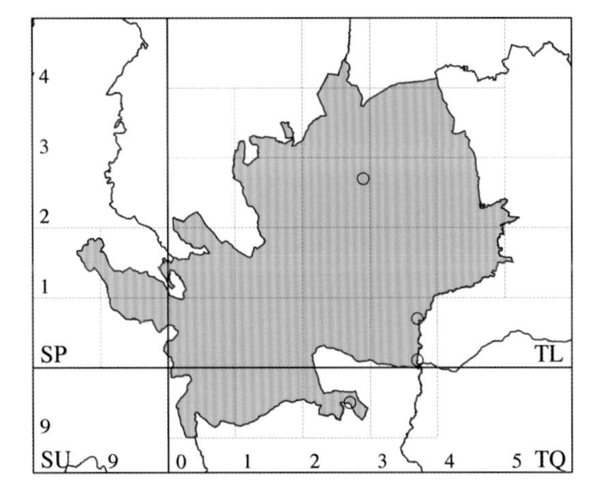

Our earliest record is from Haileybury College area (Bowyer, 1888), and the moth was presumably either on the adjacent Lea Valley marshes or a wanderer from there. It was certainly present at Cheshunt Marsh, where it was said to be scarce (Boyd, 1901) and Broxbourne Marshes, where it 'used to be common (Foster, 1937). It is not hard to imagine that the freshwater marshes of the River Lea Valley, perhaps even those along the River Stort, as suitable habitat for this wetland moth from throughout much of their length. There is an old record from East Barnet (Gillum, given in Foster, 1937) which dates between 1860 and 1937. During the 1940s it was 'not common', but was reported as taken along the River Beane, below the village green at Walkern, by J. Birdsall. There are no other records and it is unlikely that the species is overlooked as it is now more or less confined to coastal areas in the south-east of Britain.

2063 *Diaphora mendica* (Cl.) Muslin Moth

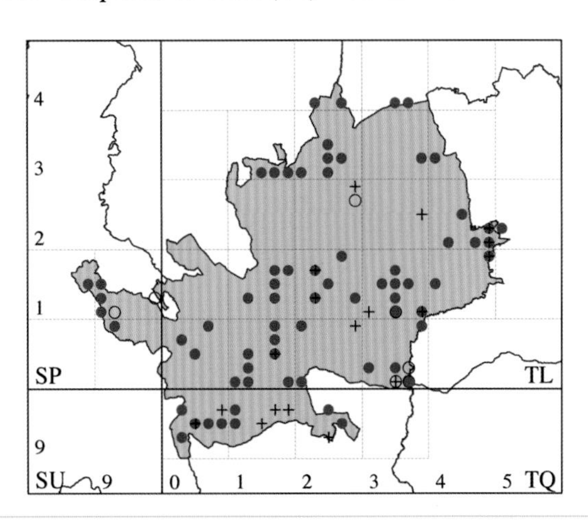

Recorded:	1888 – 2006
Distribution / Status:	Widespread / Common resident
Conservation status:	Herts Stable
Caterpillar food plants:	Not recorded. Elsewhere, polyphagous on low plants
Flight period:	April/May
Records in database:	433

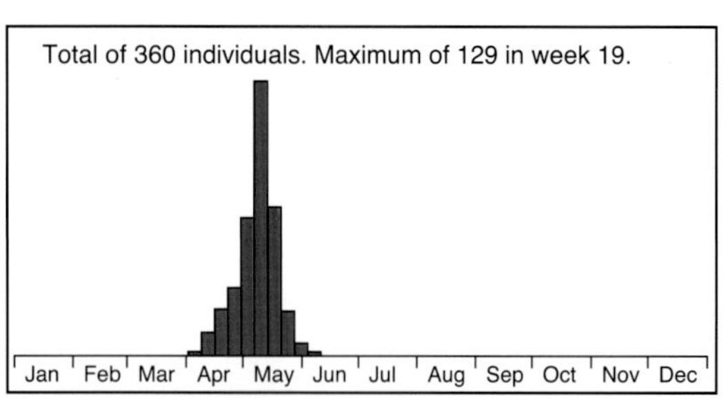

Almost all records relate to the darker males; the white females rarely come to light. My suggestion (Plant, 1993) that the moth was under-recorded in Hertfordshire appears to have been correct.

2064 *Phragmatobia fuliginosa* (L.) Ruby Tiger

Recorded:	1828 – 2006
Distribution / Status:	Widespread / Common resident
Conservation status:	Herts Stable
Caterpillar food plants:	Not recorded. Elsewhere, polyphagous
Flight period:	April/May then late June to August, occasionally a third brood in September
Records in database:	571

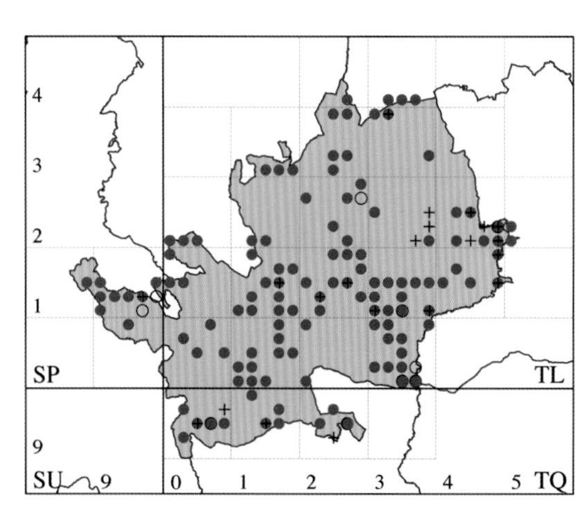

The Ruby Tiger is normally a bivoltine species, with the spring generation being markedly smaller than the summer one. A third generation of adults was produced in the years 2003, 2005 and 2006. The moth is likely to be represented on most site lists in the county.

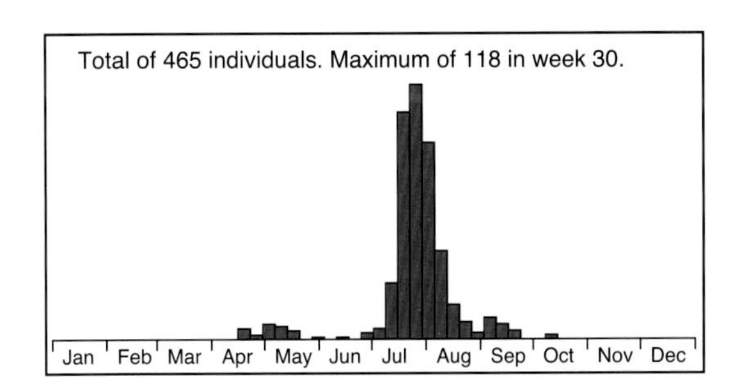

2067 *Euplagia quadripunctaria* (Poda) Jersey Tiger

Recorded: 1934 – 1934
Distribution / Status: Absent / Former immigrant or vagrant
Conservation status: -
Caterpillar food plants: Not recorded. Elsewhere, on many herbaceous plant species
Flight period: Not recorded. Elsewhere, mid-July to early September
Records in database: 1

A single example of the Jersey Tiger was noted at a garden in North Road, Stevenage in August 1934 by C. H. Tindall-Lucas (Foster, 1937).

2068 *Callimorpha dominula* (L.) Scarlet Tiger

Recorded: 1872 – 1952
Distribution / Status: Absent / Possible former temporary resident
Conservation status: -
Caterpillar food plants: Not recorded. Elsewhere, on many herbaceous plant species
Flight period: Not recorded. Elsewhere, June/July
Records in database: 5

There are five Hertfordshire records: from Hitchin, where one was found on a doorstep in 1872 by J. H. Durrant; from Ickleford, near Hitchin, where larvae were found in 1912 (R. Palmer), from Northchurch, 'at light several times' by J. Bell (Foster, 1942) and from Little Tring, in 1952, and again in 1953 'possibly a wanderer from the 'planted colony' near Tring Museum' by S. B. Hodgson (Bell, 1954). This implies two foci, one in the Tring/Berkhamsted area arising from an introduced colony (about which I have no information) and one in the Hitchin area which may perhaps have arisen from an initial immigration of a gravid female.

2069 *Tyria jacobaeae* (L.) Cinnabar

Recorded: 1828 – 2006
Distribution / Status: Ubiquitous / Abundant resident
Conservation status: UK BAP Watch List
No perceived threats in Herts
Caterpillar food plants: Oxford Ragwort; Common Ragwort; Groundsel; Coltsfoot
Flight period: May to July
Records in database: 419

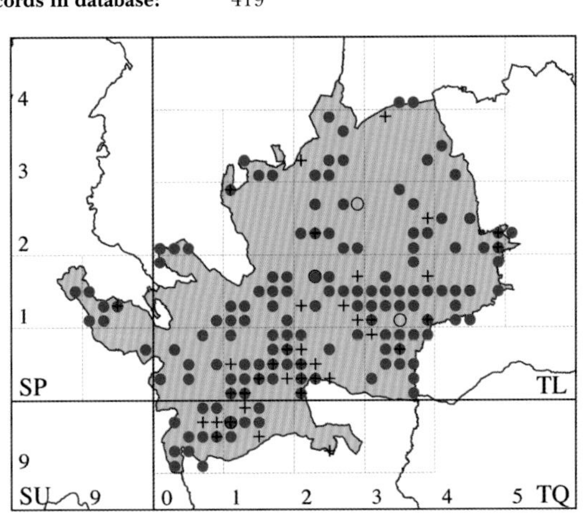

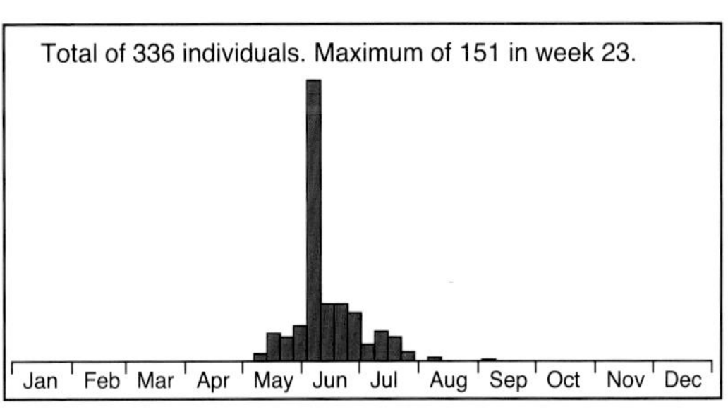

The Cinnabar is probably one of the most widespread and abundant moths in Hertfordshire and almost any ragwort plant is likely to produce the familiar larvae; there is no hint of any decline in either range or population. A particular abundance was noted in the Ashridge area of Pitstone Common, Moneybury Down, Aldbury Down and Aldbury Nowers (Hodgson, 1936). Bell (1954) notes 'larvae in coltsfoot when ragwort was available' at Kings Langley by H. C. Dunk, adding that this was also reported in *The Entomologist* (without actually giving the reference). This seems surprising, and one is led to wonder if they were actually observed eating the coltsfoot or whether they were merely resting on it having been dislodged from adjacent ragwort plants.

NOLIDAE

The position of the Nolidae is uncertain with some authors treating them as members of the Noctuidae and others retaining them as a separate family, but grouping them with noctuid subfamilies Chloeophorinae (nycteolines) and Eariadinae (Cream-bordered Green Pea). I follow current British practice here placing them just before the start of the Noctuidae. The family is characterised, in part, by a peculiar projection on the side of the first antennal segment and by the presence of scale-tufts on the forewings. Four of the five British species are recorded in Hertfordshire, though two are no longer present.

2075 *Meganola strigula* ([D.& S.]) Small Black Arches

Recorded: Pre-1937 – 1938
Distribution / Status: Absent / Former resident
Conservation status: Herts Extinct
Caterpillar food plants: Not recorded. Elsewhere, on oak
Flight period: Elsewhere, June/July
Records in database: 2

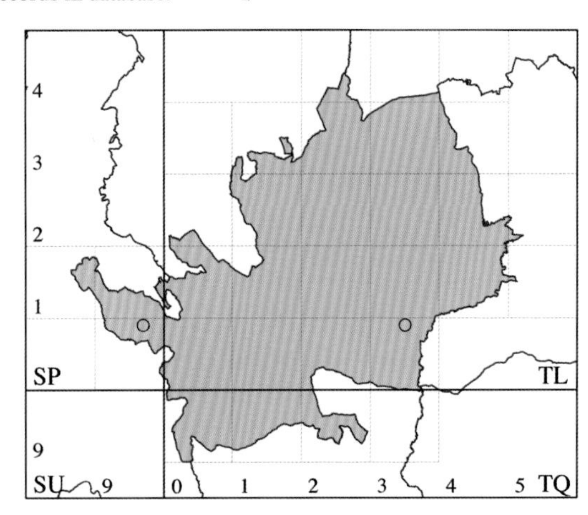

The report of this mature oak woodland species as 'fairly plentiful' at Hodd Park, Hoddesdon, by G. V. Bull, given in Foster (1937) without a year, is the source of the mapped dot in TL 31 in *Moths and Butterflies of Great Britain and Ireland* volume 9. Bull contributed records to Foster after 1902, so the record relates to the early twentieth century, but we can be no more precise than that. Later (Foster, 1942) there is a report of two on Northchurch Common in 1938, reported by J. Bell. Although initially seeming to be unlikely localities, these do fit a general pattern of old records extending over a wide area of southern Britain and it is clear that the species has contracted its range considerably.

2076 *Meganola albula* ([D.& S.]) Kent Black Arches

Recorded: 1954 – 1954
Distribution / Status: Absent / Former immigrant
Conservation status: -
Caterpillar food plants: Not recorded. Elsewhere, on Dewberry
Flight period: August
Records in database: 1

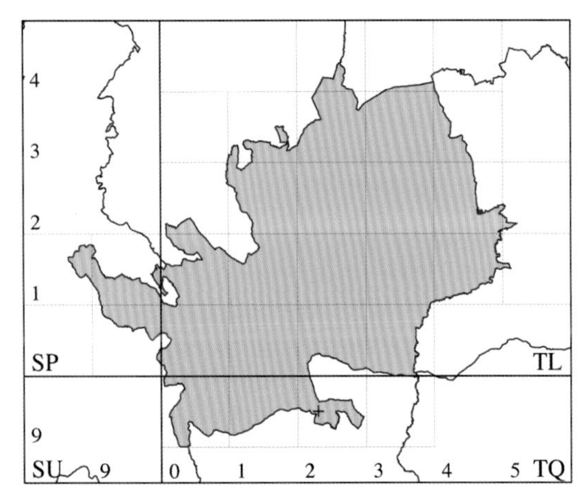

A single report from Arkley, on 5th August 1954 (*Entomologist's Gazette* **5**: 232) is considered to relate to an immigrant example. There are no other Hertfordshire records.

2077 *Nola cuculatella* (L.) Short-cloaked Moth

Recorded: 1884 – 2006
Distribution / Status: Widespread / Common resident
Conservation status: Herts Stable
Caterpillar food plants: Common Hawthorn. Elsewhere, also on apple, Blackthorn and Plum
Flight period: June to early August
Records in database: 349

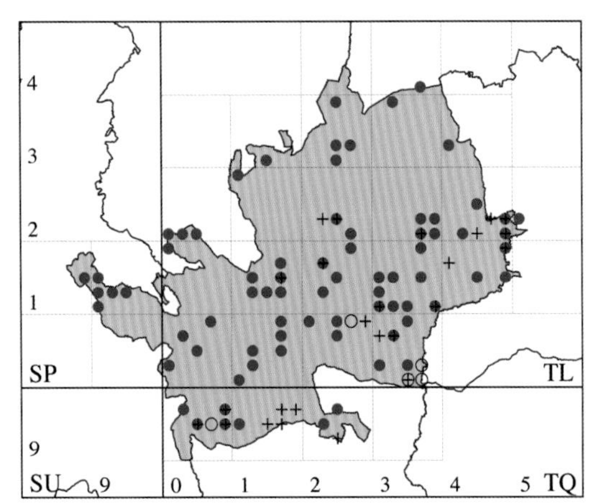

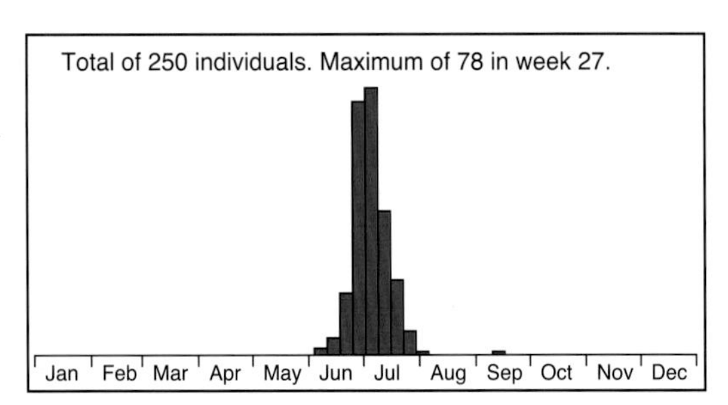

The Short-cloaked Moth is a common visitor to most moth traps, though some newcomers to moth recording may dismiss it as a 'micro'. A late example is recorded at Chorleywood, on 13th September 2006 (Richard Ellis), though this was, technically, a few yards inside Buckinghamshire (vice-county 24).

2078 *Nola confusalis* (H.- S.) Least Black Arches

Recorded: 1934 – 2006
Distribution / Status: Widespread / Common resident
Conservation status: Herts Stable
Caterpillar food plants: Not recorded. Elsewhere, on various trees
Flight period: April to June
Records in database: 141

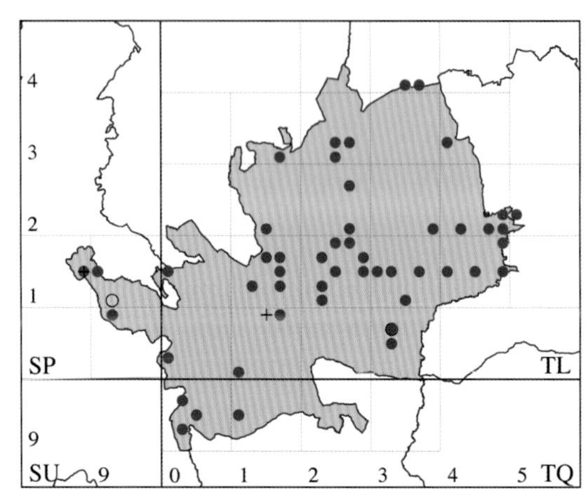

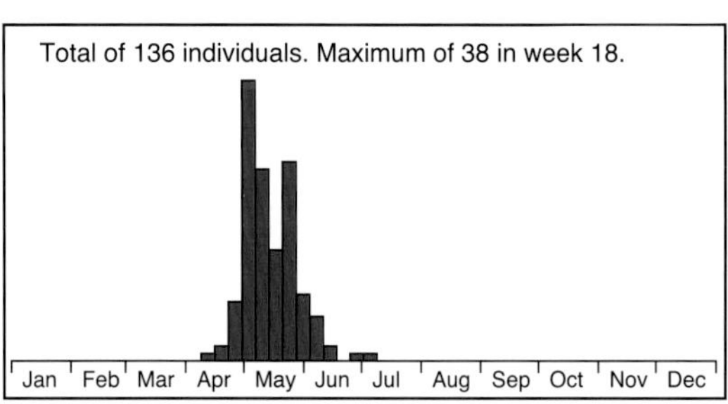

The Least Black Arches was for a long time considered a rarity and was first recorded in the county from Broxbourne Woods as recently as 1934 by Eric Classey, where it was found again by Eric in 1936, (Foster, 1942). Apart from a report from the woods around Tring in 1945 (Goodson) there are no more Hertfordshire records until one at St Albans on 20th July 1971 (C. H. C. Lyal). Another long gap follows until Alan Bernard caught the next example at Long Marston in 1983; more were caught here several years later in 1996, 1997 and 1998 suggesting that a small local population was established. During 1998, Mardley Heath was added to the list of localities by Rob Souter and in 1999 the moth was detected at three new and widely spaced sites in Harpenden, Bishops Stortford and Royston hinting of things yet to come. Over the next two or three years the moth appeared in many new places and established itself as a breeding species in the county. Today it is more or less expected in most sites. The grey aberration *columbina* Image was said to be confined to Epping Forest in Essex, across the River Lea to the east. Whilst that may or may not have been true in the past, it certainly is no longer the case and *columbina* is occasionally caught at sites in the east of the county.

NOCTUIDAE

With at least 25,000 species worldwide, this is one of the largest moth families. Its classification is ongoing, but at present 14 subfamilies are recognised in Europe and these contain around

1,400 species. In dealing with the 265 Hertfordshire species I have followed British tradition in excluding the Nolidae as a separate family. I also exclude 2020: *Diloba caeruleocephala* which I have placed in the Notodontidae, but I retain the Chloephorinae and Eariadinae (which some believe should be moved to the Nolidae) and the Pantheinae (which some treat as a separate family). For ease of use I have retained the sequence and names used in the British checklist (Bradley, 2000) and where this may not be correct I have made comments. Those interested in forming their own opinions are referred to the ongoing series *Noctuidae Europaeae,* available from Apollo Books in Denmark. This taxonomic review of the Noctuidae introduces several changes to established wisdom.

NOCTUINAE

[2080 *Euxoa obelisca* ([D.& S.]) Square-spot Dart

In a list sent in approximately 1974 to the then county recorder Peter Waterton, John (Jack) Newton reports catching one adult at mv light in Stevenage on 17th September 1970, the specimen apparently being in the collection of D. Ruston. This is a surprising record of a species that is, apart from the anomaly of an apparent colony in the Rugby district of Warwickshire from the 1980s to present, entirely restricted in Britain to the coast, clockwise from Sussex round to north-east Scotland. The moth is not noted for migrations, though some unlikely species may wander during exceptional conditions (for example, the Sand Dart *Agrotis ripae* (Hb.), an equally coastal species, turned up in David Agassiz's garden in Enfield, Middlesex on 27th June in the exceptionally hot summer of 1976 (see *Ent. Rec.* **89**: 153). The Ruston collection has not been found and so the specimen cannot be examined, but no particular freak weather or other conditions appear to have prevailed on or just before the date of the report. In spite of the captor, this must be treated as a doubtful record and cannot be accepted unless the specimen is traced and examined. Two examples recorded tentatively from Essendon in 1945 (Foster, 1946) proved, subsequently, to be examples of ab. *aquilina* ([D.& S.]) of 2081: White-line Dart (see, Fryer, 1948).]

2081 *Euxoa tritici* (L.) White-line Dart

Recorded:	1895 – 1998
Distribution / Status:	Extremely local or absent / Rare resident or extinct
Conservation status:	UK BAP Priority Species Herts Endangered
Caterpillar food plants:	Not recorded. Elsewhere, on various herbaceous plants
Flight period:	September
Records in database:	16

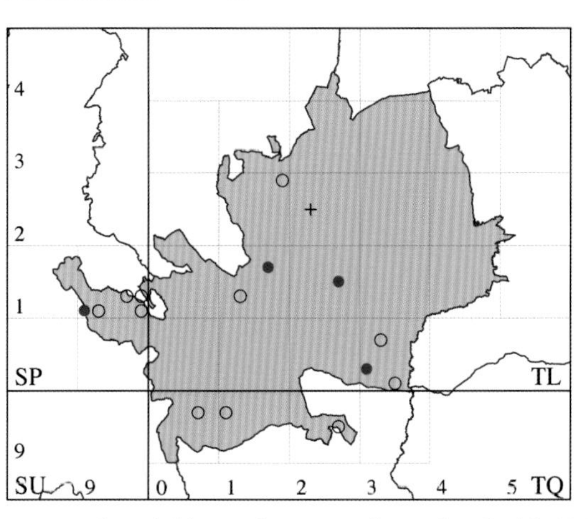

Some examples of this species are easily confused with 2082: Garden Dart. The map seems to indicate scattered records in the south-west half of the county; there appears never to have been any reports from the north-east portion. The first known county occurrence is from Watford, where one was captured by S. H. Spencer in 1895. It was recorded at Waltham Cross in 1902 by W. C. Boyd and two were taken by 'Mr. Grellett, of Hitchin' during 1902, and reported by A. H. Foster (Gibbs, 1904a). In his 1937 list, Foster also gives East Barnet, Berkhamsted, Broxbourne and Watford, suggesting that this is a less widespread species than many others in his county list. Hodgson (1939) notes a var. *aquilina* at sugar on the Ashridge Estate in 1934 and two others were noted at Essendon in 1945 (Fryer, 1948) and at Tring in the same year. One was caught at light on the Rothamsted Estate in Harpenden in 1948. More recently, records are all of single moths from Stevenage in 1970 (Jack Newton), Tewin in 1995 (Rob Souter), Tring in 1995 (Brian Jessop), Kimpton in 1997 (Vincent & Betty Judd) and Cuffley in 1998 (Alan Bolitho). According to recent research the national population of White-line Dart has declined by 92 per cent since 1970. Hertfordshire data from the map indicates a loss of this species from 75 per cent of its sites occupied prior to 1995, but since there have been no reports for eight years this species may in fact already have become extinct in Hertfordshire.

2082 *Euxoa nigricans* (L.) Garden Dart

Recorded:	1887 – 2006
Distribution / Status:	Extremely local / Rare resident
Conservation status:	UK BAP Watch List Herts Endangered
Caterpillar food plants:	Not recorded. Elsewhere, on a wide variety of herbaceous plants
Flight period:	July/August
Records in database:	88

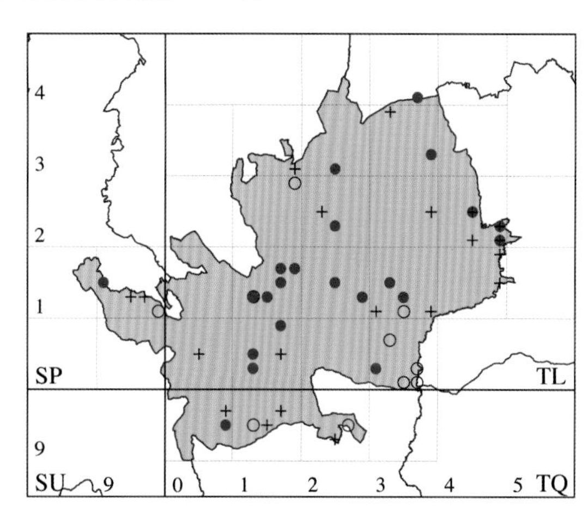

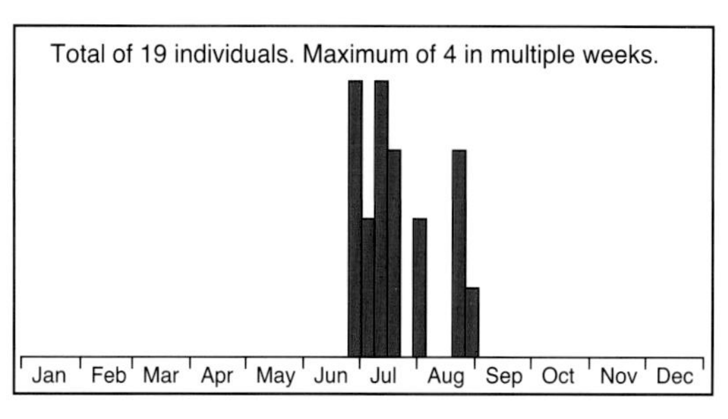

Some examples of this species are easily confused with 2081: White-line Dart and caution is required in identification. At the national level there is a reported 97 per cent reduction in population since 1970 and although this moth seems still to be hanging on in Hertfordshire, there are places from which the moth has certainly disappeared. The distribution map suggests a 57 per cent decline in Hertfordshire sites since 1995 and a 72 per cent decline since 1999. At the end of 2006, it appears to persist at Bricket Wood, but may have vanished from most other sites. It was first listed for the county for the Haileybury College area (Bowyer, 1888) and in 1937 Foster listed several localities indicating it to have been moderately widespread (although the record from Berkhamsted is in error – corrected in Hodgson (1939). In 1950, P. B. M. Allan noted it as 'Occasional; sometimes common' in his list for the Bishops Stortford area and in the 1985 revision by the Bishops Stortford Natural History Society it is dismissed as 'Common' with no further comment. This latter, somewhat superficial work is unlikely to have been correct; since moving to this town in October 1986 I have caught only five individuals in my garden (on 15th July 1987, 12th August 1988, two on 7th August 1989 and one on 30th June 2006), in spite of near nightly trapping and none in the surrounding woodlands and other habitats.

2083 *Euxoa cursoria* (Hufn.) Coast Dart

Recorded:	1959 to 1959
Distribution / Status:	Absent / Former rare vagrant
Conservation status:	-
Caterpillar food plants:	Elsewhere, on various coastal plants
Flight period:	Elsewhere, July/August
Records in database:	1

One was taken at light in Bishops Stortford on 6th August 1959 by Geoffrey Sell and is mentioned in the 1985 list published by the Bishops Stortford and District Natural History Society. The specimen has been examined by Mark Parsons, Bernard Skinner and myself. This very surprising record remains the only one for Hertfordshire of this otherwise coastal species.

2084 *Agrotis cinerea* ([D. & S.]) Light Feathered Rustic

Recorded:	1897 to 1982
Distribution / Status:	Absent / Former resident/rare vagrant
Conservation status:	Herts Extinct
Caterpillar food plants:	Not recorded. Elsewhere on Thyme (*Thymus* spp.) and probably other plants
Flight period:	Insufficient data. Elsewhere May and June
Records in database:	9

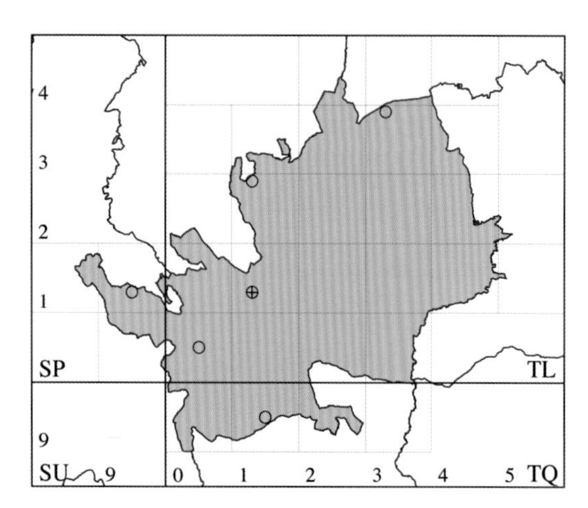

The few records that we have seem to indicate that the Light Feathered Rustic was once resident on the chalk downs in the north and west of the county, but that it has since become extinct. There are inadequate records to draw a complete time-line, but it was common in the late 1930s and was probably eliminated by habitat change arising from the introduction of the rabbit disease myxomatosis in the 1950s. The record from Bushey Heath in the south of the county is rather surprising since the geology here appears to be unsuitable and it is a pity that Foster's 1937 list gave so little information. All available records are given: 'Three males were taken at Felden, Boxmoor, at light, by Mr. Albert Piffard in 1897, and he kindly gave them to me. This is a new record for the County, and a particularly interesting one' (Cottam, 1901). Foster (1937) lists this as 'Felden, Boxmoor, 1887', but the date in the original reference is the correct one; 'I have taken this species on Pegsdon Hills flying in sunshine in July and have seen other specimens in the same locality' (Foster, 1914). Foster (1937) repeats his Pegsdon Hills record and adds Royston Heath [= Therfield Heath], Bushey Heath and Berkhamsted (all undated) and Harpenden (1933). Hodgson (1939) notes that it was common on the downs at Ashridge and Aldbury Nowers, though it is possible that the 'downs at Ashridge' may refer to land within Buckinghamshire. Riley (1999) confirms the 1933 record from the Rothamsted Estate at Harpenden and adds two more in 1950 and 1982. Ian Woiwod of the Department of Entomology at Rothamsted has kindly checked their database and supplied me with the full dates for all three records as follows: Trap 1: Barnfield, 18th May 1933; Trap 6: on a laboratory roof, 24th May 1950 and Trap 26: GI site, 2nd July 1982. These Harpenden records were perhaps of dispersing vagrants rather than local residents? A record from the Apsley area on 30 June 1976 by N. E. Gammon is rejected. Gammon did not retain specimens and recorded other unlikely species at the same place; his letter, which accompanies the list submitted to the county recorder at the time, states that he was not an expert at moth identification.

[2085 *Agrotis vestigialis* (Hufn.) Archer's Dart

Bell (1952) records an example taken by C. B. Williams in the light traps at Rothamsted (Harpenden) in 1948 and notes that this was a new species for the county. However, this species is omitted by Adrian Riley (1999) from his definitive review of larger moths on the Rothamsted Estate; it is assumed that the original identification may have been an error, although Riley did not discuss rejected records in his otherwise comprehensive paper. In adjacent Essex, the moth is confined to the east coast and there are no reports from anywhere near our borders whilst in Bedfordshire to our north-west there are seven reports of individual moths in recent years, but all confined to the Upper Greensand ridge that runs from north-east to south-west across that county. Taking all the information into account, Archer's Dart cannot be admitted to the Hertfordshire fauna without better evidence.]

2087 *Agrotis segetum* ([D.& S.]) Turnip Moth

Recorded:	1881 to 2005
Distribution / Status:	Ubiquitous / Common resident and primary immigrant
Conservation status:	Herts Stable
Caterpillar food plants:	Not recorded. Elsewhere on roots and lower stems of plants
Flight period:	May to early December in two, or perhaps three, generations, confused by immigration.
Records in database:	1041

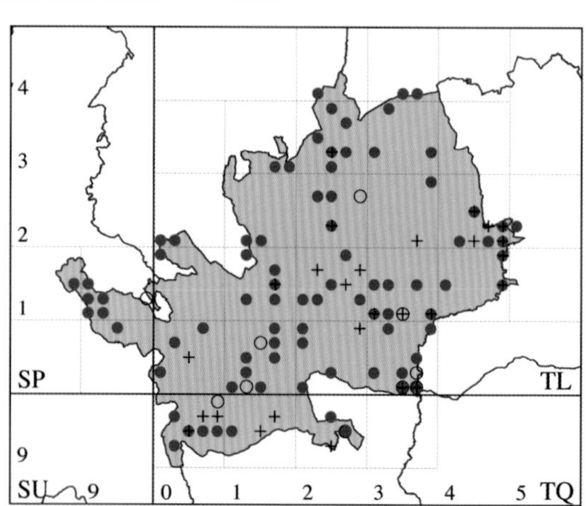

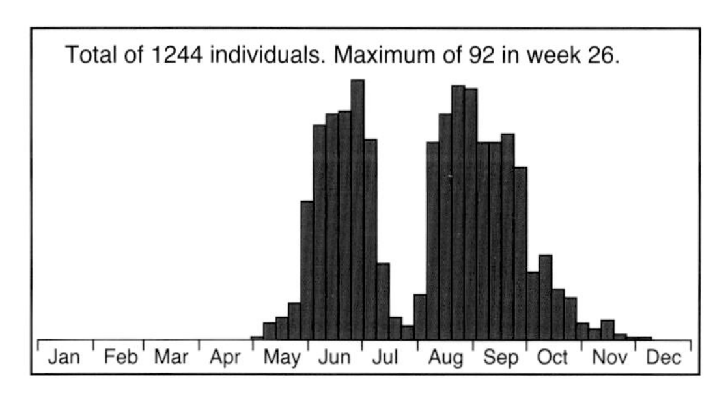

The flight chart shows very clearly that this is a double-brooded species, with adults flying from mid-May to mid- July and again from early August to early October. There is a suggestion of a third generation in October/November, but the whole picture is obfuscated by the regular arrival of immigrants from continental Europe and the moths can plainly be found in light traps continuously from May to December! The Turnip Moth has always been common with us and is likely to be in every map tetrad of the county and may attain huge numbers. The caterpillars are one of several agricultural pests termed 'cut worms' because they feed at the base of plant stems felling the plant in the process. At Harpenden, 'several large larvae' were seen crossing a road 24th July 1881 (Willis, 1882).

2088 *Agrotis clavis* (Hufn.) Heart and Club

Recorded: 1828 to 2005
Distribution / Status: Widespread / Common resident
Conservation status: Increasing
Caterpillar food plants: Not recorded. Elsewhere on herbaceous plants
Flight period: June/July
Records in database: 685

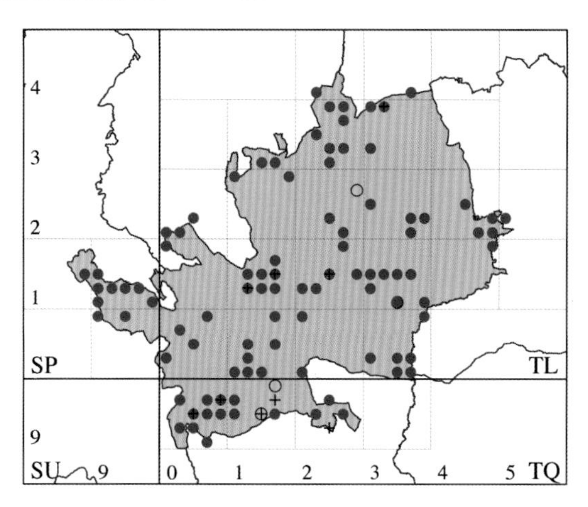

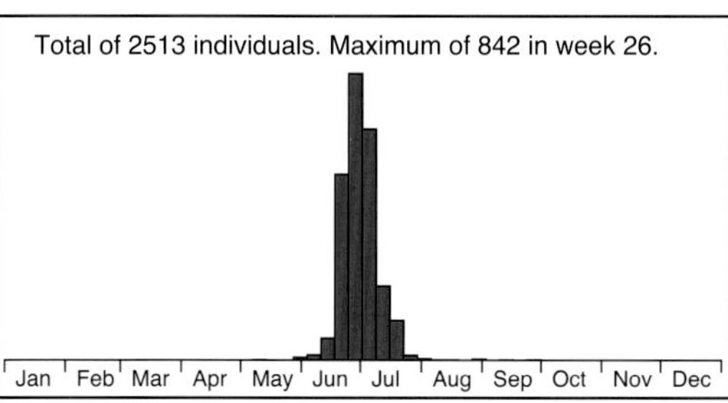

The Heart and Club has increased in its frequency of capture since about 2000, turning up in many sites where it was almost certainly absent beforehand; the paucity of old records in the map reflects this. Writing about the Bishops Stortford district in 1950, P. B. M. Allan noted this moth as 'Not uncommon formerly', gave a single record from the town and added 'Has not been taken for many years'. The species is not included in the 1985 revision of the Bishops Stortford area list, which implies that there had been no records since the 1950 publication in spite of at least two people actively recording in the area. In my own garden in Bishops Stortford, trapped almost nightly from October 1986 to December 2006, I did not record Heart and Club until 2001; it is now expected in single or perhaps low double figures each year. It appeared for the first time during the same year in the trap run on the other side of the town in adjoining gardens by James Fish and Julian Reeve on a near nightly basis since 1995. Away from Bishops Stortford, Liz Goodyear, whose garden trap is in Ware, does not seem to have taken this species until 2002 and it does not appear on Andrew Wood's list for the Bengeo area of Hertford until 2001. Doubtless there are other examples.

2089 *Agrotis exclamationis* (L.) Heart and Dart

Recorded: 1883 to 2005
Distribution / Status: Ubiquitous / Abundant resident
Conservation status: Herts Stable
Caterpillar food plants: Not recorded. Elsewhere on various plants
Flight period: late May to late July
Records in database: 2,273

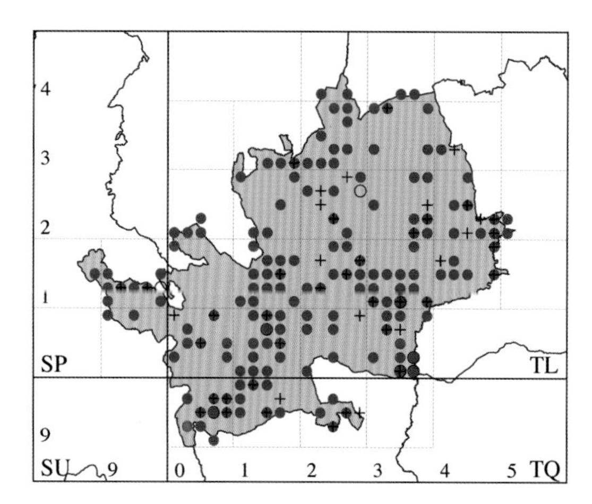

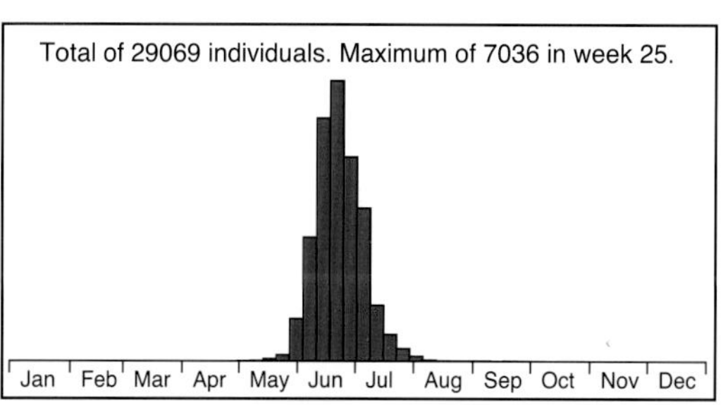

The Heart and Dart, with only 2,273 records in the database, is not the most frequently reported moth in Hertfordshire – that accolade is reserved for 2107: Large Yellow Underwing which is reported on 3,353 occasions. In fact the Heart and Dart lies a feeble sixth. The value of persisting with what is often a tedious process of counting Heart and Darts in the moth trap every morning is evident from the flight chart with just under 7,000 individuals reported in week 25 (18th – 24th June) and an approximate 29,000 individuals counted altogether it is possible to have a high degree of confidence in the chart. It is clear that there is only a single generation of adults per year, though there are some exceptional dates: 19th September 2003 (James Fish and Julian Reeves in Bishops Stortford) and 20th September 2003 (my garden in the same town). An even later male was caught in my garden on 18th October 2006 in the same trap as a single example of 2321: Dark Arches.

2091 *Agrotis ipsilon* (Hufn.) Dark Sword-grass

Recorded:	1883 to 2006
Distribution / Status:	Random / Immigrant
Conservation status:	-
Caterpillar food plants:	Not recorded.
Flight period:	April to November, occasionally records December and January
Records in database:	318

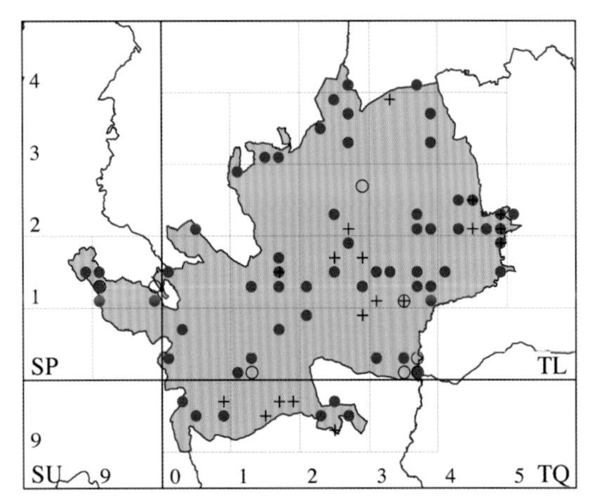

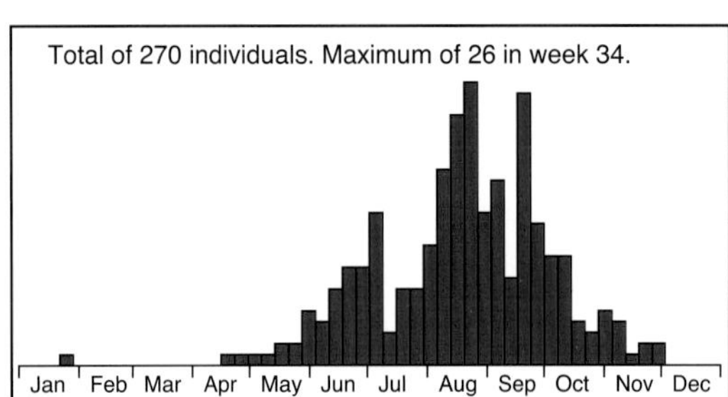

There is no evidence at all to suggest that the Dark Sword-grass breeds in Hertfordshire and it is probable that all records relate to primary immigrants from overseas. On this basis, any apparent population peaks in the flight chart should be regarded as artefacts, since numbers of immigrants are governed by conditions at the site of origin rather than here in Britain. Numbers attending moth traps are usually low (the graph shows a peak in week 34 of just 26 individuals for the period 1995 to 2006), but at Bishops Stortford, on the night of 7th October 1959 there were, according to Bell (1961), no less than 35 in Clifford Craufurd's trap, along with 117 examples of 2306: Angle Shades, 19 adult 2441: Silver Y and 5 of 2119: Pearly Underwing – all primary immigrants. The exceptionally early bar in the flight chart relates to one taken on 21st January 2001 at Cuffley by Alan Bolitho.

2092 *Agrotis puta* (Hb.) Shuttle-shaped Dart

Recorded:	1893 to 2006
Distribution / Status:	Ubiquitous / Abundant resident
Conservation status:	Herts Stable
Caterpillar food plants:	Not recorded. Elsewhere on a range of herbaceous plants
Flight period:	Late April to late June, late July to late August and then late September to early October in three generations
Records in database:	2,019

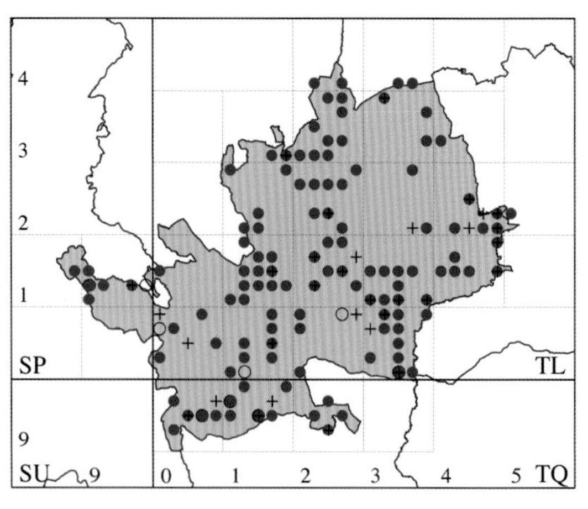

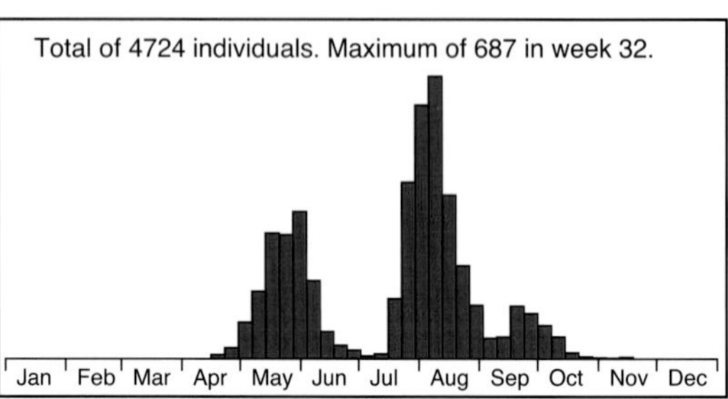

This familiar moth is absent from all of the major county lists of the nineteenth century and is not listed for Hertfordshire until 1893, when S. H. Spencer found one in his garden in Gladstone Road, Watford (Gibbs, 1896). It was described as 'Scarce' at Waltham Cross by Boyd (1901), but in 1937 Foster listed several localities indicating it to have been widespread by that date. It is of some interest that the first record of Shuttle-shaped Dart in Hertfordshire was not forthcoming until people started using electric arc lamps to attract moths. Indeed, the moth was reported as generally rather scarce until more people got going with the new-fangled electric lamps whereupon it was discovered to be really rather common. Of course, the moth *could* have been genuinely rare a hundred years ago, but that cannot be assured and this true tale serves as an illustration of the pitfalls of assigning status categories to moths. Today it is an ubiquitous species, whose numbers in moth traps may reach three figures. The adult flight chart shows two clear peaks of adults in May/June and August; these are well separated in most years and the apparent continuous brooded nature of the moth is merely a consequence of the graph combining all the records from 1995 to 2006. There is a smaller third peak discernible for the September/October period which has been an annual event from 2001 to 2006, but apparently not before. The two sexes are different in appearance with the females being more or less uniformly dark, apart from the 'shuttle' mark, on the forewing and the males being much lighter brown with darker markings. Rarely males may assume the all-dark female wings, but if this has happened in Hertfordshire it has passed unrecorded. All Hertfordshire examples of Shuttle-shaped Dart are referable to subspecies *puta* (Hübner). Forms approaching the pattern exhibited by the Scilly Isles subspecies *insula* Richardson, which does not occur here (and which may or may not be the same as the Greek species *Agrotis syricola* Corti & Draudt), are sometimes encountered and should be recorded.

[2097 *Actinotia polyodon* (Cl.) Purple Cloud

Now regarded as a member of the subfamily Amphipyrinae and placed after species 2306. A report from Ashridge in 1938 refers to *polyodon* of Linnaeus – an old name for 2321: Dark Arches.]

2098 *Axylia putris* (L.) Flame

Recorded: 1883 to 2006
Distribution / Status: Ubiquitous / Common resident
Conservation status: Herts Stable
Caterpillar food plants: Not recorded. Elsewhere on herbaceous plants
Flight period: June/July
Records in database: 1,217

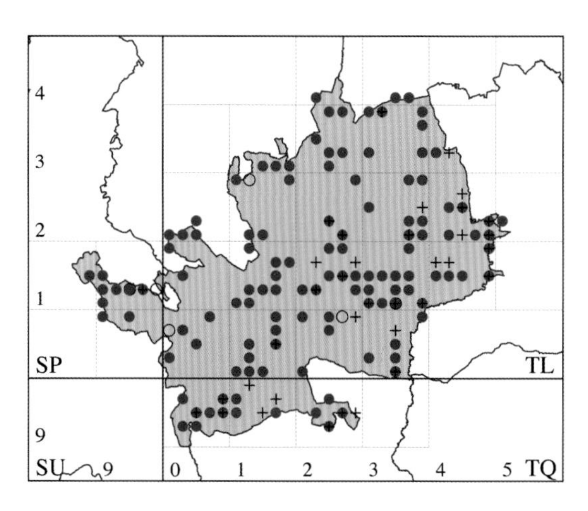

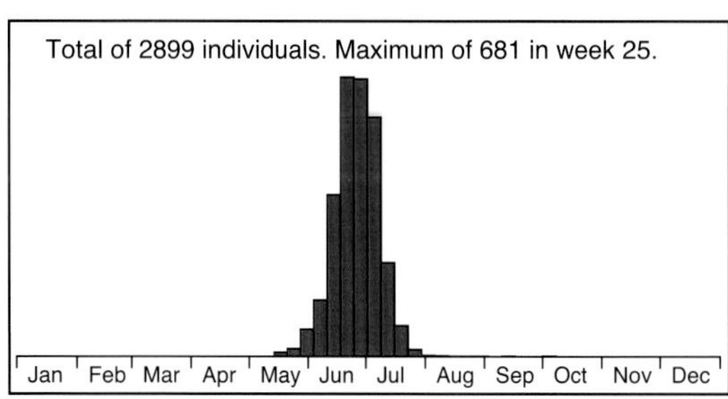

The Flame is a more or less ubiquitous moth in Hertfordshire and as far as I am aware no regular trap site has failed to produce at least one example. The single generation of adults flies throughout June, starting in mid-May and finishing towards the end of July, varying between years with the advancement or otherwise of the season. The scale of the graph does not allow us to see that there are three late records, on 11th August 2001 (Hitchin, John Webb), 13th August 2005 (Totteridge Fields, John Hollingdale) and 23rd August 2004 (Bishops Stortford, in my own garden trap).

2099 *Actebia praecox* (L.) Portland Moth

Recorded: 1913 only
Distribution / Status: Absent / Former vagrant
Conservation status: -
Caterpillar food plants: Not recorded
Flight period: September
Records in database: 1

A single published Hertfordshire record for this distinctive green moth, from 'Hoddesdon, two specimens at sugar, Sept. 1913. G. V. Bull', was presented by Foster (1937). The moth, which flies in August and September, is a local resident in some coastal sandhills of Britain, the nearest to Hertfordshire being Essex and Dorset. It occurs inland only in northern England. It is a very distinctive moth and it is hard to imagine that it could have been confused with any other species, except perhaps by a beginner who might misidentify 2247: Merveille Du Jour, which flies from late September in woodlands. It is assumed that the moth was a vagrant from one of the coastal localities in the south-east and it would be desirable to locate Bull's collection and examine the specimen.

2102 *Ochropleura plecta* (L.) Flame Shoulder

Recorded: 1884 – 2006
Distribution / Status: Ubiquitous / Common resident
Conservation status: Herts Stable
Caterpillar food plants: Not recorded. Elsewhere, on a variety of herbaceous plants
Flight period: April to September in two generations
Records in database: 1,852

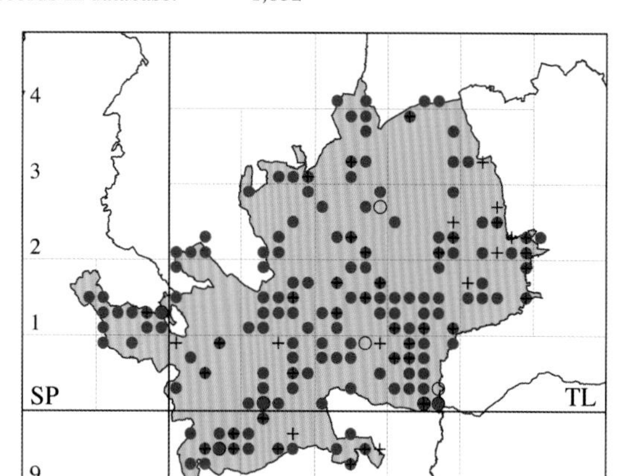

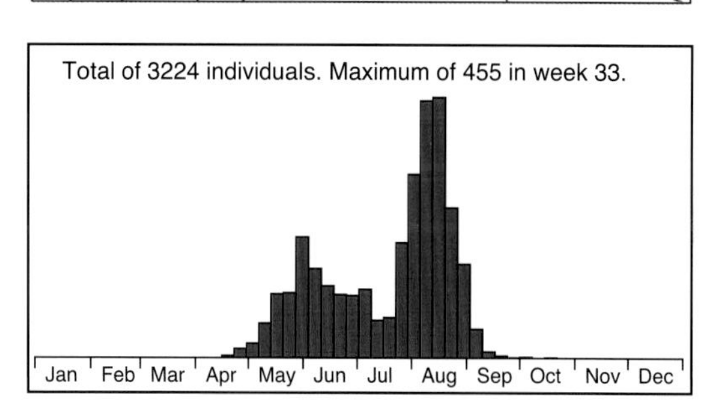

Apart from possible confusion in the autumn with the rare immigrant Radford's Flame Shoulder (*Ochropleura leucogaster* Freyer), which has yet to be recorded in Hertfordshire the present species is immediately recognisable. It was 'Common in all districts' according to Foster (1937) and that remains the case at the end of 2006. The Flame Shoulder is the eleventh most frequently reported moth in the county.

[2103 *Eugnorisma depuncta* (L.) Plain Clay

Foster (1941) adds this most surprising species to the county list from 'Ware (Gerard)' and later (Foster, 1942) records one taken at light in Berkhamsted by J. Bell in 1938. During the 1930s, Gerard made a number of records that could be interpreted as probable errors; in addition to Plain Clay these include 2217: Star-wort, 2219: Striped Lychnis, 2455: Dark Crimson Underwing and 1644: Kentish Glory. Young (1991) in discussing the latter species notes that 'Records are hopelessly confused by specimens labelled from place of emergence rather than capture and this may explain doubtful past records from ... Hertfordshire ...'. This seems a likely explanation. The record from Berkhamsted by J. Bell is very likely to have arisen from a misidentification. Neither record is accepted and the species is omitted from the county list.]

2105 *Rhyacia simulans* (Hufn.) Dotted Rustic

Recorded: 1963 – 2005
Distribution / Status: Extremely local, perhaps now absent / Rare resident
Conservation status: Herts Endangered
Caterpillar food plants: Unknown. The wild larva has not been found in Britain
Flight period: June to August, elsewhere June to October, with a period of aestivation in July
Records in database: 40

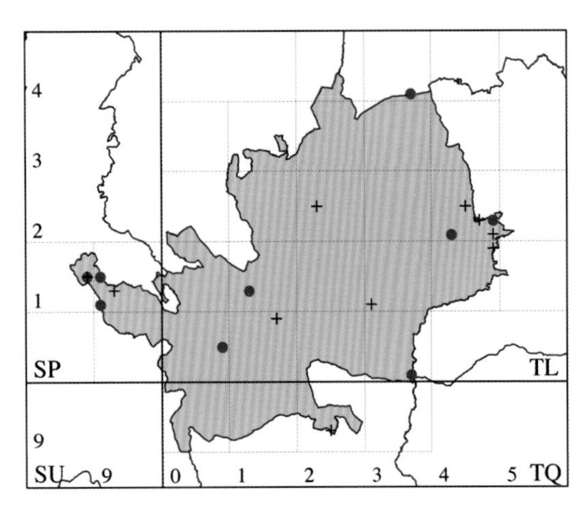

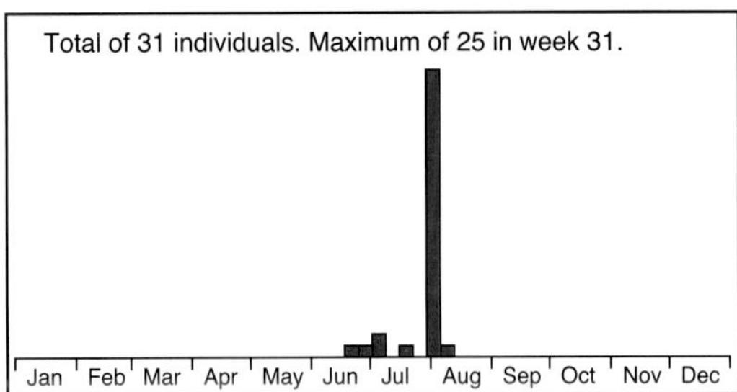

Formerly restricted to the north-west of England, where it flies continuously from July to October, the Dotted Rustic suddenly appeared in southern central England. One at the light trap on the Rothamsted Estate at Harpenden in 1963 (R. A. French) was reported by Bell (1964) as being the first county record, but another example taken by P. Ward at Whetstone on 11th August 1963 and also reported in Bell (1964) was in fact in the Middlesex vice-county. De Worms (1964) in discussing this latter report remarked that this was an extremely unusual record of a species normally associated with downland and rocky coasts in the north and west of England, adding that the only other London Area record was from Ewell, Surrey, in 1949. An example taken at light in Totteridge, during September 1969 (Ian Lorimer) – seems to be the next Hertfordshire record; there were further examples at Totteridge, on 2nd October 1972 and 1 July 1976 (Ian Lorimer). Subsequent records were from Bayfordbury in 1974 (Jim Reid), Totteridge again on 1st July 1976 (Ian Lorimer), Bishops Stortford town, 17th September 1980 and again in 1981, and Bloodhounds Wood near Bishops Stortford on 27th July 1981 (Charles Watson). In the far west of the county, Alan Bernard recorded this species in 1983, 1984, 1985, 1986, 1997 and 2001 whilst in the same area it was recorded by Peter Bygate on 27th June 2000, in 2003 and on 2nd and 30th July 2005 (the last Hertfordshire records available). During 1987 there was a flurry of reports, from Bishops Stortford (Charles Watson and me), St Albans (Wendy Hatton) and Tring (D. Wingrove). It seems to have remained widespread, but apparently rather local in the county for at least a few years, and there are occasionally reports up to about 1999, after which all records have already been listed above. There were no reliable reports in 2006 and it appears that the insect is retreating again, at a national level. Unlike their northern counterparts, southern English Dotted Rustics emerge in June, but after no more than two weeks enter a period of aestivation (summer equivalent of hibernation) and awaken to fly in September and October. Localised declines may be due in part to a lack of aestivation sites: When I moved to Bishops Stortford, I built an extension to the house and in the summer months could easily show people adult Dotted Rustic by turning over bricks or large stones on rubble piles in the garden, but since the work was completed and the debris cleared I saw no more aestivating adults. Sheds and other structures are also used, but the critical factor is that these places should remain completely undisturbed during July and August.

2107 *Noctua pronuba* (L.) Large Yellow Underwing

Recorded:	1884 – 2006
Distribution / Status:	Ubiquitous / Abundant resident
Conservation status:	Herts Stable
Caterpillar food plants:	Common Couch Grass; Dandelion. Elsewhere, polyphagous on various low plants and grasses
Flight period:	June to October
Records in database:	3,353

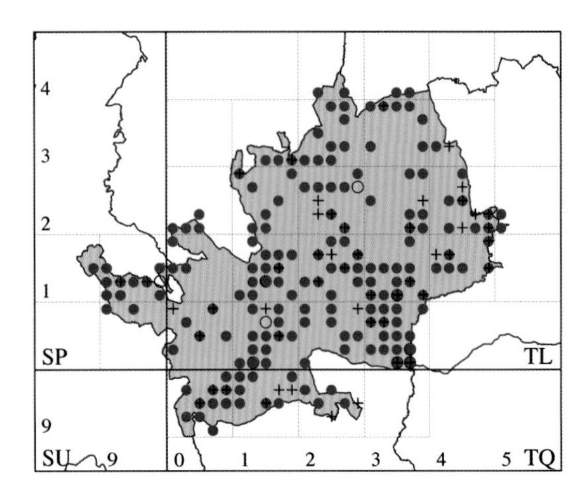

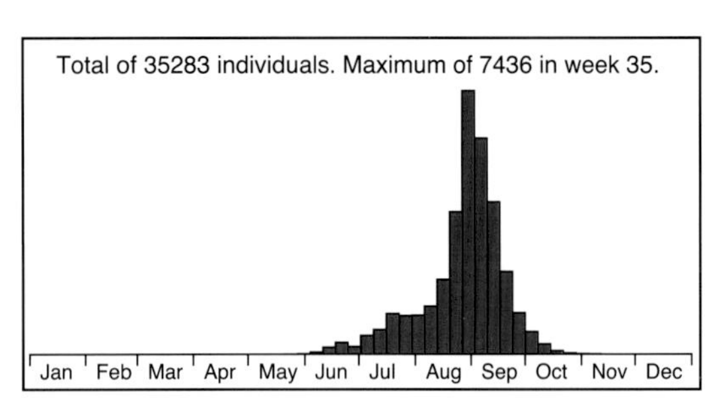

The Large Yellow Underwing appears on every significant list of moths in Hertfordshire; indeed it would be a great surprise if even the briefest of lists obtained from July to September lacked it. It is the single most frequently reported of all Hertfordshire's moths (3,353 records) and also the most numerous, with 37,166 adults reported (the nearest rival is 2089: Heart and Dart, with 30,863 adults reported). A great many colour forms exist, but no data on the frequency of these appears to have been collated. Many forms were named by Tutt (1892). Early examples were noted on 22nd March 1988 at Patmore Heath by me, and on 30th March 2002 at Garston by Colin Everett.

2108 *Noctua orbona* (Hufn.) Lunar Yellow Underwing

Recorded:	1940 – 1940
Distribution / Status:	Absent / Former vagrant or immigrant
Conservation status:	UK BAP Priority Species
Caterpillar food plants:	Not recorded. Elsewhere, on various 'fine' grasses
Flight period:	Elsewhere, July to September
Records in database:	1

The only valid records appear to be of four specimens collected by J. Birdsall in the Walkern area between 1940 and 1950. The exact location is uncertain and so no map is presented. Several more recent reports have been received, but where specimens or photographs have been examined all have proved to be 2109: Lesser Yellow Underwing. Any additional, unreported records of this species in Hertfordshire must be supported by a specimen or, in exceptional circumstances, a clear photograph.

2109 *Noctua comes* (Hb.) Lesser Yellow Underwing

Recorded:	1884 – 2006
Distribution / Status:	Ubiquitous / Abundant resident
Conservation status:	Herts Stable
Caterpillar food plants:	'grasses'. Elsewhere, on various herbaceous plants and grasses
Flight period:	Late June to late October
Records in database:	2,009

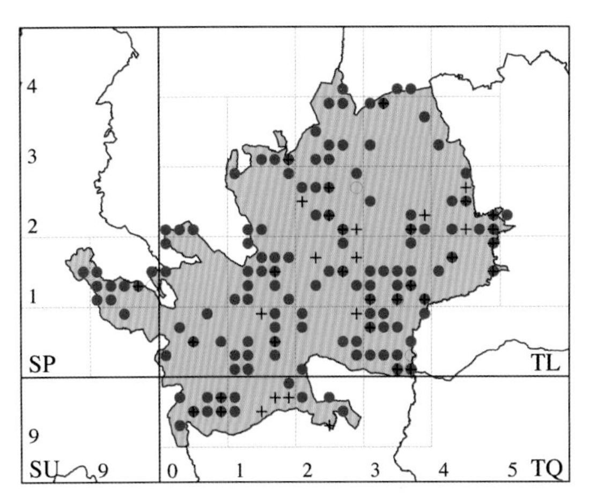

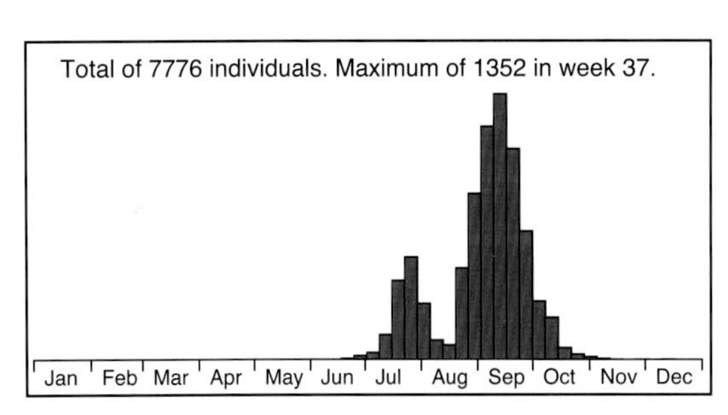

Caterpillars are easily obtained by using a sweep net on tall grasses at night time during the spring; unfortunately, collectors rarely report the species of grasses upon which these larvae are found! The adults of the last species (2108: Lunar Yellow Underwing) aestivate for a short period after emergence and before egg-laying, but this behaviour is not reported in the Lesser Yellow Underwing, which is said to be single-brooded. There is, nevertheless, an interesting and unexplained dip in the Hertfordshire flight chart during August. This might normally be explained in terms of two generations of adults, but the possibility that this species also aestivates is perhaps overlooked? An exceptionally late adult was caught at mv light in Ware on 12th December 2003 by Elizabeth Goodyear.

2110 *Noctua fimbriata* (Schreb.) Broad-bordered Yellow Underwing

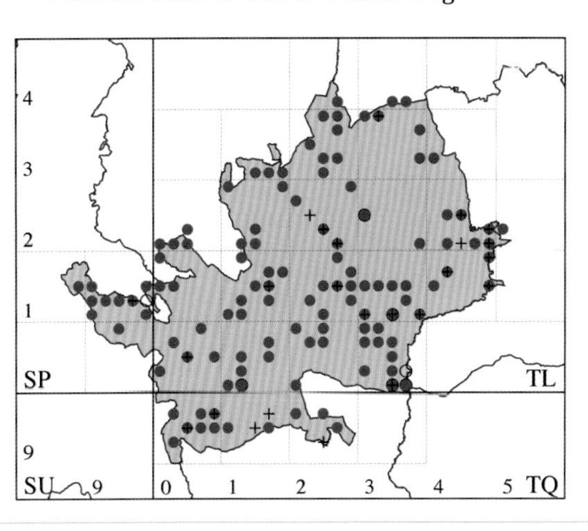

Recorded:	1884 – 2006
Distribution / Status:	Widespread / Common resident
Conservation status:	Herts Stable
Caterpillar food plants:	Not recorded. Elsewhere on various shrubs and herbaceous plants
Flight period:	Late June to early October in two generations
Records in database:	862

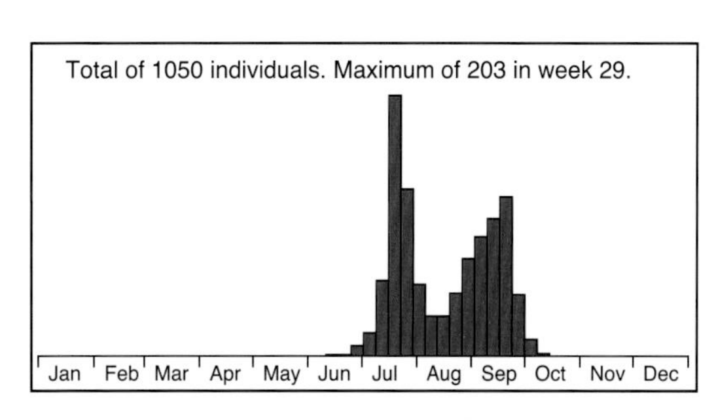

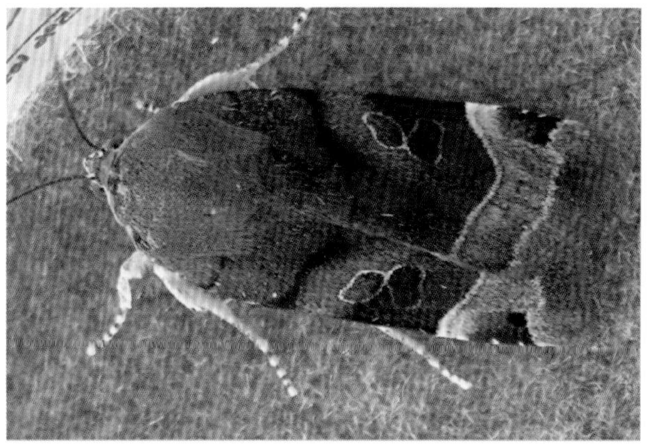

Although listed as single-brooded in various identification guides, this moth evidently has two generations of adults per year in Hertfordshire, peaking in July and September. The sexes differ, with the females assuming an overall pale fawn colour and the males being darker to varying degrees. A similar Iberian species, *Noctua tirrenica* Biebinger, Speidel & Hanigk, has recently spread into southern France and as climate change progresses could conceivably migrate north, although it may take several years to reach us; both sexes resemble our female in colour and the two are only reliably separated by characters of the genitalia.

2111 *Noctua janthe* (Borkh.) Lesser Broad-bordered Yellow Underwing

Recorded:	1884 – 2006
Distribution / Status:	Ubiquitous / Abundant resident
Conservation status:	Herts Stable
Caterpillar food plants:	Not recorded. Elsewhere, on various herbaceous plants, shrubs and even trees
Flight period:	Mid-July to mid September
Records in database:	1,370

4
3
2
1
SP
TL
9
SU 9
0 1 2 3 4 5 TQ

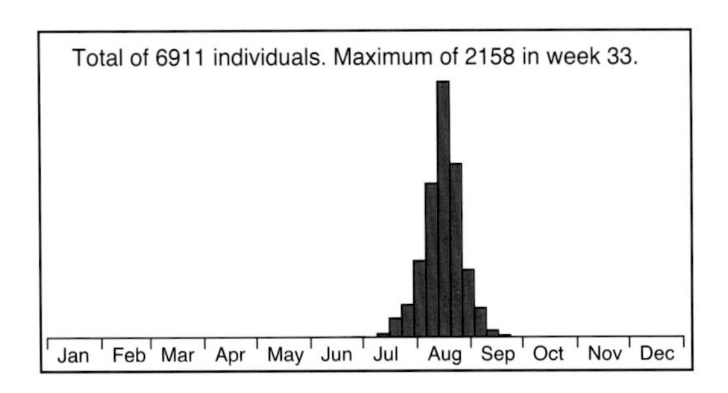

Old text books refer to this species as *Noctua janthina*, but Mentzer et al (1991) showed that this was the correct name for the European species and that the taxon present in Britain is *Noctua janthe*. In recent years, *N. janthina* has started to appear in Britain as an immigrant and has been called Langmaid's Yellow Underwing; it may yet appear in Hertfordshire. The ordinary Lesser Broad-bordered Yellow Underwing is a familiar sight throughout the county.

2112 *Noctua interjecta* Hb. ssp. *caliginosa* (Schaw.) Least Yellow Underwing

Recorded: 1828 – 2006
Distribution / Status: Widespread / Common resident
Conservation status: No perceived threats
Caterpillar food plants: Not recorded. Elsewhere, on various grasses and herbaceous plants
Flight period: July to early September
Records in database: 371

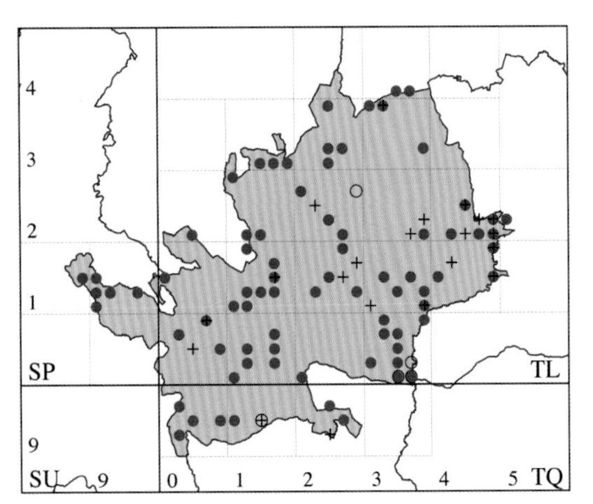

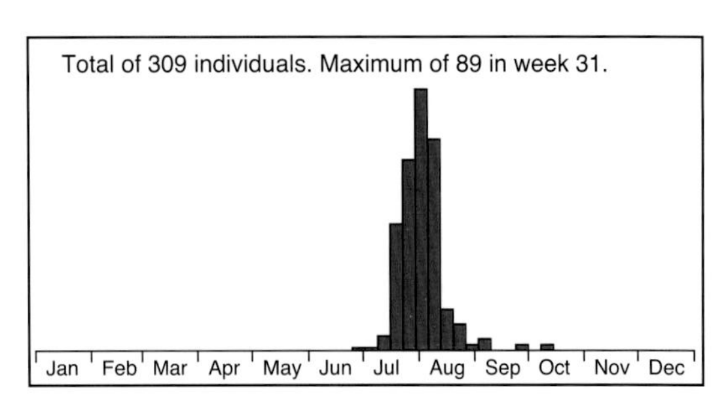

The nominotypical subspecies *interjecta* Hübner is found in southern Europe; British and northern European examples are all referable to subspecies *caliginosa* (Schawerda). It rarely presents in large number at light traps, but is nevertheless a widespread and very common species in Hertfordshire. Late examples were recorded as singles, in Tom Casey's light trap at Wyddial on 8th October 2005 and 14th October 2006.

2113 *Spaelotis ravida* ([D. & S.]) Stout Dart

Recorded: 1887 – 2001
Distribution / Status: Absent / Immigrant; perhaps former resident
Conservation status: Insufficiently known
Caterpillar food plants: Not recorded. Elsewhere, on herbaceous plants
Flight period: August to October
Records in database: 26

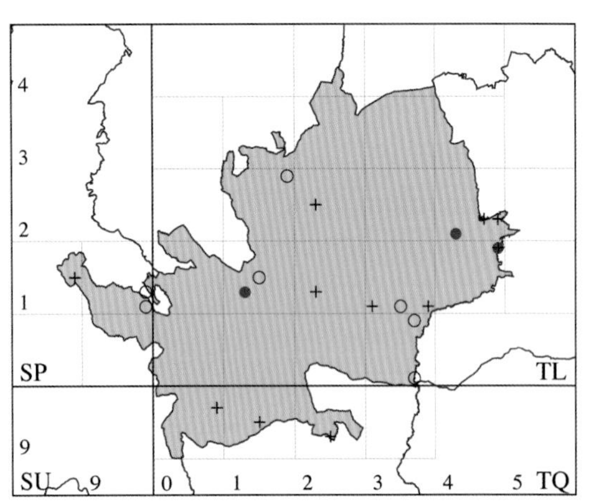

This is a species that undergoes huge population swings as a resident and which is also known as a primary immigrant. Old records are sparse, and come from Haileybury (Bowyer, 1888) and Cheshunt (Boyd, 1901), Hitchin (Foster, 1916), East Barnet and Hoddesdon [about the year 1900] and Berkhamsted [1934] and Harpenden [in the 1930s] (Foster, 1937). There is no evidence of it ever having bred in Hertfordshire, though it may have done so. Records since 1937 are few; one at Watford in September 1958 (Ray Penrose) as well as at Bushey on 23rd August 1965 and a female there on 5th September 1965 (Barry Goater) coincide with immigrant activity and of the latter records de Worms (1966) comments that 'This sporadic insect was apparently fairly numerous in the Eastern Counties at this period'. Most, if not all, records since that date also relate to immigrants and are as follows: Rye Meads, 1972, Totteridge, 1973 (Ian Lorimer); Bayfordbury, 1974 (Jim Reid); Totteridge, 3 in 1977, one in 1979 (Ian Lorimer); Lemsford Springs, 1979 (Tom Gladwin); Little Hadham, 1999 (Geoff Senior); Rothamsted Estate, 1999 (Adrian Riley); Stevenage, 6th September 1966 (Jack Newton); Bushey, 18th and 23rd August 1967 and 30th August 1968 (Barry Goater); Totteridge, September 1974 (Ian Lorimer); Bloodhounds Wood, 27th July 1981 (Charles Watson); Long Marston, 4th October 1987 (Alan Bernard); Bishops Stortford, 26th July 1994 (Charles Watson); Bishops Stortford, 27th July 1994 (James Fish and Julian Reeves) and Twyford Lock, Bishops Stortford, 14th August 2001 (Rodney Cook).

2114 *Graphiphora augur* (Fabr.) Double Dart

Recorded: 1828 – 2006
Distribution / Status: Extremely local / Rare resident
Conservation status: UK BAP Watch List. Herts Endangered
Caterpillar food plants: Not recorded. Elsewhere on blackthorn, sallow, hawthorn, birch, elm and occasionally dock
Flight period: June/July
Records in database: 59

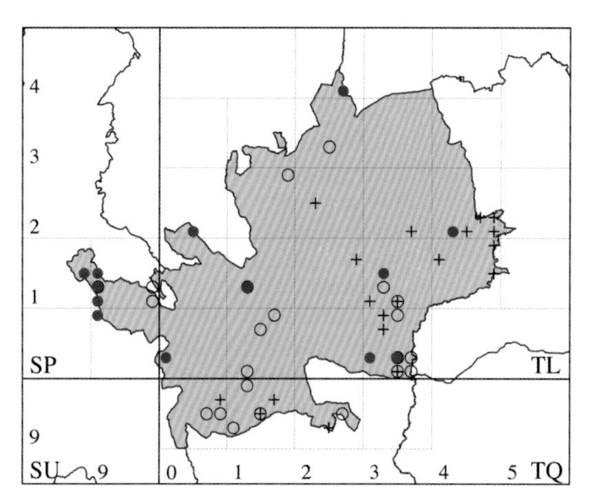

The map shows all post-1994 records as solid red dots but this masks the fact that there are only six Hertfordshire sightings since the turn of the Millennium. These were at Wilstone Reservoir, 1st July 2000 (I. Burrus) and again on 2nd July 2006 (Colin Lambert), Zouches Farm near Dunstable on the Herts Moth Group field trip of 14th June 2003, Grove Wood, on the Buckinghamshire border to the south of Tring when one came to the sheet on another Herts Moth Group field trip, on 2nd July 2005, Long Marston on 16th June 2006 (Peter Bygate) and Bovingdon Brick Pits on 24th June 2006 – another Herts Moth Group recording trip. Thus, there has been a decline of about 90 per cent in the number of sites where this species may be found in the county; this value coincides well with the reported 97 per cent national decline in numerical population since 1970. Given that the most intensively recorded areas of the county are in the central and mid-eastern zones it is likely to be significant that all of the more recent sightings of Double Dart are from the west of the county. The low level of recording effort prior to the 1990s makes it difficult to pinpoint the start of the decline or to suggest reasons for it.

2117 *Eugnorisma glareosa* (Esper) Autumnal Rustic

Recorded: 1903 – 2005
Distribution / Status: Extremely local or absent / Former resident, now perhaps vagrant
Conservation status: UK BAP Watch List. Herts Endangered
Caterpillar food plants: Not recorded. Elsewhere on various low plants
Flight period: September/October
Records in database: 9

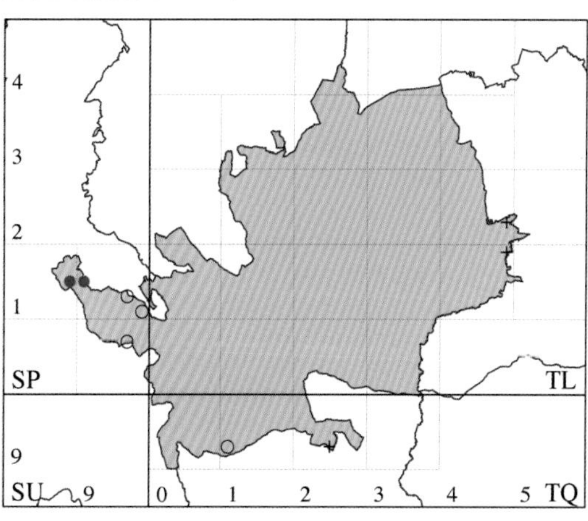

This has never been a common moth in Hertfordshire. A 'good series' was found on Ashridge Common by searching heather-bloom at night with a lantern in 1903 (Gibbs, 1904a) and provides the first county record. Foster (1937) listed this and also Berkhamsted, where it was 'very local at sugar, 1933 etc'. It was noted at Berkhamsted Common by Hodgson, in 1938, and in the same year at Oxhey Wood, on our border with Middlesex, by Eric Classey. These are probably the only records from the county that may relate to breeding populations and the remaining records probably relate to either vagrants or immigrants. An example of ab. *rosea* Tutt was taken in his garden at Totteridge by Ian Lorimer, on 30th September 1980. In the east of the county, Clifford Craufurd took this species on 14th September 1958 at Bishops Stortford and Charles Watson light trapped one in his garden further south in the same town on 14th October 1985. The two recent records on the map are both from different parts of Long Marston near our boundary with Buckinghamshire – one on 23rd September 2000 by Peter Bygate and one on 24th September 2005 by Alan Bernard. This species is reported to have declined nationally by 92 per cent since 1970; in Hertfordshire we appear to have lost it as a breeding species long before 1970. Nevertheless, it may yet be found and if so it should be regarded as Endangered for the purpose of conservation planning.

2118 *Lycophotia porphyrea* ([D.& S.]) True Lover's Knot

Recorded: 1884 – 2006
Distribution / Status: Random / Rare vagrant/immigrant
Conservation status: –
Caterpillar food plants: Not recorded. Elsewhere, on Heather and Bell Heather
Flight period: June/July
Records in database: 22

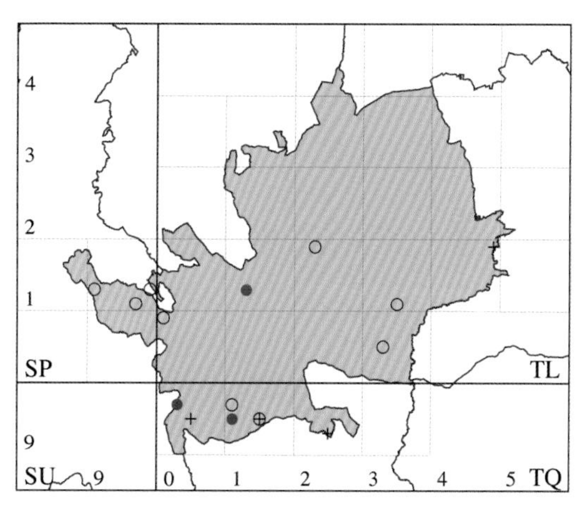

The True Lover's Knot is first listed for the county from the Sandridge area (Griffith, 1884; 1890) and Haileybury (Bowyer, 1888), whilst Cottam (1901) records a single example coming into his room at Watford, attracted by the light, on 18th July 1898 and notes that 'Where it can have come from is a mystery, as the nearest heather must be several miles away'. (Foster, 1914) reports that 'H. A. Leeds takes this species fairly commonly at Potter's Heath, near Knebworth' and later (Foster, 1937) also lists Tring, Bushey Heath, St Albans, Wormley Woods, Berkhamsted and Harpenden. Hodgson (1939) notes it as 'occasionally at light on commons, Ashridge'. More recently, Barry Goater reported one in his garden in Bushey on 14th July 1968, Charles Watson caught one at light in Bishops Stortford on 25th July 1978 and Ian Lorimer caught another at Totteridge in 1979. There was one in Rickmansworth on 27th June 1990 (Ric Sandifer), another in the light trap on the Rothamsted Estate at Harpenden in 1999 (Adrian Riley) and one at Oxhey in 2001 (Joan Thompson). Finally, I caught one at light on Chorleywood Common on 7th July 2000 and it is of relevance that in his garden near the common, a few metres into the Buckinghamshire vice-county, Richard Ellis caught examples on 17th June and on five nights between 1st and 10th July 2006. Apart from this latter spate of records, which may suggest a resident population in the Hertfordshire/ Buckinghamshire border area, there is no convincing evidence that Hertfordshire examples of the True Lover's Knot are anything other than vagrants or immigrants.

2119 *Peridroma saucia* (Hb.) Pearly Underwing

Recorded:	1828 – 2006
Distribution / Status:	Random / Occasional immigrant
Conservation status:	-
Caterpillar food plants:	Not known to breed in Britain
Flight period:	April to November
Records in database:	42

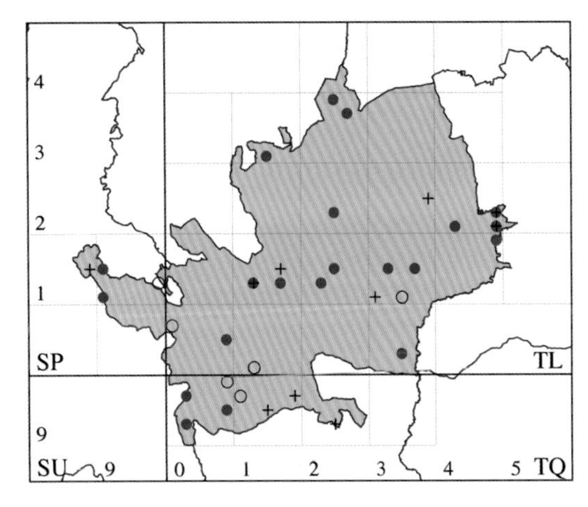

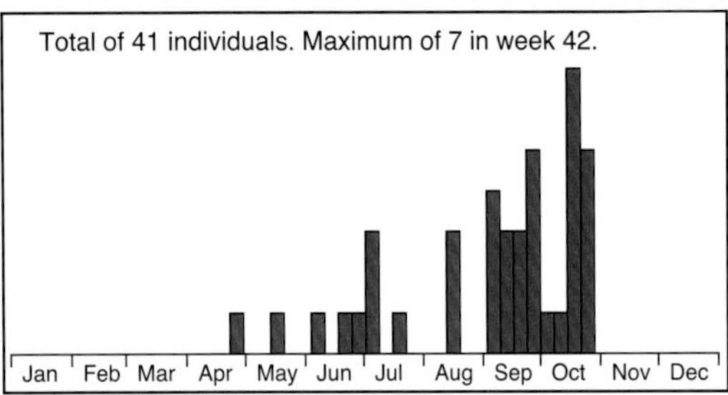

This is an immigrant species to Britain, reaching us in many, but not all, years and rarely in large number. Five in Clifford Craufurd's trap in Bishops Stortford, on the night of 7th October 1959 is an all-time Hertfordshire high and these were in the company of 35 *Agrotis ipsilon,* 19 *Autographa gamma* and 117 *Phlogophora meticulosa* (Bell, 1961). Remaining reports since Foster's 1937 list are given, as follows: Bushey, 21st September 1965 (Barry Goater); Borehamwood, 23rd October 1967 (Eric Bradford); Bayfordbury, 1974 (Jim Reid); Totteridge, 1975 (Ian Lorimer); Totteridge, 1979 (Ian Lorimer); Bushey, 1983 (C. M. StG. Kirke); Bishops Stortford, 29th August 1987 (Colin Plant); Bishops Stortford, 18th September 1987 (Colin Plant); Rothamsted Estate, Harpenden, 1990 (Adrian Riley); Braughing, 1992 (Ray Thompson); Long Marston, 11th Jun 1994 (Alan Bernard); Marshalls Heath, 30th August 1994 (John Murray); Bishops Stortford, 1994 (James Fish and Julian Reeves); Bishops Stortford, 6th Jun 1995 (Charles Watson); Bedmond, 22nd July 1995 (S. Farrell); Bishops Stortford, 11th October 1995 (Charles Watson); Bishops Stortford, 1995 (James Fish and Julian Reeves); Bishops Stortford, 1996 (James Fish and Julian Reeves); Maple Cross, 1996 (anon.); Pirton, 18th August 1997 (D. Heath); Bishops Stortford, 1997 (James Fish and Julian Reeves); Hertford, 2nd October 1998 (Andrew Wood); Bishops Stortford, 1998 (James Fish and Julian Reeves); Bishops Stortford, 1999 (James Fish and Julian Reeves); Little Hadham, 1999 (Geoff Senior); Watford, 1999 (Ray Penrose); Cheshunt, 2002 (Hilary Cooper); Digswell, 2000 (Tom Gladwin); Rothamsted Estate, Harpenden, 4th July 2000 (Adrian Riley); Bishops Stortford, 4th July 2000 (James Fish and Julian Reeves); Wheathampstead, 6th July 2000 (Trevor Chapman); Digswell, 23rd September 2000 (Tom Gladwin); Stevenage, 29th September 2000 (Mark Gurney); Bishops Stortford, 19 October 2000 (Colin Plant); Tring, 20th October 2000 (Ian Burrus); Hertford, 27th October 2000 (Andrew Wood); Lemsford Springs, 28th October 2000 (Vincent and Betty Judd); Bishops Stortford, 26th October 2001 (Colin Plant); Bishops Stortford, 4th September 2002 (James Fish and Julian Reeves); Long Marston, 25th September 2002 (Peter Bygate); Rothamsted Estate, Harpenden, 28th April 2003 (Phil Gould); Rothamsted Estate, Harpenden, 18th May 2003 (Phil Gould); Hertford, 14th August 2003 (Andrew Wood); Bishops Stortford, 30 September 2003 (Tom Lewis); Bishops Stortford, 15th October 2004 (James Fish and Julian Reeves); Arbury Banks, 19 Jun 2005 (Jim Reid); Bishops Stortford, 4th September 2005 (James Fish and Julian Reeves); Ashwell Quarry, 2005 (Emil de Maria); Hertford, 06 September 2006 (Andrew Wood); Ware, 13th September 2006 (Elizabeth Goodyear); Ware, 15th September 2006 (Elizabeth Goodyear); Chorleywood Common, 20th October 2006 (Colin Plant); Bishops Stortford, 27th October 2006 (James Fish and Julian Reeves).

2120 *Diarsia mendica* (Fabr.) Ingrailed Clay

Recorded:	1828 – 2006
Distribution / Status:	Widespread / Common resident
Conservation status:	Herts Stable
Caterpillar food plants:	Not recorded. Elsewhere, on bilberry, bramble, hawthorn and other plants
Flight period:	May to July
Records in database:	406

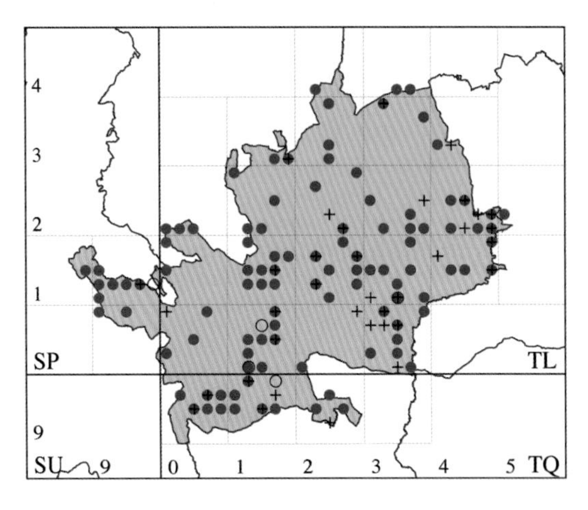

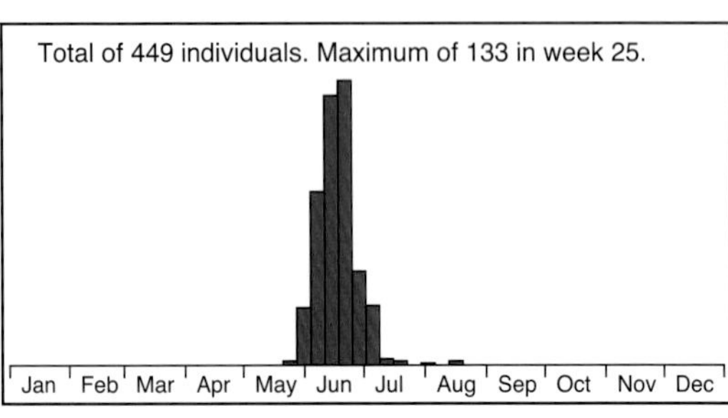

This is a widespread and common moth in Hertfordshire woodlands, but is less well-represented in non-woodland sites and is either absent from several garden lists or represented on them by occasional singe moths. During 2004, there were three later than expected records, on 4th August at Dane End (J. King), on 13th August at Long Marston (Peter Bygate) and on 14th August at Hertford (Andrew Wood). There is a great degree of variation on colour and pattern of the forewings, but this has not been documented for Hertfordshire.

2121 *Diarsia dahlii* (Hb.) Barred Chestnut

Recorded: 1888 – 1932
Distribution / Status: Absent / Extinct
Conservation status: Herts Extinct
Caterpillar food plants: birch. Elsewhere, on various trees
Flight period: August/September
Records in database: 2

Foster (1937) notes a single record – from Haileybury (Stockley). J. Bell notes one at light in Berkhamsted in 1932 (Foster, 1942). There are no other valid records, although it is not beyond the bounds of possibility that this species is present and overlooked.

2122 *Diarsia brunnea* ([D.& S.]) Purple Clay

Recorded: 1884 – 2006
Distribution / Status: Local / Uncommon resident
Conservation status: Herts Scarce
Caterpillar food plants: Not recorded. Elsewhere, polyphagous
Flight period: June to August
Records in database: 52

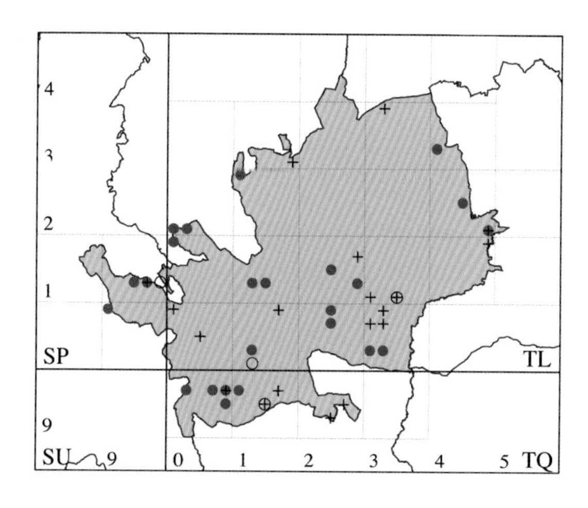

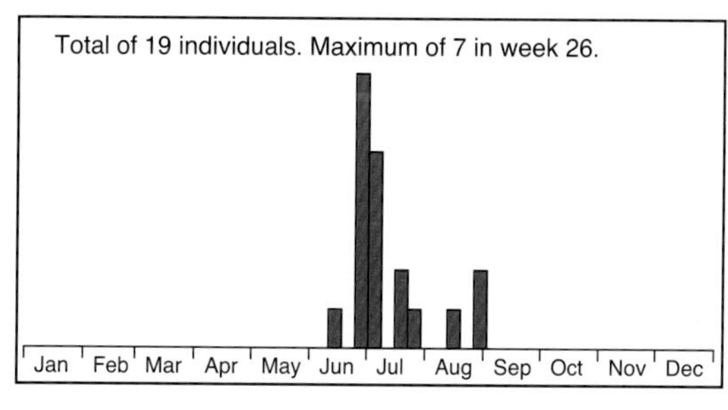

Most records of this rather scarce moth fall within the June/July period, but we have four from August, on 16th August 1987 at St Albans (Wendy Hatton), 29th August 1987 at Therfield Heath and 18th August 2001 at Hexton Chalk Pit both by myself and 31st August 2006 at Bricketwood (Henry Ellis). There are large areas of the county from which this moth appears to be absent at present; additionally, the map shows an apparent loss of the species from 18 of the overall total of 42 recorded sites for this species, suggesting a decline of around 43 per cent across the county.

2123 *Diarsia rubi* (View.) Small Square-spot

Recorded: 1884 – 2006
Distribution / Status: Widespread / Common resident
Conservation status: UK BAP Watch List. Herts Stable
Caterpillar food plants: Not recorded. Elsewhere, on various herbaceous plants
Flight period: May/June and August/September
Records in database: 463

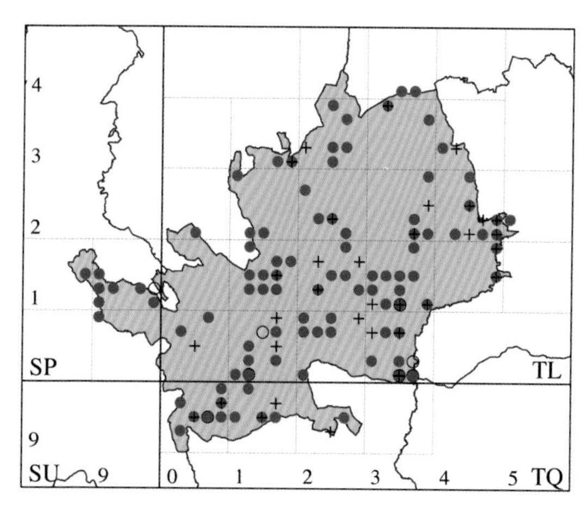

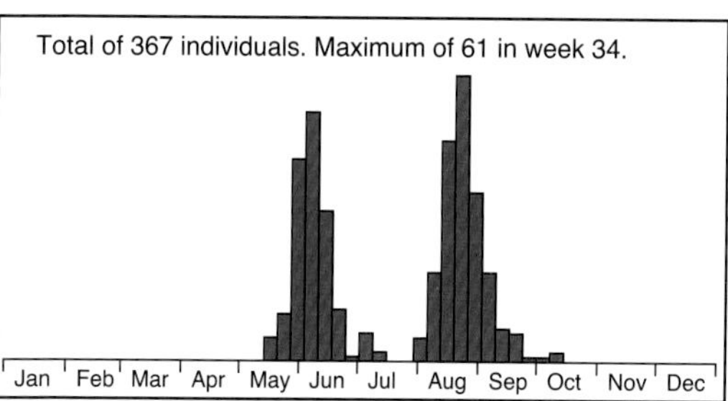

There can be few properly recorded places in the county that do not have this species and generally it is equally well represented in both the spring and autumn broods. The small peak of adults in early July, evident in the chart, relates to individuals caught from 2004 to 2006 and probably represents later emergence in these years rather than any suggestion of an extra generation.

2126 *Xestia c-nigrum* (L.) Setaceous Hebrew Character

Recorded: 1828 – 2006
Distribution / Status: Ubiquitous / Abundant resident
Conservation status: Herts Stable
Caterpillar food plants: dock, Dandelion
Flight period: May to July then August to October in two peaks
Records in database: 2,193

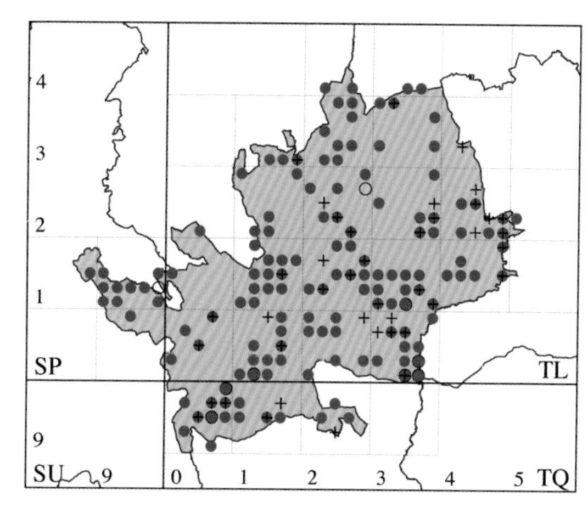

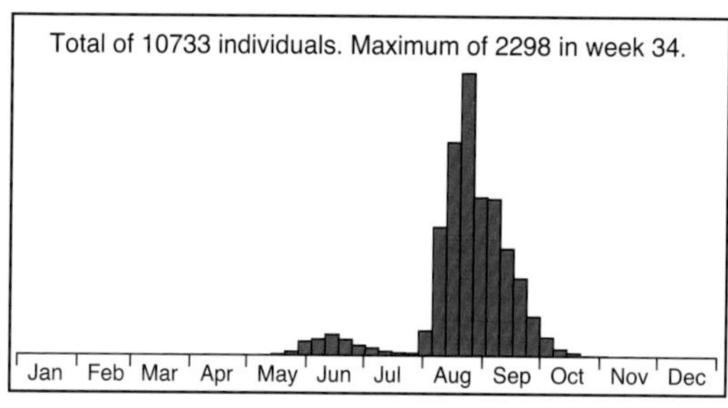

There are two clear peaks in the flight chart for this ubiquitous moth, but whilst that in June almost certainly represents the resident population the second is confused by a large number of immigrant examples that arrive in some years. One especially good year for the species was 2003, though it is unclear if the exceptional weather favoured successful breeding or if there was a massive immigration to the county. Overnight counts in excess of one hundred individuals in a single trap during August of that year are from Liz Goodyear's garden in Ware (156 on 17th, 139 on 18th and 114 on 23rd), from the Bengeo area of Hertford in Andrew Wood's garden (102 on 10th, 105 on 12th and 140 on 13th) and from Bishops Stortford, where James Fish and Julian Reeves produced 108 on 21st. However, these figures are dwarfed by the numbers that undoubtedly arrived as immigrants during 1951. There are no nightly counts from garden traps for that year, but a trap on the Rothamsted Estate in Harpenden recorded 5,338 examples during September of that year (Bell, 1953). The same trap also recorded 179 Silver Y (*Autographa gamma*) in the same period.

2127 *Xestia ditrapezium* ([D.& S.]) Triple-spotted Clay

Recorded: 1914 – 2006
Distribution / Status: Extremely local / Rare resident
Conservation status: Herts Scarce
Caterpillar food plants: Not recorded. Elsewhere, on various trees
Flight period: June/July
Records in database: 21

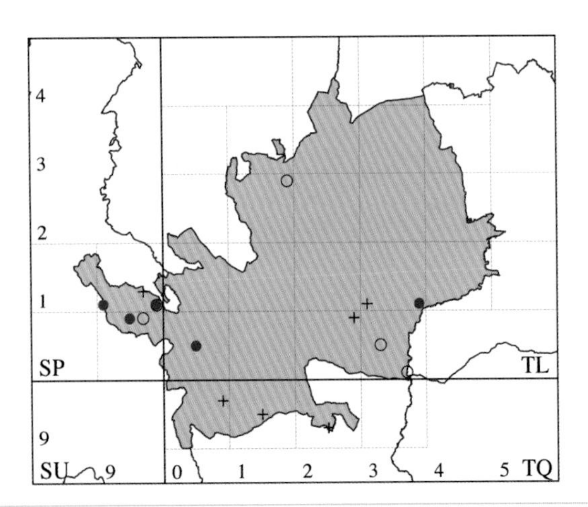

This species appears to be confined to the extreme west in Hertfordshire, where it is decidedly local, though locally common. Elsewhere in Hertfordshire it is an extreme rarity and the only recent report is from Rye Meads RSPB nature reserve where adults were taken at light on 26th June, 1st and 7th July 2006 by Paul Roper. Older records seem to be largely south-western, the exceptions being at Waltham Cross (Boyd, 1901), in the Hitchin area, where there were 'one or two specimens only' (Foster, 1914), Wormley Woods (Foster, 1937), Howe Green in 1971 and Bayfordbury in 1974 (Jim Reid). At our southern boundary one at Totteridge in July 1955 and a male there on 7th July 1976 (the hot summer), were undoubtedly wanderers from further afield whilst for the Watford area Penrose (1980) notes it as 'rare – June 1957' in his report which covered the years from 1948 to 1962). Some of the yet un-recorded woodlands in the Tring area are likely to produce this moth, revealing it to be present in more places than the map indicates, but it is not expected elsewhere in the county.

2128 *Xestia triangulum* (Hufn.) Double Square-spot

Recorded: 1828 – 2006
Distribution / Status: Widespread / Common resident
Conservation status: Herts Stable
Caterpillar food plants: Stinging Nettle. Elsewhere, said to feed on various trees and plants
Flight period: June to early August
Records in database: 953

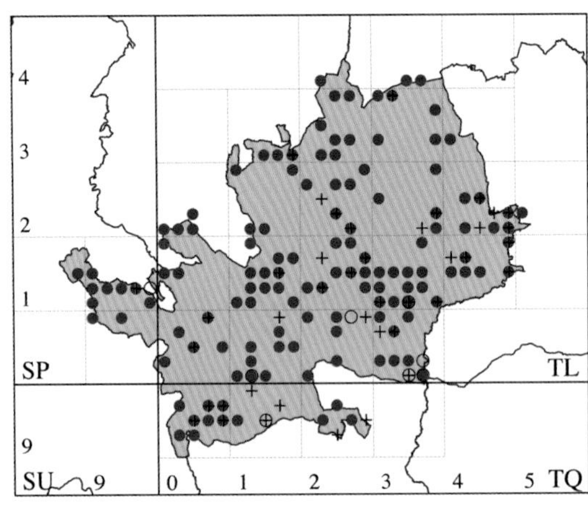

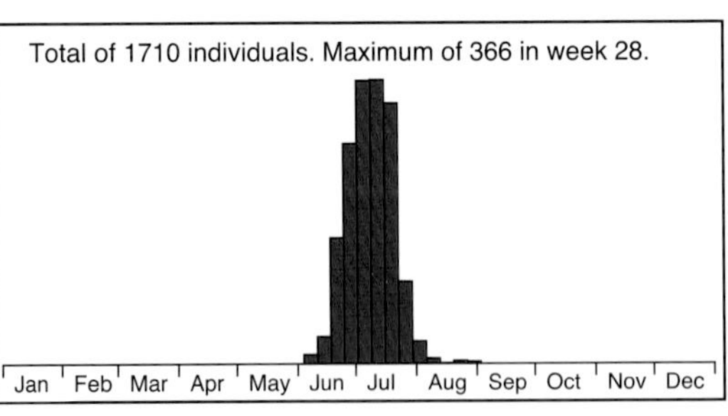

It is unfortunate that various text books appear to repeat the words of earlier authors when it comes to recording the foodplant of this species as 'various trees and shrubs'; the little information we have for Hertfordshire suggests that Stinging Nettle is the favoured pabulum here, from which it may be found by using a sweep net on the plants from about 9pm onwards – only exceptionally earlier in the evening. The adult moth is a familiar site in most light traps in the county.

2130 *Xestia baja* ([D.& S.]) Dotted Clay

Recorded: 1884 – 2001
Distribution / Status: Perhaps absent / Former resident
Conservation status: Herts Endangered
Caterpillar food plants: Not recorded. Elsewhere, apparently widely polyphagous
Flight period: Elsewhere, late July and August
Records in database: 22

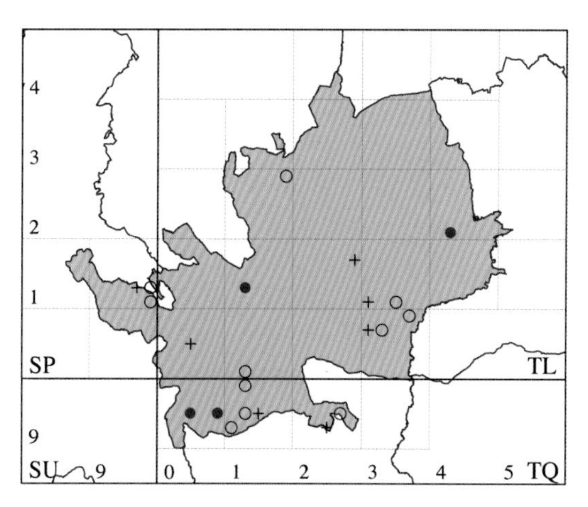

Historical records listed by Foster (1937) are from Aldenham, Bushey, Broxbourne, Berkhamsted School, Hoddesdon, Oxhey Wood, Hitchin, East Barnet, Bricket Wood, the Sandridge area and Haileybury College. Since then, the moth is recorded from Ashridge in 1938 and then not again until one was caught by Barry Goater at Bushey, on 8th August 1965. Scattered records during the 1970s are from Bramfield Wood, Bayfordbury and Wormley Wood (Jim Reid), Apsley (N. E. Gammon), Aldbury Common (Barry Goater) and Totteridge (Ian Lorimer). There are three reports in 1999, from Watford (Ray Penrose), Little Hadham (Geoff Senior) and Harpenden (Adrian Riley) and finally one in 2001 at Rickmansworth (Paul Clark). There are no other reports of the Dotted Clay in Hertfordshire and it is probable that we have lost this species from our county fauna.

2131 *Xestia rhomboidea* (Esp.) Square-spotted Clay

Recorded:	1884 – 2006
Distribution / Status:	Widespread / Common resident
Conservation status:	Increasing
Caterpillar food plants:	Not recorded. Elsewhere, on Stinging Nettle
Flight period:	August
Records in database:	84

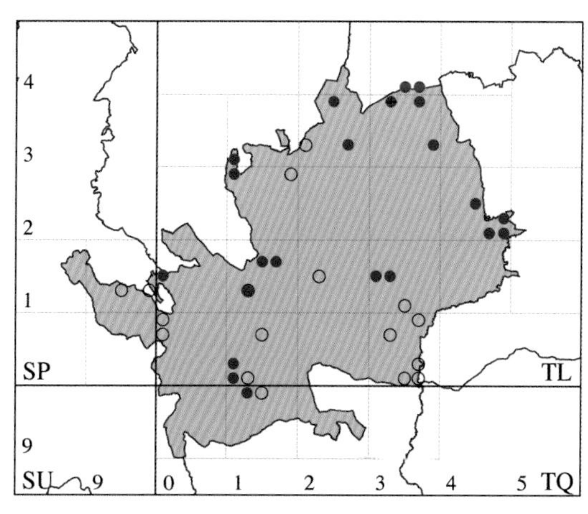

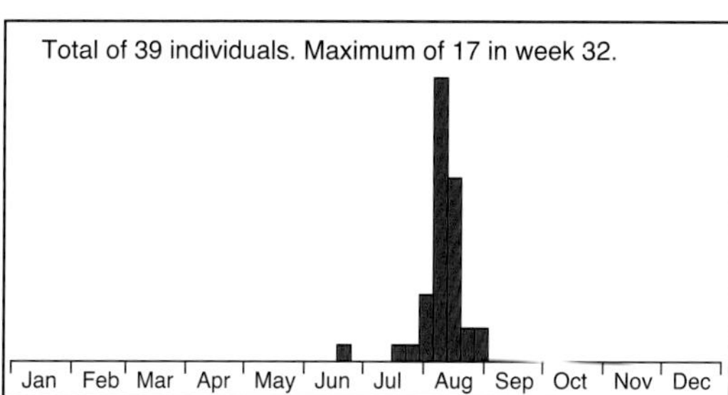

The Square-spotted Clay has been regarded recently as a rare moth in Britain and until recently was categorised as a UK Biodiversity Action Plan species and included in English Recovery Programme'. Its past fortunes in Hertfordshire are vague; it has certainly been present for many years, but perhaps not continuously so and probably at a low population density. (Griffith, 1884) lists it for the Sandridge area – our earliest record. Bowyer (1888) includes it in the list from Haileybury College and Gibbs (1896) notes five at sugar collected by Bowyer, in autumn 1894. In recording this species for Bricket Wood, in 1899, Cottam (1901), summarising past records for the county notes that 'Mr. Gibbs has recorded that five specimens of it were taken at Haileybury by Mr Bowyer in 1893 (*sic*)... and Mr Griffith has taken it at Sandridge. It is by no means a common insect'. Interestingly, Foster (1937) lists several additional localities, including several (St Albans, Bricket Wood, Waltham Cross and Berkhamsted), that were almost certainly made prior to 1901, though dates are not given. One report is dated – from Letchworth in 1922; the remainder, from Tring Hoddesdon, Broxbourne, Hitchin, Aldenham, and Harpenden were probably made between 1901 and 1937. Hodgson (1939) had it as scarce and irregular at sugar at Ashridge, Aldbury Nowers and Long Green, Berkhamsted, but Bell (1952) notes examples 'at sugar most nights in August' during 1949 in Welwyn (D. A. B. MacNicol). There are no more reports at all until 29th August 1987 when I caught examples on Therfield (= Royston) Heath; this is perhaps no surprise as the UK stronghold of the moth lies not far from our north-east boundary, but another ten-year gap followed by an adult in the middle of the county at Hertford, on 9th August 1997 (Andrew Wood) was a portent of things to come and during 1999 the moth began its apparent south-westwards spread. This spread is still continuing in 2006.

[2132 *Xestia castanea* (Esp.) Neglected Rustic

A record 'published' in a newsletter of an adult Neglected Rustic at Hertford Heath in 1994 is certainly an error. It is a heathland and moorland species not present in our region of England.]

2133 *Xestia sexstrigata* (Haw.) Six-striped Rustic

Recorded:	1884 – 2006
Distribution / Status:	Widespread / Uncommon resident
Conservation status:	Increasing
Caterpillar food plants:	Not recorded. Elsewhere, on herbaceous plants
Flight period:	August/September
Records in database:	225

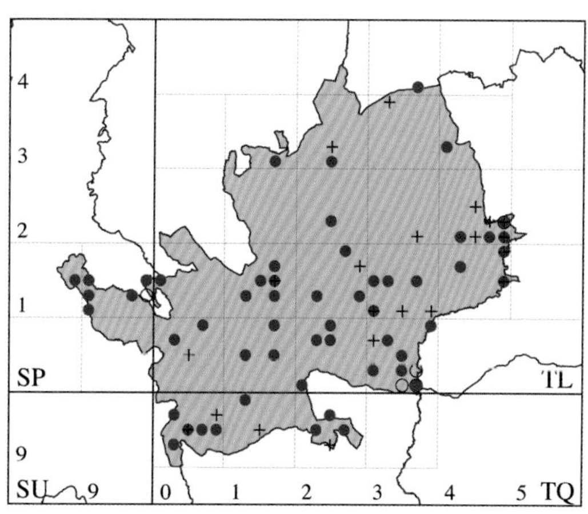

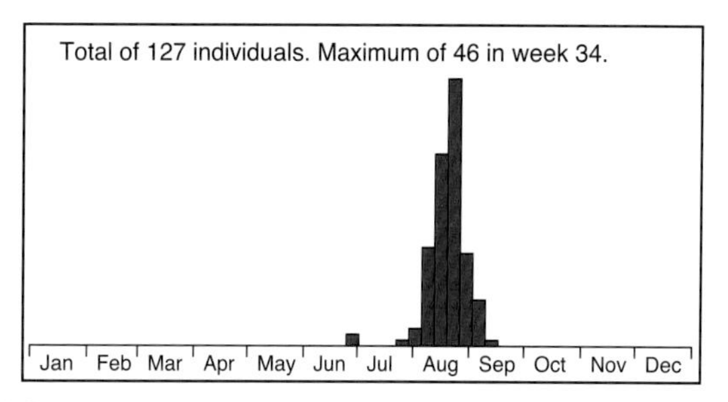

The map shows the Six-striped Rustic to be moderately widespread, but rather local and that is a fair representation of the current situation, but it never turns up in number when encountered. In the years since 1999 it has started to appear at new sites and appears likely to be extending its range within the county. An early adult was caught in St Albans on 30th June 1998 (Wendy Hatton), but otherwise the moth flies from the end of July to mid-September.

2134 *Xestia xanthographa* ([D.& S.]) Square-spot Rustic

Recorded: 1884 – 2006
Distribution / Status: Ubiquitous / Abundant resident
Conservation status: Herts Stable
Caterpillar food plants: Cock's-foot Grass; unidentified fine grasses. Elsewhere on grasses and herbaceous plants
Flight period: August to early October
Records in database: 1469

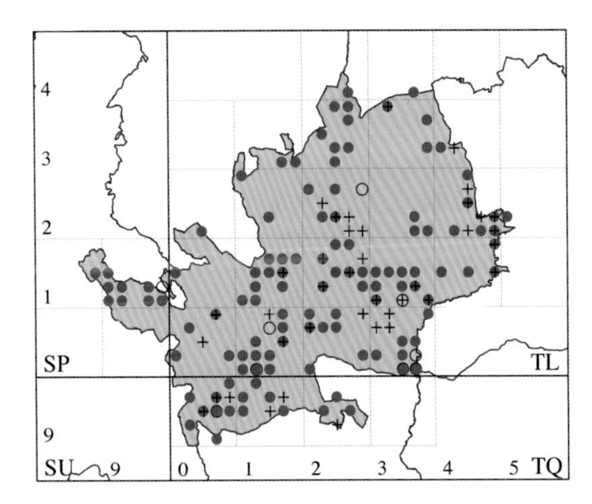

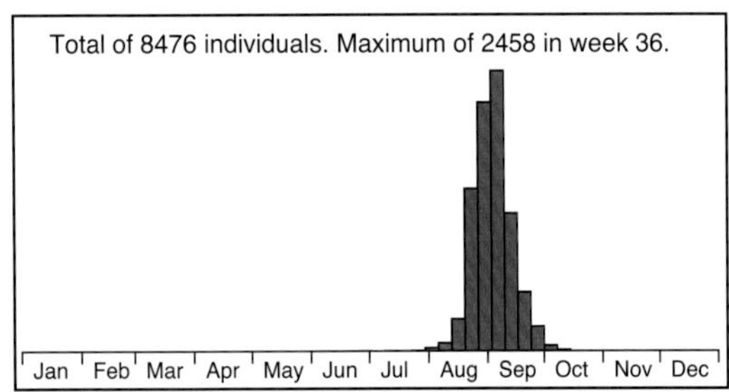

The Square-spot Rustic was reported as 'Common in all districts' by Foster (1937) and the same situation applies today. Adult numbers in excess of 150 per trap per night were obtained by most people during the drought year of 2003, though in a 'normal' year a count of 50 or so may be nearer expectation. Caterpillars can be collected easily by sweep-netting the tops of grasses about two or three hours after darkness on dry nights in March.

2136 *Naenia typica* (L.) Gothic

Recorded: 1884 – 2006
Distribution / Status: Local / Uncommon resident – declining
Conservation status: Herts Vulnerable
Caterpillar food plants: Not recorded. Elsewhere, supposedly polyphagous
Flight period: June to August
Records in database: 59

There are rather few recent records of The Gothic and several of those lack specific dates so that creation of a flight chart adds nothing useful to the discussion. Perusal of existing texts indicates that gardens, waste places, river banks and similar habitats support this species, whilst Skinner (1998) states in particular that it is most numerous on 'the old slag heaps in parts of the Midlands'. This all seems to point to a species that favours ruderal habitats – those in which the ground is recently disturbed and this would fit nicely with the apparent decline in the moth in Hertfordshire where such habitat is in actively being lost. Mowing, spraying, the incessant 'tidying' of road verges and other places, the mania for planting trees in every available grassland, the ploughing of field margins and the absence of sheltering hedges in places where field margins are actually retained are all contributing factors in the decline of the habitat, as is the redevelopment of brownfield sites within the county.

2137 *Eurois occulta* (L.) Great Brocade

Recorded: 1944 – 2006
Distribution / Status: Random / Rare immigrant
Conservation status: -
Caterpillar food plants: Not recorded. Elsewhere, on Bog Myrtle
Flight period: Late July to early September
Records in database: 17

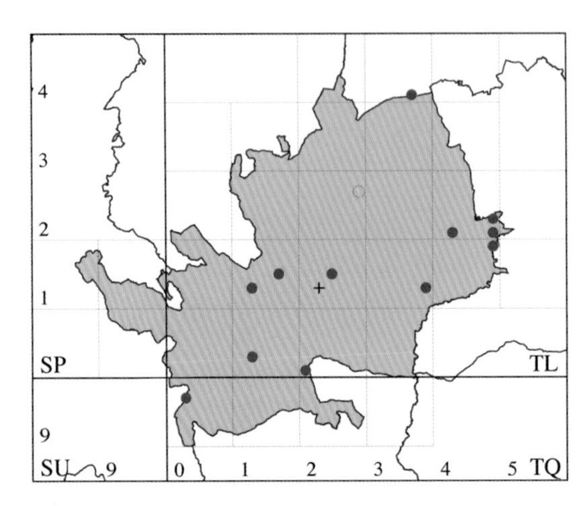

There is a resident population of the Great Brocade in Scotland, but 'down south' all reports relate to primary immigrants; these are typically lighter in colour than the

Scottish residents and are thought to originate from Denmark, northern Germany and The Netherlands. There was a large-scale invasion of the coast of Britain by this species on 3rd and 4th August 2006 and this resulted in several Hertfordshire records over the following few days. All known Hertfordshire records are given: Walkern, 1944 (J. Birdsall); Bishops Stortford, 6th August 1955 (Clifford Craufurd); Lemsford Springs, 1970 (Tom Gladwin); Bishops Stortford, 6th August 1995 (James Fish and Julian Reeves); Marshalls Heath, 7th August 1995 (John Murray); Digswell, 11th August 1995 (Tom Gladwin); Easneye, 22nd August 1995 (Morris Pledger); Easneye, 15th August 1996 (Morris Pledger); Bishops Stortford, 1st September 1996 (Charles Watson); Rothamsted Estate, Harpenden, 1996 (Adrian Riley); Little Hadham, 1999 (Geoff Senior); Bishops Stortford, one female on 4th August 2006 (Colin Plant); Bricket Wood, 5th August 2006 (Henry Ellis); Bishops Stortford, 6th August 2006 (James Fish and Julian Reeves); Shenley, 7th August 2006 (Bill and Pearl Page); Bishops Stortford 13th August 2006 (James Fish and Julian Reeves), Royston 21st August 2006 (John Chainey & Jenny Spence) and Much Hadham, 2 during 2006 (Geoff Senior).

2138 *Anaplectoides prasina* ([D.& S.]) Green Arches

Recorded:	1884 – 2006
Distribution / Status:	Very local / Uncommon resident
Conservation status:	Herts Scarce
Caterpillar food plants:	Wild Honeysuckle
Flight period:	June to early July
Records in database:	42

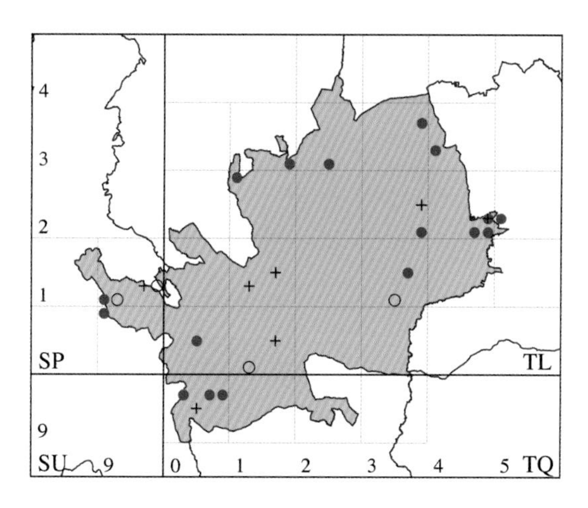

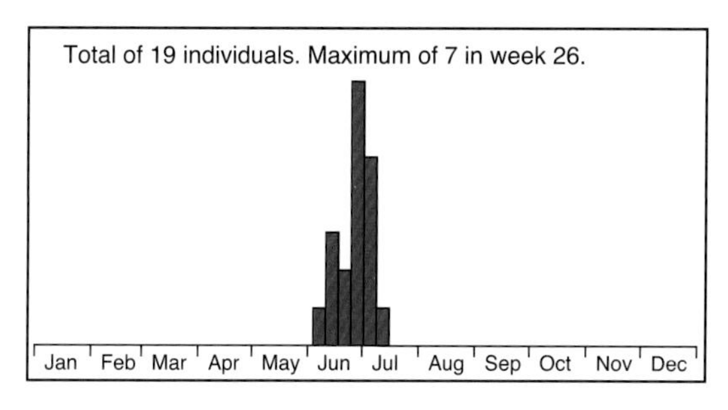

Most woodlands in the south of the county will, if they contain Wild Honeysuckle, support this species, but there are records from the north-east of the county in sites that do not fit this profile. Garden varieties of honeysuckle might be used, though there is no evidence for this in Hertfordshire and so some other foodplant is almost certainly involved; elsewhere, bramble, sallow and dock are also utilised. In spite of some under-recording, the moth is decidedly local in its distribution though apparently neither increasing nor declining in terms of either population or geographical range.

2139 *Cerastis rubricosa* ([D.& S.]) Red Chestnut

Recorded:	1884 – 2006
Distribution / Status:	Widespread / Common resident
Conservation status:	Herts Stable
Caterpillar food plants:	Not recorded. Elsewhere, on various herbaceous plants
Flight period:	Mid-March to early May
Records in database:	172

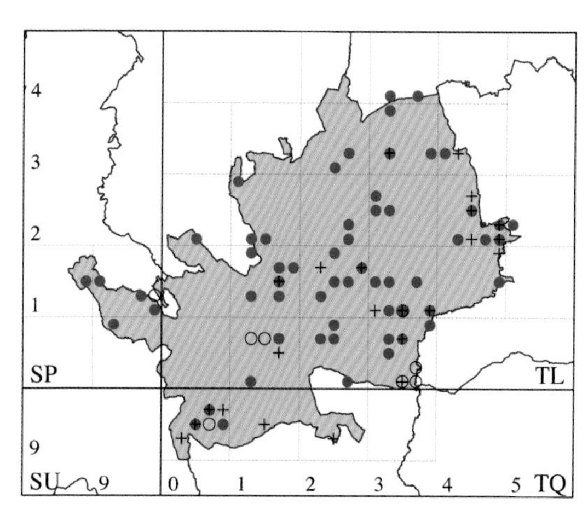

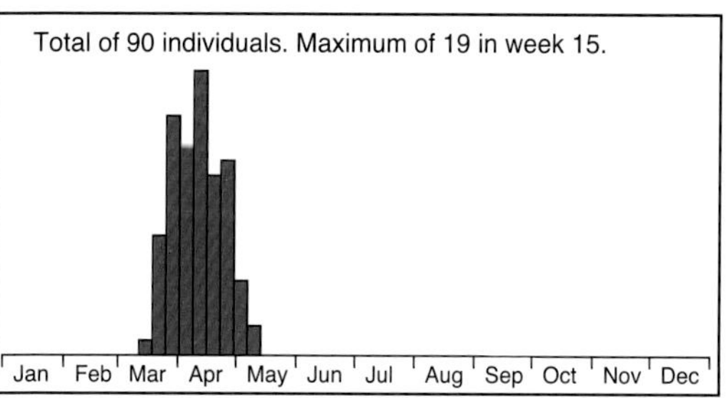

The Red Chestnut is a common species of the spring and its absence from some parts of Hertfordshire is more likely to reflect seasonal lethargy on the part of lepidopterists than any real lack of the insect itself. Almost every garden trap list has the species; about half of non-garden sites (those to which special trips need to be made to gather records) lack this species.

2140 *Cerastis leucographa* ([D.& S.]) White-marked

Recorded:	1930 – 2006
Distribution / Status:	Extremely local / Uncommon resident
Conservation status:	Herts Scarce
Caterpillar food plants:	Unknown in Britain
Flight period:	Mid-March to early May
Records in database:	23

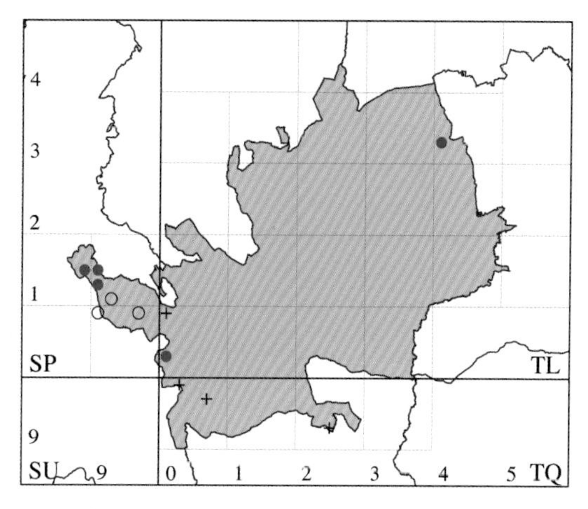

Interestingly, our earliest report of this species in the county is not until 1930, when an adult was found feeding on sallow catkins near Hastoe by A. L. Goodson (Foster, 1941). Later

(Foster, 1942) the second record, of two at light in Northchurch in 1937 and collected by J. Bell, is reported. Hertfordshire lies at the extreme north-east of the range of this moth in Britain; its distribution extends south-westwards via Buckinghamshire and Berkshire to Hampshire, although there is also a population in Gloucestershire and Wales. It is no surprise, therefore that all bar one of our records are from the south-west edge of the county. The single locality in the north-east is Scales Park, where adults were first recorded at light on 22nd March 2002 by Jim Reid and subsequently found to be quite common there by Phil Jenner and myself during 2005. There may be other localities as yet undetected? The easiest way of finding adult White-marked is apparently by beating the blossom-bearing boughs of sallows at night over a sheet, whereupon the moths will drop to the ground and remain there whilst being examined!

HADENINAE

2142 *Anarta myrtilli* (L.) Beautiful Yellow Underwing

Recorded:	1899 – 1939
Distribution / Status:	Absent / Former resident
Conservation status:	Herts Extinct
Caterpillar food plants:	Not recorded. Elsewhere, on heathers
Flight period:	Elsewhere, June and early July
Records in database:	3

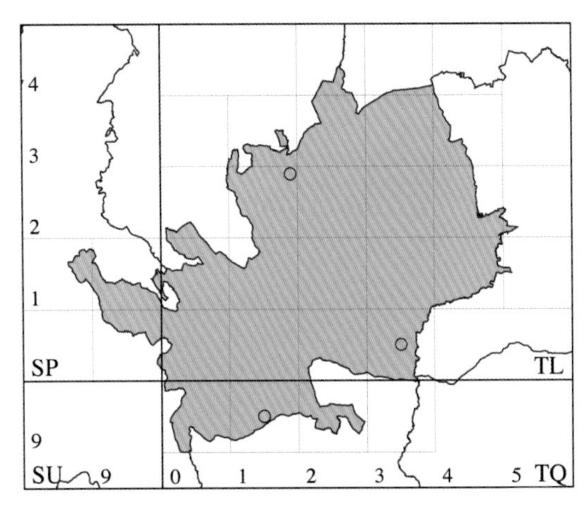

Wormley, 1899 (Edelsten) and Hitchin, undated (Tuke) are the only records given by Foster (1937). It is also noted from Bushey Heath in 1939 by E. W. Classey (Foster, 1942). There are no other records. The accuracy of the record by Eric Classey is beyond question and so too, probably is that of Edelsten; nothing in my research has indicated any unreliability on the part of Tuke, though Hitchin is hardly a suitable locality resting, as it does, on the mostly calcareous solifluction deposits laid on top of the Chalky Boulder Clay. The moth is not known for its migratory movements and is generally regarded as fairly sedentary. The decline of heathland in lowland Britain took place very largely during and after the Second World War and it is not hard to imagine that heather may well have grown in heathland habitat in all three areas at the time of the records. Nationally, the moth is well distributed to the south of us from Sussex to Hampshire with scattered localities in Breckland to our north-east; there are also thriving populations north-west of a line drawn between about Bristol and Lincolnshire. Taking all this into account, it seems likely that the Beautiful Yellow Underwing was once resident in Hertfordshire, presumably confined to heathland with heathers and so extremely local in its distribution.

2145 *Discestra trifolii* (Hufn.) Nutmeg

Recorded:	1884 – 2006
Distribution / Status:	Local / Common resident
Conservation status:	Herts Stable
Caterpillar food plants:	Not recorded. Elsewhere, on goosefoots and oraches
Flight period:	May to September in two generations
Records in database:	251

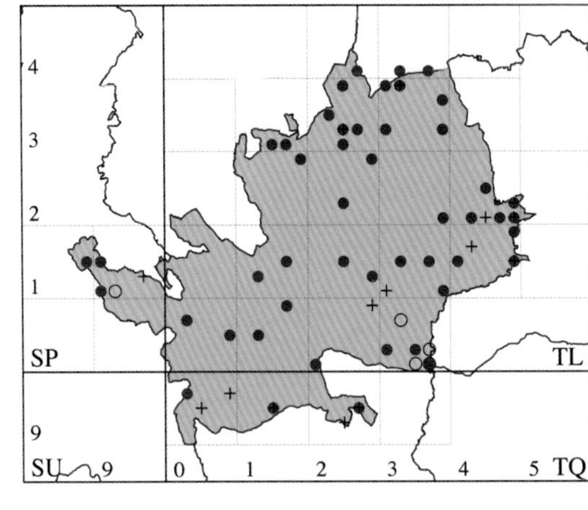

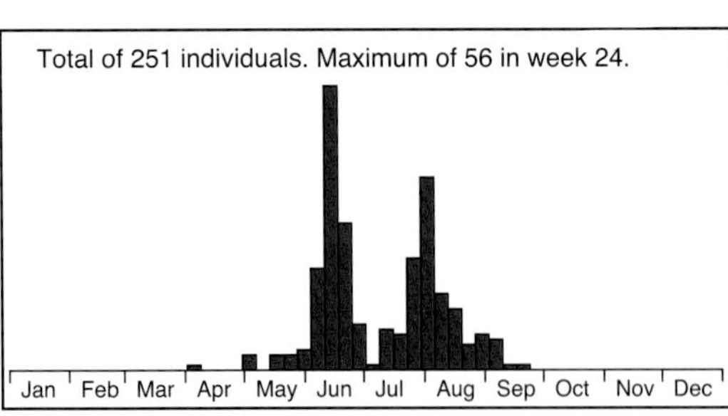

The goosefoots (*Chenopodium*) and oraches (*Atriplex*) that provide the caterpillar with food are characteristic plants of disturbed (ruderal) ground, and so the moth may be expected, at least fancifully, along field margins, railway embankments, road verges and in gardens. The reality in Hertfordshire is that all of these places are subjected to excessive 'tidying': verges are mown so that only coarse grasses thrive, railway embankments are sprayed, field edges, though becoming fashionable again, lack hedges to provide shelter and in most gardens the foodplants are regarded as being weeds. Consequently, the moth is actually very much a locally distributed species, though not uncommon where it is found. The first appearance of adults in the spring varies with the advancement of the season, but is typically at the very end of May. Most of the early May records shown in the flight chart were made in 2005; an exceptionally unseasonal adult was noted by Peter Bygate on 3rd April 2003 at Long Marston.

2147 *Hada plebeja* (L.) Shears

Recorded: 1884 – 2006
Distribution / Status: Local / Common resident
Conservation status: Herts Stable
Caterpillar food plants: Not recorded. Elsewhere, on various Compositae
Flight period: Late May to early July
Records in database: 453

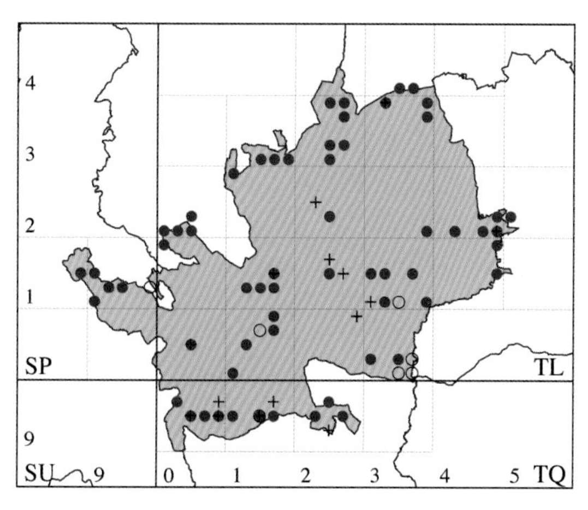

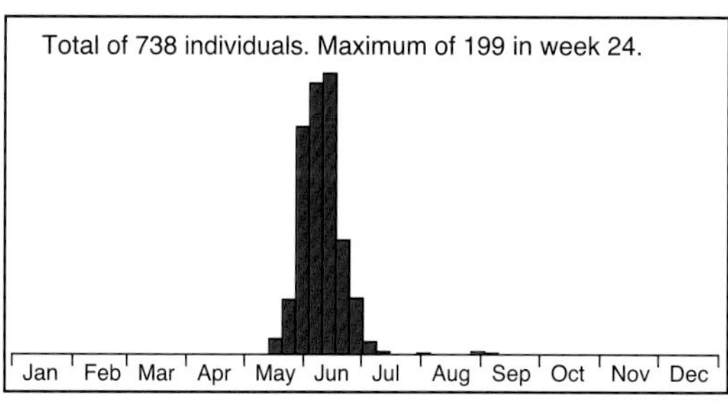

The Shears is occasionally recorded at flowers in afternoon sunshine, though it more normally flies at night. Open, herb-rich grasslands seem to be the favoured habitat and it seems to matter little if these are acidic, neutral or basic. Skinner (1998) states that there is a partial second generation in the south in August, but in Hertfordshire this is generally not the case, with a scattering of August records in 2002, 2004 and 2005 only and with September reports confined to 2004 at a single locality. During 2007, beyond the period covered by the above account, the Shears evidently underwent a considerable population increase in Hertfordshire and adults became a nightly feature of light trap catches in May and June of that year, including at places where only a handful were normally caught in any given year. This phenomenon also evidently affected a wider area and a similar increase was also noted on the western end of the Isle of Wight by Sam Knill-Jones.

2148 *Polia bombycina* (Hufn.) Pale Shining Brown

Recorded: 1888 – 2006
Distribution / Status: Extremely local / Rare resident
Conservation status: UK BAP Priority Species. Herts Endangered
Caterpillar food plants: Apparently unknown in the wild
Flight period: June/July
Records in database: 56

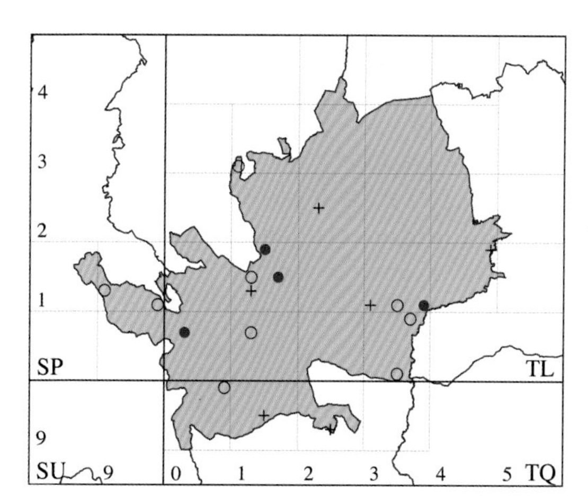

The Pale Shining Broom has declined drastically at a national level and until very recently there was some fear that it was doomed to extinction. During 2006 it seems to have made a remarkable comeback, although it is too soon to know if this is permanent. For historical reference, all Hertfordshire records are listed and mapped; the open circle symbols relating to Berkhamsted, St Albans and Pegsdon Hills are plotted arbitrarily because the precise location is not know. Records are from Haileybury (Bowyer, 1888); Nascot Wood Road, Watford, at sugar in the garden in 1892 by J. E. K. Cutts (Gibbs, 1893); 'Two at Waltham Cross, 1900' (Boyd, 1901); Pegsdon Hills, occasionally elsewhere [in the north Herts district] (Foster, 1914) – this is the 'Hexton' record given in Foster (1937), who also adds St Albans, Wilstone, Berkhamsted, Hoddesdon and Harpenden; Berkhamsted, 'regularly' by J. Bell (Foster (1942); 'The Pale Shining Brown (*Polia nitens*) and Bordered Gothic (*Heliophobus anceps = saponariae*) also enjoyed good years' (Bell, 1954) – unfortunately, Bell does not say where this good year was enjoyed and there is no specific reason to suggest that he was necessarily referring to Hertfordshire; Southway, Totteridge, where the trap was run from 1954 to 1980 – three in 1958, one in 1959 and one 1969 (Ian Lorimer); Stevenage, one at mv light on 26 June 1966 (Jack Newton); Reddings Avenue, Bushey, recorded from 1965 to 1976 as follows: 1965: 26th June, 1st, 4th and 8th July; 1966: 9th and 14th July; 1968: 17th, 28th, 29th and 30th June and 1st, 5th, 7th, 8th, 11th, 12th and 15th July; 1969: 25th, 26th and 29th June, 3rd, 4th, 9th, 11th, 12th, 14th, 15th, 16th and 17th July; 1970: 3rd, 4th, 19th and 25th June and 4th July; 1973: 4th July; 1975: 1st July and finally 1976: 30th July (Barry Goater); Bayfordbury, one in 1974 (Jim Reid); Thorley Park Road, Bishops Stortford, one on 7th July 1981 and one on 30th June 1982 (Charles Watson); Rothamsted Estate, Harpenden, 1986 (Adrian Riley); Marshall's Heath, one on 28th June 1996 (John Murray); Hemel Hempstead area, one on 19th June 2004 (Dave Kirk); Rye Meads, one on 8th June 2006 (Paul Roper); Peters Green, 2 on 30th June and one on each of 5th and 7th July 2006 (Matt Best; Jane Best).

2149 *Polia trimaculosa* (Esper) Silvery Arches = *hepatica* auctt.

Recorded: 1937 – 1970
Distribution / Status: Absent / Former resident
Conservation status: Herts Extinct
Caterpillar food plants: birch
Flight period: Elsewhere, June/July
Records in database: 2

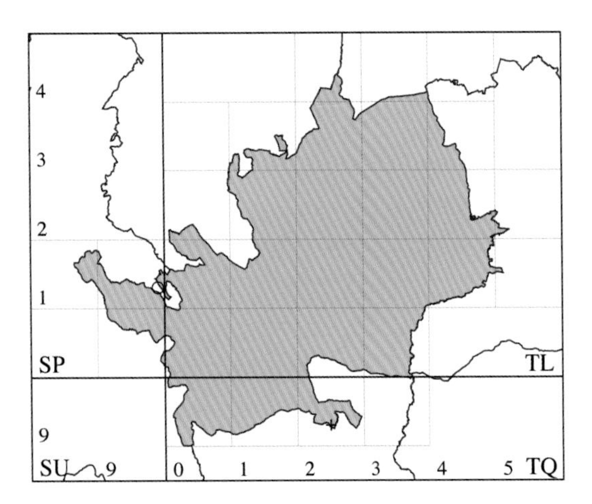

This is a species of open woodland on acid soils, especially heaths, in Britain. An adult was bred from a single larva found on birch at Ashridge in May 1937 by D. Frost and was reported to the Hertfordshire Natural History Society by S. B. Hodgson, (1937. *Transactions* **20**(5): 354). Commenting on Hodgson's reading of this communication to the Society's meeting at St Albans, A. H. Foster commented that this was the first record for Hertfordshire. Since then, one was taken at light at Totteridge on 22nd June 1970 – the only one in the trap from 1954 to 1980. There are no other Hertfordshire records.

2150 *Polia nebulosa* (Hufn.) Grey Arches

Recorded:	1888 – 2006
Distribution / Status:	Local / Common resident
Conservation status:	Herts Stable
Caterpillar food plants:	Wild Honeysuckle. Elsewhere, on various trees and shrubs
Flight period:	June/July
Records in database:	86

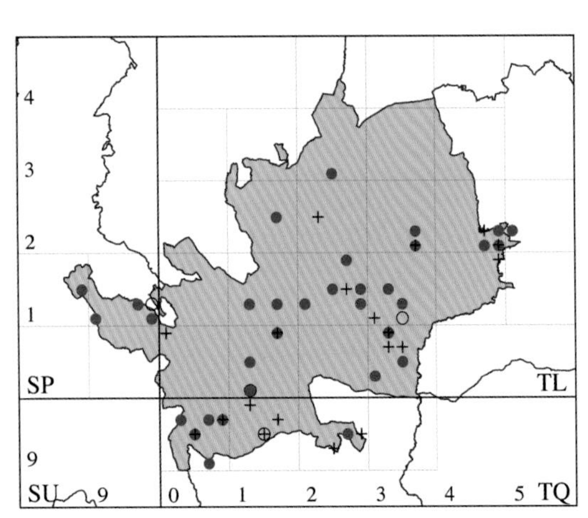

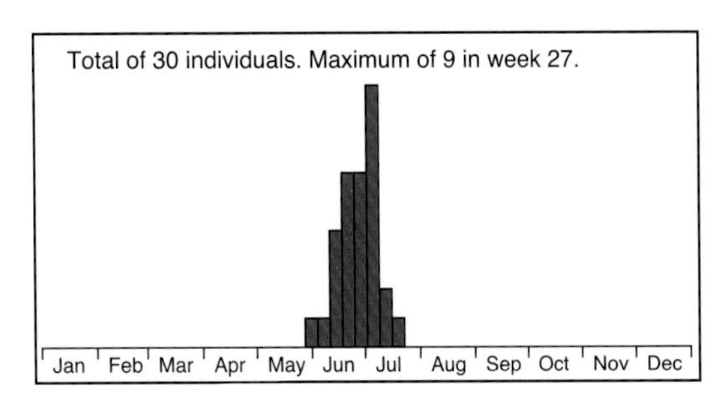

The Grey Arches is a common and expected moth in most of our woodlands, but it rarely attends light traps before midnight and so is sometimes missed by those lesser mortals who place sleep before moths! Caterpillars can be beaten very easily from honeysuckle, especially where this forms large clumps on trees, and in the spring may be found wandering around on tree trunks at around three hours after darkness has fallen. It is almost certainly under-recorded, though probably genuinely absent from much of the north-east of the county.

2153 *Heliophobus reticulata* (Goeze) ssp. *marginosa* (Haw.) Bordered Gothic

Recorded:	1884 – 1994
Distribution / Status:	Absent / Former resident/vagrant
Conservation status:	UK BAP Priority Species. Herts Extinct
Caterpillar food plants:	Sea Campion
Flight period:	Elsewhere, June/July
Records in database:	17

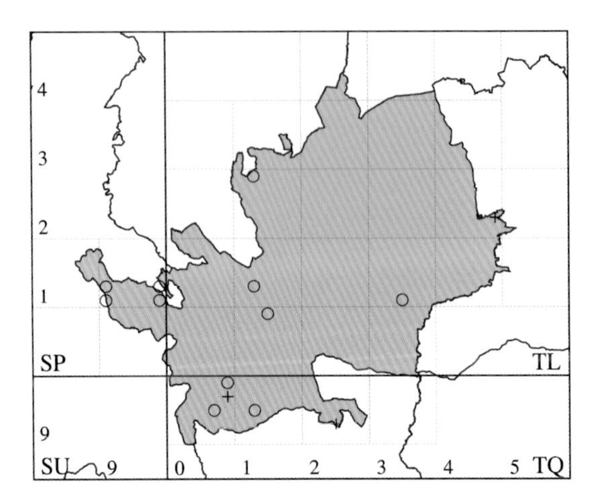

As a resident moth, the Bordered Gothic was said to be most numerous in the East Anglian Breckland with further populations in England south of the Thames and sparse, isolated localities in the Midlands. Looking at the distribution map in volume 9 of *Moths and Butterflies of Great Britain and Ireland* it is clear that the insect was formerly resident in a continuous north-east to south-west strip from north-east Norfolk coast to Dorset – a band that includes Hertfordshire – with a south-easterly side shoot to the south of London and into Kent. This pattern more or less precisely follows the Chalk on a map of Solid Geology of Britain. On this basis, it is clear that most of the elderly records from Hertfordshire probably relate to a resident population, whilst the most recent record from Bishops Stortford must surely relate to either a wanderer or an immigrant example. As a breeding species, the Bordered Gothic now appears to be extinct in Hertfordshire. All records are given: Sandridge area, prior to 1884 (Griffith, 1884); Haileybury area (Bowyer, 1888); St Albans area (Gibbs, 1889), Nascot Wood Road, Watford, at sugar in the garden in 1892 by J. E. K. Cutts (Gibbs, 1893); Elmcote, Watford, 1896 (S. H. Spencer); Battlefield Road, St Albans, 1905 (A. E. Gibbs); Pegsdon Hills in Herts, 1906 (A. H. Foster – this is the same locality as 'Hexton' in Foster, 1937); Bushey, Tring, Berkhamsted and Harpenden (Foster, 1937); Ashridge, 1938 – 'scarce' (S. B. Hodgson); Wilstone Reservoir, 1938 – 'scarce' (S. B. Hodgson); Rothamsted Estate, Harpenden, 1948 (Riley, 1999); Totteridge, three during 1955 were the only examples caught from 1954 to 1980 (Ian Lorimer); Mildred Avenue, Watford, July 1957 (Ray Penrose) and Bishops Stortford, 20th July 1994 (James Fish and Julian Reeves).

2154 *Mamestra brassicae* (L.) Cabbage Moth

Recorded:	1881 – 2006
Distribution / Status:	Widespread / Common resident
Conservation status:	Herts Stable
Caterpillar food plants:	Spinach; Cabbage; Brussels Sprouts, Cauliflower.
Flight period:	April to September in two overlapping generations
Records in database:	733

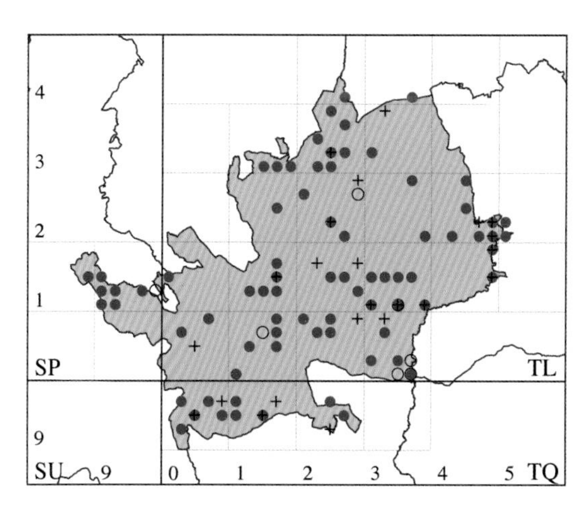

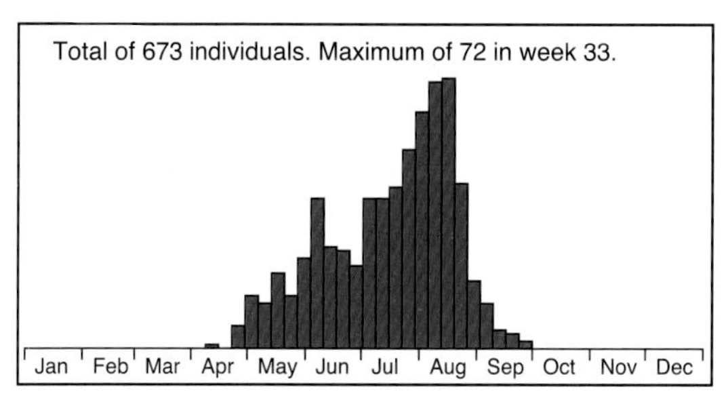

The apparent confinement of larvae to cultivated *Brassica* species is misleading – they are just easier to find in monocultural fields. Since larvae on these crops are usually destroyed others must be raised on the many species of wild *Brassica* and related Cruciferae that grow in Hertfordshire, otherwise the moth would be extremely rare. It is a generally common and widespread insect and according to sources consulted appears always to have been so since at least the 1880s. Though two peaks are just about discernible in the flight chart, Cabbage Moths are on the wing more or less throughout the year from mid-April to the end of September and can be encountered at any time in that period during any given year.

2155 *Melanchra persicariae* (L.) Dot Moth

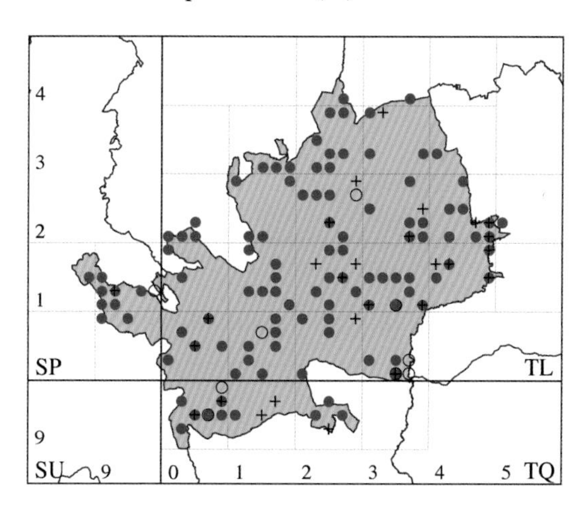

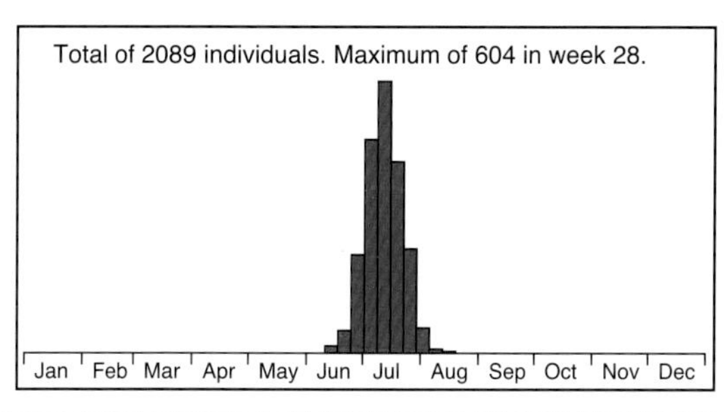

Recorded:	1828 – 2006
Distribution / Status:	Ubiquitous / Common resident
Conservation status:	UK BAP Watch List Herts Stable
Caterpillar food plants:	Stinging Nettle. Elsewhere, on many low plants
Flight period:	Mid-June to mid-August
Records in database:	872

First listed for the county from Hertford in Stephens' *Illustrations of British Entomology* **2**: 196 (published in 1829), the Dot Moth has apparently always been common in Hertfordshire. In the 1937 list, Foster records it as abundant in all districts; at the end of 2006 that situation is unaltered. It was, therefore, surprising to learn that catches in British Isles Rothamsted Light Traps, which take quantitative samples on a nightly basis, indicate that the British population has declined by 88 per cent since 1970. This notion is not supported by the Hertfordshire data. However, we do have evidence that the population varies across the county. Thus, whilst my garden trap in Bishops Stortford was producing nightly counts of twenty or so individuals during mid-July in 2003, 2004 and 2005, other observers in the south of the county (and in the north London area of Middlesex) reported the species as absent. The reasons for this discrepancy are not at all clear. A moth from Knebworth in 1875, originally reported as 2246: *Valeria oleagina* by Benjamin Brown in *Entomologist* **8**: 164, was a Dot Moth. This was corrected in 1876 (*Entomologist* **9**: 279).

[2156 *Lacanobia contigua* ([D.& S.]) Beautiful Brocade

The record from Broxbourne Common in 1924, given in Foster (1937) is withdrawn by Foster in his 1940 list of *Corrigenda* (Foster, 1940).]

2157 *Lacanobia w-latinum* (Hufn.) Light Brocade

Recorded:	1828 – 2006
Distribution / Status:	Local / Common resident
Conservation status:	Herts Stable
Caterpillar food plants:	Not recorded. Elsewhere, Broom, Dyer's Greenweed and other plants
Flight period:	May/June
Records in database:	172

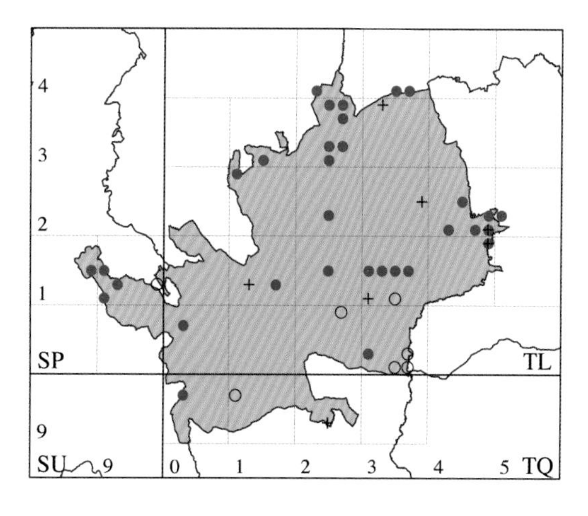

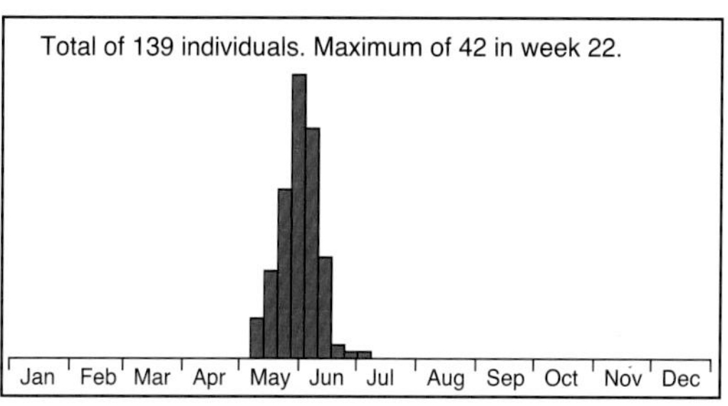

Gibbs (1896) states that a record from Gladstone Road, Watford, by S. H. Spencer in 1893, was the first Hertfordshire record, but he evidently overlooked the fact that the moth is illustrated from a Hertford specimen by J. F. Stephens in *Illustrations of British Entomology* **2**: 184 (published in 1829). However, the Light Brocade has always been a rather locally distributed moth in Hertfordshire. It seems to prefer calcareous soils, though it is by no means restricted to the chalk and is present on the Chalky Boulder Clay in the north and east.

2158 *Lacanobia thalassina* (Hufn.) Pale-shouldered Brocade

Recorded:	1884 – 2006
Distribution / Status:	Local / Common resident
Conservation status:	Herts Stable
Caterpillar food plants:	Not recorded. Elsewhere, on various 'trees and plants'
Flight period:	June/July
Records in database:	104

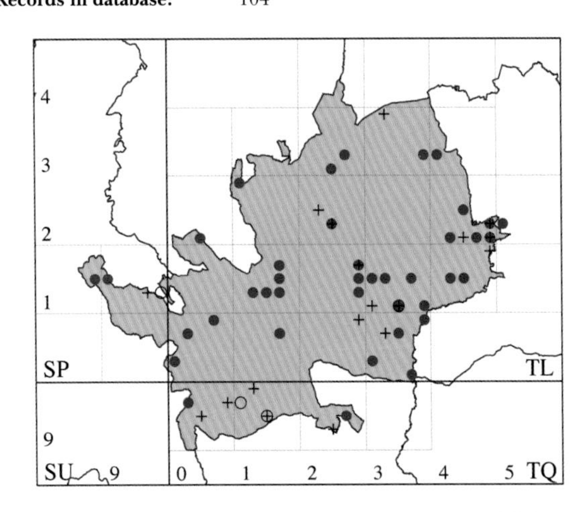

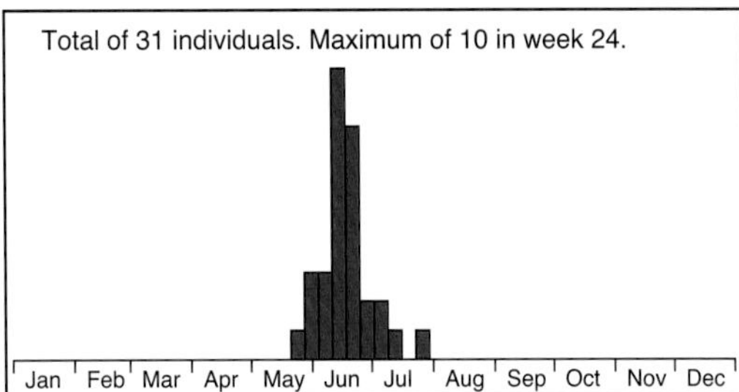

Though quite widespread across the county the Pale-shouldered Brocade is decidedly local in its occurrence and there are a great many places that simply do not seem to support this species. A high proportion of reports are from woodlands, or from sites adjacent to such habitat and this may be a limiting factor in Hertfordshire. In spite of this, adult moths may be quite numerous in light traps operated in the places where they are found.

2159 *Lacanobia suasa* ([D.& S.]) Dog's Tooth

Recorded:	1893 – 2004
Distribution / Status:	Local / Rare vagrant
Conservation status:	-
Caterpillar food plants:	Not recorded. Elsewhere, on herbaceous plants
Flight period:	Elsewhere May/June and late July to early September in two generations
Records in database:	18

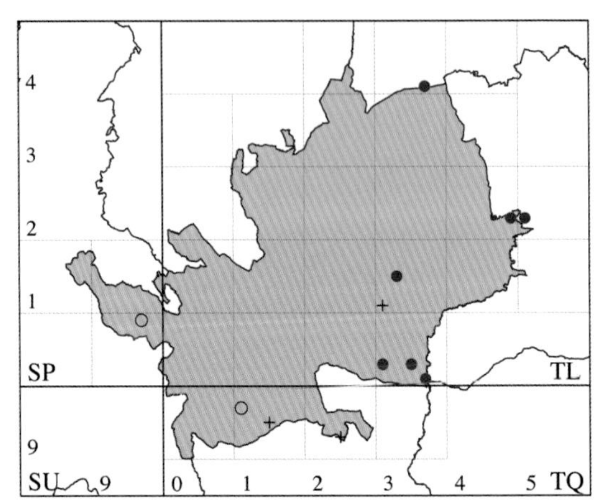

Historically, this was a rare moth in Hertfordshire, the first report being that from Gladstone Road, Watford, in 1893 (S. H. Spencer). Apart from one taken in Bishops Stortford by C. S. Coleman in 1912 (Foster, 1945), there are no more records until the singletons reported by J. Bell from Berkhamsted in 1938 and Northchurch Common in 1941. Ian Lorimer took single examples at his garden light trap in Totteridge in 1954 and 1970 (trap run from 1954 to 1980) and then Jim Reid caught one at Bayfordbury in 1974 followed by one in Bushey on 8th August 1981 (Barry Goater). More recently there are increasing numbers of records from the east of the county at Holdbrook in 1995, 1997 and 2001 (Alan Downie), Hertford in August 2000 (Andrew Wood), Bishops Stortford in May 2001 (James Fish and Julian Reeves), Birchanger Wood in 2001 (Colin Plant), Cuffley in 2003 (Alan Bolitho), Royston in 2003 (John Chainey & Jenny Spence) and Cheshunt in 2004 (Mark Cooper). These more recent records, at least probably relate to vagrant individuals from the Thames Estuary or Greater London area where the species is a common resident.

2160 *Lacanobia oleracea* (L.) Bright-line Brown-eye

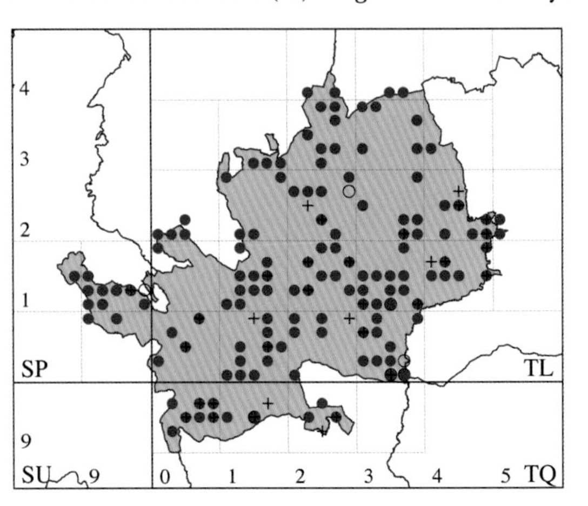

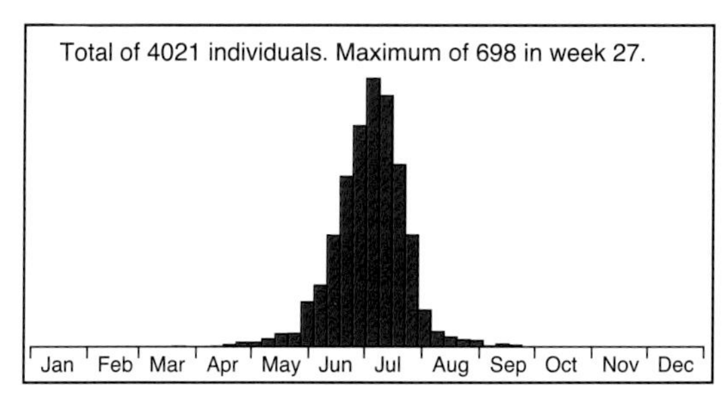

Recorded: 1884 – 2006
Distribution / Status: Ubiquitous / Common resident
Conservation status: Herts Stable
Caterpillar food plants: Tomato. Elsewhere polyphagous on various plants
Flight period: May to August
Records in database: 1,765

The Bright-line Brown-eye is one of the commonest moths in Hertfordshire, ranking 14th in the list of most frequently reported species. It is regularly found feeding on tomato plants in my greenhouse and elsewhere in the county, but is able to survive on a wide range of other foodplants. Occasional caterpillars are found on organically grown vegetables in supermarkets.

2163 *Melanchra pisi* (L.) Broom Moth

Recorded: 1888 – 2006
Distribution / Status: Local / Uncommon resident
Conservation status: UK BAP Watch List. Herts Threatened
Caterpillar food plants: Broom. Elsewhere, also on, Bracken, various trees and other plants
Flight period: Late May to the end of June
Records in database: 70

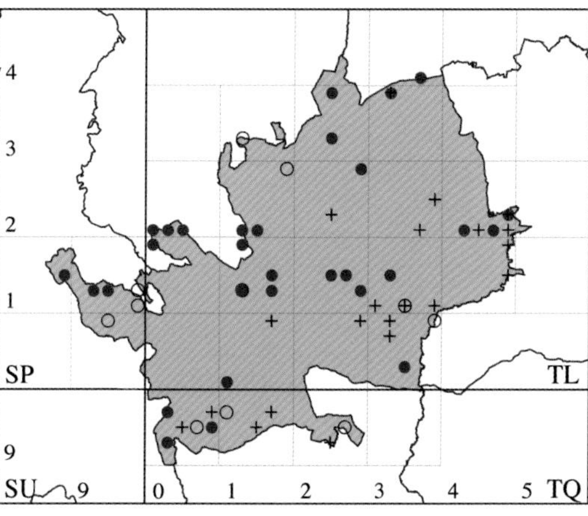

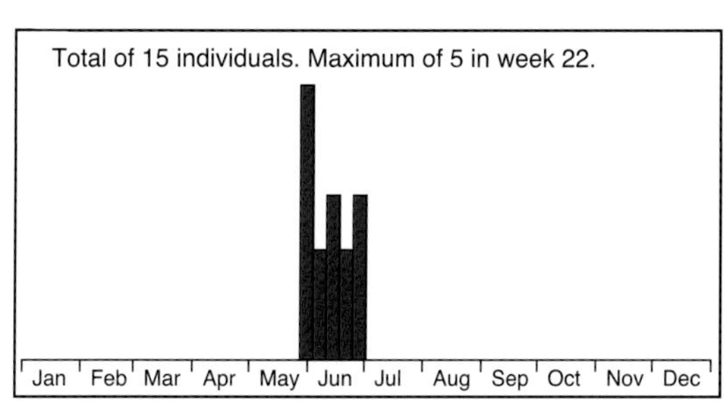

The adult moth is seldom caught and the distinctive caterpillar almost never found when beating for larvae and the inevitable conclusion that is drawn is that the species is scarce in Hertfordshire. Examination of the map reveals that about half of all recorded sites (28 out of 57) have not yielded the moth in the post-1995 period and this suggests a possible decline may be in progress; this fits with a supposed national decline of 77 per cent since 1970, as measured by the catches in Rothamsted traps across the whole of Britain. For this reason, the Broom Moth should be regarded as Threatened in Hertfordshire.

2164 *Hecatera bicolorata* (Hufn.) Broad-barred White

Recorded: 1828 – 2006
Distribution / Status: Widespread / Common resident
Conservation status: Herts Stable
Caterpillar food plants: Not recorded. Elsewhere, on hawkweeds and hawk's-beards and probably other plants
Flight period: June/July
Records in database: 273

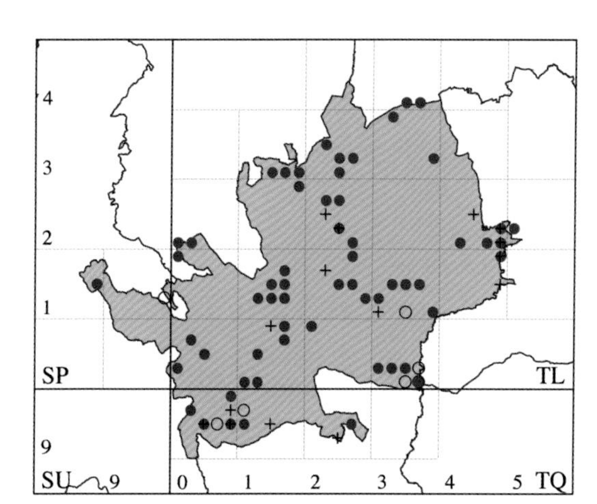

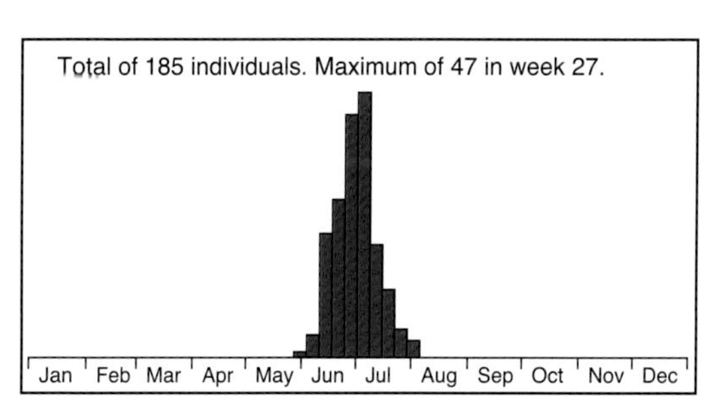

The distribution map clearly shows the barren arable area in the north-east, centred upon ten-kilometre grid square TL 32, but elsewhere the moth may be under-recorded. It is a familiar species in light traps and, for those prepared to make the effort to get out and look, is one of the more frequently encountered noctuids feeding from flowers at dusk.

2165 *Hecatera dysodea* ([D.& S.]) Small Ranunculus

Recorded: 1828 to 1886; 1930s; 2003 to 2006
Distribution / Status: Widespread / Common resident
Conservation status: Increasing
Caterpillar food plants: Prickly Lettuce. Elsewhere also on Great Lettuce
Flight period: Mid-April to mid-October, perhaps continuously brooded
Records in database: 60

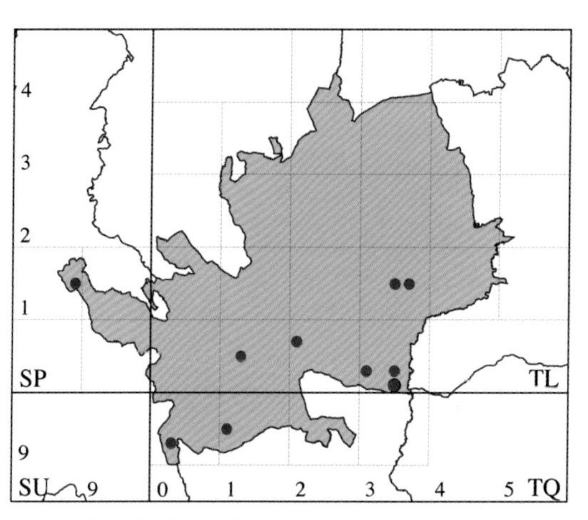

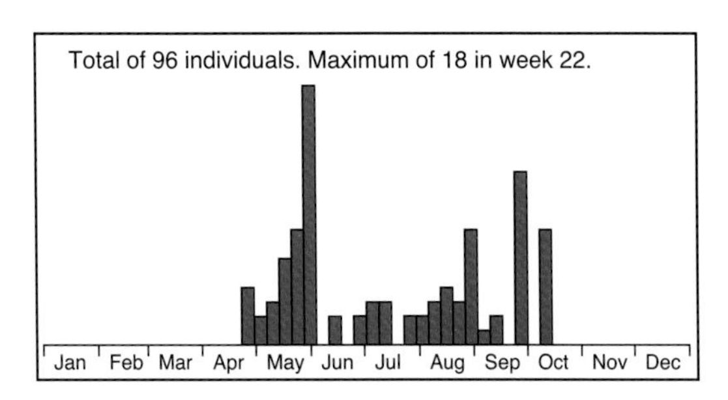

During the nineteenth century, the Small Ranunculus was present in the southern part of Britain, more or less from Oxfordshire and Northamptonshire southwards, though absent from the West Country. It was especially common in Norfolk, Suffolk, Essex, Cambridgeshire, Huntingdonshire, Greater London, Surrey and north-west Kent (Pratt, 1986). During the last quarter of the nineteenth century, the moth disappeared from most of the localities where it had been common away from the east; the most striking decline occurred over the decade following the mid 1880s, when inroads were made in more eastern areas. Barrett (1897) notes that 'thirty years ago it was one of the most reliable ... of visitors ... but no such attractive visitant now haunts our London gardens'. The adult is illustrated by J. F. Stephens in his *Illustrations of British Entomology* **3**: 32 (published in 1829) using a specimen collected in the Hertford area; this is our first record. Griffith (1884) includes it in his list for the Sandridge area, which included records made over several years and it is included in the list for the Haileybury College area (Bowyer, 1888), although the year is not given and may have been much earlier. It is mentioned as having been taken at Cheshunt Street by Boyd (1901), but the date of the record is unknown. According to Pratt (1986) it was a fairly common species in the glasshouses of the Lea Valley in Essex and so its presence in this area of Hertfordshire is scarcely a surprise. One was 'obtained' by John Hartley Durrant at Hitchin Station on 10th July 1886 (field meeting report in *Trans. Herts.* **4**: 32 and the record in Foster (1914) of 'A few specimens at light in Hitchin, but not in recent years' probably relates to this single specimen. In his 1937 county list, Foster lists Hitchin and Bishops Stortford without dates, but Allan (1950) omits the Bishops Stortford record from his comprehensive list – presumably deliberately? Later (Foster, 1942) it is reported as 'several at flowers and light' in the Berkhamsted district by Bell, though no date is given. From 1912 onwards the moth became rare over the entire country and after the First World War there were no sightings in Britain until the 1930s, when it was seen in Hertfordshire, Somerset and Sussex, the last record being in 1939. These were the last British records until the 1990s and the moth was regarded as extinct here. Pratt (1986) notes that it was briefly established at Berkhamsted in Hertfordshire during the 1930s. The Small Ranunculus reappeared in Britain in 1997 and was discovered on 26th June in that year when David Agassiz found one in his trap at Gravesend, in north-west Kent; subsequent searches for larvae proved it to be established in the local area (Agassiz & Spice, 1998). Since then the moth has spread rapidly from this focus, and is frequent in parts of the London area in particular. The caterpillars feed on the developing seeds of Prickly Lettuce and Great Lettuce, two plants that are currently quite common on railway embankments and many 'post-industrial' sites in London and elsewhere. I predicted that the moth would spread into Hertfordshire via the Lea Valley and it was therefore no surprise to me when Mark Cooper reported its arrival at Cheshunt in 2003. Since then it has invaded the south of the county on a broad front and in extending its range steadily northwards. The map shows records for 2003 to 2006 only, largely because the bulk of earlier records lack sufficient detail for them to be included.

2166 *Hadena rivularis* (Fabr.) Campion

Recorded:	1892 – 2006
Distribution / Status:	Widespread / Common resident
Conservation status:	Herts Stable
Caterpillar food plants:	Red Campion; White Campion; Bladder Campion – on the unripe seeds
Flight period:	May/June and July to September
Records in database:	386

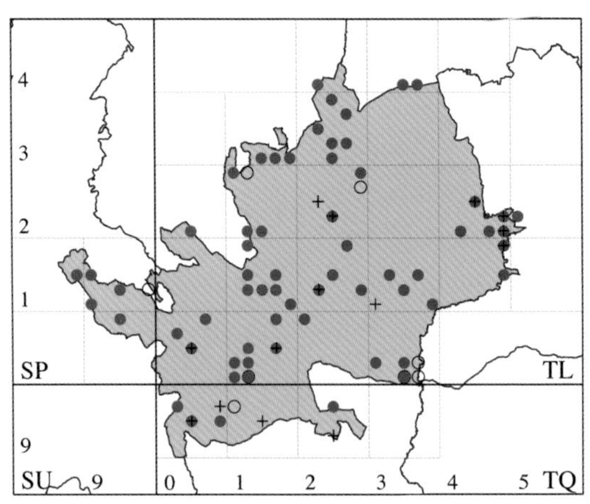

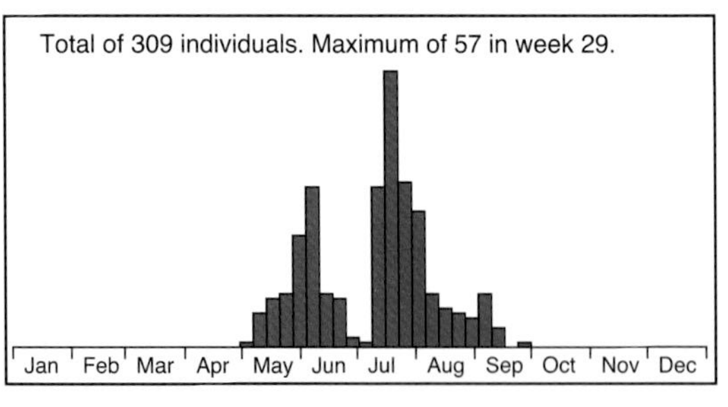

The Campion is a frequent visitor to garden light traps, but is easily confused with 2173: The Lychnis which has an identical flight period in Hertfordshire. Apart from a probably genuine blank patch in the north-east, the moth is probably under-recorded in the county. The flight chart shows a small third peak of adult moths in late August and early September and this has occurred in all years from 2002 to 2006, suggesting a small third generation of adults.

2167 *Hadena perplexa* ([D.& S.]) ssp. *perplexa* ([D.& S.]) Tawny Shears

Recorded: 1888 – 2006
Distribution / Status: Very local / Rare resident
Conservation status: Herts Vulnerable
Caterpillar food plants: Bladder Campion
Flight period: May/June and August in two generations
Records in database: 53

Subspecies *perplexa* is referred to as the Tawny Shears in Britain, whilst subspecies *capsophila* Duponchel is the Pod Lover, which is neither present nor expected in Hertfordshire. The Tawny Shears appears to have retreated north-eastwards in Hertfordshire and is seldom seen in the south-western portion of the county. It is most frequent in association with campion plants growing in the edge habitats associated with the more diverse woodlands in the county and this is reflected in the distribution map, although several 'good' woodlands do not appear to be represented.

2170 *Hadena compta* ([D.& S.]) Varied Coronet

Recorded: 1954 – 2006
Distribution / Status: Widespread / Common resident
Conservation status: Herts Stable
Caterpillar food plants: Sweet William
Flight period: June/July
Records in database: 255

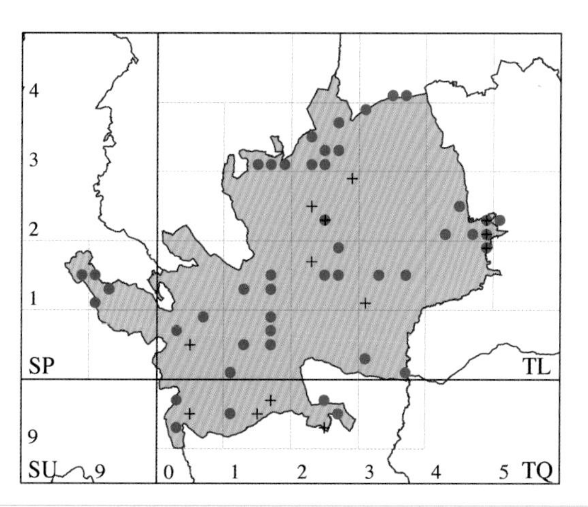

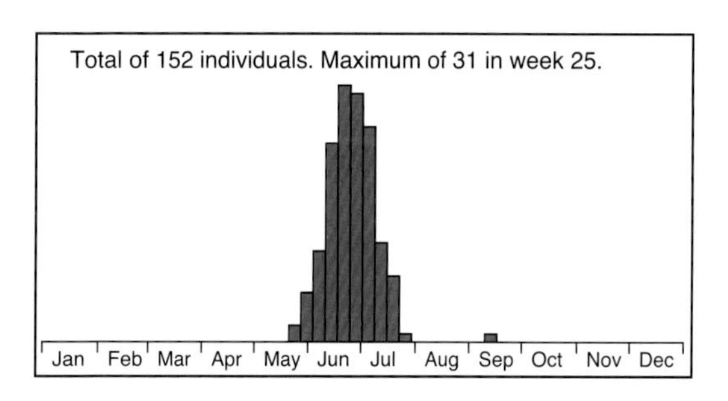

A single moth caught at Bishops Stortford on 20 June 1954 by Clifford Craufurd appears to be the first Hertfordshire record (Bell, 1956) of a species that was first found in Britain at Dover in 1948. In a later article, Bell (1959) informs us that this was taken 'on a garage window in Rye Street' and continues by noting that 'this very rare moth was discovered breeding in a nursery garden at Colchester a few years ago, Sweet William being the foodplant'. He then reports that Craufurd had a further example in Bishops Stortford in July 1956, two in 1957 and two more in 1958 and that four were bred from Sweet William seed heads collected in his garden [Galloway Road, Bishops Stortford]. He adds, interestingly, that 'there is, incidentally, a nursery within 200 yards of his house where Sweet William is grown'. In 1959, Craufurd caught 13 examples between 12 and 30 June (Bell, 1961). One was taken at mv light in Stevenage on 22 June 1962, in which area larvae were 'common on Sweet Williams in gardens 1964 1965, 1966' (Jack Newton). At Totteridge, Ian Lorimer's first garden record came on 6th July 1968 and this seems to be the first report from the south of the county. Today, the moth is widespread but decidedly localised across Hertfordshire, a fact that may be explained by the knowledge that, as far as we can tell, Sweet William remains its only larval foodplant

2171 *Hadena confusa* (Hufn.) Marbled Coronet

Recorded: 1888 – 2006
Distribution / Status: Local / Rare resident
Conservation status: Herts Scarce
Caterpillar food plants: Not recorded. Elsewhere, on campion species
Flight period: Late May to the end of July
Records in database: 26

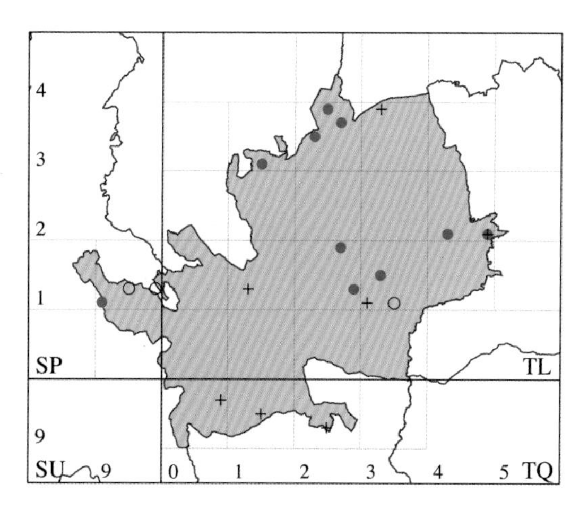

The Marbled Coronet appears to have been neither widespread nor numerically common in Hertfordshire. It seems to have retreated away from the south of the county: the three most southerly 'crosses' on the map are for Watford in 1953 and 1957 (Ray Penrose), Totteridge in 1961 and 1979 (Ian Lorimer) and Bushey in 1970 (Barry Goater). In the central and northern areas it is present at low density in woodland edge habitats, usually in association with White Campion plants.

[2172 *Hadena albimacula* (Borkhausen) White Spot

There is an unsubstantiated record from the Apsley area on 30th June 1976 by N. E. Gammon. An equally unlikely record of 2084: Light Feathered Rustic was made at the same place on the same date. Gammon did not retain specimens and his letter, which accompanies the list submitted to the county recorder at the time, states that he is not an expert at moth identification. The record is rejected.]

2173 *Hadena bicruris* (Hufn.) Lychnis

Recorded: 1884 – 2006
Distribution / Status: Widespread / Common resident
Conservation status: Herts Stable
Caterpillar food plants: Red Campion (seeds). Elsewhere, also other campions and Sweet William
Flight period: Late May to early July then August, in two generations
Records in database: 235

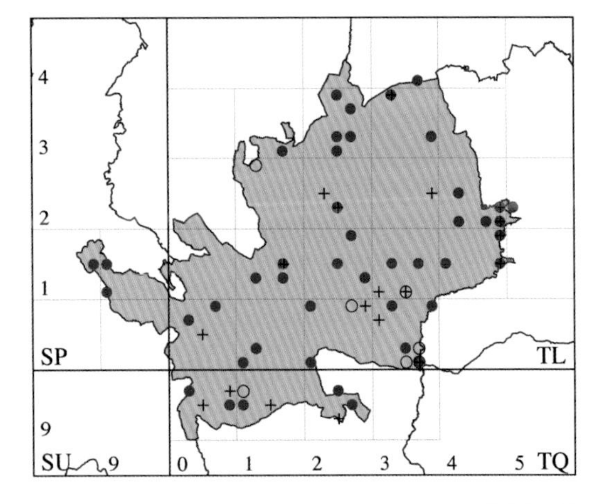

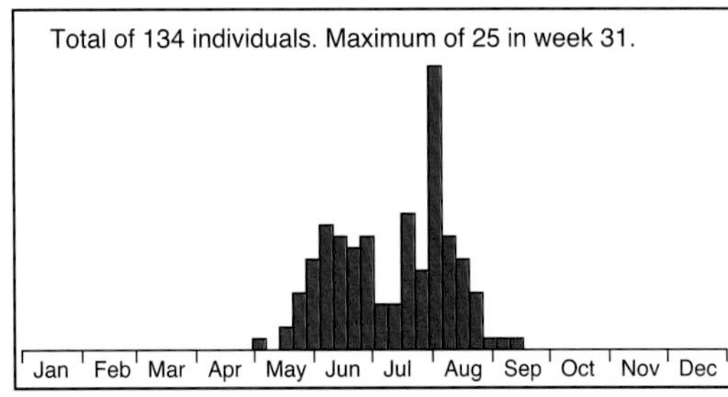

The adult is frequently confused with that of 2166: Campion and the two species fly together in the same localities. Indeed, there is little difference in the wider distribution pattern of the two species both being at least to some degree under-recorded, but probably absent from the arable area of the north-east.

2176 *Cerapteryx graminis* (L.) Antler Moth

Recorded: 1888 – 2006
Distribution / Status: Local / Common resident
Conservation status: Herts Scarce
Caterpillar food plants: Not recorded. Elsewhere, various grasses
Flight period: Mid-July to early September
Records in database: 36

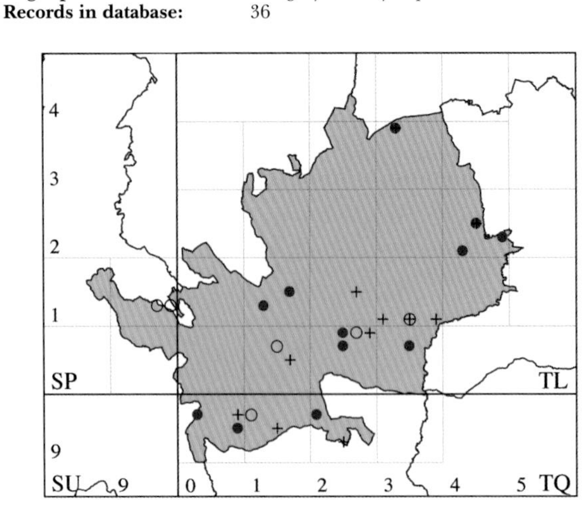

In places where this moth is found it can be numerically abundant and several hundred can be caught easily in a single moth trap set in a suitable grassland habitat. In Hertfordshire, however, we have rather few grasslands of any quality; where we have recorded in such habitats we have found the moth, suggesting that it has yet to be discovered in some unvisited sites, perhaps in particular those in the west around Ashridge and Tring. In the north of the county there is precious little suitable habitat available and the large blank area on the map probably truthfully represents the overall distribution pattern in the county.

2177 *Tholera cespitis* ([D.& S.]) Hedge Rustic

Recorded: 1893 – 2004
Distribution / Status: Extremely local / Rare resident
Conservation status: UK BAP Watch List
Herts Endangered
Caterpillar food plants: Not recorded. Elsewhere on *Deschampsia* and other grasses.
Flight period: August/September
Records in database: 35

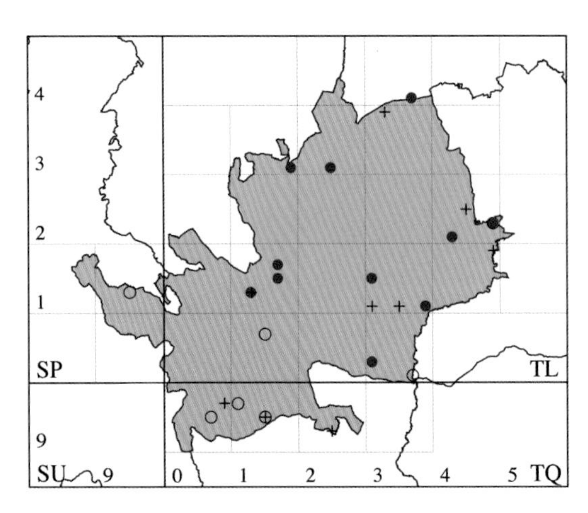

This appears to have become a very rare moth indeed in our area, though the historical records available do not particularly indicate that it has ever been widespread with us. Around 60 per cent of Hertfordshire sites producing the moth (including some that cannot be mapped for want of detail) have not supported it in the 1995 – 2006 period and the number of sites generating the moth in the present millennium are very few indeed – just one in 2001 (Wheathampstead), one in 2002

(Weston), two in 2003 (Rye Meads and Waterford Heath), one in 2004 (Harpenden), none in 2005 and only one in 2006 (Royston). If we take only the post-1999 sites as being current, the decline in Hertfordshire is 76 per cent, but it is by no means clear if the moth is still extant at these sites and it is likely that it has already become extinct with us. Nationally, this species is thought to have declined by 97 per cent since 1970. The reasons for the decline are not at all clear.

2178 *Tholera decimalis* (Poda) Feathered Gothic

Recorded:	1828 – 2006
Distribution / Status:	Local / Uncommon resident
Conservation status:	UK BAP Watch List Herts Stable
Caterpillar food plants:	Not recorded. Elsewhere on grasses
Flight period:	Late August to mid-September
Records in database:	121

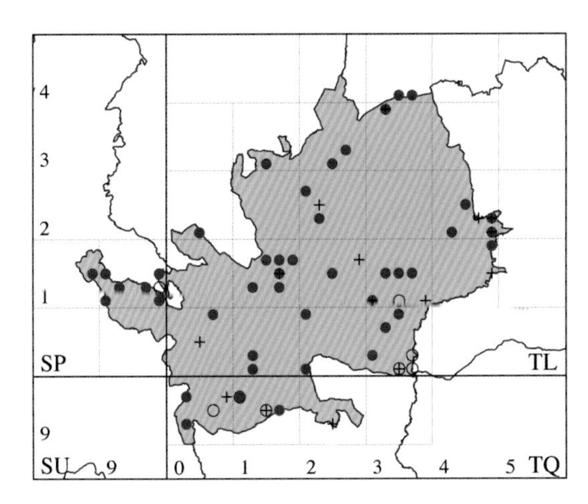

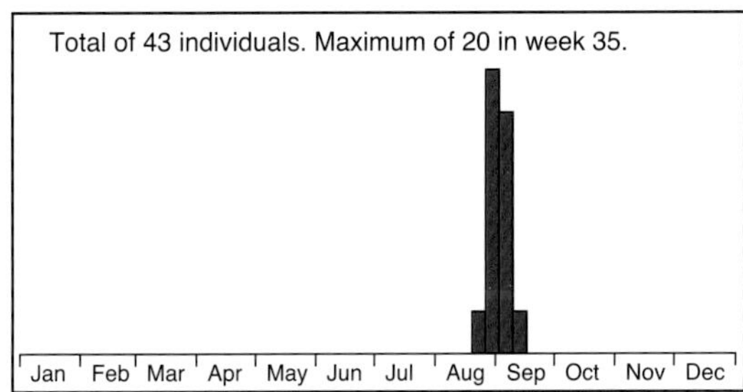

The first record in the county comes from Royston in 1828 (Stephens, 1829). During 2006, the Feathered Gothic was included on a list of species that had undergone a significant decline in Britain – its population having fallen in Rothamsted Light Traps by 90 per cent since 1970. Numerical data for Hertfordshire does not extend far enough back to make comparisons with the national situation, but an overall appraisal suggests that this trend is not reflected in this county, where the moth is local and uncommon, but it has always been so.

2179 *Panolis flammea* ([D.& S.]) Pine Beauty

Recorded:	1810 – 2006
Distribution / Status:	Local / Common resident
Conservation status:	Herts Stable
Caterpillar food plants:	Scots Pine – probably also on other pines
Flight period:	March to mid-May
Records in database:	144

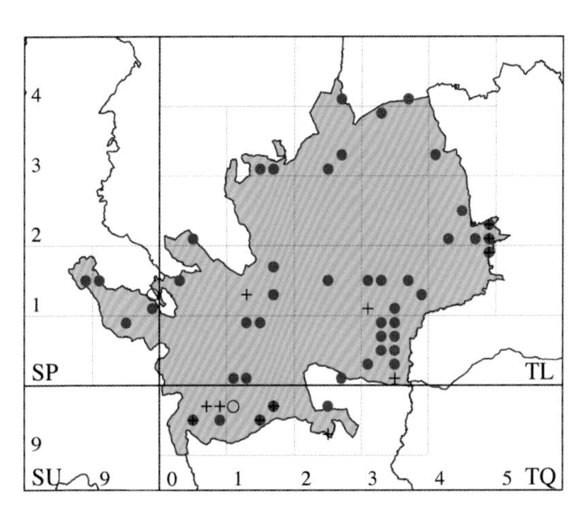

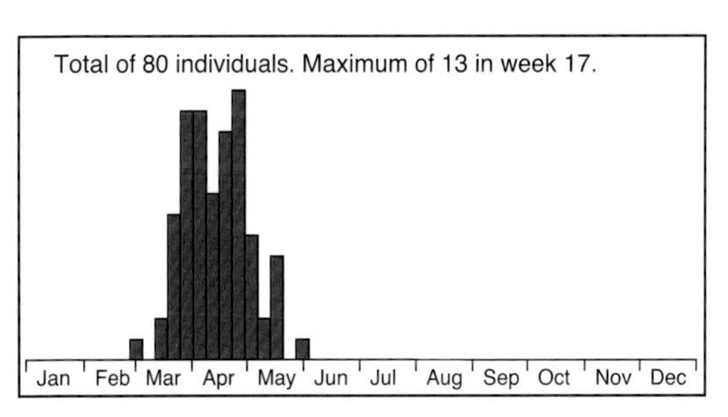

The Pine Beauty is listed by J. F. Stephens for Hertford, April 1810, in *Illustrations of British Entomology* **3**: 20 (published in 1829) – a record claimed by Durrant (1888) and repeated by Gibbs (1905) to be the first British occurrence of the species. Today it is regarded as a pest species by those who regard conifer plantations as desirable and the population may vary considerably from year to year. The spread of this rather attractive moth in Hertfordshire is not at all well documented. It is listed for the Sandridge area (Griffith, 1884), but apparently features on no other list of that period. Gibbs found it at St Albans in 1904 (Gibbs, 1905) and comments that it had '... only been taken at one other Hertfordshire locality in recent years, viz. Watford, by Mr. Wig'. Foster (1937) also added 'Wilbury Hill, Hitchin (Wightman), Ashridge Park – larvae on fences (Benson), Broxbourne Woods – at sallow (Edelsten) and Bushey Heath (Hervey)'. Foster never provided any greater detail and any records that he may have kept are no longer extant. However, both Wightman (Wilbury Hill, Hitchin) and Benson (Ashridge Park – larvae on fences) are listed by Foster as new contributors of records since 1902 and so these records possibly affect the period 1903 to 1937. The widespread planting of pine trees by the newly established Forestry Commission in the early twentieth century doubtless allowed this moth to spread in Britain and it is the lack of pine trees in some areas of Hertfordshire ensures that the distribution of the Pine Beauty in Hertfordshire is rather localised today.

2182 *Orthosia cruda* ([D.& S.]) Small Quaker

Recorded:	1887 to 2005
Distribution / Status:	Widespread / Abundant resident
Conservation status:	Herts Stable
Caterpillar food plants:	English Oak, Hornbeam. Elsewhere also on other trees
Flight period:	March/April,
Records in database:	686

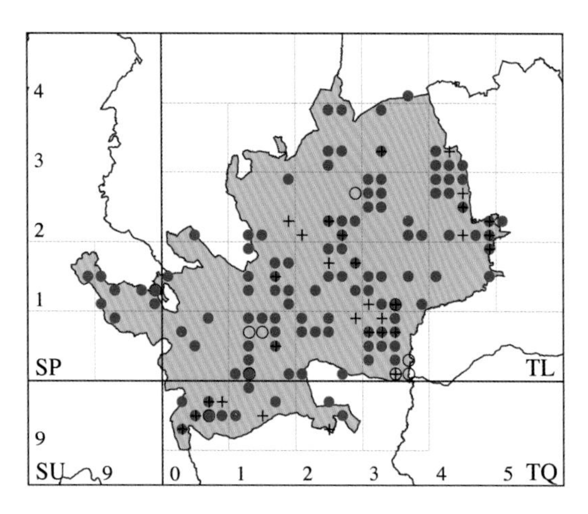

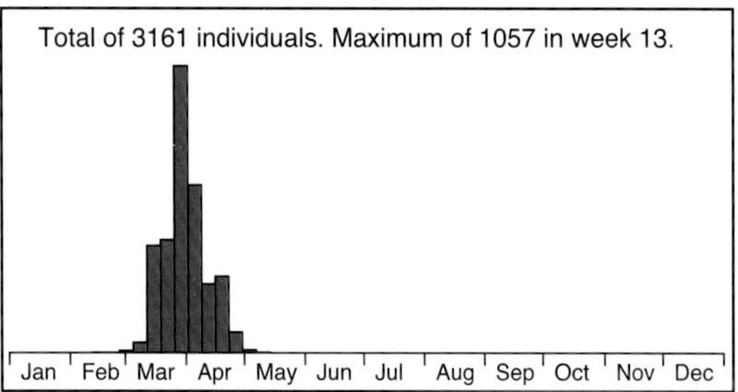

This is one of the most abundant moths in many spring light traps, but some people have never caught it at all in their gardens. The reason is probably that it is mostly confined to woodland areas, especially those containing oak. A trap placed under an oak tree can generate several hundred moths within a couple of hours. By way of illustration, on the night of 1st April 2006, four lights run by Rachel Terry and others at Fir and Pond Woods Nature Reserve (just across the southern border in Middlesex) attracted approximately a thousand Small Quakers between 8pm and midnight; the previous night four lights run by me for the same time period at Fox Covert near Therfield, in the far north of Hertfordshire, caught 2 examples of this species! Old records indicate that the status and distribution of the Small Quaker in Hertfordshire has always been as it is today. The start and end of the flight period varies with season, with moths emerging earlier in mild springs and later in cold ones. Our extreme dates are 20th February 2002 and 7th May 2004.

2183 *Orthosia miniosa* ([D.& S.]) Blossom Underwing

Recorded: 1884 – 1980
Distribution / Status: Absent / Former resident
Conservation status: Herts Extinct
Caterpillar food plants: Not recorded. Elsewhere on oak
Flight period: April/May
Records in database: 12

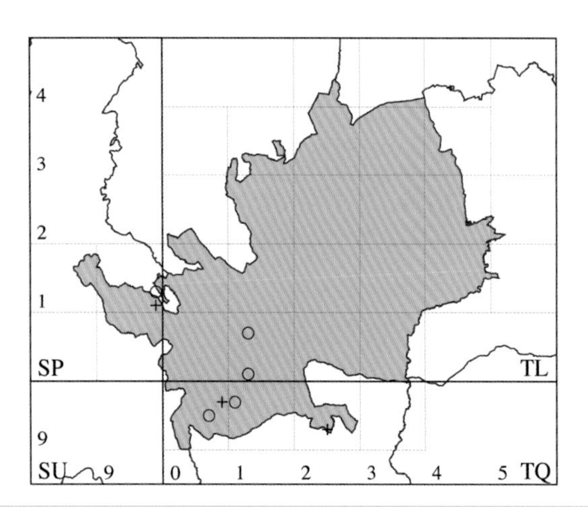

The records seem to suggest that the Blossom Underwing was well-established as a resident at Bricket Wood and the Watford area in the late nineteenth century, although only one, from Watford on 10th April 1895, is dated. Outlying records may suggest a wider distribution that affected the Ashridge Estate and perhaps other oak-dominated areas of the south-west of the county. More recently, Hodgson (1939) writes that J. H. Bell reported it as fairly common at light in the Ashridge district from 1932 to 1936. At Totteridge, where the garden trap was run from 1954 to 1980, one was caught during 1955 but there were no others (Ian Lorimer). There are still (2006) many veteran oaks in the general area around Totteridge though most are along roadsides or in other places where light trapping is near impossible, so there is a small chance that the moth may still persist in a very few places. Since 1955, there has been just a single record, of larvae at Berkhamsted Common, found by L. A. Smart on 25th May 1980. Given the long gap between this breeding record and the previous records for the Ashridge area (of which Berkhamsted Common is a part), there was hope that it may still be present, but the numerous light trapping sessions in appropriate habitat undertaken by me in both 2006 and 2007, at dates when the moth was certainly on the wing elsewhere in southern England, failed to reveal any moths. Primary immigration has been suggested as an explanation for some records that do not fit the expected distribution pattern in Britain.

2184 *Orthosia opima* (Hb.) Northern Drab

Recorded: [1930] – 1985
Distribution / Status: Absent / Former resident
Conservation status: Herts Extinct
Caterpillar food plants: Not recorded. Elsewhere, on various low plants and sallow,
Flight period: April/May
Records in database: 12

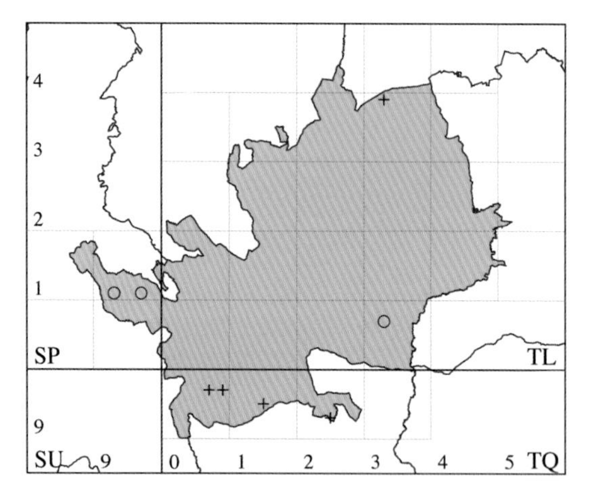

Our first record of Northern Drab in the county is of one taken at Tring by A. L. Goodson (Foster 1941). The year is not given, but Goodson was collecting from about 1930 to the mid 1950s and so his record was probably made during the 1930s. Later, Foster (1942) adds several at light in Northchurch by J. Bell (late 1930s) and 'not uncommon' at Broxbourne by E. W. Classey in the same period. Eric Classey has informed me that the latter relates to Broxbourne Wood *sensu stricto*. Records from the Watford area in 1962 by a single observer may or may not be reliable; there are no specimens available for checking and one record at least seems improbable. More recently there were two areas of the county where the Northern Drab was resident and may still be so. At Bushey, Barry Goater caught examples on 6th May 1965 (a female of the dark form then prevalent on Mitcham Common, Surrey and elsewhere), 20th April 1968 and 5th May 1970. At Therfield Heath (referred to as Royston Heath in older publications) a resident population seems to have been mostly of the paler form. For example, on 4th May 1971 Barry Goater found 12 moths, 1 brown and 11 grey, on grass stems after dark and on 15th May 1979 he again located 12 moths, 2 brown and 10 grey, on grass stems after dark, as well as four egg-batches. Our most recent record from this site was made on 15th May 1985, when Bernard Skinner saw a number of females egg-laying and the egg-batches laid on dead plant stems were quite numerous. It is known that at least some collectors went there looking for it during the 1990s and during May 2006 Phil Jenner, Beatrix Spencer and I searched for adults. However, there are no reports from Therfield since 1985 and it is feared that this moth may have been lost from the county's fauna.

2185 *Orthosia populeti* (Fabr.) Lead-coloured Drab

Recorded:	1892 to 2006
Distribution / Status:	Local / Uncommon resident
Conservation status:	Herts Stable
Caterpillar food plants:	Aspen
Flight period:	March to early May
Records in database:	81

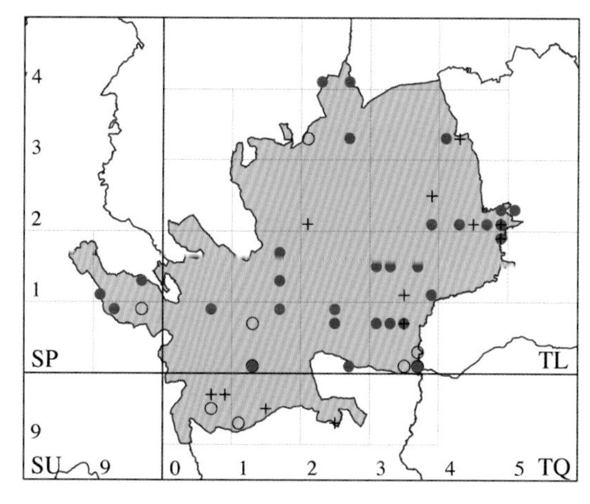

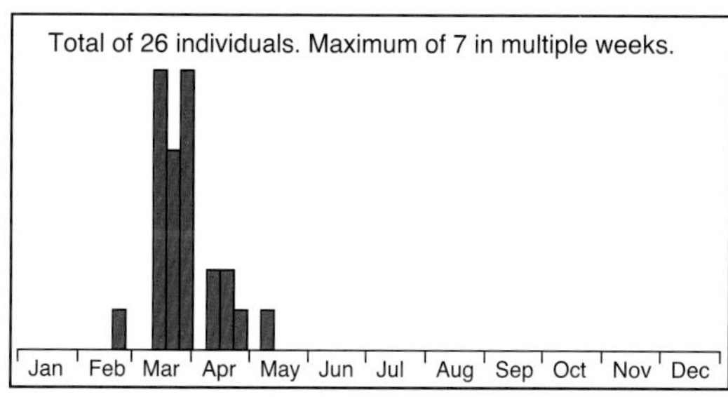

The Lead-coloured Drab may well be under-recorded since there is possible identification confusion with some forms of 2188: Clouded Drab. Positive separation of males in the field is very easy, because the antennae of the Lead-coloured Drab are feathered whilst they comprise a single filament, at least to the unaided eye, in Clouded Drab. However, this does not work for females and whilst Lead-coloured Drabs are fairly constant in appearance the Clouded Drab has a form that is easily confused. Past records are rather vague, but it does not appear likely that the overall Hertfordshire status of this moth has altered in the past hundred years or more. The most northerly of the records prior to Foster's 1937 list was from Letchworth, but all other records at that date were from the south of the county.

2186 *Orthosia gracilis* ([D.& S.]) Powdered Quaker

Recorded:	1828 – 2006
Distribution / Status:	Widespread / Common resident
Conservation status:	UK BAP Watch List Herts Stable
Caterpillar food plants:	Not recorded. Elsewhere, polyphagous
Flight period:	Late March to late May
Records in database:	232

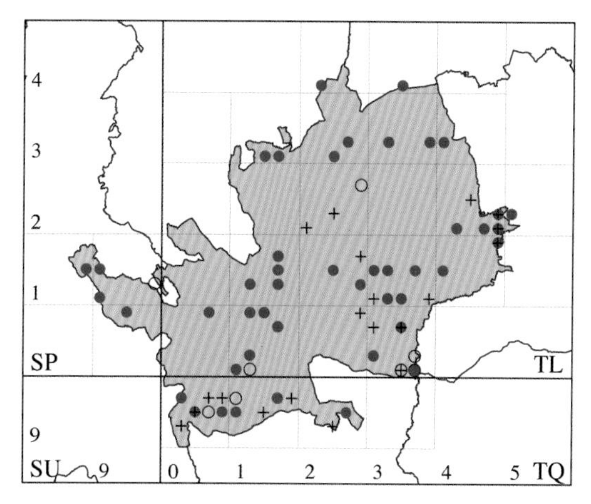

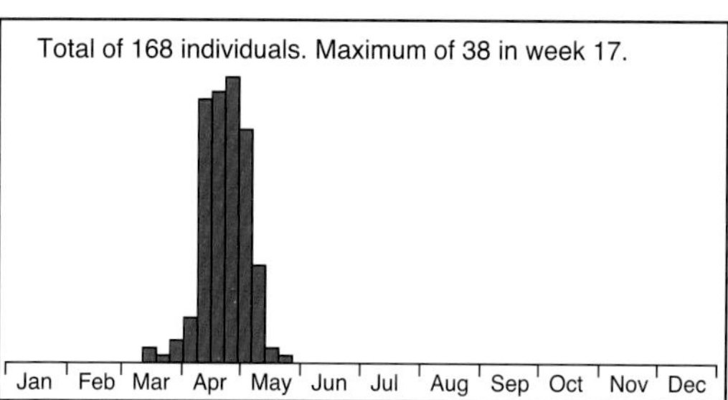

The Powdered Quaker is relatively widespread across the county, though apparently rather local with many sites not recording it and always in small number. Adults tend to fly later in the evening than most species and so, at a time of year when trapping necessarily starts fairly early in the evening, it might be under-recorded as a consequence of packing up too early. Examination of the records shows clearly that the bulk of the records are from garden traps and not from sites 'out and about', yet when one ventures out to such sites, and stays late enough, the moth is caught. The paucity of dots on the map may, therefore, reflect nothing more than post-winter lethargy on the part of moth catchers! Recent research has suggested that there has been a 76 per cent population decline of this species recorded at Rothamsted Light Traps since 1970. No such decline can be detected in Hertfordshire at present; the old records indicated in the distribution map might suggest a decline but the reader's attention is drawn to a similar pattern of old records in the map for 2187: Common Quaker, which is certainly not declining.

2187 *Orthosia cerasi* (Fabr.) Common Quaker

Recorded:	1884 – 2006
Distribution / Status:	Ubiquitous / Abundant resident
Conservation status:	Herts Stable
Caterpillar food plants:	Hornbeam, English Oak. Elsewhere on other deciduous trees
Flight period:	March to mid-May
Records in database:	1567

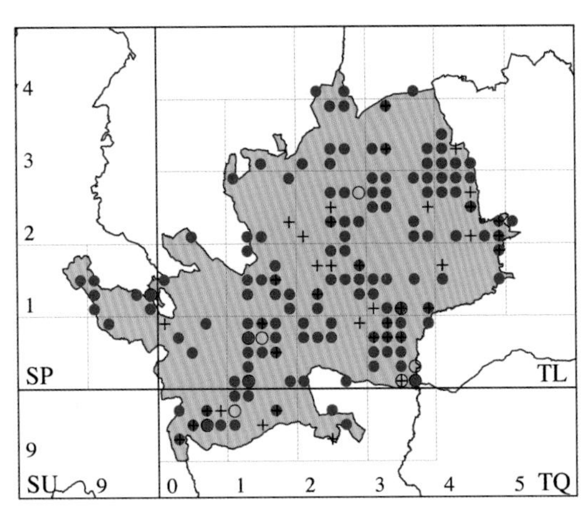

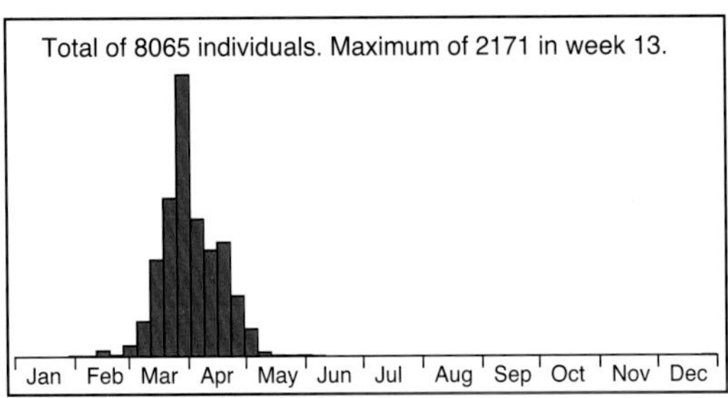

The Common Quaker was first listed for Hertfordshire from the Sandridge area (Griffith, 1884) and features on all published lists since then. Foster (1937) stated that it was 'Recorded from all districts: usually abundant' and absolutely nothing seems to have changed between then and now. The bulk of the adult population flies in March and April, with the peak in all years at the junction between these months, regardless of any variation in first and last date. During 2002 and 2004 adults persisted into early June, with the extreme date of 6th June in 2002.

2188 *Orthosia incerta* (Hufn.) Clouded Drab

Recorded:	1884 – 2006
Distribution / Status:	Ubiquitous / Common resident
Conservation status:	Herts Stable
Caterpillar food plants:	English Oak. Elsewhere also on other trees
Flight period:	March to mid-May
Records in database:	999

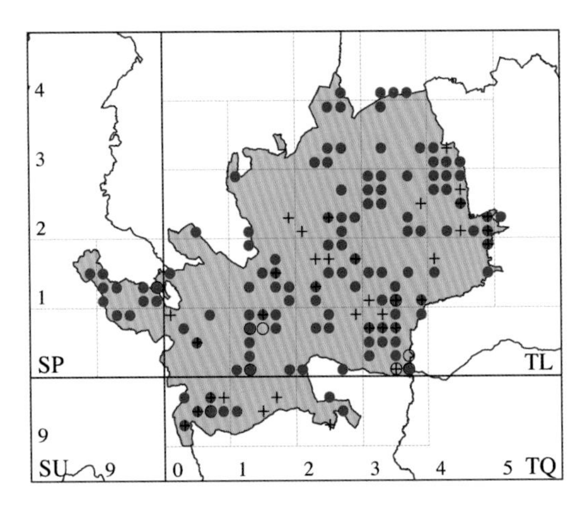

Traditionally, the Clouded drab flies throughout March and April, in most years continuing to about the middle of May. It occasionally appears in February in mild seasons, though the earliest year for which we have a record for flight in this month is 1990. Foster (1937) stated that it was usually abundant in all districts; there has been no apparent change in status since that time. The moths tend to be found in far lower number than

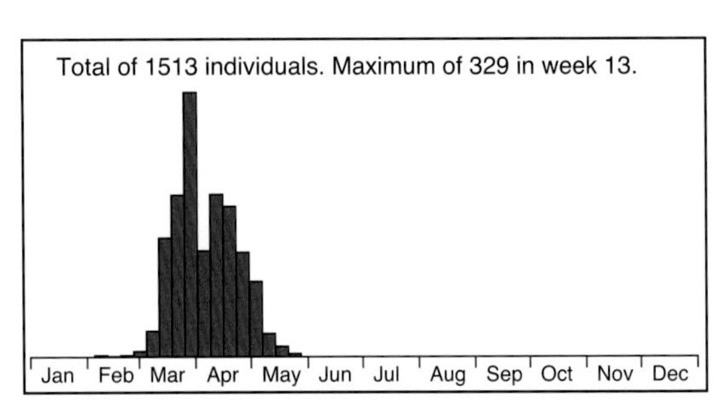

Common Quakers, Small Quakers and Hebrew Characters and may only attend traps as singletons at some sites. There is also some evidence that in some places they arrive at the light trap later in the evening than other species (though this is not the case everywhere) and so may pass unrecorded by those who pack up and go home early. In any event, the blank areas on the map are confidently predicted to reflect under-recording and the Clouded Drab is regarded as being ubiquitous within the county.

2189 *Orthosia munda* ([D.& S.]) Twin-spotted Quaker

Recorded:	1888 – 2006
Distribution / Status:	Widespread / Common resident
Conservation status:	Herts Stable
Caterpillar food plants:	Not recorded. Elsewhere, on various trees
Flight period:	March/April
Records in database:	383

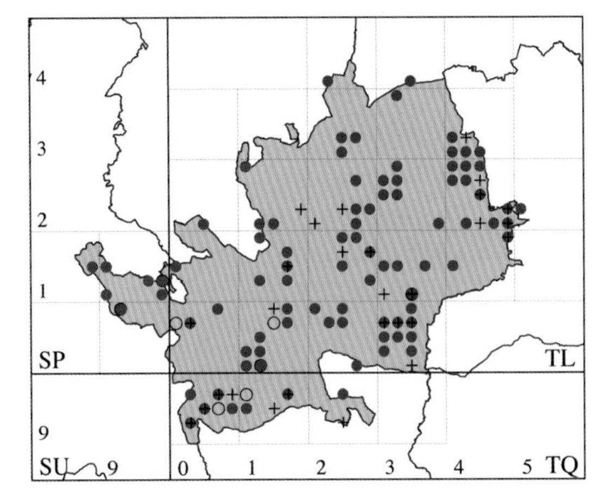

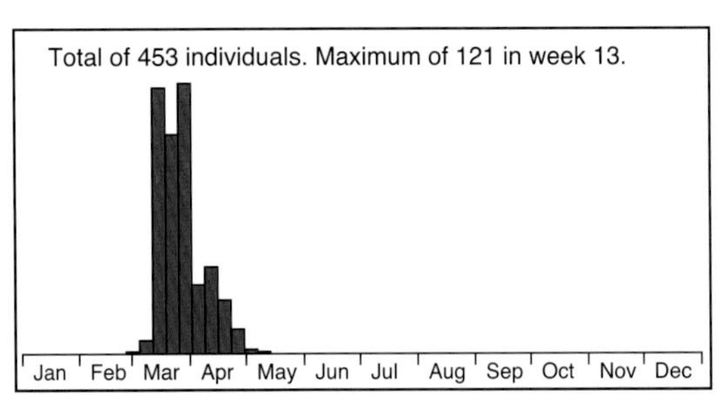

The Twin-spot Quaker seems to have a relatively narrow band of dates over which adults may be seen when compared to the other common *Orthosia* species; almost all records are strictly within the two months of March and April and there are only a handful of records in May and none beyond 3rd of that month. Generally speaking this moth also appears in lower numbers than the other common *Orthosia* species, though this is compensated for a by a reasonable variety of colour forms; examples completely lacking the paired spots from which the English name derives are not uncommon in Hertfordshire and are referable to ab. *immaculata* Staudinger. There does not seem to have been any discernible change in status in this species since at least the mid 1880s in Hertfordshire.

2190 *Orthosia gothica* (L.) Hebrew Character

Recorded: 1884 – 2006
Distribution / Status: Ubiquitous / Abundant resident
Conservation status: Herts Stable
Caterpillar food plants: Horse Chestnut; English Oak. Elsewhere on various trees and other plants
Flight period: Late February to end of May
Records in database: 1847

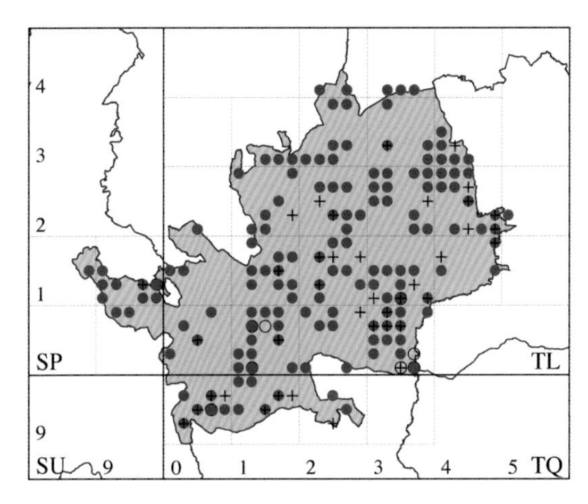

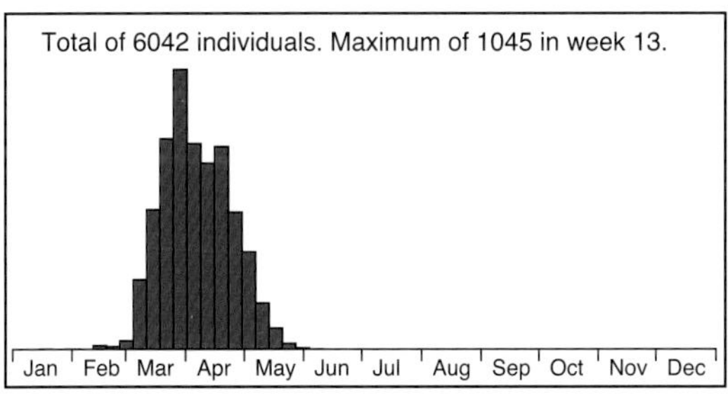

This is one of our commonest moths and numbers can reach the hundreds in light traps run in woodland sites on mild nights during March and April. Such extraordinary large numbers from one-off trips are, however, excluded from the flight chart which involves only garden traps where regular recording by a large number of observers smoothes out any anomalies. Foster had the moth as 'Generally common in all districts' in his 1937 list and this is still the situation. There can surely not be a single map square in Hertfordshire that will not produce this species? The adult is variable to some degree in colour and to a greater degree in the form of the black Hebrew-alphabet character on its wing. An example of ab. *circumsignata*, in which the black mark on the forewing forms a complete circle, was noted at Bushey in 1965 (Barry Goater).

2191 *Mythimna turca* (L.) Double Line

Recorded: 1885 – 1938
Distribution / Status: Absent / Former resident
Conservation status: Herts Extinct
Caterpillar food plants: Not recorded
Flight period: Elsewhere, mid-June to mid-July
Records in database: 8

In Britain, the Double Line is found in Devon and South Wales, and in a band from Surrey to Hampshire, via Berkshire. There is a handful of old records from Hertfordshire where it was presumably once resident. These are from Knebworth Great Wood, 1885 (Durrant), St Albans in 1889 and Bricket Wood in 1892 (Gibbs), Broxbourne Woods (Edelsten), Berkhamsted (Hodgson) and Ashridge (Fryer) – the last three in Foster (1937). Berkhamsted (in the Northchurch district) and Broxbourne Woods feature again in the records of J. Bell and E. W. Classey, respectively, in the late 1930s (Foster, 1942). Eric Classey informs me that his last sighting at Broxbourne Wood was in 1938. A specimen apparently collected by A. L. Goodson, in the R. S. Ferry collection at Mill Green Museum, is labelled 'Albury, 24th October 1953'. There is no doubt about the identity, but this is an unacceptably late date for a species that flies in June. It is possible that the date may refer to when the larva was found but it is more likely that the wrong label was put on the pin; the record is not accepted. Since Goodson operated in the Tring area it is also entirely possible that 'Aldbury' rather than 'Albury' was intended.

2192 *Mythimna conigera* ([D.& S.]) Brown-line Bright-eye

Recorded: 1828 – 2006
Distribution / Status: Local / Common resident
Conservation status: Herts Stable
Caterpillar food plants: Not recorded. Elsewhere, on various grasses
Flight period: Late June to early August
Records in database: 242

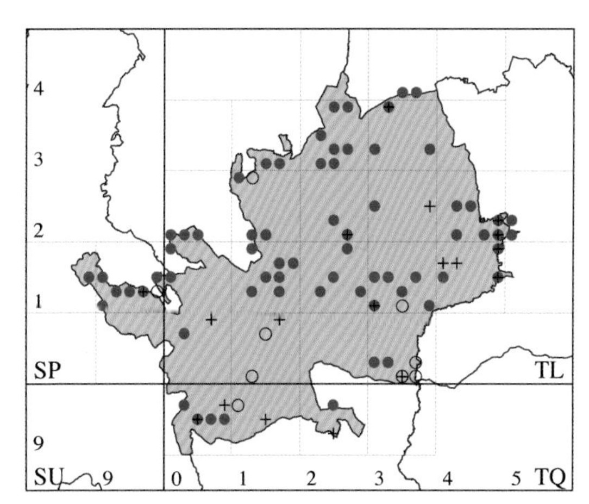

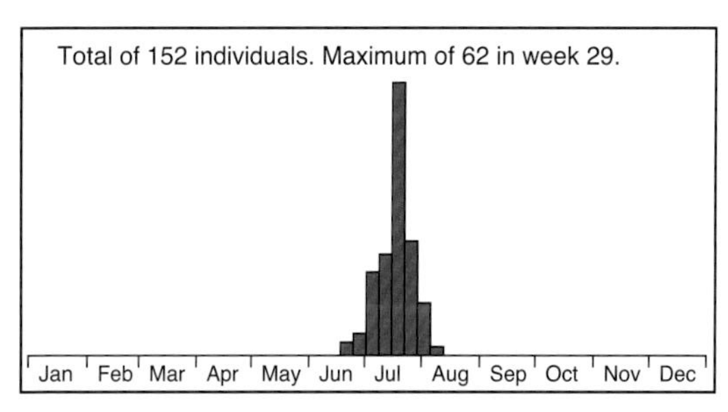

The Brown-line Bright-eye frequents a range of habitats across the county, but is by far most numerous in damp grasslands and marshes and is not reported from a number of adequately recorded dry sites. It seems to matter little if the damp grassland areas are open and exposed or within woodlands.

2193 *Mythimna ferrago* (Fabr.) Clay

Recorded: 1888 – 2006
Distribution / Status: Widespread / Common resident
Conservation status: Herts Stable
Caterpillar food plants: Not recorded. Elsewhere, on grasses and herbaceous plants
Flight period: Late June to early August
Records in database: 628

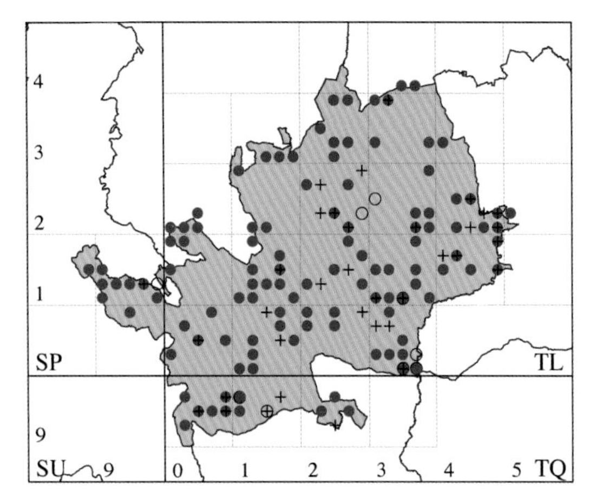

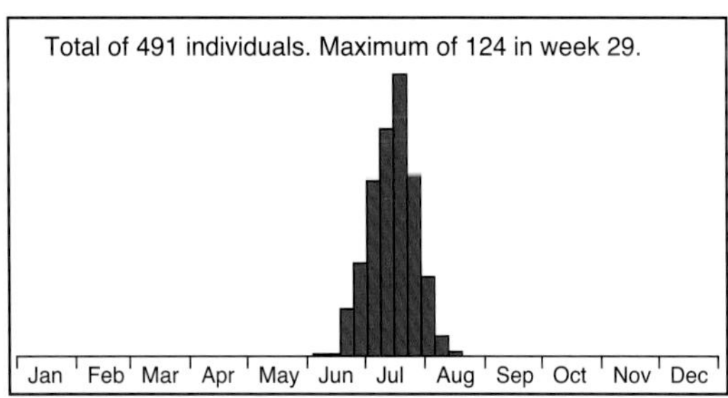

Although present throughout the county, this moth seems to be present in variable frequency, with some places consistently producing large numbers at light traps and others producing rather few. The reasons behind this are unclear.

2194 *Mythimna albipuncta* ([D.& S.]) White-point

Recorded: 1959 – 2006
Distribution / Status: Random / Occasional immigrant
Conservation status: -
Caterpillar food plants: Not recorded. Elsewhere, on Cock's-foot and other grasses
Flight period: June to November
Records in database: 15

This is an immigrant species to Britain, though in recent years migrants have established residency along the south coast, so the possibility exists that it may spread north. It is not listed for Hertfordshire in the *Victoria County History* (Gibbs, 1902) nor by Foster (1937). Our first record was of one in A. L. Goodson's light trap at Tring on 11 October 1959 (Bell, 1961), a part of a particularly large immigration of moths at that time. Subsequent records are from Totteridge, a male on 25th June 1960 (Ian Lorimer); Bishops Stortford, 10th November 1994 (James Fish & Julian Reeves); Hemel Hempstead, 1994 (Malcom Newland); Long Marston, 26th August 2000 (Peter Bygate); Bishops Park, Bishops Stortford, 24th September 2002 (Andrew Palmer); Radwell, 18th September 2005 (Jim Reid); Bishops Stortford, 25th September 2005 (James Fish & Julian Reeves); Bishops Stortford, 13th June 2006 (James Fish & Julian Reeves); Rye Meads, 17th June 2006 (Paul Roper); Chiswell Green, 5th July 2006 (Bill & Pearl Page); Bishops Stortford, 18th August 2006 (James Fish & Julian Reeves); Bishops Stortford, 21st August 2006 (Colin Plant); Bishops Stortford, 25th August 2006 (James Fish & Julian Reeves) and Bishops Stortford, 27th August 2006 (James Fish & Julian Reeves).

2195 *Mythimna vitellina* (Hb.) Delicate

Recorded: 1953 – 2006
Distribution / Status: Random / Rare immigrant
Conservation status: -
Caterpillar food plants: Not recorded in Britain
Flight period: August to October
Records in database: 7

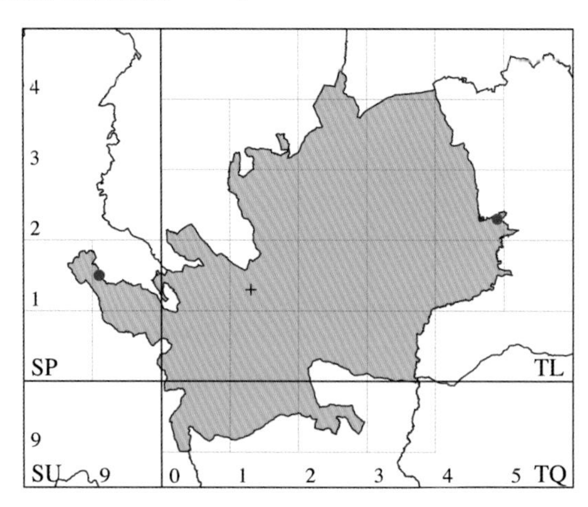

The Delicate is strictly an immigrant from overseas in Hertfordshire. The first county record was that of a single male at Arkley on 27th September 1953 taken by T. G. Howarth (*Proceedings of the South London Entomological & Natural History Society 1953 – 54:* 32 & *Ent. Gaz.* **5**: 116). This is perhaps the same record as that alluded to by Bell (1955) who writes 'I am glad to be able to report further additions to the county list amongst moths, namely ... the Delicate Wainscot (*Leucania vitellina*) ...'. Subsequent reports are from Hertford in 1974 (Geoff Senior), Bishops Stortford 20th October 2001 (James Fish & Julian Reeves), Rothamsted Estate, Harpenden, 26th August 1992 (Adrian Riley); Long Marston, 7th October 2005 (Peter Bygate), Much Hadham in 2006 (Geoff Senior) and Bishops Stortford, 10th, 18th and 20th October 2006 (James Fish & Julian Reeves).

2196 *Mythimna pudorina* ([D.& S.]) Striped Wainscot

Recorded: 1930 – 2001
Distribution / Status: Extremely Local / Resident; vagrant
Conservation status: Herts Endangered
Caterpillar food plants: Not recorded. Elsewhere, on various grasses, including Reed
Flight period: Elsewhere, mid-June to mid-July.
Records in database: 8

Foster (1941) adds this species to the county list from 'Wilstone Reservoir, scarce (A. L. Goodson)'; subsequent enquiries suggest that this record was made during 1930. Later (Foster,

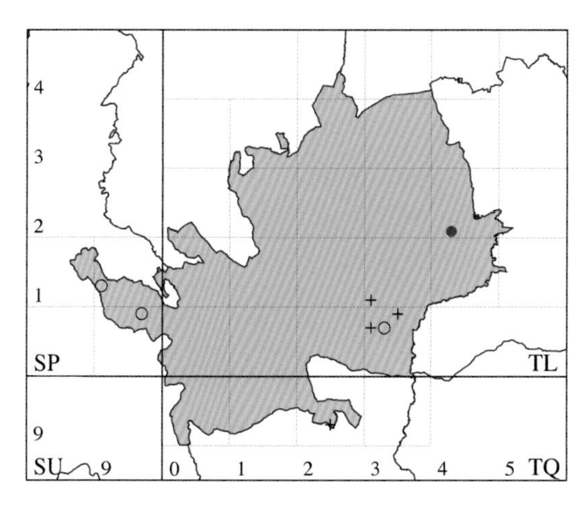

1942), he adds records by J. Bell from Northchurch in 1937. Parts of Northchurch Common and some adjacent areas appear likely to still be able to support this moth, which does not appear to have been specifically looked for here. Foster (1942) also adds a record for Broxbourne, by E. W. Classey, from where it was 'not uncommon' in the late 1930s. The terms 'Broxbourne' and 'Broxbourne Woods' have been variously applied to much of what is now the Broxbourne Woods National Nature Reserve. Within this complex of woodland, one moth was taken at Bayfordbury in 1974 and another in Wormley Wood during 1977 by Jim Reid and it was also recorded in Hoddesdon Park Wood in 1985. It is clear that the complex supported a widely scattered population and it is worth recording that no specific searching appears to have been undertaken for this moth here in the last twenty years. A single moth taken at Totteridge in July 1955 (Ian Lorimer) and one at light in Much Hadham in 2001 (Geoff Senior), were both probably vagrants from further afield.

2197 *Mythimna straminea* (Tr.) Southern Wainscot

Recorded:	1888 – 2006
Distribution / Status:	Local / Common resident
Conservation status:	Herts Stable
Caterpillar food plants:	Reed. Elsewhere also on Canary Grass
Flight period:	Mid-June to August
Records in database:	56

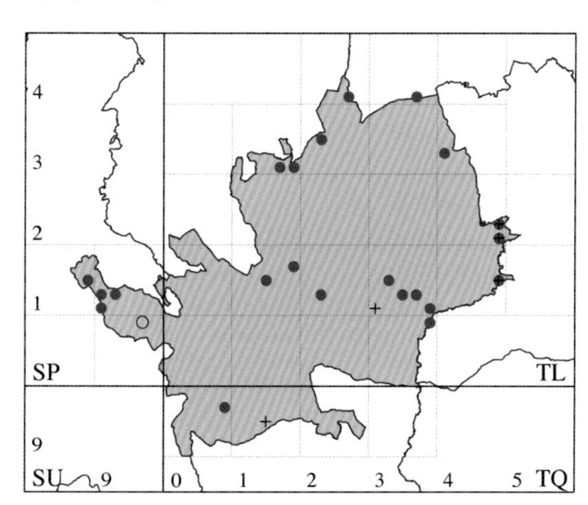

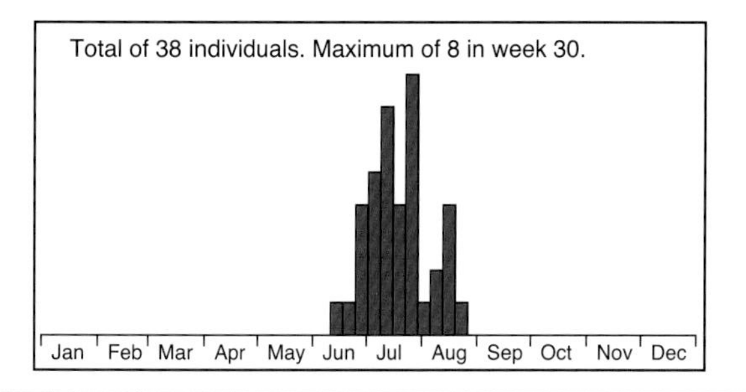

Wetlands and other damp habitats support the Southern Wainscot, and a feature of all Hertfordshire sites is the presence of reeds. The moth is usually abundant where it is found. A particularly strongly marked form persists in several places within the Lea Valley and this has been misidentified on several occasions as 2204: Obscure Wainscot; such doubtful cases are always resolved by dissection of the genitalia, when the two are easily separated.

2198 *Mythimna impura* (Hb.) Smoky Wainscot

Recorded:	1884 – 2006
Distribution / Status:	Ubiquitous / Abundant resident
Conservation status:	Herts Stable
Caterpillar food plants:	Not recorded. Elsewhere, on various grasses
Flight period:	June to September, in two generations
Records in database:	1,140

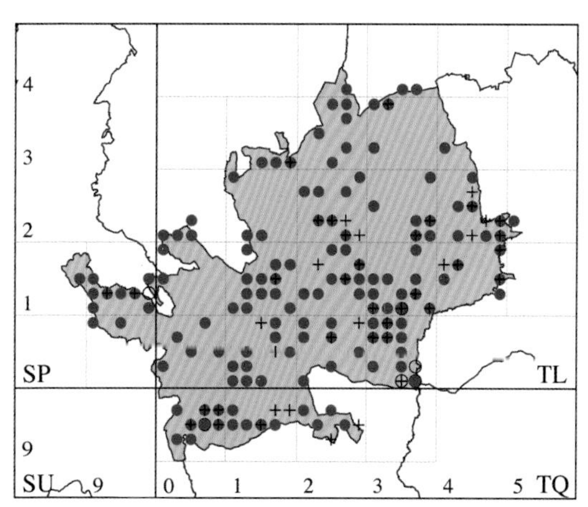

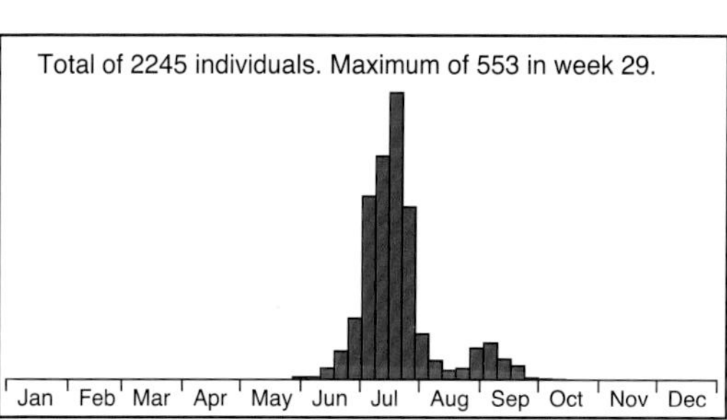

The Smoky Wainscot is amongst the commonest moths in Hertfordshire and is likely to turn up everywhere, regardless of habitat. The main peak of adult moths occurs throughout July, but in all years from at least 1995 to 2006 there is a smaller peak of freshly emerged adults in late August and September. An exceptionally early (or late?) moth was caught in my garden light trap in Bishops Stortford on 5th February 2002.

2199 *Mythimna pallens* (L.) Common Wainscot

Recorded: 1884 – 2006
Distribution / Status: Ubiquitous / Abundant resident
Conservation status: Herts Stable
Caterpillar food plants: Not recorded. Elsewhere, on various grasses
Flight period: June to September, in two generations
Records in database: 1561

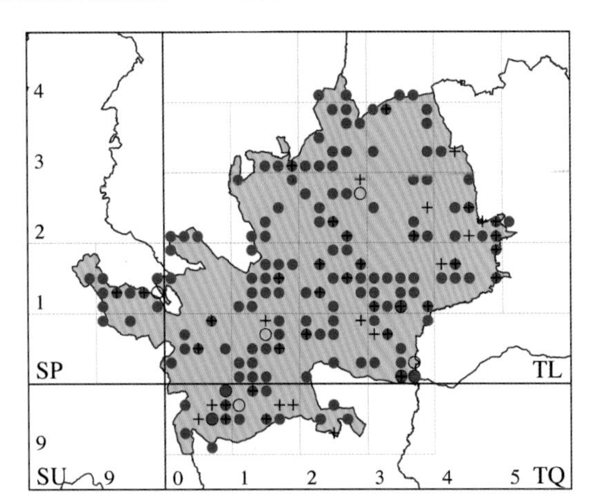

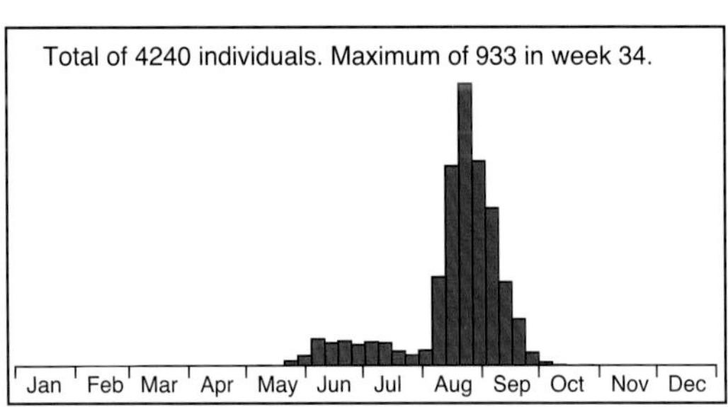

As with the last species, the Common Wainscot is likely to be found in all places wherever a light trap is put out. Although not noted as a migrant species, it is of interest that during 1959 numbers of Common Wainscot at Clifford Craufurd's light trap in Bishops Stortford suddenly soared in the first week of September and then fell away. According to Bell (1961) this 'roughly coincided with the appearance of several *Laphygma exigua*' [= 2385: *Spodoptera exigua* – a noted immigrant]. September and October 1959 were outstanding months for immigrant moths, but on the other hand the summer of 1959 was exceptional in terms of weather with a cold January and February, giving way to a mild and moist March and April, followed by 'five months ruled by the sun .... neither thunderstorm nor day or two of rain ... capable of diverting the stream of glorious warmth' (Bell, 1961). Under these conditions, localised population explosions of grassland species such as Common Wainscot would not be unexpected. The flight chart shows only data from 1995 to 2006 and a similar abrupt peak in September is observed. This peak is evident in all of the years from 1995 to 2006 and although possibly reinforced by immigrant examples clearly points to a second peak in the resident population.

[2200 *Mythimna favicolor* (Barrett) Mathew's Wainscot

Foster (1945) records an example taken at sugar in Bishops Stortford by C. S. Colman in 1896. This seems an unlikely record and unless a specimen can be traced is perhaps best treated as a form of *pallens*.]

[2202 *Mythimna l-album* (L.) L-album Wainscot

The (more or less annual) reviews of Hertfordshire moths by P. J. Bell typically terminate with a summary list of species added to the county fauna in the year under discussion. In the list that appears at the end of his combined review for 1961, 1962 and 1963 (Bell, 1964), he lists the L-album Wainscot as being added in 1960. Curiously there is no explanation for this record, which purports to have been made in a year outside the scope of the article. The review of 1960 (Bell, 1962) makes no mention of this species. The sensible course of action would seem to be to regard this record as incorrect. The record of *l-album* from Rothamsted in 2000, published in the annual report for 2000 of the Herts and Middlesex Branch of Butterfly Conservation, arises from a data entry error and the record is incorrect. There are, therefore, no valid records of this moth in Hertfordshire.]

2203 *Mythimna unipuncta* (Haw.) White-speck

Recorded: 1971 – 1971
Distribution / Status: Random / Rare immigrant
Conservation status: Herts Vulnerable
Caterpillar food plants: Not recorded in Britain
Flight period: In Britain, mostly in the autumn
Records in database: 1

There is a single record of the White-speck, also sometimes called the American Wainscot, from Broxbourne Woods in October 1971 (J. d'Arcy).

2204 *Mythimna obsoleta* (Hb.) Obscure Wainscot

Recorded: [1937] – 2006
Distribution / Status: Extremely local / Rare resident
Conservation status: Herts Vulnerable
Caterpillar food plants: Not recorded. Elsewhere, internally in the stems of reeds
Flight period: Elsewhere, late May to mid-July
Records in database: 4

Foster (1937) lists Wilstone Reservoir, 'larvae common in September' (Elliman), as the only county locality. The species persists here, though there are no further records until 9th June 2007, when two were taken at light by Lynne and Colin Lambert. On the same night, one was taken in John Chainey's light trap at Tring Sewage Works during a specific search for this species by members of the Herts Moth Group. Though 2007 is beyond the period covered by this review of Hertfordshire's moths, it is clear that the species must have been present at both sites in 2006 and so inclusion here is justified. The search at Tring Sewage Works was motivated by Ian Burrus' capture of a male there on 16th June 2005, the identification of which I confirmed by dissection. A female at light in Totteridge on 6th July 1969 was the only one there 1954 to 1980 (Ian Lorimer) and so probably a vagrant from elsewhere. The apparent absence of Obscure Wainscot from the Lea and Stort Valleys is surprising, though apparently genuine. It is worthy of note that some records from sites in the Lea Valley made during the 1990s relate to a particularly striking form of 2197: Southern Wainscot that looks closely similar (verified by genitalia examination).

2205 *Mythimna comma* (L.) Shoulder-striped Wainscot

Recorded: 1884 – 2006
Distribution / Status: Local / Common resident
Conservation status: UK BAP Watch List
Herts Stable
Caterpillar food plants: Not recorded. Elsewhere, on grasses
Flight period: June/July
Records in database: 201

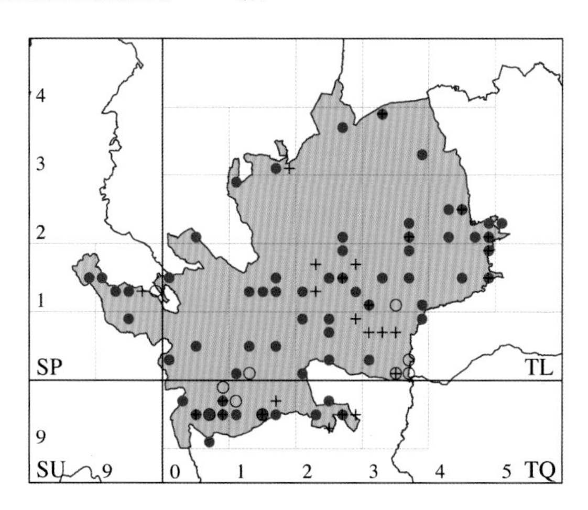

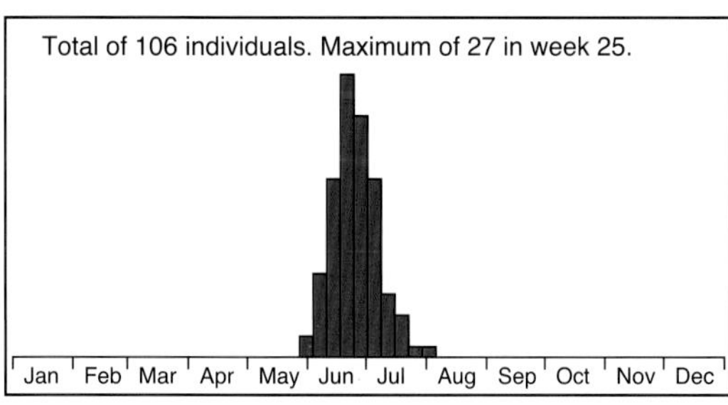

Unlike 2198: Smoky Wainscot and 2199: Common Wainscot, this species appears to require larger areas of undisturbed grassland and seems unable to thrive in small disturbed patches. Nevertheless, it is common in most of the county, though perhaps absent from tracts of the arable north-east, and wanderers sometimes arrive at garden moth traps.

2209 *Mythimna flammea* (Curtis) Flame Wainscot

Recorded: 1963 – 1963
Distribution / Status: Absent / Accidental introduction
Conservation status: -
Caterpillar food plants: Not recorded. Elsewhere, internally in stems of reed
Flight period: Elsewhere, mid-May to early July
Records in database: 1

One at Rothamsted, Harpenden on 1st June 1963 was the first and only county record. As a resident it is confined to fenland and the Broads, though it is also thought to occur as a primary immigrant elsewhere. However, according to Bell (1964) the Harpenden example could have been imported to the area in thatching reeds that were dumped nearby.

CUCULLIINAE

2211 *Cucullia absinthii* (L.) Wormwood

Recorded: 1954 – 2006
Distribution / Status: Local / Common resident
Conservation status: Herts Scarce
Caterpillar food plants: Wormwood; Mugwort
Flight period: July
Records in database: 25

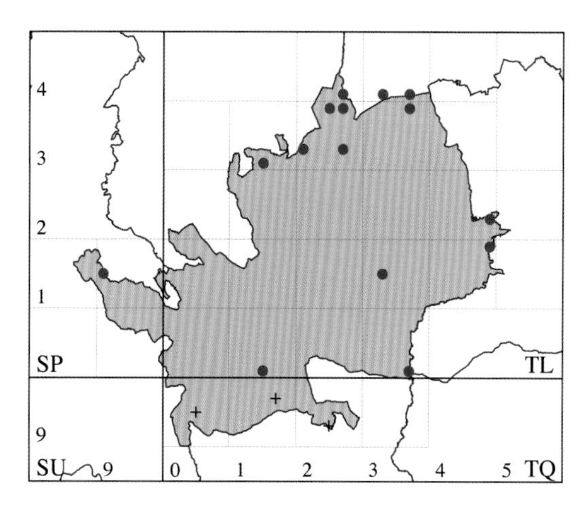

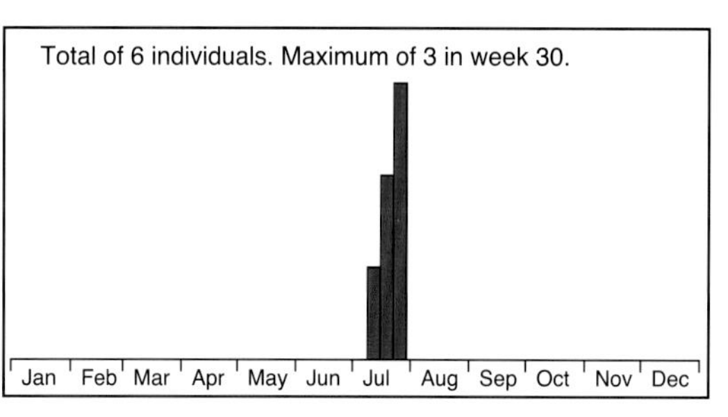

Two thirds of the Hertfordshire localities (ten out of fifteen) are from the chalky soils along the north-west border with Bedfordshire, Cambridgeshire and Buckinghamshire. Those elsewhere are either on chalky soil or base-rich ruderal habitats on post-industrial sites or similar. Prior to the Second World War the Wormwood was a rare moth in our general region of south-east England, but during the 1940s and 1950s it appears to have undergone a range expansion, spreading into the London Area (Plant, 1993) and reaching Hertfordshire by 1954, when our first record was made at Totteridge, by Ian Lorimer. Lorimer caught it again the following two years, but writing in 1980 noted it as 'rare since 1957 and not seen 1964 to end of trapping in 1980'. A record of one moth in Parsonage Lane, Bishops Stortford on 28 July 1955 by Geoffrey Sell was followed by one elsewhere in the town, across the river, in 1957 (Clifford Craufurd). Bell (1959) treats this as only the second county record, and was evidently unaware of those from Totteridge. There are then records from the Haberdashers' Aske's School at Aldenham, 22nd July 1985 (Barry Goater) and Rickmansworth, 12th July 1990 (Ric Sandifer), but these are followed by rather few sightings until 2005, when almost all of the northern records were made by John Chainey and Jenny Spence – including several larval records in September. Whilst this species is certainly restricted to a small part of the county it is doubtless under-recorded; the distinctive larvae should be searched for by beating the foodplant over a tray in the autumn, as they are far more readily found than the adults.

2214 *Cucullia chamomillae* ([D.& S.]) Chamomile Shark

Recorded: 1895 – 2006
Distribution / Status: Very local / Uncommon resident
Conservation status: Herts Vulnerable
Caterpillar food plants: Scentless Mayweed. Elsewhere, on various other mayweeds and on Chamomile.
Flight period: April/May
Records in database: 27

Most identification guides list the flight period for this moth as being from mid-April to early June; most Hertfordshire sightings are in May, but there are also two confirmed adults in

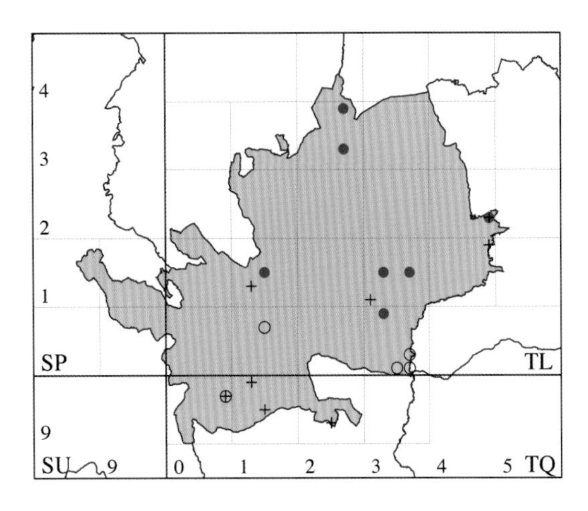

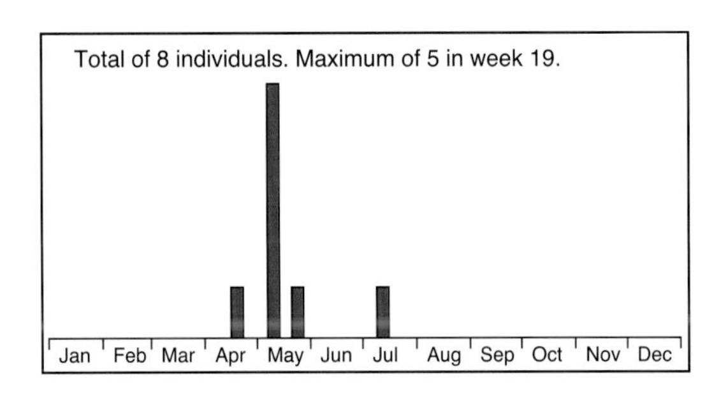

July – one in 2003 and one in 2005. Separation from 2216: Shark can be extremely difficult with worn moths and recourse to examination of the genitalia is sometimes necessary. With only 27 records for all time from the county it is difficult to interpret the map, but attention is drawn to former sites in the south of the county from which there appears to be no recent report. The loss of flower-rich grassland, the mowing and spraying of roadside verges and the loss of field margins (though now back in vogue) have probably all contributed to the decline of this species, which is regarded as 'Threatened' in the county.

2216 *Cucullia umbratica* (L.) Shark

Recorded:	1884 – 2006
Distribution / Status:	Local / Common resident
Conservation status:	Herts Stable
Caterpillar food plants:	Sow Thistle. Elsewhere also on wild lettuce
Flight period:	June/July
Records in database:	119

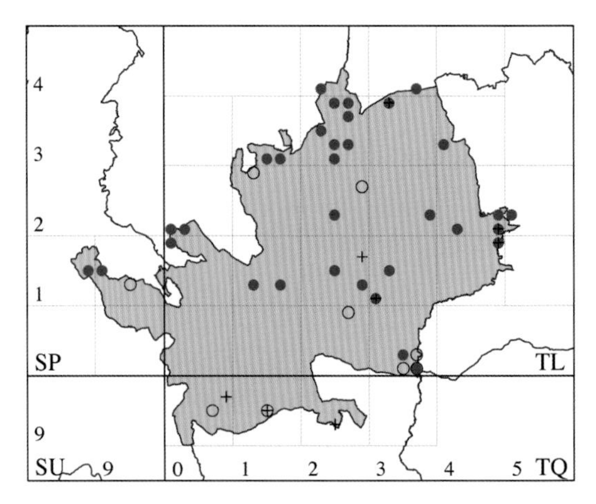

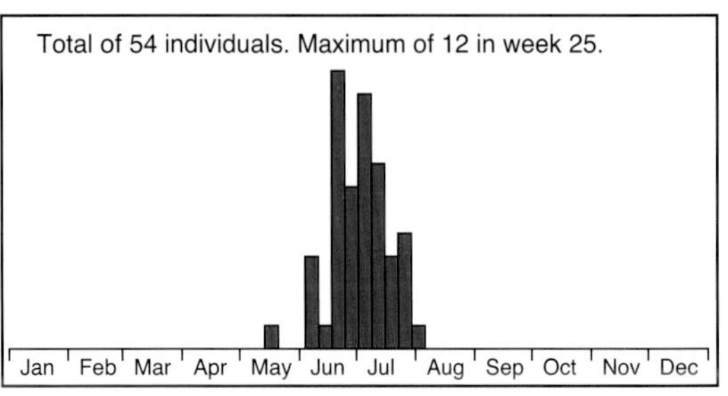

Although by no means a common moth, the Shark is as likely as not to turn up in garden light traps if they are operated for long enough, though rarely in numbers greater than one or two and the overall distribution seems to be extremely localised. Shark moths reported during May might turn out to be 2214: Chamomile Shark when looked at more carefully, but we do have one genuine May Shark – in Hertford on 18th May 2001 (Andrew Wood). Searching for larvae is likely to produce more records than light trapping, though the sorts of ruderal habitats where the foodplants grow are becoming increasing scarce in an increasingly 'tidy' county.

[2217 *Cucullia asteris* ([D.& S.]) Star-wort

Foster (1941) adds this species to the county list from 'Ware (Gerard)'. Whilst Gerard's identification of the moth is likely to have been correct the record is not acceptable as there is no evidence that this moth was actually collected in Hertfordshire. Gerard also recorded a number of other exceptionally unlikely species during the 1930s, including 1644: Kentish Glory and 2103: Plain Clay; it is generally accepted that his labels relate to his own location rather than those of the moths. This species cannot be accepted on the Hertfordshire list.]

2219 *Shargacucullia lychnitis* Rambur Striped Lychnis

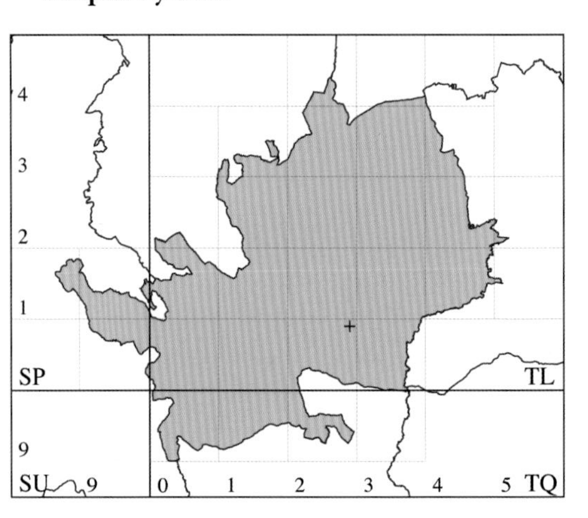

Recorded:	1970 only
Distribution / Status:	Absent / Former resident
Conservation status:	UK BAP Priority Species. Herts Extinct
Caterpillar food plants:	Great Mullein. Elsewhere, also on Dark Mullein
Flight period:	Elsewhere, June/July
Records in database:	1

Foster (1941) adds this species to the county list from 'Ware (Gerard)', but the acceptability of Gerard's records is highly questionable (see discussion under 2217: Star-wort), and this one is rejected. Our only valid record is, therefore, that from July 1970, when Jim Reid found a single larva on *Verbascum thapsus* in a disused chalk pit at Howe Green, Essendon, as well as several Mullein Shark *Shargacucullia verbasci* larvae; the adult was reared. In recent years, myself and others have searched in vain for the highly visible caterpillars of this moth, on both Light and Dark Mullein plants, in the chalky districts of the county. The moth's British range includes adjacent Buckinghamshire, but the nearest records are several kilometres from our border (Hall et al, 2006).

[2220 *Shargacucullia scrophulariae* ([D.& S.]) Water Betony

Recorded in error. The record in the *Victoria County History* (Gibbs, 1902) relates to 2221: Mullein (see Foster, 1937: 159). Separation of the Water Betony from 2219: Striped Lychnis and 2221: Mullein is discussed in Sterling & Costen (2007).]

2221 *Shargacucullia verbasci* (L.) Mullein

Recorded:	1828 – 2006
Distribution / Status:	Widespread / Common resident
Conservation status:	Herts Stable
Caterpillar food plants:	White Mullein; *Buddleia* species
Flight period:	Mid-April to early July
Records in database:	109

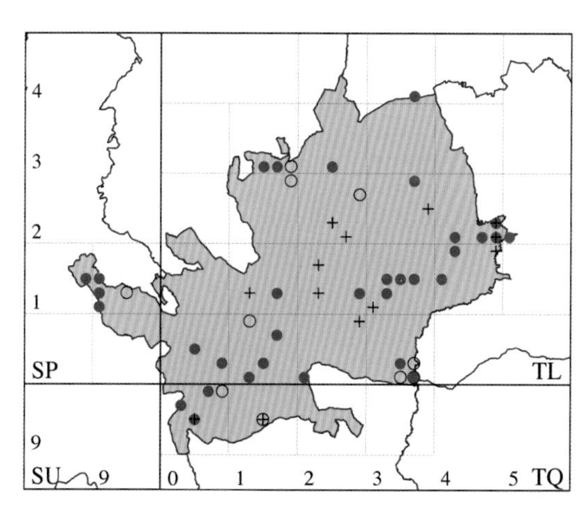

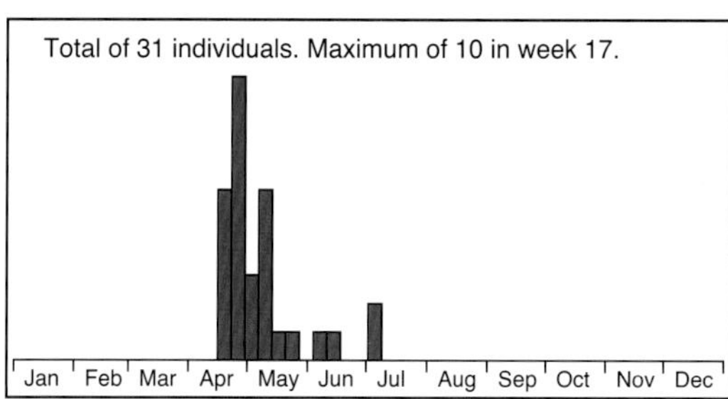

Although still probably quite widespread, the Mullein is rather locally distributed across the county and as with several other species is perhaps declining as a result of the increasing loss of ruderal habitats where Mullein plants can grow. Recording this species is easy if the strikingly obvious foodplants are searched for the brightly coloured and easily spotted caterpillars; even after they have finished feeding the large pellets of frass caught in the cupped leaf-bases provide evidence of former feasting. Larvae are reported on White Mullein as long ago as 1902 in Batch Wood, St Albans (Barraud, 1903), but more interestingly Foster (1946) records larvae in his garden at Hitchin feeding on *Buddleia*. Barry Goater also bred this species from a larva on *Buddleia* in his garden at Bushey in 1978. Most adults fly from mid-April to the end of May; we have recorded late adults at Ware on 4th June 2003 (Andrew Wood), Bishops Stortford on 11th June 2005, Much Hadham on 23rd June 2000 and two at Wilstone Reservoir on 2nd July 2006 (Colin Lambert).

2223 *Calophasia lunula* (Hufn.) Toadflax Brocade

Recorded:	2006 only
Distribution / Status:	Rare resident
Conservation status:	Increasing
Caterpillar food plants:	Purple Toadflax. Elsewhere on Yellow Toadflax
Flight period:	Elsewhere May/June and August in two generations
Records in database:	1

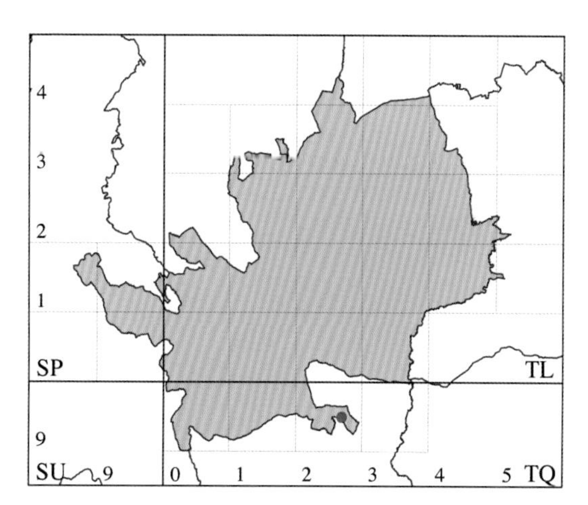

Traditionally, the Toadflax Brocade has been a rare resident restricted, in Britain, to the shingle beaches of Kent and Sussex, also occasionally recorded away from here as a primary immigrant from overseas. However, during 2002 it suddenly appeared in the northern part of London at Wembley, just a few kilometres to the south of Hertfordshire, probably as an immigrant. In 2003, larvae were found by both me and Terry Lyle, separately, on Purple Toadflax at Mile End Cemetery (also Middlesex) in East London. Since then it has become an established resident over a large area of northern London from Wembley to the Olympics site in the Lea Valley feeding mostly on Purple Toadflax, but also using the more usual yellow-flowering species where available. The spread of this moth northwards into Hertfordshire was, therefore, entirely expected, though to date we have only a single report – larvae appeared in Peter Alton's garden in Alverstone Avenue, East Barnet (on the north side of the railway line and so just inside the vice-county boundary) on Purple Toadflax during August 2006. These later produced cocoons. The insect is expected to spread northwards utilising ruderal habitats and perhaps gardens.

2225 *Brachylomia viminalis* (Fabr.) Minor Shoulder-knot

Recorded:	1828 – 2006
Distribution / Status:	Local / Common resident
Conservation status:	UK BAP Watch List. Herts Stable
Caterpillar food plants:	Common Sallow. Elsewhere, other sallows and willow
Flight period:	Mid-June to early August
Records in database:	101

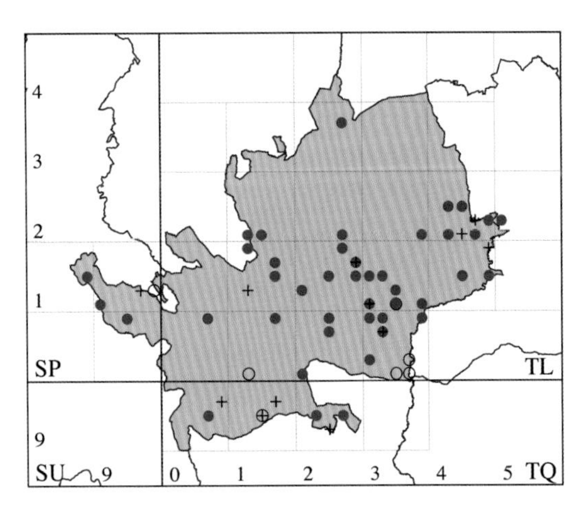

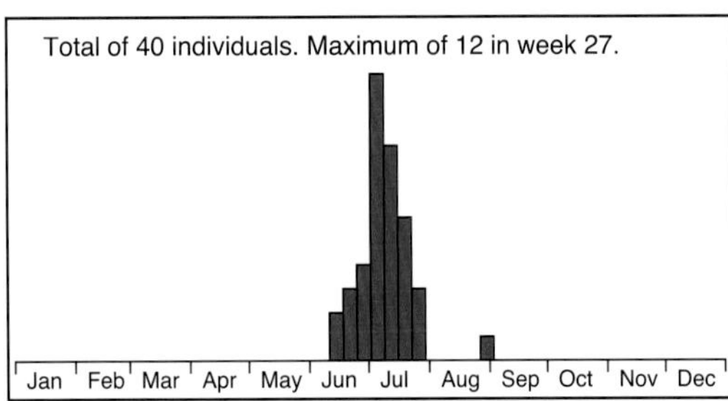

The Minor Shoulder-knot is probably more widespread than records indicate, although the apparent absence from much of the north is probably genuine; most woodlands with either sallow or willow are likely to support it – those that contain damp areas are likely to produce the greatest number. Although the moth has apparently declined nationally by 73 per cent since 1970, there is no evidence that Hertfordshire's population has declined at all. In keeping with the statement in Skinner (1998) most records where information is given relate to the pale grey form, although all the other forms or variations illustrated by Skinner have been encountered in Hertfordshire at some stage. The late record in the flight chart relates to one at Arbury Banks on 31st August 2005 (Jim Reid).

2227 *Brachionycha sphinx* (Hufn.) Sprawler

Recorded:	1828 – 2006
Distribution / Status:	Widespread / Common resident
Conservation status:	UK BAP Watch List. Herts Stable
Caterpillar food plants:	English Oak, Wych Elm. Elsewhere, also on other trees
Flight period:	Late October to early November
Records in database:	134

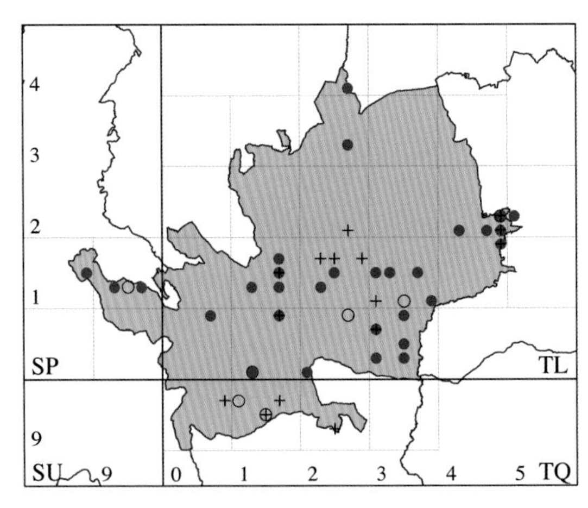

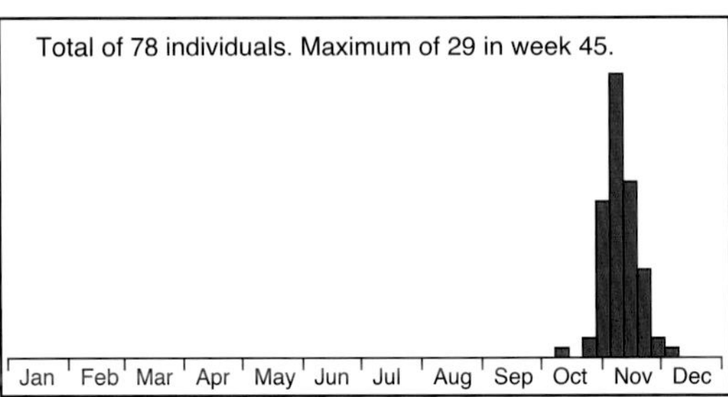

Although other tree leaves are eaten by the larvae, the best way to find this moth is to put a light trap amongst mature oak trees in oak-dominated woodland during November. It is a common moth in all of Hertfordshire's woodlands and there is no sign here of the reported decline in population of 83 per cent reported from the Rothamsted Light Trap Network. Bernard Skinner beat larvae from Wych Elm in Whippendell Wood, at the edge of the golf course, on 2nd June 1956 and 14th May 1957.

2229 *Dasypolia templi* (Thunb.) Brindled Ochre

Recorded:	1952 only
Distribution / Status:	Absent / Former vagrant
Conservation status:	UK BAP Watch List
Caterpillar food plants:	Not recorded. Elsewhere, in stems and roots of Hogweed and Wild Angelica
Flight period:	September/October
Records in database:	1

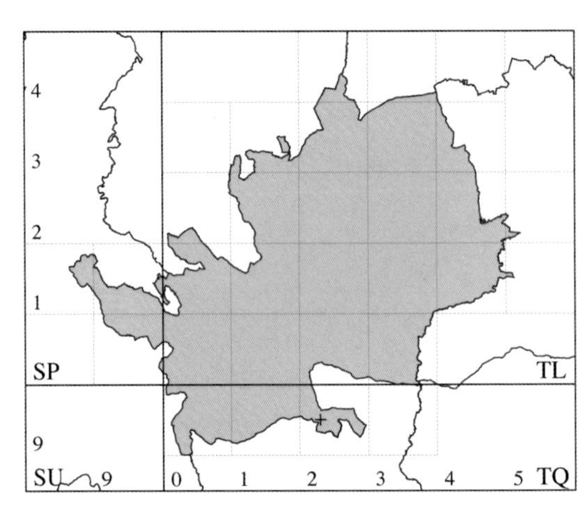

There resident population of this species in Britain affects the country from about Derbyshire northwards and around the coast of Wales, the West Country and east as far as the Isle of Wight. In the south-east we know it only as an immigrant from overseas and in Hertfordshire we can lay claim to only a single record of one taken by T. G. Howarth at Barnet Gate, Arkley on 23rd October 1952 (see *Proceedings of the South London Entomological and Natural History Society* **1953 – 54**: 32 & *Entomologist's Record* **65**: 325).

2231 *Aporophyla lutulenta* ([D.& S.]) *sensu* Bradley = *lueneburgensis* sensu Ronkay et al Deep-brown Dart

Recorded: 1901 – 2006
Distribution / Status: Local / Uncommon resident
Conservation status: UK BAP Watch List. Herts Stable
Caterpillar food plants: Not recorded. Elsewhere, allegedly on grasses
Flight period: Mid-September to mid-October
Records in database: 176

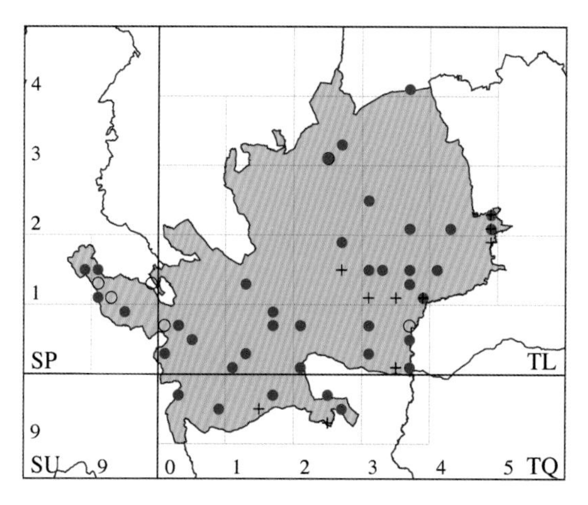

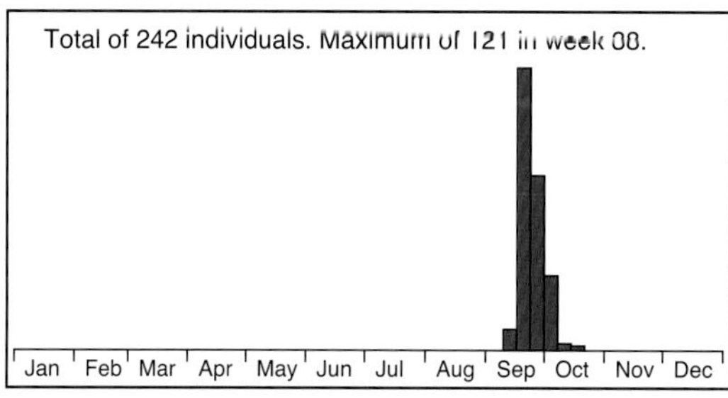

The relationship between *Aporophyla lutulenta* (Deep Brown Dart) and *Aporophyla lueneburgensis* (Northern Deep-brown Dart) supports divided opinion. In the latest British checklist (Bradley, 2000), *lueneburgensis* is given the status of a full species, but a comment is added stating that it is possibly a sibling or ecotype of *lutulenta*. In their taxonomic revision of European Noctuidae, Ronkay et al (2001) suggest that *lueneburgensis* affects all of Western Europe and that *lutulenta* extends eastwards from Eastern Europe and the Balkans. On this basis, the correct name for the Hertfordshire species should be *lueneburgensis*. Nationally, the evidence from Rothamsted Light Traps suggests a 90 per cent population decline in this species since 1970, so an examination of the Hertfordshire data may be instructive. Gibbs (1908) reports the Deep-brown Dart at Tring during 1907, noting that it was added to the county list in 1901 by Rev. G. H. Raynor and had since been recorded at Hitchin by A. H. Foster. In his 1937 list of Hertfordshire moths, Foster reveals that the 1901 record was made at Weston and that the 1907 Tring record was, in fact, made at nearby Wilstone. Foster adds records from Hoddesdon by G. V. Bull [in the early years of the twentieth century], Ashridge by Hodgson [now known to be from Berkhamsted Common in 1932] and Harpenden 'at light' by Williams [in the early 1930s at Rothamsted, where C. B. Williams was pioneering the Rothamsted Light Trap Network]. All of this suggests that the moth was not as commonly encountered as many other species. However, Foster was evidently unaware of records from Bishops Stortford in 1914 by C. S. Colman and 1935 then 1936 by P. B. M. Allan. Since then, the moth has been reported from Berkhamsted again in 1938, from Bishops Stortford in 1940 and 1945, from Tring town in 1945 and Bishops Stortford again in 1948, but then there is a gap until 1974, when Jim Reid took it at Bayfordbury, then 1979 when Ian Lorimer was surprised to catch one in his garden at Totteridge. When I moved to Bishops Stortford in 1986 I was too late in the year to find the moth, but it turned up the next year, though I caught no more until 1991, so there was a gap of three years in which trapping was more or less nightly. A single example was recorded in 1987 at the Capel Manor Environmental Centre on the border with Middlesex. More recent records are spread evenly across much of the county, indicating a moth that is widespread, but rather local and certainly not recorded in all sites. Overall, the moth appears to be local and uncommon, but has probably always been so here; if anything there may have been an extension of its range – certainly we are unable to detect any level of decline.

2232 *Aporophyla nigra* (Haw.) Black Rustic

Recorded: 1937 – 2006
Distribution / Status: Widespread / Common resident
Conservation status: Herts Stable
Caterpillar food plants: Heather. Elsewhere docks, 'other low plants' and grasses
Flight period: September to early November
Records in database: 625

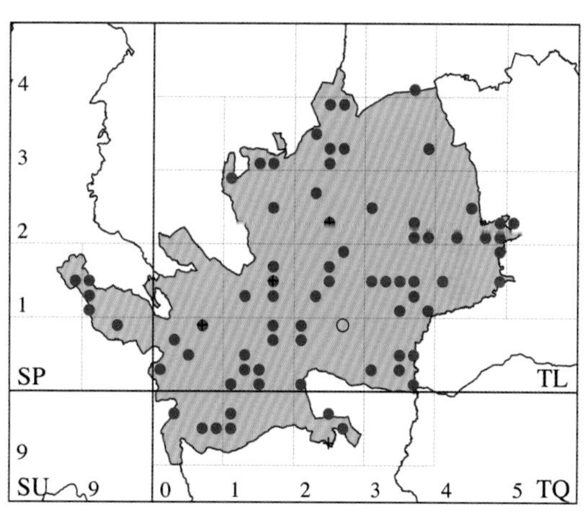

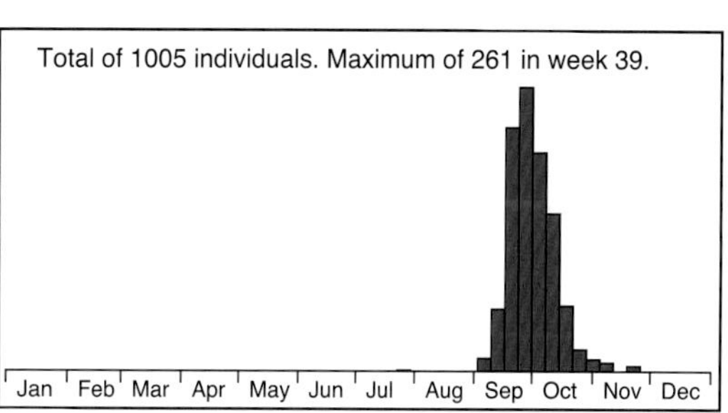

This species was added to the Hertfordshire list from Essendon, 'one to a lighted hall of a house in 1937' (Hodson, 1939). Foster (1940) later refers to this record as being from Hatfield, and gives the date as 11th September 1937. Hatfield is the general locality, which Foster has evidently taken from the title of Hodson's paper; a closer read reveals that the moth was taken at Hodson's own house in Essendon village. A second example was taken by Hodson at the same locality in 1949 and was, apparently, only the second county record (Bell, 1952). At Totteridge, the Ian Lorimer's first record was made in 1972, after having run the trap in his garden since 1954. There are no more Hertfordshire records until 1994, a 22-year gap that may reflect in part a degree of neglect by entomologists rather than a lack of moths. Since then, this moth has been steadily increasing its range north-eastwards as the years progress. It reached the far north-east of the county a few years later, with very few records prior to 2000, but many 'first records' in that year. I caught none in my Bishops Stortford garden from 1987 to 1999, but have caught it every year from 2000 onwards. Half a mile south of me, Charles Watson started catching it in 1999, but half a mile to the north of me the adjoining gardens of Jim Fish and Julian Reeves produced the first in 1995 from where an exceptionally early example was attracted to light on 29th July 1998. Today, it is trapped with increasing regularity at most sites in the county and is a common species with us. Our only larval record is from Hertford Heath West, where I found larvae on Heather on 13th July 2002. Given the dramatic range expansion of this species and the scarcity of Heather, both wild and in gardens, there must be alternative foodplants.

2233 *Lithomoia solidaginis* (Hb.) Golden-rod Brindle

Recorded:	1954 – 1996
Distribution / Status:	Random / Rare immigrant
Conservation status:	-
Caterpillar food plants:	Not recorded. Elsewhere, Bilberry, Bearberry and other plants
Flight period:	September
Records in database:	2

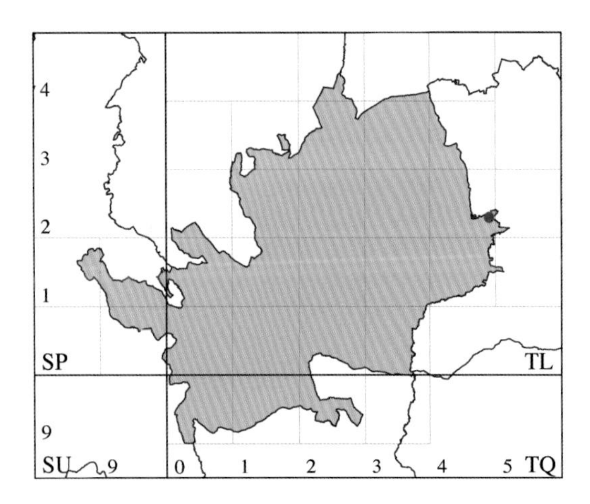

Although a resident elsewhere in Britain, the Golden-rod Brindle is a primary immigrant in Hertfordshire and we can boast just two occurrences. One was at Tring in early September 1954 (*Proc. Trans. Br. ent. Nat. Hist. Soc.* 1972: 116, *Entomologist* **88:** 128 and Bell, 1956) and was one of 17 moths recorded as a part of a wider immigration by this species from overseas. More recently, the trap in the adjoining gardens of James Fish and Julian Reeves, in Bishops Stortford, attracted a male on 1st September 1996; this moth is preserved in my own collection.

2235 *Lithophane semibrunnea* (Haw.) Tawny Pinion

Recorded:	1904 – 2006
Distribution / Status:	Very local / Uncommon resident
Conservation status:	Herts Scarce
Caterpillar food plants:	Not recorded. Elsewhere, on Ash
Flight period:	October, hibernating then flying from March to May
Records in database:	36

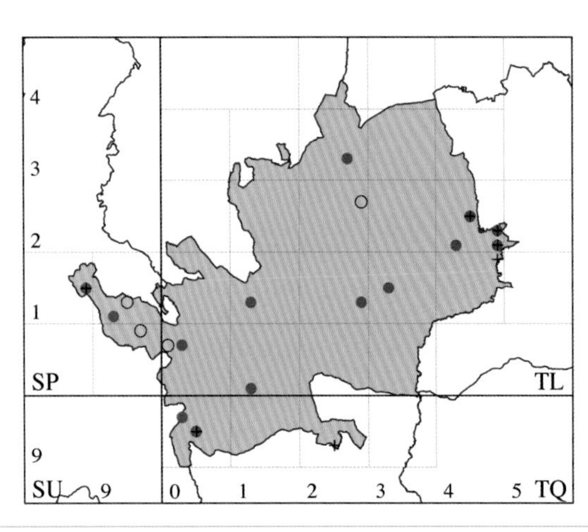

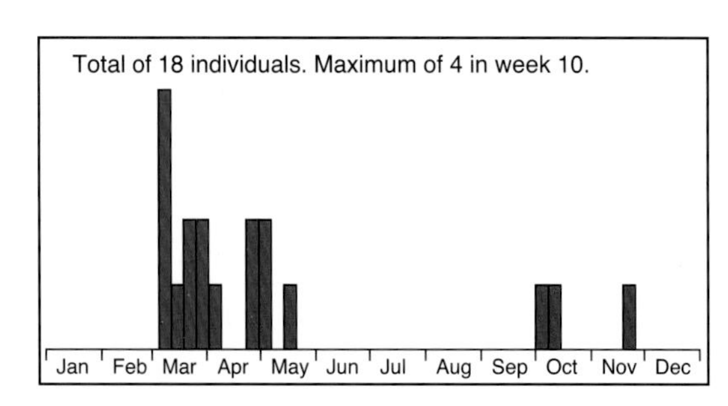

Gibbs (1905) lists the first county record from near Baldock – 4 examples in August and September 1904, all taken by A. H. Foster. Foster (1937) adds another at Hitchin, one on 6th November 1926 as well as others at Champneys, 2nd April 1933 (Frost) and 'Berkhamsted (Hodgson)'. The latter record is elaborated upon by Hodgson (1939) who notes that there were two – one at sugar at Long Green, Berkhamsted on 29th September 934 and one at light at Ashridge on 8th April 1937. J. Bell notes the species at Northchurch in 1938 (Foster, 1942). Recent records are widely scattered and are mostly from older woodlands, though not exclusively so. The moth is occasional in my Bishops Stortford garden which is bounded by a much degraded old field hedge, enclosed by the housing estate and cut off from the surrounding arable landscape in the 1930s. The hedge contained a dead elm tree with several hollows (regrettably brought down by the gales of February 2007) and a lot of very old ivy; since there is no ash tree anywhere near, it is assumed that the hedge is merely a suitable hibernation site.

2236 *Lithophane hepatica* (Cl.) Pale Pinion

Recorded:	1987 – 2006
Distribution / Status:	Local / Uncommon resident
Conservation status:	Herts Stable
Caterpillar food plants:	Not recorded. Elsewhere, on trees, including sallow
Flight period:	September onwards, hibernating then again from March to May
Records in database:	57

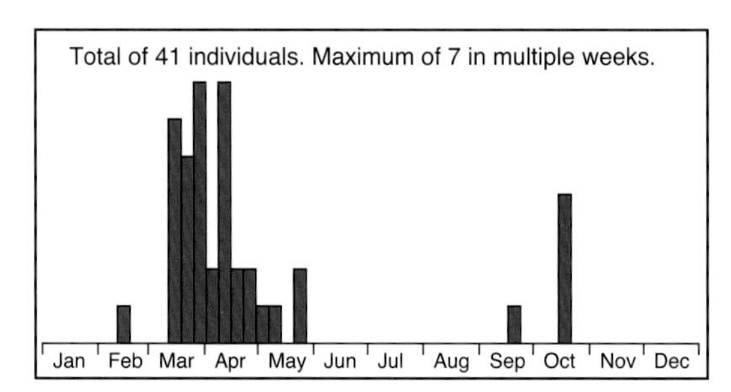

That there are more records of Pale Pinion than there are of 2235: Tawny Pinion is surprising given that there are no records for Hertfordshire prior to 1987, when our first was taken in Rickmansworth by Ric Sandifer. It appears that the

Pale Pinion has colonised us since that year. There are no records for southern Hertfordshire listed in Plant (1993), at which date I was unaware of the Rickmansworth record. Our next record was in the Rothamsted trap at Harpenden in 1989 (Adrian Riley) where he made the third county record in 2000. During 2001, Malcolm Newland caught one in Hemel Hempstead, Paul Clack caught another at Rickmansworth and, lest we began to suspect an invasion from the south-west, Tim Wilson caught one in the extreme north-east at Royston. The following year, records were made across the county and this continues to be the case in 2006; the moth is clearly resident with us now. For Essex, to our east, Goodey (2004) lists it as a rare vagrant, though Brian Goodey informs me (March 2007) that his comments are now out of date as there have been a number of records, starting in 2004 and continuing in 2005 & 2006. There appears to be north-western bias to these Essex records; perhaps it has spread from Hertfordshire? For Bedfordshire to our north Arnold et al (1997) show no confirmed record. Like the Tawny Pinion, Pale Pinions seem to fly very late at night and so under-recording is possible in places where traps are not left to operate until dawn.

2237 *Lithophane ornitopus* (Hufn.) Grey Shoulder-knot

Recorded:	1828 – 2006
Distribution / Status:	Widespread / Uncommon resident
Conservation status:	Herts Stable
Caterpillar food plants:	Not recorded. Elsewhere, on oak
Flight period:	Late September to November then after hibernation until the end of April.
Records in database:	205

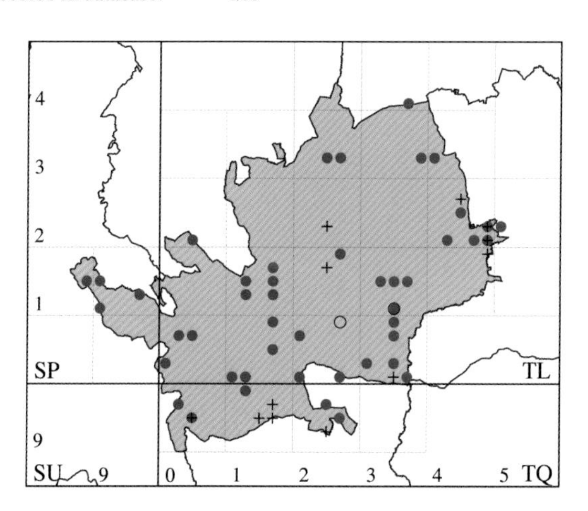

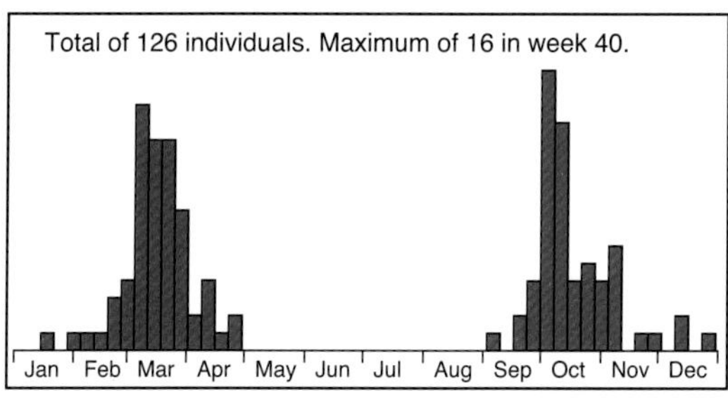

The supposed British subspecies *lactipennis* Dadd has recently been shown to be a synonym of the mainland European subspecies *ornitopus* Hufnagel (Ronkay et al, 2001). Unlike Blair's Shoulder-knot, this species hibernates in the adult stage and so there are two peaks of flight, though only a single generation. It is a widespread though somewhat local species and can be expected in places where oaks grow and where there are also suitable places to hibernate, such as tree hollows, a loose bark and synanthropic habitat, such as garden sheds. Records suggest, however, that it has been less frequently encountered in the past. Barry Goater found one at rest on an commented that it was the first he had ever seen in Hertfordshire. At Totteridge, Ian Lorimer failed to record it in his garden trap between 1954 and 1980.

2240 *Lithophane leautieri* (Boisd.) ssp. *hesperica* Boursin Blair's Shoulder-knot

Recorded:	1972 – 2006
Distribution / Status:	Widespread and under-recorded / Common resident
Conservation status:	Herts Stable
Caterpillar food plants:	Leyland Cypress; Lawson's Cypress; various unidentified *Cupressus* and *Chamaecyparis* species. Probably also on *Thuja*
Flight period:	Late September to end of November
Records in database:	738

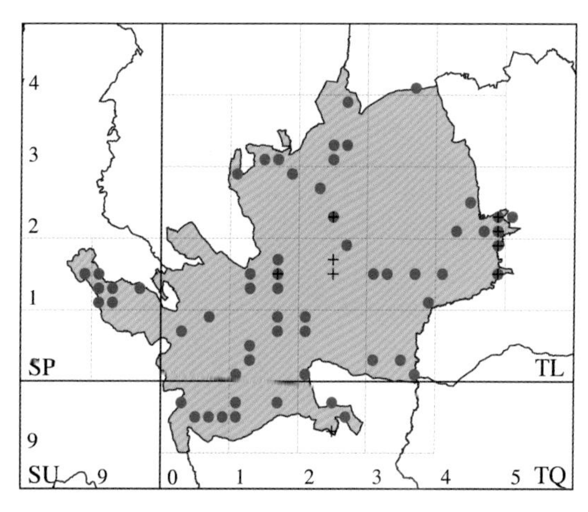

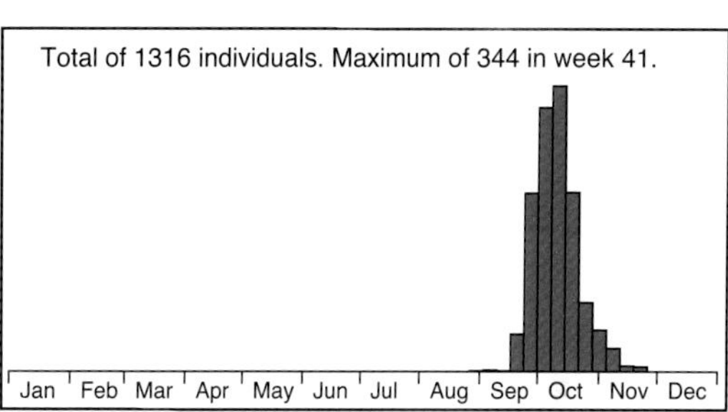

This moth was first recorded in Britain on the Isle of Wight in 1951, under the name of *Lithophane lapidea*. However, in 1957 it was realised that *lapidea* comprised two species and *leautieri* was 'split' from it. The true *lapidea* is found in south-east Europe and the two species are thought to overlap only in the region of the French-Italian border, although they can only be separated in any reliable manner by genitalia examination. The first Hertfordshire record was not until 1972, when it was caught at Totteridge on 11th November (Ian Lorimer). Another was caught there in 1976. There were no more until two in my garden trap at Bishops Stortford on 27th September 1987, but beating the three large Leyland Cypress trees next to the trap produced larvae the next year and the feeling is that the moth was already established here. Certainly by the early 1990s, as moth recording began to 'pick up speed', the moth was widely reported across the county suggesting that it was already established in most of Hertfordshire by that period. Today, it is expected wherever the foodplants grow.

2241 *Xylena vetusta* (Hb.) Red Sword-grass

Recorded:	1893 – 2004
Distribution / Status:	Random / Rare immigrant
Conservation status:	-
Caterpillar food plants:	Not recorded. Elsewhere, on various low plants
Flight period:	British upland populations fly from September to April
Records in database:	8

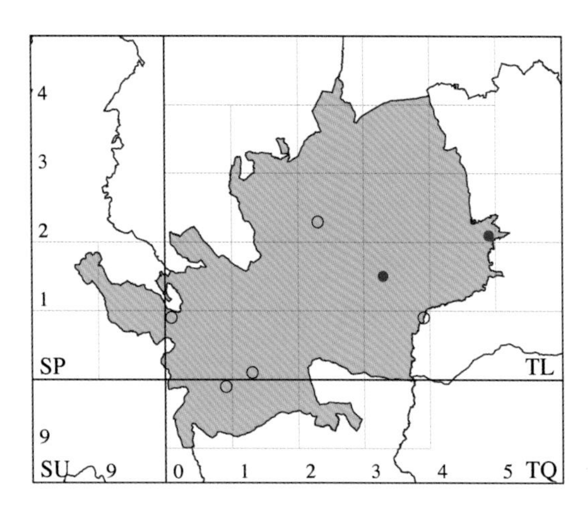

All Hertfordshire records are given: Nascott Wood Road, Watford, 1893 (J. E. K. Cutts, in Gibbs (1896); Bricket Wood, 1898 (Cottam, 1901); St. Albans, 1909 (Dickinson) – this is the same record as that credited to Gibbs by Foster (1937); Berkhamsted (Griffith), Stevenage (Matthews) and Hoddesdon (G. V. Bull) – the last three listed by Foster (1937) without any indication of dates; Bengeo Street, Hertford, 2nd November 2000 (Andrew Wood) and West Road, Bishops Stortford, 19th November 2004 (Colin Plant).

2242 *Xylena exsoleta* (L.) Sword-grass

Recorded: 1890 – 1946
Distribution / Status: Absent / Former resident
Conservation status: UK BAP Priority Species. Herts Extinct
Caterpillar food plants: Hogweed. Elsewhere, on various herbaceous plants
Flight period: Elsewhere, September to April
Records in database: 11

The Sword-grass was formerly resident in the south-east of England, but it has contracted its range drastically and is now confined to northern Britain. It is fairly certain that the Hertfordshire records relate to breeding populations that are now extinct. All Hertfordshire records are given: Larvae on *Heracleum* on the railway bank at St Albans, undated, but the text implies recently (Griffith, 1890); Bricket Wood, one in 1897, (Cottam, 1901); Haileybury (Bowyer, 1888); Cheshunt Marsh (Boyd, 1901); Hitchin (Foster, 1916), Oxhey Woods [probably late 1890s] (Cutts), Hitchin (Gatward), Stevenage (Matthews), Tring (LeQuesne, Elliman) and Chorleywood (T. Walker) are all listed by Foster (1937) without dates. (Riley, 1999) adds one in 1946 on the Rothamsted Estate, Harpenden. Foster (1937) also lists Hadley Woods (Bowden), but this refers to Monken Hadley Common in Middlesex, outside the Hertfordshire border, where the late Sydney Bowden collected in the 1930s.

2243 *Xylocampa areola* (Esp.) Early Grey

Recorded: 1888 – 2006
Distribution / Status: Widespread / Common resident
Conservation status: Herts Stable
Caterpillar food plants: Garden Honeysuckle; Wild Honeysuckle
Flight period: March to May
Records in database: 1,115

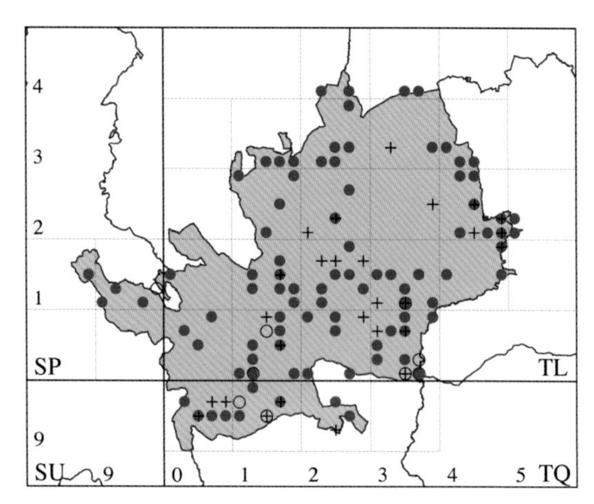

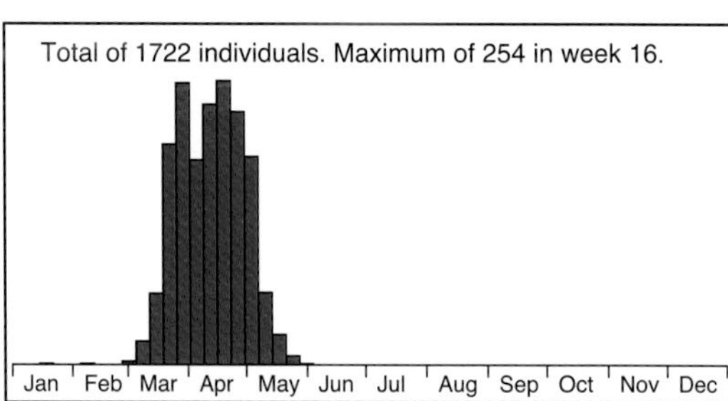

Though one of the commonest of the spring species, the Early Grey is missed by some people as it does not usually fly until after midnight. During March and April it is necessary to set up traps quite early for a relatively poor return and some people prefer not to stay out for that length of time.

2245 *Allophyes oxyacanthae* (L.) Green-brindled Crescent

Recorded: 1884 – 2006
Distribution / Status: Widespread / Common resident
Conservation status: UK BAP Watch List; Herts Stable
Caterpillar food plants: Common Hawthorn. Elsewhere, also on Blackthorn, birch and other trees
Flight period: Mid-September to November
Records in database: 289

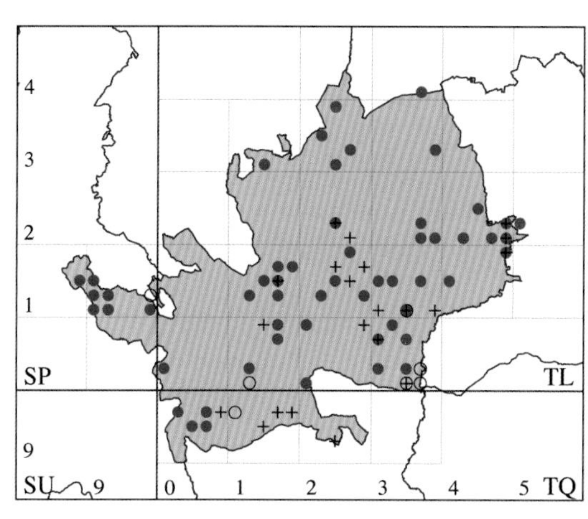

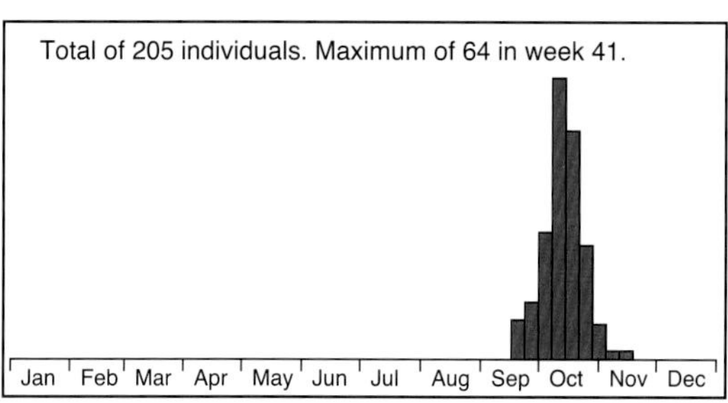

Past records indicate that the Green-brindled Crescent has always been a common moth in Hertfordshire, where it is most frequent in association with structurally well-developed woodland edges and mature, unmanaged hedges. The melanic form, *capucina* Millière, is present but seldom reported though tentative evidence suggests that it represents only about 15 – 20 per cent of the overall population.

[2246 *Valeria oleagina* ([D. & S.]) Green-brindled Dot

Recorded in error. A moth reported from Knebworth in 1875 as *Valeria oleagina* by Benjamin Brown in *Entomologist* **8:** 164) was later corrected to 2155: Dot Moth *Melanchra persicariae* in 1876 (*Entomologist* **9**: 279).]

2247 *Dichonia aprilina* (L.) Merveille du Jour

Recorded: 1828 – 2006
Distribution / Status: Widespread / Common resident
Conservation status: Herts Stable
Caterpillar food plants: Not recorded. Elsewhere, on oak
Flight period: Late September to November
Records in database: 199

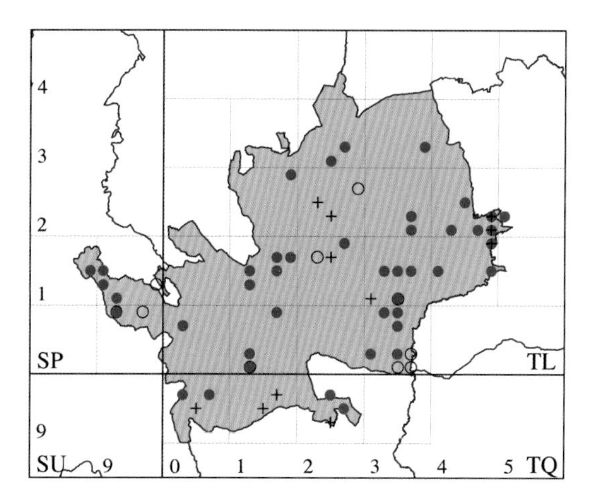

Prior to the advent of light trapping, this was a scarce moth in Hertfordshire, but when the usefulness of light was realised,

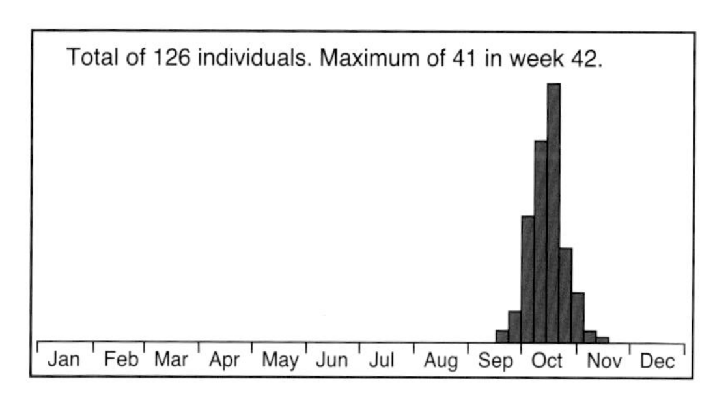

records soon increased. The conclusion must be that the moth has always been moderately common in the county. Isolated oak trees are as capable of supporting larvae as those in a woodland setting and this probably explains the presence of the moth on most garden lists.

2248 *Dryobotodes eremita* (Fabr.) Brindled Green

Recorded: 1828 – 2006
Distribution / Status: Widespread / Common resident
Conservation status: Herts Stable
Caterpillar food plants: Not recorded. Elsewhere, on oak and hawthorn
Flight period: Late August to October
Records in database: 280

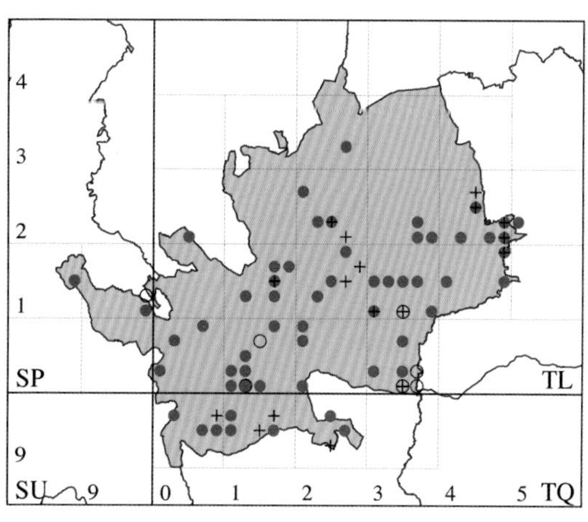

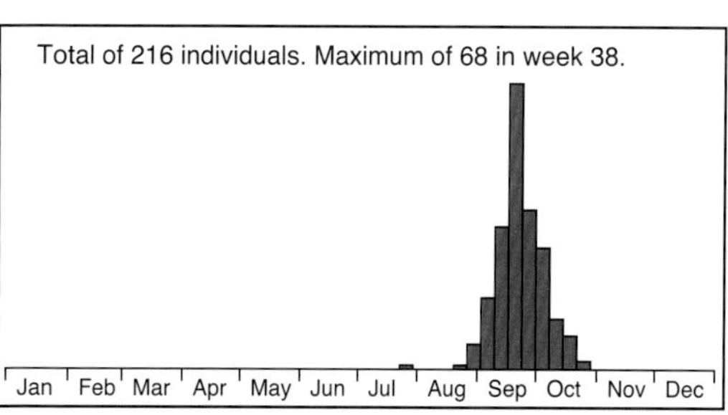

This is another common autumn species across the county and it appears always to have been so. There are no reports of the melanic ab. *nigra* Cockayne and all material that I have seen is of the typical form or close to it.

2250 *Blepharita adusta* (Esp.) Dark Brocade

Recorded: 1884 – 2006
Distribution / Status: Extremely local / Rare resident and rare immigrant
Conservation status: UK BAP Watch List. Herts Vulnerable
Caterpillar food plants: Not recorded. Elsewhere, on grasses and low plants
Flight period: June/July
Records in database: 23

The Dark Brocade is something of a mystery moth. It can be abundant where it is found, but places where it does exist are few and far between. Ian Lorimer recorded only two males at

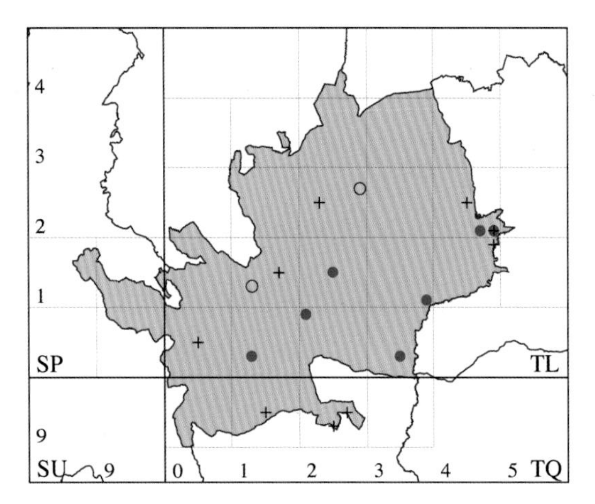

Totteridge between 1954 and 1980 (on 7th June 1965 and 7th June 1970) but 'a large number' was attracted to the Walkern Search-light during an air raid in 1940 (J. Birdsall). It also seems to fluctuate with time: there was a batch of records during the late 1960s and early 1970s, then a gap, then more records in the 1980s and early 1990s when it was occasional, for example in my garden, then another gap with no reports and finally moths appearing in 2005 and 2006. Goodey (2004) regards it as a vagrant in Essex, last seen in 1992 but he may have overlooked the large numbers taken by me in Eastend Wood at Stansted Airport during 1989 in conditions strongly suggesting residency. It does not feature on the Bedfordshire list at all (Arnold et al, 1998). It is possible that 2005 and 2006 records relate to vagrants or immigrants, in which case there is grave concern for the resident population. Nationally, it is now regarded as belonging to the 'Vulnerable' category of the IUCN Red List and this seems likely to be entirely justifiable.

2252 *Polymixis flavicincta* ([D.& S.]) Large Ranunculus

Recorded:	1828 – 2006
Distribution / Status:	Widespread / Common resident
Conservation status:	Herts Stable
Caterpillar food plants:	Garden Mint. Elsewhere, on various herbaceous plants
Flight period:	September/October
Records in database:	491

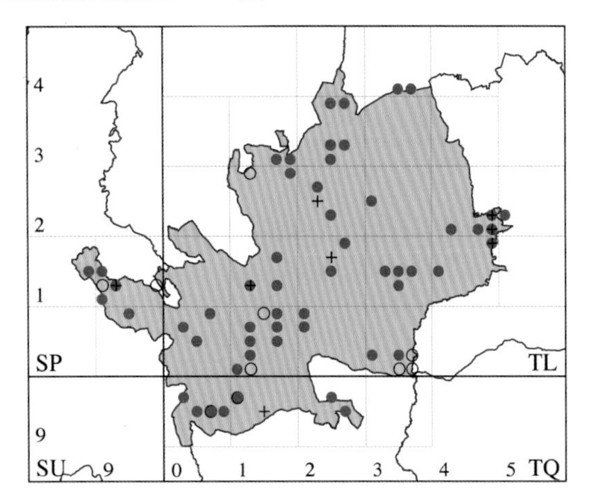

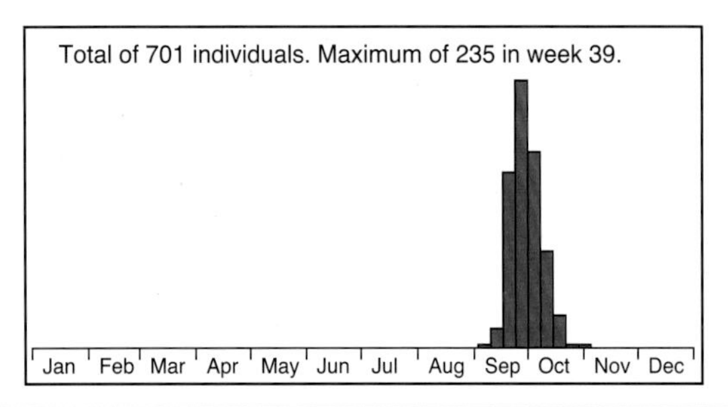

Although fairly widespread across the county, there is a definite preference on the part of this moth for gardens. This might imply a larval food plant link, microclimate variation or other factors, but whatever the reason it is entirely possible to spend a night out in the woods and catch no Large Ranunculus then return home to a garden trap not all that far away brimming with them. However, this appears to have not always been the case. Plant (1993) shows a distribution map for the London Area which includes in its northern part the entire southern third of Hertfordshire. Records of Large Ranunculus in this map for the period 1980 to 1991 are exclusively south of the River Thames (apart from a singleton in Essex) and the moth was then absent from north London and southern Hertfordshire. In 2006, both southern Hertfordshire and North London can boast this species and so there has evidently been an expansion of the species' range – either southwards from northern Hertfordshire or northwards from Surrey and Kent. Comparison with Essex, to our east, is interesting. Emmet & Pyman (1985) regard the species as resident and local, but show only pre-1960 records in the south-west and west of that county. Later, Goodey (2004) calls the same species 'resident, frequent' and maps a number of post-1990 records of adults. This suggests that south-west Essex has been recolonised at the same time as north London and Hertfordshire.

2254 *Antitype chi* (L.) Grey Chi

Recorded:	1902 – 1911
Distribution / Status:	Absent / Former vagrant/immigrant
Conservation status:	-
Caterpillar food plants:	Monkshood. Elsewhere, on herbaceous plants
Flight period:	Elsewhere, mid-August to late September
Records in database:	3

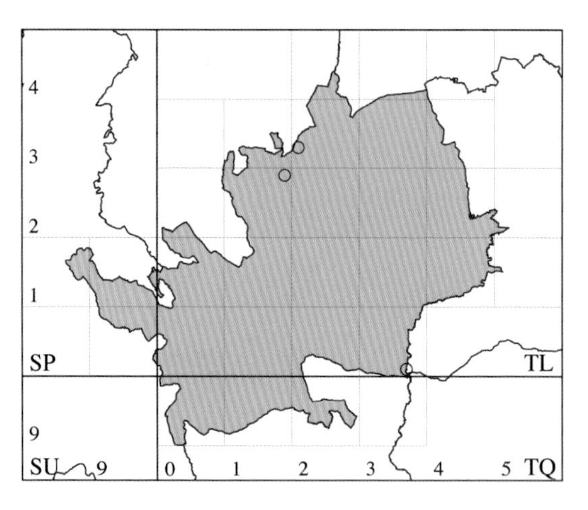

An adult was bred in 1902 from a larva found on 'Monkshood' (*Aconitum nepellum*) at Hitchin by A. H. Foster. The moth was shown to A. E. Gibbs who commented (Gibbs, 1904a) that it was 'a remarkably light-coloured variety'. Gibbs continued by stating that he had been told by C. G. Barrett that this 'northern insect has been working south recently'. Foster (1914) repeats this record and adds 'Since this record Wightman of Letchworth has taken at least a dozen specimens in 1910 and following years on a wall in a village near Hitchin'. Foster (1937) repeats his own record and adds Waltham Cross, one specimen on a wall, undated (H. M. Edelsten). Gibbs, Foster and Edelsten were all entirely competent lepidopterists and it seem unlikely that all three would misidentify this species, which is rarely seen south-east of a line between the Severn Estuary and The Wash. Presumably, these represent vagrancy or immigration, including a gravid female that laid fertile eggs; there is no evidence to suggest that the moth was in any way a temporary resident.

2255 *Polymixis lichenea* (Hb.) Feathered Ranunculus

Recorded:	1973 – 2006
Distribution / Status:	Random / Rare immigrant
Conservation status:	-
Caterpillar food plants:	Not recorded. Elsewhere, herbaceous plants
Flight period:	September/October
Records in database:	5

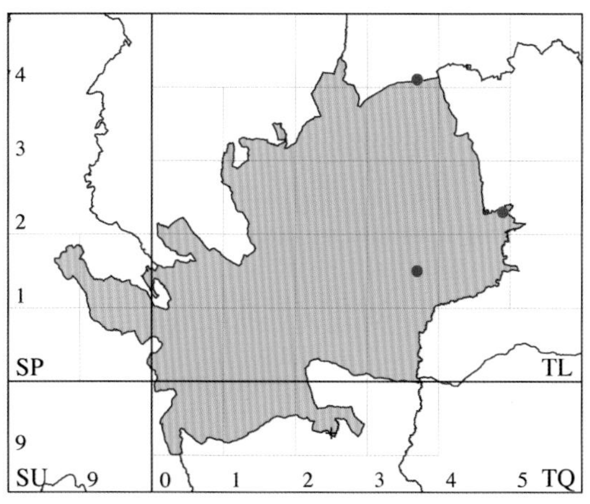

The Feathered Ranunculus is entirely an immigrant in Hertfordshire. All records are given: Totteridge, a male on 8th October 1973 (Ian Lorimer); Bishops Stortford, one in 1999, (James Fish & Julian Reeves); Royston, one on 23rd September 2000 (John Chainey & Jenny Spence); Ware, a male on 10th October 2002 (Elizabeth Goodyear) and Bishops Stortford, one on 24th September 2006 (James Fish & Julian Reeves).

ACRONICTINAE

2256 *Eupsilia transversa* (Hufn.) Satellite

Recorded:	1888 – 2006
Distribution / Status:	Ubiquitous / Common resident
Conservation status:	Herts Stable
Caterpillar food plants:	Wych Elm. Elsewhere, also on other trees
Flight period:	September to November, then after hibernation until end April
Records in database:	406

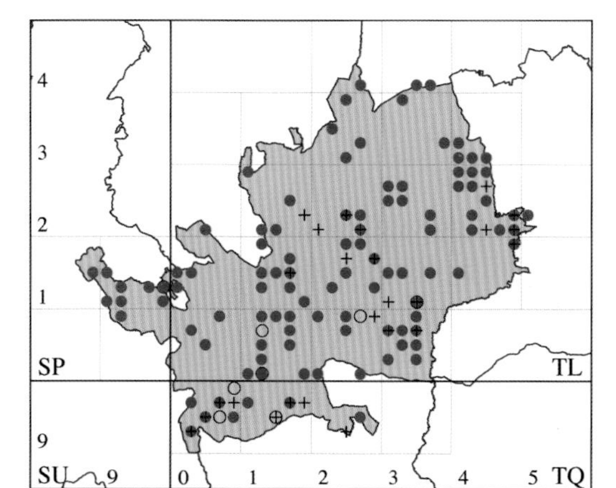

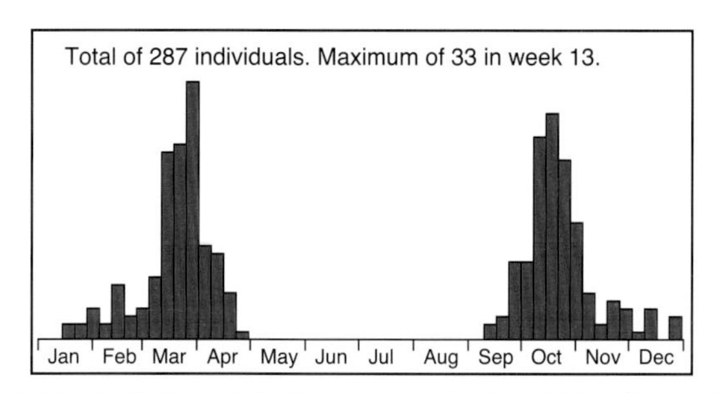

The Satellite takes its name from the two small 'satellites' in orbit around the reniform stigma of the forewing and this latter marking may be either pure white or various shades of yellow. The relative frequency of the two forms does not appear to have been recorded in Hertfordshire, but it can be said with certainty that the notion of a colour change taking place during hibernation is a myth without foundation.

2257 *Jodia croceago* ([D.& S.]) Orange Upperwing

Recorded:	1828 only
Distribution / Status:	Absent / Extinct
Conservation status:	UK BAP Priority Species. Herts Extinct
Caterpillar food plants:	Not recorded. Elsewhere, on oak
Flight period:	Elsewhere, during April
Records in database:	1

It is tempting to think that this moth's scarcity might be due in part to a lack of late-night moth trapping in oak woods during April, but our only record is that supported by the 'Hertford' specimen illustrated by J. F. Stephens (1829) in *Illustrations of British Entomology* **3**: 68. The species is Endangered at the National level.

2258 *Conistra vaccinii* (L.) Chestnut

Recorded:	1828 – 2006
Distribution / Status:	Widespread / Common resident
Conservation status:	Herts Stable
Caterpillar food plants:	Not recorded. Elsewhere, on various trees
Flight period:	September to early May, hibernating in cold weather
Records in database:	698

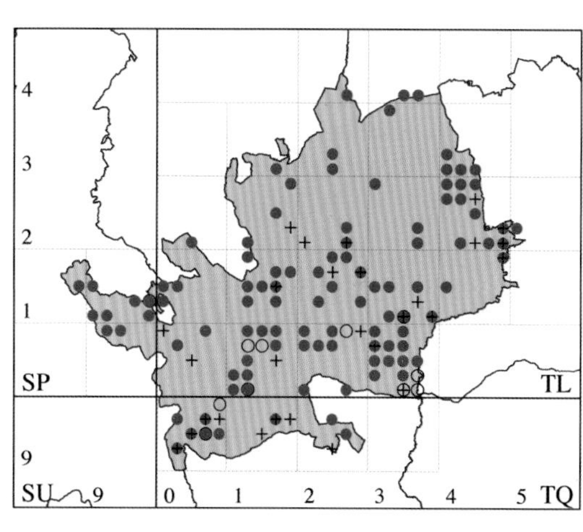

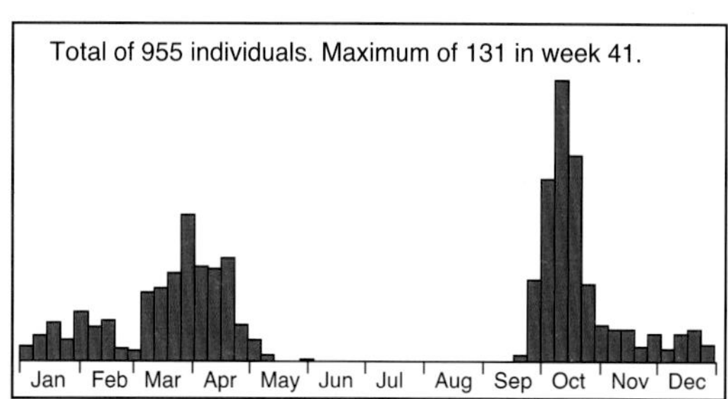

The Chestnut is often the first moth seen in any given year, since it is prone to activity during mild spells throughout its winter hibernation period. However, rarely more than one or two appear in winter catches, whilst in the spring moth traps may catch double figures; this perhaps suggests that the adults hibernate singly and away from their fellows. Confusion of worn moths in the spring is possible with 2259: Dark Chestnut; whilst the latter is always 'dark', some Chestnuts may be similarly coloured and the shape of the wing is the only reliable diagnostic character in the field.

2259 *Conistra ligula* (Esp.) Dark Chestnut

Recorded:	1884 – 2006
Distribution / Status:	Widespread / Common resident
Conservation status:	Herts Stable
Caterpillar food plants:	Blackthorn. Elsewhere, on deciduous trees then later on herbaceous plants
Flight period:	September to March, hibernating as an adult
Records in database:	157

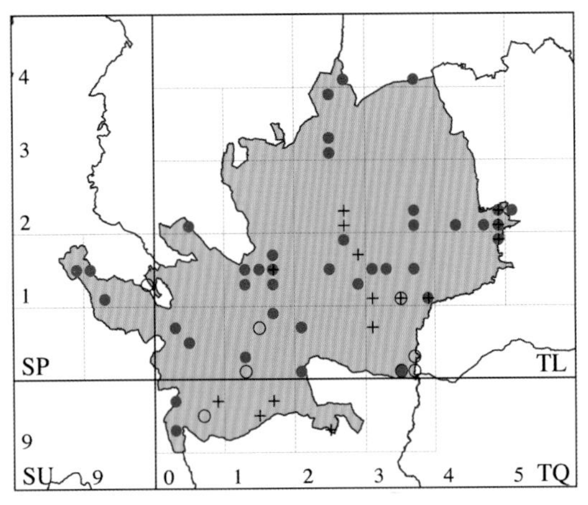

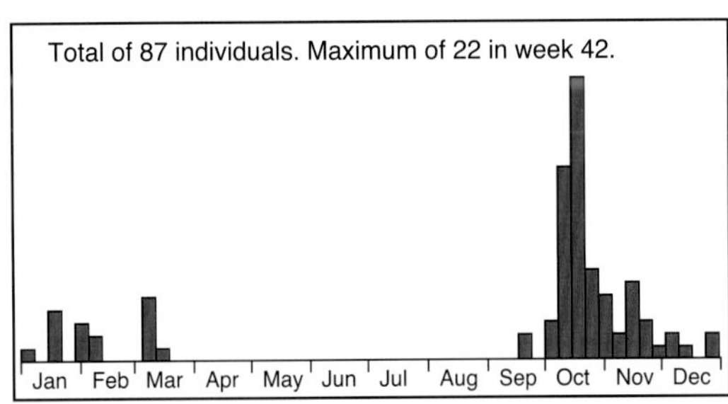

The suggestion that Dark Chestnuts are not represented in post-hibernation samples is incorrect, as the flight chart clearly shows, although it is equally clear that numbers are reduced. Some dark examples of 2258: Chestnut may be misidentified as this species, especially if the wing-tips have become worn during hibernation, though nine out of ten can probably still be named on sight by an experienced lepidopterist; the remainder may need dissection for confirmation. Only reliable records are included in the map and the flight chart.

2260 *Conistra rubiginea* ([D.& S.]) Dotted Chestnut

Recorded:	1998 – 2006
Distribution / Status:	Extremely local / Uncommon resident
Conservation status:	Increasing
Caterpillar food plants:	Not recorded. Elsewhere, on deciduous trees
Flight period:	October, then after hibernation in March/April
Records in database:	9

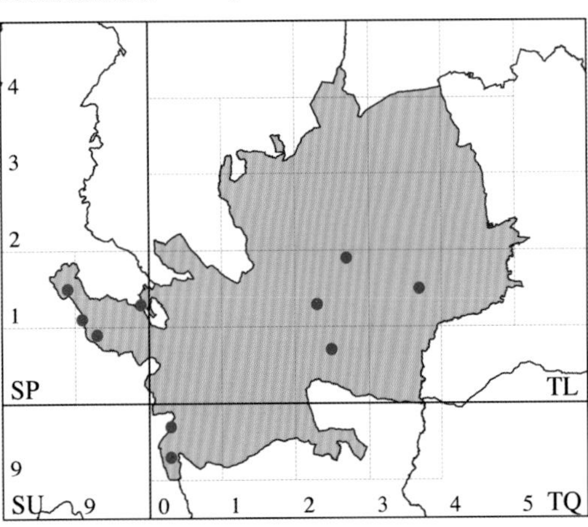

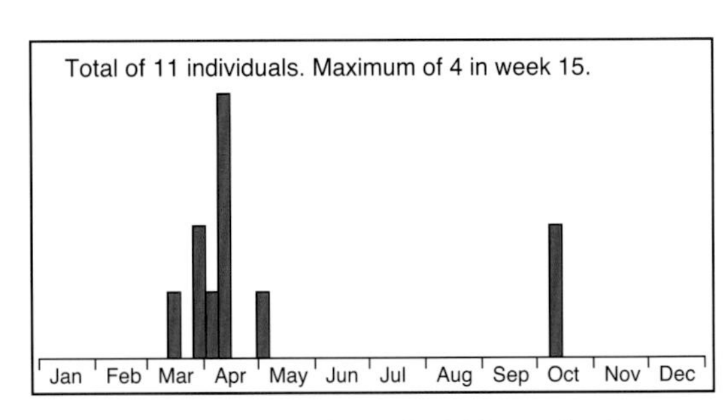

This is a recent colonist of Hertfordshire and other parts of south-east England (see Plant, 2002 for a summary of records to that date). All county records are given: Station Road, Long Marston, 28th March 1998 (Alan Bernard); Lemsford Springs, 3rd April 2002 (Colin Plant); Keley Lane, Tring, 12th April 2003 (Ian Burrus); Hares Garden Wood, 17th March 2004 (Colin Plant); Raffin Park, Datchworth, 10th April 2004 (Steve Palmer); Thunderdell Wood, Ashridge, 12th April 2006 Colin Plant); Coombe Wood, Hatfield Estate, 13th April 2006 (Colin Plant); Bottom Wood, Maple Cross, 3rd May 2006 (Ched George); Chestnut Avenue, Ware, 8th October 2006 (Elizabeth Goodyear).

2261 *Conistra erythrocephala* ([D.& S.]) Red-headed Chestnut

Recorded:	1865 – 1865
Distribution / Status:	Absent / Former immigrant
Conservation status:	-
Caterpillar food plants:	Not recorded in the wild
Flight period:	September/October
Records in database:	1

Knaggs (1866) notes that this species '... has been taken for the second time near St Albans'. This second record relates to 1865, but the source of the first record is obscure. The moth was first recorded in Britain in 1847 and was resident from that year to about 1874 in East Sussex, so it is unlikely that Knaggs intended a second *British* record – he must have meant that there was a previous Hertfordshire report? Barrett (1893 – 1907) mentions it in volume 6 as recorded at St Albans, but it is not clear if this relates to the first, second or both records.

2262 *Agrochola circellaris* (Hufn.) Brick

Recorded:	1884 – 2006
Distribution / Status:	Widespread / Common resident
Conservation status:	Herts Stable
Caterpillar food plants:	Wych Elm
Flight period:	September to November
Records in database:	296

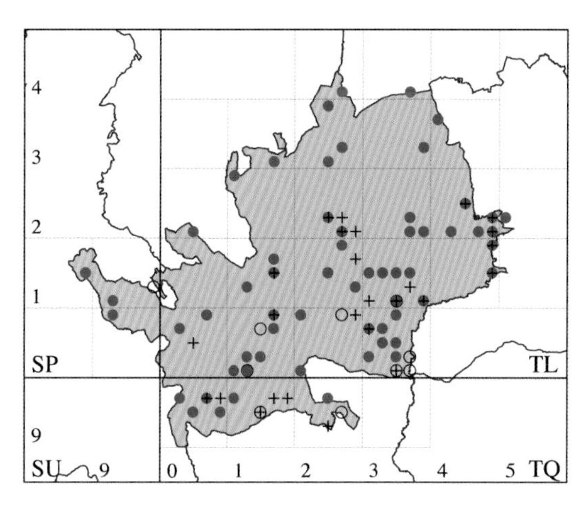

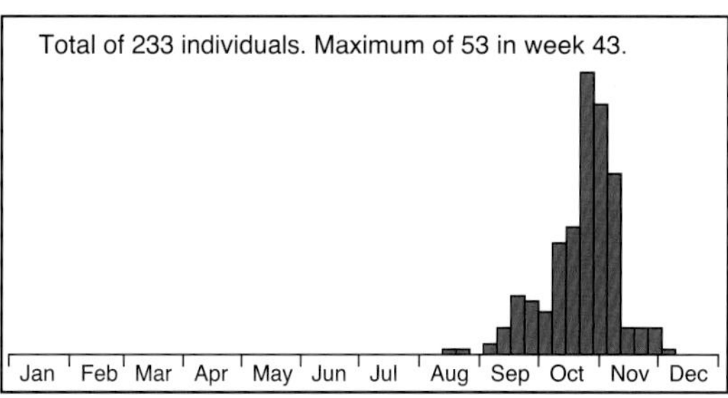

Although supposedly also recorded outside Hertfordshire on Ash and poplar, the larvae of the Brick appear likely to be restricted to Wych Elm within the county. Happily, this tree survived the ravages of Dutch Elm disease in the 1970s and the moth remains widespread and common here.

2263 *Agrochola lota* (Cl.) Red-line Quaker

Recorded: 1828 – 2006
Distribution / Status: Widespread / Common resident
Conservation status: Herts Stable
Caterpillar food plants: Not recorded. Elsewhere, sallows and willows
Flight period: Late September to November
Records in database: 318

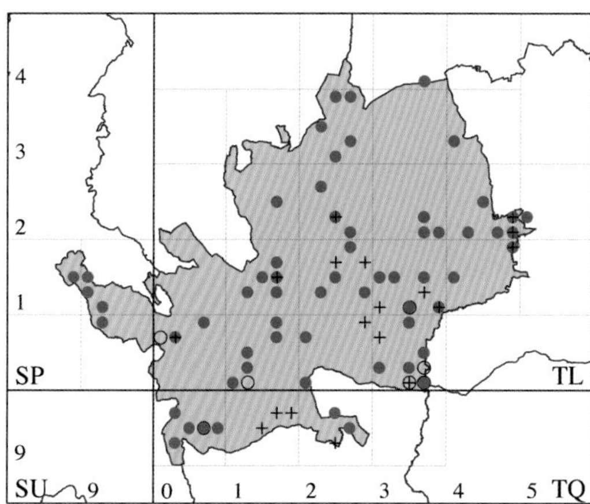

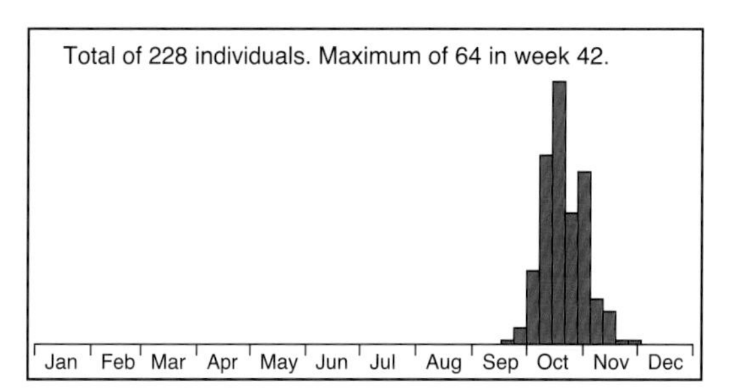

The Red-line Quaker is represented in almost all trap samples from October and is to be expected, more or less everywhere in the county where sallows and willows grow. However, this foodplant requirement means that it is absent from large tracts of arable north-east Hertfordshire.

2264 *Agrochola macilenta* (Hb.) Yellow-line Quaker

Recorded: 1828 – 2006
Distribution / Status: Widespread / Common resident
Conservation status: Herts Stable
Caterpillar food plants: Not recorded. Elsewhere, Beech, poplar catkins, hawthorn and oak
Flight period: Late September to the end of November
Records in database: 374

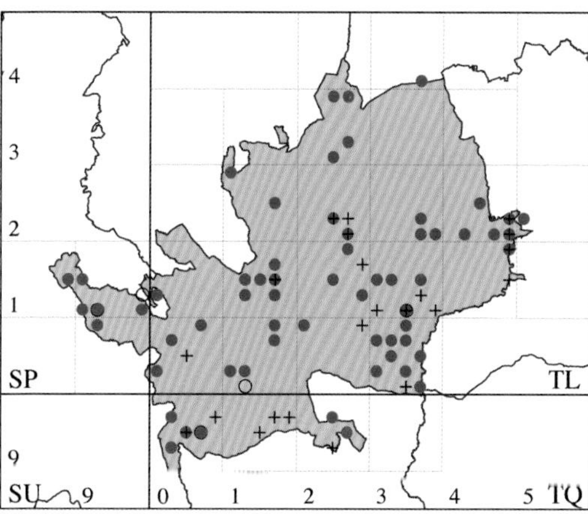

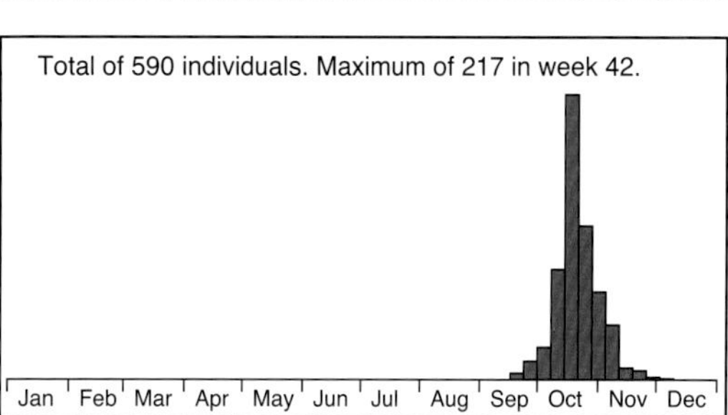

The larval foodplants of this species are rather diverse; northern British populations apparently feed on heathers whilst in the south the leaves of deciduous trees are preferred. In Hertfordshire, the moth is as widespread and frequent as 2263: Red-line Quaker, which has an identical flight period. The two are frequently caught together.

2265 *Agrochola helvola* (L.) Flounced Chestnut

Recorded: 1828 – 2006
Distribution / Status: Extremely local / Uncommon resident
Conservation status: UK BAP Watch List. Herts Endangered
Caterpillar food plants: Not recorded. Elsewhere on deciduous trees
Flight period: Late September to mid-October
Records in database: 48

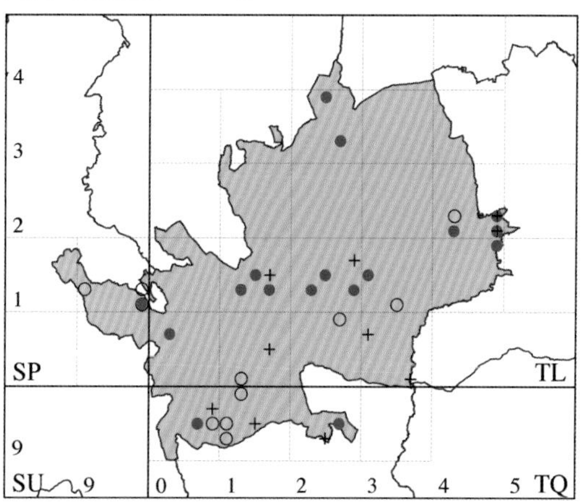

A glance at the map shows that this moth is absent from a large part of the county and that of the 34 recorded sites it has only been found at 17 since 1995; this suggests a decline of 50 per cent in occupied sites and compares with a decline of 77 per cent since 1980 in numbers attending Rothamsted light traps. Available records suggest that it was a fairly widespread species from the late nineteenth to early twentieth century in the south of the county (all such records are mapped as open circles), though we have no data on abundance. From 1937 to the 1990s records are very few, and the only area of the county that has been continuously recorded through that period (other than at the Rothamsted Estate in Harpenden) is Bishops Stortford. Nearly sixty years ago, P. B. M. Allen produced a seminal work on the moths of the Bishops Stortford District (Allen, 1950). In this, he reports 'two specimens taken in the town in October 1934' by Clifford Craufurd and 'common at sugar at Little Hadham in 1938' by S. F. Perkins. Allen continues that it has not been taken by Colman and Mellows (two of his main contributors), nor by himself and that it was 'apparently absent from the N.W., N. and N.E. area'. The 1985 update of the Bishops Stortford list (Fielding et al, 1985) is less than comprehensive; nevertheless that work adds just one record since 1950 – one in Wall Wood [Essex] on 27th October 1980. I moved to Bishops Stortford in October 1986 and in spite of trapping near nightly from 1987 to 2006 I have caught just one moth, in 2000. However, a couple of kilometres away, the adjoining gardens of James Fish and Julian Reeves, trapped from 1993 to 2006, produced the moth in 1993, 1995, 1997, 1998, 1999 and 2002. Half a mile in the opposite direction from me, Charles Watson caught only two examples, in 1999 and 2000 in spite of infrequent trapping since about 1980. Finally, in the east of the town, half a mile in a different direction again, Tony King had just one, in 1994. Little conclusion can be drawn from this other than that the Flounced Chestnut appears to have been rather rare in this well-recorded eastern district of Hertfordshire since at least the 1930s. For the wider county, there are only fifteen records from thirteen sites since the end of 1999. These divide up as follows: six sites in 2000 (East Barnet, Lemsford Springs, two locations in Bishops Stortford, Waterford Heath and Wheathampstead), two in 2001 (East Barnet and Rickmansworth), three in 2002 (Baldock, Bishops Stortford, Frithsden Beeches), one in 2003 (Hemel Hempstead), none in 2004, two in 2005 (Leasey Bridge and Ashwell) and one in 2006 (Ashwell).

2266 *Agrochola litura* (L.) Brown-spot Pinion

Recorded: 1828 – 2006
Distribution / Status: Local / Common resident
Conservation status: UK BAP Watch List. Herts Threatened
Caterpillar food plants: Not recorded. Elsewhere, widely polyphagous
Flight period: Mid-September/October
Records in database: 167

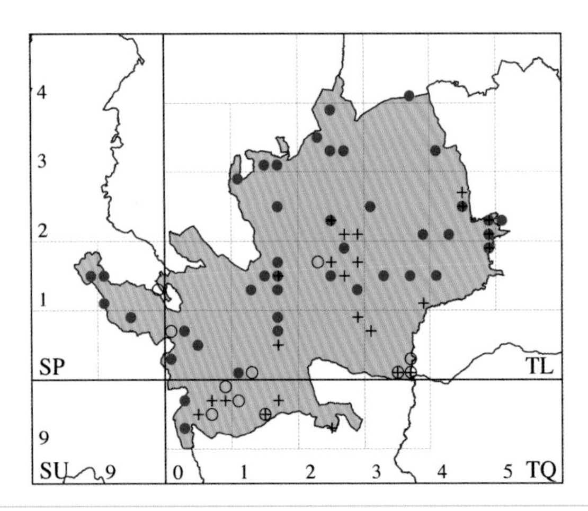

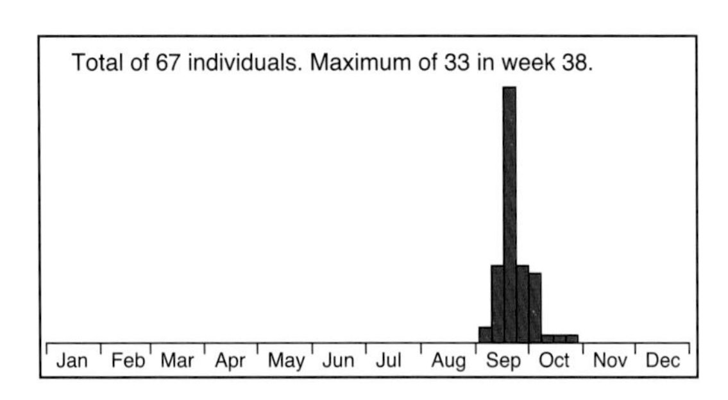

Curiously, the Brown-spot Pinion seems to have vanished from a broad band across the south-east of the county where all of the records on the map pre-date 1995. This is in sharp contrast to the rest of the county where it appears to be widespread, albeit somewhat local. This may, perhaps, represent the first stage of a north-westwards range contraction, perhaps driven by climatic changes or other factors. It is of note that the numbers recorded in Rothamsted light traps across the whole of Britain have declined by 76 per cent since 1970. Although the moth appears to be widespread in Bedfordshire, our north-western neighbour (Arnold et al, 1998), Les Hill informed me at January 2006 that modern records from that county appear to be arranged in two south-west to north-east bands – one on the chalk and one further north along the Greensand ridge. This physical alignment corresponds to that observed in Hertfordshire, but here it is difficult to relate it to any particular geological feature.

2267 *Agrochola lychnidis* ([D.& S.]) Beaded Chestnut

Recorded: 1888 – 2006
Distribution / Status: Local / Common resident
Conservation status: UK BAP Watch List. Herts Stable
Caterpillar food plants: Not recorded. Elsewhere, on grasses and other low plants
Flight period: Mid-September/October
Records in database: 296

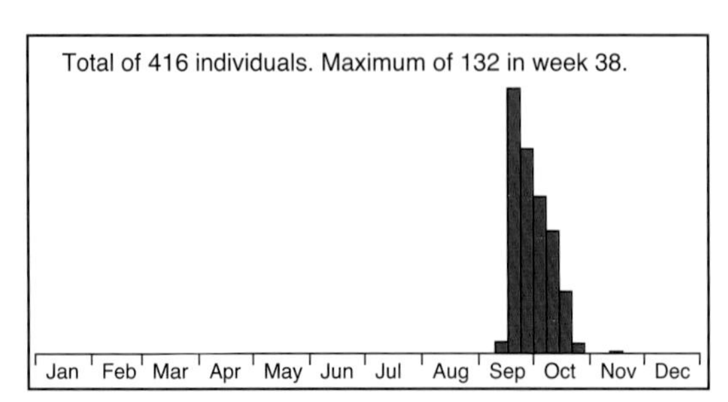

The Beaded Chestnut appears to have been a widespread species prior to at least the time of Foster's review in 1937. It has remained a common species until 2001 when, without warning, fears of a possible decline were aroused when hardly any were reported in any of the regular garden light traps. This sparked a closer examination of the available records, but unfortunately we do not have a large enough data set to determine trends with any accuracy. Other than the 'crash' of 2001, no significant change in numbers is discernible in my own garden at Bishops Stortford. However, at Digswell, Tom Gladwin reports that 'we have run the trap on 191 occasions during September and October in 27 of the 32 years from 1970 to 2001. From 1970 to 1997 there is no detectable trend in the numbers caught with the maximum ranging from 77 to 136. The maxima since then were 44 on 25th September 1998; 49 on 26th September, 1999; 5 on 22nd September, 2000; and 16 on 29th September, 2001. The trap was operated weekly on suitable nights throughout September and October 1998, 1999, and 2000; but only once, on the 18th, in October 2002, when 2 were trapped. There does seem to be a downward trend over a relatively short term'. It seems that in Hertfordshire, the sudden population decline in 2001 was a temporary affair and numbers returned to normal by 2005. The recorded national population decline of 90 per cent since 1970 does not yet appear to be mirrored by any loss of sites in Hertfordshire, but there is clearly no place for complacency.

2268 *Parastichtis suspecta* (Hb.) Suspected

Now positioned in the Amphipyrinae, after species 2313.

2269 *Atethmia centrago* (Haw.) Centre-barred Sallow

Recorded: 1884 – 2006
Distribution / Status: Widespread / Common resident
Conservation status: UK BAP Watch List
Herts Stable
Caterpillar food plants: Ash
Flight period: Mid-August/September
Records in database: 378

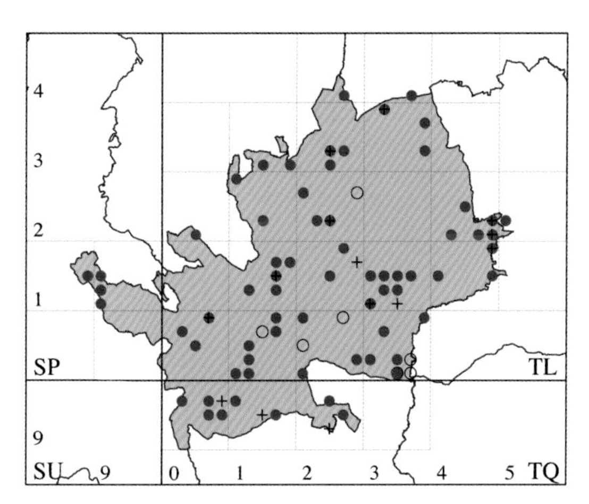

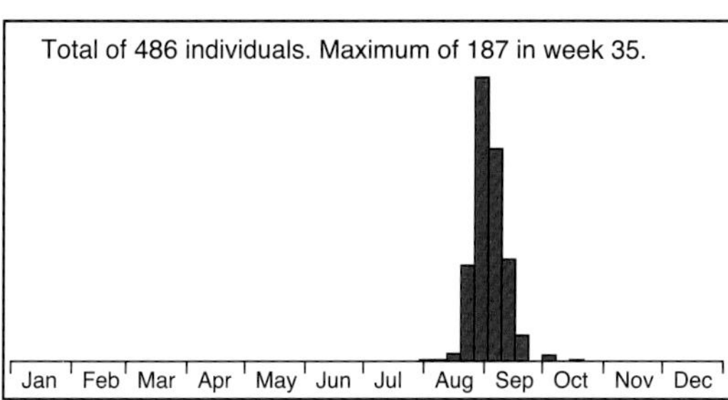

The Centre-barred Sallow is likely to be found wherever there is an Ash tree growing. Indeed, catching this species is almost guaranteed during September if a light trap is placed near or beneath a mature Ash tree – even if it is the only such tree for miles around. The gap in records in the arable north-east may be genuine, as the host tree is scarce in that area. The apparent national population decline at Rothamsted light traps of 74 per cent since 1970 is not supported by Hertfordshire data gleaned from other recording methods.

2270 *Omphaloscelis lunosa* (Haw.) Lunar Underwing

Recorded: 1828 – 2006
Distribution / Status: Widespread / Common resident
Conservation status: Herts Stable
Caterpillar food plants: Not recorded. Elsewhere, on grasses
Flight period: September/October
Records in database: 932

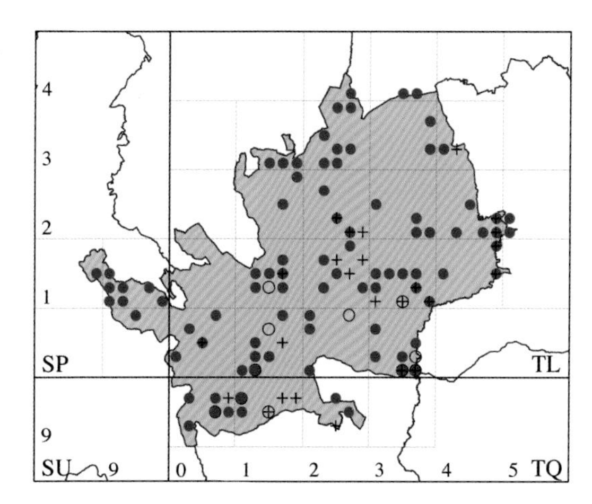

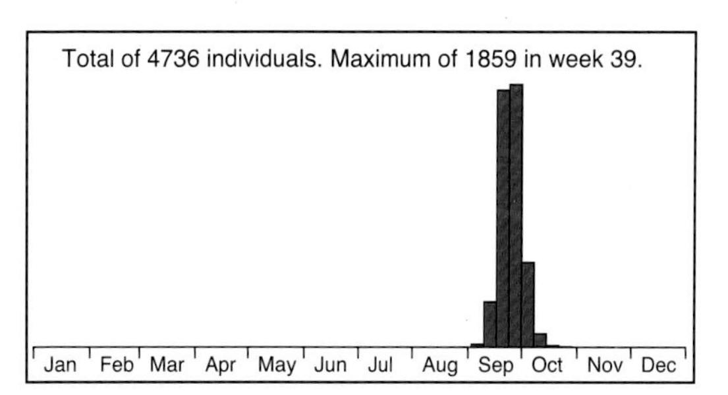

Lunar Underwing is one of the most numerous moths of the autumn and catches per trap can number in excess of 50 per night on favourable dates. The adult occurs in a range of colour forms though these tend to fall into just three categories – pale fawn, mid-brown and dark blackish brown. Pale fawn and dark brown varieties occur in more or less equal numbers, but the mid-brown types, in which the longitudinal veins are often the same colour as the rest of the wing, seems to be far less common.

2271 *Xanthia citrago* (L.) Orange Sallow

Recorded: 1888 – 2006
Distribution / Status: Very local / Rare resident
Conservation status: Herts Scarce
Caterpillar food plants: Lime
Flight period: August to October
Records in database: 100

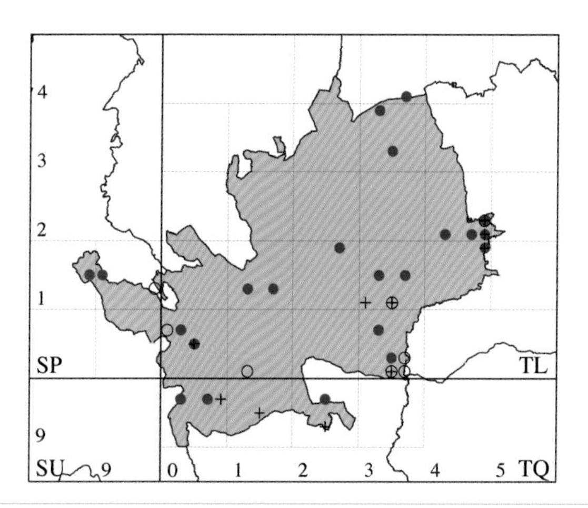

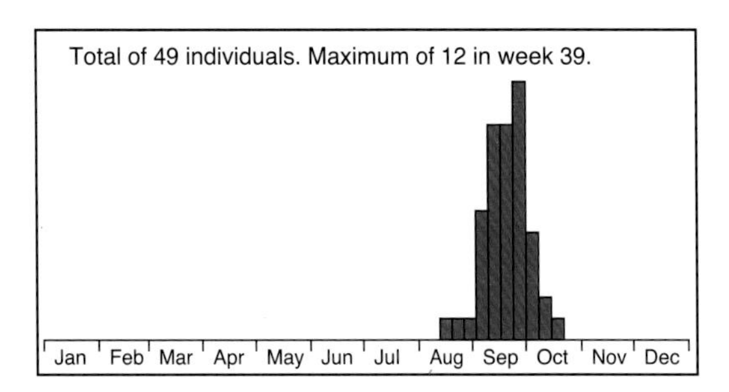

The map shows that the moth is present in scattered localities across much of the county, but the emphasis must be on the word 'scattered'. Larvae have been found on 'street' Lime in Bishops Stortford (Charles Watson) showing that there is no requirement for the native species. However, although larvae were abundant on one tree in front of Charles' house the adults very rarely attended the light trap to the rear. There are, therefore, likely to be sites in the county where the moth is present, but not recorded because light-trapping is the only recording method used. Sweeping lime foliage with a long-handled net during late April and May is likely to produce caterpillars if they are present.

2272 *Xanthia aurago* ([D.& S.]) Barred Sallow

Recorded:	1892 – 2006
Distribution / Status:	Widespread / Common resident
Conservation status:	Stable
Caterpillar food plants:	Not recorded. Elsewhere, on Field Maple and Beech
Flight period:	September to early November
Records in database:	385

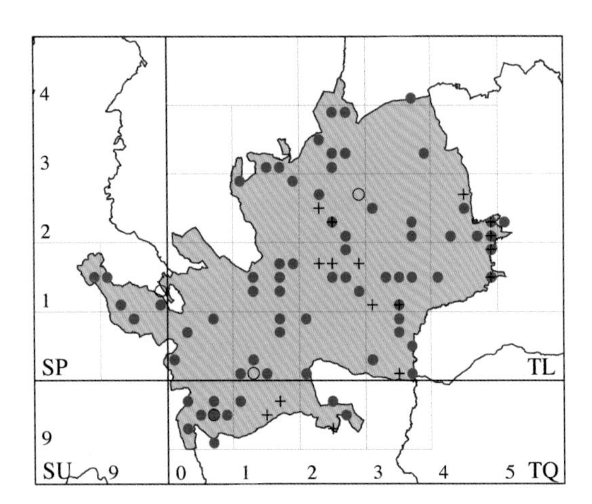

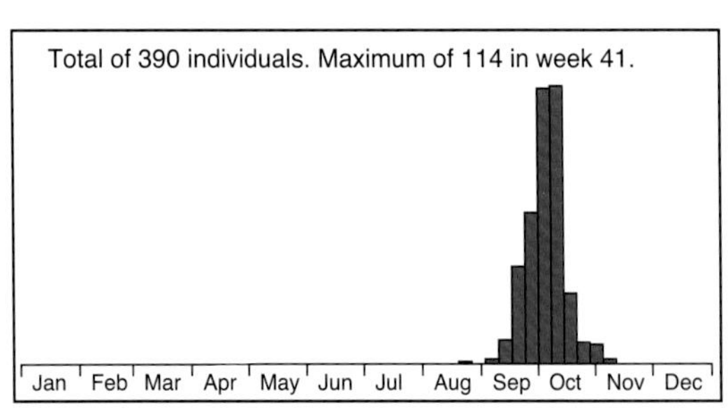

This common moth can be encountered more or less anywhere in Hertfordshire and does not appear to be restricted by any factor other than foodplant availability. Maple, in particular, is frequent across the county. However, the moth does appear with frequency in some sites where the foodplants apparently do not grow nearby – notably in my garden. In such a situation odd examples may be expected to wander through and be caught, but regular attendance tends to suggest local breeding. This in turn may suggest that another foodplant might be utilised in parts of the county.

2273 *Xanthia togata* (Esp.) Pink-barred Sallow

Recorded:	1884 – 2006
Distribution / Status:	Local / Common resident
Conservation status:	Stable
Caterpillar food plants:	Common Sallow (catkins)
Flight period:	September/October
Records in database:	125

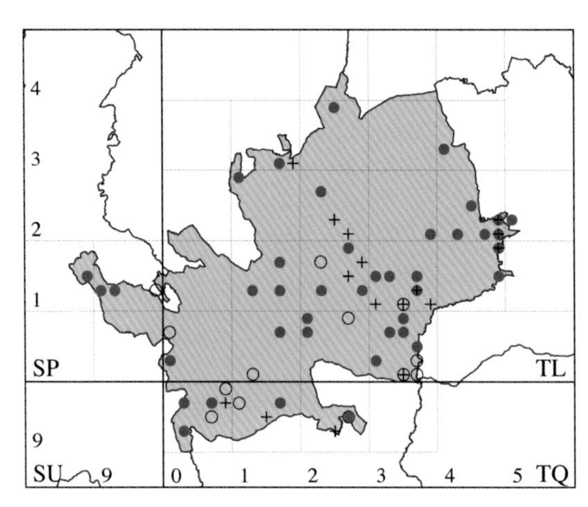

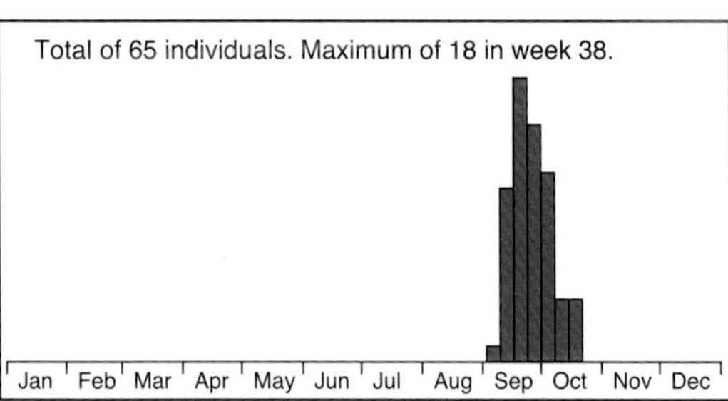

Were it not for the general absence of sallow, and hence this moth, in north-east Hertfordshire, the Pink-barred Sallow would qualify as 'Widespread', but the absence of records in much of that area is apparently genuine. As in the London Area to our south (Plant, 1993) the Pink-barred Sallow is encountered with more or less the same frequency as 2274: Sallow, but numerically can muster only about half the numbers of that other species. This is reflected in the flight chart, which shows a peak of 18 individuals for Pink-barred Sallow and of 44 (in the same week) for The Sallow.

2274 *Xanthia icteritia* (Hufn.) Sallow

Recorded:	1884 – 2006
Distribution / Status:	Widespread / Common resident
Conservation status:	UK BAP Watch List Herts Stable
Caterpillar food plants:	Common Sallow (catkins)
Flight period:	September/October
Records in database:	195

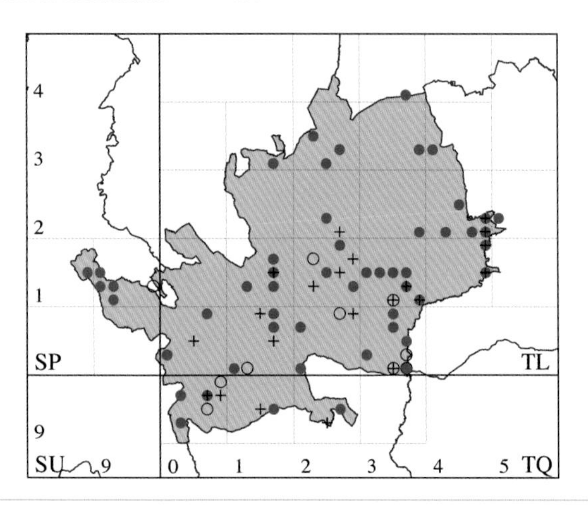

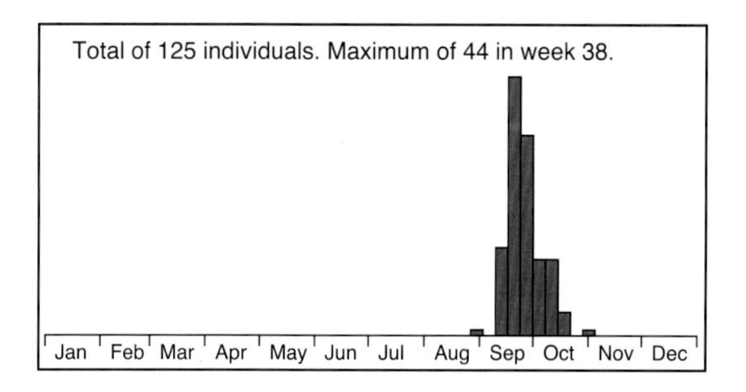

This familiar autumn species comes in both the standard 'yellow marbled with brown' format and as the more or less plain yellow ab. *flavescens* Esper. The latter is evidently uncommon in Hertfordshire, with perhaps no more than 10 per cent of the population being of this type. A number of variations of the 'marbled' form have been named – some more convincing than others. The apparent national population decline of 82 per cent since 1970 in Rothamsted light traps is not evident in Hertfordshire, though we lack a particularly long time series of numerical data.

2275 *Xanthia gilvago* ([D.& S.]) Dusky-lemon Sallow

Recorded:	1888 – 2003 / Extremely local
Distribution / Status:	Rare resident
Conservation status:	UK BAP Watch List Herts Endangered
Caterpillar food plants:	Not recorded. Elsewhere on seeds of Wych Elm and perhaps other elms
Flight period:	September/October
Records in database:	47

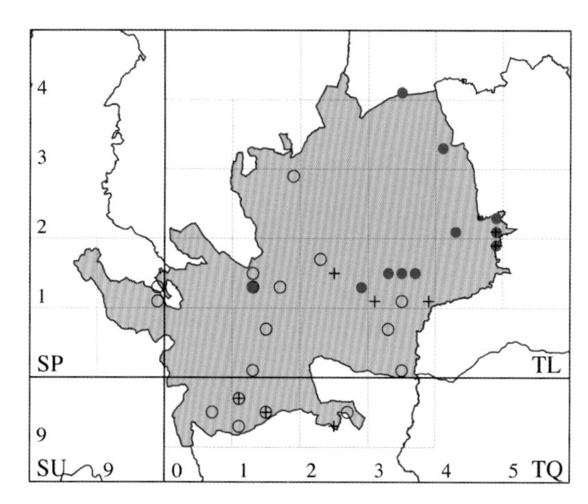

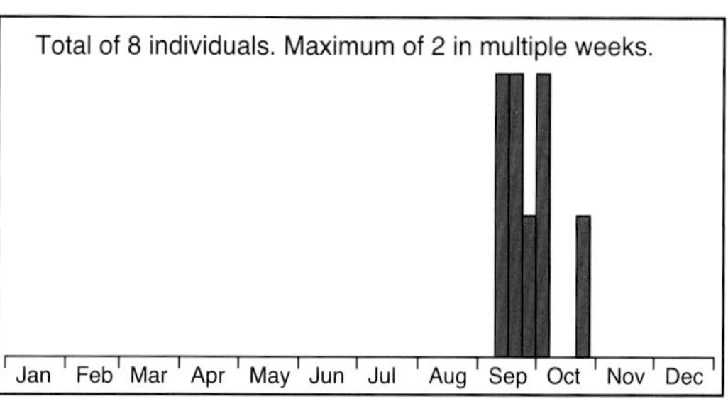

There are scattered Hertfordshire records of Dusky-lemon Sallow for most of the first half of the twentieth century and in 1937 Foster's list gives several localities indicating it to have been relatively widespread. More recent records all relate to low numbers, nearly always single moths in light traps, from a low number of sites, but the moth has been lost from 64 per cent of localities that formerly recorded it and this is in line with a nationally observed population decline at Rothamsted light traps of 92 per cent. In particular, our map shows a clear loss from the southern half of the county, corresponding in large part to the Greater London area, where this loss had already occurred by 1980 – the distribution map in *Larger Moths of the London Area* (Plant, 1993) showing only records made prior to that year. To our north, the moth fares equally poorly, with Arnold et al (1998) showing an absence from the southern half of Bedfordshire, and blaming losses on Dutch Elm Disease. Given that Wych Elm largely survived the 1970s epidemic of Dutch Elm disease it seems unlikely that this factor alone could account for the observed decline of this moth. To our east, in Essex, Goodey (2004) shows only pre-1990 records in the several ten-kilometre squares that border Hertfordshire and overall regards the moth as 'scarce'. Whatever the factors in play, this moth is in serious decline in Hertfordshire; funding for autecological research is urgently needed.

2276 *Xanthia ocellaris* (Borkh.) Pale-lemon Sallow

Recorded:	1914 – 1980
Distribution / Status:	Absent / Former vagrant
Conservation status:	Herts Extinct
Caterpillar food plants:	Not recorded. Elsewhere, on native Black Poplar
Flight period:	September/October
Records in database:	5

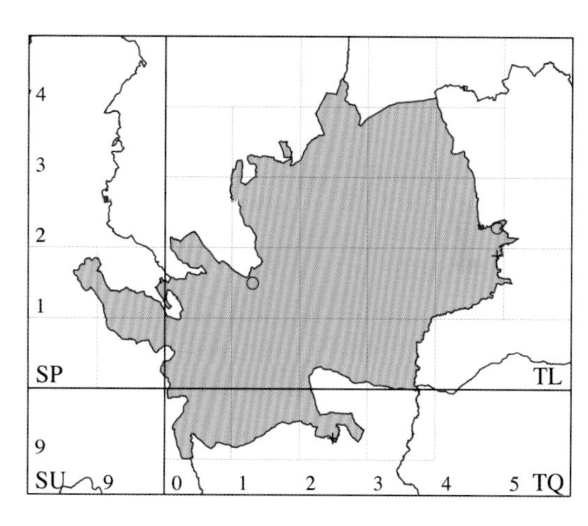

Native Black Poplar appears to be the only suitable foodplant for the larvae of this species and the various hybrid strains that are a feature of parts of the county appear quite unsuitable. These native trees appear to have their headquarters in the Vale of Aylesbury and a few just creep into our county in the extreme west. We have specifically looked for the moth in the west, but the number of occasions has been limited and it remains possible that the moth could be resident there or elsewhere in this western zone. Elsewhere, the occasional reports of single moths may suggest vagrants; it is probably significant that the two Totteridge records were both made at the end of particularly hot, drought-affected summers. Given the high level of recording in and around Bishops Stortford it seems probable that any local resident population would have been discovered if present. All Hertfordshire records are listed: Bishops Stortford, one at sugar in 1914 (J. A. Webster); Harpenden, 1933 (C. B. Williams); Bishops Stortford [Galloway Road], one in September 1955 (Clifford Craufurd); Totteridge - singletons noted on 9th October 1975 (male) and 30th September 1976 (Ian Lorimer); Thorley Park Road, Bishops Stortford, 27th September 1980 (Charles Watson).

2278 *Acronicta megacephala* ([D.& S.]) Poplar Grey

Recorded:	1828 – 2006
Distribution / Status:	Widespread / Common resident
Conservation status:	Herts Stable
Caterpillar food plants:	Lombardy Poplar; Grey Poplar; Common Sallow
Flight period:	May to August
Records in database:	338

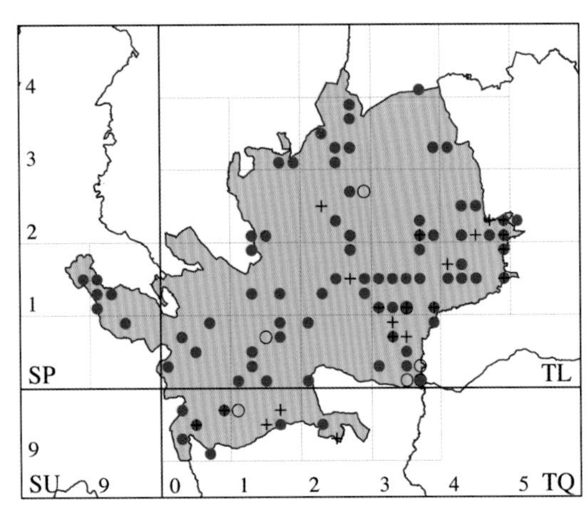

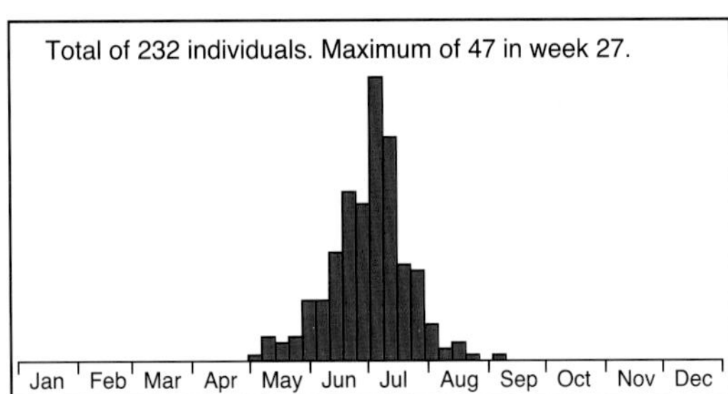

Although often confused with other *Acronicta* species the Poplar Grey is easily recognised by stepping back and looking at the general appearance of the moth rather than its detail – each forewing bears a pale patch incorporating and extending outwards from the reniform stigma; these emphasise the overall appearance of the resting insect as a 'face' – presumably intended to scare predators. It is a common moth everywhere in the county.

2279 *Acronicta aceris* (L.) Sycamore

Recorded:	1884 – 2006
Distribution / Status:	Widespread / Common resident
Conservation status:	Herts Stable
Caterpillar food plants:	English Oak; Horse Chestnut; Sycamore
Flight period:	Mid-May to early August
Records in database:	275

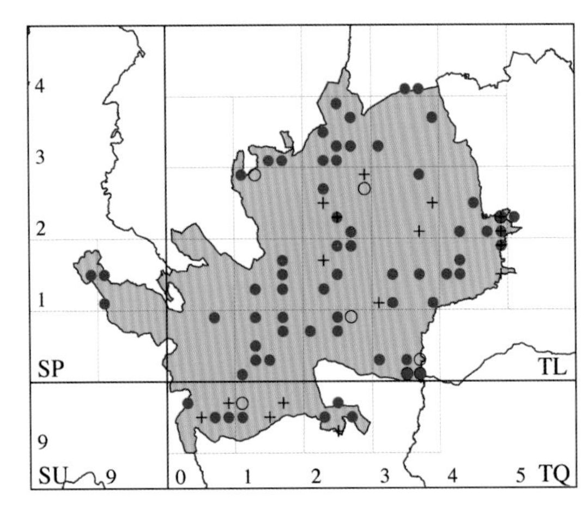

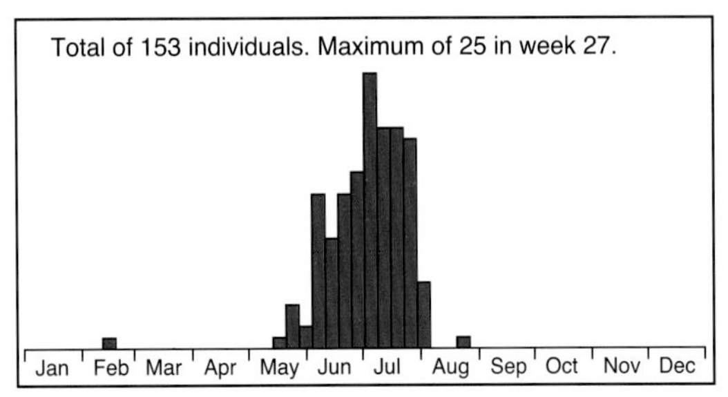

Foster (1937) lists several localities without comment, but later (Foster, 1946) he writes that '... this is a moth which, after practically disappearing, is again turning up in the county'. If there was a decline between those two years this is the only evidence that we have. Today it is a common species in the county. An exceptionally unseasonal adult was caught in my own garden light trap at Bishops Stortford on 14th February 2002. Many Hertfordshire adults are marginally darker than those further north in Britain, but the dark grey melanic ab. *infuscata* Haworth is rarely reported and usually from more southerly parts of the county. In the London Area from 1980 to 1991 it formed approximately 80 per cent of the population (Plant, 1993). I caught examples in my garden during both 1988 and 1990, but have not seen it here since then.

2280 *Acronicta leporina* (L.) Miller

Recorded:	1884 – 2006
Distribution / Status:	Widespread / Common resident
Conservation status:	Herts Stable
Caterpillar food plants:	Not recorded. Elsewhere, on birch, Alder, poplar and other trees
Flight period:	May to July
Records in database:	186

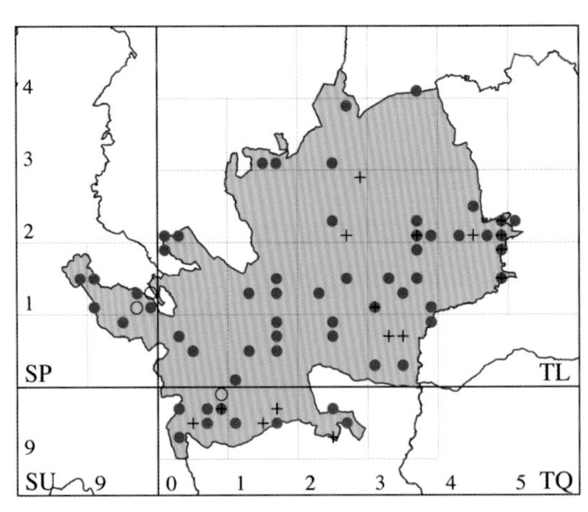

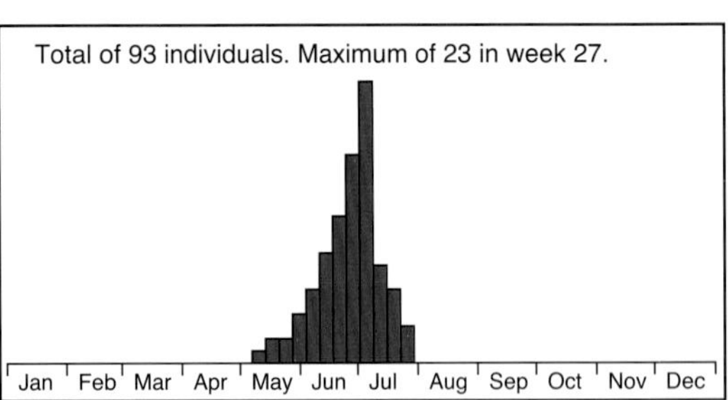

Though rarely arriving in any number, Millers are not unusual amongst Hertfordshire moth-trap samples. Distribution may, perhaps, be partly restricted by the need for soft, rotten timber into which mature larvae tunnel for pupation – a behavioural trait shared with 2281: Alder Moth, but not with the other more common members of this group. As with 2279: Sycamore, the flight period is fairly lengthy, extending from the start of May to the very end of July, but there is no evidence to suggest any more than a single generation.

2281 *Acronicta alni* (L.) Alder Moth

Recorded:	1891 – 2005
Distribution / Status:	Very local / Rare and resident
Conservation status:	Herts Vulnerable
Caterpillar food plants:	Not recorded. Elsewhere, on various trees
Flight period:	May to mid-June
Records in database:	51

A larva in a garden at Rose Hill, Hoddesdon, found by F. M. Campbell on 21st August 1891 'on some fresh-turned mould under a lime tree' was reported by Gibbs (1893) as being a new species for the county fauna. The present-day map appears to show a worrying loss from a number of sites in the south and east of the county; these losses represent exactly 50 per cent of all recorded map tetrads. This apparent loss is supported by the fact that there were no reports at all of this moth in 2006, only two in 2005 and two in 2004; it seems that the Alder Moth is in decline in our county. The start of the decline cannot be determined: Open circles on the map indicate pre-1950 data whilst crosses relate to the years 1950 – 1994. Ian Lorimer reported that the moth was 'erratic' at Totteridge, with 20 plus in 1970 and with the melanic f. *steinerti* Caspari being present in most years.

2283 *Acronicta tridens* ([D.& S.]) Dark Dagger

Recorded: 1888 – 2006
Distribution / Status: Widespread / Common resident
Conservation status: No perceived threats
Caterpillar food plants: Blackthorn; Domestic Apple
Flight period: Late May to mid-August
Records in database: 89

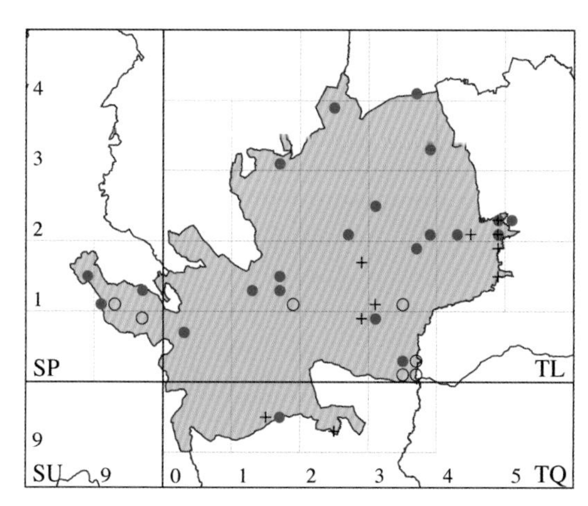

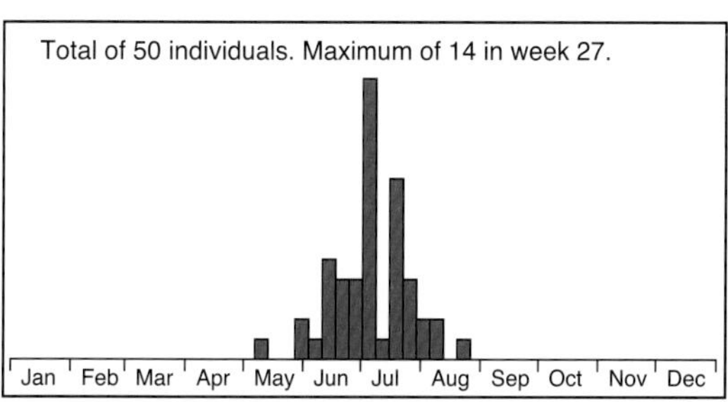

Adult Dark Daggers are identical in appearance to those of 2284: Grey Dagger, though the larvae are quite dissimilar. The map shows only the locations of adult males identified from their genital structure and of larvae. Dark Dagger is evidently far more local than Grey Dagger, is outnumbered three to one in terms of the number of records and is dominated by approximately two to one in terms of numbers of individuals.

2284 *Acronicta psi* (L.) Grey Dagger

Recorded: 1888 – 2006
Distribution / Status: Widespread / Common resident
Conservation status: UK BAP Watch List
No perceived threats in Hertfordshire
Caterpillar food plants: Rowan; Hawthorn
Flight period: Late April to early September
Records in database: 273

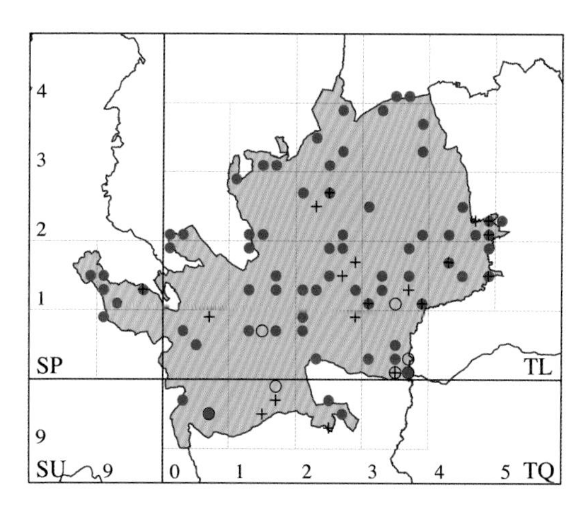

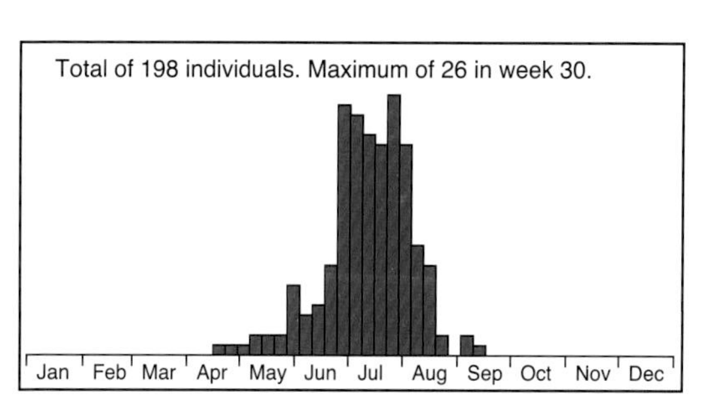

As with 2283: Dark Dagger, the map shows only the locations of adult males identified from their genital structure and of larvae. The Grey Dagger is widespread and common and although the map shows a small number of sites from which the moth appears to have been lost (16 per cent of all tetrads with records) there is no discernible decline in numbers of individuals. The apparent national population decline of 77 per cent since 1970, measured by Rothamsted light traps is not mirrored by our data from mv and actinic traps. Skinner (1998) record the adult flight period as being from June to August; in Hertfordshire, there is an increasing number of reports during May.

2289 *Acronicta rumicis* (L.) Knot Grass

Recorded: 1884 – 2006
Distribution / Status: Widespread / Common resident
Conservation status: UK BAP Watch List
No perceived threats in Hertfordshire
Caterpillar food plants: Broad-leaved Dock. Elsewhere, on many other plants
Flight period: May/June then mid-July/August in two generations
Records in database: 227

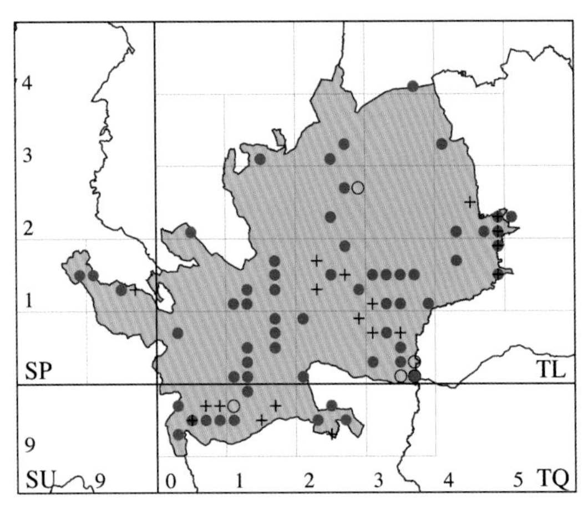

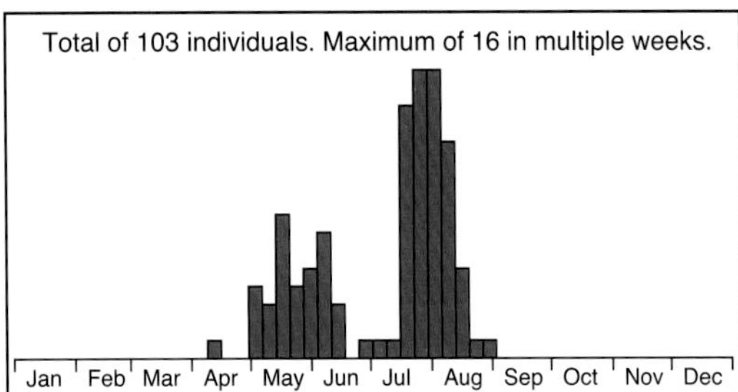

Adults fly in two well-separated generations, though the second generation is much larger than the first in terms of numbers of individuals. The apparent absence of Knot Grass from the north of the county is unexpected, although this is an agricultural area where the use of dicotyledon-specific herbicides is common practice. The melanic ab. *salicis* Curtis has apparently declined in the past thirty or so years; it was frequent in the south of the county, as well as in north London, during the 1970s, but the majority of individuals caught there recently take the typical form.

2290 *Simyra albovenosa* (Goeze) Reed Dagger

Recorded:	1928 – 2006
Distribution / Status:	Extremely local / Very rare resident
Conservation status:	Herts Endangered
Caterpillar food plants:	Not recorded. Elsewhere, on Common Reed and occasionally on sallows
Flight period:	May, then July/August, in two generations
Records in database:	3

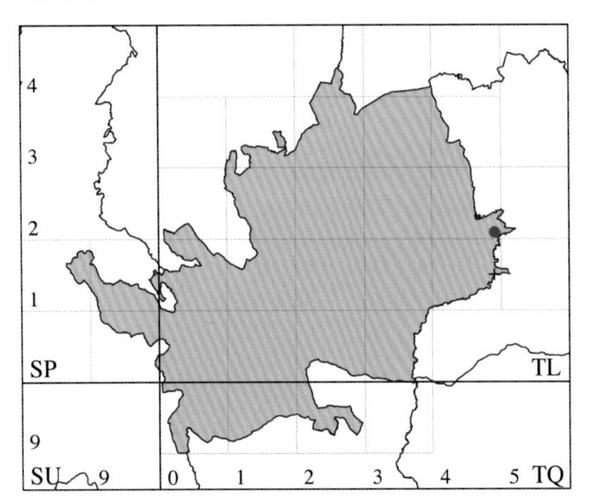

Reed Dagger is listed for Hertfordshire by Meyrick in his *Revised Handbook* (1928, page 59). This record was repeated by Foster (1937) without comment. More recently it has been recorded twice, on both occasions by me, at Sawbridgeworth Marsh on 27th July 1990 and at my garden in Bishops Stortford on 26th July 2006. Though the garden record certainly relates to a wanderer, there is a very high probability that it is resident at Sawbridgeworth Marsh; the reed beds along both the River Stort and the River Lea are inadequately surveyed for this species and it is possible that small breeding populations exist undetected elsewhere. However, these habitats are under considerable threat in Hertfordshire and this renders to moth Endangered here.

2291 *Craniophora ligustri* ([D.& S.]) Coronet

Recorded:	1882 – 2006
Distribution / Status:	Random / -
Conservation status:	–
Caterpillar food plants:	Privet
Flight period:	Elsewhere, June/July
Records in database:	5

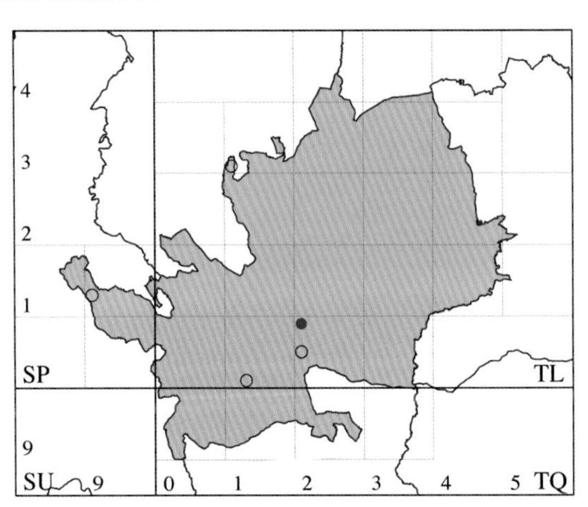

This moth is a rare visitor to Hertfordshire, presumably as a vagrant from breeding areas in Breckland and elsewhere. During 2006, Coronets appeared in a number of new and unexpected locations in the south of England, perhaps indicating primary immigration. Six of these reached Richard Ellis' garden at Chorleywood, but regrettably this site lies a few metres outside the Hertfordshire vice-county boundary, so the records belong to Buckinghamshire. Our only share of the influx was one at Hatfield on 18th July 2006 (Tony Bristow). There are a few older records and all are now listed: Bricket Wood, 1892 (Gibbs, 1893); Pegsdon Hills – scarce, larvae occasionally on privet (Foster, 1914); Wilstone (Foster, 1937); in a garden in Datchworth (TL 12 – not mapped) in 1971 by A. Newbold (on the database at the national Biological Records Centre at Monks Wood); Hatfield 18th July 2006 (Tony Bristow). One record is rejected – from Colney Heath in 1893. Of this record, Gibbs (1894) states '... Mr Pilbrow ... and he has taken *Acronycta ligustri* (?), ... in the same way'. This refers to the discovery of the moth at rest on a fence but, whilst the inference is that this event took place at Colney Heath in 1893, it is not absolutely clear that this is the case. The reason for the question mark, in parentheses, after the species name is equally unclear and Foster (1937) does not include this record in his list. Foster was not prone to offering explanations; it is assumed that he was satisfied that this record arose from a misidentification.

BRYOPHILINAE

2292 *Cryphia algae* (Fabr.) Tree-lichen Beauty

Recorded:	1996 – 2006
Distribution / Status:	Extremely local / Immigrant/vagrant
Conservation status:	Perhaps increasing
Caterpillar food plants:	Elsewhere, on lichens growing on trees
Flight period:	July/August
Records in database:	2

Formerly a rare immigrant to Britain, the Tree-lichen Beauty has recently become established as a breeding species in Kent and during 2004 it colonised much of Middlesex, perhaps elsewhere too. For Hertfordshire, we have just two records, from Bishops Stortford, on 19th August 1996 and 26th July

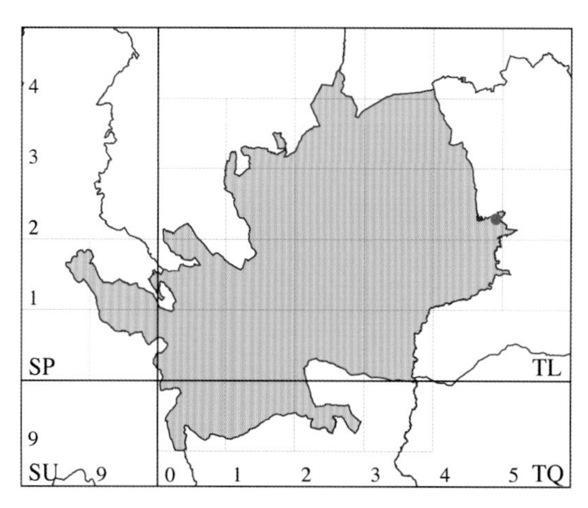

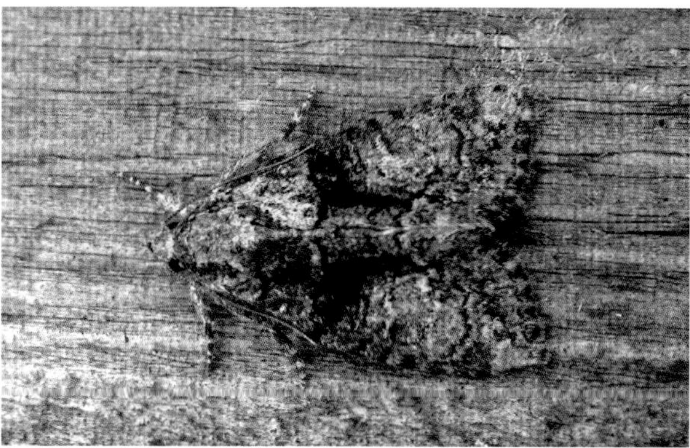

2006 (James Fish & Julian Reeves). These may have been primary immigrants or perhaps wanderers up the Lea and Stort Valley system. As yet there is no evidence of residency, but this is expected in the near future.

2293 *Cryphia domestica* (Hufn.) Marbled Beauty

Recorded:	1888 – 2006
Distribution / Status:	Widespread / Common resident
Conservation status:	Herts Stable
Caterpillar food plants:	Unidentified lichen on a roof
Flight period:	June to mid-September
Records in database:	879

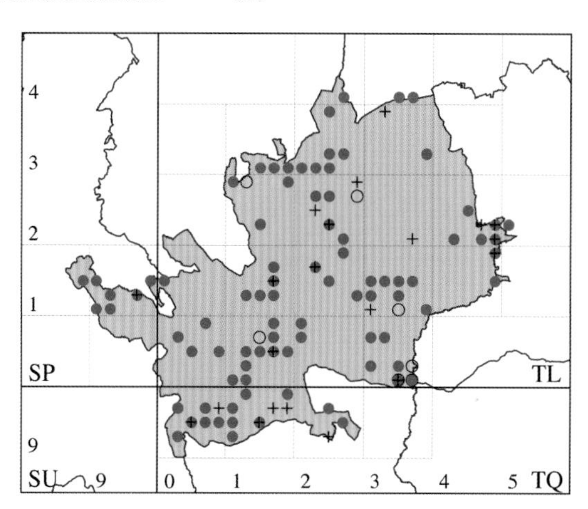

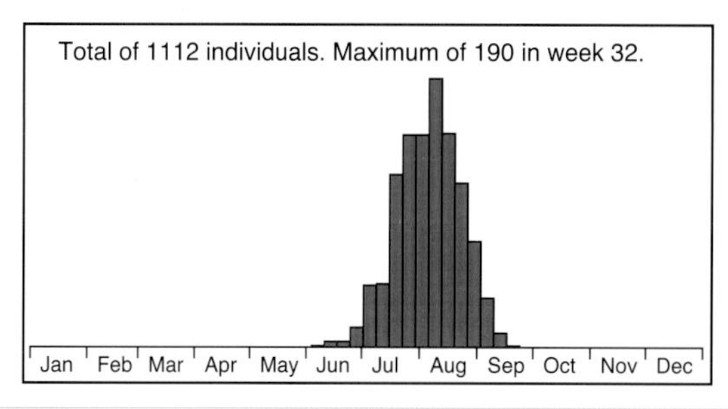

Foster (1937) records this species as common in all districts and that is the situation that persists at 2006. The single larval record is from the roof of my house in Bishops Stortford, where one was found feeding on a green foliose lichen species whilst I was reattaching a loose television aerial. I regret that I chose not to return to the roof to collect more lichen for naming after the larva had finished eating the first sample and successfully pupated, though I would be pleased to welcome visiting lichenologists!

2295 *Cryphia muralis* (Forster) Marbled Green

Recorded:	1924 – 1948
Distribution / Status:	Absent / Perhaps a former resident
Conservation status:	Herts Extinct
Caterpillar food plants:	Elsewhere, on lichens on walls, roofs etc
Flight period:	Elsewhere, July and August
Records in database:	2

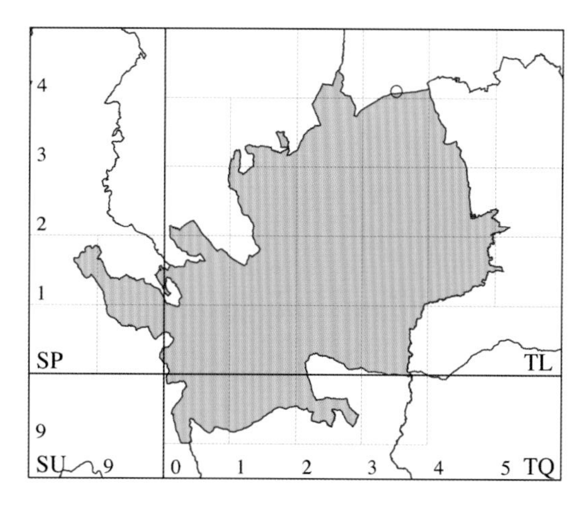

Foster (1937) records one example at Berkhamsted, on 9th July 1924 by R. B. Benson. A second was taken at Royston on 1 August 1948 by E. E. Johnson (*Entomologist* **81**: 280). In reporting the latter, Johnson noted specifically that 'Although Royston is just near the Cambridgeshire border .... it nevertheless is a Hertfordshire record'. These are our only records. There are breeding populations inland near Cambridge, where the population is regarded as belonging to subspecies *impar* Warren and this centre was perhaps the source of the Royston moth, which was probably a wanderer. The source of the Berkhamsted moth is less clear.

2297 *Amphipyra pyramidea* (L.) Copper Underwing

Recorded: 1964 – 2006
Distribution / Status: Widespread / Common resident
Conservation status: Herts Stable
Caterpillar food plants: Honeysuckle; Silver Birch. Elsewhere also on other trees
Flight period: Mid-July to mid-October
Records in database: 628

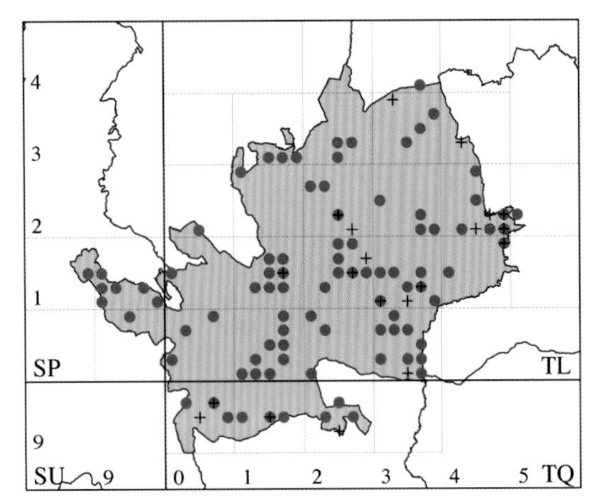

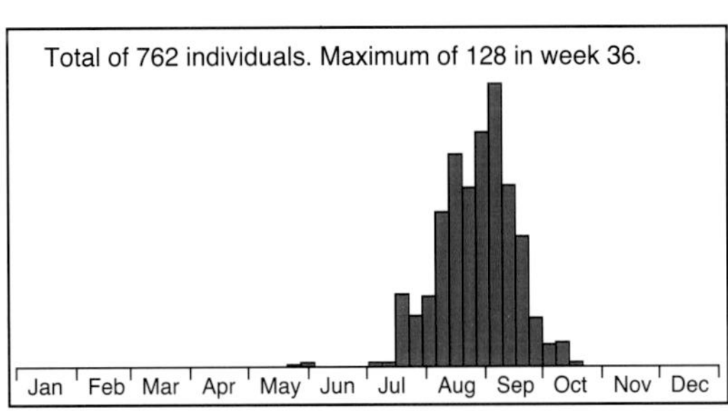

As recently as 1968 it was realised that what had, to that date, been called the Copper Underwing actually comprised two species and 2298: Svensson's Copper Underwing, also known as the Dusky Copper Underwing, was split from it (Fletcher, 1968). As a result, no records prior to that date can be accepted without sight of a voucher specimen. Thus, our first record becomes that of a moth caught at Whippendell Wood, on 11th September 1964, by Barry Goater. The Copper Underwing is a widespread and common species in Hertfordshire.

2298 *Amphipyra berbera* Rungs, ssp. *svenssoni* Fletcher Svensson's Copper Underwing

Recorded: 1968 – 2006
Distribution / Status: Widespread / Common resident
Conservation status: No perceived threats
Caterpillar food plants: Hornbeam. Elsewhere, on various trees
Flight period: Mid-July to end of September
Records in database: 265

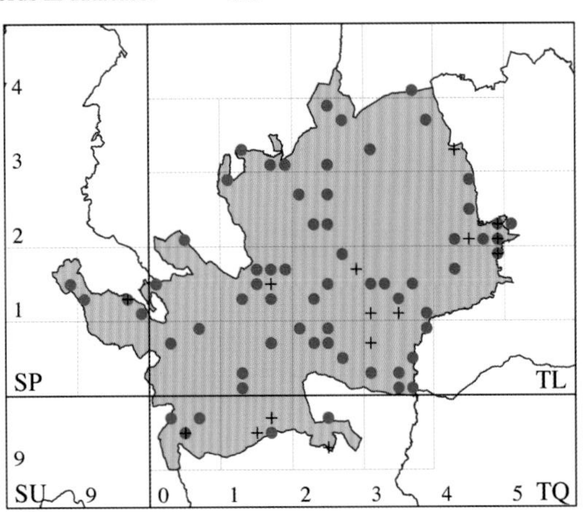

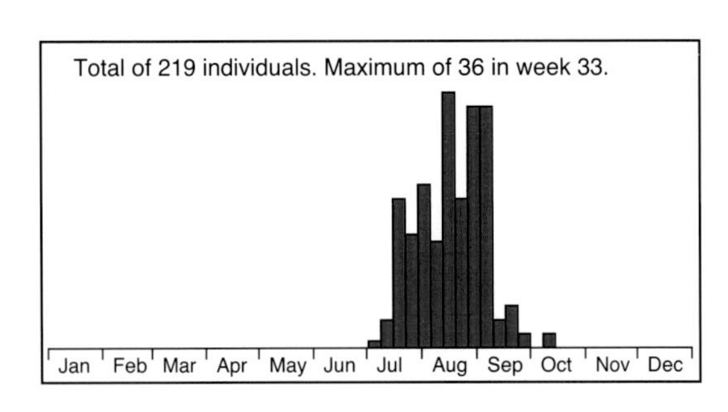

British examples of this species are referable to subspecies *svenssoni* Fletcher, whilst the typical subspecies *berbera* Rungs is found in continental Europe. Several methods of separation of this species, also known as the Dusky Copper Underwing, from 2297: Copper Underwing have been proposed; those based on wing pattern, both upper and lower, appear to work and records made this way are accepted here. However, the extent of white on the labial palps (see Winter, 1988 and subsequent plagiarists), is known to be unreliable and records that have been made using this technique alone are excluded from the map. The moth is likely to be found in most parts of the county. Our only breeding record is of a single larva beaten from Hornbeam in Broxbourne Wood on 19th August 1984 by Bernard Skinner.

2299 *Amphipyra tragopoginis* (Cl.) Mouse Moth

Recorded: 1828 – 2006
Distribution / Status: Widespread / Common resident
Conservation status: UK BAP Watch List. Herts Stable
Caterpillar food plants: Not recorded. Elsewhere, on various plants
Flight period: July to September
Records in database: 612

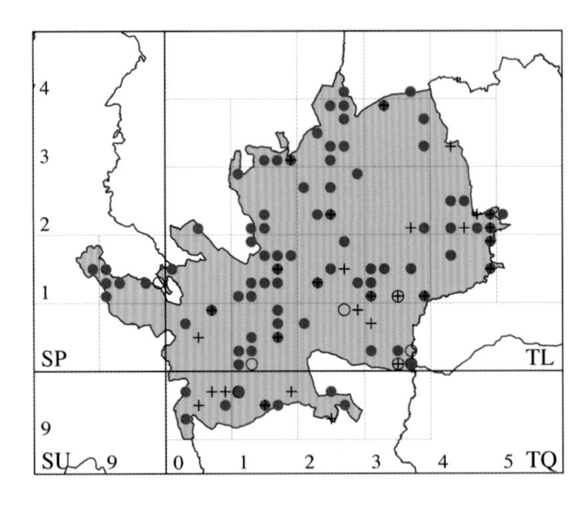

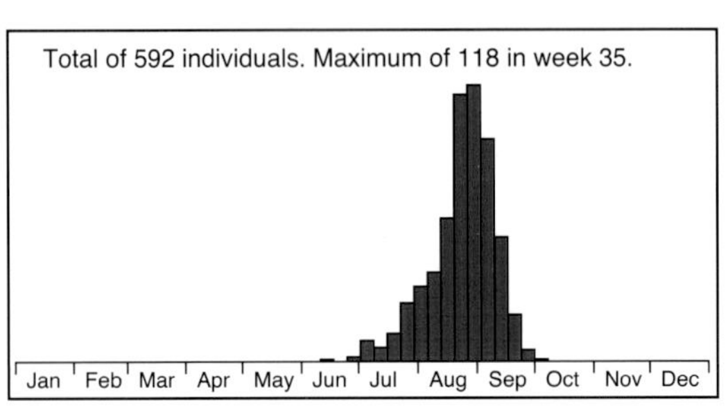

The colloquial name of the moth derives from its habit of scurrying about through vegetation (or in the moth trap) rather than flying when disturbed. It does, however, fly to light traps and appears to be widespread and numerous across the county.

2300 *Mormo maura* (L.) Old Lady

Recorded: 1828 – 2006
Distribution / Status: Widespread / Common resident
Conservation status: Herts Stable
Caterpillar food plants: Blackthorn; Common Hawthorn; English Elm
Flight period: July to early September
Records in database: 373

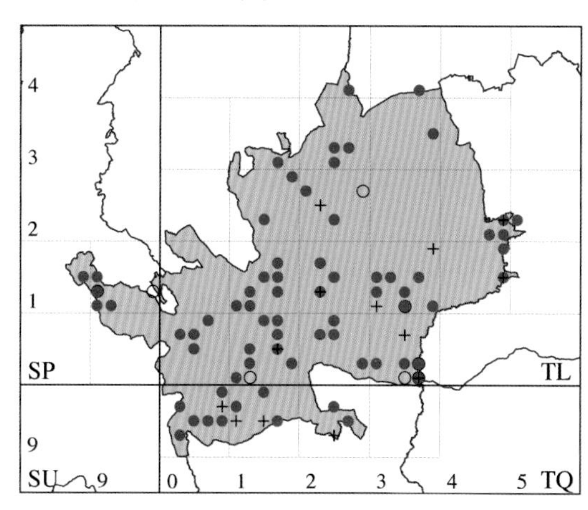

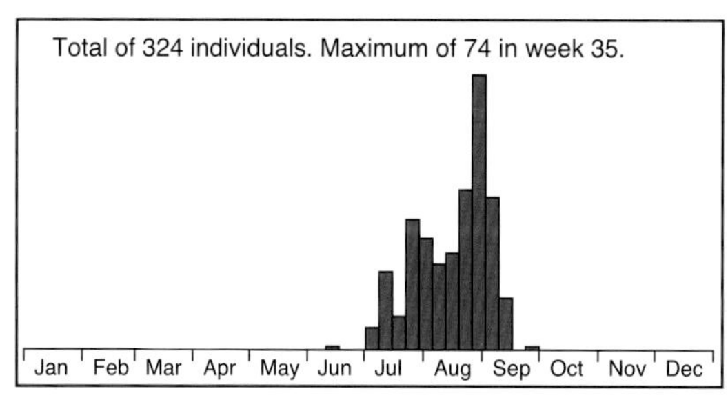

Adult Old Lady moths are rather feebly attracted to light, but are more easily found if looked for, probably on account of their size. They rest during the day in sheds, cellars and very often inside houses. Frequently, several adults will roost together: Bill and Pearl Page found 18 moths roosting under a bridge over a watercourse in London Colney in July 2002. Though I have recorded the larvae feeding on ivy in another county (Plant, 1993), this seems to be a seldom used foodplant. Larvae are most easily found by beating blackthorn, hawthorn and other bushes in hedges where these are also covered in ivy. Perhaps the ivy creates a suitable microclimate, or perhaps this is the natural roosting habitat of adults?

2301 *Dypterygia scabriuscula* (L.) Bird's Wing

Recorded: 1888 – 2006
Distribution / Status: Local / Common resident
Conservation status: Stable
Caterpillar food plants: Not recorded. Elsewhere, on docks, sorrels and other plants
Flight period: June/July
Records in database: 198

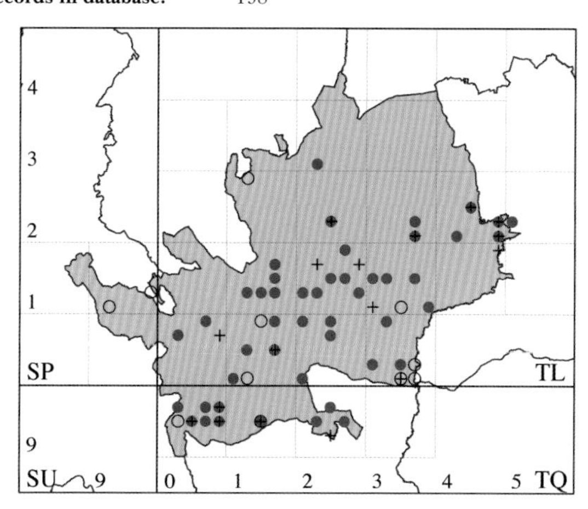

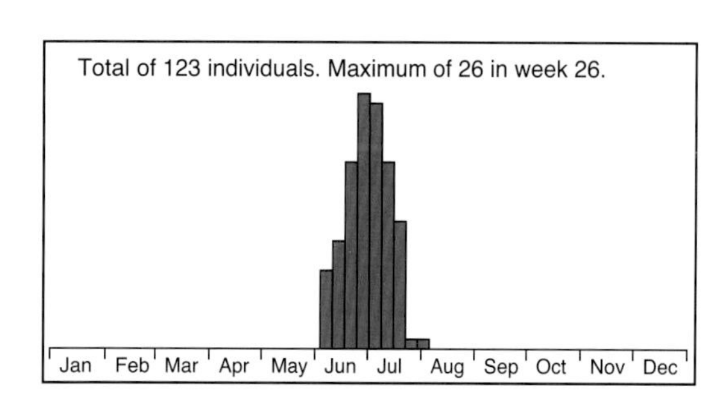

The distribution map shows that the moth is far less frequently encountered in the north of the county than it is in the south. This reflects the observed preference of the moth for woodland habitat in Hertfordshire, but rather contradicts the fact that the larvae feed on 'docks and sorrels' which, typically, are plants of more open sites. More likely, this moth is a feature of 'edge habitats' such as woodland rides, clearings and margins where the plants may be expected to grow. If so, this moth may be a useful indicator of quality in these difficult to define habitats.

2302 *Rusina ferruginea* (Esp.) Brown Rustic

Recorded: 1884 – 2006
Distribution / Status: Widespread / Common resident
Conservation status: Herts Stable
Caterpillar food plants: Not recorded. Elsewhere, on various herbaceous plants
Flight period: Late May to mid-July
Records in database: 576

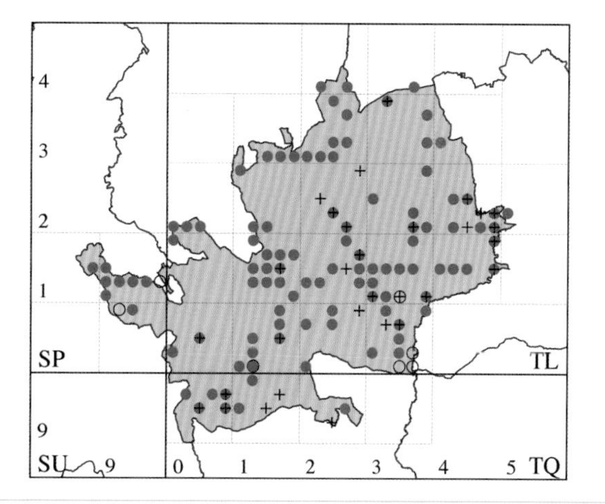

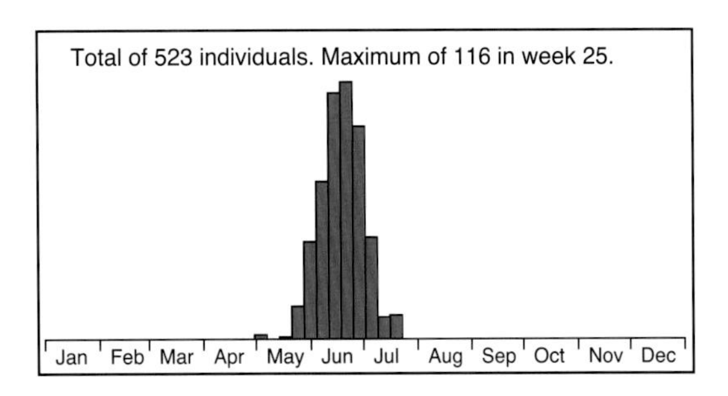

For reasons that are not immediately apparent, the Brown Rustic occupies top position amongst the 'brown noctuids' brought to me by beginners as species that they cannot recognise. Usually, the problem examples are females; males are relatively distinctive, especially since they have obviously feathered antennae that are quite unlike those of other species currently placed in the Amphipyrinae. It is a very commonly encountered moth in light traps across the county.

2303 *Thalpophila matura* (Hufn.) Straw Underwing

Recorded: 1828 – 2006
Distribution / Status: Widespread / Common resident
Conservation status: Herts Stable
Caterpillar food plants: Not recorded. Elsewhere, on grasses
Flight period: Late July/August
Records in database: 509

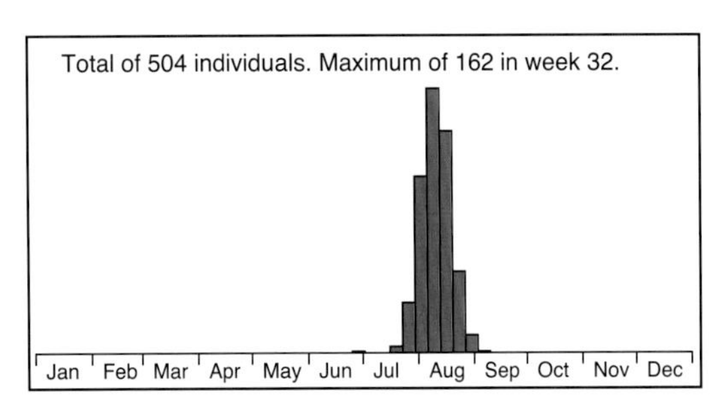

This is a familiar species of the late-summer period in most light traps across the county, though we have not yet found the larvae in Hertfordshire. This is surprising, since they feed exposed on grass stems at night and should be easily found in sweep-net samples collected in April.

2304 *Trachea atriplicis* (L.) Orache Moth

Recorded: 1888 – 1995
Distribution / Status: Random / Former vagrant; now a rare immigrant
Conservation status: -
Caterpillar food plants: Not known
Flight period: July/August
Records in database: 4

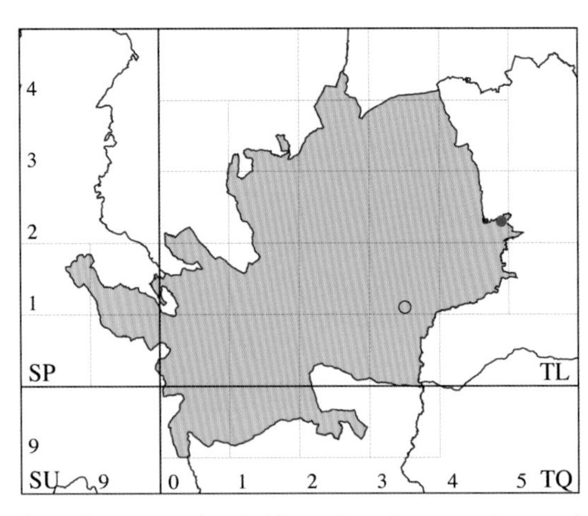

We have four records of this strikingly attractive moth as follows: Haileybury, 'once' (Bowyer, 1888) and again in 1899 (Stockley); Hemel Hempstead, one attracted to a bedroom light, 7th August 1960, I. D. Woodward (Bell, 1962); Bishops Stortford, one at mv light 10th July 1995 (James Fish & Julian Reeves). The last specimen is in my own collection. The Orache Moth was formerly resident in Britain, but became rare after about 1895 and soon afterwards became extinct. Writing in volume 10 of the series *Moths and Butterflies of Great Britain and Ireland* (1983), the late Russell Bretherton stated that 'The most common habitat of this species was round the fens and rivers of Cambridgeshire and Huntingdonshire, especially along the Cam and near Wicken and Chippenham; but it was also found in small numbers in Norfolk, Suffolk, Essex and Hertfordshire; it was reported from Buckinghamshire, and was once taken in Bishops Wood, Middlesex'. The Middlesex record was on 15th June 1865 (Plant, 1993). The 'small number' of Hertfordshire records are presumably those listed above – small number indeed and not, to my mind, indicative of breeding. The two early specimens were probably wanderers from the Fens; the two later examples are regarded as primary immigrants

2305 *Euplexia lucipara* (L.) Small Angle Shades

Recorded: 1884 – 2006
Distribution / Status: Widespread / Common resident
Conservation status: Herts Stable
Caterpillar food plants: Male Fern; Bracken
Flight period: June to early August
Records in database: 166

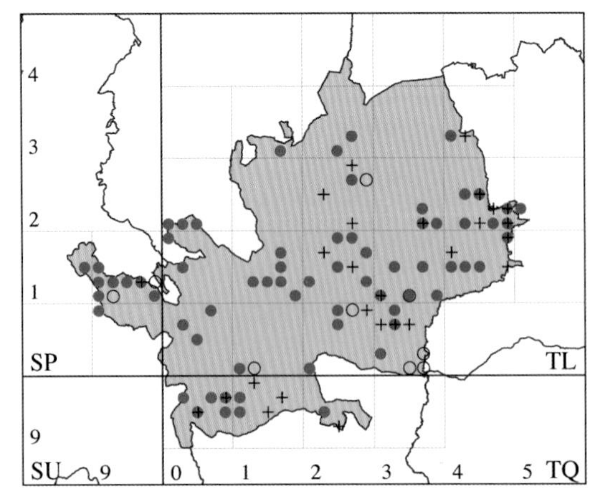

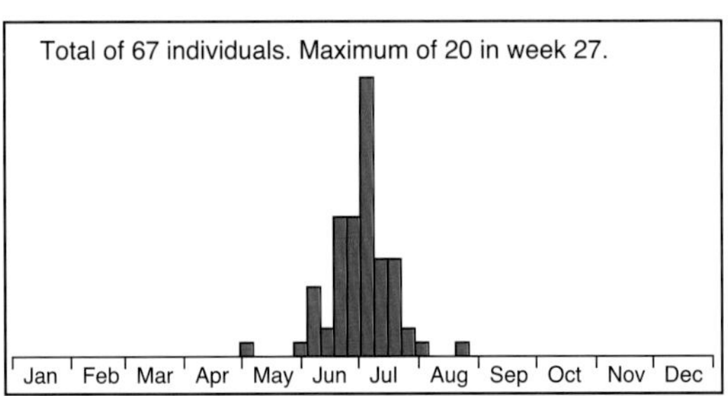

Larvae of the Small Angle Shades are sometimes found amongst potted ferns in greenhouses or other ferns planted in gardens, but the only *specific* foodplant records that we have are those quoted above. The adult moth is more or less expected in light traps set amongst areas of woodland containing bracken. Elsewhere, the larvae are said to feed on trees and herbaceous plants, but we have no evidence for that in Hertfordshire.

2306 *Phlogophora meticulosa* (L.) Angle Shades

Recorded:	1888 – 2006
Distribution / Status:	Ubiquitous / Common resident
Conservation status:	Herts Stable
Caterpillar food plants:	Bay; Lupin; Garden Honeysuckle; Broad-leaved Dock; Dandelion; greenhouse-grown Geranium.
Flight period:	All year
Records in database:	1539

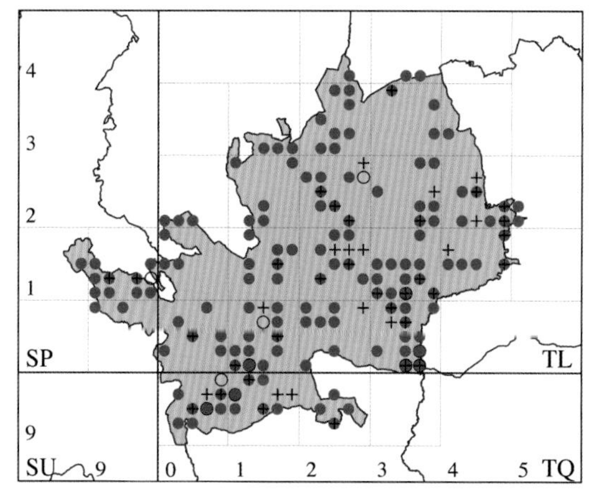

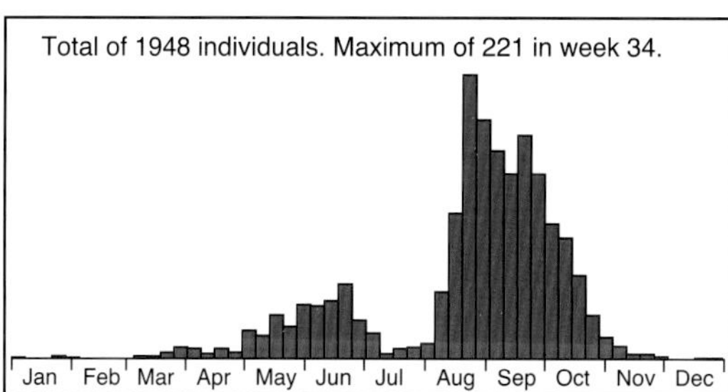

The term ubiquitous could easily have been invented to describe this moth. Adults can be found all year in mild weather, but as the chart shows there are two main peaks of activity, in May/June and then from August to October. The much larger autumn peak is certainly boosted by the arrival of primary immigrants. By way of example, at Bishops Stortford, Clifford Craufurd caught 117 on the night of 7th October 1959 in the company of 35 Dark Sword-grass 19 Silver Y and 5 Pearly Underwing (Bell, 1961). Larvae are frequently encountered, though foodplants are rarely recorded!

[2097 *Actinotia polyodon* (Cl.) Purple Cloud

A report from Ashridge in 1938 refers to *polyodon* of Linnaeus– an old name for 2321: Dark Arches.]

2311 *Ipimorpha retusa* (L.) Double Kidney

Recorded:	1828 – 1983
Distribution / Status:	Absent / Former vagrant
Conservation status:	-
Caterpillar food plants:	Not recorded. Elsewhere, on sallow and willow
Flight period:	Elsewhere, August/September
Records in database:	6

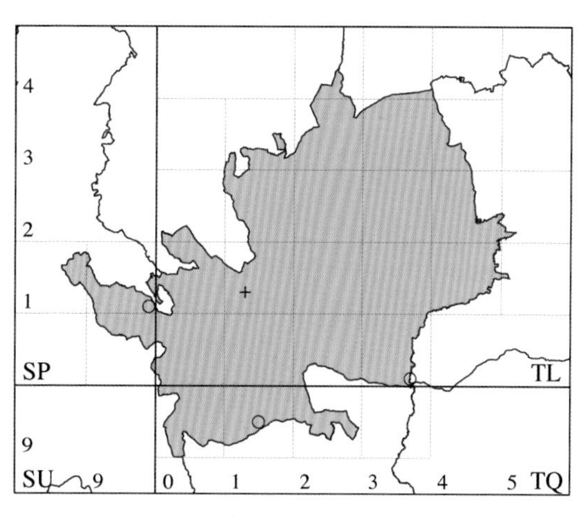

The Double Kidney is found mostly in Wales, the West Country and England south of the London – Bristol line. The Hertfordshire records are as follows: Illustrated from 'Hertford' in *Illustrations of British Entomology* **3**: 57 (Stephens 1829); Sandridge area (Griffith, 1884); 'Once, Waltham Cross' (Boyd, 1901) – this is the same record later given as 'Cheshunt Marsh' in Foster (1937); Bushey Heath, 1904 (Barraud, given in Foster, 1937); Northchurch (J. Bell, given in Foster, 1942); Rothamsted Estate, Harpenden, 1983 (Riley, 1999). The first two cannot be located accurately enough to appear in the distribution map.

2312 *Ipimorpha subtusa* ([D.& S.]) Olive

Recorded:	1884 – 2006
Distribution / Status:	Local / Uncommon resident
Conservation status:	Herts Stable
Caterpillar food plants:	'*Populus*'. Elsewhere, on Aspen and poplars
Flight period:	Mid-June to August
Records in database:	85

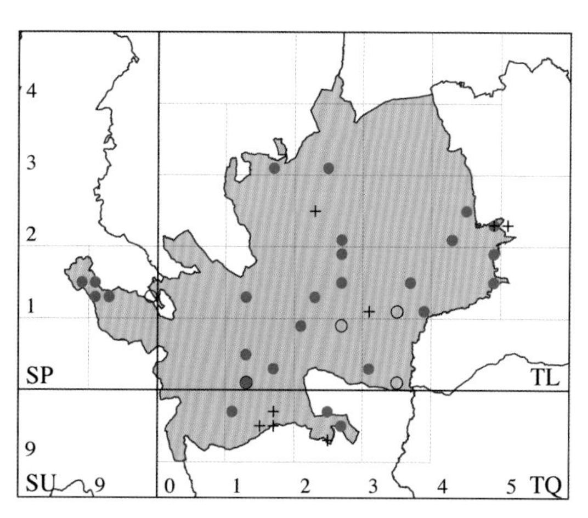

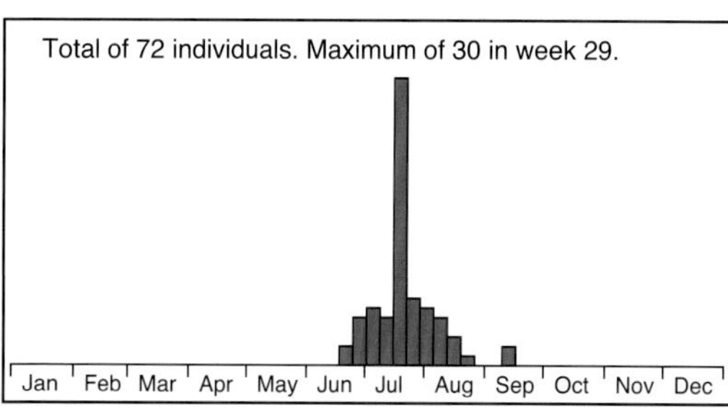

Unlike 2311: Double Kidney, to which it bears passing resemblance, the Olive is a tolerably widespread, albeit local, moth in the county. A high proportion of records are from domestic gardens and it is assumed that poplar trees in towns are providing the primary food source, though this statement is not based on any scientific data.

2313 *Enargia paleacea* (L.) Angle-striped Sallow

Recorded: 1967 – 2006
Distribution / Status: Random / Rare immigrant
Conservation status: -
Caterpillar food plants: Not recorded. Elsewhere, birch, Sallow and Aspen
Flight period: July to September
Records in database: 4

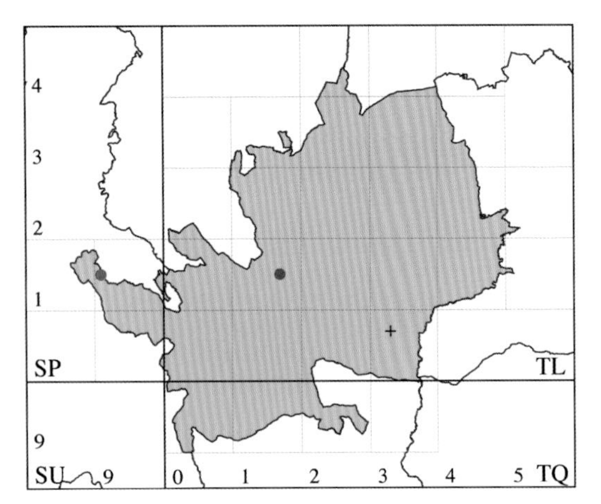

Although resident in other parts of Britain, the Angle-striped Sallow is a primary immigrant in the south-east and all Hertfordshire records fall into that category. Our records are: 'Ashridge', 21st August 1967 (Bell, 1969) – the exact locality of this 'boundary' record is unknown, though as it was an immigrant it scarcely matters a great deal; Broxbourne Woods, 24th July 1989 (Bernard Skinner); Marshall's Heath, 31st July 1995 (John Murray) and Long Marston, 12th September 2006 (Peter Bygate).

2268 *Parastichtis suspecta* (Hb.) Suspected

Recorded: 1888 – 2006
Distribution / Status: Very local / Uncommon resident
Conservation status: Herts Scarce
Caterpillar food plants: Not recorded. Elsewhere, on birch and perhaps sallow
Flight period: July/August
Records in database: 21

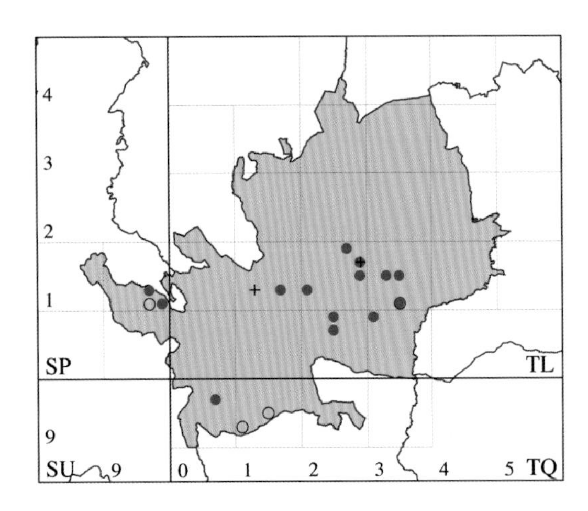

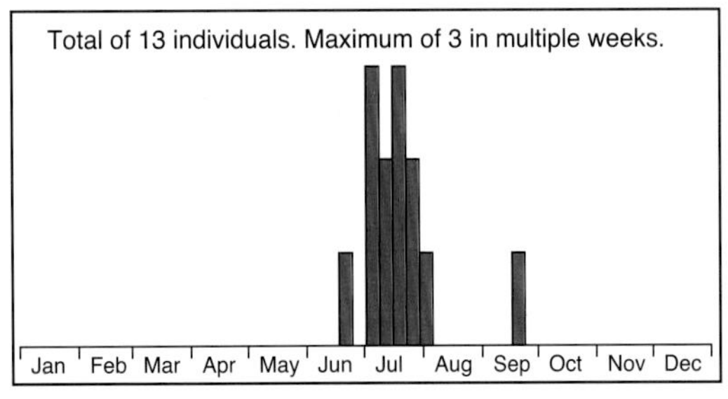

Formerly regarded as belonging with the shark moths in subfamily Cuculliinae, the Suspected is now widely accepted as belonging to the current concept of the Amphipyrinae. It is a very local species, inhabiting open woodland and lightly wooded landscapes in central and perhaps southern Hertfordshire, but so far apparently absent from the north. Two extreme dates are both recorded by Andrew Wood, with an early example on 21st June 2003 (an exceptionally hot summer) at Bramfield Park Wood and a late one on 20th September 1998 at Bengeo, Hertford.

2314 *Parastichtis ypsillon* ([D.& S.]) Dingy Shears

Recorded: 1828 – 2006
Distribution / Status: Local / Uncommon resident
Conservation status: Herts Stable
Caterpillar food plants: Crack Willow
Flight period: June/July
Records in database: 127

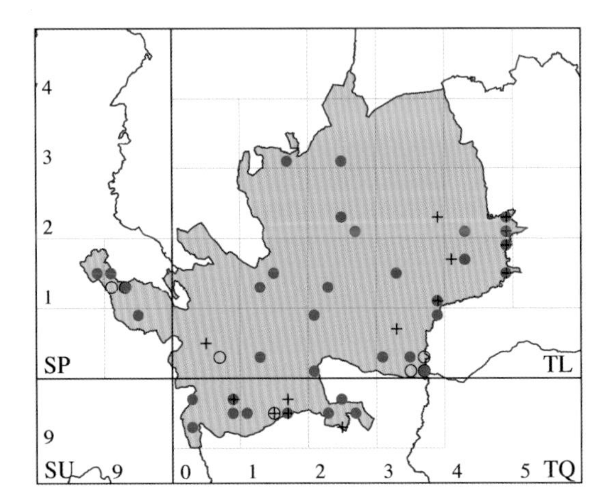

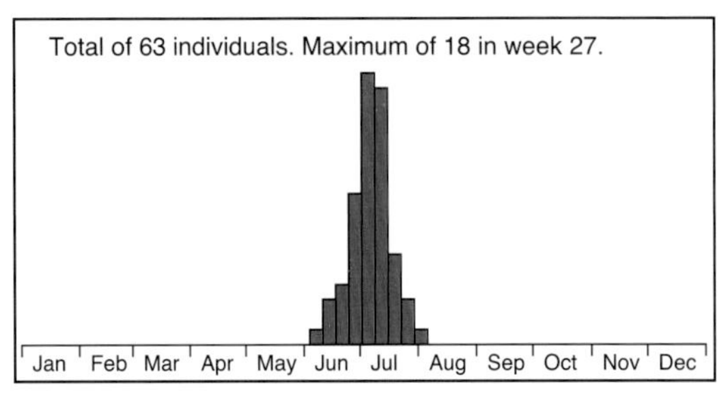

Although other willows and perhaps poplars might be eaten by the larvae, Crack Willow has a limited distribution in the county and might in part affect the distribution of the moth, which is certainly at its most numerous in the Lea and Stort Valleys. Damp woodlands with suitable trees will likely produce these species although that habitat is increasingly scarce in the county.

2315 *Dicycla oo* (L.) Heart Moth

Recorded:	1903 – 1971
Distribution / Status:	Absent / Former resident
Conservation status:	UK BAP Priority Species. Herts Extinct
Caterpillar food plants:	Not recorded. Elsewhere, on oak
Flight period:	Elsewhere, June/July
Records in database:	16

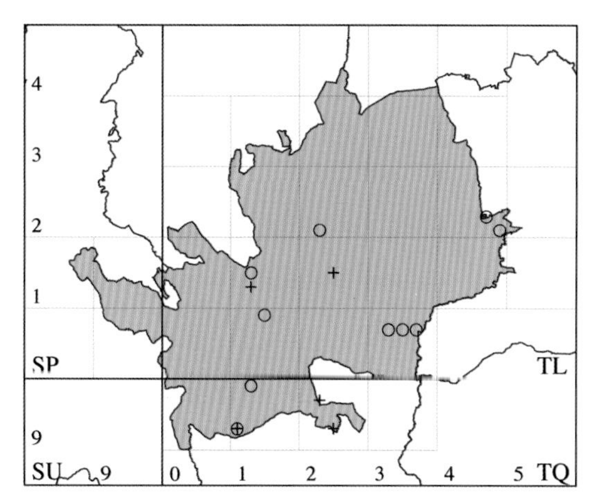

This is a moth of mature oak woodland, mature parkland with veteran oak trees and similar habitats. Bretherton, Goater and Lorimer (1983) comment that 'The most stable population seems to be in Surrey, but in the early 1950s it occurred in considerable abundance north of London, in Middlesex and the south of Hertfordshire and Essex where it still occurs but is at present very local and uncommon'. There are certainly records from this area, several of which were made by Ian Lorimer and Barry Goater themselves, but there is nothing at all to substantiate their statement that the moth was still present there in 1983: the last Hertfordshire record for that area was made in 1958 and the last ever Middlesex record heralds from 1963. All Hertfordshire records are now given: St Albans, one 'taken at sugar on an apple tree in the garden at New Farm, St Albans, on 15th July 1903, between 9 and 10 pm by Miss [Alice] Dickinson' is the first county record (Gibbs, 1904a); Oxhey Wood, 1910 'common' (Todd, given in de Worms (1956); Hoddesdon, 1920 'a few', 1922 'eighteen noted', 1924 '1 noted' (G. V. Bull, given in Foster, 1937); Broxbourne (H. M. Edelsten, given in Foster, 1937); Harpenden, one in the light trap on 29th June 1933 (C. B. Williams) appears to be the first here. Riley (1999) notes that there were eleven records from 1933 to 1952, but gives no details. At least one of these was in 1947 (listed below); Aldenham, 'at sugar' 1934 (H. King, given in Foster, 1937); Knebworth, 'at sugar' (H. A. Leeds, in Foster, 1937); Bishops Stortford, 1946 (Fryer, 1948) – this is almost certainly the same record less accurately given in Allen (1950) as 'One was taken at sugar on the college playing fields in 1948 (M[ellows]); Harpenden, in light trap 1947 (C. B. Williams); Bloodhounds Wood, 1948 (P. B. M. Allan) and Hoggets Wood [= Hoggates Wood], Bishops Stortford (Clifford Craufurd), 1948 (Allan, 1950); Arkley, 1955 'common most years' (T. G. Howarth, given in de Worms 1956); Totteridge – 'common' in 1955 (Ian Lorimer, given in de Worms 1956), 'Common to 1955: last seen 1969' Lorimer's own typed list sent during 1977 to Peter Waterton, the then county moth recorder, 1969 '... reappeared after many years' (Ian Lorimer, given in de Worms 1970); Oxhey Wood, two in 1958 (Eric Classey); Digswell, one at mv light, 18th July 1971 (Tom Gladwin). The record from Digswell is surprising and must relate to a wanderer from some distance away. The remainder clearly indicate a breeding population that reached its peak at the end of the 1950s and is now extinct. Middlesex populations centred on Scratch Wood, which is on the Hertfordshire border and from where it was recorded from 1958 to 1963, but not since – in spite of searching for it there.

2316 *Cosmia affinis* (L.) Lesser-spotted Pinion

Recorded:	1828 – 2006
Distribution / Status:	Local / Common resident
Conservation status:	Herts Scarce
Caterpillar food plants:	Wych Elm. Elsewhere, probably on other elms
Flight period:	July/August
Records in database:	92

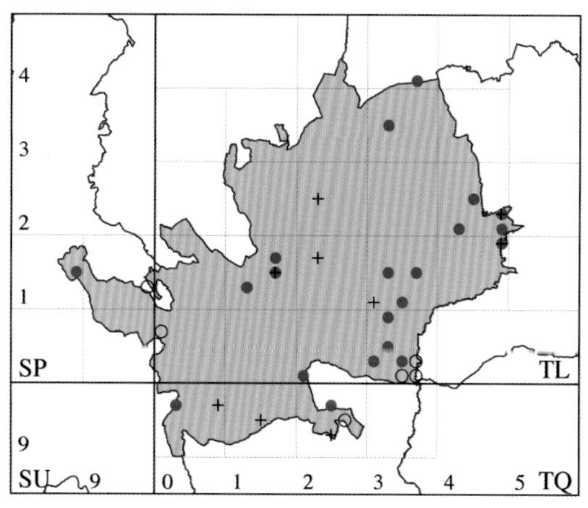

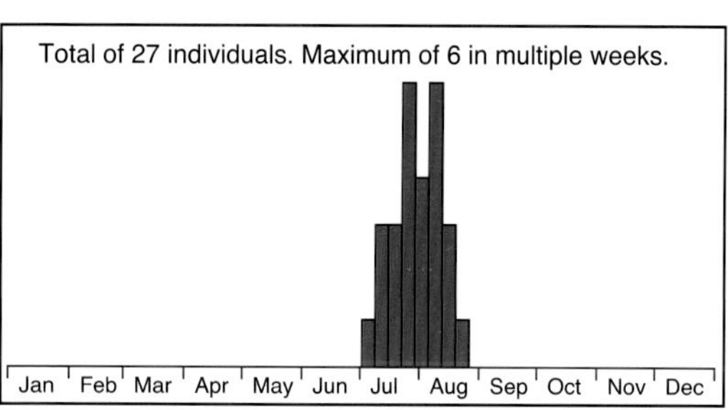

The fact that larvae of this species can thrive on Wych Elm, a tree that in general did not succumb to Dutch Elm Disease in the 1970s, is probably the reason for the relative frequency today of this species in comparison with 2317: White-spotted Pinion. However, the moth is by no means everywhere and it seems probable that there was, and remains, some dependence upon other elm species. At Golden Grove, in the extreme south-east of the county near High Wych, I disturbed dozens of the moths from semi-mature English Elm arising as 'suckers' during 2005 – although Wych Elm grows plentifully in the surrounding area as the name of the village implies.

2317 *Cosmia diffinis* (L.) White-spotted Pinion

Recorded:	1828 – 1978
Distribution / Status:	Absent / Former resident
Conservation status:	UK BAP Priority Species. Herts Extinct
Caterpillar food plants:	Not recorded. Elsewhere, on English Elm and other elms
Flight period:	Elsewhere, July to September
Records in database:	21

Prior to the 1950s (the open circles on the map), the White-spotted Pinion was apparently a widespread and quite common moth in the southern half of Hertfordshire. Outlying northern records are from Hitchin in 1914 (A. H. Foster) and from Bishops Stortford in 1936 (Clifford Craufurd). However,

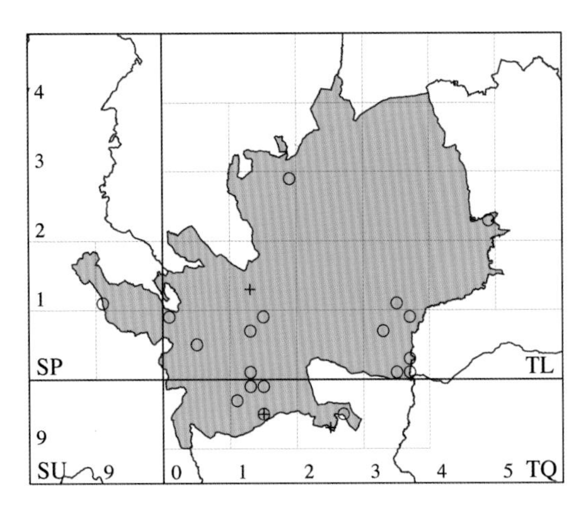

the map shows clearly that the moth had vanished long before the 1970s epidemic of Dutch Elm disease, to which the national decline is popularly attributed. Although the disease certainly contributed it may have just been the final nail in the coffin, masking whatever may have been the real reason for the sudden and drastic decline. The last Hertfordshire record is from Totteridge, on 10th September 1978 (Ian Lorimer), though most populations were extinct by about 1976.

2318 *Cosmia trapezina* (L.) Dun-bar

Recorded: 1884 – 2006
Distribution / Status: Ubiquitous / Common resident
Conservation status: Herts Stable
Caterpillar food plants: Hornbeam; English Elm, English Oak. Elsewhere, on various trees
Flight period: Late June to late August
Records in database: 904

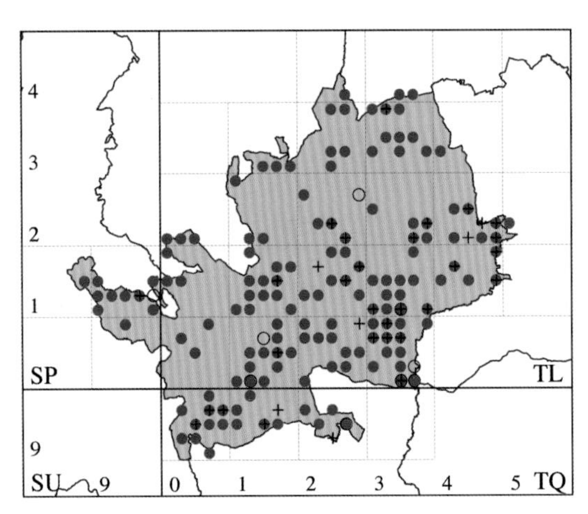

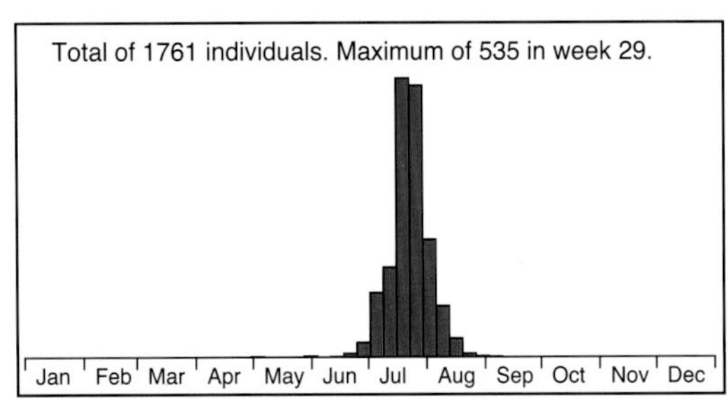

Almost all places where there are trees will produce the Dun-bar moth, which appears in a variety of colour forms, some more striking than others. The specimen of ab. *badiofasciata* Teich figured on plate 36, figure 31 in Skinner (1998), in which the central trapezoid band is entirely black was taken at Broxbourne Wood on 19th August 1984; the specimen of the equally uncommon ab. *nigra* Tutt shown on plate 36, figure 30, was also taken in Broxbourne Wood, on 4th June 1989. A

further ab. *badiofasciata* was caught by myself and Charles Watson in Lucas Wood, near Stevenage, on 23rd July 2001.

2319 *Cosmia pyralina* ([D.& S.]) Lunar-spotted Pinion

Recorded: 1888 – 2006
Distribution / Status: Local / Common resident
Conservation status: Herts Stable
Caterpillar food plants: Not recorded. Elsewhere, on elm, hawthorn, apple and other trees
Flight period: July to early August
Records in database: 131

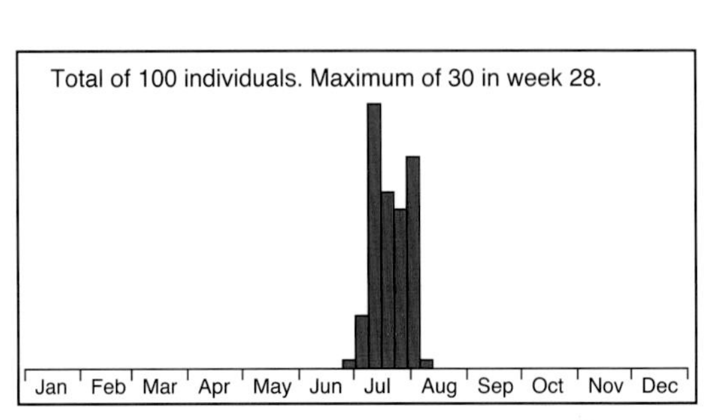

This is a tolerably widespread and frequently encountered moth in most of the county and the lack of records from the north may reflect the partially tree-less arable landscape, but the moth is surely likely to be present in several, perhaps, isolated places.

2321 *Apamea monoglypha* (Hufn.) Dark Arches

Recorded:	1884 – 2006
Distribution / Status:	Ubiquitous / Abundant resident
Conservation status:	Herts Stable
Caterpillar food plants:	Not recorded. Elsewhere, on grasses
Flight period:	June to August
Records in database:	1838

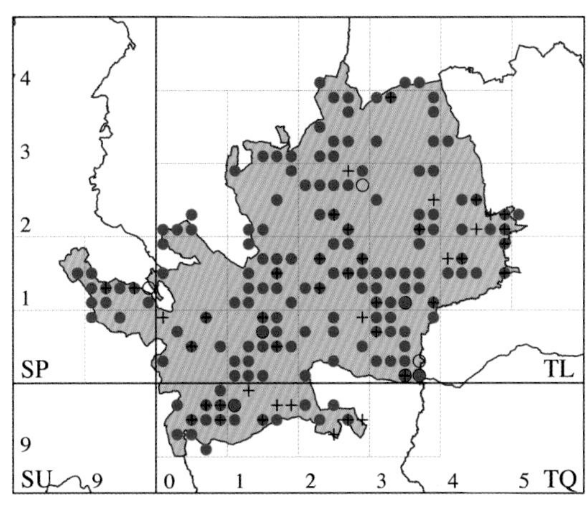

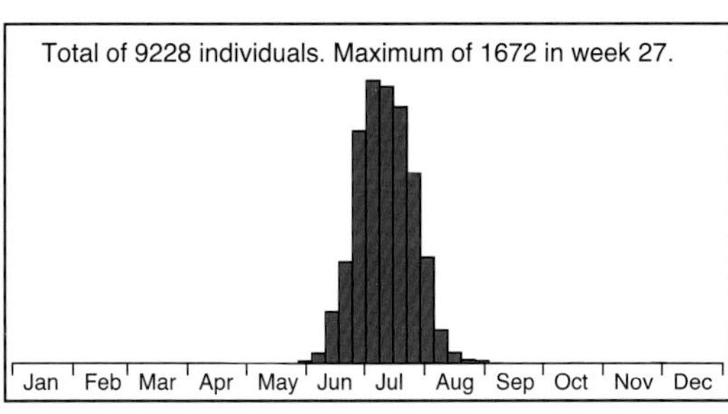

The Dark Arches often attends light traps in large number and there can surely be no site list that does not include this species. The black form, ab. *aethiops* Tutt, which affected about one third of east London examples when I lived there during the early 1980s, appears to be vanishingly rare in Hertfordshire, though doubtless some examples go unreported. Exceptionally late examples were noted by me at Bishops Stortford on 18th October 2006 (in same trap as an equally unseasonal 2089: Heart and Dart) and at Ware, on 27th November 2006 (Elizabeth Goodyear). Interestingly, on this latter date Richard Ellis also caught an example – at Chorleywood, a short distance inside the Buckinghamshire vice-county.

2322 *Apamea lithoxylaea* ([D.& S.]) Light Arches

Recorded:	1884 – 2006
Distribution / Status:	Ubiquitous / Common resident
Conservation status:	Herts Stable
Caterpillar food plants:	Not recorded. Elsewhere, on grasses
Flight period:	June/July
Records in database:	657

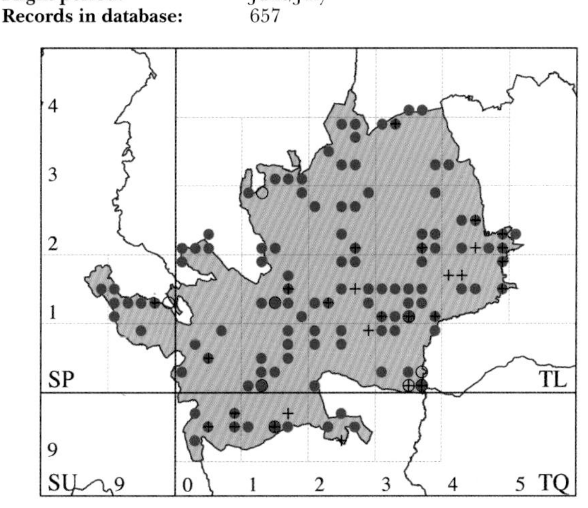

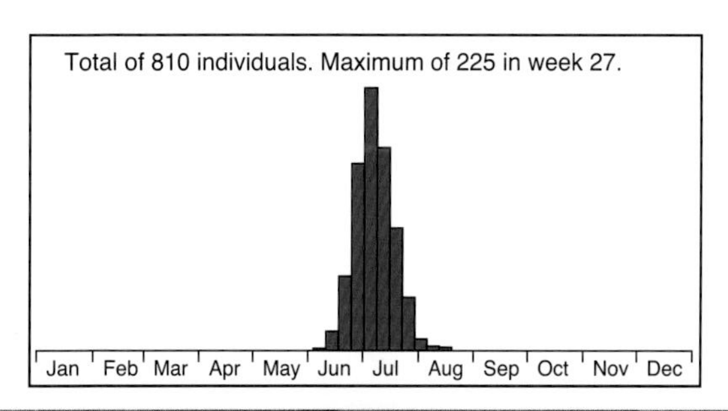

Some examples of Light Arches can be quite reddish and may be confused with 2323: Reddish Light Arches, but in such cases the absence of a post-median line on the hind wing immediately identifies the Light Arches. The moth is numerous across the entire county, yet we have no idea of the species of grass that it feeds upon.

2323 *Apamea sublustris* (Esp.) Reddish Light Arches

Recorded:	1901 – 2006
Distribution / Status:	Local / Common resident
Conservation status:	Herts Scarce
Caterpillar food plants:	Unknown in Britain
Flight period:	June/July
Records in database:	35

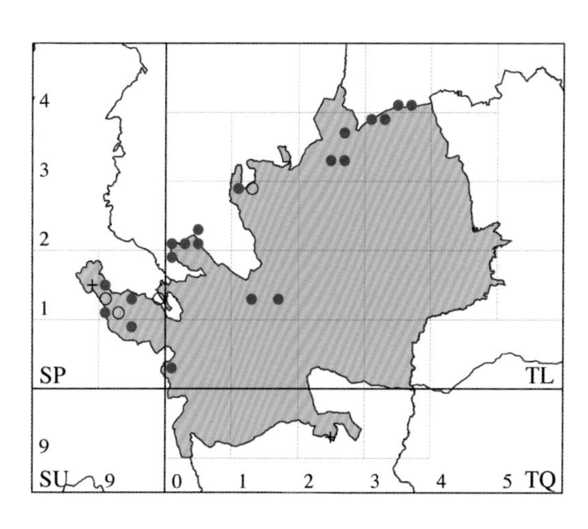

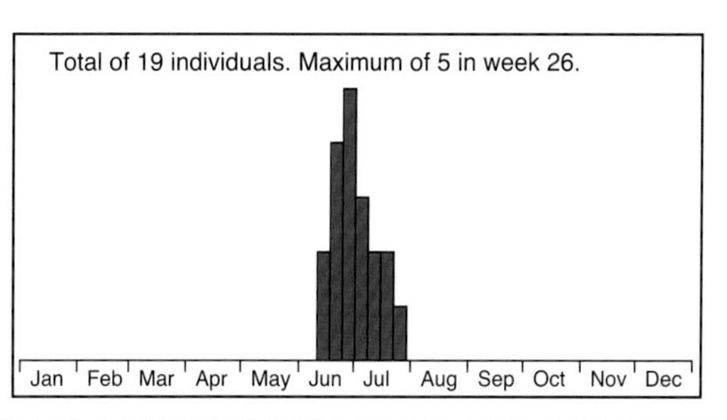

The map shows a clear association with chalk habitats on the north-west borders with Cambridgeshire, Bedfordshire and Buckinghamshire. Exceptions are at Totteridge on 4th July 1973 (Ian Lorimer), Harpenden, 23rd July 1996 (Riley, 1999), Bovingdon Brick Pits, 4th June 2006 (Colin Plant) and Wheathampstead, 18th July 2006 (Trevor Chapman). The records from Totteridge, Harpenden and Wheathampstead were probably wanderers from further afield but the Bovingdon site produced several examples suggesting a local population. This is a surprise as a clay-pit habitat is expected to be acid rather than calcareous.

[2325 *Apamea oblonga* (Haworth) Crescent Striped

Erroneously recorded. Foster (1945) records an example taken in Bishops Stortford in 1907 by C. S. Colman. This unlikely record was omitted by P. B. M. Allan from his 1950 list of moths in the Bishops Stortford district; it cannot be substantiated. The alleged example taken at Whetstone, in the administrative county of Hertfordshire, on 25 July 1962 by P. Ward and noted in both de Worms (1964) and Bell (1964) relates to Middlesex not the Hertfordshire Vice-county. Ward (1964) also notes that 'two were taken at Rothamsted in 1960 (though not then reported to me) apart from which the only record is from Bishops Stortford in 1907'. The Rothamsted records are not mentioned in the review by Riley (1999). They are not included in the permanent database at Rothamsted and no record is kept of deletions, though one assumes that these records must have been so treated and so Riley cannot be blamed for missing this information. There is, therefore, no evidence sufficient to permit the admission of this strictly coastal species to the Hertfordshire fauna.]

2326 *Apamea crenata* (Hufn.) Clouded-bordered Brindle

Recorded:	1828 – 2006
Distribution / Status:	Local / Common resident
Conservation status:	Herts Stable
Caterpillar food plants:	Not recorded. Elsewhere, on grasses
Flight period:	May to July
Records in database:	167

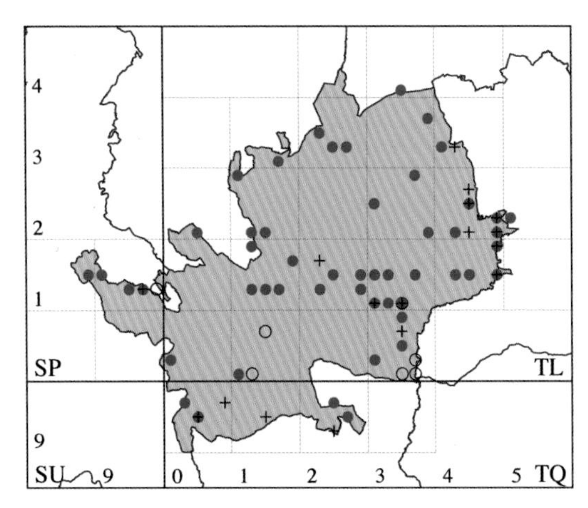

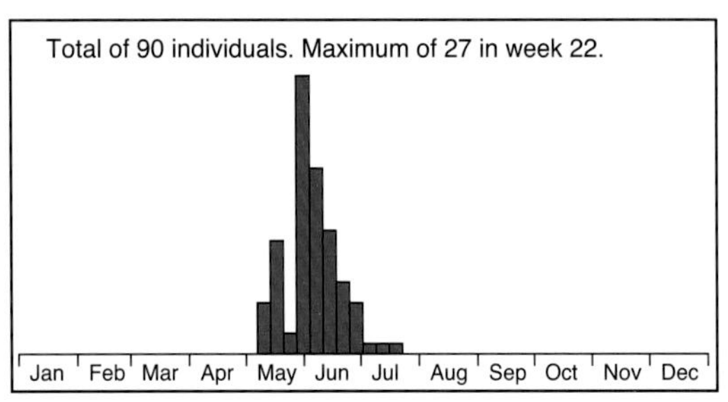

Some examples of the Clouded-bordered Brindle are confusingly similar to 2323: Reddish Light Arches, and in some sites both species can be found together during June. Most semi-natural grasslands of reasonable size are likely to support this species, including woodland clearings and rides. There is a tendency towards favouring damp grasslands, but not all records are from wet areas. Regularly mown swards and recently disturbed habitats, including most roadside verges, appear unsuitable. The more or less uniformly reddish-brown ab. *combusta* Haworth occurs occasionally, but appears to represent only about 10 per cent of the population in Hertfordshire.

2327 *Apamea epomidion* (Haw.) Clouded Brindle

Recorded:	1888 – 2006
Distribution / Status:	Local / Common resident
Conservation status:	Herts Stable
Caterpillar food plants:	Not recorded. Elsewhere, on grasses
Flight period:	Late May to July
Records in database:	181

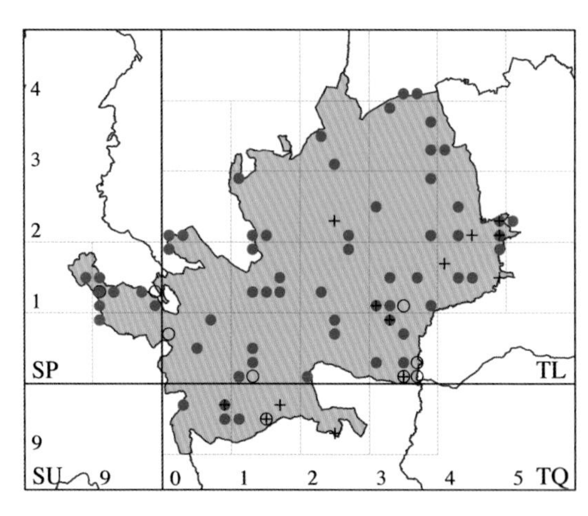

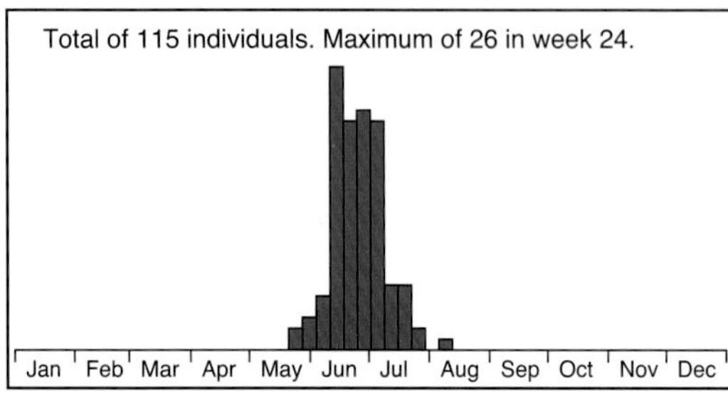

Although marginally more frequent than 2326: Clouded-bordered Brindle, the Clouded Brindle is nevertheless decidedly local in its occurrence in Hertfordshire and in numerical terms the two species are pretty much equally common. Arising from work on the London Area (Plant, 1993) was the discovery that in the northern part of that area, which included the southern third of Hertfordshire, Clouded Brindle was less common than the Clouded-bordered Brindle; for the period 1995 to 2006 this situation seems to be reversed and the map shows rather more sites for the present species.

2329 *Apamea furva* ([D.& S.]) Confused

Recorded: 1902 – 1902
Distribution / Status: Absent / Former vagrant
Conservation status: -
Caterpillar food plants: Not recorded. Elsewhere, on Rough Meadow Grass and Wood Meadow-grass
Flight period: Elsewhere, July/August
Records in database: 1

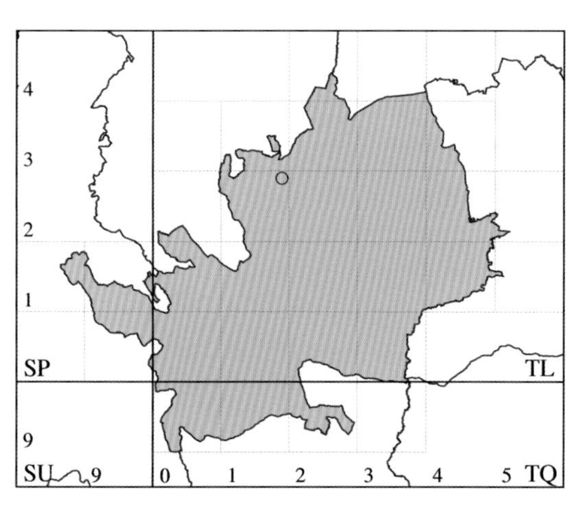

The Confused has a north-western distribution in Britain and is practically unknown south-east of the Severn – Humber line. Gibbs (1904a) records that one was taken at a light inside The Grange, Hitchin, by A. H. Foster in 1902. Gibbs was clearly aware of the significance of the record, noting that it was a 'west-country hill-frequenting species' that was entirely unexpected in Hertfordshire, but added that C. G. Barrett had confirmed the identification. It had initially been misidentified [by Foster?] as *Mamestra brassicae* – the Cabbage Moth.

2330 *Apamea remissa* (Hb.) Dusky Brocade

Recorded: 1828 – 2006
Distribution / Status: Widespread / Common resident
Conservation status: UK BAP Watch List
No peceived threats in Hertfordshire
Caterpillar food plants: Not recorded. Elsewhere, on grasses
Flight period: Late May to early September
Records in database: 185

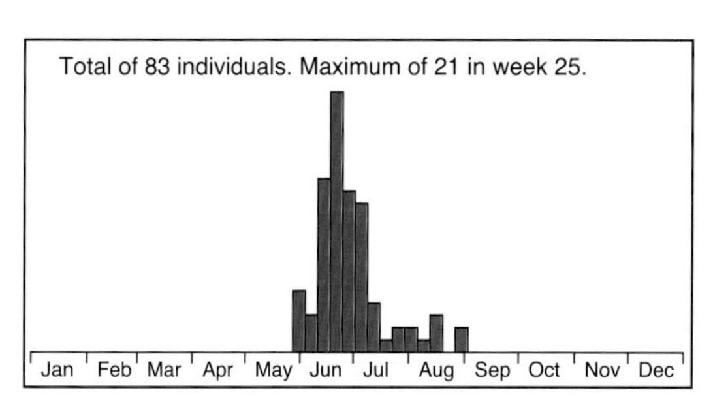

Typical forms of Dusky Brocade appear to form only a small proportion of the population in Hertfordshire and when they arrive at light traps sometime cause confusion. The bulk of the population, perhaps 80 per cent, conforms to f. *obscura* Haworth, though identification and reporting of the forms is rarely undertaken and some examples of the intermediate f. *submissa* Treitschke are probably written down as *obscura*. Nationally, this moth is said to be declining in numbers, but there is no data that confirms or denies such a trend in Hertfordshire.

2331 *Apamea unanimis* (Hb.) Small Clouded Brindle

Recorded: 1888 – 2006
Distribution / Status: Local / Common resident
Conservation status: Herts Stable
Caterpillar food plants: Striped Ribbon Grass
Flight period: May to July
Records in database: 132

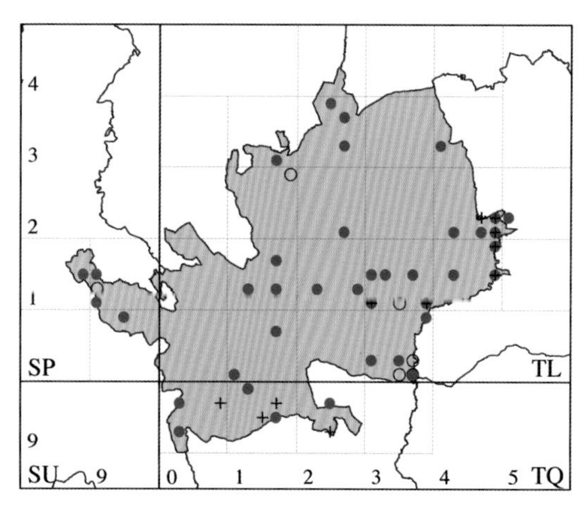

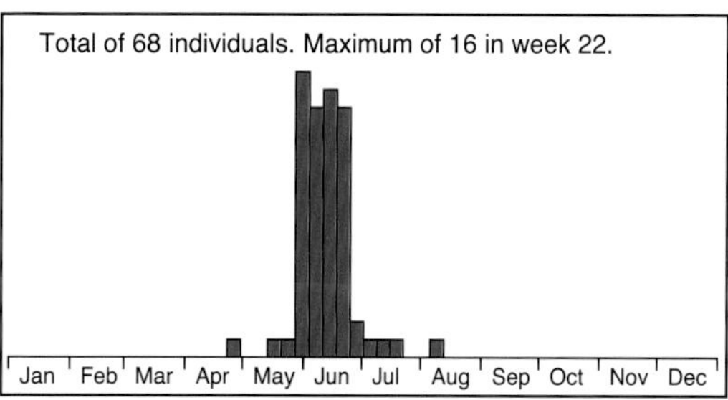

The textbooks tell us that damp grassland, of varying types, is the habitat of this moth, but whilst many records from Hertfordshire conform to this expectation the moth also has a habit of turning up in garden moth traps where the habitat appears to be unsuitable. Further investigation into this is desirable; our only larval foodplant record was made as long ago as 1902. For the London Area, I noted (Plant, 1993) an absence from urbanised areas and this seems to be more or less repeated for Hertfordshire, though our county's version of 'urban' is mild in comparison to that of London.

2332 *Eremobina pabulatricula* (Brahm) Union Rustic

Recorded: 1935 – 1935
Distribution / Status: Absent / Extinct (in Britain)
Conservation status: –
Caterpillar food plants: Not recorded. Elsewhere, on grasses
Flight period: Elsewhere, July/August
Records in database: 1

A single record from Bushey Heath in 1935 (Rev. J. A. K. Hervey) is the only Hertfordshire record of this former British resident; this is also the last known British record.

2333 *Apamea anceps* ([D.& S.]) Large Nutmeg

Recorded: 1884 – 2006
Distribution / Status: Ubiquitous / Common resident
Conservation status: UK BAP Watch List
Herts Stable
Caterpillar food plants: Not recorded. Elsewhere, on grasses
Flight period: Late May to early July
Records in database: 608

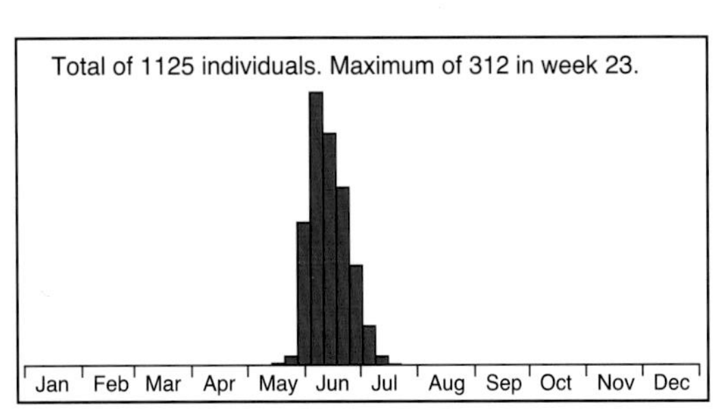

Although regarded as ubiquitous in Hertfordshire, the Large Nutmeg is generally far more numerous in towns than it is in open countryside. This may have bearing on the perceived national decline in population reported from the Rothamsted Light Trap Network – most of these traps are sited in a generally rural setting.

2334 *Apamea sordens* (Hufn.) Rustic Shoulder-knot

Recorded: 1884 – 2006
Distribution / Status: Ubiquitous / Common resident
Conservation status: Herts Stable
Caterpillar food plants: Not recorded. Elsewhere, on grasses
Flight period: May to early July
Records in database: 481

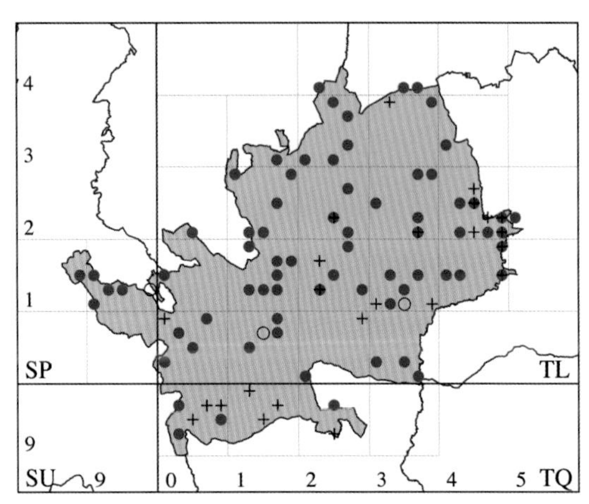

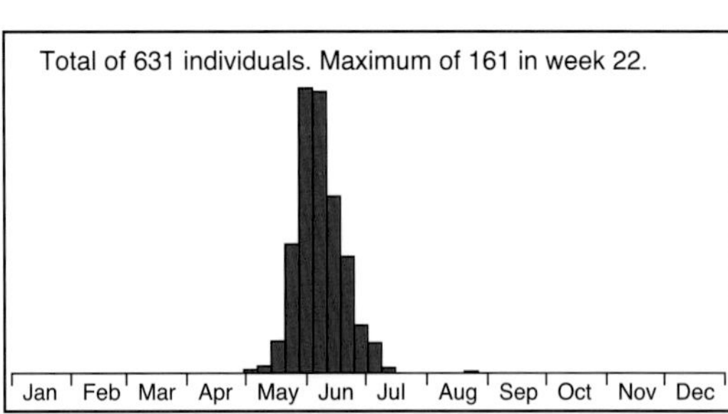

As with 2333: Large Nutmeg, this moth is at its most plentiful in suburban gardens and though present in wayside and woodland is far less numerically common there. The distribution maps for the two species are remarkably similar.

2335 *Apamea scolopacina* (Esp.) Slender Brindle

Recorded: 1932 – 2006
Distribution / Status: Local / Common resident
Conservation status: Stable or increasing
Caterpillar food plants: Not recorded. Elsewhere, on grasses
Flight period: June to August
Records in database: 107

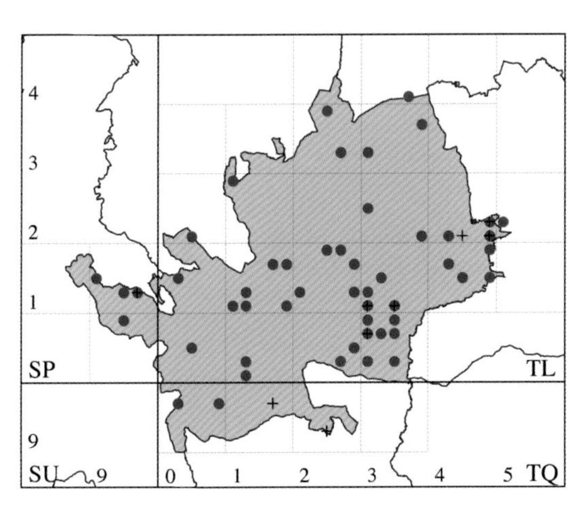

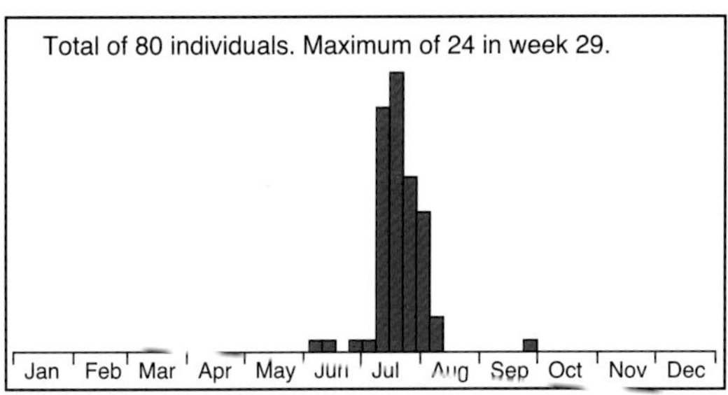

Interestingly, this appears to have been a rare moth until quite recently, as the absence of historical records on the distribution map shows. Foster (1937) lists only two captures — from Broxbourne Woods, on rush blossom (Edelsten) and Aldenham Wood, at sugar in 1932 (H. King). The Edelsten record cannot be dated, but certainly pre-dates the Aldenham sighting. Allan (1950) does not include this species in his list for Bishops Stortford; in the update to this list, Fielding et al (1985) record it as 'rare' with one example in Bishops Stortford on 12th August 1958 and another at Takeley, on the Essex side of the boundary, on 18th July 1976. For adjacent Essex, Emmet et al (1985) present a map showing the moth distributed in the south and east of that county, the only record within striking distance of our border being that from Takeley listed by Allen. However, twenty years later, Goodey (2004) shows a number of post-1990 records in the west of Essex, adjacent to our boundary, and elsewhere. Emmet et al also noted that it was 'probably increasing in numbers and extending its range'; it appears he was correct. To our north, it was listed as local and uncommon in Bedfordshire (Arnold et al, 1997). A surprisingly late, but correct record was made at Bishops Stortford on 27th September 2004 (James Fish & Julian Reeves).

2336 *Apamea ophiogramma* (Esp.) Double Lobed

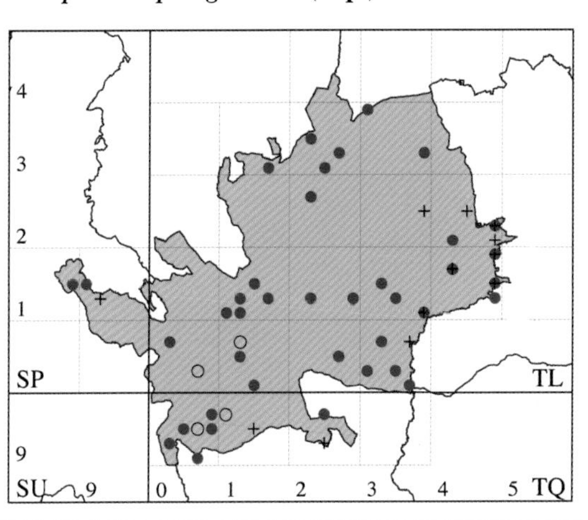

Recorded:	1892 - 2006
Distribution / Status:	Local / Common resident
Conservation status:	Herts Stable
Caterpillar food plants:	Not recorded. Elsewhere, Reed Canary-grass and Reed Sweet-grass
Flight period:	Late June to mid-August
Records in database:	99

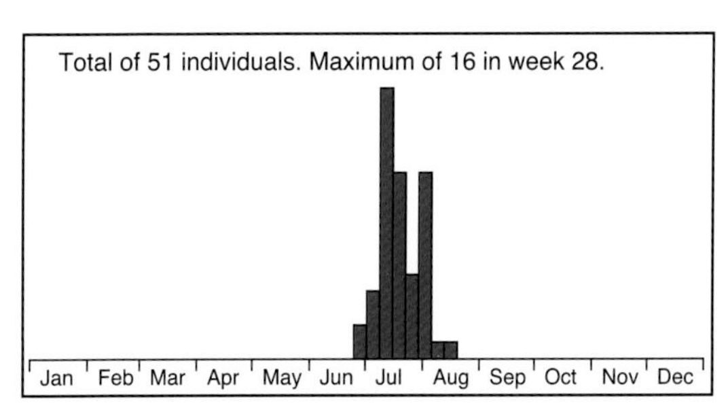

Damp habitats feature prominently at or near many of the known sites for this species, though not exclusively so perhaps suggesting that the adult moths can disperse some distance away from their natal area. However, the need for habitat that is at least partly damp goes some way towards explaining the lack of records in large parts of the north central area of the county. The melanic ab. *moerens* Staudinger, illustrated but not named in Skinner (1998), was recorded at Totteridge in 1975 and 1976, both as single examples, by Ian Lorimer.

The Marbled Minor complex

The Marbled, Tawny Marbled and Rufous Minor cannot be reliably named unless their genitalia are examined. External characters may sometimes provide an indication, but very often critical examination proves supposition incorrect. This is especially the case for Rufous Minor, of which almost all records have been shown to be wrong; this is a rare species in Hertfordshire. Only males in which the genitalia have been seen and a very few dissected females are included in the maps and flight charts for these three species. Old records of Marbled Minor largely predate the discovery of the other species and are treated as unreliable because specimens have not yet been traced and dissected.

2337 *Oligia strigilis* (L.) Marbled Minor

Recorded:	1971 - 2006
Distribution / Status:	Ubiquitous / Common resident
Conservation status:	Herts Stable
Caterpillar food plants:	Not recorded. Elsewhere, on grasses
Flight period:	Late May to July
Records in database:	441

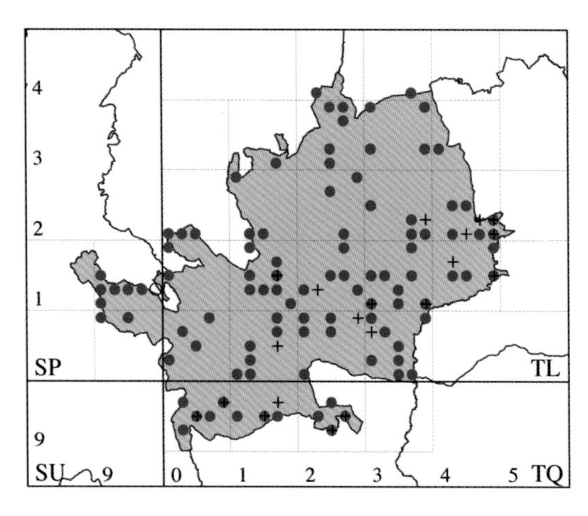

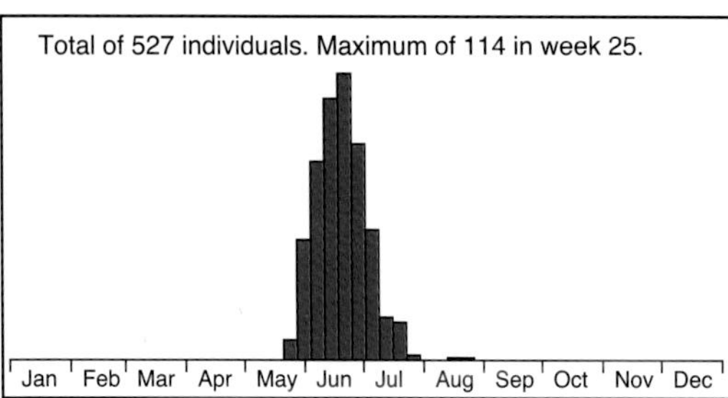

Specimens with a good deal of bright white on the outer band of the forewing are often Marbled Minor, but Tawny Marbled Minor also throws this form. More or less entirely melanic examples can be either species. Of the 23 Marbled Minors entering my light trap in Bishops Stortford during 2006, eight were of were the entirely dark form and fifteen had the white outer band.

2338 *Oligia versicolor* (Borkh.) Rufous Minor

Recorded: 1974 – 2006
Distribution / Status: Extremely local / Rare resident
Conservation status: Herts Scarce
Caterpillar food plants: Not recorded. Elsewhere, on grasses
Flight period: Late May to July
Records in database: 21

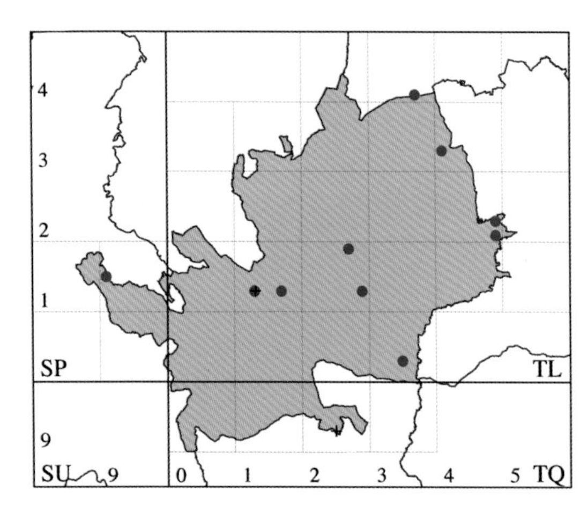

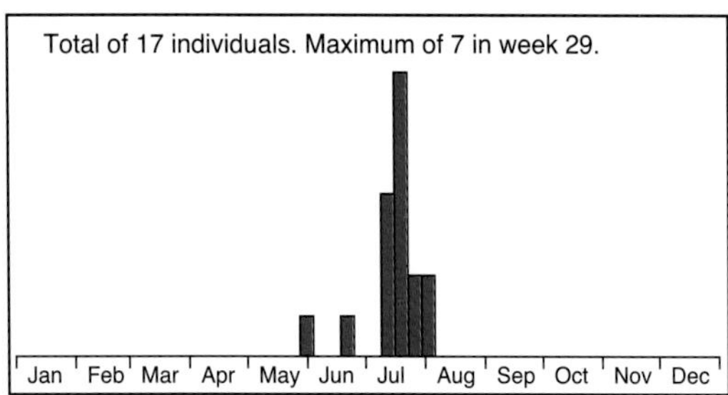

Of the 21 acceptable records in the database, half (eleven) were made during July 2005 and suggest vagrancy, immigration or both; there was only a single record in 2006 (from Royston, by John Chainey and Jenny Spence). Discounting the 2005 records, there are only six sites for this species in the county.

2339 *Oligia latruncula* ([D.& S.]) Tawny Marbled Minor

Recorded: 1971 – 2006
Distribution / Status: Ubiquitous / Common resident
Conservation status: Herts Stable
Caterpillar food plants: Not recorded. Elsewhere, on grasses
Flight period: Late May to July
Records in database: 588

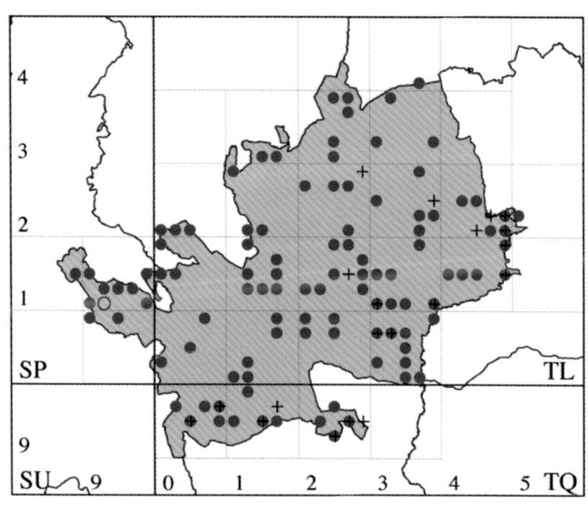

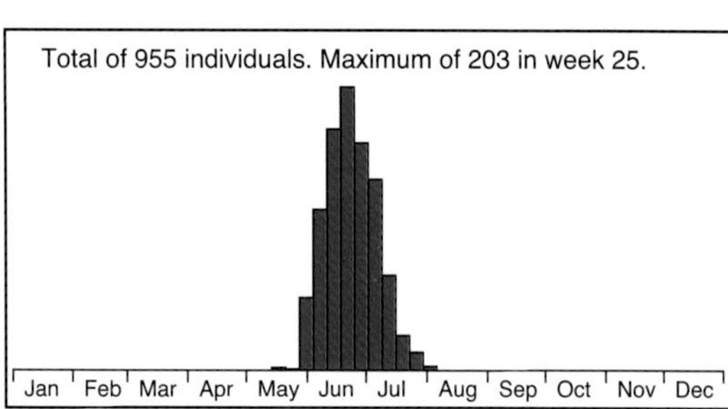

Of the 58 Marbled Minors entering my light trap in Bishops Stortford during 2006, 45 were of the entirely dark form and 13 had a white outer band.

2340 *Oligia fasciuncula* (Haw.) Middle-barred Minor

Recorded: 1828 – 2006
Distribution / Status: Widespread / Common resident
Conservation status: Herts Stable
Caterpillar food plants: Not recorded. Elsewhere, on grasses
Flight period: Late May to early August
Records in database: 305

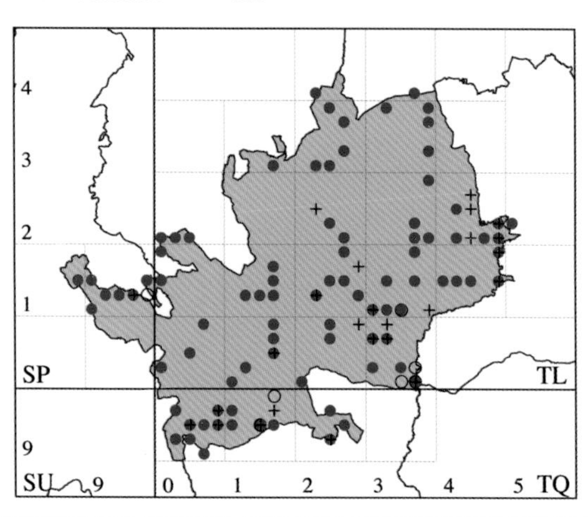

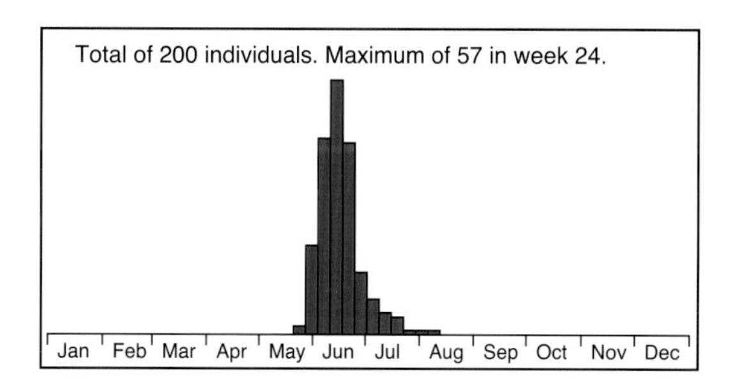

Woodland produces the bulk of the records of this distinctive species, though other sites also support it and damp habitat also seems likely to be important. There is some variation in the ground colour of the forewings, but the basic pattern is usually easily discernible making this an easy moth to identify.

2341 *Mesoligia furuncula* ([D.& S.]) Cloaked Minor

Recorded: 1828 – 2006
Distribution / Status: Widespread / Common resident
Conservation status: Herts Stable
Caterpillar food plants: Not recorded. Elsewhere, on grasses
Flight period: Late June to August
Records in database: 494

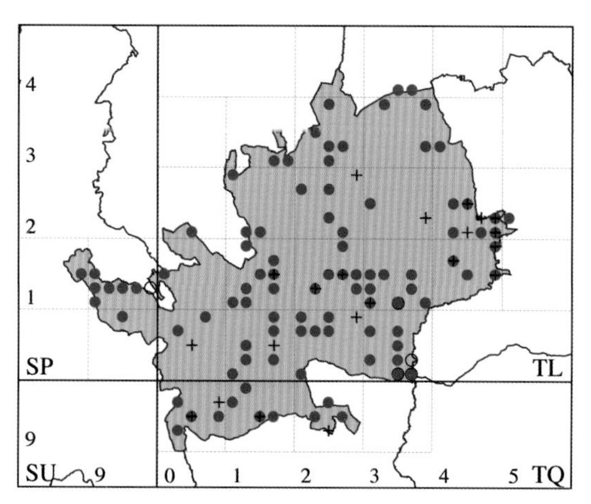

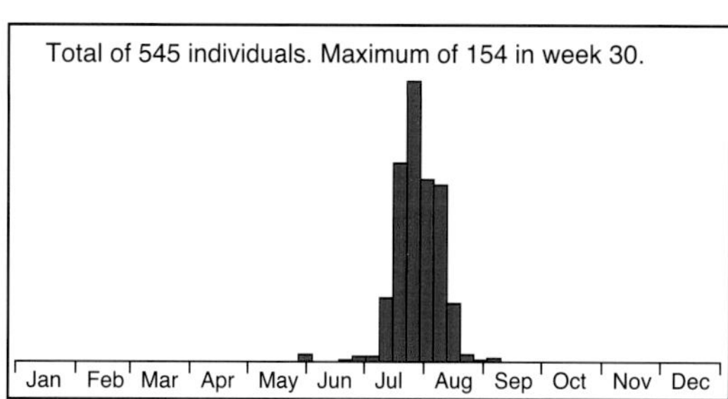

The comment that I made for the London Area (Plant, 1993) that 'almost every grassland area will produce this moth' appears to hold true for Hertfordshire. It is on most garden lists and is rarely absent from lists made on recording trips at the correct time of year. The adult moth varies considerably on the basic theme of dark inner and light outer halves to the forewings and in some examples this distinction is practically lost so that the wings are near uniform. Many varieties occur in our county, but no detailed record appears to have been kept.

2342 *Mesoligia literosa* (Haw.) Rosy Minor

Recorded: 1884 – 2006
Distribution / Status: Very local / Common resident
Conservation status: UK BAP Watch List
Herts Scarce
Caterpillar food plants: Not recorded. Elsewhere, on grasses
Flight period: Mid-June to early August
Records in database: 242

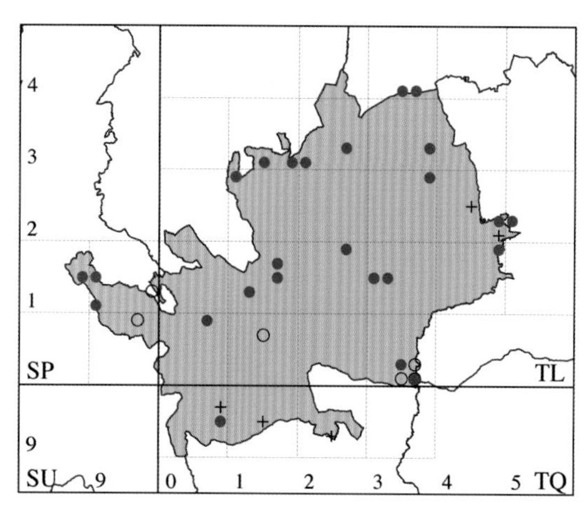

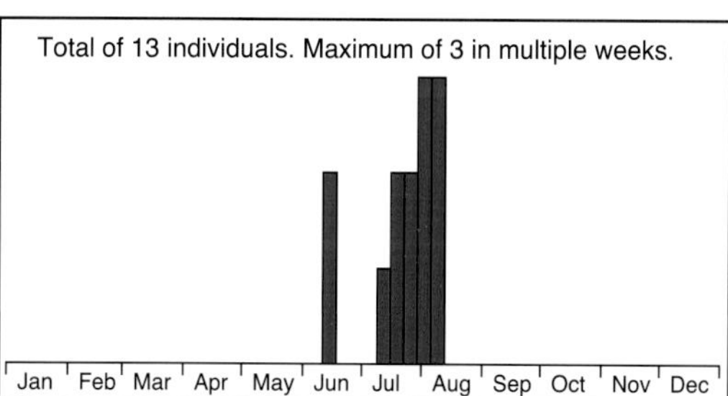

The Rosy Minor appears to be quite scarce in Hertfordshire. However, whilst the map shows many gaps the better recorded sites, those where nightly recording has been undertaken over a lengthy period of years, mostly seem to have this species listed. The attractive and distinctive ab. *aethalodes* Richardson is apparently not recorded in the county.

The Common Rustic/Lesser Common Rustic complex

Records of Common Rustic made prior to 1983, when the Lesser Common Rustic was recognised as a separate species, are disregarded. Neither species can be identified without recourse to examination of the male genitalia and only those records made in this manner are included in the maps or the flight charts for either species. Most people who record only in their gardens have supplied candidate specimens for both species until such time as both are at last recorded and then ceased collecting. As a result we have excellent and reliable distribution maps, but only limited numerical data for the proportions of each species. Although sampling in this manner has produced about twice as many records of Common Rustic as those of Lesser Common Rustic (575 compared to 224), sampling was not random and may only reflect the proportions of the colour forms selected as candidates. Local variations are likely to occur in the proportions coming to light traps.

2343 *Mesapamea secalis* (L.) Common Rustic

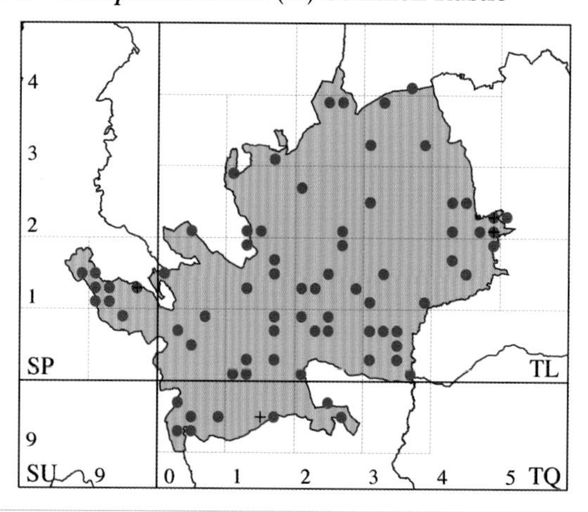

Recorded: 1973 – 2006
Distribution / Status: Widespread / Common resident
Conservation status: Herts Stable
Caterpillar food plants: Not recorded. Elsewhere, on grasses
Flight period: July/August
Records in database: 575

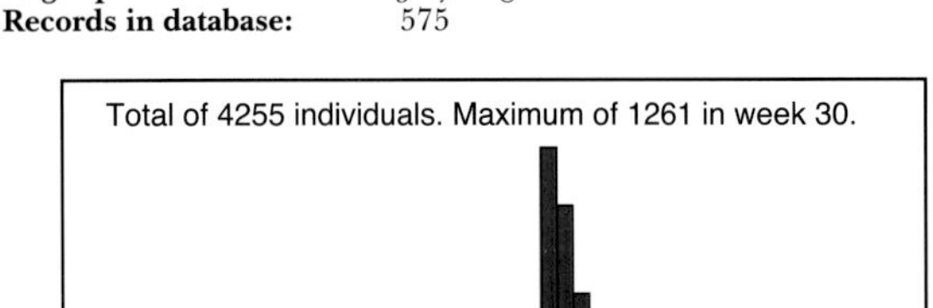

All Hertfordshire examples that conform to the pattern exhibited by the specimen at Figure 2 on Plate 38 of Skinner (1984; 1998), in which the entire hind edge of the forewing is pale and the entire costal edge is brown, have proved on dissection to be this species. However, specimens with an identical pattern, but with an all-over reddish-brown tinge to the wing tend to be *didyma*. The more unicolourous examples, with or without a prominent white discal spot (Figures 1 and 3 in Skinner), are a mixture of both species. The Common Rustic is numerically abundant in comparison with the Lesser Common Rustic.

2343a *Mesapamea didyma* (Esp.) Lesser Common Rustic

Recorded: 1975 – 2006
Distribution / Status: Widespread / Common resident
Conservation status: Herts Stable
Caterpillar food plants: Not recorded. Elsewhere, on grasses
Flight period: July/August
Records in database: 224

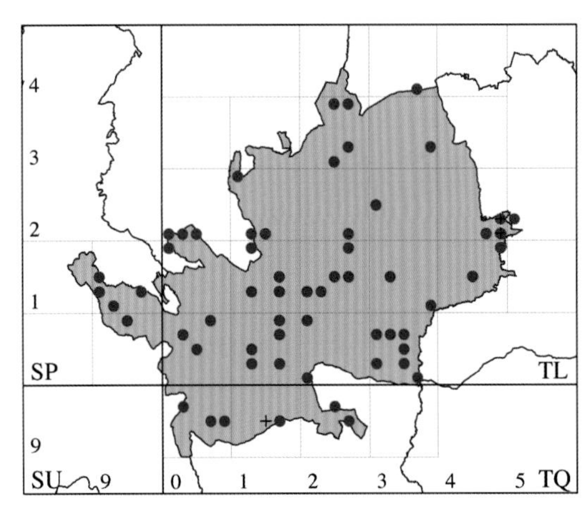

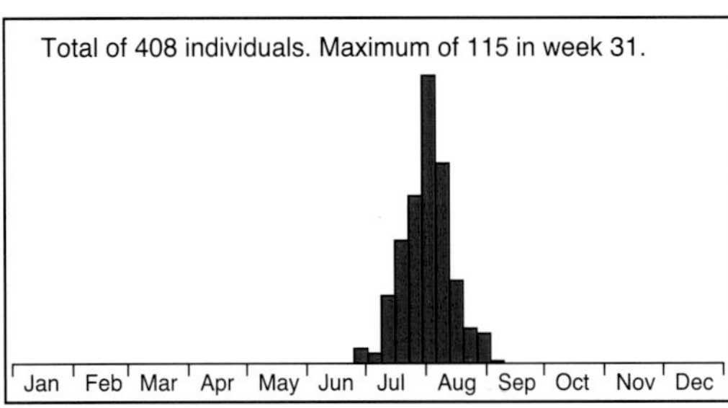

Skinner (1984; 1998) contends that all-black examples with a prominent white discal spot (his Figure 5 on Plate 38) 'are invariably *M. didyma*'. I do not have any Hertfordshire examples that contradict this, but I do indeed have one such example from Slovakia that is *secalis* not *didyma*, suggesting that placing trust in this as a diagnostic character is potentially risky.

Available data suggests that Lesser Common Rustic is considerably less numerically abundant than Common Rustic in this county.

2345 *Photedes minima* (Haw.) Small Dotted Buff

Recorded: 1828 – 2006
Distribution / Status: Widespread / Common resident
Conservation status: Herts Stable
Caterpillar food plants: Not recorded. Elsewhere, in the stems of Tufted Hair-grass
Flight period: Mid-June to early August
Records in database: 94

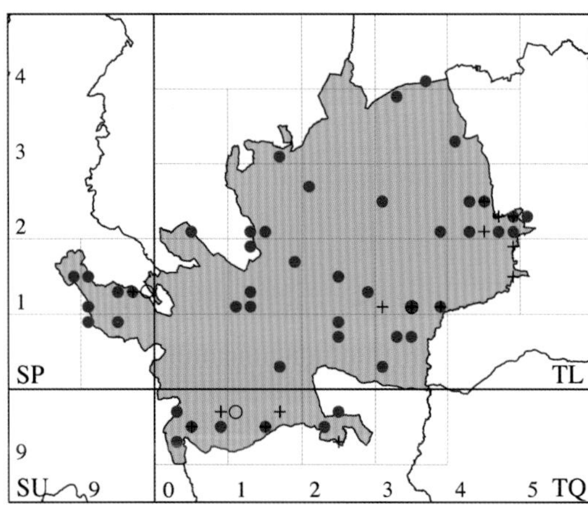

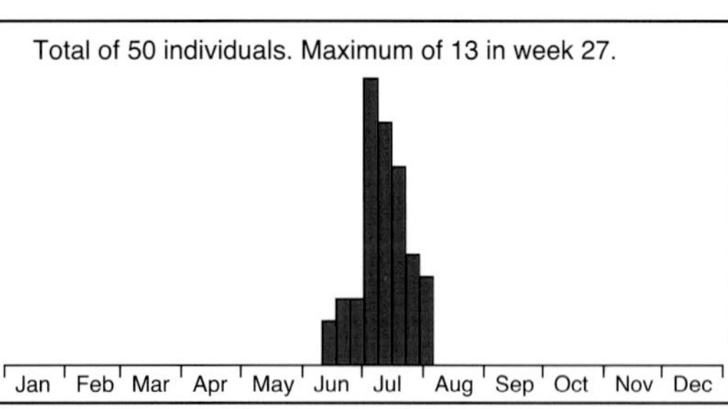

Damp habitats, especially woodlands but also more open habitats such as marshes and river banks, support this species, which is probably under-recorded in the county to some degree. Males are often encountered before dark whilst setting up the lights, in many cases disturbed by the activities of the moth enthusiast.

2349 *Chortodes fluxa* (Hb.) Mere Wainscot

Recorded: 1880 – 2000
Distribution / Status: Random / Immigrant
Conservation status: –
Caterpillar food plants: Not recorded. Elsewhere, internally in stems of Wood Small-reed
Flight period: Elsewhere, July/August
Records in database: 3

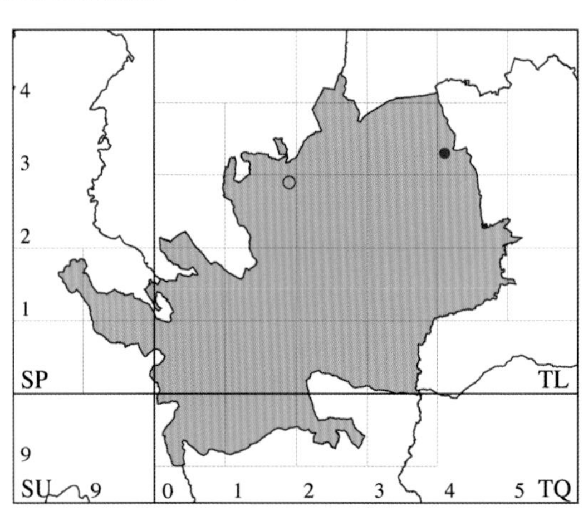

Gibbs (1904a) notes that 'One example of this species (*Tapinostola Hellmanni* Evers.) came to light at Mr Foster's residence, The Grange, Hitchin, at about 12 o'clock midnight, and being an unexpected capture .... it has been submitted to Mr C. G. Barrett ... and he pronounces it to be correctly named'. Unfortunately, the year is not given. The report is for 1903, but in opening the report and stating that nine new species have been added to the Hertfordshire list, Gibbs comments that not all were made in the year under review. However, Foster himself clarifies the situation, and adds an earlier record, in his 1937 county list where he gives 'Hitchin, 1880 (S. Tuke) and 1903 (A. H. Foster)'. Presumably the Hertfordshire record noted by Meyrick (1928, *Revised Handbook*, page 75) refers to one or both of these. Our only other record is from Scales Park, in the north-east of the county, where Jim Reid caught one on 22nd July 2000. Although this moth is resident in parts of Suffolk, Bernard Skinner informs me that it has also occurred around fifty or so times as an immigrant in Britain: the Hertfordshire reports do not seem to suggest residency.

2350 *Chortodes pygmina* (Haw.) Small Wainscot

Recorded:	1828 – 2006
Distribution / Status:	Very local / Common resident
Conservation status:	Herts Scarce
Caterpillar food plants:	Not recorded. Elsewhere, internally in stems of Lesser Pond Sedge and probably other sedges
Flight period:	July to October
Records in database:	43

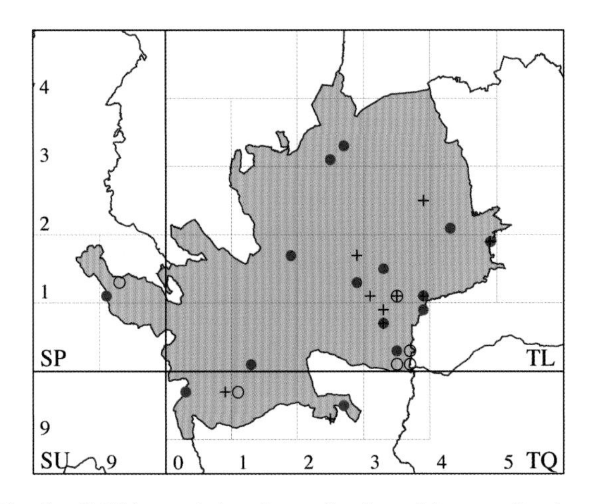

The Small Wainscot is largely confined to older woodlands on clay which are, as a result of their underlying geology, damp. Adults are recorded throughout July, August and September, but numbers are too low for any meaningful flight chart to be presented.

2352 *Eremobia ochroleuca* ([D.& S.]) Dusky Sallow

Recorded:	1916 – 2006
Distribution / Status:	Local / Common resident
Conservation status:	Herts Stable
Caterpillar food plants:	Not recorded. Elsewhere, on flowers and seeds of grasses
Flight period:	July/August
Records in database:	169

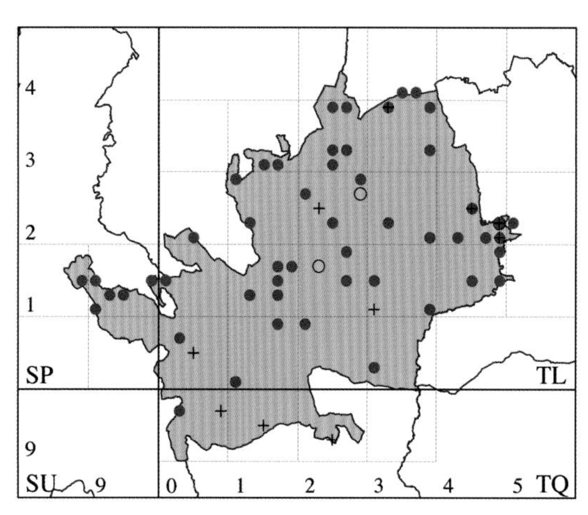

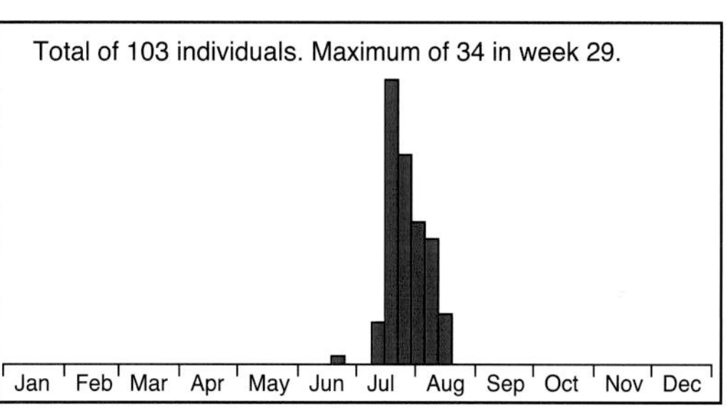

Tradition has this species more or less associated with chalk downland and closely related habitats and in the past this may well have been the case in Hertfordshire. In 1983, the authors of volume 10 of *Moths and Butterflies of Great Britain and Ireland* noted that Dusky Sallow 'appears to have spread in the last fifteen years' – unfortunately we do not have a long enough time series of data to see if this applies in Hertfordshire, but at the present time it is widespread over much of the county away from the chalk but usually associated with the Chalky Boulder Clay or some other base-rich deposit. Our earliest records are those in Foster (1916) who lists Royston Heath, without a date. Later (Foster, 1937) under the heading of '*Hadena ochroleuca* Esp.', he repeats the Royston Heath data, still without dates, but adding several new recorders and so implying that several collectors had taken specimens since the 1916 report. The 1937 paper also lists 'Hitchin' on 18th August 1927. J. Bell noted one on the 'Tring Hills' in 1938 (Foster, 1942); this very probably implies Aldbury Nowers. The spread away from the chalk may have taken place during the 1940s. In addition to the above, J. Birdsall reported one at the Walkern searchlight in 1940 and there was a small number of reports from the Bishops Stortford area – in the town in 1943 and 1944, to the north along Farnham Road and to the west at Stocking Wood, both in 1944, in the Cricket Field area in 1945 and at both Bloodhounds Wood and at Wickham Hall at around the same time (Allan, 1950). Ray Penrose caught one in Watford in 1952 then one was noted at Apsley by N. E. Gammon in 1976. Charles Watson caught one on Patmore Heath in 1980 and the revised Bishops Stortford list, produced in 1985, regarded Dusky Sallow as 'common', though it gave neither detail nor any records. The moth was certainly common across most of the county by 1991 and is perhaps still spreading.

2353 *Luperina testacea* ([D.& S.]) Flounced Rustic

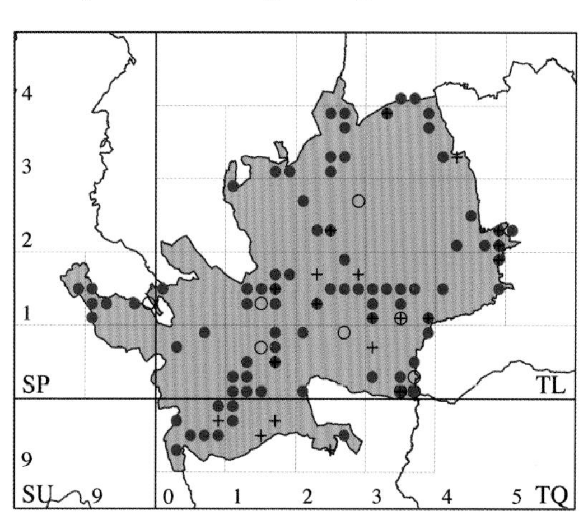

Recorded:	1884 – 2006
Distribution / Status:	Widespread / Common resident
Conservation status:	Herts Stable
Caterpillar food plants:	Not recorded. Elsewhere, on roots and stem bases of grasses
Flight period:	August/September
Records in database:	597

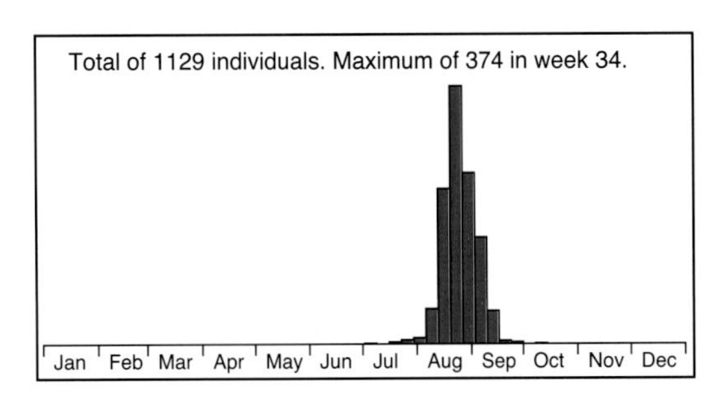

It is quite a surprise to discover that this is not an ubiquitous species; the gaps in the distribution pattern defy explanation. There is no sign of any decline in numbers and no recorded loss from previously occupied sites, so there is no real reason to not expect the moth to be widespread.

2355 *Luperina dumerilii* (Dup.) Dumeril's Rustic

Recorded:	1953 – 1974
Distribution / Status:	Random / Rare immigrant
Conservation status:	-
Caterpillar food plants:	Unknown
Flight period:	September
Records in database:	2

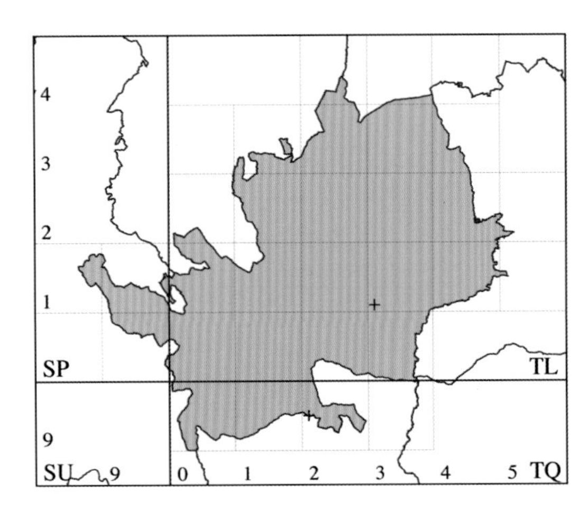

This rare immigrant from the Mediterranean Basin and Asia is reported twice in Hertfordshire: Arkley, a male was captured by T. G. Howarth on 24th September 1953 (*Proc. Trans. South London Entomological & Natural History Society* **1953 – 54**: 32 & *Entomologist's Gazette* **5**: 116); Bayfordbury, one at light on 16th September 1974 by Jim Reid (*Proc. Trans. British Entomological Natural History Society* **16:** 107).

Ear moths

There are four species of 'Ear' moth in Britain. Out of every thousand caught in Hertfordshire, it is reliably predicted that 999 will be 2360: *Amphipoea oculea*, but spotting that one which is not involves dissection of the genitalia. Although many will say otherwise, I am not of the opinion that any species of ear moth can be reliably named on sight and so I have only included in the text, charts and maps those specimens that have been collected and dissected.

2357 *Amphipoea lucens* (Frey.) Large Ear

Recorded:	1990 – 1990
Distribution / Status:	Random / Vagrant
Conservation status:	–
Caterpillar food plants:	Not recorded. Elsewhere, on grasses
Flight period:	Elsewhere, August/September
Records in database:	1

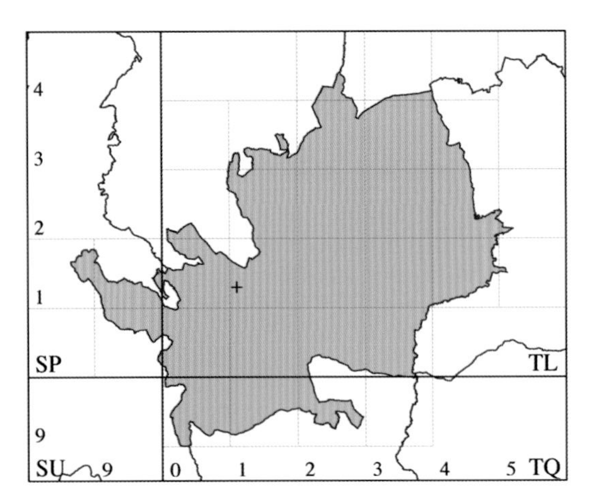

The only acceptable record is that from the Rothamsted Estate at Harpenden on 23rd August 1990 (Riley, 1999). A record for Berkhamsted in 1945 by J. H. Bell (Fryer, 1948) is not thought to have been named by dissection and is omitted from the map – even though it may be correct.

2358 *Amphipoea fucosa paludis* (Tutt) Saltern Ear

Recorded:	1949 – 1979
Distribution / Status:	Random / Rare vagrant
Conservation status:	–
Caterpillar food plants:	Not recorded. Elsewhere, on grasses
Flight period:	Elsewhere, August/September
Records in database:	2

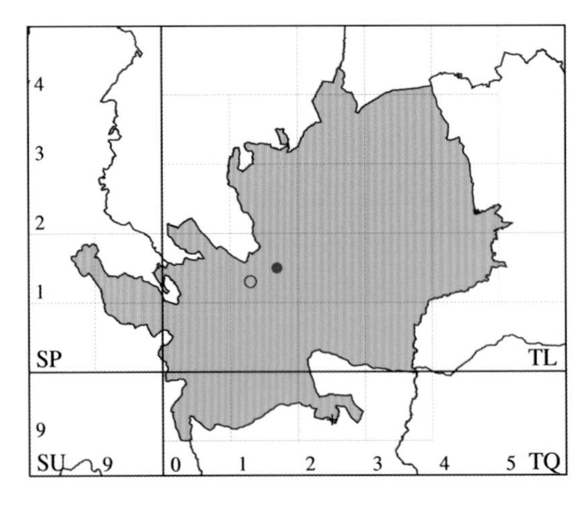

There are two acceptable Hertfordshire records: One was caught at the Rothamsted Estate at Harpenden on 25th August 1949 and one was caught at Totteridge in 1979 (Ian Lorimer).

[2359 *Amphipoea crinanensis* (Burrows) Crinan Ear

The record for Bushey Heath, at light in 1933 (Rev. J. A. K. Hervey) cannot be substantiated and seems unlikely to be correct.]

2360 *Amphipoea oculea* (L.) Ear Moth

Recorded: 1974 – 2006
Distribution / Status: Local / Uncommon resident
Conservation status: UK BAP Watch List
No perceived threats in Hertfordshire
Caterpillar food plants: Not recorded. Elsewhere, on grasses
Flight period: July to early August
Records in database: 52

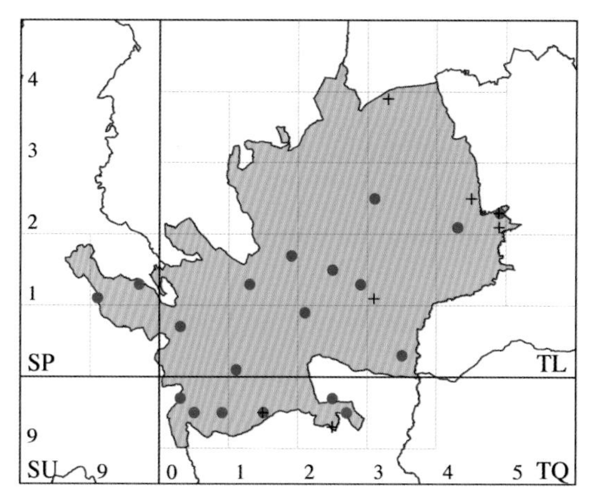

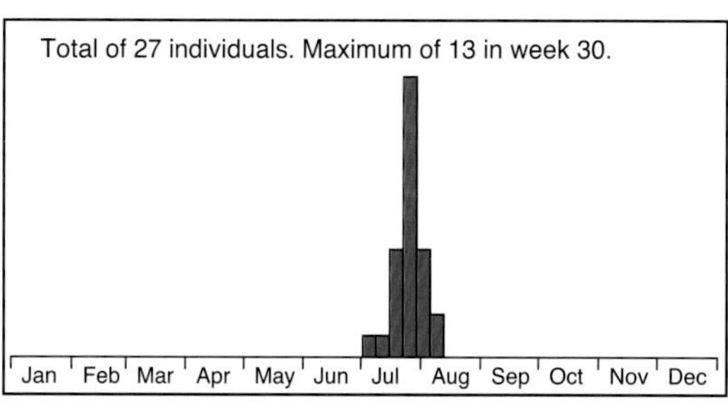

Surprisingly, perhaps, the Ear Moth is decidedly local in Hertfordshire, although the draconian criteria with regard to genitalia examination that I have rigorously imposed for record acceptance may have removed several records that are actually quite correct. However, the map presented can be relied upon as accurate and those who are aggrieved that their garden records are absent know what to do about it!

2361 *Hydraecia micacea* (Esp.) Rosy Rustic

Recorded: 1884 – 2006
Distribution / Status: Widespread / Common resident
Conservation status: UK BAP Watch List
Herts Stable
Caterpillar food plants: Not recorded. Elsewhere, internally in roots of dock and other plants
Flight period: Late July to October
Records in database: 289

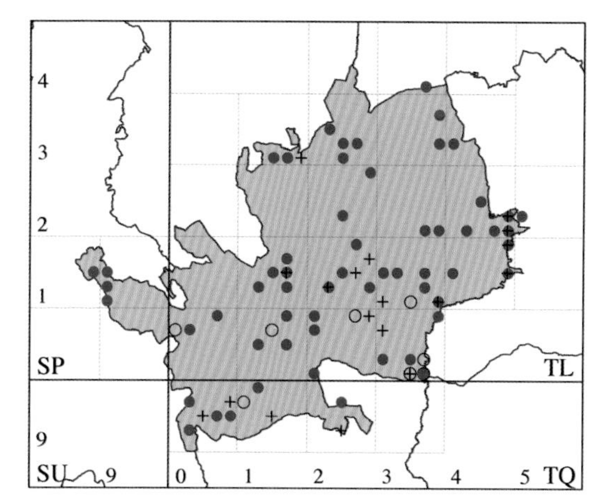

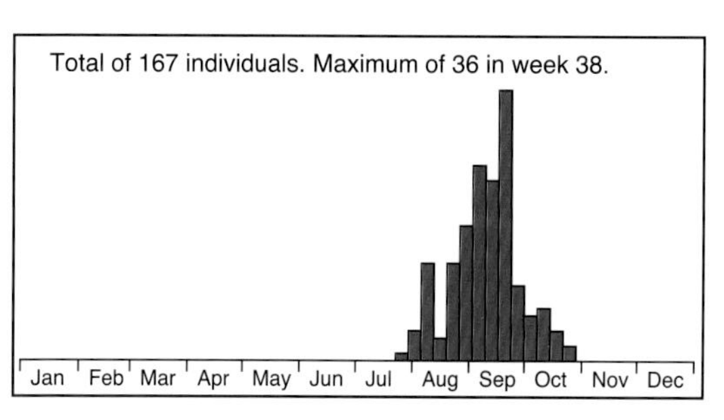

This readily recognised moth can only really be confused with 2362: Butterbur, which is much more localised in its distribution. Records seem to suggest that the Rosy Rustic has always been a fairly widespread and common species in Hertfordshire. It is a regular in many garden moth traps and is frequently encountered in the wider countryside in grassland, in woodland rides and on some field edges. The prolonged flight period, covering around twelve weeks, is more of less the same as that recorded for the London Area (Plant, 1993). Nationally, numbers of this species in Rothamsted Light Traps have apparently declined by 86 per cent since 1970, but there is no evidence to show any decline in Hertfordshire data obtained from mercury vapour and actinic light traps.

2362 *Hydraecia petasitis* Doubl. Butterbur

Recorded: 1957 – 2006
Distribution / Status: Extremely Local / Rare resident
Conservation status: Herts Endangered
Caterpillar food plants: Butterbur
Flight period: August
Records in database: 14

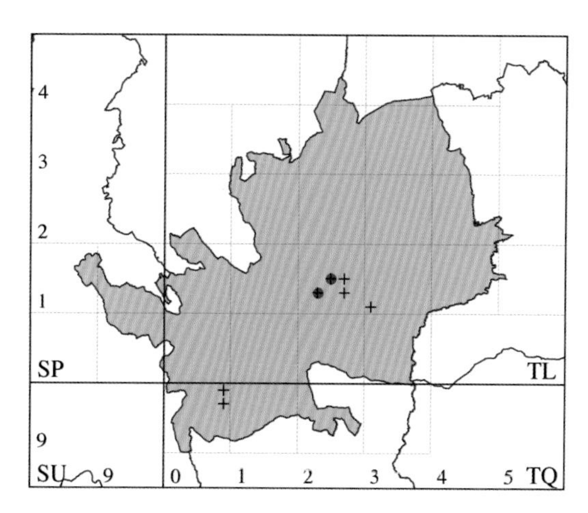

The Butterbur is generally larger and darker in colouration than the superficially similar Rosy Rustic but it would be extremely exceptional for the moth to fly more than a few feet away from the butterbur plants in whose roots it fed as a caterpillar. Indeed, if trying to light trap this species it is absolutely necessary to put the trap well in amongst the plants, preferably under taller ones so that the light can barely be seen! My own experience shows that traps so placed will catch double figures of moths whilst an identical trap placed on a footpath six feet (2 metres) away and run at the same time will catch none! The moth is extremely localised in Hertfordshire, and is restricted to large stands of the foodplant along the Rivers Lea, Mimram and Colne. Such areas are now very rare and are under threat in the county; consequently the Butterbur moth is regarded as an endangered species in Hertfordshire. All known records are listed: Casiobury Park, Watford, 2 on 17th August 1957 and 3 on 19th August, netted under *Petasites* at dusk (Barry Goater); Grove Mill, Watford, pupae frequent under *Petasites* growing in alluvial soil beside Canal, 6th & 9th August 1958 – moths bred (Barry Goater); Mill Lane, Watford, 12th August 1963 (Bernard Skinner); Digswell Lake, 1963 – the foodplant and the moth are still present in 2006, with moths caught on 10th August in that year (Tom Gladwin), Bayfordbury, three close to a patch of *Petasites albus*, east of the university buildings, on 13th October 1969 (Jim Reid); River Mimram at Archers Green, 1991 and River Mimram at Tewinbury in 1993 (Tom Gladwin); Lemsford Springs, 1970 and 1991 (Tom Gladwin) and 10th August 2002 – several at light on the Herts Moth Group recording trip; Digswell Lake, 10th August 2006 (Tom Gladwin).

2364 *Gortyna flavago* ([D.& S.]) Frosted Orange

Recorded:	1884 – 2006
Distribution / Status:	Widespread / Common resident
Conservation status:	Herts Stable
Caterpillar food plants:	Not recorded. Elsewhere, internally in stems of thistles, burdock etc
Flight period:	Late August/September
Records in database:	151

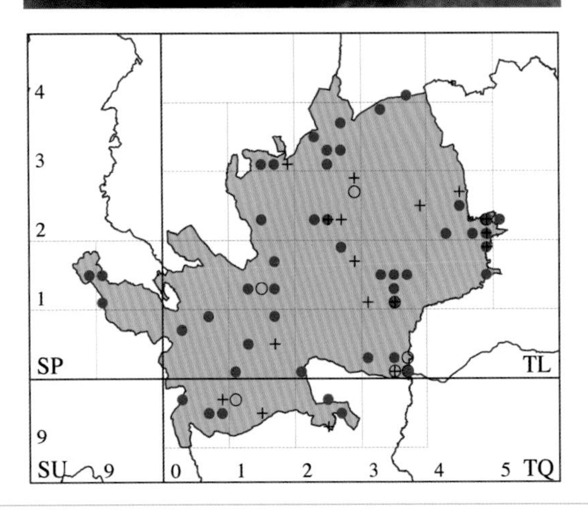

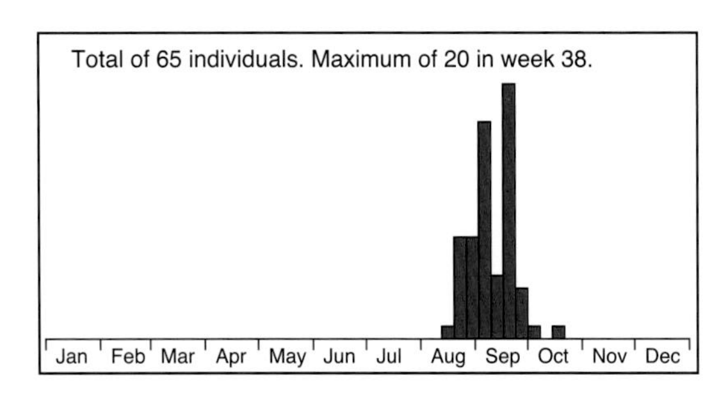

Though quite widespread across the county the Frosted Orange is somewhat locally distributed and never arrives at the light trap in any great number. The need for thistles, burdocks or similar plants that will survive the summer without being cut or pulled must be a limiting factor.

2368 *Celaena leucostigma* (Hb.) Crescent

Recorded:	1888 – 2006
Distribution / Status:	Widespread / Common resident
Conservation status:	Herts Threatened
Caterpillar food plants:	Not recorded. Elsewhere, on Iris, Saw Sedge and other fen plants
Flight period:	July/August
Records in database:	24

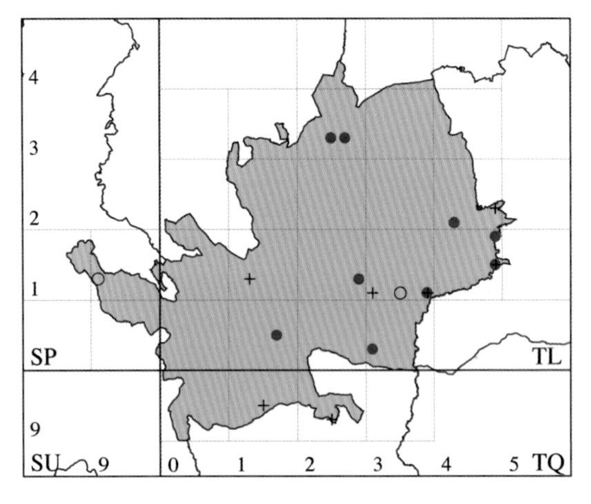

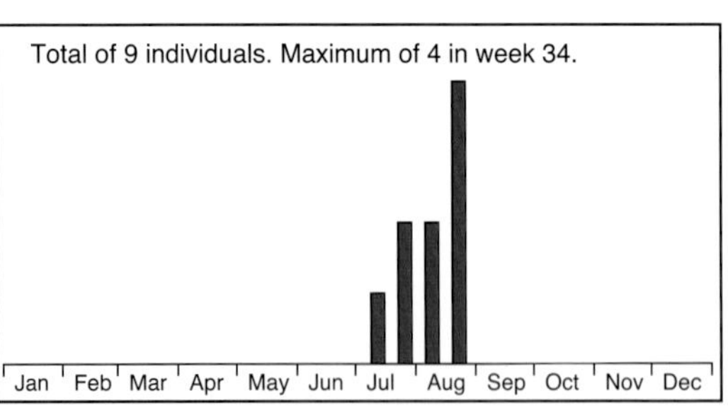

The distribution map is deceptive; in the years since 1999 the only sites where the Crescent appears to be breeding are Sawbridgeworth Marsh and Rye Meads – almost all the other records are of single adults in light traps in gardens or elsewhere and clearly relate to vagrant individuals. These two sites are nature reserves, but climate change and other factors beyond the control of land managers necessitate the designation of this moth as 'Threatened' in Hertfordshire. There are probably other breeding sites, but for the moment they remain obscure. Places such as the Wilstone Reservoir, where the moth was last seen in 1938, could usefully be searched. Occasional records at several sites in Bishops Stortford must indicate a population somewhere in the Stort Valley, though light trapping in the town area is fraught with difficulties these days; the earliest record for Bishops Stortford is 1948 (Allan, 1950).

2369 *Nonagria typhae* (Thunb.) Bulrush Wainscot

Recorded: 1884 – 2006
Distribution / Status: Local / Common resident
Conservation status: UK BAP Watch list. Herts Stable
Caterpillar food plants: Greater Reedmace; Lesser Reedmace
Flight period: July to September
Records in database: 70

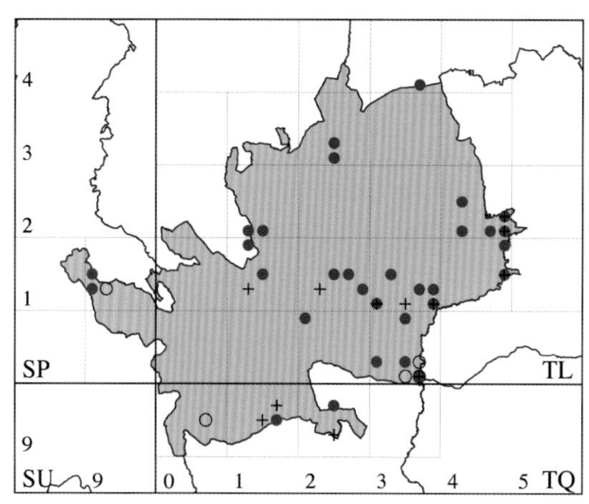

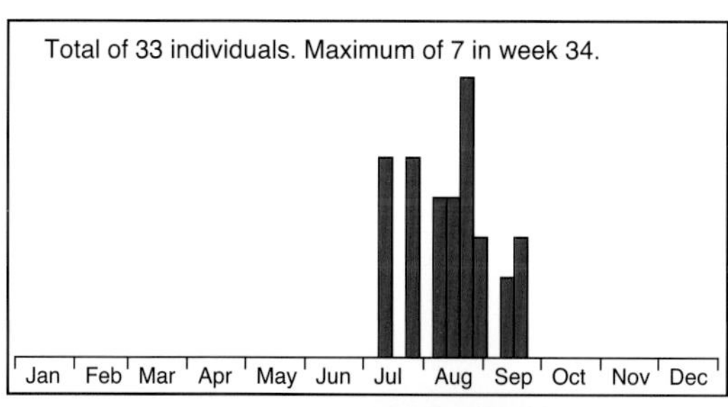

Almost any reedmace growth will do as far as this moth is concerned and several records are from the plant growing in garden ponds. Larvae are very easily found by looking for stunted plants then pulling them apart in two directions from the top: as the stem splits to the base the larvae or pupae will be revealed feeding or pupating head downwards – if the larva or pupa is aligned head-upwards it will be 2273: Webb's Wainscot (or 2374: Rush Wainscot which is currently absent from Hertfordshire). Moorhens are particularly good at finding larvae and damaged stem bases may indicate a former presence. The melanic ab. *fraterna* Treitschke is recorded in the Lea and Stort Valleys. The only numerical data for this colour form results from fifty pupae collected at Sawbridgeworth Marsh in the early 1990s by me and Charles Watson – these produced 5 ab. *fraterna* and 45 typical adults.

2370 *Archanara geminipuncta* (Haw.) Twin-spotted Wainscot

Recorded: 1925 – 2006
Distribution / Status: Extremely local / Rare resident
Conservation status: Herts Vulnerable
Caterpillar food plants: Internally in reed stems
Flight period: Late July/August
Records in database: 13

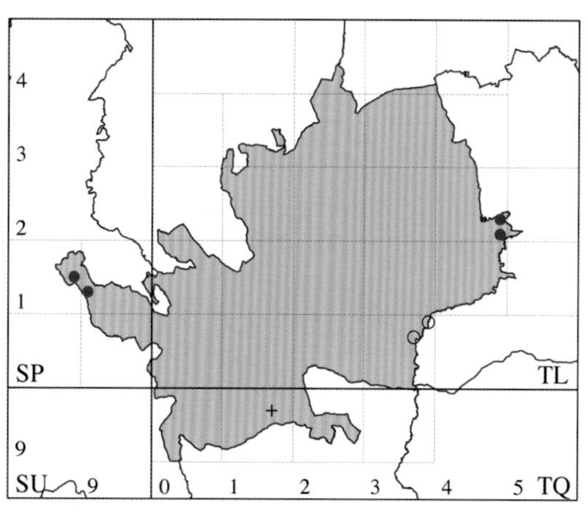

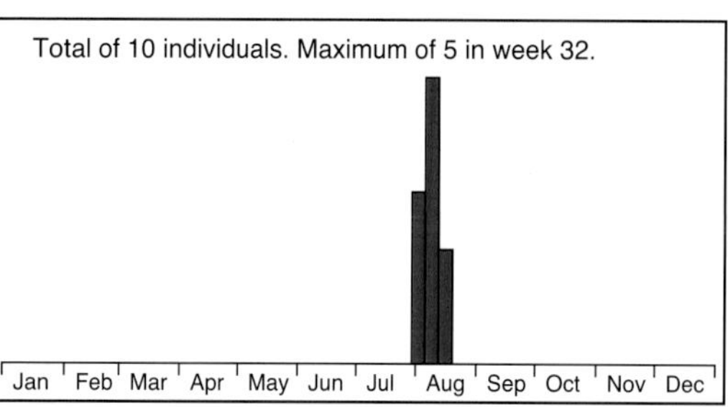

Foster (1937) gives two records as follows: Hoddesdon, one at light on 8 August 1925 (G. V. Bull) and near Rye House, in the angle formed by the junction of the Stort and the Lea (Edelsten). At Tykeswater Pond, Barry Goater found one pupa in *Phragmites* and other workings were seen in this tiny patch of foodplant on 27th July 1966. Modern records are from Bishops Stortford where the regularity of records suggests strongly that there must be a resident colony in the Stort Valley, perhaps at the Town Meads and from the far west where there appears to be another population associated with the reed beds at Wilstone Reservoir. The future of Bishops Stortford Town Meads is not certain whilst unfavourable reed-cutting regimes at Wilstone may cause problems for this moth. Consequently, it must be categorised as being Vulnerable in Hertfordshire.

2371 *Archanara dissoluta* (Tr.) Brown-veined Wainscot

Recorded: 1953 – 2006
Distribution / Status: Extremely local / Rare resident
Conservation status: Herts Vulnerable
Caterpillar food plants: Internally in reed stems
Flight period: July/August
Records in database: 14

As with 2370: Twin-spotted Wainscot, the Lea and Stort Valleys in the east (at Amwell, Rye Meads and Sawbridgeworth Marsh) and the Wilstone Reservoir area, in

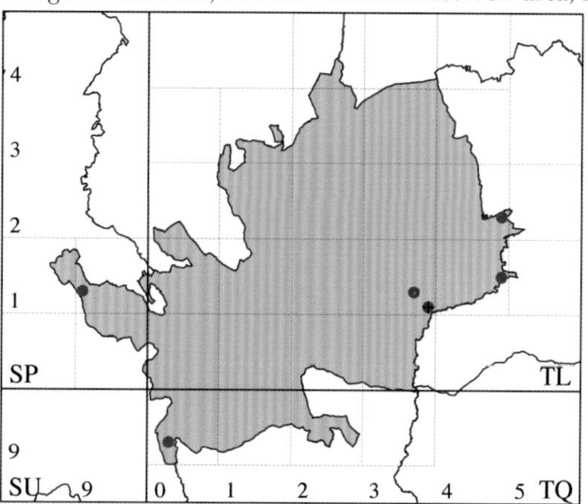

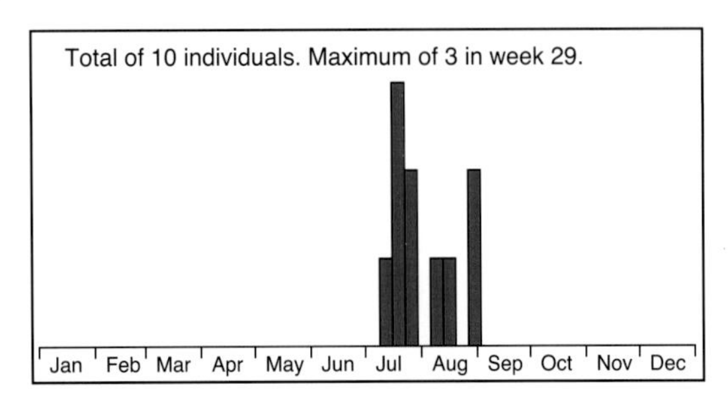

the west are the only centres of population for Brown-veined Wainscot in Hertfordshire, though there are also records from the Colne Valley at Maple Cross in 1996. The sites are not under threat as all are nature reserves, though inappropriate reed cutting could cause problems and so this, together with the rarity and isolation of appropriate habitat, renders this moth Vulnerable in Hertfordshire. In the London Area to the south, the Brown-veined Wainscot is very rare, but breeds in several places along the River Lea. There is strong evidence to suggest that the moth is a recent colonist in Hertfordshire. Bell (1955) comments that 'A. L. Goodson attracted to his Tring and Ashridge M.V. lamps what was evidently part of a migration of *dissoluta*, 30 moths attending over a couple of nights in August [*1953*], mostly at Tring. A single specimen came to my own light on the 11th of that month'. These records are not mapped as the exact locations are unclear. Though Bell does not say so, this is the earliest Hertfordshire record that I have been able to locate and there are no more until 1977 when it was discovered in Sawbridgeworth Marsh (Fielding et al, 1985). It may or may not be a coincidence that this resident population was discovered the year following one of the longest and hottest summers on record at that date; vagrant moths from the east coast could easily have found the Stort Valley and elsewhere to their liking.

2373 *Archanara sparganii* (Esp.) Webb's Wainscot

Recorded:	1994 – 2006
Distribution / Status:	Local / Uncommon resident
Conservation status:	Herts Vulnerable
Caterpillar food plants:	Greater Reedmace. Elsewhere, also on Iris and other plants
Flight period:	July to early September
Records in database:	17

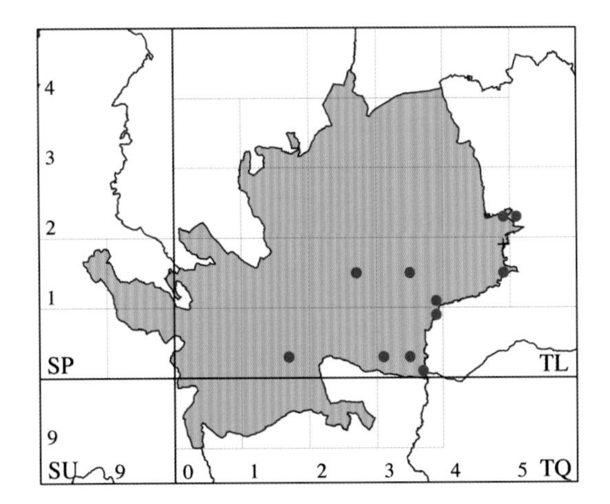

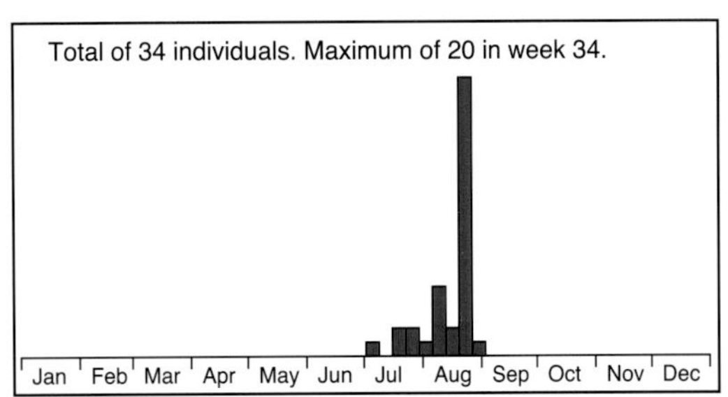

There are no Hertfordshire records of this moth until 1994, when Charles Watson caught one in his garden in Bishops Stortford on 28th September 1994. Motivated by this report I searched for and found larvae in reedmace stems the following year at Rushey Mead (on the North Essex side of the River Stort) and in Hertfordshire at Sawbridgeworth Marsh, four kilometres to the south, where it still thrives in 2006. It is currently established as a resident in the Stort and Lea Valleys; the only map dot that does not follow this pattern relates to adults caught on the Herts Moth Group recording trip to Broad Colney Lakes Nature Reserve on 5th August 2006. This is evidently a moth that is extending its range to include suitable wetland sites in Hertfordshire, but because it belongs to a suite of wetland species it could easily be lost through inappropriate management of the vegetation and so is ranked as Vulnerable in Hertfordshire.

2375 *Rhizedra lutosa* (Hb.) Large Wainscot

Recorded:	1893 – 2006
Distribution / Status:	Local / Uncommon resident
Conservation status:	UK BAP Priority Species. Herts Scarce
Caterpillar food plants:	Internally in stems of Reed
Flight period:	September to early November
Records in database:	86

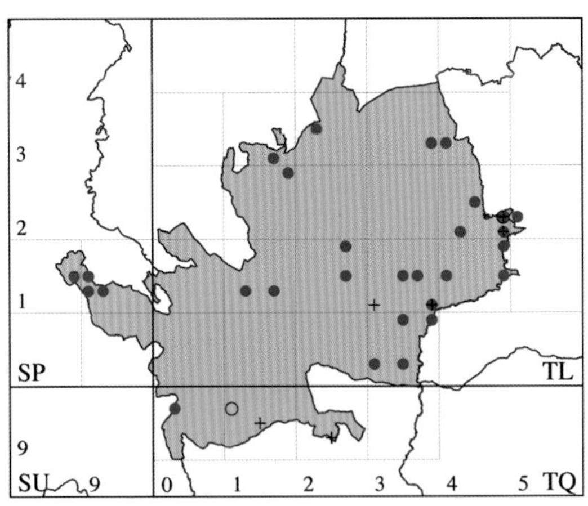

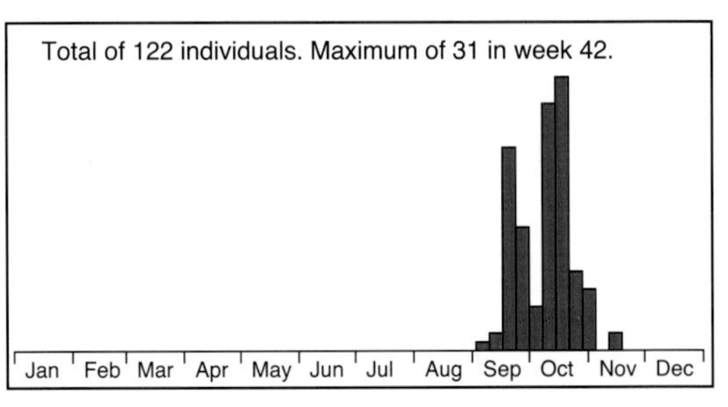

The large Wainscot was first noted in the county by S. H. Spencer in his garden at Gladstone Road, Watford, during 1893. Most of our records are made in wetland areas, mainly river valleys, though not necessarily in the immediate vicinity of the foodplant, but there are records away from this habitat and though a few undoubtedly represent wanderers the possibility that garden and village ponds can support this species should not be overlooked. The moth appears numerically uncommon with us, but has probably always been so and it is not possible to determine if the reported decline of 86 per cent since 1970 in the national population is repeated here.

2377 *Arenostola phragmitidis* (Hb.) Fen Wainscot

Recorded:	1880 – 2006
Distribution / Status:	Very local / Uncommon resident
Conservation status:	Herts Vulnerable
Caterpillar food plants:	Internally in Reed stems
Flight period:	Late June to August
Records in database:	28

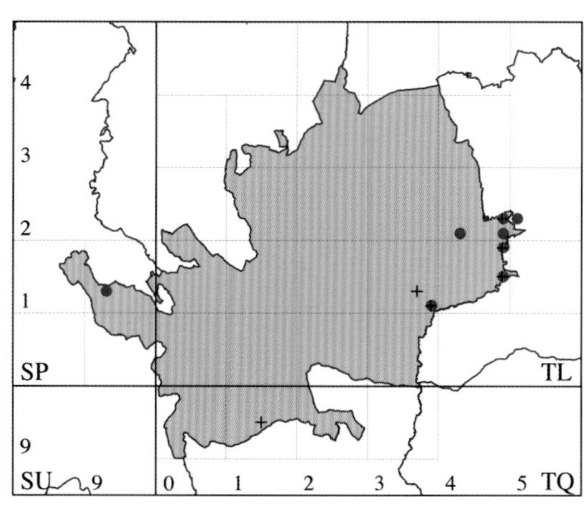

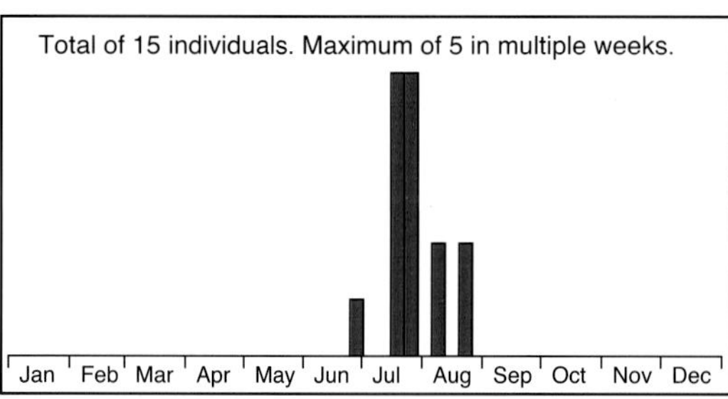

This is another of the wetland suite of species and again the significance of the Stort Valley is clear from the distribution map. Foster (1937) lists only Hitchin in 1880 by S. Tuke for this species; it is quite likely, given that Foster's definition of the Hitchin area was rather liberal, that Oughtonhead Common was the site involved; the moth could easily be present there today and it would be desirable to search for it there.

2379 *Coenobia rufa* (Haw.) Small Rufous

Recorded: 1901 – 2006
Distribution / Status: Very local / Uncommon resident
Conservation status: Herts Scarce
Caterpillar food plants: Not recorded. Elsewhere, in stems of rushes
Flight period: Mid-July to August
Records in database: 30

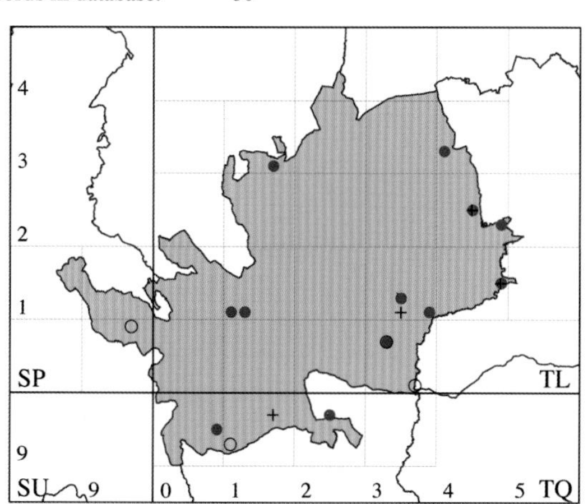

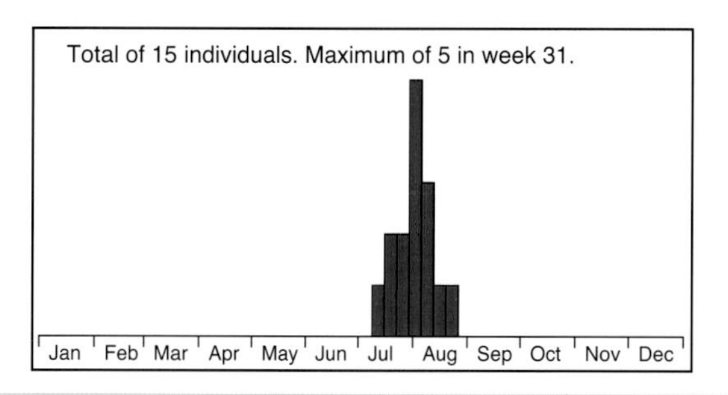

Slightly damp grassland habitats with plenty of rushes, usually on the acidic side of neutral, are the places where this small moth can be found. Confusion is possible with 2350: Small Wainscot, especially if the grassland is within a wider woodland habitat, but the Small Rufous is a much more slender insect and always has a characteristic grey thorax contrasting with the brown of the rest of the body. The best sites in the county for Small Rufous are Sawbridgeworth Marsh and Croxley Common Moor and at these two sites the populations appear to be stable, though the moth would clearly be sensitive to any drastic changes in the grazing regime at Croxley. At other known localities the populations may be rather smaller and more fragile.

2380 *Charanycha trigrammica* (Hufn.) Treble Lines

Recorded: 1828 – 2006
Distribution / Status: Widespread / Common resident
Conservation status: Herts Stable
Caterpillar food plants: Not recorded. Elsewhere,
Flight period: Mid-May/June
Records in database: 308

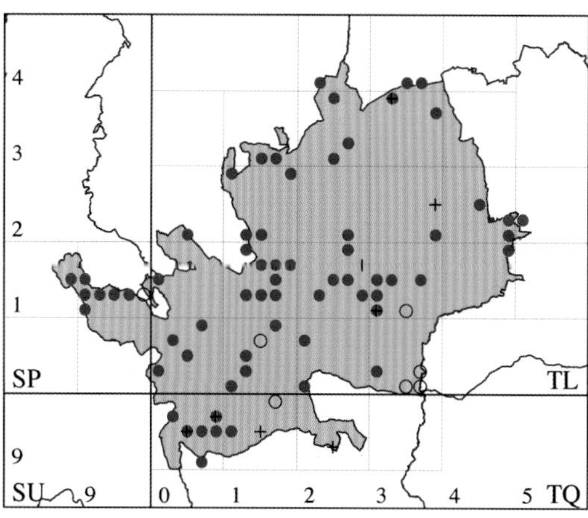

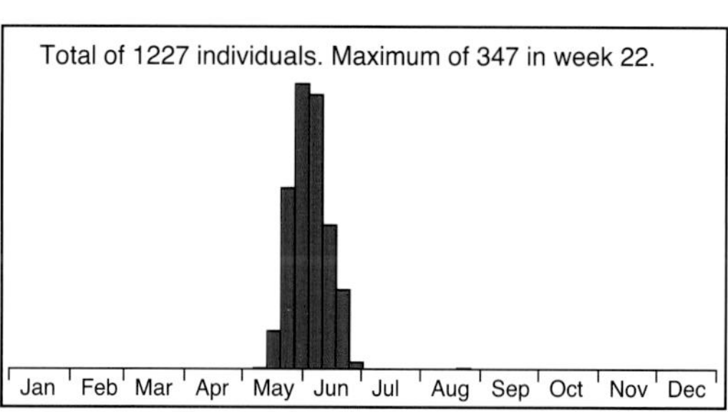

It appears that this has always been a relatively widespread moth across the county but the distribution is patchy, and some areas fail to produce the insect. For example, the trap in the adjoining gardens of James Fish and Julian Reeves in northern Bishops Stortford produced this species in 1995 (first year of trapping), 1997, 1998, 1999 and then each year from 2002 to 2006. Meanwhile, further south in the same town, where I started trapping in late 1986, I recorded it is 2002, 2003 and 2004, but not in any earlier or later year. The two sites are scarcely a mile apart. Half a mile south of my garden, Charles Watson caught it once only, in 1997 in spite of trapping since the 1970s until his death in October 2005. A sudden dramatic increase in numbers, coupled with its arrival at new sites, was noted during 2004, in the east of the county in particular and this was repeated during 2007 – beyond the scope of the present review, but worthy of passing mention.

2381 *Hoplodrina alsines* (Brahm) Uncertain

Recorded: 1884 – 2006
Distribution / Status: Ubiquitous / Abundant resident
Conservation status: Herts Stable
Caterpillar food plants: Not recorded. Elsewhere, on various herbaceous plants
Flight period: Mid-June to early August
Records in database: 1543

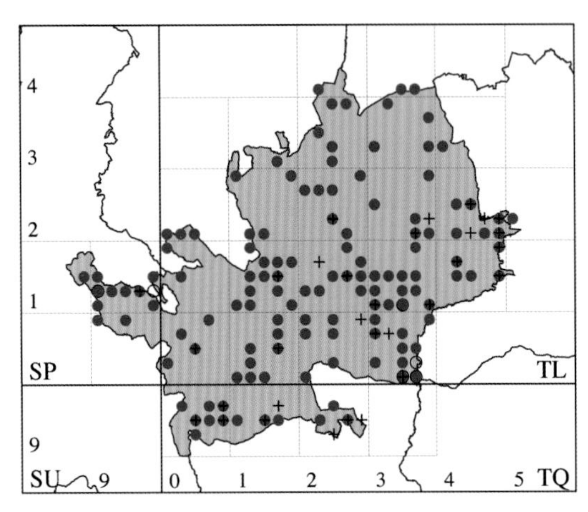

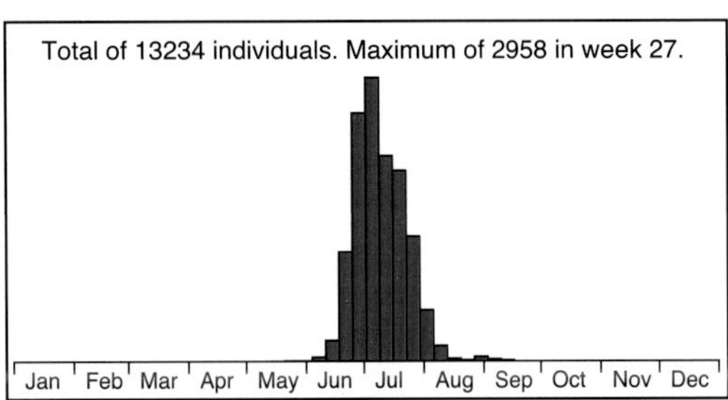

The Uncertain is likely to be found in every map square across the county, regardless of habitat and the fact that it is not represents poor recording effort only. During July, this can be the most numerous species in garden light traps, but this is rarely the case elsewhere, suggesting strongly that garden plants may provide an important larval food resource. Care should be taken by beginners in separating this species from 2382: Rustic, which can be confusingly similar.

2382 *Hoplodrina blanda* ([D.& S.]) Rustic

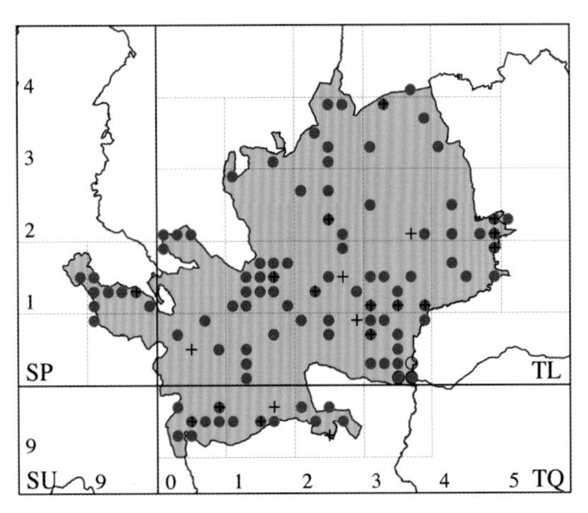

Recorded:	1884 – 2006
Distribution / Status:	Widespread / Uncommon resident
Conservation status:	UK BAP Watch List No perceived threats in Hertfordshire
Caterpillar food plants:	Not recorded. Elsewhere,
Flight period:	Mid-June to late September
Records in database:	987

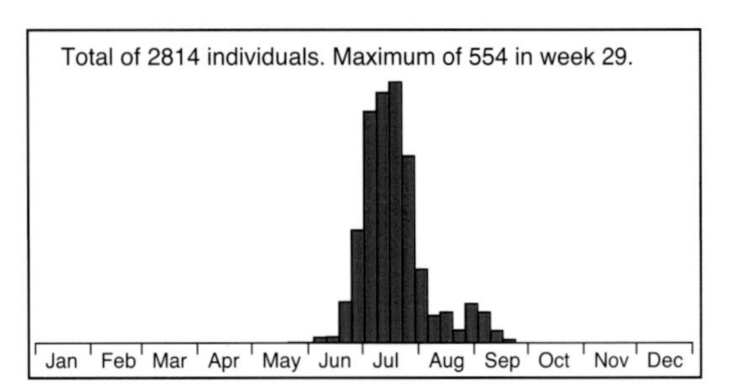

The Rustic is far and away less numerous than 2381: Uncertain, as the numbers of individuals used to plot the flight charts betrays, and when there are several hundred Uncertains in the trap it is perhaps not unexpected that the occasional Rustic will be overlooked. Nevertheless, it is likely to be present in all areas of the county. Both species fly together, but the chart shows that the Rustic peaks about two weeks after the Uncertain. The peak of adults during September shown in the flight chart is made up of adults recorded in 2005 and 2006 only; in earlier years the moth was finished by the end of August.

2384 *Hoplodrina ambigua* ([D.& S.]) Vines Rustic

Recorded:	1945 – 2006
Distribution / Status:	Widespread / Abundant resident and Immigrant
Conservation status:	Herts Stable
Caterpillar food plants:	Not recorded. Elsewhere, on herbaceous plants
Flight period:	Late May/June then August/September
Records in database:	1,487

Although known as an immigrant to Britain as long ago as 1879, there were only temporarily resident populations on the south coast until 1949 when the moth suddenly moved inland and became established in Surrey. Since then it has steadily moved northwards and is now a familiar resident in southern Britain, though still boosted by primary immigrants in the autumn. The first Hertfordshire record was at Berkhamsted, where one was seen by J. H. Bell in 1945. Writing about this, Fryer (1948) noted that it was '... doubtless an immigrant to Herts, although it is apparently established along the south and south-west coasts'. Our next was at Welwyn, one in 1953 (D. A. B. Macnicol), then at Bushey, one on 3rd August 1965 (Barry Goater) – 'a rare insect in this part of the [London] area' (de Worms (1966). At Totteridge, it was noted as increasing greatly during the 1970s, with the second generation especially abundant in 1978, but 'after the hard winter, gen. 1 was not seen and only about 50 in all of gen. 2 came to the trap' (Ian Lorimer). Lorimer noted 100 at light in his Totteridge garden on 25th August 1976, the drought year, and in that year further range expansions were noted by the moth in Britain. Today, the moth is resident in the entire county and it is inevitably hard to separate residents from immigrant examples.

2385 *Spodoptera exigua* (Hb.) Small Mottled Willow

Recorded: 1932 – 2006
Distribution / Status: Random / Immigrant
Conservation status: -
Caterpillar food plants: Overseas, on herbaceous plants
Flight period: June to November
Records in database: 46

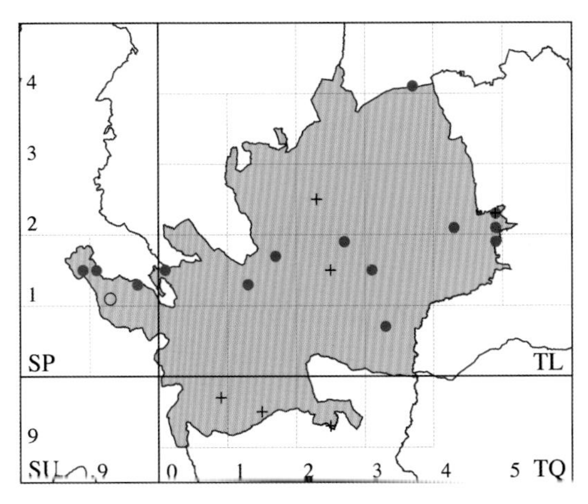

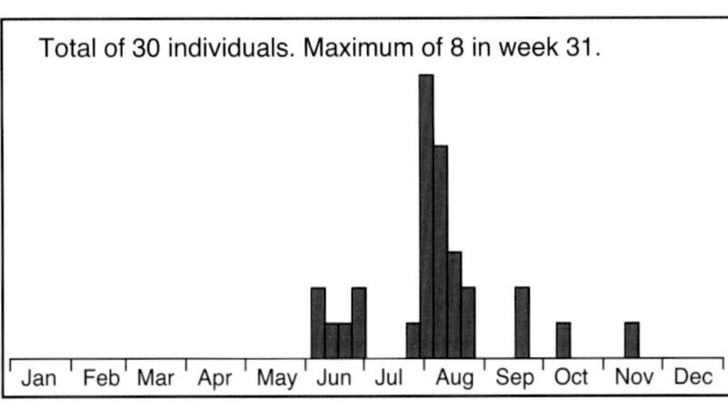

One at light at Northchurch (Berkhamsted) in 1932 by J. Bell (Foster, 1942) is the first county record of this immigrant from southern Europe. Until quite recently, records were rather sparse, though that might reflect a lack of active recorders in the county. Other records up to the end of 1999 are: Tring, one in 1945 (A. L. Goodson); Stevenage, one at mv light, 8th August 1966 (Jack Newton); Tring, 6 males and one female in August 1952 (A. L. Goodson); Harpenden, four in 1952 (C. B. Williams); Watford, one in September 1952 (Ray Penrose); Tring, seven in 1953 (Bell, 1955) and two in 1957 (Bell, 1959); Tring, in October 1959 (Bell, 1961); Totteridge, one on 6th May 1962 by Ian Lorimer (Bell, 1964) and another in 1969 (Ian Lorimer); Bushey, one on 7th June 1966 (Barry Goater); Stevenage, 8th August 1966 (Jack Newton); Totteridge, one in 1969 (Ian Lorimer); Bushey, one on 21st October 1969 (Barry Goater); Digswell, one on 3rd August 1985 (Tom Gladwin); Bishops Stortford, September 1994, 1995 and 1996 (James Fish & Julian Reeves); Rothamsted Estate, Harpenden, 1996 (Riley, 1999); Long Marston, 14th August 1996 (Alan Bernard); Wheathampstead, 1997 (Vincent & Betty Judd); Little Hadham, 1999 (Geoff Senior) and Waterford Heath 1999 (Vincent & Betty Judd). In the present millennium, we have recorded one in year 2000, at Bishops Stortford (Charles Watson); none in 2001; two in 2002 (Long Marston, 6th June by Alan Bernard and Bishops Stortford, 26th June, by James Fish & Julian Reeves); six in 2003 (Royston, by John Chainey; Broxbourne Wood, 4th August, Ravensdell Wood, 9th August, Millhoppers Pasture, 23rd August, all by Colin Plant, and Bishops Stortford on 18th September (James Fish & Julian Reeves); none in 2004; one in 2005 (Datchworth, 12th October, by Steve Palmer); and 12 in 2006, at three localities (Ashridge Monument area, 29th July, by Colin Plant, Long Marston, on 29th July and 5th August by Peter Bygate, and in Bishops Stortford on 18th June, 30th July and 1st, 5th, 6th, 11th, 14th, 17th and 24th August (James Fish & Julian Reeves). A number of records from Chorleywood made by Richard Ellis are excluded since they were made just over the border in Buckinghamshire.

2387 *Caradrina morpheus* (Hufn.) Mottled Rustic

Recorded: 1828 – 2006
Distribution / Status: Ubiquitous / Common resident
Conservation status: UK BAP Watch List. Herts Stable
Caterpillar food plants: Not recorded. Elsewhere, on herbaceous plants
Flight period: Late May to early August
Records in database: 962

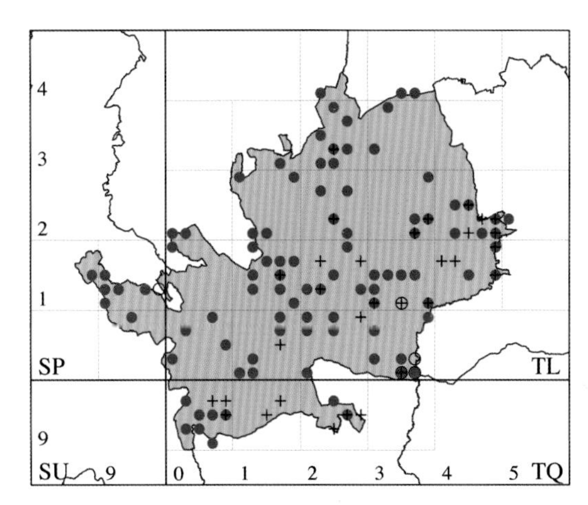

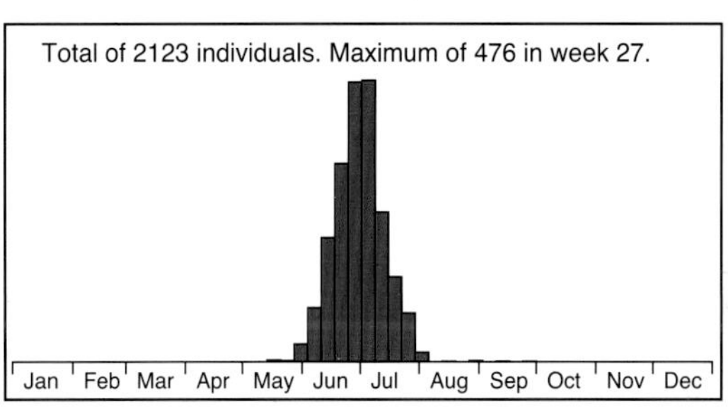

The Mottled Rustic is one of the more common 'brown and boring' moths in Hertfordshire, though it is never present in such large numbers as 2381: Uncertain. The number of records per year in the database shows neither decline nor rise in population. It is expected in all trap samples across the county.

2388 *Paradrina flavirena* (Guen.) Lorimer's Rustic

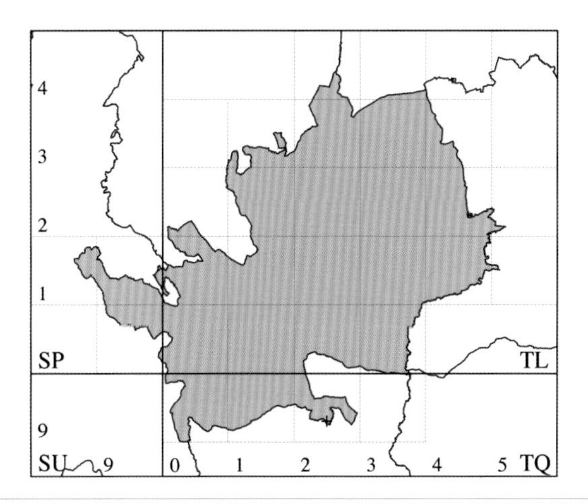

Recorded:	1967 – 1967
Distribution / Status:	Random / Former immigrant
Conservation status:	–
Caterpillar food plants:	Unknown
Flight period:	October
Records in database:	1

A male at a garden light trap at Southway, Totteridge by Ian Lorimer on 8th October 1967 is the first British record of this species. It arrived at a time of high migrant activity and is thought to have originated in south-west France. The specimen is in the National Collection at the Natural History Museum.

2389 *Paradrina clavipalpis* (Scop.) Pale Mottled Willow

Recorded:	1884 – 2006
Distribution / Status:	Widespread / Common resident
Conservation status:	Herts Stable
Caterpillar food plants:	Not recorded. Elsewhere, grasses and stored grain
Flight period:	Mid-March to mid-November
Records in database:	2,798

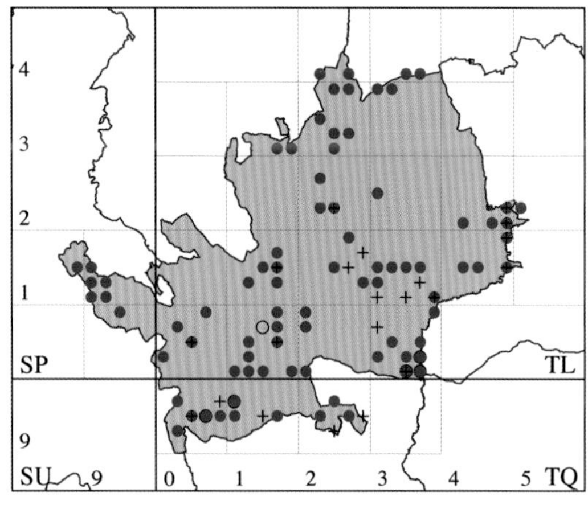

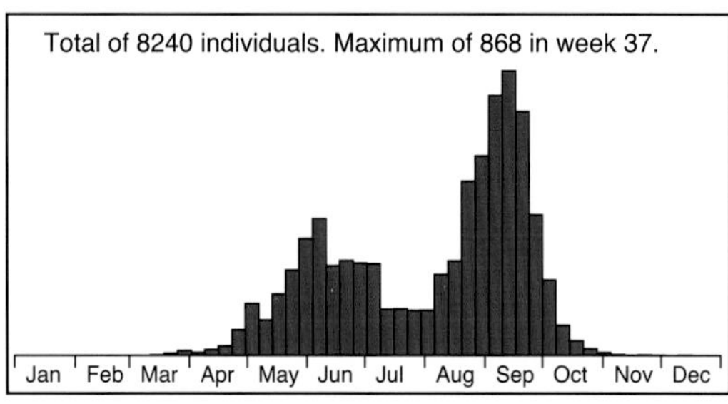

With almost 3,000 records, the Pale Mottled Willow ranks second, after 2107: Large Yellow Underwing, in the table of most frequently recorded species. It is curious, therefore, to discover that the distribution map sports a number of gaps. Presumably, this is a result of patchy recording, although it is certain that this moth is more frequent in gardens than it is in the countryside and perhaps it prefers feeding on garden plants? It is interesting, however, to note the relationship between number of records and number of reported individuals. There are 2,798 records of Pale Mottled Willow reporting 8,683 individuals – an average of 3 individuals per record. For Large Yellow Underwing there are 3,353 records of 37,166 individuals, an average of 11 individuals per record.

2391 *Chilodes maritimus* (Tausch.) Silky Wainscot

Recorded:	1905 – 2002
Distribution / Status:	Extremely local / Rare resident and vagrant
Conservation status:	Herts Vulnerable
Caterpillar food plants:	Not recorded. Elsewhere, carnivorous, preying on other insects inside the stems of Reed
Flight period:	Mid-June to mid-August
Records in database:	6

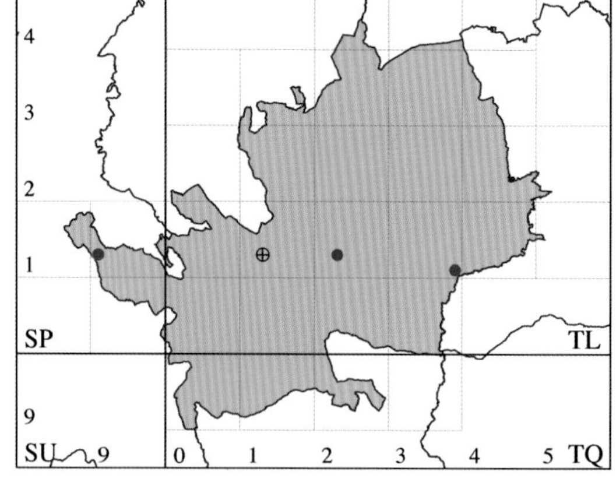

Our first report of Silky Wainscot in the county is from Tring in 1905 (A. T. Goodson), given in Gibbs (1906) and repeated by Foster (1937). This is also the Hertfordshire record mentioned by South (*The Moths of the British Isles*. Series 1, page 300). Subsequent records are from the Rothamsted Estate on 24th June 1935 (C. B. Williams) and 10th August 1991 (Adrian Riley) then Rye Meads, 17th June 2000, Wilstone Reservoir, 1st July 2000 and Lemsford Springs, 15th July 2002 all recorded by me. At the last three sites the moth is regarded as resident and it is a surprise that it has not yet been found at Amwell Pit or Sawbridgeworth Marsh. Given the fragility of its habitat the breeding populations of this moth must be regarded as Vulnerable in Hertfordshire.

2396 *Elaphria venustula* (Hb.) Rosy Marbled

Recorded:	1974 – 2006
Distribution / Status:	Extremely local / Resident and Vagrant
Conservation status:	Herts Rare
Caterpillar food plants:	Not recorded. Elsewhere, on the flowers of various plants
Flight period:	Elsewhere, May to July
Records in database:	3

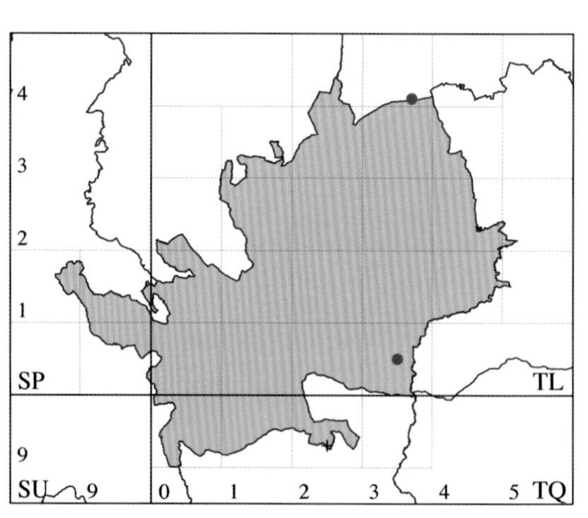

We have just three records of the Rosy Marbled in Hertfordshire. Two of these, from Totteridge on 9th July 1974 (Ian Lorimer) and from Royston on 6th July 1999 (John Chainey & Jenny Spence) probably relate to vagrants from elsewhere, but one caught amongst Sessile Oak/ Hornbeam/birch woodland by Mark Cooper in the eastern portion of Thunderfield Grove on 2nd June 2007 probably indicates a resident population and so is included in the map even though the record was made after the end of the formal survey period on 31st December 2006. It is a moth of open woodlands, usually occurring where there is bracken, but not always so, and the caterpillars feed on the flowers of various plants, but especially those of Common Tormentil. Though almost certainly extremely localised, and perhaps only resident in the Broxbourne complex of woodlands, the adult moth appears to shun mercury-vapour lamps. Additionally, to the uninitiated it looks extremely similar to an *Epiblema* species (Tortricidae) and may be overlooked by those who only record 'macros'.

STIRIINAE

2397 *Panemeria tenebrata* (Scop.) Small Yellow Underwing

Recorded: 1828 – 2006
Distribution / Status: Local / Uncommon resident
Conservation status: Herts Stable
Caterpillar food plants: Not recorded. Elsewhere, on mouse-ears
Flight period: May to early June
Records in database: 79

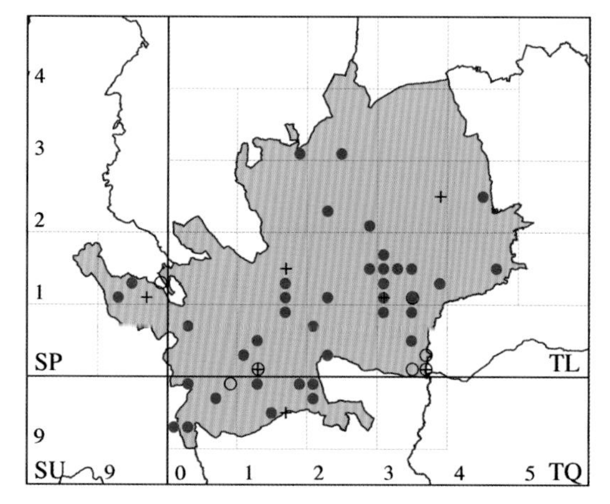

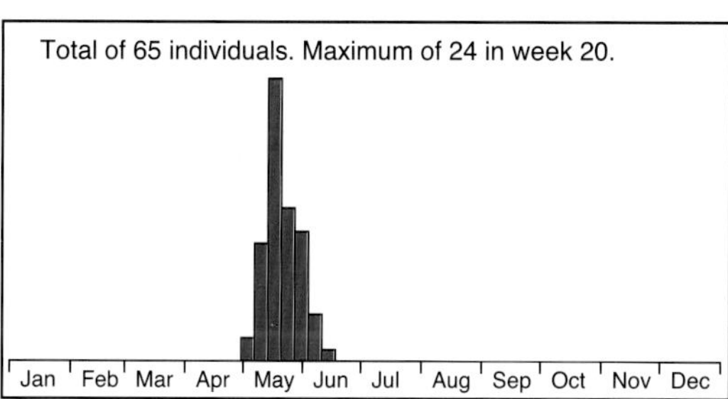

Judging by the surprise that is generally expressed when this species is seen, people evidently think it is rare; I suspect that it is often overlooked as a species of *Pyrausta* (Pyralidae) and so ignored. It flies in afternoon sunshine and most records originate from butterfly recorders. Adults are recorded 'nectaring' at flowers of Field Speedwell. The moth is likely to be widespread, but local across most of the county.

HELIOTHINAE

2399 *Pyrrhia umbra* (Hufn.) Bordered Sallow

Recorded: 1884 – 2006
Distribution / Status: Local / Uncommon resident
Conservation status: Herts Stable
Caterpillar food plants: Not recorded. Elsewhere, on restharrow
Flight period: June/July
Records in database: 92

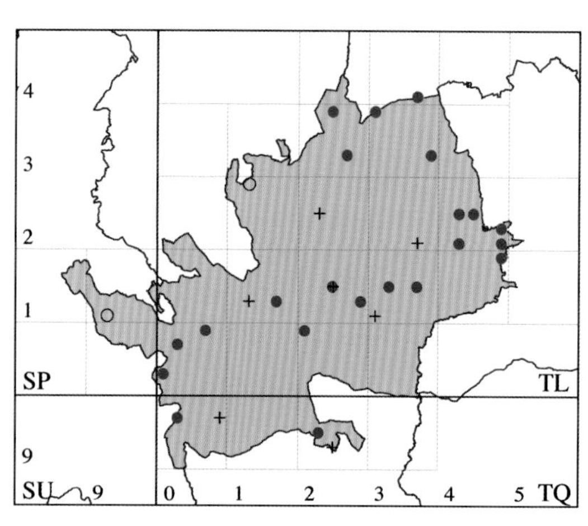

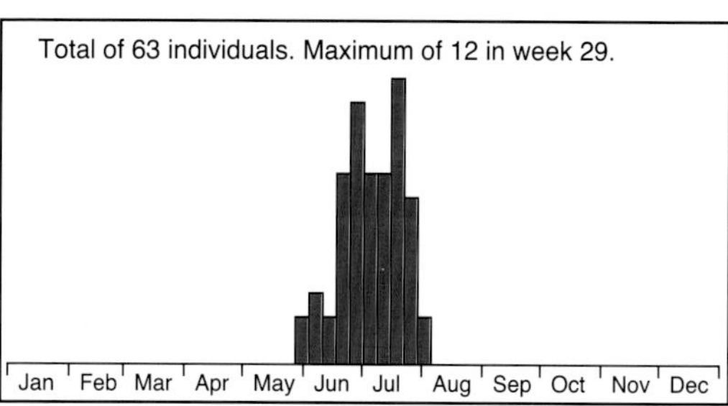

Examination of the records given by Foster (1937) suggests that this moth was not especially widespread or common at that period in Hertfordshire. Today, though there is a wide spread of records some may relate to vagrants and as a breeding species it remains rather local. Although alternative foodplants have been implicated elsewhere, Restharrow is the pabulum of choice and the moth is probably restricted to sites where this plant grows. I have suggested elsewhere (Plant, 1993), that Bordered Sallow adults are more readily attracted to tungsten-filament light sources than to mercury-vapour lamps.

2400 *Helicoverpa armigera* (Hb.) Scarce Bordered Straw

Recorded: 1873 – 2006
Distribution / Status: Random / Immigrant/accidental import
Conservation status: A pest species overseas
Caterpillar food plants: Imported Mung Beans
Flight period: August to November
Records in database: 42

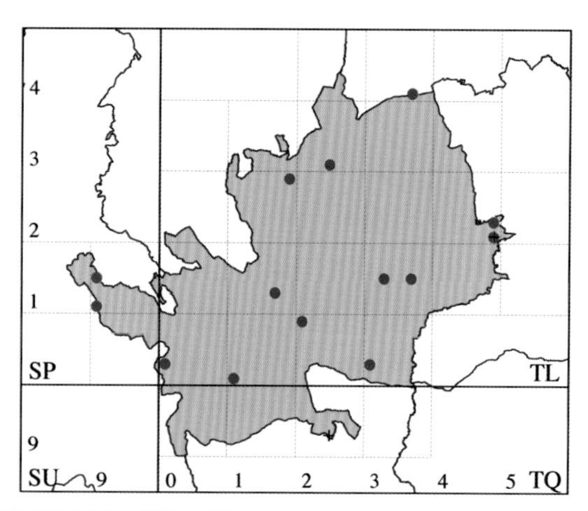

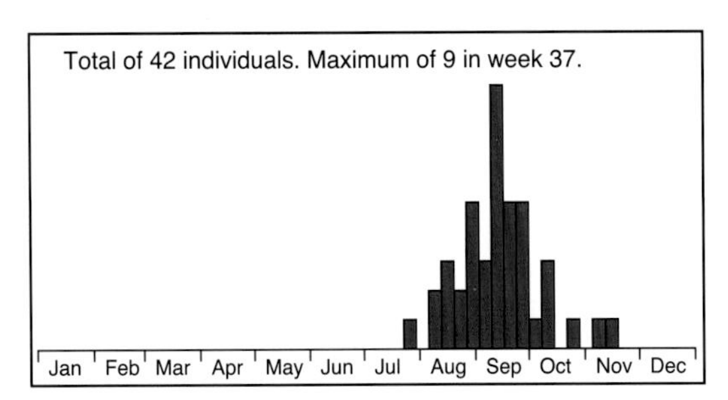

Formerly a very rare immigrant, the Scarce Bordered Straw arrived in Britain in force during 2006. In Hertfordshire the records are as follows: One listed for his garden at Sandridge in September 1873 (Griffith, 1884); Totteridge, one on 3rd October 1962 (Ian Lorimer manuscript list), but given erroneously as 1st October 1962 by Bell, 1964) and another on 17th September 1969; Grange Road, Bishops Stortford, 26th September 1994 (Tony King); Bishops Stortford, 1996 and 13th October 1998 (James Fish & Julian Reeves); Hertford, 30th September 1999 (Andrew Wood); Garston, 26th September 2000 (Colin Everett); Bishops Stortford, 6th August 2003 (James Fish & Julian Reeves); Tring, 2004 (Ian Burrus); Bishops Stortford, 13th and 26th August 2004 (James Fish & Julian Reeves); Cuffley, 26th October 2005 (Alan Bolitho); Bishops Stortford, 17th and 31st August, 6th, 14th, 15th, 16th, 17th and 18th September then 2nd and 14th October 2006 (James Fish & Julian Reeves); Bishops Stortford, 2nd, 14th, 16th and 26th September 2006 (Colin Plant); Royston, 29th July, 20th & 22nd August 2006 (John Chainey & Jenny Spence); Hertford, 31st August, 2nd, 3rd & 4th September 2006 (Andrew Wood); Long Marston, 15th September 2006 (Peter Bygate), Wheathampstead, 23rd September 2006 (Trevor Chapman); Bovingdon Brick Pits, 23rd September 2006 (Colin Plant); Ellenbrook, Weston, 27th September 2006 (Alan Cockburn); Hatfield, 12th October 2006 (Tony Bristow); Ware, 10th November 2006 (Elizabeth Goodyear) and Long Marston, 18th November 2006 (Peter Bygate). Hitchin, A larva was found with imported, pre-packed Mung Beans at Hitchin in July 2003 and the adult reared (Kerry Robinson).

2401 *Heliothis viriplaca* (Hufn.) Marbled Clover

Recorded:	1946 – 1997
Distribution / Status:	Random / Vagrant or Immigrant
Conservation status:	-
Caterpillar food plants:	Elsewhere, on various low plants
Flight period:	August. Elsewhere, also in June
Records in database:	5

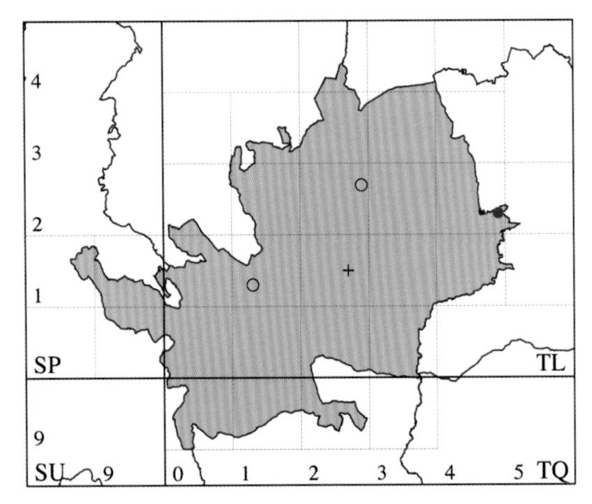

This moth is a resident of the Breckland district of Suffolk and Norfolk and our Hertfordshire examples are perhaps wanderers from here, although they could have been primary immigrants. In the Walkern area, it was described as being 'frequent in the clover fields' during the 1940s by J. Birdsall (the first Hertfordshire record). It is tempting to suggest that this implies residency, but that is most unlikely, particularly in view of the vagueness of that statement. The 1940s included some very good migrant years, especially 1947. There are two other 1940s records, both strongly indicative of moths entering the area from further afield. Fryer (1948) reports that C. B. Williams took an example during 1946 'at Harpenden in his light trap'. This record is also reported by Riley (1999) who notes another example in 1947 (also reported in Fryer, 1950). There are no more records until 3rd August 1995 and 11th August 1997 when examples were caught in Bishops Stortford by James Fish and Julian Reeves.

2403 *Heliothis peltigera* ([D.& S.]) Bordered Straw

Recorded:	1884 – 2006
Distribution / Status:	Random / Immigrant/accidental import
Conservation status:	A pest species overseas
Caterpillar food plants:	Elsewhere, on many herbaceous plants
Flight period:	May/June and August/September
Records in database:	45

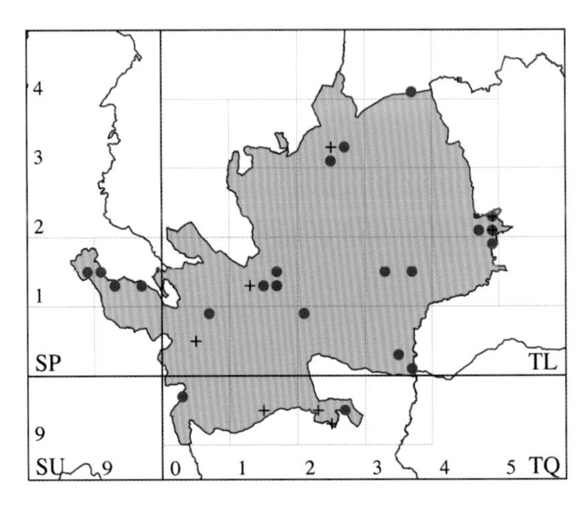

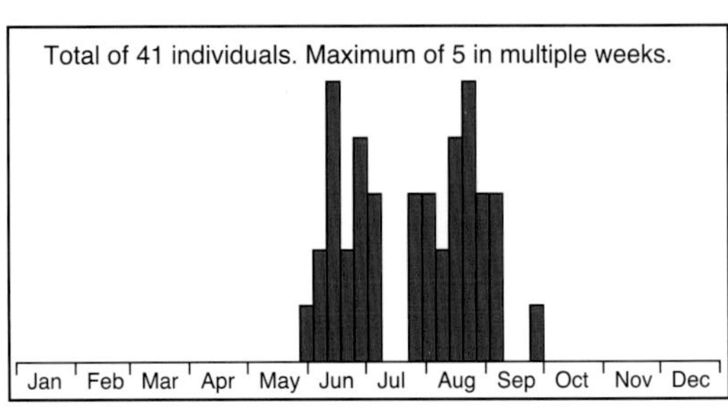

Prior to 2000 we have only 20 records for this moth as an immigrant adult in Hertfordshire: Hitchin, one in 1884 (Durrant); Tring, one in 1906 (Goodson); Bishops Stortford – one at Valerian, 1938 (Colman); Berkhamsted, one on 16 May 1945 (S. B. Hodgson); Hitchin Priory, one on 20 May 1945 (D. W. H. Ffennell); Rothamsted Estate, Harpenden, 1951 (Riley, 1999); Tring, one on 18 August 1955 (Bell, 1957); Totteridge, one in March 1957 (Ian Lorimer); Arkley, one on 12 June 1958 (T. G. Howarth); Apsley, 21 September 1975 by N. E. Gammon (Bell, 1977); Totteridge, one in May 1968 (Ian Lorimer); Bushey, 19th July 1982 (Barry Goater); Baldock, 10th July 1994 (Kerry Robinson); Bishops Stortford, 30th August 1994 (Tony King); Bishops Stortford, 1994 (James Fish); East Barnet, 10th June 1996 (Peter Alton); Bishops Stortford, 12th & 17th June 1996 (Charles Watson); Hertford, 1996 (Andrew Wood); Marshall's Heath, 1996 (John Murray) and Bishops Stortford, 1996 (James Fish and Julian Reeves). For the period 2000 to 2006 we have 25 records – more than for the last hundred years and spread across the whole county. These divide into three in 2000, none in 2001, seven in 2002, 13 in 2003, 2 in 2004, 1 in 2005 and 14 in 2006. For reasons of space these are not listed here but are stored in the database for access by anyone who needs them.

EUSTROTINAE

2410 *Protodeltote pygarga* (Hufn.) Marbled White Spot

Recorded:	1888 – 2006
Distribution / Status:	Widespread / Common resident
Conservation status:	Herts Stable
Caterpillar food plants:	Not recorded. Elsewhere, on various grasses
Flight period:	Late May to the end of July
Records in database:	157

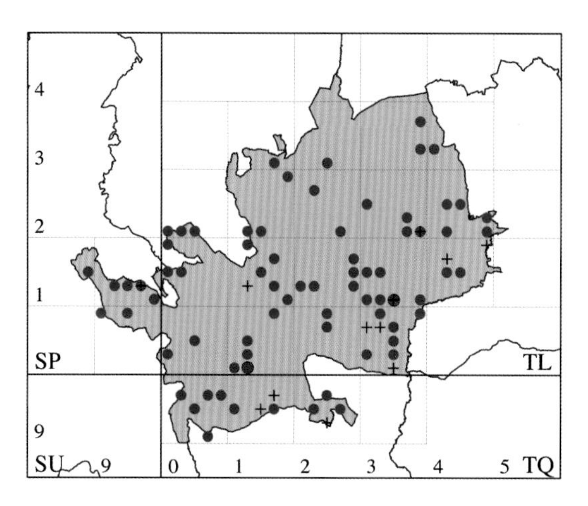

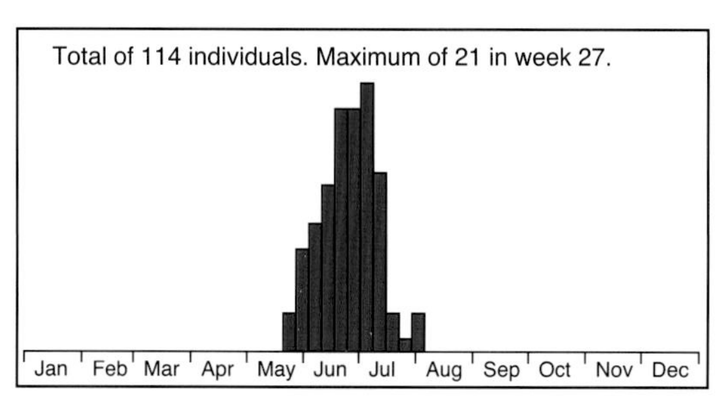

The Marbled White Spot is a tolerably common moth that is regularly encountered when running light traps in Hertfordshire woodlands. The larvae are said to feed on grasses that grow in damp areas in clearings, rides and at the woodland edge and so the moth may have value as an indicator species for edge habitat quality.

2412 *Deltote uncula* (Cl.) Silver Hook

Recorded:	1930 – 1970
Distribution / Status:	Absent / Vagrant. Possible former resident
Conservation status:	Herts Extinct
Caterpillar food plants:	Not recorded. Elsewhere, on sedges
Flight period:	Elsewhere, late June to August
Records in database:	5

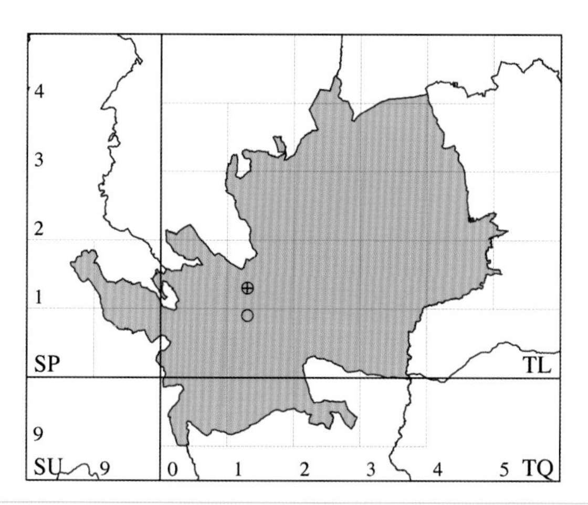

Four examples of the Silver Hook were taken at Harpenden in 1948 by C. B. Williams, according to Fryer (1950). In this same report, Fryer comments that he had thought the species already to be on the county list on the strength of his own recollection of examples by the Shafford Bridge across the River Ver, but regrettably he does not give a date, nor even a year, though some evidence points to it having been 1930. However, Riley (1999) in summarising records from the Harpenden Estate, differs by stating that four examples were caught there in two different traps during 1947, with only one in 1948 and one more in 1970. There are no other records. All of the Harpenden records are surely vagrants, but the vague reference to Shafford Bridge, at a time when the habitat would likely have been quite suitable, might suggest a remnant breeding population.

EARIADINAE

2418 *Earias clorana* (L.) Cream-bordered Green Pea

Recorded:	1901 – 2006
Distribution / Status:	Local / Uncommon resident
Conservation status:	Herts Threatened
Caterpillar food plants:	Osier, Common Sallow
Flight period:	Late May/June
Records in database:	13

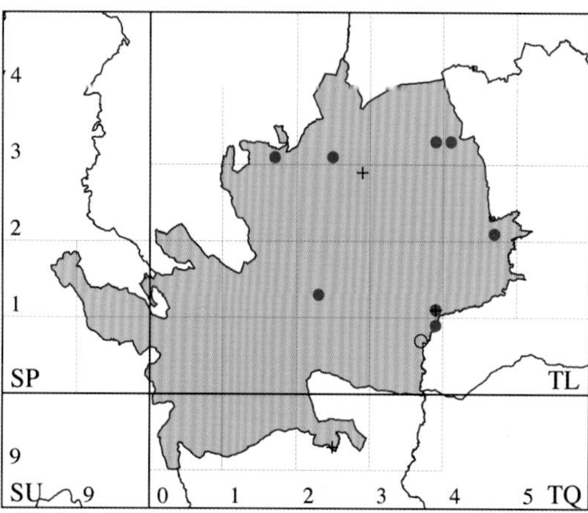

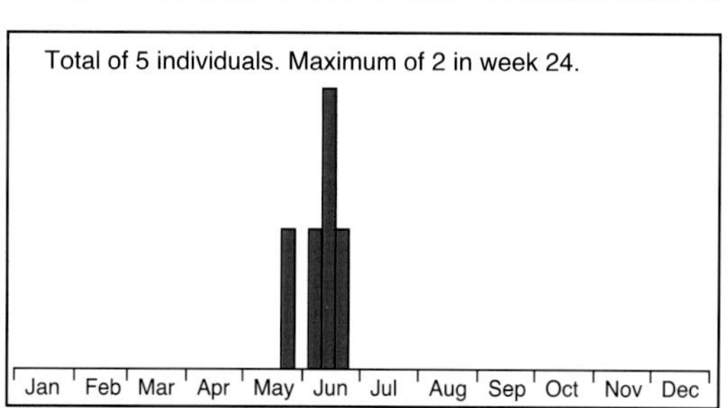

Cream-bordered Green Pea prevails where sallows, osiers and other *Salix* species thrive, though these do not necessarily need to be in wet habitats. The distribution shows that the moth has a clear affinity with the north-east of the county, although the 1993 maps for the London Area show this species extending up the Lea Valley towards our boundary and it would be no real surprise to record the moth both there and along the Stort. Sallows are frequently cleared on nature reserves and this might be a factor in limiting the spread of the moth; for this reason it is classed as Threatened in Hertfordshire.

CHLOEPHORINAE

The Green/Scarce Silver-lines species

Interpretation of old records of these next two species presents some difficulties. Before 1939, 2421: Scarce Silver-lines was referred to as *bicolorana*, as now, but from 1939 for the next fifty or so years it was referred to as *prasinana*. Today, and prior to 1939, the name *prasinana* implies 2422: Green Silver-lines, but during the interim that species was known as *fagana*. The situation is also confused by the accidental application of the wrong name of the day by some less careful authors!

2421 *Bena bicolorana* (Fuessly) Scarce Silver-lines

Recorded: 1884 – 2006
Distribution / Status: Local / Common resident
Conservation status: Herts Stable
Caterpillar food plants: English Oak. Elsewhere, allegedly on birch
Flight period: Late June to late August
Records in database: 162

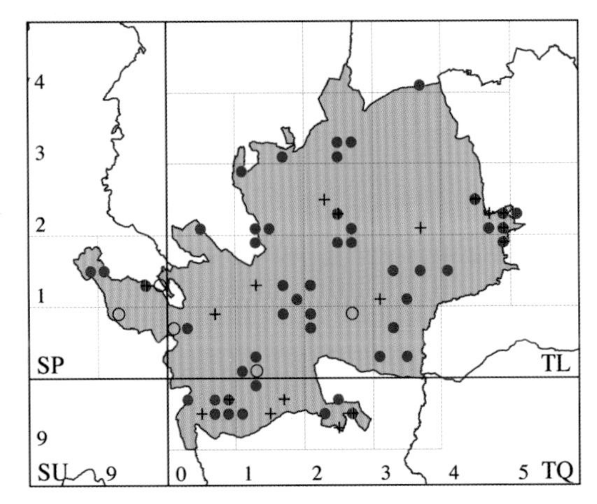

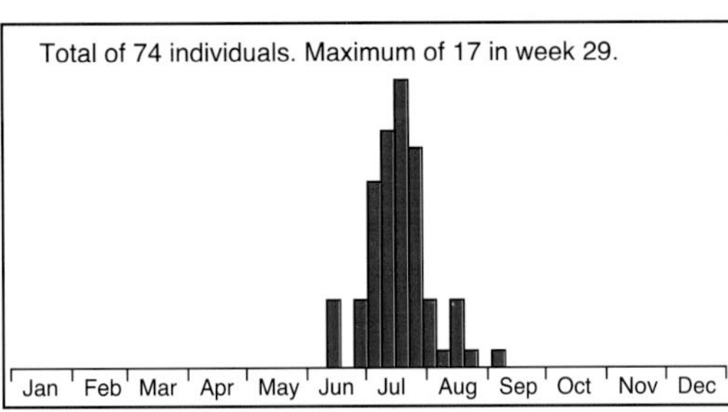

Though rarely presenting itself in numbers greater than one, this is nevertheless a widespread and relatively common moth in the county and is likely to be present wherever there are oaks – both in woodland and growing in hedgerows, parks and gardens. However, it appears that the oaks need to be at least semi-mature in order to support larvae and the moth may be genuinely absent from parts of the north-east.

2422 *Pseudoips prasinana* (L.) ssp. *britannica* Warren Green Silver-lines

Recorded: 1884 – 2006
Distribution / Status: Widespread / Common resident
Conservation status: Herts Stable
Caterpillar food plants: English Oak. Elsewhere, also on Beech, Hazel and birch
Flight period: Mid-May to late July
Records in database: 232

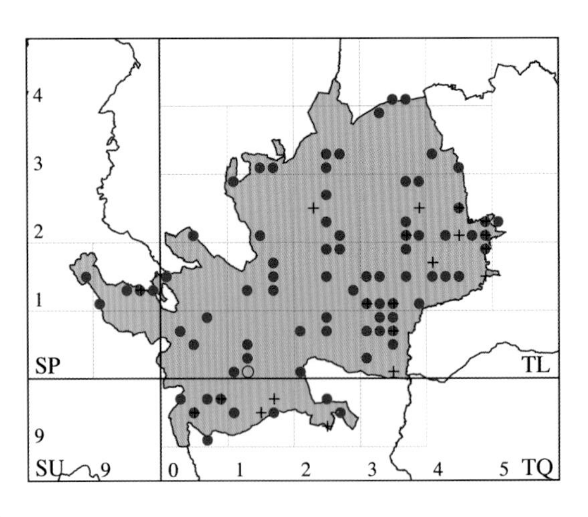

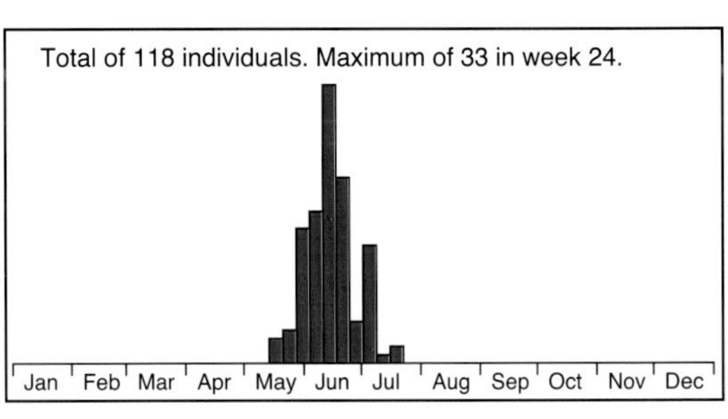

Subspecies *prasinana* Linnaeus is found in continental Europe and in Britain is replaced by subspecies *britannica* Warren. The moth is far more frequently encountered than 2421: Scarce Silver-lines and sometimes presents in larger numbers; doubtless the wider range of foodplants accounts for its presence in areas of the north-east where the last species is apparently absent.

2423 *Nycteola revayana* (Scop.) Oak Nycteoline

Recorded: 1899 – 2006
Distribution / Status: Local / Common resident
Conservation status: Stable or incresing
Caterpillar food plants: English Oak
Flight period: September/October then after hibernation from March to May then late June to early August
Records in database: 159

4
3
2
1
SP
TL
9
SU 9
0 1 2 3 4 5 TQ

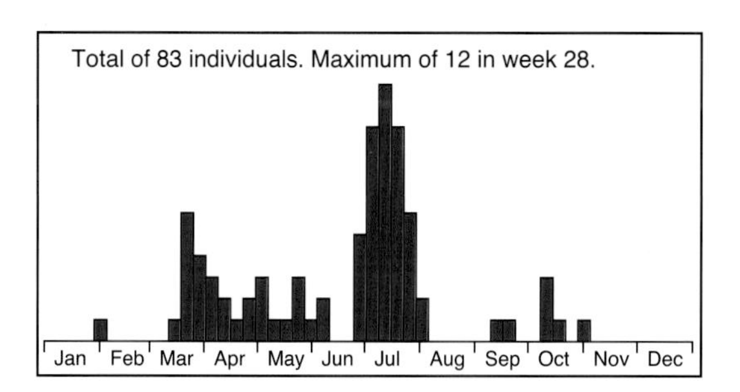

The recent addition of the Eastern Nycteoline (*Nycteola asiatica* (Krulikovsky) to the British list means that care must now be taken when naming nycteolines in Hertfordshire; in several cases examination of the genital structure may be necessary to provide a reliable answer. British populations of Oak Nycteoline are supposedly univoltine, but in Hertfordshire there are certainly two generations of adults rather than one. Summer adults are on the wing from late June to early August and give rise to a second generation, flying from September, but entering hibernation soon after emergence to fly again in the spring. In spite of reasonable coverage of the county for the preceding forty or so years, our first record comes as late as 1899, at Bricket Wood (Gibbs, 1901). The moth was subsequently found at Felden, in 1900 (A. Piffard) and Bushey Heath in the same year (Barraud) and then again at Bricket Wood in 1932 (Fryer). It was still evidently quite rare when a cocoon from Hertfordshire was exhibited at a meeting of the South London Entomological & Natural History Society on 9 July 1931. Later, Foster (1942) reported it from Northchurch (also recorded by others as 'Ashridge'), by J. Bell. At Totteridge, Ian Lorimer trapped moths from 1954 to 1980 and recorded the Oak Nycteoline twice only, in 1973 and 1979 – 'always melanic'. The Bishops Stortford district list (Allen, 1950) makes no mention of this species other than at a site in Essex further east and it is not mentioned in the 1985 update (Fielding et al, 1985). The first record ever for Bishops Stortford is probably my own from my garden on 15th July 1987; Charles Watson caught the next in 1989. However, by the early 1990s it had started to extend its range and by 1995 was present in most places across the county. In 2006 it is expected in most site lists from the county.

PANTHEINAE

2425 *Colocasia coryli* (L.) Nut-tree Tussock

Recorded:	1893 – 2006
Distribution / Status:	Widespread / Common resident
Conservation status:	Herts Stable
Caterpillar food plants:	Not recorded. Elsewhere, on various deciduous trees
Flight period:	Late March to June then July/August, in two generations
Records in database:	589

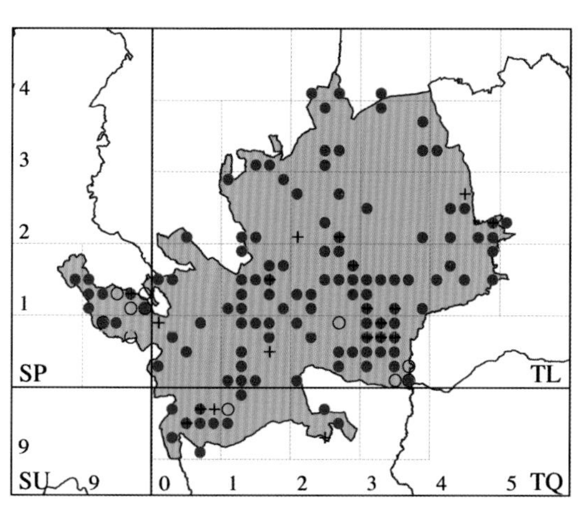

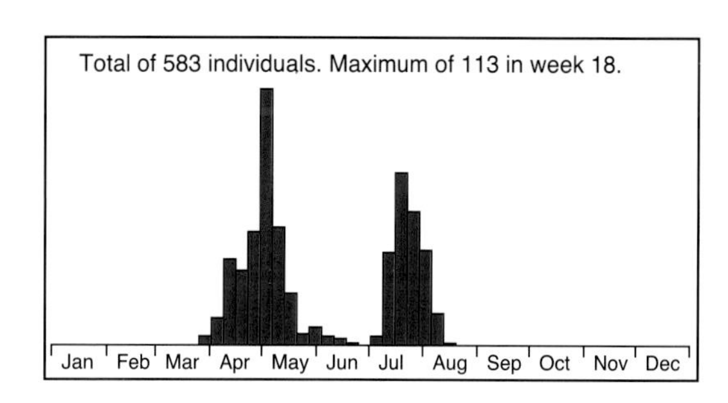

This widespread and common species is a familiar sight across the county wherever there are trees, though it may prove to be absent from some of the arable areas in the north-east of the county. The melanic ab. *melanotica* Havercampf typically forms less than 5 per cent of the population, but this rises to about 10 per cent in the Broxbourne Woods complex and occasionally it becomes more frequent, as during 2003 when about 60 per cent of captures at Hertford Heath West, Balls Wood and other areas of the Broxbourne complex were of this form.

2427 *Raphia frater* (Grote) Brother

Recorded:	1949 – 1949
Distribution / Status:	Random / Former immigrant
Conservation status:	
Caterpillar food plants:	Not known
Flight period:	July. In America, May to July
Records in database:	1

This North American species was added to the British list when a single example arrived at the light trap on the Rothamsted Estate in Harpenden, on 3 July 1949 (C. B. Williams). There are no other British records of this species.

PLUSIINAE

2428 *Chrysodeixis chalcites* (Esper)

Recorded:	1990 – 2004
Distribution / Status:	Random / Rare immigrant
Conservation status:	-
Caterpillar food plants:	Not recorded.
Flight period:	September/October
Records in database:	6

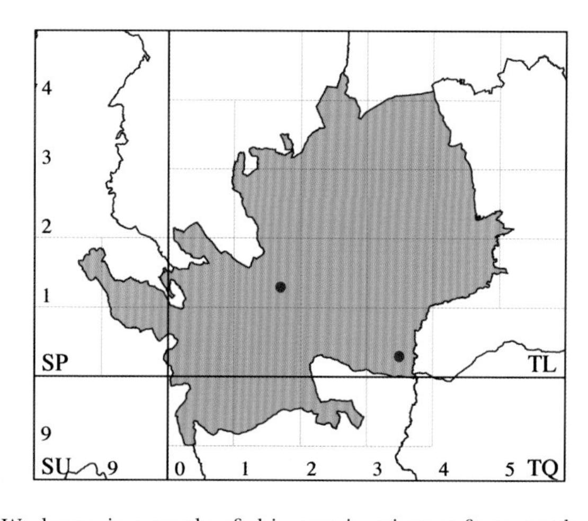

We have six records of this rare immigrant from southern Europe and North Africa as follows: Green Tye, 18th October 1990 (David Wilson); Hobbs Close, Cheshunt, 1st and 4th September 2004 (Mark Cooper); Churchgate, Cheshunt, 4th September 2004 (Paul Roper); Wheathampstead, 11th and 13th October 2004 (Trevor Chapman).

2432 *Trichoplusia ni* (Hb.) Ni Moth

Recorded: 1952 – 2006
Distribution / Status: Random / Rare immigrant
Conservation status: -
Caterpillar food plants: Not recorded. Elsewhere, marigold, Sea Rocket and other plants
Flight period: July/August
Records in database: 4

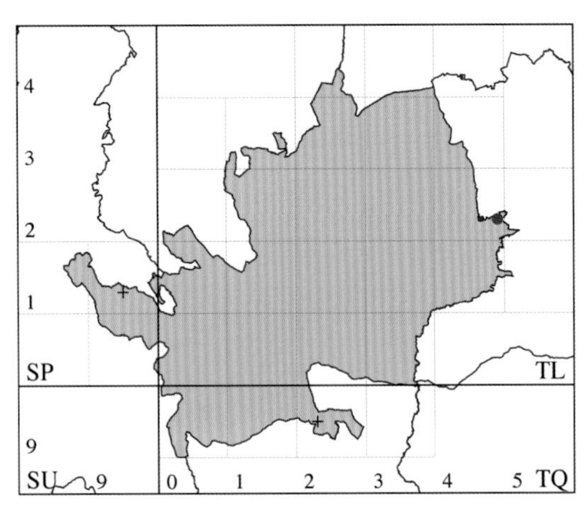

The Ni Moth is a southern European species that reaches Britain as a primary immigrant. Our four records from Hertfordshire are: Tring, 23rd August 1952 by A. L. Goodson (Bell, 1954); Arkley, 27th August 1964 by T. G. Howarth (Bell, 1966) and Bishops Stortford, 28th July and 5th August 2006 (James Fish & Julian Reeves).

2433 *Thysanoplusia orichalcia* (Fabr.) Slender Burnished Brass

Recorded: 2000 – 2000
Distribution / Status: Random / Immigrant
Conservation status: -
Caterpillar food plants:
Flight period: November
Records in database: 1

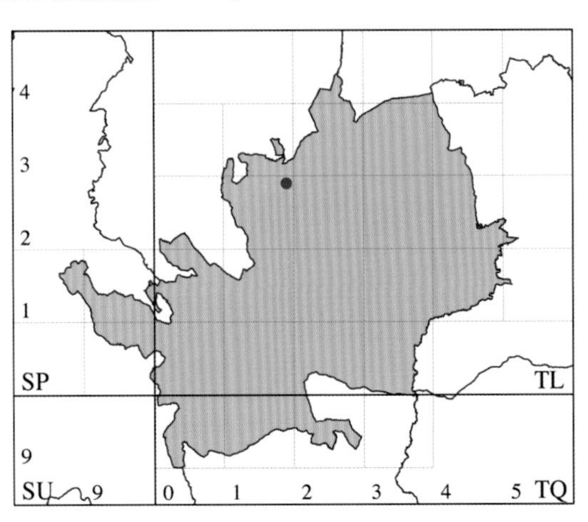

We have a single record of this rare immigrant for Hertfordshire: One was seen flying around a kitchen in Hitchin, on 18th November 2000 and was found dead the next day (D. Hudson, reported in *Atropos* number 12, page 69).

2434 *Diachrysia chrysitis* (L.) Burnished Brass

Recorded: 1884 – 2006
Distribution / Status: Ubiquitous / Common resident
Conservation status: Herts Stable
Caterpillar food plants: Stinging Nettle
Flight period: June/July then August/September in two generations
Records in database: 928

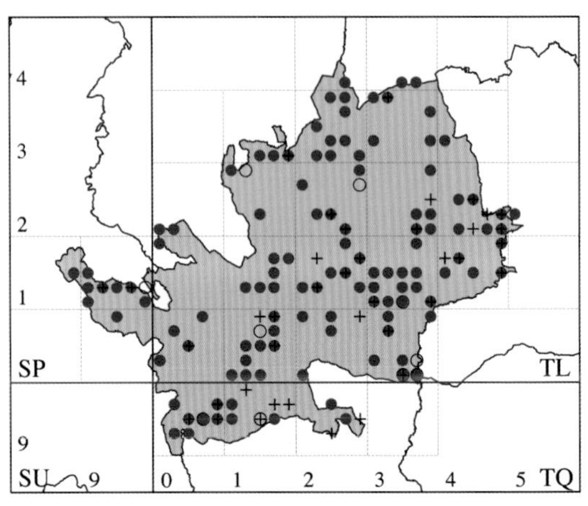

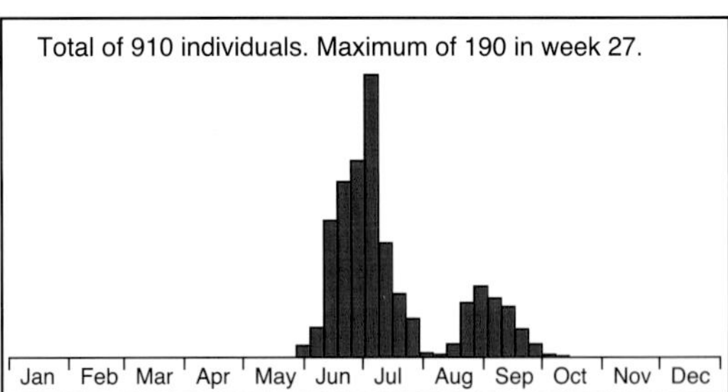

Goater et al (2003) alerted us to potential problems with our concept of the Burnished Brass, with three 'species' to consider in Britain – *chrysitis* Linnaeus (Burnished Brass), *tutti* Kostrowicki (Northern Burnished Brass) and *stenochrysis* Warren (Pacific Burnished Brass) [the English names are mine]. In Britain we have regarded typical *chrysitis* as being the form in which the forewings bear two more or less parallel brassy bands that are separated by the darker ground colour; where these two bands coalesce to create an effective 'H' shape we have regarded this as being either ab. *juncta* Tutt or ab. *tutti* Kostrowicki. The status of *tutti* is not at all clear; it may be a valid species or it may be a form. The status of *stenochrysis* seems pretty certain, however – it is a valid species and almost certainly occurs in Britain. It sports the 'H' shape marking. Representative voucher specimens should be kept where possible and until such time as the problem may be resolved recorders ought, as a minimum, note whether moths caught are of the typical form ('parallel' bands) or the *tutti/stenochrysis* form ('H' form). In the present work it has been impossible to segregate records; both 'parallel' and 'H' forms are widespread across the county in both generations, although 'H' forms appear to be numerically superior.

2436 *Macdunnoughia confusa* (Steph.) Dewick's Plusia

Recorded: 1995 – 1995
Distribution / Status: Random / Rare immigrant
Conservation status: -
Caterpillar food plants: Not recorded. Elsewhere, on various herbaceous plants
Flight period: Elsewhere, August to October
Records in database: 1

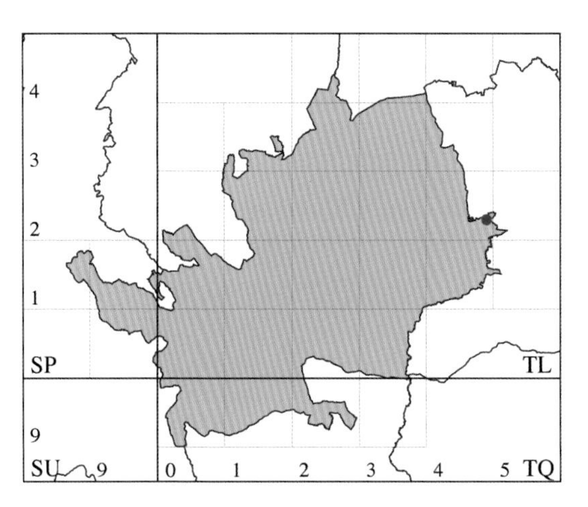

Our only record is of one at Bishops Stortford on 30th August 1995, caught by James Fish and Julian Reeves. The moth is an increasingly regular immigrant in Britain; it originates in southern Europe.

2437 *Polychrysia moneta* (Fabr.) Golden Plusia

Recorded:	1896 – 2006
Distribution / Status:	Local / Common resident
Conservation status:	Stable
Caterpillar food plants:	Monk's-hood; garden *Delphinium* species
Flight period:	June to early August
Records in database:	95

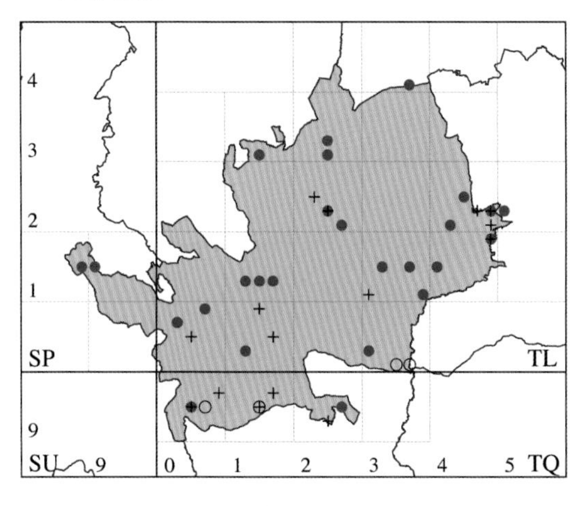

The first British specimen of the Golden Plusia was taken by a schoolboy at Dover, East Kent, on 25th June 1890 and reported by Barrett in the same year (*Entomologist's Monthly Magazine* **26:** 255) who gives other reports. The first Hertfordshire example was captured by Arthur Cottam, in the company of Clarence E. Fry, in Fry's garden at Elmcote, Watford, on 19th June 1896. It was taken at Honeysuckle blossom at about 10 pm. In the last week of June and the first week of July 1896 about 8 examples were also captured in Tring. Foster caught it at Hitchin in 1898 (Foster, 1916) and it 'appeared in some numbers' at Watford during 1902 (Barraud, 1903). In the years between its discovery and Foster's 1937 county list it was reported from Bushey Heath, Waltham Cross, Letchworth, Hoddesdon, Baldock, Stevenage, Berkhamsted, New Barnet and Harpenden; in reporting these localities Foster noted that it was 'now [1937] common all over the county'. It was first noted at Bishops Stortford in 1910 and by 1950 was 'now common in most of our gardens' (Allan, 1950). Today, it is widespread, but rather local, perhaps limited by the need for delphiniums unaffected by garden sprays on which to feed.

2439/2440 *Plusia festucae* (L.)/*putnami* Grote ssp. *gracilis* Lempke Gold Spot/Lempke's Gold Spot

Neither the Gold Spot nor Lempke's Gold Spot breed in Hertfordshire and all our records are of vagrants or immigrants from elsewhere. Since we did not realise that Lempke's Gold Spot occurred in Britain until 1969 any records prior to that date which are not supported by a voucher specimen could refer to either species. These are: Elmcote, Watford, 31st August 1896 (S. H. Spencer); Cheshunt Marshes, by Edelsten, undated in Foster (1937); Bishops Stortford, one at light in 1938 (C. S. Colman); Bishops Stortford, one at a house light in Galloway Road in 1945 and another in 1949 (Clifford Craufurd); Rothamsted Estate, 1947 (C. B. Williams), Totteridge, September 1956 (Ian Lorimer) and Bishops Stortford, 8th August 1959 (Geoffrey Sell). The last listed was reported as *putnami* in the 1985 Bishops Stortford list, which was compiled by Sell himself, but is simply given as 'Gold Spot' (apparently added at a later date) in his diaries which he gave to me upon retirement to Dorset.

2439 *Plusia festucae* (L.) Gold Spot

Recorded:	1896 – 2006
Distribution / Status:	Extremely local / Vagrant
Conservation status:	–
Caterpillar food plants:	Not recorded. Elsewhere,
Flight period:	June; August. Elsewhere, June/July then August/September
Records in database:	10

Records made since 1969 that are attributed specifically to *festucae* are from Rickmansworth, 10th June 2002 (Paul Clack); Hemel Hempstead, 6th August 2006 (Roger Prue) and Hatfield, 13th August 2006 (Tony Bristow).

2441 *Autographa gamma* (L.) Silver Y

Recorded: 1882 – 2006
Distribution / Status: Ubiquitous / Regular immigrant; temporary resident
Conservation status: –
Caterpillar food plants: Stinging Nettle. Elsewhere, polyphagous
Flight period: May to December
Records in database: 2,491

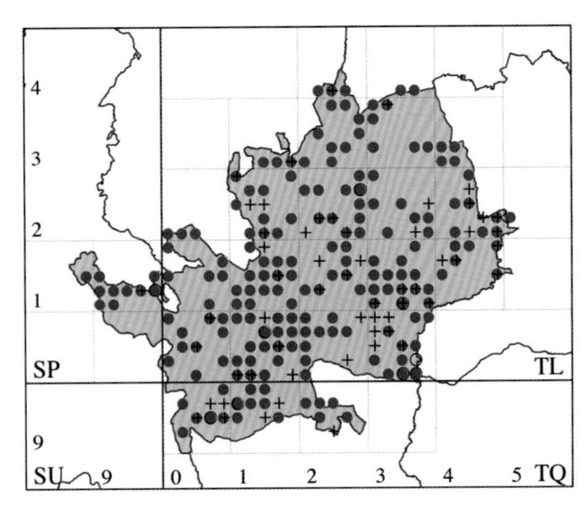

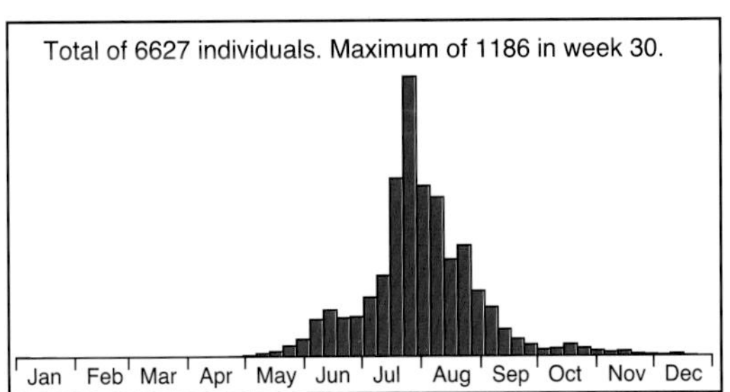

Silver Y moth records rank third in the table of most frequently reported species in Hertfordshire. Early-season immigrants usually lay eggs and there is a generation of adults produced in July/August that is boosted by fresh immigration from September to November. We have no evidence to suggest that any Silver Y moths ever survive a Hertfordshire winter and each new year depends upon a fresh batch of immigrants arriving. At Harpenden, large numbers of larvae were encountered whilst 'taking up a mangel-wurtzel crop' during 1882 (Willis, 1882). Bell (1972) referred to 1971 as being 'the year of the Silver Y' to moth-ers or the year of the 'Small Tortoiseshell' to butterfly enthusiasts. Clearly both were abundant that year; given that the larvae of both species feed on the same plants it is probable that this was a good year for home bred moths rather than immigration, for which the butterfly is not particularly noted.

2442 *Autographa pulchrina* (Haw.) Beautiful Golden Y

Recorded: 1888 – 2006
Distribution / Status: Widespread / Common resident
Conservation status: Herts Stable
Caterpillar food plants: Not recorded. Elsewhere on low plants
Flight period: Late May to early August
Records in database: 264

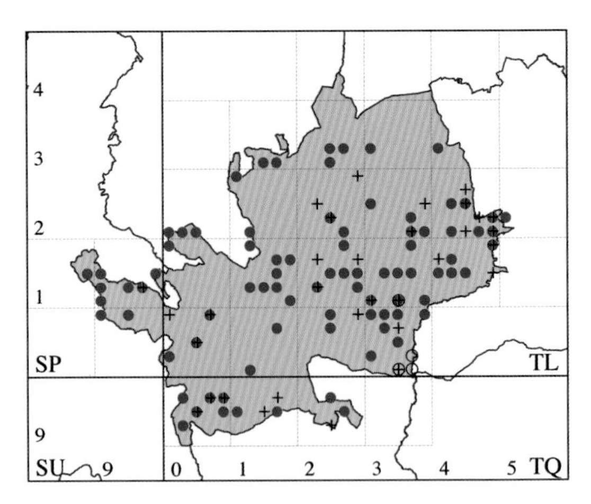

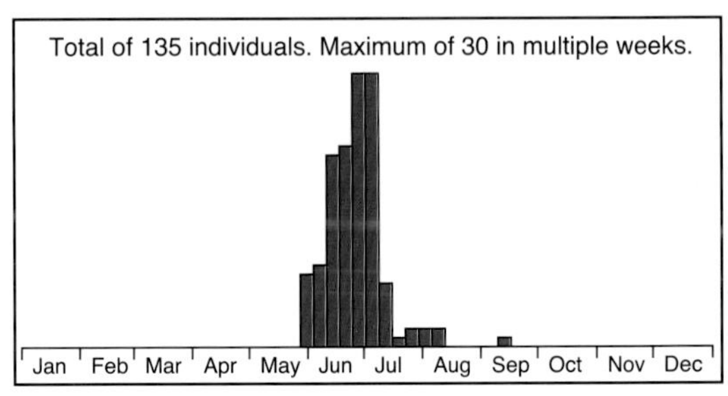

Both this species and the next fly together in similar habitat. The Beautiful Golden Y is probably present in most map squares in Hertfordshire.

2443 *Autographa jota* (L.) Plain Golden Y

Recorded: 1828 – 2006
Distribution / Status: Local / Scarce resident
Conservation status: Herts Threatened
Caterpillar food plants: Stinging nettle
Flight period: Late May to early August
Records in database: 190

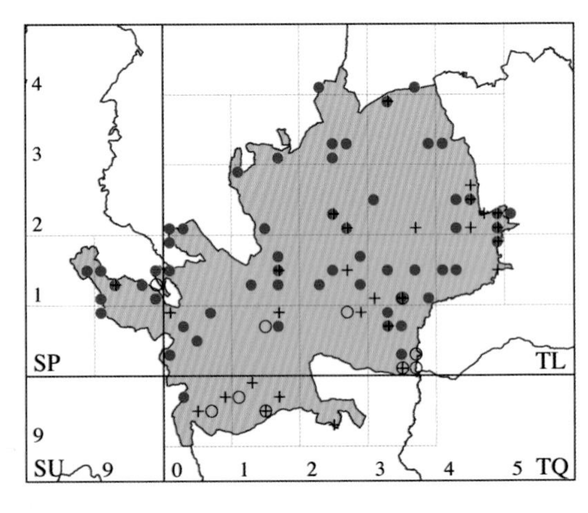

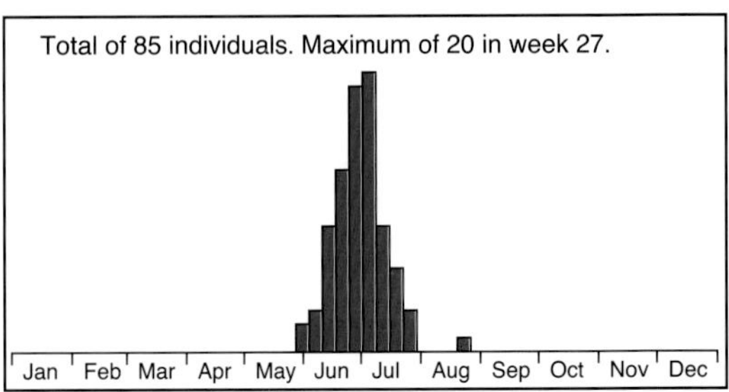

Interestingly, the Plain Golden Y appears now to be absent from several places in the south of Hertfordshire where it once flourished. This is surprising, since 2442: Beautiful Golden Y seems to like the same habitat and is evidently doing well there. There may be a difference in foodplant preference or perhaps there are other, as yet unknown factors operating.

2444 *Autographa bractea* ([D.& S.]) Gold Spangle

Recorded: 1956 – 1982
Distribution / Status: Random / Former vagrant
Conservation status: -
Caterpillar food plants: Not recorded. Elsewhere, on low plants
Flight period: Elsewhere, July/August
Records in database: 2

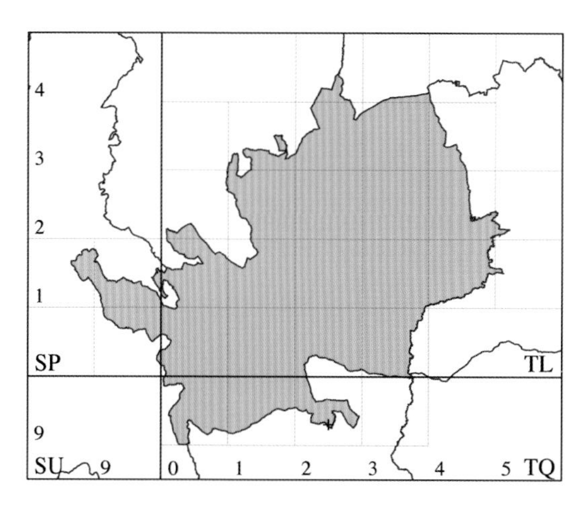

We have two records. The first was caught at light in Totteridge on 22nd July 1956 (Ian Lorimer, *Entomologist's Gazette* **9:** 20 and Bell, 1959). The second was in David Wilson's garden light trap at Much Hadham on 31st July 1982 (reported in Bretherton & Chalmers-Hunt, *Entomologists Record* **95**: 151). The moth is resident in Wales, the north-west, Scotland and Ireland and during the 1950s underwent a southwards range expansion of which the Totteridge example was presumably a part; the origin of the Much Hadham example is less clear.

2447 *Syngrapha interrogationis* (L.) Scarce Silver Y

Recorded: 1901 – 1960
Distribution / Status: Random / Rare immigrant
Conservation status: -
Caterpillar food plants: Not recorded. Elsewhere, Heather and Bilberry
Flight period: August
Records in database: 2

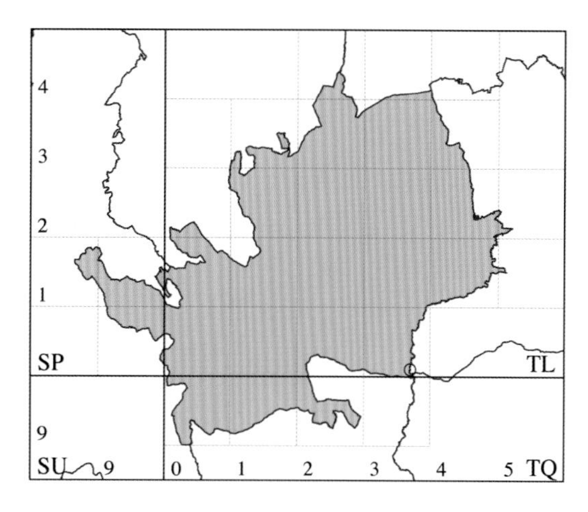

Although the Scarce Silver Y is resident in north-west Britain, examples recorded in the south-east are generally regarded as immigrants from the European mainland. We have two records only for Hertfordshire: Cheshunt Street, 'once' (Boyd, 1901) and Tring, one taken by A. L. Goodson on 19 August 1960 (Bell, 1962). The year of the Cheshunt Street example is unclear.

Spectacle moths

There is confusion in older literature between the two spectacle moths that are found in Britain and in some cases it is impossible to be certain which species is being referred to. This is because the two names *triplasia* and *tripartita* have been interchanged over the years. However, the old name of *trigemina* has never been used for the ordinary Spectacle and similarly *urticae* has never been used for the Dark Spectacle – as far as I am aware. In his list for Hitchin, Foster (1916) helpfully includes English names and thus we know that he used *triplasia* for Dark Spectacle and *tripartita* for the ordinary Spectacle. Foster's two entries in the 1937 county list are *triplasia* Linnaeus and *tripartita* Hufnagel (= *urticae* Hübner). Thus, it is possible to conclude that Foster retains in his 1937 work the same names that he used in his 1916 paper. This is important, because the relative status of the two species has evidently reversed.

2449 *Abrostola triplasia* (L.) Dark Spectacle

Recorded: 1828 – 2005
Distribution / Status: Random / Vagrant
Conservation status: -
Caterpillar food plants: Not recorded. Elsewhere, Stinging Nettle and Hop
Flight period: Late June to early September
Records in database: 30

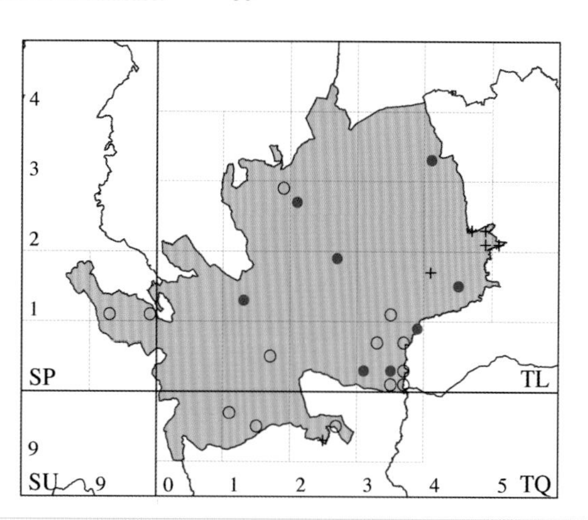

Having sorted through the nomenclatural confusion it is evident that the Dark Spectacle was a common and widespread moth in Hertfordshire whilst 2450: Spectacle was rather infrequently seen. Thus, at Hitchin in 1916 Foster has it as 'very common' and in his 1937 county list he gives several localities where it was found. It was evidently common in the Bishops Stortford area and Allan (1950) noted that it was 'Common enough at light' here. In the 1985 update to the Bishops Stortford list by John Fielding and others, there is no mention of Dark Spectacle, even though Charles Watson took one at light in Bloodhounds Wood in 1981; the entry for the Ordinary Spectacle reads 'Common'. At some stage, however, the Dark Spectacle declined to its present state of rarity in the county and was replaced by the ordinary Spectacle, which was then rare and is now more or less ubiquitous. At Totteridge, Ian Lorimer records just six Dark Spectacles in his garden trap from 1954 to 1980, suggesting that in his area, at least, the moth was not common by as early as 1954. By 1983, the authors of volume 10 of *Moths and Butterflies of Great Britain and Ireland* were able to report that the Dark Spectacle was then '... much more local [than ordinary Spectacle] over much of Britain. More common in the west than the east ...'. There is very little additional data that sheds light on the situation. The present-day map shows a number of solid dots for records made recently, but these were all made from 2001 to 2005 and the 1981 Bloodhounds Wood record is the last one in Hertfordshire prior to this more recent flurry, which perhaps relates to vagrant examples? All but one of these are from light traps: Scales Park, 22nd July 2001 (Jim Reid); Cuffley, 21st July 2001 (Alan Bolitho); Rothamsted, 21st August 2001 (Phil Gould); Lucas Wood, Todd's Green, 25th August 2001 (Colin Plant); Churchgate, Cheshunt, 4th September 2001 (Paul Roper); Rothamsted Estate, 29th June and 27th July 2002 (Phil Gould); Golden Grove, Gilston, 11th July and 4th August 2005 (Colin Plant); Datchworth, 17th July 2005 (Steve Palmer) and Rye House Power Station, one male in a Malaise trap, 18th September 2005 (Colin Plant).

2450 *Abrostola tripartita* (Hufn.) Spectacle

Recorded:	1884 – 2006
Distribution / Status:	Widespread / Common resident
Conservation status:	Herts Stable
Caterpillar food plants:	Stinging Nettle
Flight period:	Late April to early September
Records in database:	1,250

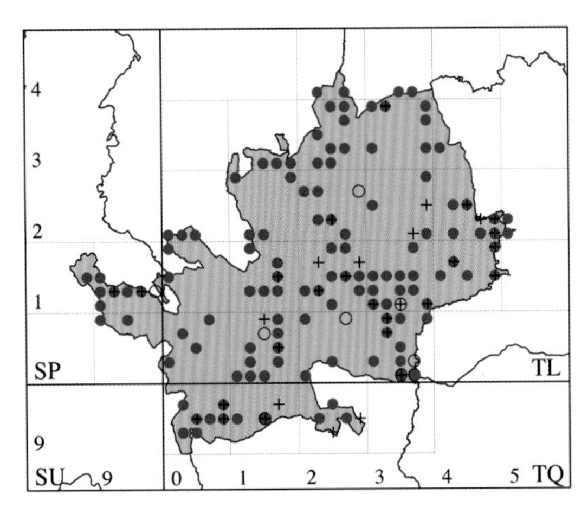

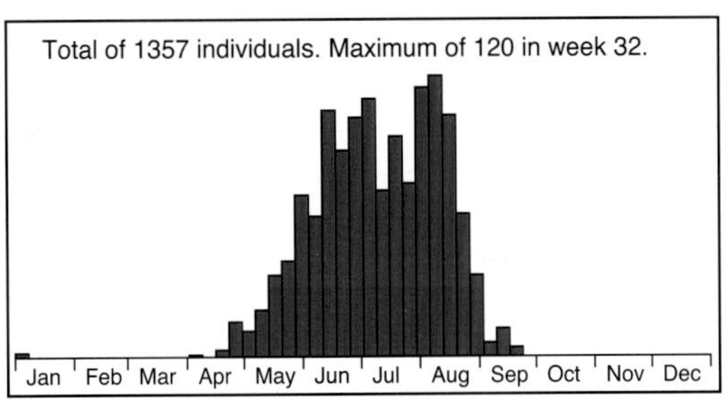

The fact that the database contains 1,250 records of this species and only 30 of 2449: Dark Spectacle emphasises the comments under that species. The change in fortunes of the Spectacle by which it ascended from scarcity to near ubiquity are not recorded, but today this is a very common moth everywhere in Hertfordshire.

CATOCALINAE

2451 *Catocala fraxini* (L.) Clifden Nonpareil

Recorded:	1887 – 1945
Distribution / Status:	Random / Rare immigrant
Conservation status:	-
Caterpillar food plants:	In Europe, on Aspen
Flight period:	September
Records in database:	3

This large moth occasionally migrates to Britain from southern Europe and there are three records for Hertfordshire as follows: Haileybury, one on 23rd September 1887 recorded by R. W. Bowyer – '... a specimen .... was brought to me; it had been picked up on a path under some ivy which had been trimmed in the course of the day. Unfortunately it has suffered from rough treatment' (*Entomologist* **20**: 306); Waltham Cross, 'has been seen', (Boyd, 1901), but the year is not given and Boyd's list covered 'the last fifty years'; Walkern, one on 15 August 1945 was 'captured under a tumbler' by the Rev. W. D. W. Greenham's housekeeper on the wall at Walkern rectory. Although the moth escaped when the tumbler was knocked over, the (unnamed) housekeeper described it as a large moth that showed its blue hind wings when being captured. This same record appears in a number of hand-written lists variously dated 1940 and 1943, some of which appear to be claiming credit for the capture of the moth by the list-writer!

2452 *Catocala nupta* (L.) Red Underwing

Recorded:	1884 – 2006
Distribution / Status:	Widespread / Common resident
Conservation status:	Herts Stable
Caterpillar food plants:	Not recorded. Elsewhere, on willows
Flight period:	Late July to early October
Records in database:	177

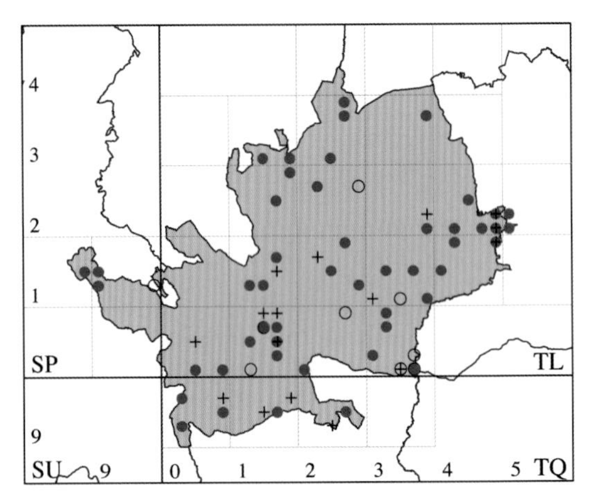

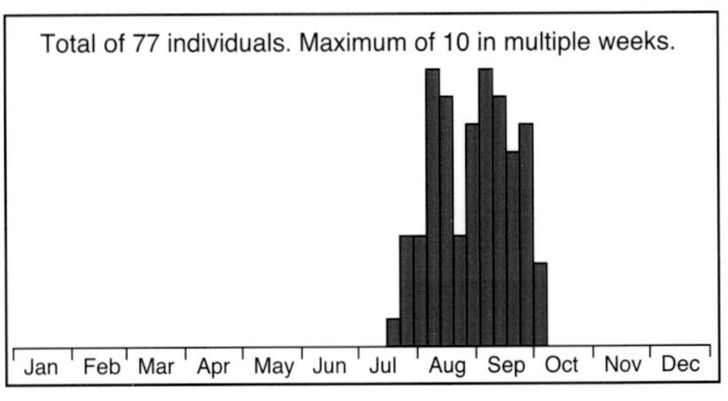

Elsewhere in Britain, the caterpillars thrive on a variety of willow species including Weeping Willow and this tree grows in a number of places around dwellings in the arable north-east of the county, where records on the map currently thin out. It is expected that if sufficient recording was undertaken in those areas the moth may be found, though there will be some intensely arable parts where it is absent. An example of ab. *nigra* Cockayne (= f. *nigrata* Lempke) in which the forewings are entirely black was taken at Totteridge on 30th September 1962 (P. Barnes, reported in de Worms 1964). The specimen was exhibited by Ian Lorimer at the 1962 Annual Exhibition of the South London Entomological & Natural History Society and was subsequently figured in the *Proceedings* of that Society for the year. Further examples were captured there on 14th September 1969 and 29th September 1970, but none appear to have been recorded elsewhere in the county.

2453 *Catocala electa* (View.) Rosy Underwing

Recorded:	1927 – 1927
Distribution / Status:	Random / Rare immigrant
Conservation status:	-
Caterpillar food plants:	Not recorded. Elsewhere, on willows, sallows and poplars
Flight period:	Elsewhere, mid-July to late September
Records in database:	1

The Rosy Underwing is an extremely rare immigrant to Britain from southern Europe. There is a single Hertfordshire record, from Hoddesdon on 15th September 1927, 'one specimen on a window' (Molesworth, 1928. *Entomologist* **61:** 139).

[2455 *Catocala sponsa* (L.) Dark Crimson Underwing

The Dark Crimson Underwing was formerly resident in several of the 'better' oak woodlands of southern Britain, but is now more or less confined to the New Forest. Foster (1941) adds it to the Hertfordshire list from 'Ware, one at rest, August 1937, one at light September, 1940 (Gerard)'. There is some evidence that examples of this species away from the Hampshire area probably relate to primary immigrants (Skinner, 2004). These records may support that theory, but during the 1930s, Gerard made a number of records that could be interpreted as probable errors, though taken in the context of other records for each individual species, several could be correct. These include 2103: Plain Clay, 2217: Star-wort, 2219: Striped Lychnis and the present records of Dark Crimson Underwing. The fact that Gerard has so many 'unusual' records is suspicious, as is the fact that he is responsible for *both* the Hertfordshire sightings. In discussing his (frankly, unbelievable) Hertfordshire record of Kentish Glory, Young (1991. in *Moths and Butterflies of Great Britain & Ireland* volume 7) notes that 'Records are hopelessly confused by specimens labelled from place of emergence rather than capture and this may explain doubtful past records from .... Hertfordshire ...'). Tempting though it is to treat these records as valid, I am of the opinion that there is insufficient data to substantiate the claims.]

2462 *Callistege mi* (Cl.) Mother Shipton

Recorded:	1884 – 2006
Distribution / Status:	Local / Common resident
Conservation status:	Herts Stable
Caterpillar food plants:	Not recorded. Elsewhere, on grasses or legumes – depending on which book is believed
Flight period:	May/June
Records in database:	126

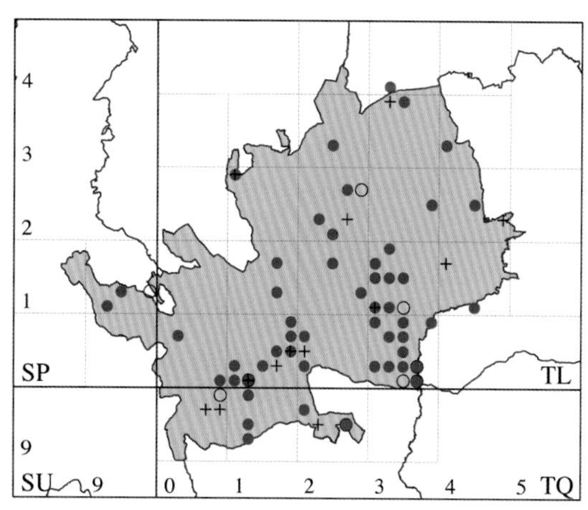

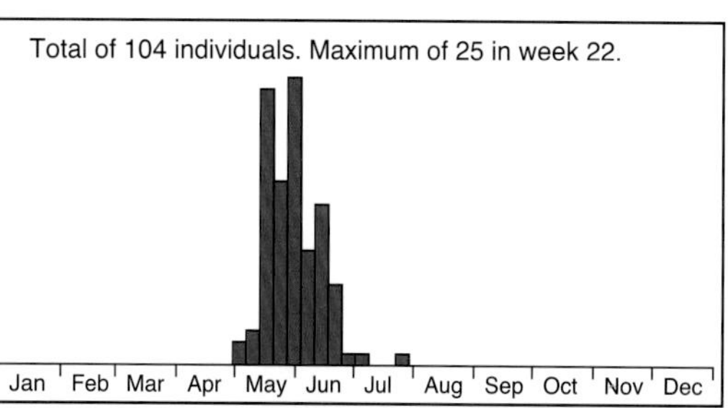

The Mother Shipton moth takes it name from the markings on the forewings which, if viewed with the outer edge of the wing to the bottom bear an uncanny resemblance to the face of a witch. The adults fly in sunshine over grasslands and the abundance of modern records reflect the rise in the number of butterfly observers that also report day-flying moths. It would be surprising if the areas currently lacking records do not also support the moth.

2463 *Euclidia glyphica* (L.) Burnet Companion

Recorded:	1884 – 2006
Distribution / Status:	Local / Common resident
Conservation status:	Herts Stable
Caterpillar food plants:	Not recorded. Elsewhere, on clovers and trefoils
Flight period:	May/June
Records in database:	123

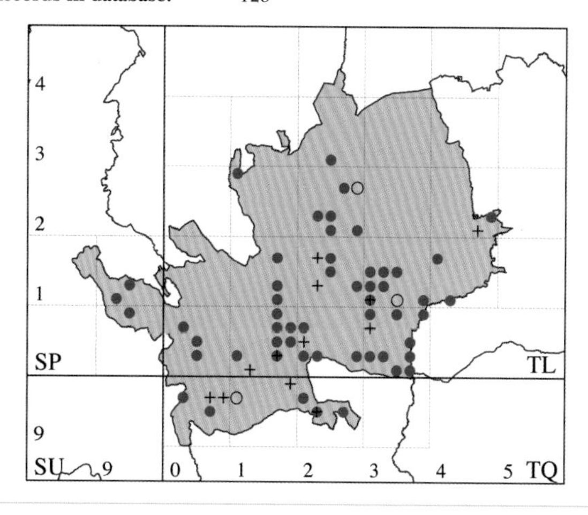

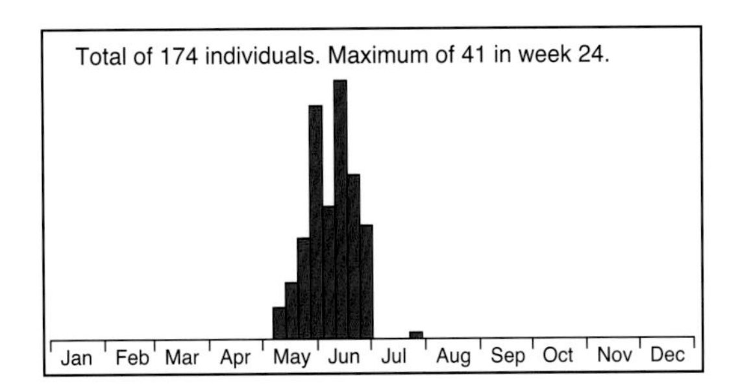

The Burnet Companion is recorded on an equal number of occasions to 2462: Mother Shipton, but these records report approximately twice the number of individuals, suggesting that the Burnet Companion is the more common of the two day-flying species.

OPHIDERINAE

2465 *Tyta luctuosa* ([D.& S.]) Four-spotted

Recorded:	1828 – 2005
Distribution / Status:	Extremely local / Resident
Conservation status:	UK BAP Priority Species. Herts Endangered
Caterpillar food plants:	Not recorded. Elsewhere, on Field Bindweed
Flight period:	Elsewhere, mid-May to mid-August in two generations
Records in database:	19

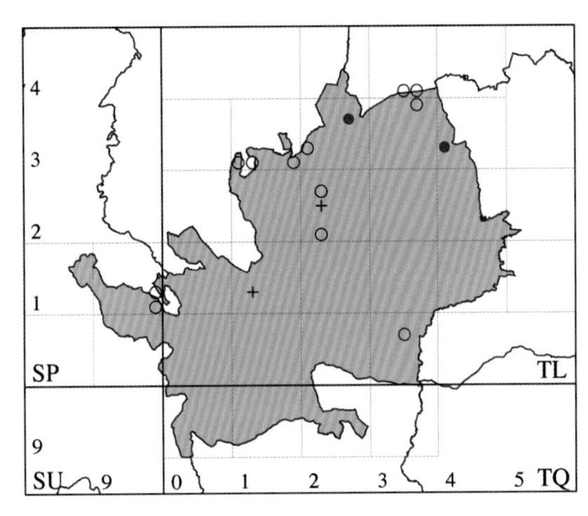

The Four-spotted is listed by J. F. Stephens for Hertford in his *Illustrations of British Entomology*, published in 1829. Because Stephens' definition of Hertford was somewhat all encompassing, the record cannot be mapped. Foster (1916), noted that it 'may usually be met with singly in clover-fields and meadows in many parts of the [north Hertfordshire] district. In 1912 I found this species occurring fairly commonly on one of the railway banks near Hitchin, and in 1915 discovered a spot on this railway bank where the specimens were very abundant; indeed it being possible to take three or four in the net at once'. Later (Foster, 1937), he lists Letchworth, Graveley, Hitchin, Hexton, Highdown, nr. Hitchin, Willbury Hill, nr. Hitchin, Hoddesdon, Royston, Berkhamsted and Harpenden 'at light'. All records are mapped, though the accuracy of some may be a little dubious; the Hoddesdon report in particular is 'geologically' surprising. Hodgson (1939) notes it as not uncommon at light at Ashridge and at Long Green, Berkhamsted and Roger S. Ferry captured one in flight at Knebworth in June 1946 (specimen at Mill Green Museum and seen by me). It was common in 1934 in the Bishops Stortford district and also noted at Little Hadham (Allan, 1950); Fielding et al (1985) add that 'one was taken in a clover field just outside Bishops Stortford in August, 1949' (though it is uncertain if this was in Hertfordshire or Essex). Jack Newton records it at Stevenage, at mv light in a garden on 17th July 1964. It was apparently well-established in the early 1970s in the Royston area, though there are no precise records and it is uncertain if Hertfordshire, Cambridgeshire or both are implied; this serves as a good example of a moth that was poorly reported because it was common, but which then became rare and left us with no documentation of its decline. Today, the national distribution of this species more or less follows the Chalk from Portland in the south-west to Peterborough in the north-east line passing north of Hertfordshire, though it is found in rather few sites along this band. There is a strong population just to the north-east of Hertfordshire at Littlebury, Essex, in association with field margins above a chalk cutting, where I saw approximately 100 adults on a single day and so it was no real surprise to discover that Jim Reid had found it in Hertfordshire at Arbury Banks in the same year. The colony covers a large area of verges and other habitats where the foodplant grows and adults ought to be counted annually. Jim also found it in June 2001 at Scales Park, not very far away from the known Essex sites. These are our only current records, but it is surely under-recorded. Although I saw about a hundred adults on one field margin and associated road verge on a single day in 2005 at the Essex site, the next day I saw only two or three – and they had to be searched for on the bindweed flowers. Where they all went is a mystery, but one assumes they must have been there somewhere. It may be, very specifically, a case of being at the right place at the right time. Any roadside verge that lies on the chalk along the boundary of Hertfordshire with Cambridgeshire and perhaps also Bedfordshire, on which Field Bindweed grows, may well support hidden colonies of this allegedly rare moth. The adults fly by day, though males at least also come in to mv light traps at night.

2466 *Lygephila pastinum* (Tr.) Blackneck

Recorded:	1881 – 2006
Distribution / Status:	Local / Uncommon resident
Conservation status:	No perceived threats
Caterpillar food plants:	Not recorded. Elsewhere, on Tufted Vetch
Flight period:	Mid-June/July
Records in database:	57

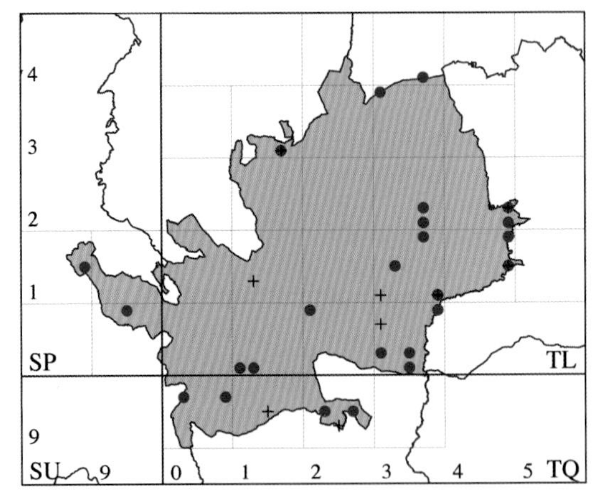

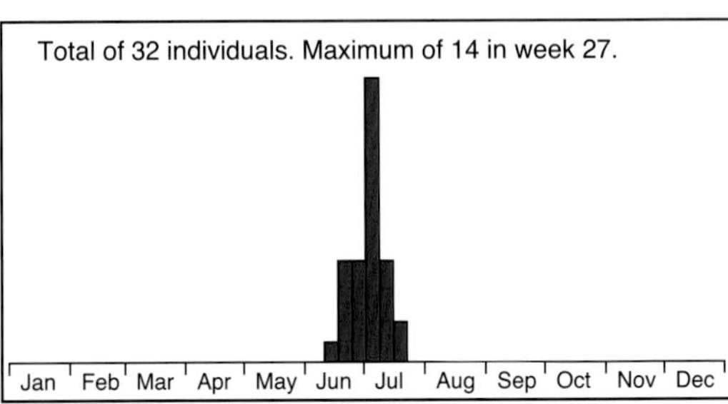

Numerically, the Blackneck is not a common species in Hertfordshire, though it is distributed widely across the south-east half of the county and on the calcareous soils in the north-west. Past records indicate that is was formerly rather scarce. It was first noted here in 1881, when Benjamin Brown caught a single example at Burleigh Heath, near Knebworth (Foster,

1916). Foster himself found it at a new locality 'quite near Hitchin' where he collected four in 1914 and three in 1915. It was also recorded at Norton Common in 1921 (Foster, 1937). It is absent from the 1950 list for the Bishops Stortford district (Allan, 1950) and was first recorded in this area in 1956, then again in 1958 (Fielding et al, 1985). During 1981 it was caught on several occasions at Sawbridgeworth Marsh (Charles Watson, Geoffrey Sell and others); I caught it on my first trip there in 1987 and it is still there in 2006. The record for Whetstone, on 18th July 1963 (P. Ward), remarked upon in de Worms (1964) as being noteworthy, is actually in Middlesex, though it nevertheless serves to demonstrate that the species was still scarce at that date whilst singles at light in Totteridge, in July 1974 (Ian Lorimer) and at Bushey, on 10th July 1975 (Barry Goater) were also worthy of comment at the time. David Wilson caught a number in his garden at Green Tye in 1976, the hot summer, and that may have been the start of its increase in population – and perhaps the number of occupied sites.

2469 *Scoliopteryx libatrix* (L.) Herald

Recorded:	1884 – 2006
Distribution / Status:	Widespread / Common resident
Conservation status:	Herts Stable
Caterpillar food plants:	Not recorded. Elsewhere, on willows and poplars
Flight period:	March to May then June to August in two generations and then hibernating
Records in database:	313

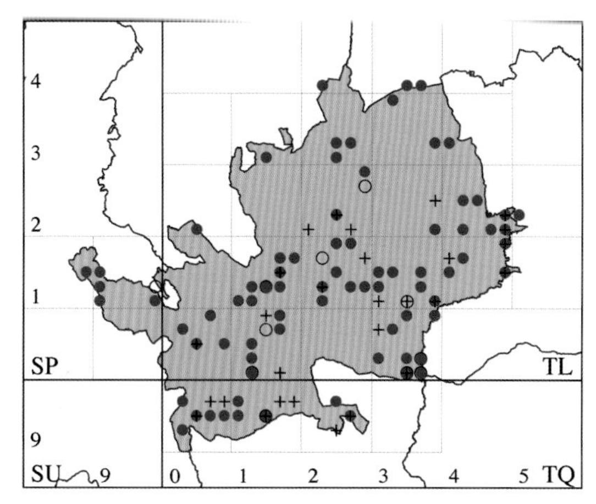

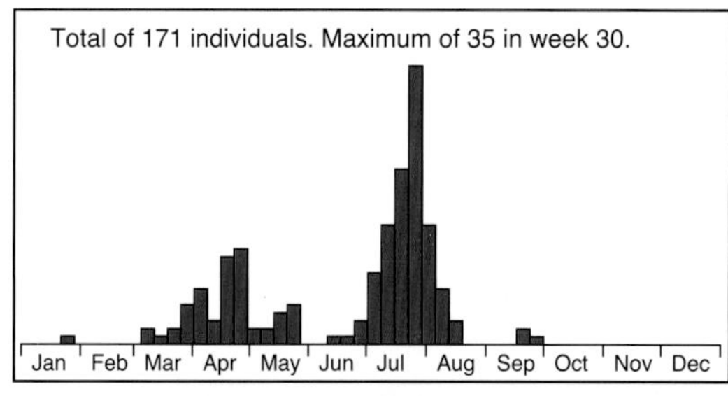

The Herald is a familiar site in Hertfordshire. Hibernating adults are excluded from the flight chart, but they can of course be found throughout the winter in sheds, hollow trees and other places away from the frosts. There will be few places in Hertfordshire where the Herald is not present.

2470 *Phytometra viridaria* (Cl.) Small Purple-barred

Recorded:	1828 – 2001
Distribution / Status:	Extremely local / Rare resident
Conservation status:	Herts Endangered
Caterpillar food plants:	Not recorded. Elsewhere, Common Milkwort and Heath Milkwort
Flight period:	Elsewhere, Mid-May to July
Records in database:	19

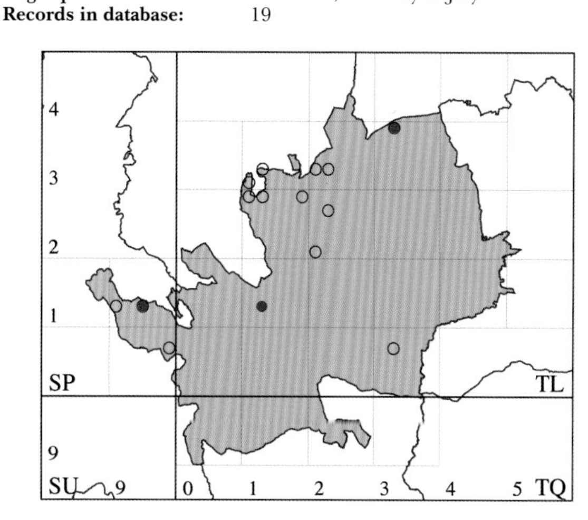

Therfield Heath is the only current locality for this species in Hertfordshire; it was first recorded here by A. H. Foster in 1916 and last seen by me on 27th July 2001, on Church Hill; it should be looked for to check if it is still present. The Broxbourne record in the south-east, which was given by Boyd in his 1901 list for the Cheshunt area, is surely suspect and at best may relate to a vagrant, as do the singletons recorded in 1999 and 2000 in the light trap on the Rothamsted Estate at Harpenden. All remaining records indicate a former resident of the chalk downland that used to occur in the north-west of the county. It is possible that this day-flying moth might still persist in a few places where the foodplant is present. Trevor James informs me (April 2007) that Heath Milkwort is now found only on Bricket Wood Common, where it is rare. Other sites, like rides in Knebworth Woods and Claypits Meadow at Bayford have all succumbed since the 1970s. Common Milkwort is still reasonably frequent on the best chalk sites, but increasingly rare on non-chalk sites and has declined significantly (43 per cent) since the 1960s.

RIVULINAE

2473 *Laspeyria flexula* ([D.& S.]) Beautiful Hook-tip

Recorded:	1884 – 2006
Distribution / Status:	Local / Common resident
Conservation status:	Herts Stable
Caterpillar food plants:	Not recorded. Elsewhere, on lichens growing on trees
Flight period:	June/July. In 2006, also mid-September to early October
Records in database:	106

The Beautiful Hook-tip is widespread, but decidedly local in Hertfordshire and apparently absent from much of the north-west part of the map and apparently absent from some of its former haunts in the south, near to London. Given the larval requirement for lichens growing on trees this may not be too surprising. The larvae prefer lichens in dense thickets rather than on exposed branches, where the humidity of the air is

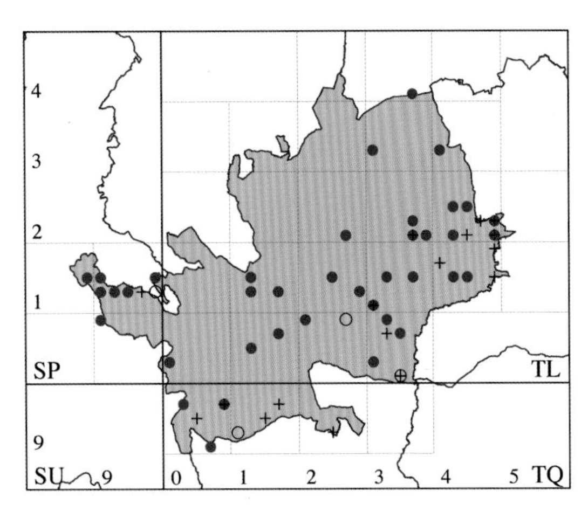

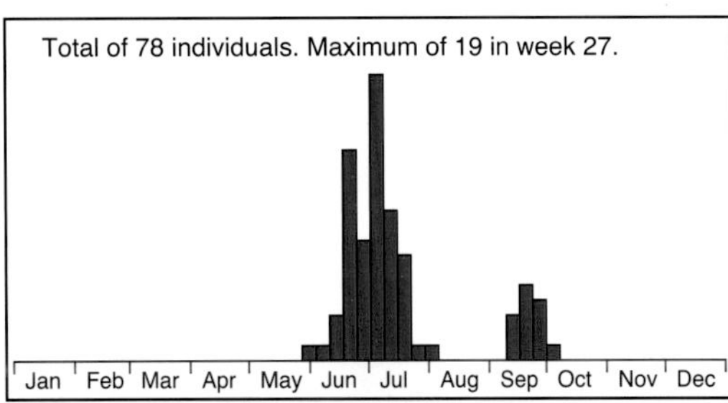

slightly raised. This implies that well-structured woodlands are more likely to support the moth than open habitats, though this may not be a hard and fast rule. It is normally single-brooded, but a flurry of autumn adults in 2006 perhaps indicate a partial second generation.

2474 *Rivula sericealis* (Scop.) Straw Dot

Recorded:	1884 – 2006
Distribution / Status:	Ubiquitous / Common resident
Conservation status:	Herts Stable
Caterpillar food plants:	Not recorded. Elsewhere, on grasses
Flight period:	Late May to early July then late July to August – sometimes to September/October
Records in database:	1,062

Past records suggest that the Straw Dot was an uncommon and very local moth in Hertfordshire during the late 1800s and at least the first forty years of the twentieth century. For example, Foster (1916) reports one example at Rabley Heath, near Knebworth (by Leeds) and says that 'a specimen is mentioned by Durrant in his Hitchin list' – hardly the sort of words written about a moth that is commonly encountered. Old records are available from Sandridge (pre-1884), St Albans (pre-1889), Knebworth – as mentioned above (pre-1885), Hitchin – as mentioned above (pre-1885), East Barnet and Tring only. The apparent scarcity of this species is supported by de Worms (1955), who said that is 'seems scarce in the London Area' and

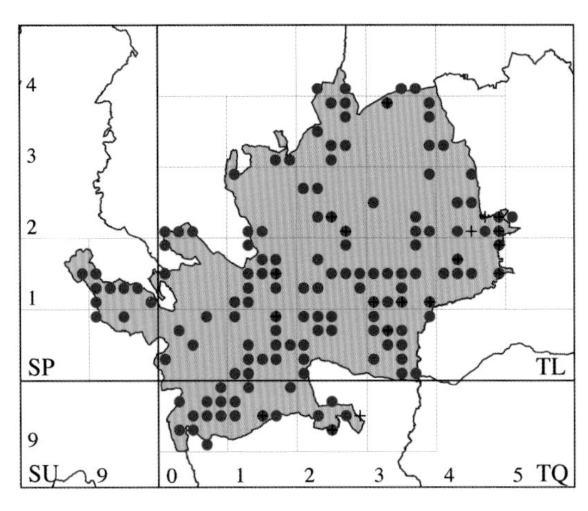

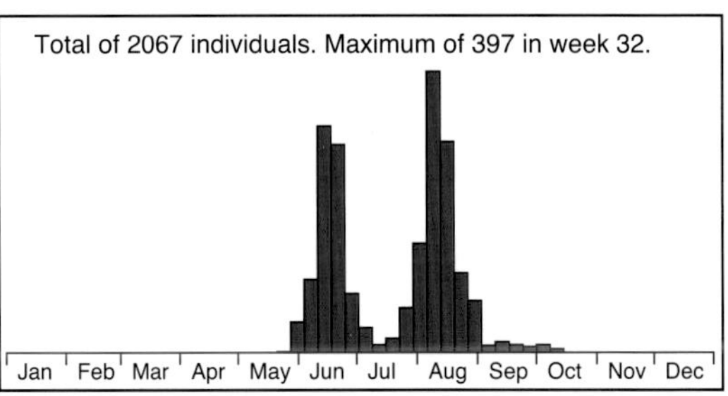

whose list of records did not include any in the Hertfordshire sector. An increase in population strength and an expansion of range appears to have taken place in parts of England from the late 1940s onwards, but there are no more Hertfordshire records at all until one turned up in Ian Lorimer's garden light trap at Totteridge in 1969. Between then and now it has become abundant everywhere. The number of generations per year of Straw Dot adults has been discussed in detail elsewhere (Plant, 2004). There are two well-separated generations in Hertfordshire, though in 2006 there was a September emergence of adults; the peak on the graph is entirely for this year.

2475 *Parascotia fuliginaria* (L.) Waved Black

Recorded:	1954 – 2006
Distribution / Status:	Local / Rare resident
Conservation status:	No perceived threats
Caterpillar food plants:	Not recorded. Elsewhere, on fungi under fallen logs and synanthropically on timbers in the dark
Flight period:	July/August
Records in database:	52

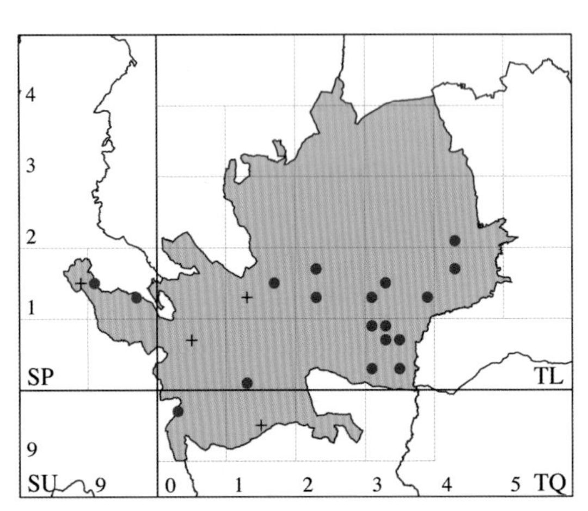

The Waved Black was discovered as a British species in London, where it had evidently adapted to feeding on the fungi growing on rotting timbers in cellars and other dark places. For many years it was regarded as a London speciality as

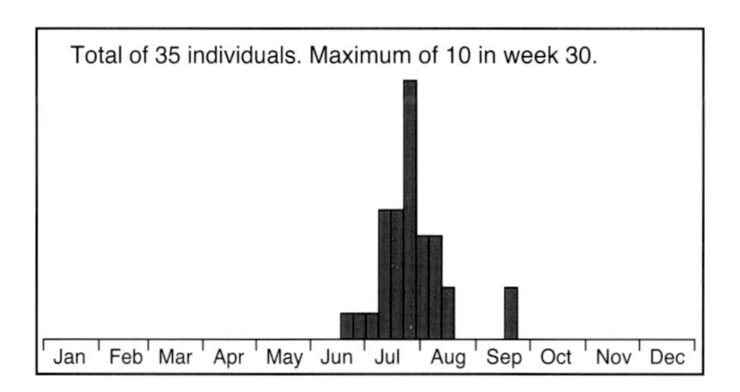

it exploited this habitat; more recently, damp timbers have become a thing of the past and the moth has had to revert to its natural habit of feeding on fungi under fallen logs and other timber. There are no Hertfordshire reports until 1954, and again in 1957, at Arkley, taken by T. G. Howarth and reported in de Worms (1966). Later, Bell (1977) in his final review of the county's macrolepidoptera, records one taken by N. E. Gammon 'lurking in an old greenhouse' on 18th May 1975. Regrettably, in spite of believing this to be a new species to the Hertfordshire fauna he omitted to say where in the county Mr Gammon had made this important discovery; it was probably in Hemel Hempstead, where Gammon resided. A published record for Whetstone, on 16th July 1964, relates to Middlesex, not Hertfordshire. There are no more reports until the mid-1980s when it was again found in the south of the county and there are then occasional records from the same general area for the next few years until the mid-1990s when suddenly adults started to appear in light traps at new sites across the county, with a drastic rise in numbers during 2000. It has been suggested that fungal infestations of the timber left lying after the October 1987 hurricane might, by the mid-1990s, have achieved optimum conditions for the larvae of the moth to feed. This would not be unexpected for a strictly saproxylic species; its numbers may be expected to decline then rise again over the coming years.

HYPENINAE

2476 *Hypena crassalis* (Fabr.) Beautiful Snout

Recorded: 1956 – 2002
Distribution / Status: Random / Vagrant
Conservation status: -
Caterpillar food plants: Not recorded. Elsewhere, on Bilberry
Flight period: Elsewhere, June/July
Records in database: 5

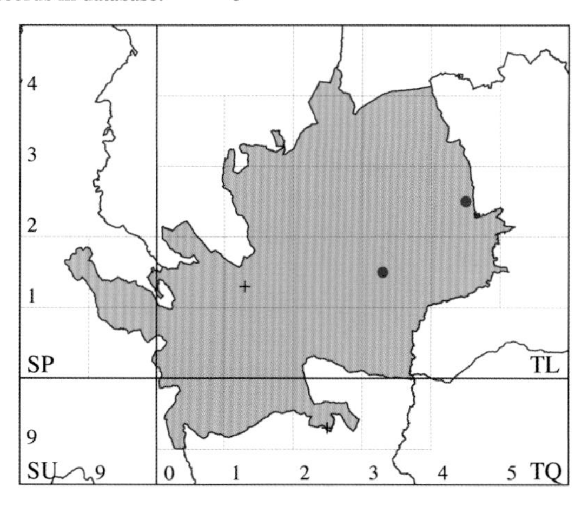

The first record of this species in the county was made at Bishops Stortford when one was taken by Clifford Craufurd on 9th July 1956 (Bell, 1958). A male was recorded by Ian Lorimer at Totteridge on 11th July 1967 (Plant, 1993) and then a single female was recorded on the Rothamsted Estate, in the Geescroft trap (trap 22), on 13th July 1985 (Riley, 1986). Interestingly, in a later review of records, Riley (1999) gives

trap 26 as the source, though this scarcely matters a great deal. Another female was caught on a Herts Moth Group recording trip held at Patmore Heath, on 29th June 2002 (Plant, 2002a) and finally Andrew Wood caught another female at Hertford, on 7th July 2002. According to Trevor James, the Hertfordshire botanical recorder, Bilberry is extinct as a native wild plant in Hertfordshire; it was last recorded before 1960 from the Chipperfield area, and before that it was present at Oxhey Woods and a couple of other sites, but never common. Suggested alternative larval foodplants are dismissed by Plant (2002a).

2477 *Hypena proboscidalis* (L.) Snout

Recorded: 1934 – 2006
Distribution / Status: Ubiquitous / Abundant resident
Conservation status: Herts Stable
Caterpillar food plants: Stinging Nettle
Flight period: June/July then mid-August to late October in two generations
Records in database: 1,400

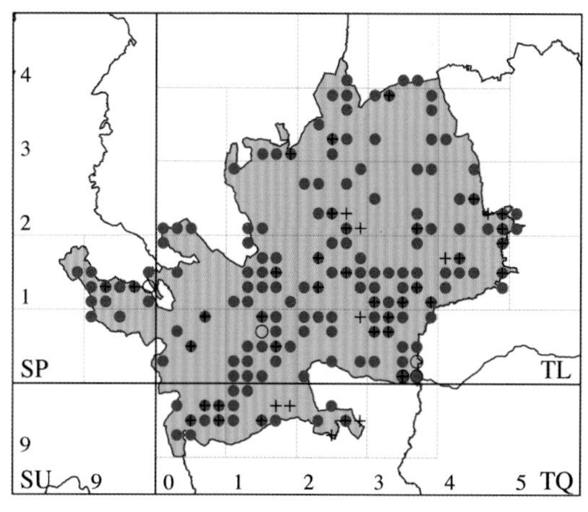

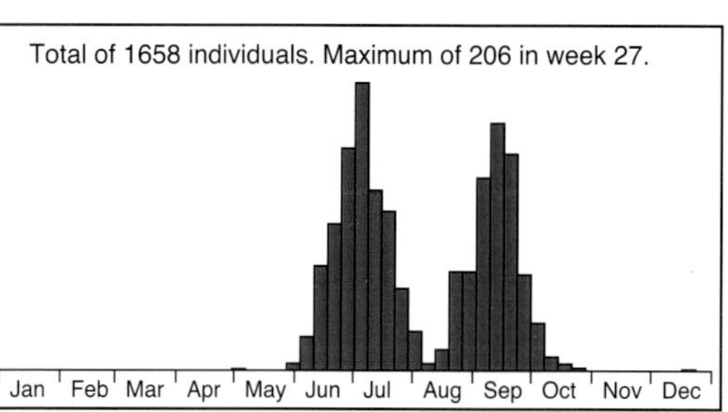

The Snout is one of the most numerically abundant species of moth in the county and is easily disturbed from nettle beds or observed flying in country lanes at night. It can be found wherever Stinging Nettles grow and has doubtless benefited from the long-term eutrophication of Hertfordshire's soils over the past hundred years.

2480 *Hypena rostralis* (L.) Buttoned Snout

Recorded: 1900 – 2006
Distribution / Status: Local / Common resident
Conservation status: Herts Scarce
Caterpillar food plants: Hop, including garden varieties
Flight period: August to early June, hibernating from September onwards
Records in database: 69

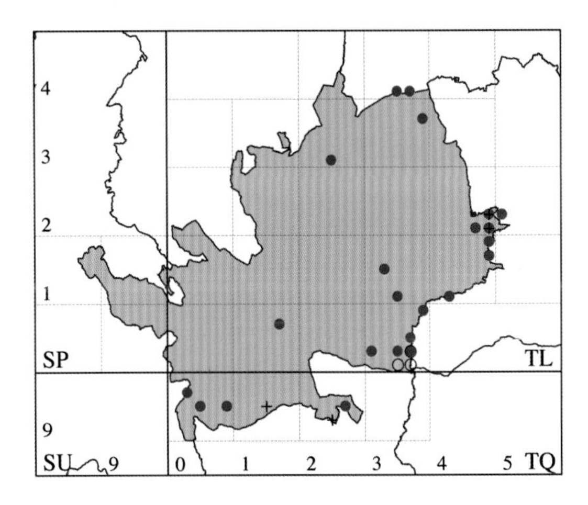

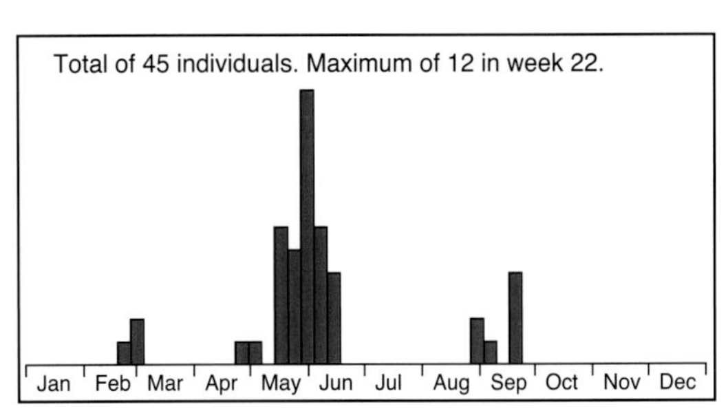

This supposedly Nationally Scarce moth is present throughout the south-east of England. Its distribution depends on the presence of a combination of Hop plants and suitable hibernation sites, such as hollow trees, cellars, ice houses and similar places. Throughout much of the county hops are absent from the hedges and the moth is simply not present. Hops are, however, particularly prevalent in neglected synanthropic habitats, notably along railway lines, and in the unkempt areas of quarries and other sites to which there is no theoretical public access. In these places the moth thrives. Thus, the Lea and Stort Valleys act as corridors, primarily along the railway lines, and from here it spreads out to colonise the many plants of Golden Hop grown in gardens of Bishops Stortford. In the south, the London area provides one continuous synanthropic habitat and the moth is present throughout – doubtless under-recorded for want of access to people's back gardens.

2482 *Schrankia taenialis* (Hb.) White-line Snout

Recorded: 1937 – 2002
Distribution / Status: Extremely local / Rare resident
Conservation status: Herts Rare
Caterpillar food plants: Unknown
Flight period: July to early August
Records in database: 6

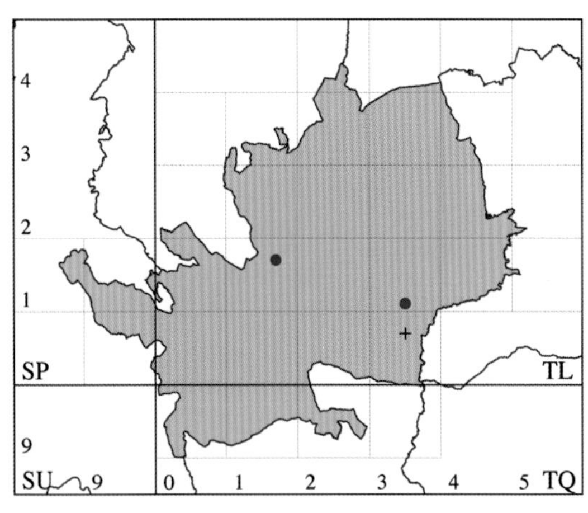

This rare species of damp woodland in southern Britain is recorded only six times in Hertfordshire; five of these records relate to the Broxbourne Woods National Nature Reserve complex in the south-east, from where it is listed by Foster in 1937 (Hoddesdon and Broxbourne, both without dates and precise localities) and later from Danemead Wood in 1971 and 13th July 1982 (David Wilson) and Balls Wood on 13th July 2002 (Jim Reid). The stray record is from Hall Wood, Kimpton, in 2001 (Vincent & Betty Judd); it is unclear if this might represent another breeding locality or if the moth was merely a wanderer. The conservation requirements of this species need to be addressed in the management plan for the National Nature Reserve.

2483 '*Schrankia intermedialis* Reid' Autumnal Snout

The taxonomic status of his 'species' has been resolved by Anderson et al (2007) who examined DNA markers and showed conclusively that it is a hybrid between 2482: *Schrankia taenialis* and 2484: *Schrankia costaestrigalis*. The findings are summarised by Gould (2007). It was described as a species new to science by Jim Reid from a moth taken in an mv light trap in Hoddesdonpark Wood on 20th October 1971, with a second example taken the next night, 21st October 1971. A third was taken by Jim at mv light at Bayfordbury, east of the university buildings on the edge of the estate on 5th October 1973 and a fourth was netted at dusk in Danemead Wood on 1st October 1982. All four examples were male.

2484 *Schrankia costaestrigalis* (Steph.) Pinion-streaked Snout

Recorded: 1906 – 2006
Distribution / Status: Very local / Rare resident
Conservation status: Herts Scarce
Caterpillar food plants: Not known
Flight period: Late May to end of August
Records in database: 22

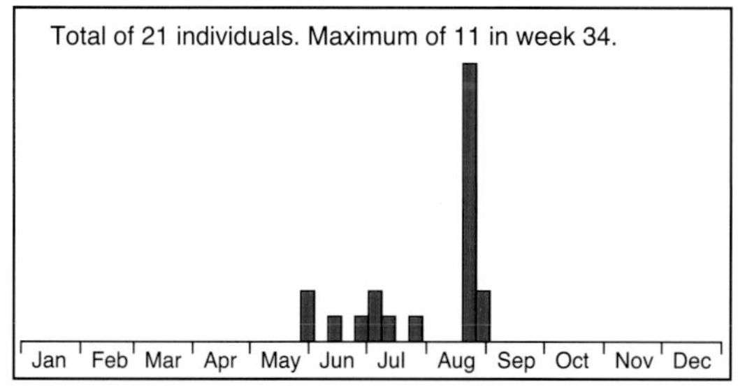

Two examples of the Pinion-streaked Snout, caught on the Ashridge Estate on 24th July and 22nd August 1907, were reported as new to the county, though a worn example was also taken there in 1906 by the same captor, A. T. Goodson, who was unable to identify it until better examples were found in the next year (Gibbs, 1908). Foster (1937) repeats these records and the moth appears to be unreported again until 3rd August 1983, when it was caught at Green Tye, west of Bishops Stortford, by David Wilson. Today, it is widespread, but local in damp woodland and marshes, including at Sawbridgeworth Marsh where catching examples is more or less guaranteed at the appropriate time of year.

HERMINIINAE

2488 *Pechipogo strigilata* (L.) Common Fan-foot

Recorded: 1834 – 1950
Distribution / Status: Absent / Former resident
Conservation status: UK BAP Priority Species. Herts Extinct
Caterpillar food plants: Not recorded. Elsewhere, on withered oak leaves on broken branches
Flight period: Elsewhere, late May and June
Records in database: 6

The Common Fan-foot ought to be renamed as the Rare Fan-foot and its existing name transferred to 2489: Fan-foot, which is common. It was formerly resident in deciduous woodlands on clay soils in the South-east but has declined and Parsons et al (2005) regarded it as occurring in only 12 British sites from 1980 to 1997. In Hertfordshire it was recorded by Stephens from the Hertford area in 1834, but Boyd (1901) does not include it in his list for the Cheshunt area, which included the Broxbourne Woods complex – the area of the county most likely to have supported it. Foster (1916) notes, under the heading of '*Pechipogon barbalis* (Common Fan-foot)' that it was 'frequent in the larger woods' in the Hitchin area, though he does not list 2489: Fan-foot. In the later county list Foster (1937), under the heading of *Herminia barbalis* Clerck, repeats the records from Hertford and Hitchin, adding Hoddesdon (G. V. Bull) and Northaw (H. E. Bull). Later (Foster, 1942) he adds Northchurch by J. Bell, also without any year. Allan (1950) records 'one specimen' by C. S. Colman in his list for the Bishops Stortford area, rather oddly commenting that the larva 'feeds on birch catkins in the spring'. There are no other acceptable Hertfordshire records known to me.

2489 *Zanclognatha tarsipennalis* (Tr.) Fan-foot

Recorded: 1884 – 2006
Distribution / Status: Widespread / Common resident
Conservation status: Herts Stable
Caterpillar food plants: Not recorded. Elsewhere, on withered tree leaves
Flight period: June/July
Records in database: 527

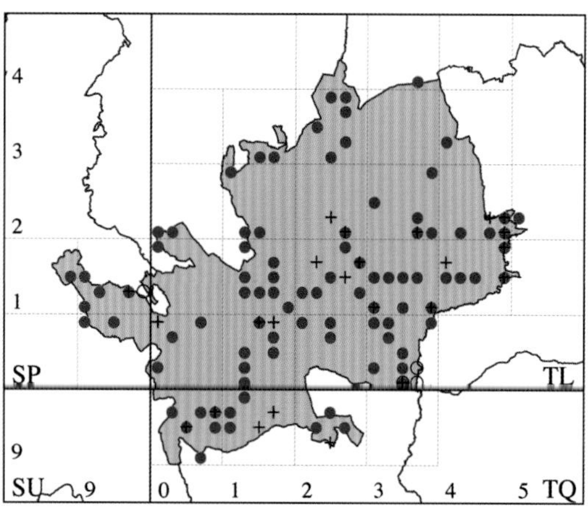

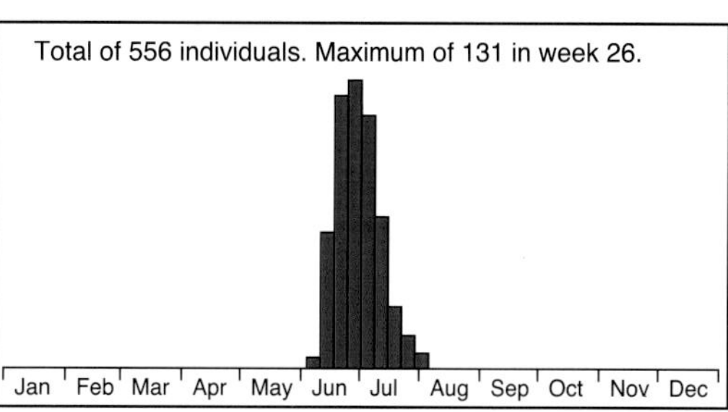

This is a widespread and common moth in Hertfordshire and may yet prove to be ubiquitous, as it seems as much at home in gardens as it does in woodlands and other more rural habitats.

2492 *Herminea grisealis* ([D.& S.]) Small Fan-foot

Recorded: 1884 – 2006
Distribution / Status: Widespread / Common resident
Conservation status: Herts Stable
Caterpillar food plants: Not recorded. Elsewhere, on fresh and withered tree leaves
Flight period: June/July
Records in database: 375

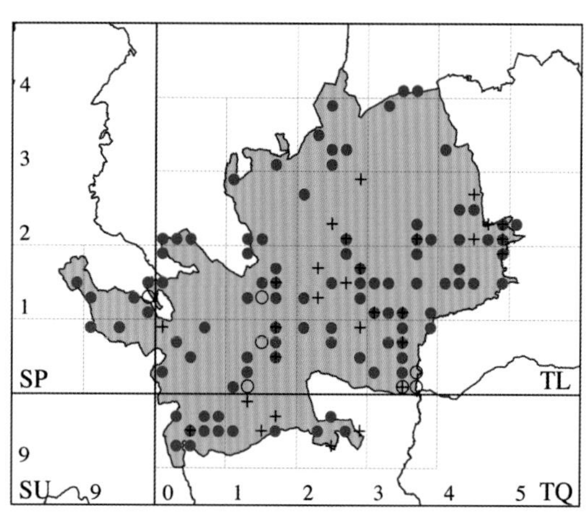

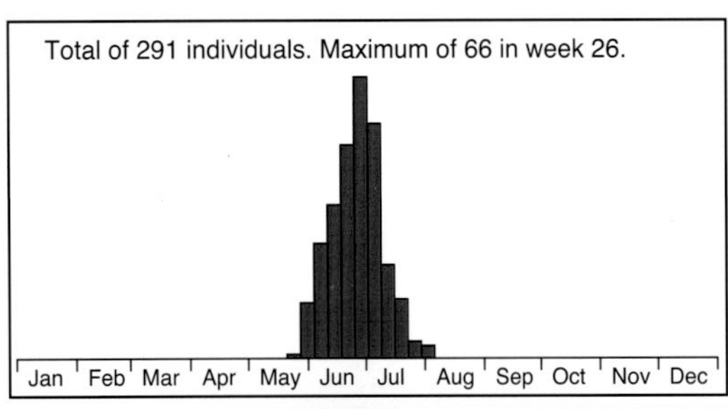

The Small Fan-foot, like 2489: Fan-foot, is likely to prove to be an ubiquitous species in Hertfordshire, although there are slightly fewer records and the number of reported individuals is only about half of that species.

2493 *Macrochilo cribrumalis* (Hb.) Dotted Fan-foot

Recorded:	1990 – 2006
Distribution / Status:	Widespread / Common resident
Conservation status:	Herts Vulnerable
Caterpillar food plants:	Not recorded. Elsewhere, on sedges and some grasses
Flight period:	Mid-June to early August
Records in database:	11

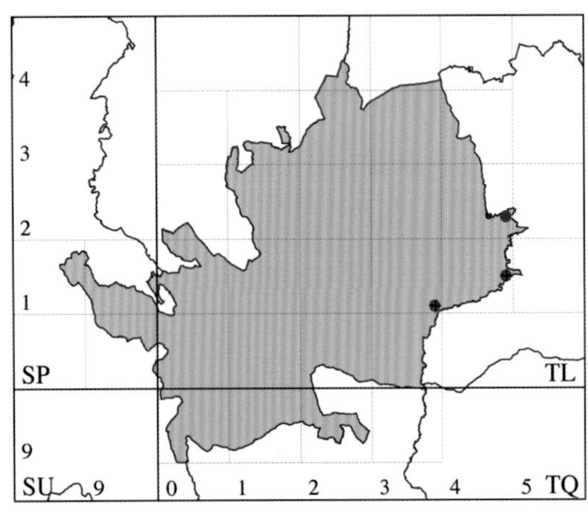

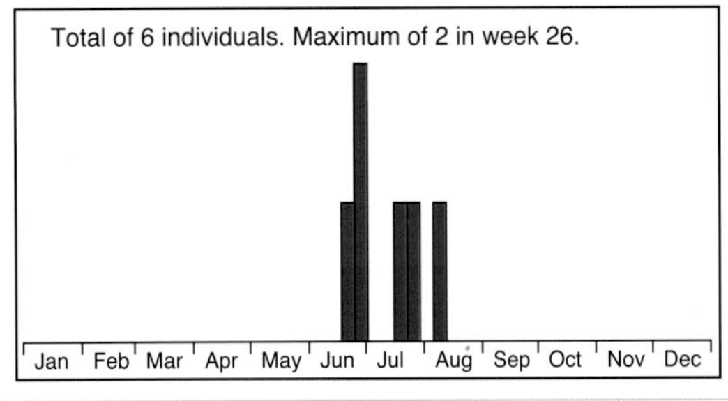

This moth is confined in Hertfordshire to the Lea and Stort river valleys, with apparently thriving populations at Rye Meads and Sawbridgeworth Marsh and vagrant examples in Bishops Stortford that must surely have originated a few hundred metres away in the Town Meads or some other adjacent part of the Stort Valley. Other sites in both the Stort and Lea may support the moth, but dedicated searches elsewhere in the county have failed to find additional populations. Although both known sites are nature reserves the moth is nevertheless susceptible to both hydrological changes and unintentional mismanagement and must therefore be regarded as Vulnerable in Hertfordshire.

REJECTED SPECIES

Inevitably, as the County Moth Recorder I occasionally receive reports of moths that have been misidentified. These are usually corrected and go no further, but sometimes incorrect records may appear in print. To ignore these would leave the reader in doubt as to whether or not I am aware of them and so it is important that they are mentioned and the reasons for their rejection clearly stated. This I have done, at the relevant position within the species accounts, enclosing the entire entry for each unacceptable species within square brackets. However, for ease of reference it seems to make sense to summarise the rejected species here, together with their checklist numbers, so that interested parties can locate them more easily. If any species is neither here nor in the species accounts, then I have missed it – please send me the details.

173	*Apoda limacodes* (Hufn.) Festoon
344	*Phyllonorycter strigulatella* (Zell.)
889	*Mompha divisella* H.- S.
950	*Aethes francillana* (Fabr.)
971	*Pandemis cinnamomeana* (Tr.)
1039	*Acleris comariana* (Lienig & Zeller)
1100	*Endothenia pullana* (Haw.)
1119	*Ancylis geminana* (Donovan)
1208	*Pseudococcyx posticana* (Zett.)
1296	*Crambus silvella* (Hb.)
1298	*Crambus ericella* (Hb.)
1299	*Crambus hamella* (Thunb.)
1335	*Scoparia ancipitella* (La Harpe)
1430	*Paralipsa gularis* (Zell.) Stored Nut Moth
1482	*Homoeosoma nimbella* (Duponchel)
1484	*Phycitodes saxicola* Vaughan
1635	*Malacosoma castrensis* (L.) Ground Lackey
1644	*Endromis versicolora* (L.) Kentish Glory
1650	*Sabre harpagula* (Esper) Scarce Hook-tip
1656	*Tetheella fluctuosa* (Hb.) Satin Lutestring
1688	*Scopula rubiginata* (Hufn.) Tawny Wave
1694	*Scopula ternata* (Schrank) Smoky Wave
1698	*Idaea muricata* (Hufn.) Purple-bordered Gold
1701	*Idaea sylvestraria* (Hb.) Dotted Border Wave
1744	*Entephria caesiata* ([D.& S.]) Grey Mountain Carpet
1770	*Thera cognata* (Thunb.) Chestnut-coloured Carpet
1779	*Hydriomena ruberata* (Freyer) Ruddy Highflier
1831	*Eupithecia goossensiata* Mabille Ling Pug
1833	*Eupithecia expallidata* Doubleday Bleached Pug
1901	*Cepphis advenaria* (Hb.) Little Thorn
1966	*Siona lineata* (Scop.) Black-veined Moth
2027	*Dicallomera fascelina* (L.) Dark Tussock
2036	*Setina irrorella* (Hb.) Dew Moth
2046	*Eilema pygmaeola* (Doubleday) Pygmy Footman
2080	*Euxoa obelisca* ([D.& S.]) Square-spot Dart
2085	*Agrotis vestigialis* (Hufn.) Archer's Dart
2097	*Actinotia polyodon* (Cl.) Purple Cloud
2103	*Eugnorisma depuncta* (L.) Plain Clay
2132	*Xestia castanea* (Esper) Neglected Rustic
2156	*Lacanobia contigua* ([D.& S.]) Beautiful Brocade
2172	*Hadena albimacula* (Borkh.) White-spot
2200	*Mythimna favicolor* (Barrett) Mathew's Wainscot
2202	*Mythimna l-album* (L.) L-album Wainscot
2217	*Cucullia asteris* ([D.& S.]) Star-wort
2220	*Shargacucullia scrophulariae* ([D.& S.]) Water Betony
2246	*Valeria oleagina* ([D.& S.]) Green-brindled Dot
2325	*Apamea oblonga* (Haw.) Crescent Striped
2359	*Amphipoea crinanensis* (Burrows) Crinan Ear
2455	*Catocala sponsa* (L.) Dark Crimson Underwing

An overview of Hertfordshire's moth fauna

The first attempt at a list of Hertfordshire's moths, produced by A. E. Gibbs in the 1902 *Victoria County History*, contained references to 1136 species – around 55% of the then recognised British total of 2061. Gibbs later withdrew some of these published records and in 1909 he reported a revised tally of 1148, commenting that 'many species of Lepidoptera were only recorded by J. F. Stephens in 1834 and are long gone'. Manuscript lists indicate that by the time he died in 1917 Gibbs had added a further seven to the list raising the overall score to 1155. Foster's 1937 list added a further 104 species, to bring the Hertfordshire total up to 1259 (59%) of the 2143 British species listed in Meyrick's revised *Handbook* (1928). By the end of 1945 (Foster, 1946) a short-term increase in recording effort following the publication of Foster's list raised the total to 1300 (61%). This present work lists a total of 1548 species for Hertfordshire at the end of 2006, representing 62% of currently known British Isles moths. These species fall within 58 families (42 families of micro-Lepidoptera, and 16 macro-Lepidoptera families) as indicated in the following table:

Family	British species*	all time Herts	presumed or possibly extinct (not seen for at least 20 years)	currently in Herts
Micropterigidae	5	5	2	3
Eriocraniidae	8	8	0	8
Hepialidae	5	5	0	5
Nepticulidae	99	69	7	62
Opostegidae	4	2	1	1
Tischeriidae	6	4	1	3
Incurvariidae	5	5	1	4
Prodoxidae	7	3	3	0
Adelidae	15	11	0	11
Heliozelidae	5	5	0	5
Cossidae	3	3	2	1
Zygaenidae	10	5	3	2
Limacodidae	2	0	0	0
Psychidae	18	7	0	7
Tineidae	61	26	8	18
Bucculatricidae	12	9	1	8
Douglasiidae	2	0	0	0
Roeslerstammiidae	2	1	0	1
Gracillariidae	93	74	9	65
Sesiidae	15	9	0	9
Choreutidae	6	3	1	2
Glyphipterigidae	8	6	2	4
Heliodinidae	2	0	0	0
Yponomeutidae	81	59	6	53
Lyonetiidae	9	5	0	5
Coleophoridae	109	59	7	52
Elachistidae	49	25	9	16
Oecophoridae	26	15	5	10
Stahmopodidae	1	1	0	1
Amphisbatidae	5	3	1	2
Chimabacidae	3	3	1	2
Depressariidae	51	30	8	22
Ethmiidae	6	1	0	1
Gelechiidae	162	84	22	62
Autostichidae	4	3	0	3
Blastobasidae	3	2	0	2
Batrachedridae	3	2	0	2
Agonoxenidae	6	6	0	6
Momphidae	15	11	1	10
Cosmopterigidae	12	4	0	4
Scythrididae	12	4	2	2
Tortricidae	390	235	30	205
Epermeniidae	8	4	2	3
Schreckensteiniidae	1	1	0	1
Alucitidae	1	1	0	1
Crambidae	136	67	9	58
Pyralidae	85	47	10	37
Pterophoridae	41	24	6	18
Lasiocampidae	12	8	2	6
Saturniidae	1	1	0	1
Endromidae	1	0	0	0
Drepanidae	7	5	0	5
Thyatiridae	9	8	0	8
Geometridae	318	233	36	197
Sphingidae	26	16	2	14
Notodontidae	27	19	1	18
Thaumetopoeidae	3	1	1	0
Lymantriidae	11	8	1	7
Arctiidae	35	24	4	20
Ctenuchidae	6	0	0	0
Nolidae	5	4	2	2
Noctuidae	451	265	42	223
All micros	**1612**	**956**	**160**	**797**
All macros	**912**	**592**	**91**	**501**
All families	2524	1548	251	1298

*numbers of British species may not be precise

Thus we have gained 248 species in the sixty years since 1946, an average of just over four per year; this compares with the 104 added by Foster in his 1937 *magnum opus* to Gibbs' revised total produced in 1917, an average of just over five species per year. It is interesting to note that of those 248 that we have added, no less than 117 were encountered since the start of the intensive surveys undertaken specifically for the production of this book; the numbers in each of those years, 1995 to 2006, are shown as follows: 1995 – 7; 1996 – 3; 1997 – 12; 1998 – 9; 1999 – 2000 – 19; 2001 – 13; 2002 – 13; 2003 – 9; 2004 – 9; 2005 – 10; 2006 – 7.

These average out to 9.75 additions per year and leave 131 species added from 1937 to 1994 – an average of only 2.6 per year. It is clear that specific survey allows for the discovery of more species than does casual recording.

Of course, although recording effort will play a major role there will also be genuine changes in the fauna with time. Excessive changes in either direction may be an indication of a more fundamental alteration of wider environmental factors. Although we can be reasonably certain that there are no overlooked macro moths in the county, amongst the micros it is very likely that some overlooked species may yet be found. It is hoped that this present summary of Hertfordshire's moths to the end of 2006 will provide a baseline of information against which future changes may be properly assessed.

Most frequently recorded species

Whilst some moths are easily found, others are less often encountered. Some shun the light trap and are scarcely seen at all, yet they may be numerically abundant, as has been demonstrated through the use of pheromone attractants to record clearwings (Sesiidae). Counting both the number of records and the number of individuals making up those records of the most regularly reported species provides a potentially useful means of monitoring changes in moth populations over time. The following 'league table' therefore places on record Hertfordshire's top 50 macro-moths, arranged by the number of records received for the years 1995 to 2006 inclusive. The table is annotated in the right hand columns with the number of individual moths recorded and the 'chart position' indicated by these values. The Large Yellow Underwing ranks first using both parameters; the positions of some of the remaining species almost coincide, but there are some interesting discrepancies. The Heart and Dart ranks second in terms of numbers of moths, but only sixth in relation to the number of records received.

Chart position	Number of records	English name	Scientific name	Chart position	No of individuals
1	3353	Large Yellow Underwing	*Noctua pronuba*	1	36807
2	2798	Pale Mottled Willow	*Paradrina clavipalpis*	9	8515
3	2491	Silver Y	*Autographa gamma*	14	7114
4	2438	Willow Beauty	*Peribatodes rhomboidaria*	12	7483
5	2339	Brimstone Moth	*Opisthograptis luteolata*	20	4650
6	2273	Heart and Dart	*Agrotis exclamationis*	2	30320
7	2193	Setaceous Hebrew Character	*Xestia c-nigrum*	5	11351
8	2173	Riband Wave	*Idaea aversata*	3	14970
9	2019	Shuttle-shaped Dart	*Agrotis puta*	18	5081
10	2009	Lesser Yellow Underwing	*Noctua comes*	10	8431
11	1852	Flame Shoulder	*Ochropleura plecta*	26	3702
12	1847	Hebrew Character	*Orthosia gothica*	15	6659
13	1838	Dark Arches	*Apamea monoglypha*	6	9944
14	1765	Bright-line Brown-eye	*Lacanobia oleracea*	21	4576
15	1599	Garden Carpet	*Xanthorhoe fluctuata*	36	2471
16	1567	Common Quaker	*Orthosia cerasi*	8	8528
17	1561	Common Wainscot	*Mythimna pallens*	19	4734
18	1543	Uncertain	*Hoplodrina alsines*	4	13958
19	1539	Angle Shades	*Phlogophora meticulosa*	41	2280
20	1526	Common Marbled Carpet	*Chloroclysta truncata*	32	2947
21	1487	Vine's Rustic	*Hoplodrina ambigua*	11	7540
22	1469	Square-spot Rustic	*Xestia xanthographa*	7	9063
23	1400	Snout	*Hypena proboscidalis*	48	2027
24	1370	Lesser Broad-bordered Yellow Underwing	*Noctua janthe*	13	7425
25	1281	Double-striped Pug	*Gymnoscelis rufifasciata*	47	2035
26	1250	Spectacle	*Abrostola tripartita*	56	1667
27	1217	Flame	*Axylia putris*	30	3210
28	1215	Common Footman	*Eilema lurideola*	25	4106+
29	1140	Smoky Wainscot	*Mythimna impura*	33	2700
30	1115	Early Grey	*Xylocampa areola*	49	2007
31	1065	Scalloped Oak	*Crocallis elinguaria*	55	1703
32	1062	Straw Dot	*Rivula sericealis*	42	2269
33	1045	Peppered Moth	*Biston betularia*	65	1382
34	1041	Turnip Moth	*Agrotis segetum*	63	1469
35	1031	Elephant Hawk-moth	*Deilephila elpenor*	54	1812
36	1006	Buff Ermine	*Spilosoma luteum*	52	1849
37	999	Clouded Drab	*Orthosia incerta*	53	1831
38	987	Rustic	*Hoplodrina blanda*	31	3110
39	962	Light Emerald	*Campaea margaritata*	70	1334
40	962	Mottled Rustic	*Caradrina morpheus*	38	2430
41	953	Double Square-spot	*Xestia triangulum*	44	2094
42	932	Lunar Underwing	*Omphaloscelis lunosa*	17	5097
43	928	Burnished Brass	*Diachrysia chrysitis*	80	1221
44	927	Poplar Hawk-moth	*Laothoe populi*	89	1065
45	909	Common Carpet	*Epirrhoe alternata*	77	1245
46	904	Dun-bar	*Cosmia trapezina*	43	2122
47	884	Single-dotted Wave	*Idaea dimidiata*	67	1359
48	879	Marbled Beauty	*Cryphia domestica*	64	1464
49	874	Small Quaker	*Orthosia cruda*	27	3462
50	872	Dot Moth	*Melanchra persicariae*	39	2365

League table of moths recorded in Hertfordshire.

Species of conservation significance

Definitions of rarity have, in the past, sometimes varied with the experience of the person passing the opinion. In recent years, however, far greater emphasis has been placed upon the accurate and comprehensive recording of the distributions of species, a process greatly facilitated by the advent of the personal computer, and this has placed entomologists in a far better position to determine both the distribution and the numerical abundance of our moths. Coupled with this is a far greater awareness amongst the general public of environmental issues and, amongst entomologists in particular, of the usefulness of individual moth species in acting as monitors of environmental changes. By investigating which species have declined (or for that matter increased) and by understanding the reasons why, we open the door to a much wider understanding of the many factors affecting our own health and well-being. This next section is, therefore, concerned with categorising Hertfordshire's moths so that they can be of such use by others.

UK Biodiversity Action Plan Species

UK Biodiversity Action Plan Species are those that have been identified as requiring conservation action as species of principal importance for the conservation of biodiversity in England. Local authorities are required by *Planning Policy Statement 9: Biodiversity and Geological Conservation* (PPS9), published by the Office of the Deputy Prime Minister during 2005, to take measures to protect the habitats of these species from further decline through policies in local development documents. Planning authorities are required to ensure that these species are protected from the adverse effects of development, where appropriate, by using planning conditions or obligations. Planning authorities are advised to refuse permission where harm to the species or their habitats would result unless the need for, and benefits of, the development clearly outweigh that harm.

The current UK Biodiversity Action Plan divides the moths into two lists. The first contains those species defined as 'Priority Species' – species that are scarce, threatened or declining in Britain. The presence of one or more of these moth species on a site in Hertfordshire is indicative that the site is of National (Great Britain) significance. There are 81 such species, of which 27 have been recorded in Hertfordshire. Of these, eight are or may still be present; these are regarded as Endangered in the county.

Code	Species	English name	Year of last Herts record
133	*Lampronia capitella*	Currant Shoot Borer	1970
144	*Nemophora fasciella*		2006
162	*Cossus cossus*	Goat Moth	1999
163	*Adscita statices*	Forester	1947
482	*Epermenia insecurella*		1987
715	*Agonopterix capreolella*		1868
848	*Syncopacma albipalpella*		2003
1381	*Anania funebris*		1931
1679	*Cyclophora porata*	False Mocha	1996
1696	*Idaea ochrata cantiata*	Bright Wave	1983
1731	*Scotopteryx bipunctaria cretata*	Chalk Carpet	2001
1787	*Rheumaptera hastata*	Argent & Sable	1972
1880	*Trichopteryx polycommata*	Barred Tooth-striped	1937
1967	*Aspitates gilvaria*	Straw Belle	1924 [2006]
1982	*Hemaris tityus*	Narrow-bordered Bee Hawk	1946
2025	*Orgyia recens*	Scarce Vapourer	1884
2081	*Euxoa tritici*	White-line Dart	1998
2108	*Noctua orbona*	Lunar Yellow Underwing	1940
2148	*Polia bombycina*	Pale Shining Brown	2006
2219	*Shargacucullia lychnitis*	Striped Lychnis	1970
2242	*Xylena exsoleta*	Sword-grass	1946
2257	*Jodia croceago*	Orange Upperwing	1828
2315	*Dicycla oo*	Heart Moth	1971
2317	*Cosmia diffinis*	White-spotted Pinion	1978
2375	*Rhizedra lutosa*	Large Wainscot	2006
2465	*Tyta luctuosa*	Four-spotted	2005
2488	*Pechipogo strigilata*	Common Fan-foot	1950

UK Biodiversity Action Plan Priority Species of moths recorded in Hertfordshire

The second list within the UK Biodiversity Action Plan contains a number of moths that are still widespread and common at the national level, but which are nevertheless rapidly declining usually numerically, though some may also be contracting their distributional range). This 'Watch List' has caused some confusion amongst British Lepidopterists, but one only has to consider our past attitude to the once ubiquitous and now rapidly declining House Sparrow (*Passer domesticus*) to appreciate the value of such a list. A total of 71 species currently includes the White-line Dart and the Large Wainscot which apparently are here by reason of clerical error and ought to feature in the Priority Species list (though the latter species is not under any apparent threat in Hertfordshire). Sixty-one 'Watch List' species have been recorded in Hertfordshire, as follows:

Code	Species	English name
14	*Hepialus humuli*	Ghost Moth
1632	*Trichiura crataegi*	Pale Eggar
1634	*Malacosoma neustria*	Lackey
1658	*Cymatophorima diluta hartwiegi*	Oak Lutestring
1673	*Hemistola chrysoprasaria*	Small Emerald
1682	*Timandra comae*	Blood-vein
1689	*Scopula marginepunctata*	Mullein Wave
1719	*Orthonama vittata*	Oblique Carpet
1725	*Xanthorhoe ferrugata*	Dark-barred Twin-spot Carpet
1732	*Scotopteryx chenopodiata*	Shaded Broad-bar
1740	*Epirrhoe galiata*	Galium Carpet
1749	*Pelurga comitata*	Dark Spinach
1757	*Eulithis mellinata*	Spinach
1759	*Ecliptopera silaceata*	Small Phoenix
1784	*Melanthia procellata*	Pretty Chalk Carpet
1807	*Perizoma albulata*	Grass Rivulet
1864	*Chesias legatella*	Streak
1894	*Chiasmia clathrata*	Latticed Heath
1897	*Macaria wauaria*	V-Moth
1912	*Ennomos quercinaria*	August Thorn
1914	*Ennomos fuscantaria*	Dusky Thorn
1915	*Ennomos erosaria*	September Thorn
1927	*Lycia hirtaria*	Brindled Beauty
2020	*Diloba caeruleocephala*	Figure of Eight
2057	*Arctia caja*	Garden Tiger
2060	*Spilosoma lubricipeda*	White Ermine
2061	*Spilosoma luteum*	Buff Ermine
2069	*Tyria jacobaeae*	Cinnabar
2082	*Euxoa nigricans*	Garden Dart
2114	*Graphiphora augur Fab*	Double Dart
2117	*Eugnorisma glareosa*	Autumnal Rustic
2123	*Diarsia rubi*	Small Square-spot
2155	*Melanchra persicariae*	Dot Moth
2163	*Melanchra pisi*	Broom Moth
2177	*Tholera cespitis*	Hedge Rustic
2178	*Tholera decimalis*	Feathered Gothic
2186	*Orthosia gracilis*	Powdered Quaker
2205	*Mythimna comma*	Shoulder-striped Wainscot
2225	*Brachylomia viminalis*	Minor Shoulder-knot
2227	*Asterocopus sphinx*	Sprawler
2229	*Dasypolia temple*	Brindled Ochre
2231	*Aporophyla lutulenta*	Deep-brown Dart
2245	*Allophyes oxyacanthae*	Green-brindled Crescent
2250	*Blepharita adusta*	Dark Brocade
2265	*Agrochola helvola*	Flounced Chestnut
2266	*Agrochola litura*	Brown-spot Pinion
2267	*Agrochola lychnidis*	Beaded Chestnut
2269	*Atethmia centrago*	Centre-barred Sallow
2274	*Xanthia icteritia*	Sallow
2275	*Xanthia gilvago*	Dusky-lemon Sallow
2284	*Acronicta psi*	Grey Dagger
2289	*Acronicta rumicis*	Knot Grass
2299	*Amphipyra tragopoginis*	Mouse Moth
2330	*Apamea remissa*	Dusky Brocade
2333	*Apamea anceps*	Large Nutmeg
2342	*Mesoligia literosa*	Rosy Minor
2360	*Amphipoea oculea*	Ear Moth
2361	*Hydraecia micacea*	Rosy Rustic
2368	*Celaena leucostigma*	Crescent
2382	*Hoplodrina blanda*	Rustic
2387	*Caradrina morpheus*	Mottled Rustic

UK Biodiversity Action Plan 'Watch List' Species of moths recorded in Hertfordshire

A Hertfordshire Biodiversity Action Plan for Moths

The Creation of Hertfordshire Biodiversity Action Plans is a matter for the appropriate local government authority – in our case, Hertfordshire County Council. This section of the book now recommends a list of candidate species for inclusion in that process through the creation of a categorised 'Red List' of Hertfordshire moths. All the recorded species of moth in Hertfordshire have been given a 'Conservation Status' in the species accounts. These categories are defined in the table below.

THREAT CATEGORIES		
Category	**Code**	**Attributes**
Herts Extinct	**X**	1. Moths considered to be extinct as breeding species in Hertfordshire at 31st December 2006.
Herts Endangered (Highest threat category)	**E**	1. 'Priority Species' within the UK Biodiversity Action Plan; 2. Species categorised as 'Herts Rare' **and** believed to be declining in Hertfordshire **and** where none of these sites has a long term management plan that includes specifically identified proposals for this moth species; 3. Species that would otherwise be categorised as Vulnerable or Threatened, but which have declined rapidly in either distribution or population strength in recent years and which are continuing to so decline in spite of conservation efforts **or** which are confined to a single site in the county even if that site is not currently threatened; 4. Species that may be extinct in the county, but for which exists the possibility that they are overlooked rather than absent.
Herts Vulnerable (Middle threat category)	**V**	1. Species categorised as 'Herts Rare' **and** believed to be declining in Hertfordshire **but** present on sites that **either** have a long term management plan that includes specifically identified proposals for this moth species **or** which are not under any specific threat; 2. Species categorised as 'Herts Scarce' **and** believed to be declining in Hertfordshire **and** where none of these sites has a long term management plan that includes specifically identified proposals for this moth species; 3. 'Herts Rare' species associated with a rare and threatened habitat, microhabitat or foodplant even if the moth itself does not appear to be declining; 4. Nationally Rare (Red Data Book category 3) and Nationally Scarce (Nationally Notable) species not included elsewhere.
Herts Threatened (Lower threat category)	**T**	1. Species categorised as 'Herts Scarce' **and** believed to be declining in Hertfordshire **but** present on at least one site that has a long a long term management plan that includes specifically identified proposals that will benefit this moth species; 2. Species categorised as 'Herts Scarce' for which suitable habitat is in very short supply in the county even if there are no immediate threats to the habitat the balance could easily be tipped; 3. Species not yet 'Herts Scarce' where these have undergone a significant decline in Hertfordshire.
Herts Stable	**N**	1. Species that are expected to continue to thrive without intervention in spite of existing or reasonably predictable human activities.
No perceived threats		1. Species for which there is inadequate data for us to allocate a threat category with any reasonable degree of certainty, but which we do not consider likely to be declining.
Insufficiently known		1. Species for which there is inadequate data for us to pass any opinion at all.
Increasing		1. Species whose range or population strength has increased in Hertfordshire over the period 1995 to 2006.

STATUS CATEGORIES		
Category	**Code**	**Attributes**
Herts Rare*	**R**	1. Species known from or predicted to be resident and breeding in five or less localities within the county regardless of the number of map tetrads that are affected); 2. Species occurring in 6-10 'localities' but known to be under threat; 3. Species recorded in more localities, but for which Hertfordshire is known to support a large proportion of the population regionally; 4. Nationally Scarce (Nationally Notable) and British Red Data Book species regardless of their Hertfordshire status.
Herts Scarce	**S**	1. Species known or predicted to be resident and breeding in six to thirty localities within the county regardless of the number of map tetrads that are affected).
Non-residents		1. Immigrants, vagrants and others that do not form long term breeding populations in Hertfordshire. Species that may breed on arrival, but which do not on data gathered to 31st December 2006), survive the ensuing winter are included here.

Species that are 'Herts Rare' or which are listed in any of the threat categories specified above are summarised in the following table; this forms the overall **Hertfordshire Red List of Moths**.

ENDANGERED SPECIES IN HERTS

Code	Taxon	UK BAP Status	Herts Status	Vernacular
57	*Stigmella filipendulae*		E4	
58	*Stigmella ulmariae*		E4	
144	*Nemophora fasciella*	P	E1	
162	*Cossus cossus*	P	E2	Goat Moth
164	*Adscita geryon*		E4	Cistus Forester
211	*Haplotinea ditella*		E4	
243	*Tinea dubiella*		E4	
245	*Tinea pallescentella*		E4	Large Pale Clothes Moth
252	*Ochsenheimeria urella*		E4	
336	*Phyllonorycter dubitella*		E4	
339	*Phyllonorycter ulicicolella*		E4	
340	*Phyllonorycter scopariella*		E4	
367	*Phyllocnistis saligna*		E4	
381	*Synanthedon culiciformis*		E2	Large Red-belted Clearwing
388	*Prochoreutis myllerana*		E4	
445	*Ocnerostoma friesei*		E4	
478	*Phaulenis fulviguttella*		E4	
482	*Epermenia insecurella*	P	E1	
487	*Metriotes lutarea*		E4	
510	*Coleophora juncicolella*		E2	
546	*Coleophora genistae*		E2	
561	*Coleophora therinella*		E4	
572	*Coleophora vestianella*		E4	
740	*Monochroa hornigi*		E4	
752	*Aristotelia ericinella*		E2	
764	*Pseudotelphusa scalella*		E4	
768	*Carpatolechia notatella*		E4	
775	*Teleiodes sequax*		E2	
792	*Mirificarma mulinella*		E4	
802a	*Gelechia sororculella*		E4	
825	*Phthorimaea operculella*		E4	Potato Tuber Moth
831	*Caryocolum proxima*		E4	
848	*Syncopacma albipalpella*	P	E1	
849	*Syncopacma cinctella*		E4	
880	*Mompha langiella*		E4	
884	*Mompha miscella*		E2	
914	*Scythris crassiuscula*		E2	
920	*Scythris potentillella*		E3	
1116	*Ancylis comptana*		E4	
1122	*Ancylis obtusana*		E4	
1198	*Eucosma pauperana*		E3	
1278	*Dichrorampha sequana*		E4	
1385	*Ebulea crocealis*		E4	
1490	*Oxyptilus parvidactylus*		E4	
1496	*Cnaemidophorus rhododactyla*		E4	
1508	*Stenoptilia bipunctidactyla*		E2	
1632	*Trichiura crataegi*	W	E2	Pale Eggar
1642	*Gastropacha quercifolia*		E2	Lappet
1665	*Pseudoterpna pruinata atropunctaria*		E4	Grass Emerald
1692	*Scopula immutata*		E2	Lesser Cream Wave
1731	*Scotopteryx bipunctaria cretata*	P	E1	Chalk Carpet
1734	*Scotopteryx luridata plumbaria*		E4	July Belle
1775	*Colostygia multistrigaria*		E3	Mottled Grey
1793	*Euphyia biangulata*		E2	Cloaked Carpet
1807	*Perizoma albulata*	W	E2	Grass Rivulet
1814	*Eupithecia plumbeolata*		E3	Lead-coloured Pug
1821	*Eupithecia valerianata*		E3	Valerian Pug
1897	*Macaria wauaria*	W	E2	V-Moth
1924	*Angerona prunaria*		E3	Orange Moth
2040	*Cybosia mesomella*		E3	Four-dotted Footman
2057	*Arctia caja*	W	E2	Garden Tiger
2081	*Euxoa tritici*	P	E1	White-line Dart
2082	*Euxoa nigricans*	W	E2	Garden Dart
2105	*Rhyacia simulans*		E4	Dotted Rustic
2114	*Graphiphora augur*	W	E3	Double Dart
2117	*Eugnorisma glareosa*	W	E4	Autumnal Rustic
2130	*Xestia baja*		E4	Dotted Clay
2148	*Polia bombycina*	P	E1	Pale Shining Brown
2177	*Tholera cespitis*	W	E2	Hedge Rustic
2196	*Mythimna pudorina*		E3	Striped Wainscot
2265	*Agrochola helvola*	W	E3	Flounced Chestnut
2275	*Xanthia gilvago*	W	E3	Dusky-lemon Sallow
2290	*Simyra albovenosa*		E3	Reed Dagger
2362	*Hydraecia petasitis*		E2	Butterbur
2465	*Tyta luctuosa*	P	E1	Four-spotted
2470	*Phytometra viridaria*		E2	Small Purple-barred

VULNERABLE SPECIES IN HERTS

Code	Taxon	UK BAP Status	Herts Status	Vernacular
119	*Opostega salaciella*		V3	
374	*Synanthedon vespiformis*		V2	Yellow- legged Clearwing
431	*Yponomeuta sedella*		V3	
470	*Orthotelia sparganella*		V1	
652	*Alabonia geoffrella*		V1	
776	*Teleiopsis diffinis*		V1	
796	*Aroga velocella*		V1	
797	*Neofaculta ericetella*		V3	
799	*Neofriseria singula*		V1	
816	*Scrobipalpa obsoletella*		V3	
818	*Scrobipalpa atriplicella*		V3	
902	*Chrysoclista lathamella*		V4	
1050	*Acleris kochiella*		V2	
1102	*Endothenia nigricostana*		V4	
1290	*Chilo phragmitella*		V1	
1328	*Schoenobius gigantella*		V1	
1382	*Anania verbascalis*		V3	
1387	*Nascia cilialis*		V1	
1388	*Udea lutealis Hübne*		V2	
1462	*Pempeliella dilutella*		V1	
1512	*Merrifieldia baliodactylus*		V3	
1721	*Xanthorhoe biriviata*		V2	Balsam Carpet
1749	*Pelurga comitata*	W	V2	Dark Spinach
1755	*Eulithis testata*		V2	Chevron
1757	*Eulithis mellinata*	W	V2	Spinach
1778	*Hydriomena impluviata*		V2	May Highflyer
1784	*Melanthia procellata*	W	V2	Pretty Chalk Carpet
1789	*Rheumaptera undulata*		V1	Scallop Shell
1790	*Triphosa dubitata*		V1	Tissue
1864	*Chesias legatella*	W	V2	Streak
1870	*Odezia atrata*		V3	Chimney Sweeper
1885	*Abraxas sylvata*		V2	Clouded Magpie
1907	*Epione repandaria*		V2	Bordered Beauty
1995	*Cerura vinula*		V3	Puss Moth
2020	*Diloba caeruleocephala*	W	V2	Figure of Eight
2136	*Naenia typica*		V2	Gothic
2167	*Hadena perplexa perplexa*		V2	Tawny Shears
2204	*Mythimna obsolete*		V3	Obscure Wainscot
2214	*Cucullia chamomillae*		V2	Chamomile Shark
2250	*Blepharita adusta*	W	V2	Dark Brocade
2281	*Acronicta alni*		V2	Alder Moth
2370	*Archanara geminipuncta*		V3	Twin-spotted Wainscot
2371	*Archanara dissoluta*		V3	Brown-veined Wainscot
2373	*Archanara sparganii*		V3	Webb's Wainscot
2377	*Arenostola phragmitidis*		V3	Fen Wainscot
2391	*Chilodes maritimus*		V3	Silky Wainscot
2493	*Macrochilo cribrumalis*		V3	Dotted Fan-foot

THREATENED SPECIES IN HERTS

Code	Taxon	UK BAP Status	Herts Status	Vernacular
145	*Nemophora minimella*		T2	
735	*Monochroa tenebrella*		T2	
1161	*Rhopobota stagnana*		T2	
1329	*Donacaula forficella*		T1	
1330	*Donacaula mucronellus*		T1	
1634	*Malacosoma neustria*	W	T3	Lackey
1674	*Jodis lactearia*		T3	Little Emerald
1725	*Xanthorhoe ferrugata*	W	T3	Dark-barred Twin-spot Carpet
1732	*Scotopteryx chenopodiata*	W	T3	Shaded Broad-bar
1788	*Rheumaptera cervinalis*		T1	Scarce Tissue
1822	*Eupithecia pygmaeata*		T2	Marsh Pug
1874	*Euchoeca nebulata*		T1	Dingy Shell
1894	*Chiasmia clathrata*	W	T3	Latticed Heath
1915	*Ennomos erosaria*	W	T1	September Thorn
1918	*Selenia lunularia*		T1	Lunar Thorn
1927	*Lycia hirtaria*	W	T3	Brindled Beauty
2031	*Leucoma salicis*		T3	White Satin
2163	*Melanchra pisi*	W	T3	Broom Moth
2266	*Agrochola litura*	W	T3	Brown-spot Pinion
2368	*Celaena leucostigma*	W	T2	Crescent
2418	*Earias clorana*		T2	Cream-bordered Green Pea
2443	*Autographa jota*		T3	Plain Golden Y

RARE SPECIES IN HERTS

Code	Taxon	UK BAP Status	Herts Status	Vernacular
1	*Micropterix tunbergella*		R	
8	*Eriocrania unimaculella*		R	
9	*Eriocrania sparrmannella*		R	
19	*Bohemannia quadrimaculella*		R	
22	*Ectoedemia louisella*		R	
24	*Ectoedemia turbidella*		R	
36	*Ectoedemia quinquella*		R	
40	*Bohemannia pulverosella*		R	
74	*Stigmella assimilella*		R	
78	*Stigmella incognitella*		R	
82	*Stigmella paradoxa*		R	
107	*Stigmella regiella*		R	
127	*Emmetia angusticollella*		R	
128	*Phylloporia bistrigella*		R	
146	*Nemophora cupriacella*		R	
147	*Nemophora metallica*		R	
154	*Heliozela sericiella*		R	
156	*Heliozela resplendella*		R	
157	*Heliozela hammoniella*		R	
158	*Antispila metallella*		R	
188	*Proutia betulina*		R	
199	*Psychoides verhuella*		R	
223	*Nemaxera betulinella*		R	
237	*Niditinea fuscella*		R	Brown-dotted Clothes Moth
265	*Bucculatrix cristatella*		R	
271	*Bucculatrix albedinella*		R	
272	*Bucculatrix cidarella*		R	
276	*Bucculatrix demaryella)*		R	
290	*Caloptilia semifascia*		R	
296	*Calybites phasianipennella*		R	
299	*Parectopa ononidis*		R	
337	*Phyllonorycter hilarella*		R	
358	*Phyllonorycter froelichiella*		R	
389	*Choreutis pariana*		R	Apple Leaf Skeletoniser
397	*Glyphipterix thrasonella*		R	
405	*Argyresthia arceuthina*		R	
412	*Argyresthia pygmaeella*		R	
416	*Argyresthia glaucinella*		R	
443	*Cedestis subfasciella*		R	
463	*Ypsolopha vittella*		R	
473	*Acrolepiopsis assectella*		R	Leek Moth
525	*Coleophora solitariella*		R	
545	*Coleophora saturatella*		R	
547	*Coleophora discordella*		R	
550	*Coleophora silenella*		R	
565	*Coleophora saxicolella*		R	
566	*Coleophora sternipennella*		R	
568	*Coleophora versurella*		R	
646	*Telechrysis tripuncta*		R	
660	*Pseudatemelia josephinae*		R	
661	*Pseudatemelia flavifrontella*		R	
670	*Depressaria daucella*		R	
674	*Depressaria badiella*		R	
676	*Depressaria pulcherrimella*		R	
682	*Depressaria chaerophylli*		R	
700	*Agonopterix pallorella*		R	
704	*Agonopterix scopariella*		R	
709	*Agonopterix liturosa*		R	
713	*Agonopterix angelicella*		R	
714	*Agonopterix yeatiana*		R	
727a	*Metzneria aprilella*		R	
736	*Monochroa lucidella*		R	
748	*Ptocheuusa paupella*		R	
757	*Recurvaria nanella*		R	
773	*Pseudotelphusa paripunctella*		R	
809	*Pexicopia malvella*		R	Hollyhock Seed Moth
841	*Sophronia semicostella*		R	
843	*Aproaerema anthyllidella*		R	
877	*Stathmopoda pedella*		R	
879	*Batrachedra pinicolella*		R	
885	*Mompha conturbatella*		R	
889a	*Mompha bradleyi*		R	
890	*Mompha jurassicella*		R	
891	*Mompha sturnipennella*		R	
894	*Cosmopterix zieglerella*		R	
899	*Pancalia leuwenhoekella*		R	
906	*Blastodacna atra*		R	Apple Pith Moth
908	*Sorhagenia rhamniella*		R	
942	*Aethes piercei*		R	
949	*Aethes dilucidana*		R	
952	*Commophila aeneana*		R	
981	*Archips rosana*		R	Rose Tortrix
982	*Choristoneura diversana*		R	
1026	*Exapate congelatella*		R	
1027	*Neosphaleroptera nubilana*		R	
1029	*Eana osseana*		R	
1034	*Spatalistis bifasciana*		R	
1061	*Acleris literana*		R	
1089	*Apotomis semifasciana*		R	
1094	*Apotomis capreana*		R	
1110	*Bactra furfurana*		R	
1130	*Epinotia pygmaeana*		R	
1144	*Epinotia signatana*		R	
1187	*Epiblema costipunctana*		R	
1236a	*Pammene herrichiana*		R	
1237	*Pammene germmana*		R	
1256	*Cydia servillana*		R	
1340	*Eudonia truncicolella*		R	
1366	*Pyrausta nigrata*		R	
1445	*Pempelia formosa*		R	
1457	*Hypochalcia ahenella*		R	
1461	*Assara terebrella*		R	
1465	*Nephopteryx angustella*		R	
1494	*Capperia britanniodactyla*		R	
1498	*Amblyptilia punctidactyla*		R	
1739	*Epirrhoe rivata*		R	Wood Carpet
1794	*Euphyia unangulata*		R	Sharp-angled Carpet
1836	*Eupithecia denotata denotata*		R	Campanula Pug
1846	*Eupithecia nanata*		R	Narrow-winged Pug
1851	*Eupithecia virgaureata*		R	Golden-rod Pug
1865	*Chesias rufata*		R	Broom-tip
1903	*Plagodis pulveraria*		R	Barred Umber
1949	*Paradarisa consonaria*		R	Square Spot
2396	*Elaphria venustula*		R	Rosy Marbled
2482	*Schrankia taenialis*		R	White lined Snout

EXTINCT IN HERTS

Code	Taxon	UK BAP Status	Herts Status	Vernacular
2	*Micropterix mansuetella*		X	
3	*Micropterix aureatella*		X	
30	*Ectoedemia arcuatella*		X	
47	*Trifurcula beirnei*		X	
59	*Stigmella poterii*		X	
91	*Stigmella minusculella*		X	
121	*Pseudopostega crepusculella*		X	
132	*Incurvaria praelatella*		X	
133	*Lampronia capitella*	P	X	Currant Shoot Borer
136	*Lampronia corticella*		X	Raspberry Moth
137	*Lampronia morosa*		X	
160	*Phragmataecia castaneae*		X	Reed Leopard
163	*Adscita statices*	P	X	Forester
170	*Zygaena trifolii*		X	Five-spot Burnet
217	*Nemapogon wolffiella*		X	
225	*Triaxomera fulvimitrella*		X	
234	*Trichophaga tapetzella*		X	Tapestry Moth
236	*Tineola bisselliella*		X	Common Clothes Moth
253	*Ochsenheimeria vacculella*		X	
270	*Bucculatrix frangutella*		X	
316	*Phyllonorycter roboris*		X	
319	*Phyllonorycter kuhlweiniella*		X	
347	*Phyllonorycter anderidae*		X	
354	*Phyllonorycter emberizaepenella*		X	
365	*Phyllonorycter comparella*		X	
393	*Glyphipterix equitella*		X	
394	*Glyphipterix forsterella*		X	
403	*Argyresthia glabratella*		X	
407	*Argyresthia dilectella*		X	
409	*Argyresthia ivella*		X	
457	*Ypsolopha lucella*		X	
534	*Coleophora currucipennella*		X	
594	*Elachista gleichenella*		X	
595	*Elachista biatomella*		X	
599	*Elachista alpinella*		X	
603	*Elachista subnigrella*		X	
623	*Elachista bisulcella*		X	
625	*Biselachista cinereopunctella*		X	
630	*Biselachista albidella*		X	
637	*Crassa tinctella*		X	
638a	*Denisia albimaculea*		X	
640a	*Batia internella*		X	
645	*Borkhausenia minutella*		X	
650	*Esperia oliviella*		X	
662	*Pseudatemelia subochreella*		X	
665	*Dasystoma salicella*		X	
666	*Semioscopis avellanella*		X	
671	*Depressaria ultimella*		X	
677	*Depressaria douglasella*		X	
691	*Agonopterix purpurea*		X	
694	*Agonopterix nanatella*		X	
710	*Agonopterix conterminella*		X	
711	*Agonopterix curvipunctosa*		X	
715	*Agonopterix capreolella*	P	X	
744	*Monochroa arundinetella*		X	
759	*Coleotechnites piceaella*		X	
766	*Altenia scriptella*		X	
777	*Bryotropha basaltinella*		X	
788	*Bryotropha politella*		X	
790	*Chionodes fumatella*		X	
791	*Chionodes distinctella*		X	
793	*Mirificarma lentiginosella*		X	
806	*Gelechia nigra*		X	
807	*Gelechia turpella*		X	
834	*Caryocolum tricolorella*		X	
836	*Caryocolum kroesmanniella*		X	
856	*Anarsia spartiella*		X	
861	*Acompsia schmidtiellus*		X	
911	*Scythris grandipennis*		X	
918	*Scythris limbella*		X	
959	*Cochylidia rupicola*		X	
960	*Falseuncaria ruficiliana*		X	
1046	*Acleris shepherdana*		X	
1068	*Celypha rivulana*		X	
1087	*Orthotaenia undulana*		X	
1098	*Endothenia oblongana*		X	
1101	*Endothenia ustulana*		X	
1103	*Endothenia ericetana*		X	
1104	*Endothenia quadrimaculana*		X	
1118	*Ancylis uncella*		X	
1119a	*Ancylis diminutana*		X	
1121	*Ancylis upupana*		X	
1125	*Ancylis unculana*		X	
1129	*Ancylis apicella*		X	
1145	*Epinotia nanana*		X	
1152	*Epinotia maculana*		X	
1154	*Epinotia caprana*		X	
1180	*Epiblema tetragonana*		X	
1217	*Eucosmomorpha albersana*		X	
1231	*Pammene spiniana*		X	
1232	*Pammene populana*		X	
1238	*Pammene ochsenheimeriana*		X	
1254	*Cydia strobilella*		X	Spruce Seed Moth
1280	*Dichrorampha consortana*		X	
1321	*Thisanotia chrysonuchella*		X	
1343	*Eudonia delunella*		X	
1373	*Paratalanta pandalis*		X	
1374	*Paratalanta hyalinalis*		X	
1381	*Anania funebris*	P	X	
1386	*Opsibotys fuscalis*		X	
1420	*Aglossa caprealis*		X	Small Tabby
1441	*Oncocera semirubella*		X	
1450	*Ortholepis betulae*		X	
1463	*Pempeliella ornatella*		X	
1480	*Homoeosoma nebulella*		X	
1486	*Apomyelois bistriatella*		X	
1489	*Oxyptilus pilosellae*		X	
1510	*Merrifieldia leucodactyla*		X	
1514	*Pterophorus galactodactyla*		X	
1515	*Pterophorus spilodactylus*		X	
1633	*Eriogaster lanestris*		X	Small Eggar
1638	*Macrothylacia rubi*		X	Fox Moth
1679	*Cyclophora porata*	P	X	False Mocha
1687	*Scopula ornata*		X	Lace Border
1691	*Scopula emutaria*		X	Rosy Wave
1718	*Phibalapteryx virgata*		X	Oblique Striped
1719	*Orthonama vittata*	W	X	Oblique Carpet
1740	*Epirrhoe galiata*	W	X	Galium Carpet
1761	*Chloroclysta miata*		X	Autumn Green Carpet
1774	*Colostygia olivata*		X	Beech-green Carpet
1787	*Rheumaptera hastata*	P	X	Argent & Sable
1820	*Eupithecia insigniata*		X	Pinion-spotted Pug
1826	*Eupithecia trisignaria*		X	Triple-spotted Pug
1843	*Eupithecia distinctaria constrictata*		X	Thyme Pug
1878	*Minoa murinata*		X	Drab Looper
1880	*Trichopteryx polycommata*	P	X	Barred Tooth-striped
1881	*Trichopteryx carpinata*		X	Early Tooth-striped
1945	*Cleorodes lichenaria*		X	Brussels Lace
1952	*Ematurga atomaria*		X	Common Heath
1964	*Charissa obscurata*		X	Annulet
1969	*Dyscia fagaria*		X	Grey Scalloped Bar
1970	*Perconia strigillaria*		X	Grass Wave
1982	*Hemaris tityus*	P	X	Narrow-bordered Bee Hawk
1983	*Hemaris fuciformis*		X	Broad-bordered Bee Hawk
2017	*Clostera pigra*		X	Small Chocolate-tip
2025	*Orgyia recens*	P	X	Scarce Vapourer
2038	*Nudaria mundana*		X	Muslin Footman
2056	*Parasemia plantaginis*		X	Wood Tiger
2062	*Spilosoma urticae*		X	Water Ermine
2075	*Meganola strigula*		X	Small Black Arches
2084	*Agrotis cinerea*		X	Light Feathered Rustic
2121	*Diarsia dahlia*		X	Barred Chestnut
2142	*Anarta myrtilli*		X	Beautiful Yellow Underwing
2149	*Polia trimaculosa*		X	Silvery Arches
2153	*Heliophobus reticulata*		X	Bordered Gothic
2183	*Orthosia miniosa*		X	Blossom Underwing
2184	*Orthosia opima*		X	Northern Drab
2191	*Mythimna turca*		X	Double Line
2219	*Shargacucullia lychnitis*	P	X	Striped Lychnis
2242	*Xylena exsoleta*	P	X	Sword-grass
2257	*Jodia croceago*	P	X	Orange Upperwing
2276	*Xanthia ocellaris*		X	Pale lemon Sallow
2295	*Cryphia muralis*		X	Marbled Green
2315	*Dicycla oo*	P	X	Heart Moth
2317	*Cosmia diffinis*	P	X	White-spotted Pinion
2412	*Deltote uncula*		X	Silver Hook
2488	*Pechipogo strigilata*	P	X	Common Fan-foot

Species recommended for Biodiversity Action Planning in Hertfordshire

The creation of Biodiversity Action Plans is a matter for the County Council, not for voluntary bodies or individuals. The following are, therefore, merely recommendations which it is earnestly hoped will be acted upon.

UK Biodiversity Action Plan Priority Species
All sites that contain a resident population of a UKBAP species are by default sites of **National Significance** to biodiversity conservation. These all warrant designation as Sites of Special Scientific Interest (SSSI) and most, though not all, are already so designated. It is imperative that the sites supporting UKBAP species remain protected and that site management plans include measures specific to the well-being of the moth.

One Hertfordshire site is now the only remaining locality in Britain for 848: *Syncopacma albipalpella*. This moth may now be confined to one small patch of foodplant and is clearly likely to be adversely affected by collecting of its easily spotted early stages. The site name is withheld, though it should be added that the site owners and managers are aware of its presence.

Moths regarded as Endangered in Hertfordshire
(76 species)
Without doubt, these species should be designated as **Priority Species** within Hertfordshire County Council's Biodiversity Action Planning process. Any site supporting a resident population of a *Herts Endangered* moth is of **County Significance**. Such sites may have a higher significance (Regional or National) if they support more than one *Herts Endangered* species.

Moths regarded as Vulnerable in Hertfordshire
(47 species)
These species are also recommended, without exception, for immediate designation as **Priority species** within Hertfordshire County Council's Biodiversity Action Planning process. Any site supporting a resident population of a *Herts Endangered* moth is also of **County Significance**.

Moths regarded as Threatened in Hertfordshire
(22 species)
These species are recommended for monitoring within the county. They do not yet qualify for entry into the main Biodiversity Action Planning process, but may do so in the future. It is most strongly urged that funding should be made available for research into these species in Hertfordshire. The presence of a resident population of a *Herts Threatened* species on a site nevertheless renders that site of **County Significance**.

Moths regarded as Rare in Hertfordshire
(115 species)
Occasional examples of *Herts Rare* moths may be expected on most sites from time to time as wanderers and it should be remembered that not only do many adult moths disperse over a wide area, but also that mercury vapour light-traps are not necessarily drawing moths just from the site where they are operated. However, the presence of resident populations of two or more *Herts Rare'* species that share similar habitat requirements on a site confers **County Significance** on the relevant habitat units on that site. The presence of resident populations of two or more *Herts Rare* species that have different habitat requirements on a site that supports all the appropriate habitats as a 'habitat mosaic' also confers **County Significance** on the site as a whole.

Moths regarded as Scarce in Hertfordshire
(149 species – not included in the table above)
The presence of an assemblage of several *Herts Scarce* species may suggest that the site either supports a prime example of a particular habitat type (if all species have similar ecological requirements) or else supports an important mosaic of interacting habitats (if the species requirements are varied). In either case the significance of the site is raised and should be regarded as being of District Significance. It is suggested that the presence of five or more *Herts Scarce* species on a site should be the defining parameter. In this context, the 'Districts' of Hertfordshire are the areas currently administered by Broxbourne Borough Council, Dacorum Borough Council, East Herts District Council, Hertsmere Borough Council, North Hertfordshire District Council, St Albans City And District Council, Stevenage Borough Council, Three Rivers District Council, Watford Borough Council and Welwyn Hatfield Borough Council.

Moths regarded as extinct in Hertfordshire
(157 species)
General consensus is that a species needs to have been absent for at least fifty years **and** needs to have been specifically searched for during that period of absence before it can be declared extinct. Yet some species famously 'return from the dead' after a far greater period – the best example perhaps being 2165: Small Ranunculus (*Hecatera dysodea*) whilst others can be reliable treated as absent after a far shorter period of time. In most cases in Hertfordshire the candidate species fall between these two extremes and in defining extinction in our area I have had to deploy a good deal of extrapolation of known data and then inject a significant degree of personal opinion. It goes almost without saying that to qualify as extinct the moth must at some stage have been resident here (so excluding immigrants that have not turned up for ages). However, the rediscovery of an extinct species as a resident in Hertfordshire would automatically promote that species to the *Herts Endangered* threat category until such time as it may become established (at which point a qualified lepidopterist ought to be asked to recommend recategorisation).

Appendix 1: Some Hertfordshire Moth-ers

Throughout the course of the field survey work for this book a number of people have petitioned me to include some biographical information on selected Hertfordshire moth-ers. Extremely brief biographies are, therefore, presented below. For further interest, photographs of the subjects are also presented where I have been able to get hold of them. Clearly, there is not space for a word about everyone who has ever looked at Hertfordshire moths and so inclusion of a person in the list is rather arbitrary. I have tried to include all those who have published on the subject, since their names are 'in the public domain'. I have also tried to include lepidopterists who are relatively well-known at a level beyond the county boundary if they do or have in the past lived or worked in the county and contributed in some way. I have made a particular attempt to include the living as well as the dead. If anyone is excluded and feels this unjust, I apologise profusely. The list is presented alphabetically by surnames and if it encourages someone who has the time and patience to do some more detailed research and write a book on the subject then it will have been worthwhile.

Allan, Philip Bertram Murray, MBE, MA, FSA, FRES (1884 – 1973)

Photograph by A. E. Hick, 1945.

Known to many older entomologists as 'Old Moth Hunter', frequently signing himself as 'OMH', P. B. M. Allan lived in Windhill, Bishops Stortford, directly opposite St Michael's Churchyard where he is now buried in view of his front room window. Educated at Charterhouse, he intended to become a doctor and commenced training at The Middlesex Hospital. However, illness caused him to change course and instead read English and Mediaeval History at Clare College, Cambridge. After serving in Military Intelligence during World War I, he set up Phillip Allan and Co, a publishing company that produced several of his own non-entomological books, including some under the pseudonyms 'Alban M. Phillip', 'Philip Murray' and 'O. Eliphaz Keat'. In 1928 he founded *The Police Journal* and, later, the *Journal of Criminal Law*. His numerous entomological writings are of greater interest to us and these include the famous *Talking of Moths* (1943) and *Leaves from a Moth-hunter's Notebooks*, published posthumously in 1980. Although Allan was also active at a much wider geographical level, he made a significant contribution to the pool of moth records from Hertfordshire and was a particular proponent of 'sugaring' in the middle part of the twentieth century. During 1950, he authored the first edition of *The Macrolepidoptera of Bishops Stortford district*, published as volume 1 part 1 of the *Transactions of the Bishops Stortford and District Natural History Society* and it was he, along with Clifford Craufurd, who founded that society in 1935. The journal is no longer published, though the society thrives. It is regrettable that because the then Vicar at St Michaels objected to the burial of cremated remains, OMH's grave lacks a headstone.

Ashwell, Derek A. (1913 – 1972)

Photograph by A. E. Hick, 1945.

Ashwell was a resident of Bishops Stortford, attending the Bishops Stortford College and later working as an optician in the town. Together with Clifford Craufurd and P. B. M. Allen, Ashwell was an active field worker in the Bishops Stortford area and contributed many records to the 1950 publication authored by Allan. However, he was not a collector and was more interested in breeding experiments, particularly trying to predict the percentages of extreme forms in a population.

Baker, Charles, MA (b. 1933)

Charles Baker worked as an entomologist at the Plant Pathology Laboratory (later the Central Science Laboratory) in Harpenden, mostly on problems associated with imported insect pests. He contributed a chapter on pest species in volume 1 of *The Moths and Butterflies of Great Britain and Ireland* and was a co-author of *The Butterflies and Moths of Bedfordshire* (Arnold et al. 1997). He has been an active member of the Herts Moth Group in recent years, attending many recording trips.

Bell, J. H., (? – c.1950)

Bell lived at Berkhamsted and appears to have been active with regard to moths from about 1909 to 1914 at which point reference to him in the Herts Natural History Society journal ceases until he 'returned to the district in 1932'. Perhaps he left to go to war? He certainly sent moth records to Fryer in 1947 and was Joint Recorder of Lepidoptera with his son Captain Peter J. Bell in 1949. He appears to have died around 1950.

Bell, Captain Peter J., MBE, MA, FLS

A native of Northchurch, Berkhamsted he moved to The Old Cottage, Wiggington, Tring in about 1955 and in 1966 he moved to a different address in the same town, at Goldfield Mill House, Miswell Lane. He was the Hertfordshire Macrolepidoptera Recorder from 1949 to 1976. His last annual review of Hertfordshire moths was published in 1977 and covered the years 1973 – 1976, being especially noted for listing several interesting records without localities! For the last few reviews it was clear that Bell was receiving fewer and fewer records from observers and his published summaries were typically less than two pages in length and of increasingly minimal interest.

James Birdsall

Recorded Lepidoptera in and around Walkern between 1940 and 1950, including at the 'Walkern Searchlight', which evidently attracted large numbers of moths whilst he was trying to illuminate the Luftwaffe. He authored the books *The Boys and the Butterflies* (1988) and *Moths in Memory* (1990). In the late 1980s he was evidently living at T'owd Smithy, Main Street, Bradley, Keighley, West Yorkshire. There is little more information available, except that his brother Timothy (1926 – 1963) was an actor, cartoonist & illustrator who appeared on The Cambridge Footlights in 1958/59 and in the TV program 'That was the week that was' in 1962 as both writer & actor.

Bowden, Sydney R. (1904 – 1991)
A resident of Letchworth, Bowden was mainly interested in butterflies rather than moths and was especially noted for his research on genetic variation in European *Pieris* species. He also published notes in the Journal of the Letchworth Natural History Society. His geographical interest was in the border area with Bedfordshire, particularly the Pegsdon Hills, where he collected from 1917 to the late fifties. He sent some moth records to Foster in 1945. Most of his butterflies are at the Natural History Museum, but some others are in the present writer's collection, donated during 1983.

Bowyer, Robert Wiliam (? – 1905)

From 1869 to 1901 Bowyer was a Master at the Haileybury and Imperial Service College (now Haileybury School), which had been founded a few years earlier in 1862. He was instrumental in establishing the Haileybury Natural Science Society on 6th November 1872, which had as its objective the studying natural history in the college grounds and nearby areas. Under the guidance of the Masters, including Bowyer, the boys set about recording work and produced several annual reports. Though Bowyer, by his own admission, knew nothing of moths when he took up his post, in 1888 he authored a list of macrolepidoptera of Haileybury School in the *Transactions of the Hertfordshire Natural History Society and Field Club* **5**: 23 – 32.

Boyd, William Christopher, JP (? – 1906)
Boyd, who lived in The Grange at Waltham Cross, made a significant contribution to our knowledge of the county's moths in 1901, when he produced his list of 745 species of Lepidoptera of Cheshunt and its surrounding area (*Transactions of the Hertfordshire Natural History Society and Field Club.* **11**: 75 – 86). The area covered included '*on the east ... the long extent of marshland which runs from Hackney northwards to Hertford and Bishops Stortford, and on the north and west there are many good woods, while at the pollards near Wormley West End, on the north, there is a most excellent little patch of heather, mixed with* Genista anglica*, bracken, and bushes of oak and poplar*'. Also incorporated were three gardens where '*I have sugared pretty regularly ... namely at my father's house in Cheshunt Street for 18 years, then three quarters of a mile farther south at College Road for 14 years; and lastly, another half mile farther south, in Crossbrook Street, for 9 years*'. The latter locality is probably The Grange, Waltham Cross. Boyd's list nicely complements the Haileybury list, which covered an adjacent area slightly further north and the two together form a comprehensive list for the Lea Valley/Broxbourne Woods area of south-east Hertfordshire. Interestingly, Boyd's paper was presented to the Hertfordshire Natural History Society, on 23rd April, 1901, not by himself but by A. E. Gibbs. Boyd also contributed to knowledge of the Cornish fauna through the publication of lists of Trichoptera and Odonata for that county in the early 1900s. He and his cousin Thomas (1829 – 1912), who lived at South Norwood, were evidently close friends of the H. T. Stainton. His death is reported by A. E. Gibbs, who provides some additional comments, in *Transactions of the Hertfordshire Natural History Society and Field Club* **13**: 204.

Eric Bradford (1921 – 1995)

Born in Holloway, North London and educated in nearby Hornsey, Eric left school at 14 and took up work as a sign-writer. However, he continued to study in the evenings at Hornsey School of Arts and Crafts. In 1940 he joined the RAF at Brize Norton and served his country in North Africa. After the war he first worked as a freelance illustrator and then as a graphic designer for the Associated Television (ATV) studios at Borehamwood before taking early retirement to Pean Hill, in Kent where he had already purchased several acres of the Blean Woods which he was managing as a nature reserve. Eric was an active recorder, particularly of microlepidoptera, in Hertfordshire during the 1960s and 1970s, contributing many records and his entomological illustrations were much sought by fellow lepidopterists who wished to illustrate their publications. His tragic death in a road accident robbed the world of a microlepidopterist who still had much to contribute.

Bull, George Vernon MB, BChir (1872 – 1959)
Bull was educated first at Harrow School, where he eventually became a Senior Master, and then at Caius College Cambridge. After qualification he became House-physician at St Bartholomews Hospital and House-surgeon at Great Ormond Street Hospital for Sick Children. Later, he took up a rural medical practice at first in Derbyshire and then at Hoddesdon in our county before retiring to Sandhurst. During his years in Hertfordshire he collected moths in and around the Hoddesdon area and was regularly to be found with a net in a woodland ride in the dead of night 'working' his car headlights.

Classey, Eric William (b. 1916)

Eric Classey was born in Queen's Park, west London on 2nd November 1916. During the 1930s he collected moths regularly on the borders of Hertfordshire and Middlesex, mainly by 'sugaring' and with a 'Tilley' lamp and groundsheet, particularly on the old woodland at Oxhey which, at that time was separated from London and other urban areas. Much of his time was spent trying to confirm the continued presence of species based on old records and reports, especially the Heart Moth (*Dicycla oo*) and the Double Line (*Mythimna turca*). After the end of the Second World War, he moved further into Middlesex, but continued to collect in the same area, sometimes in the company of Hertfordshire residents Barry Goater and Graham Howarth. During 1934 he joined the staff of the Department of Entomology at the British Museum (Natural History) but with the outbreak of war he joined the Royal Army Medical Corps and worked in the Entomological Laboratory in the Army School of Hygiene at Mytchett, Surrey, mainly teaching newly fledged doctors and Mobile Laboratory staff the elements of medical and forensic entomology. After the cessation of hostilities, he was offered and accepted the post of Manager of the famous naturalists' supply business *Watkins and Doncaster*, then situated in The Strand, London. Here he stayed until the early 1950s when he left to set up the now world famous entomological bookseller business that shared his name. Whilst at Watkins and Doncaster he co-founded, with the owner Richard L. E. Ford, the journal *Entomologist's Gazette* in 1950. During 1974, he retired to Gloucestershire where he now lives.

Colman, Charles Stacey (1871 – 1955)

Photograph by A. E. Hick, 1945.
Copyright © Bishops Stortford Natural History Society.

Born in Peterborough on 11th October 1871, 'Chips' Colman was a pupil at Bishops Stortford College from 1886 to 1889 before going up to Queen's College Oxford. In 1902, the Headmaster at Bishops Stortford College asked him to join the staff, which he did, teaching Classics and History and becoming a House Master in 1914. As early as 1905 he was keenly collecting moths. A memorial tribute by an unknown author in *The Stortfordian* notes that in 1905 and 1906 '*on fine nights, after lights were out* [in the college] *we sallied forth with net and acetylene lamp to go round 'the treacle' and wander up 'The Lane'* [thought to refer to what is now the main road into Bishops Stortford from the west] *looking for moths, and one or other might be seen climbing lamp posts in the hunt. This prompted C.S.C.'s remark ... when proposing the health of a junior house master, that he was 'a promising young mother*'. Colman's many other interests included cricket, soccer, mountain climbing, boating on the Norfolk Broads (his boat was called 'Moth'), skating and playing Fives. He was an Assistant Editor of *The Sportsman's Yearbook*, a keen gardener and a knowledgeable natural historian, running the school natural history society for many years before retiring in 1936. He became particularly active in the Bishops Stortford Natural History Society after his retirement and contributed many records to P. B. M. Allan's 1950 list of Lepidoptera of the Bishops Stortford area. His name is perpetuated by 'Colman Field', which he raised the funding for and presented to Bishops Stortford College.

Cottam, Arthur FRAS (1837-1911)

Cottam was a founder member of the Hertfordshire Natural History Society and its first Treasurer; according to the 1902 membership list he lived at Eldercroft, Watford. He produced a review of the Lepidoptera of west Herts in *Transactions of the Hertfordshire Natural History Society and Field Club* **10**: 185-190. In 1906, Gibbs (*Transactions of the Hertfordshire Natural Society and Field Club.* **13**: 5-9) noted his removal from Watford during 1905 and his death was reported to the HNHS meeting of 29th November 1911, again by A. E. Gibbs.

Craufurd, Clifford (c.1883 – c.1969).

Photograph by A. E. Hick, 1945.
Copyright © Bishops Stortford Natural History Society.

A contemporary of P. B. M. Allan and others associated with the Bishops Stortford College, Craufurd lived in Galloway Road, Bishops Stortford. A banker by profession, he contributed many records to the 1950 moth list for Bishops Stortford authored by Allan. He was a dedicated collector and regularly accompanied Baron Charles de Worms and other legendary collectors on trips over the entire of the British Isles, especially his home country of Scotland. In a letter to Peter Bell, dated 1969, he says he '*gave up the moth trap three years ago, when I was 83 and no longer cared to get up at dawn to attend to it*'. In 1960 he was Treasurer of the *Entomologist's Record and Journal of Variation*. There are conflicting reports concerning the final resting place of his moth collection. It may have gone to Cambridge University Zoology Department, but if so it was evidently dispersed; no collections remain at the Bishops Stortford College.

Durrant, John Hartley (1863 – 1928)

A Native of Hitchin, Durrant wrote *Lepidoptera of Hitchin & Knebworth* in 1885 (*Trans. Herts* **3**: 261) amongst others. In 1917, acquired the manuscript lists etc of A. E. Gibbs and provided A. H. Foster with much valuable information and clarification on the VCH lists.

Edelsten, Hubert McDonald (1877 – 1959)

Edelsten was born in Stamford Hill in North London, but in 1887 moved to his ancestral home at Enfield, an isolated rural area. He developed a great interest in the natural world and at the end of the nineteenth century was an extremely active lepidopterist in both Hertfordshire and Middlesex, adding many new species to the lists for both counties. The White-mantled Wainscot was originally named *Nonagria edelsteni* in his honour, though later it was realised that the species which Edelsten was found was the same as Hübner's *Nonagria neurica* and so *edelsteni* had to be dropped. In 1902 he was elected a Fellow of the Royal Entomological Society. In 1935 he commenced work at the British Museum (Natural History) and was occupied with reorganising the collections of British Lepidoptera, eventually becoming in charge of them. He was a friend of Sir John Fryer, with whom he had an interest in Wood Walton Fen and other fenland areas and with whom he worked out the life histories of the Marsh Moth (*Athetis pallustris*) and the Brighton Wainscot (*Oria musculosa*).

Ferry, Ralph (alias Roger) Stanton, (? – 1983)
Ferry resided at Fulling Mill House, in Fulling Mill Lane, Welwyn and collected butterflies and moths in his local area and in the Pegsdon Hills area on the Bedfordshire border from 1938 to 1977. His collection is preserved in Mill Green Museum and the moths are housed entirely within two drawers (probably not the originals) in a cabinet that also houses his butterflies and birds' eggs collections. Notable specimens in the collection include a Narrow-bordered Bee Hawk-moth (*Hemaris tityus*), taken in his garden in May 1940 and a Double-line (*Mythimna turca*) labelled as originating from the A. L. Goodson collection and taken at Albury on 24 October 1953 (though that the date is inconsistent with the normal flight period of the moth). Ferry's notebooks constantly refer to page numbers in 'NHHS' – a work that evidently contains information on Coleoptera as well as Lepidoptera, but which I am unable to name or trace. His minimal card index is created on the blank reverse sides of dental appointment cards.

Fielding, John Lewis (b.1919)
A resident of Little Hallingbury then Bishops Stortford, John Fielding has been a leading member of the Essex Wildlife Trust for many years. He was co-author, with Geoffrey Sell and Charles Watson, of the 1985 revision of the Bishops Stortford and District Natural History Society's *List of Macrolepidoptera*, which updates the 1950 work by P. B. M. Allan.

Fish, James (b. 1938)

Jim was born and educated in Bishops Stortford and has lived there all his life, working in a variety of professions including periods as a gentlemen's outfitter and as a distribution manager for a large supermarket chain. A member of the Bishops Stortford and District Natural History Society, his interest in moths was stimulated and encouraged by Clifford Craufurd, whose garden in Galloway Road is within sight of his own in Lyndsey Close. During 1993, he teamed up with fellow moth enthusiast Julian Reeves, whose home is also adjacent, and the two commenced a programme of moth nightly recording, alternating the position of the Robinson trap between the two gardens. This has been rewarded with a list of 420 species of macro-moths from 1993 to 2007 making it the 'best' site for moths in the county in recent years and with a list that is beaten only by the all-time inventory from the Rothamsted Estate at Harpenden where, apart from during the war years, light trapping has been undertaken nightly since 1933.

Foster, Dr Arthur Herbert, MRCS, LRCP, FRES, MBOU (? – 1946)
Foster, who was Medical Officer at the Hitchin Union Work House from 1908, joined the Hertfordshire Natural History Society in 1904 and Gibbs (*Transactions of the Hertfordshire Natural History Society and Field Club* **12**: 109) refers to 'Our new observer, Mr A. H. Foster, of The Grange, Hitchin, who, I am glad to say, has become a member of the Society ... and five of the new records have been supplied by him '). In 1916 he prepared *A list of macrolepidoptera occurring in north Hertfordshire, with notes on each species* in the *Transactions* (**16**: 237 – 258) and then in 1934 he contributed the chapter *Butterflies and Moths* in the book *The Natural History of the Hitchin Region*, edited by R. L. Hine for the Hitchin and District Regional Survey Association. However, Foster's major contribution to our knowledge of Hertfordshire's moths came in 1937 with the publication of his *A list of the Lepidoptera of Hertfordshire* in the *Transactions* (**20**: 157 – 259), at which time his address was 13 Tilehouse Street, Hitchin. Additions, deletions and corrections to the list were published in the same journal in 1940, 1941, 1942, 1944 and 1945. At the request of the Council of the Hertfordshire Natural History Society, he revived the annual reports on Lepidoptera that Gibbs had started in 1892, but his death in 1946 meant that only one was produced – covering 1945 and published posthumously in 1946. Foster's collections were donated to the North Herts Museum Service. His death is reported in the *Transactions*. (**22**(4): xxxv), in which it is stated that 'An obituary notice will be included in the next part of the *Transactions*.' No such notice seems to have appeared and no photographic image of the man appears to exist.

French, Roy Arthur (1921-1985)
French worked in the Entomology Department at Rothamsted Experimental Station from November 1948 to November 1981. He lived most of his life in Luton, except during his wartime career. He worked initially with C. B. Williams on light-trap investigations into the effects of weather on moth populations and behaviour, on moth diversity and insect migration. He took over the Insect Migration Recording Scheme from Captain Danreuther and continued it until he retired. He later worked with Professor Kenneth Mellanby on fruit flies before helping Roy Taylor set up the Rothamsted Insect Survey's network of light and suction traps throughout the UK.

Fryer, Sir John Claud Forteuseue FRS, FRES (1886 – 1948)
Sir John Fryer resided at 31 Milton Road, Harpenden. In 1914 he was appointed Entomologist to the Ministry of Agriculture and soon after became Director of the Ministry's Plant Pathology Laboratory which, in 1920, was established at Harpenden. He was appointed Secretary of the Agricultural Research Council in 1944 and knighted in 1946 in recognition of his official services. A keen lepidopterist, with a special interest in fenland moths, he looked after Wood Walton Fen for the Society for the Promotion of Nature Reserves and was involved with the management of Wicken Fen. Together with H. M. Edelsten and A. Robinson he worked out the life-history of the Marsh Moth *Athetis pallustris*. He amassed large collections of Lepidoptera, Coleoptera and Heteroptera, all of which were a team effort

between himself, his father and his grandfather; the moths remain at Rothamsted. He sent lists to Foster, especially of micros, and took over as county Recorder after Foster died, though he passed away himself a couple of years later.

Gibbs, Arthur Ernest, FLS, FZS, FES, FRHS (1859 – 1917)

Gibbs was a native of St Albans and after several moves finally resided in the town at Kitcheners Field (later called Kitchener's Meads and now partly beneath Fishpool Street). Apparently a 'small but active man', he seems to have been on almost every committee available at the time! The son of a St Albans Alderman, he was a member of the St Albans Education Committee and the St Albans Library Committee and was very largely responsible for establishing St Albans High School for Girls (at a time when most girls were not expected to be educated). He was one of the owners of the '*Herts Advertiser*', '*St Albans Times*' and '*Luton News*' newspapers, all of which appeared weekly. He was also a proprietor of the St Albans Gas Company and was a director of his fathers printing company of Gibbs & Bamforth. At the time of his death on 3rd March 1917, Gibbs was serving as President of the Hertfordshire Natural History Society and Field Club, having joined in 1879; from 1889 to 1899 he was Curator of the society's collections. He was a significant supporter of the establishment of the Hertfordshire County Museum (Now the Museum of St Albans) and donated to it a large amount of material from his own collections. He seems to have done a lot of collecting of moths at Bricket Wood, mainly by sugaring and larva beating, and often in the company of Mr Arthur Lewis of Sparrowswick, St Albans. Gibbs authored papers on the Lepidoptera of St Albans in 1889 and 1909 (*Transactions of the Hertfordshire Natural History Society and Field Club* **5**: 181 and **14**: 236, respectively). He was our County Lepidoptera Recorder from 1893 to 1917 and in that role he produced reports in the *Transactions* from 1893 (covering 1892 and earlier) to 1907 (with a few years missed through illness) and in 1902 he authored the Lepidoptera section of the *Victoria County History of Hertfordshire* – an invaluable summary of the county fauna to the end of the nineteenth century. His interests also extended beyond moths and he was, for example, co-author with P. J. Barraud of a 'List of Hertfordshire Diptera'. After his death, his various papers were said to have been acquired by John Hartley Durrant. Throughout his life he religiously ensured that the type specimens of taxa that he described were lodged at the British Museum (Natural History); remaining material is in the Museum of St Albans and some has recently been transferred to Maidstone Museum. He was a married man and had three daughters.

Gillum, Lieutenant-Colonel William

Gillum collected moths throughout the Barnet area, passing his records to A. E. Gibbs for his annual reviews. During the siege of Sebastopol in 1855, he lost a leg and thought he was going to die. He was forced to retire from the Army, but was so grateful to be alive that he decided to dedicate his life to helping homeless children. So in 1860, after marrying the sister of a headmaster and buying a farmhouse at Church Hill Park, East Barnet (now demolished), he set up Barnet's first and only industrial school. Located in Burlington Rise, East Barnet, behind St Mary's Church, it became known as Church Farm School for Street Urchins.

Gladwin, The Reverend Thomas W. (b. 1935)

Brother of the Right Reverend John Gladwin, Bishops of Guildford to 2003 and then Bishop of Chelmsford, Tom gave up a career in local government planning to combine a vocation as an Anglican clergyman with ecological consultancy work. His wide ranging interests in natural history and wildlife conservation were encouraged and nurtured by his father and paternal grandfather. Childhood memories include annual visits to see fritillaries, hairstreaks and Purple Emperors in Broxbourne Woods. Tom is responsible for a good many moth records from central Hertfordshire in particular and he has trapped and listed mostly macro-Lepidoptera at sites such as Lemsford Springs Nature Reserve and Panshanger, and continues to do so at Amwell Nature Reserve. An account of the 349 species of macro-Lepidoptera he and his wife Janet recorded in their Digswell garden between 1970 and 2001 appeared in *Transactions of the Hertfordshire Natural History Society and Field Club* 34(1) in 2002. Principal co-author with Bryan Sage of *The Birds of Hertfordshire*, and a former recorder of dragonflies (*Odonata*), he is currently working on the county's lacewings (*Neuroptera*) and allied insects.

Goater, Barry (b. 1930)

Barry Goater was Biology Master at the Haberdashers' Aske's School, Hampstead and Elstree, from 1954 to 1958 and Head of Biology from 1958. He lived at Reddings Avenue, Bushey, in the south of the county from 1964 to 1991, and contributed a considerable number of moth records, from there, from the school grounds and from other areas of the county. In 1988, he took early retirement to devote time to the study of European Lepidoptera, mainly Noctuidae and Pyralidae, travelling widely in Europe between Portugal, Swedish Lappland, Czech Republic and Bulgaria, but mostly in Spain and France. In 1991, he returned to his childhood home in Chandlers Ford, Hampshire. He has made numerous contributions to the entomological literature, prominent amongst which are The *Butterflies and Moths of Hampshire and the Isle of Wight* (E. W. Classey, 1974) and *British Pyralid Moths. A Guide to their Identification* (Harley

Books, 1986). He has also contributed to several volumes of *The Moths and Butterflies of Great Britain and Ireland* (Harley Books) and to volume 10 of *Noctuidae Europaeae* (Entomological Press, 2003). In 2005, he co-authored, with Nuss and Spiedel, the seminal work *Microlepidoptera of Europe, Volume 4. Pyraloidea I (Crambidae: Acentropinae, Evergestinae, Heliothelinae, Schoenbiinae, Scopariinae)*, published by Apollo Books. The noctuid moth *Armada barrygoateri* L. & G. Ronkay, 2003 is named in his honour. A large part of his extensive and extremely important collection of European Lepidoptera has already been transferred to the Copenhagen Museum, in Denmark.

Goodson, Arthur Leslie (1904 – 1976)
Goodson was an assistant at the Tring Museum, under Lord Rothschild. He became Senior Assistant in 1947 and then in 1957 became 'Experimental Officer'. He co-authored with Derek Read an annotated list of all named aberrations of British Lepidoptera, an immensely important document which rests unpublished in the Natural History Museum. He lived in Tring and sent garden moth records annually to Foster and subsequently to Bell. An example of the Double Line (*Mythimna turca*) allegedly taken by him at Albury in 1953 (though labelled with an improbable date), is preserved in the R. S. Ferry Collection at Mill Green Museum, though the bulk of his collection is at the City Museum, St Albans.

Gould, Philip John Lewis (b. 1973)

Phil Gould is currently a Research Scientist at Rothamsted Research, where he is co-ordinator and chief taxonomist for the national light-trap network. He grew up in the wilds of the Isle of Purbeck in Dorset, allowing for a great love of all things Natural History to flourish. However, he has always been most interested in our insect fauna and moths in particular, running light traps from a very early age. After gaining a degree in Biology from Southampton he worked in the university's Biodiversity and Ecology Division, honing his skills as an entomological taxonomist, identifying most of the insects found in agricultural ecosystems. In 2001, after a contract in Costa Rica identifying banana plantation arthropods, he joined Rothamsted – where he is now being paid to do his hobby!

Griffith, Arthur Forster, BA (1857 – 1933)
Son of the Vicar of St Swithins, Winchester, Griffith appears, from 1881 census data, to have been born in Brighton; at the date of the census he was in residence at Sandridge Vicarage and is listed as 'teacher private tutor Cambridge B.A., unmarried'. His major contribution to Hertfordshire moths was also amongst the first, in the form of his paper on the *Lepidoptera of Sandridge* published in 1884 and followed up with additional records in 1890. References in the introduction to the 1894 paper date back as far as 1874, when he would have been 17 years old. His brother, F. Ll. Griffith, apparently undertook most of the field work with him, but does not appear to have published anything himself. Arthur Griffith joined the Hertfordshire Natural History Society and Field Club in 1883, but is no longer listed as a member in the 1894 list (though there was an Acton F. Griffith given in that list). He retired to Cardiff and his collection went there, but various enquiries made of it have not borne fruit. Griffith was amongst the first to recommend that collectors should put data labels on their specimens!

Hervey, Canon J. Aidan K.
There seems to be little information on Hervey, who apparently carried out surveys of microlepidoptera at Ashridge in spring and summer of 1934 on behalf of the Herts Natural History Society; there is no trace of any report that he may have written, but his lists were included by Foster in the 1937 county list and included the last known record of 1321: *Thisanotia chrysonuchella*). The resting place of his moth collection is unknown. He left Hertfordshire after the summer of 1934 and there is no further mention of him in the county entomological literature.

Hodgson, S. B. (? – 1967)
Hodgson was partially deafened by a shell-burst during the First World War and this became progressively worse throughout life until he became totally deaf in his final years. He collected moths in the Berkhamsted area and sent records to Foster in 1945 onwards and to Bell to the early 1960s. A notice of his death appears in the Transactions of the Herts Natural History Society for 1966, published in 1968, but the date of his death is not given. His entomological diaries are with the North Herts Museum Service.

Howarth, Thomas Graham, BEM, FRES, FZS (b. 1916)
Graham Howarth was a Senior Scientific Officer in the Entomology Department of the Natural History Museum, retiring in 1976. A resident of Arkley his main interest has been in butterflies, but his contributions to knowledge of Hertfordshire's moths include catching a Silver-striped Hawk (*Hippotion celerio*) in 1958 and first county records of both Dumeril's Rustic (*Luperina dumerilii*) and The Delicate (*Mythimna vitellina*).

Lorimer, Ronald Ian (1919 – 1994)
Ian Lorimer was a native of Burton-on-Trent but his adult life was spent mostly at Totteridge some 600 yards within the Hertfordshire Vice-county. Here, he managed to run a light trap on most nights from the mid-1950s to 1980. In a letter to Peter Waterton, the then Hertfordshire Moth Recorder, dated 29th March 1979, he states that he had '*... been running m.v.l. here pretty regularly for about 25 years and the most surprising thing to me is that every year brings in something new*'. Although he formed his own collection, '*this was not purposeless and he did not accumulate long series but he saw that the museums in London and Orkney were provided, as far as was possible, with voucher specimens of all Orkney species, sub-species and forms; where only a single specimen was known and/or available it went to London*' (Classey, 1998). Ian's name is commemorated in Lorimer's Rustic (*Paradrina flavirena*) of which he caught the first British example at Totteridge on 8th October 1967. From 1963 onwards he

became much interested in the butterflies and moths of Orkney and he retired there in 1981. His *The Lepidoptera of the Orkney Islands* was published in 1983 and then a 1983 to 1987 supplement published in the journal *Entomologist's Gazette*. A later supplement also appeared posthumously in 1998 under the title of *Unfinished Business. A Supplement to the Lepidoptera of the Orkney Islands* (Hedera Press). Lorimer was also responsible for large sections of volumes 9 and 10 of the ongoing series *Moths and Butterflies of Great Britain and Ireland*, writing the text for the Hadeninae Cuculliinae, Acronictinae, Chloephorinae, Sarrothripinae, Pantheinae, Plusiinae, Catocalinae and Ophiderinae.

Mellows, Charles (1886 – 1967)

Chas Mellows came to Bishops Stortford College in 1898 and won a scholarship in Classics to Brasenose College Oxford, where he also swam and played Rugger. On leaving Oxford, he spent a short time at Manchester Grammar School and then the Bootham School in York, before returning to Bishops Stortford College as a master in 1912. During the First World War he served mainly in the Middle East and was torpedoed several times in the Mediterranean, distinguishing himself by using his swimming skills to rescue many of his fellow servicemen. He was demobilised with the rank of Captain and returned to Bishops Stortford College in 1919 where he remained until retirement in 1957. Amongst his many activities he ran the college natural history society for many years and was, according to his obituary in the college magazine, 'an outstanding entomologist'. His contribution to our knowledge of Hertfordshire's moths takes the form, primarily, of his provision of records to P. B. M. Allan for inclusion in the 1950 list of Bishops Stortford Lepidoptera. He apparently made a substantial moth collection, of which a very high proportion comprised Hertfordshire specimens; this latter fact that makes all the more distressing the discovery that his collection was neglected and ultimately destroyed by insect pests after his death.

Newton, John ('Jack')

A resident of Tetbury, Gloucestershire, and primarily a microlepidopterist, Newton recorded moths at mv light in a garden in Stevenage from 1962 to 1973; his hand-written list makes occasional reference to another lepidopterist – D. Ruston – and it is clear that some of his records are supported by voucher specimens in the Ruston collection. Unfortunately, it has not been possible to establish where in Stevenage the garden was located; Newton evidently did not live there and it is assumed that it must have either been his parents garden or perhaps Ruston's?

Ormerod, Eleanor Ann (1828 – 1901)

Miss Ormerod was a Cheshire born lady and Hertfordshire's first Recorder of entomology. An outstanding, no-nonsense entomologist she overcame the hurdles facing would-be women scientists by being

born into the British upper class with a considerable private income. She was the first woman to use her studies of insects in a professional capacity, albeit unpaid, as consulting entomologist to the Royal Agricultural Society from 1882 to 1892. In 1870 she received the Silver Flora medal for her services to the Royal Horticultural Society and in 1872 received a gold medal from Moscow University. In 1878 she was the first woman member of the Royal Meteorological Society and was also the first woman to be awarded an honorary Doctor of Law degree. Her published works include *Manual of Injurious Insects* (1881) and *Guide to the Methods of Insect Life* (1884). Apparently a somewhat fearsome, 'stout' lady, she was to farmers, fruit growers and market gardeners, a saint and her cheap-and-easy methods for destroying some of the world's worst agricultural scourges saved many of them from ruin. However, to others she was an evil killer and towards the end of the century, hate mail began to appear in her postbag. She was regularly reviled in the pages of *The Animal's Friend* and found herself hanged in effigy – and even shot at – because she advocated the total eradication of House Sparrows which, to her, were avian rats. Strangely, nobody objected to her schemes to control codling moth or wipe out warble fly.

Palmer, Stephen Michael, (b. 1952)

Stephen was born in Hemel Hempstead moving to Hatfield in 1955 and Datchworth in 1961. His father, Maurice, a Flight Engineer at De Havillands, had a strong interest in wildlife which was soon passed on to Stephen, significantly when he constructed a moth trap for him. Visits to grandparents back at Hemel were usually followed by a trip to Tring Museum where attempts were made to identify the moths he had caught at home. Air Traffic Control was his chosen profession and this took him to many parts of the UK. It was whilst working in Aberdeenshire that he met Dr Mark Young and Bob Palmer, whose friendship and mentoring set the scene for a lifetime interest in moths, particularly the microlepidoptera. In 1983 he moved to Wiltshire where, with his wife Carolyn and three children he lived in Dinton, west of Salisbury and was soon appointed County Recorder for the microlepidoptera. At this time he was introduced to and became good friends with John Langmaid. Frequent bug-hunting trips together to under-recorded parts of this county with John, particularly the Army ranges of Salisbury Plain, led to many fascinating species being added to the Wiltshire moth list. This culminated in his publication of the *Microlepidoptera of Wiltshire* in 1995, the year after moving to Preston, Lancashire. He is now County Recorder for the microlepidoptera in that county, runs the Lancashire Moth Group and is a fanatical follower of Preston North End football club!

Reid, James BSc (b. 1944)

Jim went to school in Stretford, Manchester and interest in biology led to a degree in Zoology and Applied Zoology at Bangor University. He spent over 20 years in research and development of insecticides, whilst at the same time becoming an enthusiastic conservationist. Interest in moths started in school, developed in university but really matured whilst running courses for the Field Studies Council with John Heath, training recorders for the National Moth Recording Scheme. The need for and concept of the series *Moths and Butterflies of Great Britain and Ireland* developed on these courses and Jim contributed the chapter on Techniques to Vol. 1. Enthusiasm for pug moths also developed on these courses and Jim has bred almost all British species from the egg, providing help to Prior and Riley for their book on British pugs and also augmenting the Geometridae section in Friedrich's *Breeding Butterflies and Moths* (UK edition). His main interest is recording and breeding and he has added new species to three Greek island butterfly lists whilst on holidays and he has published articles and short notes on many Lepidoptera topics. He discovered and named an apparently new noctuid species, *Schrankia intermedialis*, in Hertfordshire during 1971 but DNA sequencing now shows this to be a naturally occurring hybrid.

Reeves, Julian BSc (b. 1954)

Born and bred in Bishops Stortford, Julian gained his degree at the University of East London and works as a pharmacologist for a large pharmaceutical company. As a child he knew Clifford Craufurd who introduced him to moths and encouraged him to undertake their study. His home in Lyndsey Road, Bishops Stortford is on the high ground to the west of the River Stort and overlooks both James Fish's garden adjacent and Craufurd's former garden in Galloway Road. A single Robinson trap placed alternatively in his own garden and that of James Fish lower down the hill has recorded 420 macro-moth species since the start of 2003 making it the most species-rich site in Hertfordshire in recent years.

Riley, Adrian Michael (b. 1958)

Riley's formative years were spent in his native Shropshire, where his first interests were in geology and fishing rather than insects. However, he soon developed a keen interest in butterflies and rapidly rose to become an acknowledged expert on the Lepidoptera as a whole. His book *A Natural History of the Butterflies and Moths of Shropshire* was published in 1991 by Swan Hill Press and remains the standard text for that county. Fortunately for us, he moved to Hertfordshire in 1979 and took up a post at the Rothamsted Experimental Station, working his way up through the ranks to become the supervisor and chief taxonomist of the Rothamsted Light-trap Network. By the time he took early retirement in 2001, and moved to Norfolk, he had written over 150 scientific papers and articles and two more books of which the one that will be known most widely is *British and Irish Pug Moths,* co-authored with the late Gaston Prior and published by Harley Books in 2003. One of his more significant entomological papers was a summary of the macro-moths in the various light-traps that had been operating on the Rothamsted Estate at Harpenden since the inception of the scheme in the 1930s by C. B. Williams (Riley, 1999). In 2002, he took on the 'twitching' world and won the annual competition for the greatest total of birds seen in the British Isles in a calendar year. His total of 382 species in the year is more than most birders would see in a lifetime. In 2003, he determined to turn his attention back to butterflies, producing the book *British and Irish Butterflies* in late 2007 (Brambleby Books). He currently lives near Fakenham in Norfolk where amongst his other activities he leads bird-watching and bug-watching tours, supports Leeds United Football Club and several local pubs – often in conjunction!

Rothschild, Lionel Walter 2nd Baron Rothschild of Tring (1868 – 1937)

The second baron Rothschild of Tring, six feet three inches tall and weighing in at 22 stones, was the epitome of collectors. His seat was Tring Park and apart from a brief spell as Member of Parliament for Aylesbury from 1899 to 1910, during which he spent most of his time in the Natural History Museum, he devoted almost his entire life to establishing and running a private museum at Tring. This opened to the public in 1892. Here he amassed 'the greatest collection of animals ever assembled by one man, ranging from starfish to gorillas' – words attributed by Salmon M. A. (2000. *The Aurelian Legacy*. Harley Books) to his niece Miriam, the world authority on fleas who died in 2005. Over two and a half million set specimens of butterflies and moths were included; though almost none were from Hertfordshire it is interesting to note his own words that 'I have no duplicates'! His collections were later combined with those of Cockayne and Kettlewell to form the basis of the national collection, now at South Kensington in London and the empty cabinets were sold off. The present writer is pleased to be the proud owner of one of these! He was also well-known for his team of Zebra that drew his carriage in the place of horses and the many exotic large animals, including Kangaroo, Ostrich, Wild Horses and a flock of 65 Cassowaries that roamed freely on his estate at Tring Park. Walter should not be confused with his brother, The Honourable Nathaniel Charles Rothschild (1877 – 1923), who was also a naturalist and was, like his daughter Miriam, a world authority on fleas. However, Charles appears to have contributed nothing to knowledge of Hertfordshire moths, though he was extremely active elsewhere, notably at Wicken Fen and overseas in Hungary.

Sell, Geoffrey Hugh Baker (b. 1933)

Born in Bishops Stortford, Geoffrey attended the Bishops Stortford College and started recording butterflies and moths in 1947. The proposed expansion of Stansted Airport forced a move away (to Dorset) in 1971; his Lepidoptera diaries were transferred to my safe keeping at that date. He was actively involved in conservation management work in the Bishops Stortford area, especially at Birchanger Woods, and was a co-author (with John Fielding and Charles Watson) of the 1985 revision of the Bishops Stortford and District Natural History Society's *List of Macrolepidoptera* which updates the 1950 work by P. B. M. Allan.

Senior, Geoffrey (b.1938)

A Yorkshireman by birth, Geoff Senior moved to Trent Park (Middlesex) in 1950 where his childhood interest in birds and butterflies broadened to include the moths throughout the 1960s. In 1961 he went to the London College of Printing to study photography and this has been his career ever since. His first photographic contribution to the study of moths was the creation of the colour plates in the British Entomological and Natural History Society's *An identification guide to the British pugs* and later he also photographed the plates for Barry Goater's *British Pyralid Moths* (Harley Books, 1986). He moved to live in Little Hadham, near Bishops Stortford, in 1977.

Souter, Rob (b. 1963)

Initially a birder, Rob began his interest in moths in the 1980s, whilst a resident of St Albans. In 1991, whilst on a year's placement at the University Of Hertfordshire's Field Station at Bayfordbury, he had access to the university's Robinson light trap and he set to work to update the site list with almost nightly trapping over six months. After graduating, Rob spent six months in North Vietnam, studying tropical butterflies by day and trapping moths at night, running a tungsten light bulb at a sheet from a generator. The number of moths caught was staggering – use of an MV bulb would have been ridiculous! The largest moth caught had a 15 cm wingspan. He became involved with the Herts and Middlesex Branch of Butterfly Conservation from 1994 to 2000, sitting on the main and conservation committees as Branch Moth Officer. He wrote regular articles about moths for the branch newsletter and an article for the national magazine on day-flying moths, as well as conceiving and producing the moth report section in the Herts and Middlesex Branch's annual Butterfly and Moth Report. He also organised several moth evenings in Hertfordshire and Middlesex, before the formation of the Herts Moth Group. Amongst the more unusual things attracted to his lights, but perhaps not unexpected, were members of the local constabulary! When he was visited in the ride of Broxbourne Woods the officer appeared not as delighted as Rob when a Pine Hawkmoth landed on his brilliant white shirt. During this period Rob was also helping with the formation of the Herts Moth Group, joint hosting the first meeting of the Group in 2000 and also designing and managing their first website. Rob left the country after completing his PhD and travelled in New Zealand to look for birds. He met his German wife there and lived in southern Germany for a while before moving to Hampshire to work as a consultant ecologist.

Stephens, James Francis (1792 – 1852)

Stephens was born at Shoreham, Sussex, but was educated at The Bluecoat School, Hertford. At the age of 15 he entered the Admiralty office, Somerset House as a clerk. However, in 1818 he was given leave of absence to help in arranging the insect collection at the British Museum. In 1829 he published his famous *Systematic Catalogue of British Insects* in which he listed 10,116 species – more than half of which he had captured personally. His other famous work, *Illustrations of British Entomology, a Synopsis of Indigenous Insects,* was published from 1828 to 1856 in 11 volumes, the first four, published from 1828 to 1834, being concerned with the Lepidoptera and in which there are 117 references to Hertfordshire moths. He was the first to discover and publicise the value of crushed laurel leaves as a killing and relaxing agent for insect specimens. Interestingly, he steadfastly refused to use the new-fangled microscopes, on the basis that if it could not be seen with a pocket lens it was not worth seeing at all!

Sterling, Mark, MA, BCL (b. 1958)

Son of Col. Douglas Sterling (a Hampshire lepidopterist) and brother of Philip (the current county ecologist for Dorset), Mark was born in Winchester, Hampshire, but lived in St. Albans from 1988 to 1997 then again, after a brief period as a resident of Hong Kong, from 2003 to present. He is a partner of the law firm Allen & Overy, for whom he is an internationally renowned bankruptcy lawyer. He is primarily interested in microlepidoptera, but has a wider knowledge-base and was co-author, with Fred Harrison, of *Butterflies and Moths of Derbyshire*, published in three parts in 1985 and 1986. He is also an expert on the microlepidoptera of Hong Kong.

Terry, Rachel (b. 1968)

After growing up in Hertfordshire, Rachel 'defected' to Middlesex to study Graphic Design in Barnet. Although interested in all aspects of natural history, it was the chance discovery of an Elephant Hawkmoth caterpillar in her garden in 1998 that rekindled her childhood love of butterflies and moths - Rachel had once again been bitten by the 'Lepidoptera bug'. Joining the Herts Moth Group nurtured her fledging interest, while her job as a park ranger for the London Borough of Ealing gave her the opportunity to acquire and run MV lights. 'National Moth Night' soon found it's way onto the Parks and Countryside Events programme and regular trapping, especially in un-worked areas of Middlesex, increased her knowledge and interest. In spite of a career change in 2005, Rachel continues her Lepidoptera surveys for the Herts & Middlesex Wildlife Trust, though in recent years, her focus has been on the micro-Lepidoptera. The acquisition of a microscope and digital macro-photography equipment has enabled Rachel to become accomplished in the dissection and identification of micro-Lepidoptera, whilst her willingness to tackle difficult id problems for Middlesex mothing friends as well as the considerable back-log of micros from Hertfordshire, has added considerably to both garden lists and the county records. In 2007 Rachel co-authored the Middlesex Vice-County update with Colin Plant and one of her high-quality genitalia photographs has illustrated a recent paper describing *Prays peregrina* (Yponomeutidae) as new to science. She is also involved with, and is a contributor to an Internet project with the eventual aim of illustrating the genitalia of all the British Lepidoptera.

Uffen, Raymond William James MSc, DIC, ARCS, FRES (b. 1934)

Raymond's first entomological recollection is of frustration at the school bell disrupting his observation of a butterfly expanding its wings on the school wall at Cleveleys, Lancashire, at the age of six. Upon his returning to the family home in Chiswick after world war II, purchase of South's *Butterflies of the British Isles* gave him a sound introduction to the life cycle of Lepidoptera and the techniques for collecting and preserving specimens. Visits were made to the Natural History Museum to identify moths from the collection then available in the insect gallery. South (revised 1941) described the distribution of the Comma butterfly as having shrunk to the west country, but expanding again. Discovery of a comma outside Raymond's back door led to a key teenage visit to report this to the museum, where the butterfly expert Graham Howarth welcomed him behind the scenes and subsequently gave much help identifying noctuid moths that were represented in South's *Moths of the British Isles* by out-of register brown images. Raymond's real interest was in the micro moths that could be tackled only by collecting larvae and attempting to name them through L.T. Ford's *Guide to the Smaller British Lepidoptera*. So the handy B.M. (Nat. Hist.) again came to the rescue in the person of John Bradley, who eventually told him to join the South London Entomological and Natural History Society, to which nearly all the country's microlepidopterists belonged. As that Society met not much further away in the rooms of the Royal Society in Piccadilly and had experts in most of the principal orders of insects, this represented lift-off. Field work before 1970 was mainly in Kent, Surrey and west London, with occasional forays to the Essex marshes. The 1970s saw forays for leaf miners across Essex with Maitland Emmet. Collection in Hertfordshire has been mostly since 1980, a period that has seen very low populations of many insects and extreme localisation of species of wide national distribution. Raymond's wide-ranging entomological expertise is reflected in a particular knowledge of the Coleophoridae and he is also the Hertfordshire and London Area Recorder for Aculeate Hymenoptera (bees, wasps and ants).

Watson, Charles Percival (1929 – 2005)

A life-time resident of Bishops Stortford, Charles was the son of a Nurseryman and after a period of work away from home in Redbourne and National Service as a Signaller with RAF Coastal Command he returned again to Stortford and joined his father at South Road Nurseries, where he remained for over 50 years, taking over the business in 1960. As an entomologist Charles was proud to be called an amateur – but he was an exceptionally gifted amateur, with an encyclopaedic knowledge of the area around Bishops Stortford and the rarer moths to be found there. He was a co-author (with John Fielding and Geoffrey Sell) of the 1985 revision of the Bishops Stortford and District Natural History Society's *List of Macrolepidoptera* which updates the 1950 work by P. B. M. Allan. When I arrived in Stortford in 1986 we immediately teamed up and realised that we had common ground in our belief that sound conservation is based on sound species data. Although he did not collect moths himself he would always pass the micros and others that he could not name to me and in his later years, as he developed a keen interest in hoverflies and in bees and wasps, plus a parallel knack of finding rare species in unexpected places, all of his records were supported by properly labelled voucher specimens. However, Charles' greatest contribution to Hertfordshire moth knowledge was his encouragement of newcomers – of all ages – and his unfettered generosity in loaning moths traps and other equipment to those who could not afford their own.

Waterton, Peter

Waterton lived at Reynards Road, Welwyn and was County Lepidoptera Recorder from 1977 to 1981, in which year he moved from his home in Welwyn to Middlesborough for reasons associated with his employment when the chemical company ICI closed down operations. Waterton's first Lepidoptera report for Hertfordshire was for the year 1977 (published in the *Transactions* for 1979) and his last was for 1981, published in 1983.

Williams, Carrington Bonsor FRS (1889 – 1991)

Always known and addressed as 'CB', Williams lived in central Liverpool until the age of about eight, when the family moved to the Cheshire coast. He cut his natural history teeth on insects in the open fields that dominated that area at the time and progressed via the Lancashire and Cheshire Entomological Society, a Cheshire 'prep' school, and the Birkenhead School, from 1903 to 1908 to Clare College at Cambridge University where he took the Diploma of Agriculture. A varied career, including a post in the Entomological Section of the Ministry of Agriculture in Egypt, led eventually to his arrival at the Rothamsted Experimental Station, at Harpenden, in 1932, where he remained until retirement in 1955. Here, he was able to develop, in particular, his interest in insect migration but he will be remembered primarily as the man who first set up light traps across the Rothamsted Estate set about the gathering of statistical data from these; from this beginning, the present day network of Rothamsted Insect Survey (RIS) light traps across Britain sprang. A fuller account of his life can be read in *Biographical Memoirs of Fellows of the Royal Society* volume 28 (1982) by Sir Vincent Wigglesworth.

Wilson, David Escott (b.1941)

David Wilson is best known as the photographer who

produced the colour plates both for Bernard Skinner's *Colour identification Guide to Moths of the British Isles* (Viking, 1984, reprinted 1998) and for the hugely important *Noctuidae Europaeae* (Entomological Press, Denmark). He was born in Woodside Park, North London. Introduced to his life-long interest in Lepidoptera by his father, he spent many sunny days in his childhood in the fields around Woodside Park, Totteridge and Mill Hill. Educated in North London, his interest in biology and art led on to art school and advertising photography. This, via a rather circuitous route, ended in a career in the cement industry. He moved to the Hertfordshire village of Green Tye, near Much Hadham in 1965 and for thirty years collected and photographed insects there, running moth traps in and around his garden and contributing a large number of records to this book. He became a member of the British Entomological and Natural History Society in 1968 and in the early 1970s was asked if he would act as their Exhibition Photographer. This he did for the following 30 years. In the early 1970s, he and Robert Mays founded Aurelian Books as part of their mutual interest in books on Lepidoptera. He left Hertfordshire in 1997 and now tells me that he studies Lepidoptera and beer in coastal Suffolk!

Woiwod, Ian Peter BSc ARCS FRES (b. 1947)

Ian Woiwod is currently a Principal Research Scientist at Rothamsted Research and head of the Rothamsted Insect Survey's national light-trap network. He has had a life-long interest in insects ever since he started an insect collection as a school project when he was eight. He joined Rothamsted after graduating in Zoology from Imperial College in 1968. Since then he has published about 200 research papers, book chapters and reports on a wide range of entomological and ecological subjects including many on moths. Several of these make particular use of the unique datasets collected on the Rothamsted estate. Ian has served on the council and been a vice-President of the Royal Entomological Society. He is currently a member of the Conservation Committee of Butterfly Conservation, the steering group for the National Moth Recording Scheme and the council of the Bedfordshire Natural History Society.

Wood, Andrew Geoffrey (b. 1957)

Andrew started studying moths in 1991 after buying a cheap ex Open University moth trap which consisted of a cardboard box, waste sack and some electricals. At that time he was based in Yiewsley, Middlesex, but in 1994 he moved to Bengeo, a northern suburb of Hertford and began studying moths there. In the next few years he went from trapping on nights that looked good to trapping every night when he was at home and using a Skinner trap. He also progressed from being a macro only to a micro and macro man. In 2000 he took over from Rob Souter as the local branch of Butterfly Conservation's moth officer and joined the newly formed Herts Moth Group, reinforcing the link between the two bodies. He is also currently co-author of Butterfly Conservation's annual butterfly and moth report for the Hertfordshire and Middlesex and is the keeper of the primary back-up copy of the Herts Moth Database. Wearing his Butterfly Conservation 'hat' he continually tries to persuade butterfly recorders to also note moths that they find and he has organised a number of moth trapping events for both organisations. He has been a keen photographer for a number of years and began photographing moths using an SLR and macro lenses in 1991, progressing to digital equipment in 2002 and amassing a large library of digital images of moths. Andrew has also collated, sorted and edited the moth photographs sent in by others and used in this book.

Appendix 2: How to catch moths ....

You can't learn 'mothing' from books and there really is no substitute for practical experience. We will always warmly welcome you at the Herts Moth Group's meetings, which consist entirely of field trips except for one annual indoor meeting where we all get together informally. If you are outside Hertfordshire we can quickly point you to moth groups that are active in your own area. The field trips have three purposes. First and foremost they are fun – the moment it stops being fun we go home! Second, the trips are designed to allow people to see and learn about moths in different habitats in the presence of one or more experts who are competent at naming them. Finally, they are recording trips – lists of species encountered are compiled and used to produce books such as this.

Our trips are open to all regardless of experience. We welcome photographers and we encourage scientific collecting (for example, micro-moths for identification purposes, so that the database contains only accurate records), but we also warmly welcome people who prefer not to collect specimens. Outings are made to places across the whole of the county and sometimes southwards into Middlesex; by spreading ourselves around we not only get good recording coverage, but we also give everyone an equal chance to attend without travelling too far. We try to include wetland, woodland and grassland habitats as these are most likely to produce a wide range of species.

An early instar author pretends he can identify the leaf-mine presented to him by a Herts Moth Group member at Broxbourne Woods during a daytime field trip in 2004. Note the facial cilia and the elongate 'hair-pencil' on the dorsal surface of the vertex – features that have been lost in later instars (photograph © Richard Bigg).

Members of the Herts Moth Group around the sheet at Hazel Grove, on the University of Hertford's Hatfield Campus. Traditionally, in England, the sheet is laid flat on the ground and a bulb is suspended a few feet above it from a tripod, but in Hertfordshire we have found that the Continental method of having the sheet vertical works far better. Interestingly, we have not noticed any increase in catches if we place a bulb on both sides of the sheet and it is also interesting that several species of Geometridae might favour the side of the sheet *away* from the bulb. In recent years we have noticed a sharp decline in the numbers of moths arriving at the sheet, but we have at least proved that the number of moths is directly proportional to the interest of members as this picture seems to indicate!

If you want to start looking at moths in your garden or elsewhere, this is a relatively easy exercise. To look at moths in your garden all you will need is some sort of light trap, some pots to put moths in and the time to look at them (**tip**: Put potted moths in the fridge and look at them when you come home from work; they will suffer no harm at all even if left for several days). Problem specimens can be brought along to moth group trips for naming by the experts.

Frankly, it is just as easy to buy a light trap as it is to make your own – it all depends on how practical you are feeling and how much money you want to spend. There are many kinds of trap, but all have three basic component parts – the light source, the trap container and a funnel or some other means of preventing the live moths from escaping before you can look at them in the morning.

The light source can be almost any light bulb, but those with a high proportion of ultra-violet (UV) light in their spectrum are best. There are two kinds – actinic tubes and mercury-vapour bulbs. We are happy to provide details of our recommended supplier. Both will attract a different range of moth species, but in general mercury-vapour bulbs tend to attract more than the actinics and are recommended for overnight sessions in the garden. On the other hand, actinic tubes can be run from a car battery so that you can use the trap in the local woods without needing to buy an expensive generator. Mercury vapour bulbs get hot and should be protected by a rain shield to prevent them cracking on contact with large, cold drops of rain. The trap container can be purchased or home-made and one good method is to use a plastic dustbin and cut a hole in the lid to take the light source and funnel. Whatever you use, line it with large cardboard egg trays so that the moths have somewhere to settle and hide otherwise they will just fly around in circles and lose all their scales so you can't identify them. Make sure the top of the trap is transparent so that the moths know when it is morning and settle down so you can examine them. The funnel is designed to keep moths in the trap and works on the principal that moths will always try to escape upwards towards the light and not downwards. Robinson-pattern traps are far and away better at retaining moths after capture than Skinner-pattern traps. On the other hand, Skinners can be folded up and carried around (**tip**: whatever you decide, do not place the trap where the morning sunshine will 'fry' the catch before you can examine it).

One of the author's rather elderly 6-watt actinic traps. Modern actinic traps may be of a different design and bulbs of greater power are available. The actinic tube in this trap sits vertically in the translucent funnel and transparent baffles help direct flying moths downwards.

Robinson-pattern light traps are round and therefore cannot be folded flat for transport, but they retain almost all the catch with very few moths escaping. These traps are ideal for abandoning overnight in gardens and elsewhere. Note the rain shield (home made with wire coat-hanger and supermarket plastic fruit container); this trap is left in the garden in all weathers.

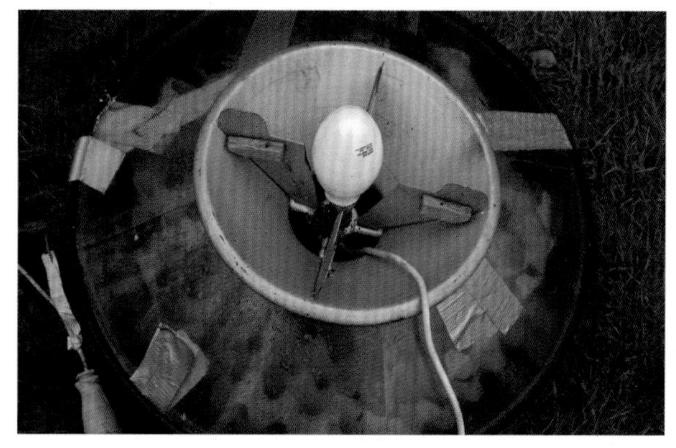

In the Robinson-pattern light trap, the transparent circular lid rises up to the centre of the trap and the funnel hangs down at the centre. The entrance holes are at the base of the funnel. This design minimises the number of moths escaping before they can be examined. The rain shield has been removed for the photograph; note the four baffles around the bulb which help to direct flying moths down into the funnel and the egg trays under which moths can settle.

Robinson-pattern traps are ideal for abandoning in awkward situations. This one is balanced on top of a bramble bush to overlook a reed bed through the only gap in a hawthorn hedge.

Skinner-pattern traps fold flat and can be stored or carried easily, but the long slots at the base of the perspex top panels allow more moths to escape. These traps are best in situations where regular inspection throughout the night is proposed. A base is optional – most do not have one and for this reason need to be placed on a sheet. This wooden trap slots together and is inspected regularly throughout the night and so there is no need for a rain shield, but note also that this design lacks baffles around the bulb.

Older 'Skinners' like this one being examined by Marcel Ashby (left) and Les Hill (right) were constructed of hinged aluminium sheets.

Artificial pheromones placed in a bag and hung from the vegetation in appropriate habitat is very effective at attracting male clearwings.

Of course, there is far more to moth-ing than sitting around a light trap on a warm, balmy evening with a bottle of red and a few like-minded souls (honest!). Light trapping will provide you with a good basic list of the macro-moths in your garden, but there will be many species that don't come to light. The clearwings (Sesiidae) are good examples. It was always assumed that these moths were rare, but since the invention of synthetic pheromones this has proved to be incorrect. Pheromones are the 'sex scents' emitted by virgin females in order to attract males; hanging lures soaked in artificial pheromones from vegetation is effective at attracting male adults.

A great many micro-moths are much more easily found by looking for their feeding signs. In some cases these will be leaf-mines (for example species 19 to 127), or holes in leaves (see, for example, 1150: *Epinotia abbreviana*). Others form galls whilst the frass (droppings) of some can be a giveaway sign of caterpillars inside fungi, under loose bark or in other less obvious places. Less obvious signs might include the disintegration of a reedmace seed head (a sign of probable feeding by larvae of 898: *Limnaecia phragmitella*) or a withered plant of Wood Sage that supports a larva of the plume moth 1494: *Capperia britanniodactyla*, amongst thousands of normal plants on the woodland floor. The easy availability of light traps, the tendency to shy away from specimen collecting and a degree of laziness on the part of naturalists who can't really be bothered with the fuss of breeding caterpillars through to determine what species they are from the adult have combined to render this type of field craft, and hence real entomologists, endangered. Very little can be learned from books; the only way is to go out in the field with others and learn from them.

Appendix 3. Moths in folklore, literature and humour

First to come in was a flying moth,
She laid out the tablecloth

From Froggy went a'courting
(Traditional)

There is an almost universal dislike of some animals, such as snakes, bats and spiders and a corresponding, but equally illogical, universal love of others, such as butterflies and some song birds. Moths, on the other hand, occupy a sort of middle ground. On the one hand they are creatures of the darkness, and so are probably evil; on the other hand they don't suck blood or give poisonous bites and so are probably harmless after all. It is interesting, therefore, to see how, and how frequently, moths get a mention in literature, poetry, music and other areas. Emily Bronte ends *Wuthering Heights* by giving the impression that she likes them ... "*I lingered around them, under that benign sky: watched the moths fluttering among the heath and harebells; listened to the soft wind breathing through the grass, and wondered how anyone could ever imagine unquiet slumbers for the sleepers in that quiet earth.*" On the other hand, Thomas Harris used the Death's-head Hawk Moth to suggest death by placing a chrysalis of the (albeit incorrectly identified) moth in the mouth of one of the victims of the serial killer Hannibal Lecter in his novel *The Silence of the Lambs*. Just for fun – here are some other aspects of moths!

First, it is interesting to note the application of the female gender to moths in the traditional *Froggy went a'courting*, above. It is unclear if moths were traditionally perceived as female (like cats, for example) or whether laying out the tablecloth was merely a task undertaken by females. In a great many poems and literary works, moths are consistently treated in a romantic vein and perhaps it is this romanticism that was the origin of the view that moths are female. Percy Bysshe Shelley in his 'One word is too often profaned' (1824) refers to:

The desire of the moth for the star,
Of the night for the morrow,
The devotion to something afar
From the sphere of our sorrow.

whilst twenty years later that other romantic poet Robert Browning, in his 1842 poem *In a Gondola*, says:

The moth's kiss, first!
Kiss me as if you made believe
You were not sure, this eve,
How my face, your flower, had pursed
Its petals up . . .
The bee's kiss, now!
Kiss me as if you entered gay
My heart at some noonday.

In spite of the sentiment in the Froggy went a'courting verse that moths came first there is no mention of moths in the book of Genesis, although the earliest mention of moths in literature probably is indeed in the bible. Moths actually get a rather bad press here; they are mentioned only as destroyers of things, including clothes. The book of Job, in Chapter 4, verse 19, clearly regards moths as dispensable when it says 'How much more those who live in houses of clay, whose foundations are in the dust, who are crushed more readily than a moth'. Isaiah (51:8) knows them only as pests when he says 'For the moth will eat them up like a garment; the worm will devour them like wool.' The New Testament chapters are scarcely better, with Matthew (6: 19) advising 'Do not store up for yourselves treasures on earth, where moth and rust destroy, and where thieves break in and steal'.

Moths were clearly in the minds of more recent writers. William Shakespeare deploys a moth in Othello, Act 1 Scene 3:

'*If I be left behind,*
A moth of peace, and he to go to the war,
The rites for which I love him are bereft me,
And I a heavy interim shall support
By his dear absence.
Let me go with him'

Whether troublesome pests or symbols of romanticism, moths are clearly a group of insects long known to people in general. It is not that surprising, therefore, to discover that knowledge of their metamorphosis from egg to adult, via caterpillar and then chrysalis, is also a matter of familiarity. One of my favourite references to this (even though it refers to a butterfly not a moth) can be found in *Alice's adventures in Wonderland* by Lewis Carol. Here, Alice is in conversation with a caterpillar:

'Alice replied very politely ... *being so many different sizes in a day is very confusing. It isn't*, said the Caterpillar. *Well, perhaps you haven't found it so yet,* said Alice; *but when you have to turn into a chrysalis – you will some day, you know – and then after that into a butterfly, I should think you'll feel it a little queer, won't you? Not a bit,* said the Caterpillar.

Moths have, it seems, worked their way into almost all aspects of human life even into politics. For example, on 30th June 2005, in a debate in the Upper House on the matter of decentralisation, Lord Kirkwood of Kirkhope stated

'*I will settle for conspiracy. It is a quintessentially British process: the metamorphosis from having been a green legislative caterpillar in the House of Commons to a red legislative moth here in the House of Peers*'.

The attractiveness of light to moths is also well documented. William Shakespeare has, in *The Merchant of Venice*:

Thus hath the candle sing'd the moth.

whilst more recently English poet and playwright John Gay has, in Act 4, Scene 4 of *The Beggar's Opera* (1728):

How, like a moth, the simple maid
Still plays about the flame!

The existence of moths in folklore and, consequently, the arts, is perhaps not really a surprise. Nor is this a phenomenon restriced to England. There is an (apparently old) Albanian proverb which I am reliably informed translates as:

He dreads a moth who has been stung by a wasp

Whilst there is, apparently, a Palestinian 'saying' that runs:

If only I were a bird! Ah, but eating caterpillars?

However, it is in humour that moths feature most prominently. In researching this section of the book I was only mildly surprised that the number of 'witticisms' received on the subject far outweighed the volume of artistic and literary references sent to me by various people. So – at the great risk of lowering the tone – here are some of said humourous items to close with.

One-Liners

What is a myth?
A female moth!

What do insects learn at school?
Mothmatics!

What's the biggest moth in the world?
A mammoth!

What do leaf-miners do on New Years day?
Promise to turn over a new leaf.

What is the definition of a caterpillar?
A worm in a fur coat!

If you have a moth-ball in each hand, what have you got?
- A very big moth.

How about the WW II moth – 'Turn that bloody light off'!

Especially for Clothes Moths ...

What insect lives on nothing?
A moth, because it eats holes.

Why do stones stop moths eating your clothes?
Because rolling stones gather no moths!

Why did the moth nibble a hole in the carpet?
He wanted to see the floor show!

Why was the moth so unpopular?
He kept picking holes in everything!

What do you get if you cross a firefly and a moth?
An insect who can find its way around a dark wardrobe!

Slightly longer ones ...

A man goes into a dentist's one evening.
'Can you help me I keep thinking I'm a moth!'
'You need to see a psychiatrist not me' replies the dentist
'I know' says the man 'but your light was on and I just couldn't resist coming in'.

A woman was having a passionate affair with an inspector from a pest-control company. One afternoon they were carrying on in the bedroom together when her husband arrived home unexpectedly. 'Quick' said the woman to her lover, 'into the closet!' and she pushed him in the closet, stark naked. The husband, however, became suspicious and after a search of the bedroom discovered the man in the closet. 'Who are you?' he asked him.' 'I'm an inspector from Bugs-B-Gone' said the exterminator. 'What are you doing in there?' the husband asked. 'I'm investigating a complaint about an infestation of clothes moths' the man replied. 'And where are your clothes? asked the husband. The man looked down at himself and said. 'Those little *******.'

Veteran Rocker Mick Jagger, singer with the Rolling Stones, was being interviewed for a rock music program on the radio when he accidentally let it slip that he used to collect butterflies as a child. The interviewer happened to be a moth enthusiast and quickly seized the opportunity to broaden the scope of the interview. Questions on butterflies were expertly answered by Jagger, to the amazement of the radio audience, who couldn't quite relate to the image of the aged rocker chasing around with a butterfly net. The interviewer expertly steered the discussion round to moths but was surprised that Mick had no interest in collecting moths. Pressed for a reason why, Jagger replied simply ... *everybody knows that a Rolling Stone gathers no moths*!

Limericks etc

I've just bought a fully trained moth
Who can swim like a fish in Scotch broth
To end his routine
He farts 'God save the Queen'
Has anyone here got a cloth?

If I were a caterpillar
life would be a farce,
I'd climb up all the leaves and trees
and slide down on my .. hands and knees!

And finally ... a clever one

The following appeared as a part of an obituary for Maitland Emmet and was penned by David Agassiz and John Langmaid (see British Journal of Entomology and Natural History **14**: 173 – 184). The following story is told entirely in the names of Lepidoptera as given by Kloet & Hincks (1972), and those of their authors, abbreviated where appropriate. The theme is 'incorrect combination' (which is also a taxonomic term!) and this is reflected in the nomenclature.

Impura, dissoluta adonis (Rich.) cautella, immaculatella, virginiensis.

"Hylas!"

"Imella".

Arte lecheana humerella, confusella:

"Mi nisella, decentella, udea splendididella".

Saucia, Elachista hermannella, oo, ciliella. Subsequana Frölich costella dia.

Nudaria prostratella (Bed.). *Impudens* Mann *lixella* (Tutt). *Degenerata* Coverd. *modestella. Grandipennis elongata, erectana verticalis, incerta abdominalis; piercella* (Forst.)*; servella* (Fuchs); *plumbella, upupana, ramella* (Cram.) *continuella Bjerk., faginella* (Fab.); *comes. Augasma saturatella. Genitalana Schrank psi. "Myella, io tenerella"* (Pey.). *Inconstans desertella* (Ratz.). *Hadena similella, rapae* Sod. *Adaina, Cynthia ausonia.*

Seqella bigella, rotundella, distentella Pod. *Pima suspecta quaestionella:*

"Nodosella or pilella!"

"Gnoma", sedella. "Unitella". "Ino angelicella", wailesella.

Desperatella Prays. Par fumatella Knaggs.

"Bena badiella, ignobilella, vilella, horridella, putridella, cinerella Haw.*".*

Dispar harrisella, canella, lambdella. Alienata, castigata, abjecta fugitivella. Gemina Hatch. *Pinella* (Constant). *Neglecta, solitariella, pallidella, siccella. Luzella* (Ob.) *Funerella. Terminella.*

Appendix 4: Scientific names of foodplants mentioned in the text

Common name	Scientific name
agrimony	*Agrimonia* spp.
Alder	*Alnus glutinosa*
Alder Buckthorn	*Frangula alnus*
Alder, Grey	*Alnus incana*
Almond	*Prunus dulcis*
Angelica	*Angelica sylvestris*
apple	*Malus* spp.
Apricot	*Prunus armeniaca*
Ash	*Fraxinus excelsior*
Aspen	*Populus tremula*
Barren Strawberry	*Potentilla sterilis*
Bastard Toadflax	*Thesium humifusum*
Bay	*Laurus nobilis*
Bearberry	*Arctostaphylos uva-ursi*
bedstraws	*Galium* spp.
Beech	*Fagus sylvatica*
Bell Heather	*Erica cinerea*
Betony	*Betonica officinalis*
Bilberry	*Vaccinium myrtillus*
Bindweed	*Convolvulus arvensis*
birch	*Betula* species
Bird's-foot trefoil	*Lotus corniculatus*
Bird-cherry	*Prunus padus*
Bittersweet	*Solanum dulcamara*
Black Bindweed	*Fallopia convolvulus*
Black Horehound	*Ballota nigra*
Black Mullein	*Verbascum nigrum*
Black Poplar	*Populus nigra*
Blackberry	*Rubus fruticosus* agg.
Blackcurrant	*Ribes nigrum*
Blackthorn	*Prunus spinosa*
Bladder Campion	*Silene vulgaris*
Bluebell	*Endymion non-scriptus*
Bog Stitchwort	*Stellaria alsine*
Bog-myrtle	*Myrica gale*
Bracken	*Pteridium aquilinum*
Bramble	*Rubus fruticosus* agg.
Bristly Ox-tongue	*Picris echioides*
Broad-leaved Dock	*Rumex obtusifolius*
Broad-leaved Willow-herb	*Epilobium montanum*
Broom	*Cytisus (= Sarothamnus) scoparius*
Brussels Sprouts	*Brassica oleracea* (variety)
Buckthorn	*Rhamnus catharticus*
Bugle	*Ajuga reptans*
Burdock, Great	*Arctium lappa*
Burnet Saxifrage	*Pimpinella saxifraga*
burnets	*Sanguisorba* spp.
bur-reeds	*Sparganium* spp.
Butterbur	*Petasites hybridus*
Cabbage	*Brassica oleracea*
Calamint	*Calamintha* spp.
campions	*Silene* spp.
Canary Grass	*Phalaris canariensis*
Carline Thistle	*Carlina vulgaris*
Carnation Grass	*Carex flacca*
carnations	*Dianthus* spp.
Cat's-ear	*Hypochaeris radicata*
Cauliflower	*Brassica oleracea* (variety)
Chamomile	*Matricaria recutita*
Cherry Plum	*Prunus cerasifera*
Chervil	*Chaerophyllum temulentum*
chickweeds	*Cerastium* spp.
cinquefoils	*Potentilla* spp.
Cleavers	*Galium aparine*
Cloudberry	*Rubus chamaemorus*
clovers	*Trifolium* spp.
club rushes	*Scirpus* spp.
Clustered Bellflower	*Campanula glomerata*
Cock's-foot Grass	*Dactylis glomerata*
Coltsfoot	*Tussilago farfara*
Common Centaury	*Centaurium pulchellum*
Common Club Rush	*Schoenoplectus(= Scirpus) lacustris*
Common Couch Grass	*Agropyron repens*
Common Cow-wheat	*Melampyrum pratense*
Common Fleabane	*Pulicaria dysenterica*
Common Gromwell	*Lithospermum officinale*
Common Hawthorn	*Crataegus monogyna*
Common Lime	*Tilia* X *europaea*
Common Melilot	*Melilotus officinalis*
Common Milkwort	*Polygala vulgaris*
Common Orache	*Atriplex patula*
Common Osier	*Salix viminalis*
Common Ragwort	*Senecio jacobaea*
Common Rock Rose	*Helianthemum nummularium*
Common Sallow	*Salix cinerea*
Common Skullcap	*Scutellaria galericulata*
Common Sorrel	*Rumex acetosa*
Common Spike-rush	*Eleocharis palustris*
Common Toadflax	*Linaria vulgaris*
Common Tormentil	*Potentilla erecta*
Common Valerian	*Valeriana officinalis*
Conglomerate Rush	*Juncus subuliflorus*
Corn Mint	*Mentha arvensis*
Corsican Pine	*Pinus nigra* var. *maritima*
Cotton Grass	*Eriophorum angustifolium*
Cow Parsley	*Anthriscus sylvestris*
Cowslip	*Primula veris*
Crab Apple	*Malus sylvestris*
Crack Willow	*Salix fragilis*
Creeping Thistle	*Cirsium arvense*
Creeping Thyme	*Thymus praecox*
Cross-leaved Heath	*Erica tetralix*
Curled Dock	*Rumex crispus*
Dame's Violet	*Hesperis matronalis*
Damson	*Prunus interstita*
Dandelion	*Taraxacum officinale* agg.
Dark Mullein	*Verbascum nigrum*
Deadly Nightshade	*Solanum nigra*
Devil's-bit Scabious	*Succisa pratensis*
Dewberry	*Rubus caesus*
docks	*Rumex* spp.
Dog Rose	*Rosa canina*
Dog Violet	*Viola canina*
Dogwood	*Cornus sanguinea*
Domestic Apple	*Malus domesticus*
Downy Birch	*Betula pubescens*
Dropwort	*Filipendula vulgaris*
duckweeds	*Lemna* spp.
Dwarf Gorse	*Ulex minor*
Dyer's Greenweed	*Genista tinctoria*
Eared Sallow	*Salix aurita*
Elder	*Sambucus nigra*
elm	*Ulmus* spp.
Enchanter's Nightshade	*Circaea lutetiana*
English Elm	*Ulmus procera*
English Oak	*Quercus robur*
False-brome	*Brachypodium sylvaticum*
fescues	*Festuca* spp.
Field Bindweed	*Calystegia sepium*
Field Maple	*Acer campestre*
Field Milk-thistle	*Sonchus arvensis*
Field Mouse-ear Chickweed	*Cerastium arvense*
Field Scabious	*Knautia arvensis*
Field Southernwood	*Artemisia campestris*
Field Speedwell	*Veronica officinalis*
Field Woodrush	*Luzula campestris*
fir	*Abies* sp.
Fleabane	*Pulicaria dysenterica*
Fool's Watercress	*Apium nodiflorum*
Foxglove	*Digitalis purpurea*
French Bean	*Phaseolus vulgaris*
Gallingale	*Cyperus longus*
Garden Barberry	*Berberis vulgaris*
Garden Blackcurrant	*Ribes nigrum*
Garden Hollyhock	*Alcea rosea*
Garden Lettuce	*Lactuca sativa*
Garden Mint	*Mentha spicata*
Gentian	*Gentiana* spp.
Germander Speedwell	*Veronica chamaedrys*
Giant Bellflower	*Campanula latifolia*
Gipsy-wort	*Lycopus europeus*
Goat Willow	*Salix caprea*
Golden Rod	*Solidago virgaurea*
Golden Samphire	*Inula crithmoides*
Gooseberry	*Ribes uva-crispa*
goosefoots	*Chenopodium* spp.
Gorse	*Ulex europaeus*
Great Burdock	*Arctium lappa*
Great Lettuce	*Lactuca virosa*
Great Mullein	*Verbascum thapsus*
Great Pond-sedge	*Carex riparia*
Great Sallow	*Salix caprea*
Great Willow-herb	*Epilobium hirsutum*
Greater Bindweed	*Calystegia sepium*
Greater Bird's-foot Trefoil	*Lotus uliginosus*
Greater Knapweed	*Centaurea scabiosa*
Greater Reedmace	*Typha latifolia*
Greater Stitchwort	*Stellaria holostea*
Grey Alder	*Alnus incana*
Grey Poplar	*Populus canescens*
Grey Willow	*Salix cinerea*
Ground Elder	*Aegopodium podagraria*
Ground Ivy	*Glechoma hederacea*
Groundsel	*Senecio vulgaris*
Guelder Rose	*Viburnum opulus*
Hairy Violet	*Viola hirta*
Hairy Willow-herb	*Epilobium hirsutum*
Hard Rush	*Juncus inflexus*
Hardheads	*Centaurea nigra*
Hart's-tongue Fern	*Phyllitis scolopendrium*
hawk's-beards	*Crepis* spp.
Hawkweed Ox-tongue	*Picris hieracioides*
hawkweeds	*Hieracium* spp.
hawthorn	*Crataegus* species
Hazel	*Corylus avellana*
Heath	*Erica* sp.
Heath Milkwort	*Polygala serpyllifolia*
Heather	*Calluna vulgaris*
Hedge Garlic	*Alliaria petiolata*
Hedge Woundwort	*Stachys sylvatica*
Hemlock	*Conium maculatum*
Hemp Agrimony	*Eupatorium cannabinum*
hemp-nettles	*Galeopsis* spp.
Herb Bennet	*Geum urbanum*
Himalayan Honeysuckle	*Leycesteria formosa*
Hoary Pepperwort	*Cardaria draba*
Hoary Rock Rose	*Helianthemum oelandicum*
Hogweed	*Heracleum sphondylium*
Holly	*Ilex aquifolium*
Holm Oak	*Quercus ilex*
Honeysuckle	*Lonicera periclymenum*
Hop	*Humulus lupulus*
Hornbeam	*Carpinus betulus*
Horse Chestnut	*Aesculus hippocastanum*
Horse-shoe Vetch	*Hippocrepis comosa*
Ice Plant	*Sedum spectabile*

Iris	*Iris* spp.
Italian Alder	*Alnus cordata*
Ivy	*Hedera helix*
Jointed Rush	*Juncus articulatus*
Juniper	*Juniperus communis*
Kidney Vetch	*Anthyllis vulneraria*
knapweeds	*Centaurea* spp.
Laburnum	*Laburnum anagyroides*
Lady's Smock	*Cardamine Pratensis*
Larch	*Larix decidua*
Large Bird's-foot trefoil	*Lotus uliginosus*
Lawson's Cypress	*Chamaecyparis lawsoniana*
Lawson's Cypress	*Chamaecyparis lawsonii*
Leek	*Allium ampeloprasum*
Lemon Geranium	*Pelargonium crispum*
Lesser Knapweed	*Centaurea nigra*
Lesser Pond Sedge	*Carex acutiformis*
Lesser Reedmace	*Typha angustifolia*
Lesser Skull-cap	*Scutellaria minor*
Lesser Stitchwort	*Stellaria graminea*
Leyland Cypress	*Chamaecyparis leylandii*
Lilac	*Syringa vulgaris*
lime	*Tilia* spp.
Lime, Street	*Tilia* X *europaea*
Loganberry	*Rubus* X *loganbaccus*
Lombardy Poplar	*Populus nigra italica*
Lousewort	*Pedicularis sylvatica*
Lupin	*Lupinus polyphyllus*
Male Fern	*Dryopteris filix-mas*
Mallow	*Malva* spp.
marigold	*Calendula* sp.
Marjoram	*Origanum vulgare*
Marsh Thistle	*Cirsium palustre*
Marsh Valerian	*Valeriana dioica*
Marsh Woundwort	*Stachys palustris*
Meadow Vetchling	*Lathyrus pratensis*
Meadowsweet	*Filipendula ulmaria*
melilots	*Melilotus* spp.
Midland Hawthorn	*Crataegus laevigata*
Mint, Corn	*Mentha arvensis*
Mint, Garden	*Mentha spicata*
Mint, Water	*Mentha aquatica*
mints	*Mentha* spp.
Monkshood	*Aconitum nepellum*
Mouse-ear Hawkweed	*Hieracium pilosella*
mouse-ears	*Cerastium* spp.
Mugwort	*Artemisia vulgare*
Mullein, Common	*Verbascum thapsus*
Mullein, Dark	*Verbascum nigrum*
Mullein, Great	*Verbascum thapsus*
Mung Bean	*Phaseolus aureus*
Musk Thistle	*Carduus nutans*
Nettle-leaved Bellflower	*Campanula trachelium*
Norway Maple	*Acer platanoides*
Norway Spruce	*Picea abies*
Nottingham Catchfly	*Silene nutans*
oak	*Quercus* species
oraches	*Atriplex* spp.
Orange Balsam	*Impatiens capensis3*
ornamental cherry	*Prunus* sp.
Orpine	*Sedum telephium*
Osier	*Salix viminalis*
Ox-eye Daisy	*Leucanthemum vulgare*
Oxford Ragwort	*Senecio squalida*
pea	*Pisum sativum*
Pear	*Pyrus communis*
Perennial Sow-thistle	*Sonchus arvensis*
Perforate St John's-wort	*Hypericum perforatum*
Petty Whin	*Genista anglica*
Pignut	*Conopodium majus*
pine	*Pinus* spp.
plantains	*Plantago* spp.
Ploughman's Spikenard	*Inula conyza*
Plum	*Prunus domesticus*
Pomegranate	*Punica granatum*
poplar	*Populus* species
Poplar, Grey	*Populus canescens*
Prickly Lettuce	*Lactuca serriola*
privet	*Ligustrum* spp.
Purple Toadflax	*Linaria purpurea*
quince	*Cydonia* spp.
Ragwort, Common	*Senecio jacobaea*
Ragwort, Oxford	*Senecio squalida*
Raspberry	*Rubus idaeus*
Rat-tail Plantain	*Plantago major*
Red Bartsia	*Odontites verna*
Red Campion	*Silene dioica*
Red Centaury	*Centaurium erythraea*
Red Clover	*Trifolium pratense*
Red Valerian	*Centranthus ruber*
Redcurrant	*Ribes rubrum*
Reed	*Phragmites australis*
Reed Canary-grass	*Phalaris canariensis*
Reed Sweet-grass	*Glyceria maxima*
Reed-grass	*Phalaris arundinacea*
restharrow	*Ononis* spp.
Ribbon Grass	*Phalaris arundinacea*
Ribwort Plantain	*Plantago lanceolata*
rock rose	*Helianthemum* spp.
rose	*Rosa* spp.
Rosebay Willow-herb	*Chamaenerion angustifolium*
Rough Chervil	*Chaerophyllum temulentum*
Rough Meadow Grass	*Poa trivialis*
Rowan	*Sorbus aucupariae*
Rugose Rose	*Rosa rugosa*
rushes	*Juncus* spp.
Sallow, Common	*Salix cinerea*
sallows	round-leaved species of *Salix*
Saw Sedge	*Cladium mariscus*
Saw-wort	*Serratula tinctoria*
Scabious, Devil's-bit	*Succisa pratensis*
Scabious, Small	*Scabiosa columbaria*
Scentless Mayweed	*Tripleurospermum inodorum*
Scots Pine	*Pinus sylvestris*
Sea Campion	*Silene maritima*
Sea Lavender	*Limonium vulgare*
Sea Rocket	*Cakile maritima*
Sea Wormwood	*Artemisia maritima*
sedges	*Carex* spp.
Sessile Oak	*Quercus petraea*
Sharp-flowered Rush	*Juncus acutiflorus*
Sheep's Sorrel	*Rumex acetosella*
Shepherd's-purse	*Capsella bursa-pastoris*
Silver Birch	*Betula pendula*
Silver Fir	*Abies alba*
Sitka Spruce	*Picea sitchensis*
Skullcap, Common	*Scutellaria galericulata*
Slender Bird's-foot trefoil	*Lotus tenuis*
Sloe	*Prunus spinosa*
Small Balsam	*Impatiens parviflora*
Small Scabious	*Scabiosa columbaria*
Sneezewort	*Achillea ptarmica*
Snowberry	*Symphoricarpos rivularis*
Soft Rush	*Juncus effusus*
sorrel	*Rumex* spp.
Sour Cherry	*Prunus cerasus*
Sow Thistle	*Sonchus* species
Spear Thistle	*Cirsium vulgare*
Spearmint	*Mentha spicata*
Spinach	*Spinacia oleracea*
Spindle	*Euonymus europaeus*
Spiny Restharrow	*Ononis spinosa*
spruce	*Picea* spp.
Square-stemmed Willow-herb	*Epilobium tetragonum*
St John's-wort	*Hypericum* spp.
Stinging Nettle	*Urtica dioica*
Stinking Mayweed	*Anthemis cotula*
stitchworts	*Stellaria* spp.
stonecrops	*Sedum* spp.
Strawberry	*Fragaria vesca*
Strawberry, Barren	*Potentilla sterilis*
Street Lime	*Tilia* X *platyphyllos*
Striped Ribbon Grass	*Phalaris arundinacea*
Sweet Chestnut	*Castanea sativa*
Sweet Vernal Grass	*Anthoxanthum odoratum*
Sweet William	*Dianthus barbatus*
Sycamore	*Acer pseudoplatanus*
Tall Fescue	*Festuca arundinacea*
Tamarisk	*Tamarix gallica*
Tansy	*Chrysanthemum vulgare*
Teasel	*Dipsacus fullonum*
thistles	*Cirsium* spp.
Thrift	*Armeria maritima*
Thyme, Wild	*Thymus drucei*
Tomato	*Lycopersicum esculentum*
Tormentil, Common	*Potentilla erecta*
Travellers Joy	*Clematis vitalba*
Tree Mallow	*Lavatera arborea*
Tufted Hair-grass	*Deschampsia cespitosa*
Upright Brome	*Bromus erectus*
vetches	*Viccia* spp.
water dropworts	*Oenanthe* spp.
Water Mint	*Mentha aquatica*
Wayfaring Tree	*Viburnum lantana*
Weeping Willow	*Salix babylonica*
White Bryony	*Bryonia dioica*
White Campion	*Silene alba*
White clover	*Trifolium repens*
White Horehound	*Marrubium vulgare*
White Mullein	*Verbascum thapsus*
White Poplar	*Populus alba*
White Willow	*Salix alba*
Whitebeam	*Sorbus aria*
Whitebeam	*Sorbus aria*
Wild Angelica	*Angelica sylvestris*
Wild Basil	*Clinopodium vulgare*
Wild Carrot	*Daucus carota*
Wild Cherry	*Prunus avium*
Wild Currant	*Ribes* sp.
Wild Honeysuckle	*Lonicera periclymenum*
Wild Parsnip	*Pastinaca sativa*
Wild Privet	*Ligustrum vulgare*
Wild Service	*Sorbus torminalis*
Wild Thyme	*Thymus drucei*
willows	long-leaved species of *Salix*
Winter Cress	*Barbarea vulgaris*
Wood Meadow-grass	*Poa nemoralis*
Wood Sage	*Teucrium scorodonia*
Wood Small-reed	*Calamagrostis epigejos*
Wood Spurge	*Euphorbia amygdaloides*
woodrush	*Luzula* spp.
Woody Nightshade	*Solanum dulcamara*
Wormwood	*Artemisia absinthium*
woundworts	*Stachys* spp.
Wych Elm	*Ulmus glabra*
Yarrow	*Achillea millefolium*
Yellow Water-lily	*Nuphar lutea*
Yellow-rattle	*Rhinanthus minor*
Yellow-wort	*Blackstonia perforata*

Appendix 5. References mentioned in the Species Accounts

Agassiz, D. J. L., 1982. *Oegoconia caradjai* Popescu-Gorj & C_pu_e (Lep.: Gelechiidae) recognised as British. *Proceedings and Transactions of the British Entomological and Natural History Society* **15**: 1 – 15.

Agassiz, D. J. L., 1996. *Invasions of Lepidoptera*. In Emmet, A. M. (Ed.) *Moths and butterflies of Great Britain and Ireland* **3**: 9 – 36 (Harley Books).

Agassiz, D. J. L., 1996b. Lepidoptera, Pyralidae, (China Mark) Moths. *In* Nilsson, A, N., *Aquatic insects of North Europe – A taxonomic handbook*. Apollo Books.

Agassiz, D. J. L. & Langmaid, J. R., 2004. The *Eucosma hohenwartiana* group of species (Tortricidae). *Nota Lepidopterologica* **27**(1): 41 – 49.

Agassiz, D. J. L. & Spice, W. M., 1998. The return of the Small Ranunculus. *Entomologist's Rec. J. Var.* **110**: 229 – 232.

Agassiz, D. J. L. & Tuck, K. R., 1999. The Cypress Tip Moth *Argyresthia cupressella* Walsingham, 1890 (Lepidoptera: Yponomeutidae) new to Britain. *Entomologist's Gazette* **50**: 11 – 16.

Agassiz, D. J. L., 2003. The names of Engrailed moths (Geometridae). *Entomologist's Rec. J. Var.* **115**: 223.

Allan, P. B. M., 1950. The macrolepidoptera of Bishop's Stortford and district. *Transactions of the Bishop's Stortford Natural History Society*. **1**(1): 1 – 45.

Anderson, S. J., Gould, P. & Freeland, J. R., 2007. Repetitive Flanking Sequences (ReFS): novel molecular markers from microsatellite families. *Molecular Ecology Notes* **7**: 374 – 376.

Arnold, V. W., Baker, C. R. B., Manning, D. V. & Woiwod, I. P., 1997. *The butterflies and moths of Bedfordshire*. Bedfordshire Natural History Society.

Baldizzone, G., Van der Wolf, H. & Landry, J. - F., 2006. *World Catalogue of Insects, volume 8: Coleophoridae, Coleophorinae (Lepidoptera)*. Apollo Books.

Bankes, E. R., 1910. *Monopis weaverella*, Scott (n. syn. = *semispilotella*, Strand), specifically distinct from *M. rusticella* Hb. *Entomologist's Monthly Magazine* **46**: 221 – 228 and plate.

Bankes, E. R., 1912. Stray notes on *Monopis crocicapitella*, Clms., and *M. ferruginella* Hb. *Entomologist's Monthly Magazine* **48**: 39 – 44 and plate.

Barraud, P. J., 1903. Notes on Lepidoptera observed in Hertfordshire in the year 1902. *Transactions of the Hertfordshire Natural History Society and Field Club* **12**: 21 – 25.

Barrett, C. G. 1893 – 1907. *The Lepidoptera of the British Islands*. Volumes 1 – viii.

Beirne, B. P., 1952. British pyralid and plume moths. Warne.

Bell, P. J., 1952. Report on Lepidoptera observed in Hertfordshire in 1948 and 1949. *Transactions of the Hertfordshire Natural History Society and Field Club* **23**(5): 230 – 233.

Bell, P. J., 1953. Report on Lepidoptera observed in Hertfordshire in 1950 and 1951. *Transactions of the Hertfordshire Natural History Society and Field Club* **24**(1): 31 – 34.

Bell, P. J., 1954. Report on Lepidoptera observed in Hertfordshire in 1952. *Transactions of the Hertfordshire Natural History Society and Field Club* **24**(2): 72 – 72.

Bell, P. J., 1955. Report on Lepidoptera observed in Hertfordshire in 1953. *Transactions of the Hertfordshire Natural History Society and Field Club* **24**(4): 134 – 135.

Bell, P. J., 1956. Report on Lepidoptera observed in Hertfordshire in 1954. *Transactions of the Hertfordshire Natural History Society and Field Club* **24**(5): 188 – 189.

Bell, P. J., 1957. Report on Lepidoptera observed in Hertfordshire in 1955. *Transactions of the Hertfordshire Natural History Society and Field Club* **24**(6): 224 – 225.

Bell, P. J., 1958. Report on Lepidoptera observed in Hertfordshire in 1956. *Transactions of the Hertfordshire Natural History Society and Field Club* **25**(1): 27 – 28.

Bell, P. J., 1959. Report on Lepidoptera observed in Hertfordshire in 1957. *Transactions of the Hertfordshire Natural History Society and Field Club* **25**(2): 64 – 65.

Bell, P. J., 1960. Report on Lepidoptera observed in Hertfordshire in 1958. *Transactions of the Hertfordshire Natural History Society and Field Club* **25**(3): 93 .

Bell, P. J., 1961. Report on the Lepidoptera observed in Hertfordshire in 1959. *Transactions of the Hertfordshire Natural History Society and Field Club* **25**(5): 193 – 194.

Bell, P. J., 1962. Report on the Lepidoptera observed in Hertfordshire in 1960. *Transactions of the Hertfordshire Natural History Society and Field Club* **25**(4): 161 – 163.

Bell, P. J., 1964. Report on the Lepidoptera observed in Hertfordshire in 1961, 1962 and 1963. *Transactions of the Hertfordshire Natural History Society and Field Club* **26**(1): 31 – 33.

Bell, P. J., 1966. Report of the recorder for Lepidoptera for 1964 and 1965. *Transactions of the Hertfordshire Natural History Society and Field Club* **26**(3): 140 – 142.

Bell, P. J., 1969. Report on Herts. macrolepidoptera, 1966 to 1968. *Transactions of the Hertfordshire Natural History Society and Field Club* **27**(1): 21 – 22.

Bell, P. [J.], 1970. Macrolepidoptera in 1969. *Transactions of the Hertfordshire Natural History Society and Field Club* **27** (2): 72 – 73.

Bell, P. [J.], 1971. Macrolepidoptera in 1970. *Transactions of the Hertfordshire Natural History Society and Field Club* **27** (3): 108 – 109.

Bell, P. [J.], 1972. Macrolepidoptera in 1971. *Transactions of the Hertfordshire Natural History Society and Field Club* **27** (4): 207 – 208.

Bell, P. [J.], 1972. Macrolepidoptera in 1972. *Transactions of the Hertfordshire Natural History Society and Field Club* **27**(5): 229 – 231.

Bell, P. [J.], 1972. Macrolepidoptera of Herts — 1973 – 1976. *Transactions of the Hertfordshire Natural History Society and Field Club* **28**(1): 29 – 33.

Bowyer, R. W., 1888. Some methods of moth collecting. *Transactions of the Hertfordshire Natural History Society and Field Club* **5**: 23 [contains the first list of Macrolepidoptera of Haileybury School].

Boyd, W. C., 1868. *Entomologist's Monthly Magazine* **5**: 147.

Boyd, W. C., 1901. List of the Lepidoptera of Cheshunt and its neighbourhood. *Transactions of the Hertfordshire Natural History Society and Field Club* **11**: 75 – 86.

Bradley, J. D., 1951. A comparative study of four European species, including one new species from Britain, belonging to the genus *Mompha* Huebner (Lepidoptera; Lavernidae). *Entomologist's Gazette*. **2**: 173 – 182 & plate.

Bradley, J.D., 2000. Checklist of Lepidoptera recorded from the British Isles. Privately published.

Bradley, J. D. and Fletcher, D. S., 1979. A recorder's log book or label list of British butterflies and moths. Curwen Books.

Bradley, J. D., Tremewan, W. G. & Smith, A., 1973. *British Tortricoid Moths*. Volume 1. Ray Society.

Bradley, J. D., Tremewan, W. G. & Smith, A., 1979. *British Tortricoid Moths*. Volume 2. Ray Society.

Bretherton, R.F., Goater, B. & Lorimer, R. I., 1983. Noctuidae (continued) in Heath, J. & Emmet, A. M. (Eds.). *Moths and Butterflies of Great Britain and Ireland* volume 10. Harley Books.

Buckell, M. B. & Prout, L. B., 1898 – 1901. The fauna of the London district. Lepidoptera. *Transactions of the City of London Entomological and Natural Hitory Society* **8**: 51 – 63; **9**: 66 – 80; **10**: 62 – 74.

Burton, R. M., 1994. Watsonian vice-county boundaries in the London Area. *London Naturalist* **73**: 199 – 214.

Clancy, S. P. & Parsons, M. S., 1999. *Vitula biviella* Zell.: A pyralid new to Britain and Ireland. *Atropos* number 7: 43 – 44.

Classey, E. W., 1998. *Unfinished Business. A Supplement to the Lepidoptera of the Orkney Islands.* Hedera Press.

Cockerell, T. D. A., 1891 – 1892. A preliminary list of the insect fauna of Middlesex: Lepidoptera. *Entomologist* **24**: 65 – 69, 119 – 121, 139 – 143, 156 – 160, 280 – 283 and **25**: 115 – 118, 130 – 134, 182 – 185, 203 – 207.

Collins, G. A., 1997. *Larger Moths of Surrey*. Surrey Wildlife Trust.

Collins, G. A. & Porter, J., 2005. *Elachista nobilella* Zeller, 1839 (Lep.: Elachistidae), a micro-moth new to Britain. *Entomologist's Record & Journal of Variation* **117**: 133 – 137.

Cottam, A., 1901. Notes on Lepidoptera observed in western Hertfordshire in 1897, 1898 and 1899. *Transactions of the Hertfordshire Natural History Society and Field Club* **10**: 185 – 190.

Cottam, A., 1903. Notes on the habits of some of our lepidopterous insects. *Transactions of the Hertfordshire Natural History Society and Field Club***12**: 53 – 61.

Curtis, S. C., 1878. Parasites of *Dicranura vinula*. *Entomologist* **11**: 251 – 252.

de Worms, C. G. M., 1954 -1958. The moths of London and its surroundings. *London Naturalist* **33**: 101 – 146; **34**: 66 – 107; **35**: 33 – 76; **36**: 59 – 99; **37**: 136 – 178.

de Worms, C. G. M., 1964. A review of the macrolepidoptera of the London Area for 1962 and 1963. *London Naturalist* **43**: 26 – 33.

de Worms, C. G. M., 1966. A review of the macrolepidoptera of the London Area for 1964 and 1965. *London Naturalist* **45**: 89 – 97.

de Worms, C. G. M., 1969. Resumé of the macrolepidoptera of the London Area for 1966 and 1967. *London Naturalist* **48**: 121 – 124. .

de Worms, C. G. M., 1970. A review of the macrolepidoptera of the London Area for 1968 and 1969. *London Naturalist* **49**: 82 – 89.

de Worms, C. G. M., 1972. A review of the macrolepidoptera of the London Area for 1970 and 1971. *London Naturalist* **51**: 28 – 38.

de Worms, C. G. M., 1974. A review of the macrolepidoptera of the London Area for 1972 and 1973. *London Naturalist* **53**: 86 – 99.

de Worms, C. G. M., 1976. A review of the macrolepidoptera of the London Area for 1974 and 1975. *London Naturalist* **55**: 48 – 57.

de Worms, C. G. M., 1978. A review of the macrolepidoptera of the London Area for 1976 and 1977. *London Naturalist* **57**: 81 – 90.

Durrant, J. H., 1885. List of Lepidoptera observed in the neighbourhood of Hitchin and at Knebworth, Herts. *Transactions of the Hertfordshire Natural History Society and Field Club* **3**: 261 – 265 & Appendix by A. F. Griffith on page 266.

Durrant, J. H., 1888. Contributions to the knowledge of the entomological fauna of Hertfordshire. No. 1 – Lepidoptera. *Transactions of the Hertfordshire Natural History Society and Field Club* **5**: 63 – 75.

Emmet, A. M., 1983. Exhibits – meeting of 11 November 1982. *Proceedings and Transactions of the British Entomological and Natural History Society* **16**: 58.

Emmet, A. M., 1986. *Parornix carpinella* (Frey, 1863) a distinct species from *P. fagivora* (Frey, 1861). *Entomologist's Record & Journal of Variation* **98**: 144 – 146.

Emmet, A. M., 1991. The scientific names of the British Lepidoptera: Their history and meaning. Harley Books.

Emmet, A. M., 1991a. Chart showing the life history and habits of the British Lepidoptera. In Emmet, A. M. & Heath, J. (Eds.). The moths and butterflies of Great Britain and Ireland. Volume 7, part 2: 61 – 303.

Emmet, A. M. & Pyman, G. A., 1985. The larger moths and butterflies of Essex. *Essex Naturalist* number 8. 1 – 136.

Fletcher, D. S., 1968. *Amphipyra pyramidea* (Linnaeus) and *A. berbera* Rungs (Lep.: Noctuidae), two species confused. *Entomologist's Gazette* **19**: 91 – 106 & Plates.

Foster, A. H., 1916. A list of macro-Lepidoptera occurring in North Hertfordshire, with notes on each species. *Transactions of the Hertfordshire Natural History Society and Field Club* **16**: 237 – 258.

Foster, A. H., 1934. *Section Lepidoptera* in *Natural History of Hitchin Region*.

Foster, A. H., 1937. A list of the Lepidoptera of Hertfordshire. *Transactions of the Hertfordshire Natural History Society and Field Club* **20** (4): 157 – 279.

Foster, A. H., 1940. Hertfordshire Lepidoptera: Delenda, addenda and corrigenda. *Transactions of the Hertfordshire Natural History Society and Field Club* **21** (2): 173 – 174.

Foster, A. H., 1941. Hertfordshire Lepidoptera: Further addenda and corrigenda. *Transactions of the Hertfordshire Natural History Society and Field Club* **21** (4): 272 – 276.

Foster, A. H., 1942. Hertfordshire Lepidoptera. New species and other addenda to the list. *Transactions of the Hertfordshire Natural History Society and Field Club* **21** (5): 308 – 310.

Foster, A. H., 1944. Addenda to list of Hertfordshire Lepidoptera. *Transactions of the Hertfordshire Natural History Society and Field Club* **22** (2): 40 – 42.

Foster, A. H., 1945. Addenda to list of Hertfordshire Lepidoptera. v. *Transactions of the Hertfordshire Natural History Society and Field Club* **22** (3): 84 – 86.

Foster, A. H., 1945a. Report on Lepidoptera in Hertfordshire for 1945. *Transactions of the Hertfordshire Natural History Society and Field Club***22** (4): 125 – 129.

Fryer, J., 1948. Report on Lepidoptera observed in Hertfordshire, mostly in1946. *Transactions of the Hertfordshire Natural History Society and Field Club* **23** (1): 17 – 20.

Fryer, J., 1948. Report on Lepidoptera observed in Hertfordshire in 1947. *Transactions of the Hertfordshire Natural History Society and Field Club* **23** (13): 86 – 88.

Gibbs, A. E., 1889. Some notes on the Lepidoptera of St Albans and its neighbourhood. *Transactions of the Hertfordshire Natural History Society and Field Club* **5** (13): 181 – 186.

Gibbs, A. E., 1893. Notes on Lepidoptera observed in Hertfordshire *Transactions of the Hertfordshire Natural History Society and Field Club* **7**: 187 – 198.

Gibbs, A. E., 1896. Notes on Lepidoptera observed in Hertfordshire during the year 1893. *Transactions of the Hertfordshire Natural History Society and Field Club* **8**: 74 – 84.

Gibbs, A. E., 1896a. Notes on Lepidoptera observed in Hertfordshire during the year 1895. *Transactions of the Hertfordshire Natural History Society and Field Club* **9**: 27 – 32.

Gibbs, A. E., 1901. Notes on Lepidoptera observed in Hertfordshire during the year 1900. *Transactions of the Hertfordshire Natural History Society and Field Club* **11**: 43 – 45.

Gibbs, A. E., 1902. *Lepidoptera (Butterflies and Moths)*. In: Page, W., *The Victoria History of the County of Hertford*, volume 1. 110 – 168. Archibald Constable.

Gibbs, A. E., 1904. Notes on Lepidoptera observed in Hertfordshire during the year 1903. *Transactions of the Hertfordshire Natural History Society and Field Club* **12**: 109 – 116.

Gibbs, A. E., 1905. Notes on Lepidoptera observed in Hertfordshire during the year 1904. *Transactions of the Hertfordshire Natural History Society and Field Club* **12**: 159 – 164.

Gibbs, A. E., 1906. Notes on Lepidoptera observed in Hertfordshire during the year 1905. *Transactions of the Hertfordshire Natural History Society and Field Club* **13**: 5 – 9.

Gibbs, A. E., 1907. Notes on Lepidoptera observed in Hertfordshire during the year 1906. *Transactions of the Hertfordshire Natural History Society and Field Club* **13**: 199 – 204.

Gibbs, A. E., 1907a. Notes on Lepidoptera observed in Hertfordshire in the year 1907. *Transactions of the Hertfordshire Natural History Society and Field Club* **14**: 45 – 48.

Gibbs, A. E., 1909. St Albans and its neighbourhood. Lepidoptera. *Transactions of the Hertfordshire Natural History Society and Field Club* **14**: 236 – 238.

Goater, B., Ronkay, L. & Fibiger, M., 2003. *Noctuidae Europaeae. Volume 10: Catocalinae & Plusiinae*. Entomological Press.

Goodey, B., 2004. *The Moths of Essex*. Lopinga Books.

Gould, P. J. L., 2005. Five new records of the Autumnal Snout *Schrankia intermedialis* Reid (Lep.: Noctuidae) from Devon. *Entomologist's Rec. J. Var.* **117**: 139 – 140.

Gould, P. J. L., 2006. Further evidence of a second generation of *Chrysoteuchia culmella* (L.) (Lep.: Pyralidae) in Hertfordshire. *Entomologist's Record & Journal of Variation* **118**: 228 – 229.

Gould, P. J. L., 2007.Confirmation of the hybrid status of the Autumnal Snout *Schrankia intermedialis* Reid (Lep.: Noctuidae). *Entomologist's Record & Journal of Variation* **119**: 193 – 194.

Gould, P. J. L., 2007a.A fourth Hertfordshire (VC20) record of the Apple Pith Moth *Blastodacna atra* (Haworth(Lep.: Agonoxenidae). *Entomologist's Record & Journal of Variation* **119**: 212.

Griffith, A. F., 1884. *Notes on Lepidoptera observed in the neighbourhood of Sandridge*. *Transactions of the Hertfordshire Natural History Society and Field Club***3**: 58 – 66.

Griffith, A. F., 1890. Notes on Tineina and other Lepidoptera observed in the neighbourhood of Sandridge, Herts. *Transactions of the Hertfordshire Natural History Society and Field Club***6**: 97 – 102.

Hall, P., McVeigh, A. & Albertini, M., 2006. The Striped Lychnis Moth *Shargacucullia lychnitis* (Rambur) (Lep.: Noctuidae): A review of its distribution in Buckinghamshire (VC 24) during 2005. *Entomologist's Rec. J. Var.* **118**: 97 – 102.

Harper, M. W., 1990. *Batia internella* Jäckh (Lepidoptera: Oecophoridae) new to Britain. *Entomologist's Gazette* **41**: 99 – 101.

Higgott, J. B., 2006. *Emmelina argoteles* (Meyrick, 1922) (Lep.: Pterophoridae) – a newly recognised British plume moth. *Entomologist's Record & Journal of Variation* **118**: 195 – 197.

Hodgson, S. B.,1939. Macro-Lepidoptera in west Hertfordshire. *Transactions of the Hertfordshire Natural History Society and Field Club* **21**(1): 71 – 89.

Hodgson, S. B., 1943. The Grey Scalloped Bar Moth (*Crocata belgaria*) in Hertfordshire. *Transactions of the Hertfordshire Natural History Society and Field Club* **21**(6): 345.

Hodgson, S. B., 1944. Lepidoptera in west Hertfordshire in 1943. *Transactions of the Hertfordshire Natural History Society and Field Club* **22**(2): 54 – 55.

Hodson, L. S., 1939. Notes on the Lepidoptera of the Hatfield district in 1937 and 1938. *Transactions of the Hertfordshire Natural History Society and Field Club* **21**(1): 69 – 70.

Jackson, A. C., 1965. The macrolepidoptera of the South Herts. Plateau: Some selected records and an appeal to members. *Lond. Nat.* **44**: 73 – 76.

Jermyn, S. T., 1974. *Flora of Essex*. Essex Naturalists Trust.

Johansson, R., Nielsen, E. S., van Nieurkerken, E. J. & Gustafsson, B., 1990. The Nepticulidae and Opostegidae (Lepidoptera) of North West Europe. *Fauna Entomologica Scandinavica* **23**: parts 1 and 2. Brill, Leiden.

Kaila, L., Bengtsson, B, A., _ulcs, I. & Junnilainen, J., 2001. A revision of the *Elachista regificella* Sircom -complex (Lepidoptera: Elachistidae. *Entomologica Fennica* **12**: 153 – 168.

Kaila, L. & Langmaid, J. R., 2005. The *Elachista regificella* Sircom complex (Lep.: Elachistidae) in Britain. *Entomologist's Record & Journal of Variation* **117**: 187 – 193.

Karsholt, O., Aarvik, L., Agassiz, D., Huemer, P. & Tuck, K., 2005. *Acleris effractana* (Hübner, 1799) – a Holarctic Tortricid. *Nota Lepidopterologica* **28**(2): 93 – 102.

Knaggs, H. G., 1866. Notes on the British Lepidoptera for 1865. *Entomologists' Annual* **1866**: 139.

Koster, S. J. C. & Sinev, S. Y., 2003. Momphidae, Batrachedridae, Stathmopodidae, Agonoxenidae, Cosmopterigidae, Chrysopeleiidae. In Huemer, P., Karsholt, O. & Lyneborg, L., 2003. *Microlepidoptera of Europe*. Apollo Books.

Leech, J. H.,1886. *British Pyralides, including the Pterophoridae*. London

Manning, D., 2001. *Chrysoteuchia culmella* (L.) (Lep.: Pyralidae) flight period. *Entomologist's Record and Journal of Variation* **113**: 70.

McGavin, G.C., 2001. *Essential Entomology.* Oxford University Press.

Mentzer, E. von, Moberg, A. & Fibiger, M., 1991. *Noctua janthina* ([Denis & Schiffermüller]) sensu auctorum a complex of three species (Lepidoptera: Noctuidae). *Nota Lepidopterologica* **14**: 25 – 40.

Mironov, V., 2003. *Larentiini II. (Perizomini and Eupitheciini).* In Hausmann, A. (Ed.) *The Geometrid Moths of Europe* **4**: 1 – 463. Apollo Books.

Murray, D., 2007. *Scythris potentillella* (Zeller) (Lep.: Scythrididae) new to Hertfordshire. *Entomologist's Record and Journal of Variation* **119**: 71.

Nash, D. R., Agassiz, D. J.L., Godfray, H. C. J. & Lawton, J. H., 1995. The pattern of spread of invading species: two leaf-mining moths colonising Great Britain. *Journal of Animal Ecology* **64**: 225 – 233.

Ormerod, E. A., 1884. Notes on insects observed in Hertfordshire in 1882. *Transactions of the Hertfordshire Natural History Society and Field Club* **2**: 187 – 188.

Parsons, M. S., 1993. *A review of the scarce and threatened pyralid moths of Great Britain.* UK Nature Conservation, number 11. JNCC.

Parsons, M. S., 1995. *A review of the scarce and threatened ethmiine, stathmopodine and gelechiid moths of Great Britain.* UK Nature Conservation, number 16. JNCC.

Parsons, M. S., Hoare, D., Davis, T. & Green, D., 2005. The distribution of the UK Biodiversity Action Plan Priority Moth Species, 1999 – 2004. *Atropos* **25**: 5 – 20.

Penrose, R. J., 1980. Butterflies and moths at Watford 1948 – 1962. *Transactions of the Hertfordshire Natural History Society and Field Club* **28**(3): 92 – 100.

Pierce, F. N., 1917. Occurrence in England of *Parornix finitimella* Z., a species of Gracillariidae new to the British list. *Entomologist's Monthly Magazine* **53**: 9 – 10.

Pierce, F. N. & Metcalfe, J. W., 1935. The genitalia of the tineid families of the Lepidoptera of the British Isles. No longer in print but available form second-hand booksellers.

Plant, C. W., 1983. A review of the Lepidoptera of the London Area for 1981 and 1982. *London Naturalist.* **62**: 116 – 125.

Plant, C. W., 1985. A review of the Lepidoptera of the London Area for 1983 and 1984. *London Naturalist* **64**: 45 – 62.

Plant, C. W., 1987. A review of the Lepidoptera of the London Area for 1985 and 1986. *London Naturalist* **66**: 135 – 156.

Plant, C. W., 1989. A review of the Lepidoptera of the London Area for 1987 and 1988. *London Naturalist* **68**: 89 – 107.

Plant, C. W., 1994. *Provisional Atlas of the Neuroptera, Megaloptera, Raphidioptera and Mecoptera of the British Isles.* Huntingdon, Institute of Terrestrial Ecology.

Plant, C. W., 1994a. A map of the surface geology of the London Area. *London Naturalist* **73**: 215 - 220 & map.

Plant, C. W., 1995. A review of the butterflies and larger moths of the London Area for 1992 - 1994. *London Naturalist* **74**: 145 – 157.

Plant, C. W., 1997. A review of the butterflies and moths (Lepidoptera) of the London Area for 1995 and 1996. *London Naturalist* **76**: 157 – 174.

Plant, C. W., 1999. A review of the butterflies and moths (Lepidoptera) of the London Area for 1997 and 1998. *London Naturalist* **78**: 147 – 171.

Plant, C. W., 2000. *Chrysoteuchia culmella* (L.) (Lep.: Pyralidae) captured in September. *Entomologist's Record and Journal of Variation* **112**: 272.

Plant, C. W., 2002. Invasion of the Dotted Chestnuts *Conistra rubiginea* (D.& S.). *Entomologist's Record and Journal of Variation* **114**: 130.

Plant, C. W., 2002a. The Beautiful Snout *Hypena crassalis* (Fabr.) (Lep.: Noctuidae) taken in Hertfordshire with a note on the doubtful status of some alleged larval host plants. *Entomologist's Record and Journal of Variation* **114**: 159 – 160.

Plant, C. W., 2002b. Moths and moth recording in Hertfordshire. *Transactions of the Hertfordshire Natural History Society* **34** (1): 89 – 125.

Plant, C. W., 2003. Clearwing pheromones – useful for recording Tortricidae! *Entomologist's Record and Journal of Variation* **115**: 42.

Plant, C. W., 2004. The Straw Dot moth *Rivula sericealis* (Scop.) (Lep.: Noctuidae): how many broods? *Entomologist's Record and Journal of Variation* **116**: 32 – 36.

Plant, C. W., 2004a. The lost moths of Hertfordshire. *Trans. Hertfordshire Natural History Society* **36**(1): 47 – 68.

Plant, C. W., 2005. Separation of Red Twin-spot *Xanthorhoe spadicearia* (D.& S.) and Dark-barred Twin-spot Carpet (*Xanthorhoe ferrugata* (CL.) (Lep.: Geometridae). *Entomologist's Record and Journal of Variation* **117**: 177 – 180.

Pratt, C., 1986. A modern review of the demise of *Hecatera dysodea* D.& S.: the Small Ranunculus. *Entomologist's Record and Journal of Variation* **98**: 70 – 78; 114 – 118; 154 – 158.

Prout, L. B., 1902. The fauna of the London district: Lepidoptera. Supplement. *Transactions of the City of London Entomological and Natural Hitory Society* **8**: 51 – 63; **9**: 66 – 80; **10**: 62 – 74.

Riley, A. M., 1991. *Eupithecia ultimaria* Boisduval (Lepidoptera: Geometridae): a third record for the British Isles and the first mainland capture. *Entomologist's Gazette* **42**: 289 – 290.

Riley, A. M., 1986. *Hypena crassalis* Fabricius (Lep.: Noctuidae), the Beautiful Snout, in Hertfordshire. *Entomologist's Record and Journal of Variation* **98**: 213.

Riley, A. M., 1999. The macrolepidoptera of the Rothamsted Estate, Harpenden, Hertfordshire. *Entomologist's Record and Journal of Variation* **111**: 71 – 94.

Riley, A. M. & Prior, G., 2003. *British and Irish pug moths: A guide to their identification and biology.* Harley Books.

Robinson, G. S., 1979. Clothes moths of the *Tinea pellionella* complex: A revision of the world's species (Lepidoptera: Tineidae). *Bulletin of the British Museum (Natural History): Entomology* **38**: 57 – 128 and figures.

Ronkay, L., Yela, J. L. & Hreblay, M, 2001. *Noctuidae Europaeae, volume 5: Hadeninae II.* Entomological Press.

Rowland-Brown, H., 1893. On the Middlesex north border, 1892. *Entomologist* **26**: 57 – 58.

Silvester, F. W., 1885. Report on insects observed in Hertfordshire during the year 1885. *Transactions of the Hertfordshire Natural History Society and Field Club* **4**: 49 – 52.

Skinner, B., 1984. *The colour identification guide to moths of the British Isles.* Viking.

Skinner, B., 1998. *The colour identification guide to moths of the British Isles.* Viking. Revised edition.

Skinner, B., 2004. Notes on Dark Crimson Underwing *Catocala sponsa* and Light Crimson Underwing *C. promissa* as possible immigrants. *Atropos* **24**: 7 – 8.

Skou, P., 1986. The Geometroid Moths of North Europe. Brill/Scandinavian Science Press.

South, R. 1907. *The moths of the British Isles.* Warne.

South, R. 1920. *The moths of the British Isles.* New edition. Warne.

South, R. 1939. *The moths of the British Isles.* New edition. Warne.

South, R. 1961. *The moths of the British Isles.* New edition. Warne.

Spencer, S. H., 1897. Notes on Lepidoptera observed in the neighbourhood of Watford in 1896. *Transactions of the Hertfordshire Natural History Society and Field Club***9**: 236 – 240.

Stephens, J. F., 1828, 1829 & 1834. *Illustrations of British Entomology, "Haustellata".* Volumes 1 – 4.

Sterling, P. H. & Costen, P, D. M., 2007. Water Betony *Shargacucullia scrophulariae* (D.& S.) (Lep.: Noctuidae) new to the Channel Islands. *Record & Journal of Variation* **119**: 97 – 102.

Thomasson, A. J. & Avery, B. W., 1963. The soils of Hertfordshire. *Transactions of the Hertfordshire Natural History Society and Field Club* **25**(6): 247 – 263, plus fold-out colour map.

Townsend, M. C., 1994. *Spargania luctuata* (Denis & Schiffermüller) White-banded Carpet (Lep.: Geometridae) new to Hertfordshire. *Entomologist's Record & Journal of Variation* **106**: 151.

Townsend, M. C., & Riley, A.M., 1992. *Eupithecia sinuosaria* Eversmann (Lep.: Geometridae) in Hertfordshire. The second British record. *Entomologist's Record & Journal of Variation* **104**: 323.

Tutt, J. W., 1891 – 1892. *The British Noctuae and their varieties* **1 – 4**. London.

Wakely, S., 1947. Occurrence of a species of *Blastobasis* resembling *decolorella* Wollaston in South London. *Proceedings and Transactions of the South London Entomological and Natural History Society.* **1947-1948**: 205 – 208.

Waterton, P., 1979. Lepidoptera report 1977. *Transactions of the Hertfordshire Natural History Society and Field Club* **28**(2): 7 – 8.

Waterton, P., 1980. Lepidoptera report 1978. *Transactions of the Hertfordshire Natural History Society and Field Club* **28**(3): 7 – 8.

Waterton, P., 1981. Lepidoptera report. *Transactions of the Hertfordshire Natural History Society and Field Club* **28**(4): 9 – 10.

Waterton, P., 1982. Lepidoptera report 1980. *Transactions of the Hertfordshire Natural History Society and Field Club* **28**(6): 33 – 34.

Waterton, P., 1983. Lepidoptera report 1981. *Transactions of the Hertfordshire Natural History Society and Field Club* **29**(1): 19 – 20.

West, B. K., 2004. The Brimstone Moth *Opisthograptis luteolata* (L.) (Lep.: Geometridae). Comments on the early generation. *Entomologist's Record & Journal of Variation* **116**: 226 – 227.

Willis, J. J., 1882. *Transactions of the Hertfordshire Natural History Society and Field Club* **2**: 241.

Winter, P. Q., 1988. An additional aid to the identification of *Amphipyra pyramidea* (L.) and *A. berbera svenssoni* (Fletcher) (Lepidoptera: Noctuidae). *British Journal of Entomology and Natural History* **1**: 97 – 99.

Young, M., 1991. In Heath, J. & Emmet, A. M. (Eds.). *Moths and Butterflies of Great Britain & Ireland*, volume 7. Harley Books.

Appendix 6: Photo credits and copyright information

The photographs of moths and their early stages, cases, leaf mines etc used in the species section of this book were contributed by members of the Herts Moth Group and others and were collated by Andrew Wood. Copyright of these photographs is retained by the following photographers:

Photographer	Species number illustrated in the species accounts
Andy Banthorpe	148, 161, 360, 492, 737, 1016, 1064, 1255, 1301, 1415, 1652, 1784, 1791, 1795, 1807, 1838, 1876, 1884, 1917, 2142, 2166, 2173, 2192, 2293, 2337, 2364, 2369, 2437, 2469
Charles Baker	3, 42, 111, 116, 140, 144, 196, 228, 246, 247, 256, 293, 308, 321, 326, 332, 341, 407, 411, 415, 424, 425, 440, 452, 453, 455, 495, 499, 533, 560, 601, 640, 647, 649, 652, 658, 695, 726, 774, 874, 904, 954, 972, 1023, 1062, 1126, 1134, 1138, 1165, 1169, 1219, 1274, 1281, 1288, 1313, 1331, 1332, 1333, 1425, 1438, 1470, 1509, 1513, 1662
Tristan Bantock	162, 173, 1676, 2132
Mark Cooper	131, 1853
Trevor Chapman	1082, 2322
Rob Edmunds	28, 123, 125, 129, 185, 186, 476, 883
Ian Kimber	779
Mike Lawrence	937, 1631, 2060, 2157
Mick Massie	382
Bill & Pearl Page	1642, 1750, 1773, 1832, 1921, 1926, 1972, 1981, 1984, 1994, 2005, 2057, 2110, 2111, 2318, 2381, 2484
Adriaan Peeters	272, 918
Ann Piper	1776, 2063
Colin W. Plant	73, 95, 159, 263, 313, 368, 370, 1150
Ian Small	379
Ben Smart	519, 877
Duncan Williams	447
Andrew Wood	6, 14, 20, 150, 169, 171, 229, 282, 286, 320, 373, 385, 391, 464, 493, 663, 688, 706, 800, 862, 871a, 925,962, 980, 998, 1002, 1020, 1036, 1054, 1113, 1155, 1171, 1216, 1236, 1306, 1370, 1375, 1433, 1437, 1497, 1524, 1663, 1673, 1690, 1707, 1722, 1725, 1738, 1766, 1789, 1808, 1816, 1817, 1823, 1825, 1827, 1844, 1858, 1884, 1889, 1919, 1941, 1950, 1954, 2014, 2019, 2031, 2051, 2089, 2126, 2134, 2147, 2165, 2178, 2186, 2198, 2214, 2223, 2243, 2262, 2283, 2292, 2301, 2314, 2334, 2360, 2399, 2422, 2441, 2443, 2473, 2476, 2492

In addition, the following photographs are copyrighted by the photographers as follows:

Canary-shouldered Thorn on Front cover	Mike Lawrence
Larvae of Great Prominent on page 5	Colin W. Plant
Early Grey on page 21	Andrew Wood
Narrow-bordered Five-spot Burnet on page 23	Andrew Wood
Rhyacionia pinicolana on page 30	Andrew Wood
Ectoedemia subbimaculella on page 58	Ian Kimber

Remaining photographers and copyright holders are credited in captions accompanying their photographs.

Anyone wishing to contact the photographers is invited to do so via the author through www.hertsmothgroup.org.uk

Hertfordshire Natural History Society

Hertfordshire Natural History Society promotes the study and recording of the flora and fauna in Hertfordshire and encourages a wider interest in natural history including the conservation of wildlife, habitats and geological features.

The Society was established in Watford in January 1875 by a group of local naturalists, headed by John Hopkinson who later became secretary and president. The objectives were *'the investigation of the Meteorology, Geology, Botany and Zoology of the neighbourhood of Watford and the County of Hertford, and the dissemination amongst its members of information on Natural History and Microscopical Science'*. The Society expanded rapidly and in 1879 extended its remit to the whole county and took the name the Hertfordshire Natural History Society and Field Club.

In the early days the membership was drawn from a wealthy and scientifically minded elite group. In 1880 this included eleven titled gentlemen including the Marquis of Salisbury, five Fellows of the Royal Society, numerous fellows of other learned societies and twelve clergy, Charles Darwin was elected an Honorary Member in 1877. They had the time, inclination and resources to explore the county using the latest scientific knowledge and techniques. Despite the difficulty of travel limited to railways, horses and bicycles, they met weekly during the summer months for field trips throughout the county. These often ended with tea taken in the garden of an eminent local member.

Documenting and publishing the results of their studies was always very important. The first part of the Society's 'Transactions' was published in 1875. The initial volumes had papers on the weather, rainfall, phenology, botany, birds (the first Bird Report was published in 1878), geology, fossils, watercourses, beetles (the first paper in 1880), fungi and much more. The obvious delight in discovery leaps from the pages. The Society's Transactions have been published continuously from 1875 to the present day and now run to 39 volumes. They provide a vital and comprehensive source of information about the county and its changing flora and fauna over the last 130 years. For example the annual papers on phenology have proved one of the best long term sources of data in the whole of Britain and have been used in influential scientific publications on climate change.

Not resting on our laurels, today members of the Society continue to engage in individual projects and county wide surveys making use of modern technology to monitor and record wildlife in the county and its changing fortunes. The Society co-ordinates a network of County Recorders covering:

fungi, mosses and liverworts, lichens, vascular plants, leeches, molluscs, ants, bees, beetles, bugs, butterflies, caddis flies, cockroaches, crickets, dragonflies, earwigs, flies, grasshoppers, lacewings, mayflies, moths, stoneflies, wasps, spiders, crustacean, fish, amphibians, reptiles, birds, mammals and geology.

Records for individual species are captured in electronic databases and made available for specific studies, analysis and to support conservation work. Where appropriate, records are shared with the Hertfordshire Biological records Centre at the Hertfordshire County Council.

There are also thriving specialist activities including Herts Bird Club, Herts Moth Group and Herts Flora Group. The Society also works closely with Herts and Middlesex Wildlife Trust, Herts and Middlesex branch of Butterfly Conservation and London Natural History Society

The Society's Transactions are now published annually in two parts:

- **The Hertfordshire Bird Report** contains a systematic record of all bird species found in the year, papers on birds new to the county and results and analysis of specific studies and survey work;
- **The Hertfordshire Naturalist** covers all other wildlife groups, including fungi, flora, dragonflies, butterflies, moths and other invertebrates, amphibians, reptiles and mammals plus reports of the activities of the Society.

Other HNHS publications include:

Dragonflies and Damselflies of Hertfordshire by Alan Reynolds, the Revd Tom Gladwin and Christine Shepperson, 2008, ISBN 978-0-9521685-6-0

The Mammals Amphibians and Reptiles of Hertfordshire by Michael Clark, 2001, ISBN 1-84019-012-4

The Birds at Tring Reservoirs by Rob Young, Jack Fearnside and David Russell, 1996, ISBN 0-9521685-1-0

The Breeding Birds of Hertfordshire by K W Smith, CW Dee, J D Fearnside, E W Fletcher and R N Smith, 1993, ISBN 0-9521685-0-2.

All publications are available to purchase from the Secretary to the Society.

Future works are planned on a Flora of Hertfordshire, Geology of Hertfordshire and a Hertfordshire Avifauna including the results of the 2007-2011 Bird Atlas.

Membership of the Hertfordshire Natural History Society is open to everyone. For further information contact the Secretary, Linda Smith, at 24 Mandeville Rise, Welwyn Garden City, AL8 7JU; email herts.naturalhistorysociety@ntlworld.com or the website www.hnhs.org

Index

Note: *this index give the moth reference number as used in the species accounts, not the page number.*

Index of scientific names

Index of English names

code

Blair's Shoulder-knot........................2240

Dark Umber......................................1792

Figure of Eighty 1654